Selected Papers on

MOLECULAR GENETICS

PERSPECTIVES IN MODERN BIOLOGY

A Series of Reprint Collections

SELECTED PAPERS ON MOLECULAR GENETICS, J. Herbert Taylor (Ed.) 1965

Other titles in preparation

Selected
Papers
on
MOLECULAR
GENETICS

A COLLECTION OF REPRINTS—
WITH INTRODUCTORY MATERIAL BY

J. HERBERT TAYLOR

INSTITUTE OF MOLECULAR BIOPHYSICS
THE FLORIDA STATE UNIVERSITY
TALLAHASSEE, FLORIDA

1965

ACADEMIC PRESS   New York and London

ACADEMIC PRESS INC.
111 Fifth Avenue, New York, New York 10003

United Kingdom Edition published by
ACADEMIC PRESS INC. (LONDON) LTD.
Berkeley Square House, London W.1

Library of Congress Catalog Card Number: 65-18437

First Printing, July, 1965
Second Printing, January, 1966
Third Printing, September, 1966

PRINTED IN THE UNITED STATES OF AMERICA

Preface

"Molecular Genetics" was the title chosen for a rather extensive treatment of various aspects of replication, transmission, and control of genetic information in a spectrum of systems from viruses to higher cells ["Molecular Genetics" (J. Herbert Taylor, ed.), Part I (1963), Part II (in press). Academic Press, New York]. After the publication of Part I and during the planning of Part II of this two-volume treatise, it became apparent that certain aspects, particularly the early work in the development of present concepts, would not be properly covered. Attempts to use this work for supplementary and textual material for courses in genetics emphasized these omissions. Much of the necessary information existed in previous publications, but assignments from the original literature revealed that many of the most desirable papers were not readily available to students and even when they were, the number of copies was quite inadequate to meet the needs.

With these difficulties in mind, selections were made among the most useful and significant original papers for reprinting in a single volume. The choices which are made in assembling such a volume are limited by many considerations besides the obvious one of space. Some otherwise appropriate contributions had to be omitted because they were too long or the data were too involved for this type of presentation. No doubt some readers will consider a few of the papers finally included too verbose or too technical for such a volume. Perhaps some topics could have been presented better by selection of sections from several papers. However, the decision was made not to tamper with the original papers. In an attempt to find the first paper or at least an early publication for each new development, the clearest presentation may not always have been attained. In addition the choices were in some instances based as much on the need for a logical sequence as on the merit of individual contributions. The inclusion of the editor's papers is an attempt to add a personal touch and is without further implication. The purpose of the introductory commentary is to place the papers in an historical perspective and to fill some of the gaps in instances where a topic could not be represented by an original paper.

The development of concepts is difficult to reconstruct from a review of scientific literature. Fortunately, the events span the careers of many who are still active, but their closeness detracts from the long view which the historian requires for proper perspective and evaluation. Admittedly the selections, as well as the introductory comments, reflect the prejudices and limitations of one person. In addition to these limitations, it is common knowledge that the exchange of information and ideas is much less efficient during the lag period when an area of science is developing. Discoveries and rediscoveries are frequently a part of such progress and even the persons involved are not always aware of the factors which influenced their thinking and their experiments. Nothing is so simple as the concept proven by well-designed experiments. However, we quickly tend to forget the sometimes bewildering array of experiments and notions which go before and perhaps influence the design of a critical experiment. In spite of these difficulties and the limitations imposed by the space available and the reader's time, the selections will hopefully include some useful information, add some historical perspective, and, when used along with "Molecular Genetics," Parts I and II, provide rather broad coverage for some of the most intriguing aspects of modern genetics.

J. HERBERT TAYLOR
Tallahassee, Florida

April, 1965

CONTENTS

SECTION I:

Biochemical Genetics

SECTION II:

The Nature of Genetic Material

SECTION III:

DNA Structure and Replication

SECTION IV:

Genetic Recombination

SECTION V:

The Function of Genetic Material

Errata

Section III p. 252, bottom of 1st column, last line: ". . . the nucleic acid contained in its chain, clusters of nucleotides. . . .

Section III p. 307. Fig. 7E contains an error in which two successive links are connected between the locus a and c; two successive linkers should not be connected in any case.

Section IV p. 394. Plate XIV is reproduced in black and white instead of color as in the original paper.

SECTION I
Biochemical Genetics

Introduction

In writing of the role of the cell nucleus in 1899, E. B. Wilson could make the following statement: "On the one hand, it is a primary factor in morphological synthesis and hence in inheritance, on the other hand an organ of metabolism especially concerned with the constructive process. The building of a definite cell-product, such as a muscle-fibre, a nerve-process, a cilium, a pigment-granule, a zymogen-granule, is in the last analysis the result of a specific form of metabolic activity, as we may conclude from the fact that such products have not only a definite physical and morphological character, but also a definite chemical character. In its physiological aspect, therefore, inheritance is the recurrence, in successive generations, of like forms of metabolism; and this is effected through the transmission from generation to generation of a specific substance or idioplasm which we have seen reason to identify with chromatin."

The above concept expressed by Wilson represents the most advanced thinking of the late nineteenth century biologists concerning the inheritance of metabolic patterns. Few, if any, would have been able to express the idea so succinctly and many would not have thought in those terms at all. Biochemistry was not yet well developed enough to allow such ideas to be put to further experimental test even if appropriate biological systems had been known. The new science of genetics was just about to experience its most fundamental rediscovery and did not yet bear a name. Although Wilson and his contemporaries were already thinking in terms of units of inheritance as a result of their study of the distribution of the chromosomes during mitosis and the hypotheses concerning invisible pangenes elaborated by Weismann, De Vries, and Hertwig, they were not yet ready to associate these units with definite steps in metabolic reactions. Nevertheless, Driesch had already considered them as a storehouse of specific ferments (enzymes).

With the rediscovery of Mendel's work, those most concerned with genetics were busy for years to come with the mechanics of inheritance and evolution and with the development and verification of the chromosome theory of genetic transmission. Biochemists were busy with other problems and with a few notable exceptions did not understand or appreciate the developments in genetics and cell biology. The best documented exception was presented by Garrod in 1908 in his Croonian Lectures before the Royal College of Physicians and later in two editions of his book "Inborn Errors of Metabolism." Garrod was studying the metabolism associated with several rare human diseases. One of these, alcaptonuria, was found to result from a block in the sequence of reactions by which the amino acids, phenylalanine and tyrosine, are catabolized. The intermediate alcapton (2,5-dihydroxyphenylacetic acid) is secreted in the urine of affected individuals and produces a black color on exposure to air. By 1902 Bateson had pointed out that the defect was inherited as a simple Mendelian recessive trait, and before the second edition of Garrod's book was published in 1923, the German chemist Gross had shown that the blood serum of affected individuals was deficient in an enzyme which catalyzed the oxidation of alcapton. Therefore, this case, and several others which were less completely understood, provided direct evidence for a specific enzyme-gene relationship. In spite of Garrod's brilliant and remarkable insight his audience seems to have included few of those who were active in advancing the frontiers of Mendelian genetics. His work produced little excitement and stimulated no extensive work in either genetics or biochemistry. The missing catalyst was probably the availability of suitable experimental materials. The errors in metabolism occurred only in patients with rare diseases where genetic experiments were impossible. The search for appropriate experimental materials was continued in a few instances as exemplified by the work on the biochemical genetics of the plant pigments carried out by Onslow (1925), Scott-Moncrief, and others (see Lawrence and Price, 1940) and by the work initiated on eye pigments of *Drosophila* by Ephrussi and Beadle in the 1930's (see the review by Ephrussi, 1942). None of the systems provided the necessary experimental conditions to test further the hypothesis that genes regulated metabolism by controlling the specificity of enzymes. However, the difficulties encountered served to define some of the requirements. An organism was needed in which mutations affecting simple metabolic pathways could be induced and tested for Mendelian segregation. Not only should one be able to isolate the metabolites involved, but one must be able to supplement the growth medium of the cells with the substance necessary to bypass the block.

The break came in the early 1940's when Beadle and Tatum (1941) began their work on the fungus *Neurospora*. Much of the preliminary genetic work had already been published by B. O. Dodge and Carl C. Lindegren. The details are presented in the articles by Beadle (1950, 1959) as well as in the second paper of this collection.

The concept of a one-to-one relationship between genes and enzymes or between mutations and blocks in metabolic pathways was almost as much of a rediscovery as was the rediscovery of Mendel's work in 1900. Both biochemists and geneticists now had advanced to the point where effective use could be made of the concept, and the work quickly grew and expanded in many fruitful ways in spite of World War II. The developments are documented in the textbook "Genetics and Metabolism" by Wagner and Mitchell (1955, 1964). It would take some years to understand the relationship between mutations and enzymes primarily because so little was known concerning the structure of proteins at the time there was so much discussion of the one gene-one enzyme concept. We may have difficulty in appreciating the problem unless we keep in mind that the concepts were formulated without any clear idea of the properties of proteins which conferred specificity. Sanger's sequence analysis of one of the simplest proteins, insulin, was yet to be published. Although proteins were known to be composed of polypeptide chains which were assumed to be folded in specific ways, there was no clear concept of what determined the sequence of amino acids or whether the sequence was related to the three-dimensional shape. Did genes control the specificity of enzymes and if so how? If a mutation changed an enzyme activity was it because the protein was changed or produced in smaller amounts? Would the mutation of one gene change more than one protein? Could genes mutate in a variety of ways?

Without a clear concept of the nature of the gene or of its supposed product, a specific protein, little progress could be made. Geneticists could study the phenotypes produced by mutation as had been done for years. The improvement provided by *Neurospora*, which could be grown in a simple, completely defined medium, was that the change in phenotype could be defined much more precisely in chemical terms. In an attempt to simplify the problem, the question was put in the following form. Do any genes have a single primary function and if so what proportion of mutations produces changes of this nature? Horowitz and Leupold in the fourth paper of this section define the problem and give experimental data to test the hypothesis.

The next break came from an unexpected source. Linus Pauling, the protein chemist, and collaborators interested in human genetics decided to investigate the chemistry of the disease, sickle cell anemia. The transmission of the trait was shown by Neel (1949) to follow the simple Mendelian principle in which those severely affected were homozygous for the mutant gene. In this instance the heterozygotes could also be recognized clinically by a mild form of the disease referred to as sickle cell trait. Pauling *et al.* (1949), in the third paper of this collection, reported a chemical difference between the hemoglobin of sickle cell patients (hemoglobin S) and that of normal individuals (hemoglobin A). The two types of molecules could be separated by electrophoresis which indicated a difference in net charge on the two types of molecules. The persons who were heterozygous were found to possess both molecular species in a ratio approaching one to one (60:40).

The work on hemoglobin was significant because this was the first demonstration of an inherited change in the molecular structure of a protein. Since the change was inherited in simple Mendelian fashion the alteration was probable due to a single mutation. Both the original and the mutant genes were apparently involved in the production of a specific molecular type. Although one could not define the alteration with certainty, the work of Sanger, which was just being published, on sequences of amino acids in insulin polypeptide chains indicated that the difference might be due to amino acid substitution. Sequence studies on other proteins, ribonuclease for example, were begun within a few years, but there was little hope that a protein as large as hemoglobin could be analyzed soon. The longest polypeptide chain in insulin had only 51 amino acids, while hemoglobin with a molecular weight of 66,000 would contain about 600 amino acid residues. Although it was possible that several polypeptides were included in each molecule, the sequence analysis would almost certainly take years. Sanger's analysis of insulin had been a long and arduous task.

In spite of the magnitude of the problem, the alteration in hemoglobin S was demonstrated within a remarkably short time. A young biochemist, Vernon Ingram, who was familiar with Sanger's methods and the rapidly advancing techniques for separation of peptides and amino acids devised a short cut. He would not try to analyze the whole molecular sequence, but with the new knowledge of the specificity of trypsin, he realized that the molecule could be chopped into a number of peptides of rather small size. Trypsin had been shown to cleave polypeptide chains to the right (C-terminal) side of the residues of lysine and arginine. By separation of these derived peptides on paper by a combination of chromatography and electrophoresis one could hope to find minute differences in rather large molecules of a purified protein. This technique, which came to be called "finger printing" of proteins, was so successful that Ingram had the answer he sought within a short time. Fortunately, the difference between hemoglobin A and S showed up by the displacement of a single peptide fragment of the 28 produced in his digest of the whole protein. The isolation and analysis of the amino acid sequence in the unique peptide of hemoglobin S and its counterpart in hemoglobin A showed that the difference was due to the substitution of a single amino acid. In hemoglobin A glutamic acid, which has a free carboxyl group, had been replaced by the neutral residue of valine to form hemoglobin S. One of the most intriguing problems in molecular genetics had yielded a simple and decisive result. The way was now open to answer in precise terms the question of the relation between a gene and the specific protein under its control. The details of Ingram's experiment are presented in the fifth paper of this group on biochemical genetics. A few years later when Ingram and his colleague, J. A. Hunt, examined another mutant hemoglobin (C), he found that it had a different substitution at the same site in the polypeptide chain. In this instance the basic amino acid, lysine, was substituted for glutamic acid (see the sixth paper of the series by Hunt and Ingram, 1960). By this time hemoglobin had been shown to be composed of four peptide chains, two identical α-chains and two identical β-chains. Both substitutions mentioned above were in the β-chains. Progress in this area has been rapid and revealing for molecular genetics with many mutant hemoglobins identified and partially analyzed. The details are presented by Ingram (1963) and by Baglioni (1963). Similar studies involving the coat protein of tobacco mosaic virus and a number of induced mutants have been reported from the Virus Laboratory in Berkeley and the Max-Planck Institut in Tübingen (for details see the review by Tsugita and Fraenkel-Conrat, 1963).

A detailed genetic analysis is unfortunately not possible with either of the biological systems mentioned above. The most interesting genetic systems yet studied, where corresponding analyses can be made on the proteins, are found in *Escherichia coli*. The chemistry and genetics of the A protein of tryptophan synthetase have been studied by Yanofsky and his colleagues at Stanford University. Similar studies on alkaline phosphatase were begun at about the same time by Levinthal and his group at Massachusetts Institute of Technology. Faster progress with the tryptophan synthetase system was possible because a part of the molecule, the A protein, could be isolated for analysis. We cannot hope to review all of the developments in this rapidly expanding field, but we have reprinted one of the early papers on the tryptophan synthetase system to illustrate some new features of the relation between genes and protein structure. Certain other features of these studies cannot be fully appreciated until we have reviewed the mechanisms of protein synthesis and information transfer in the last section of this volume. Therefore, another paper by Yanofsky and his colleagues will be included in the last section after we have discussed the role of transfer RNA, activating enzymes, and the coding problem.

Although we are beginning to understand the way in which genes control protein structure, we have neglected the problem of regulation. What determines the time in the cell cycle or in the developmental cycle at which genes act? How is the rate of synthesis of a protein regulated? These problems which are basic to an understanding of differentiation have been asked many times in the past, but until recent years no answers were available. Partial answers are coming from two areas of investigation, which formerly appeared as quite unrelated problems, namely, adaptive enzyme formation and position effects. We cannot hope to follow all of the exciting developments in this field which is likely to be the most productive one in biology during the coming decade, but two papers are reprinted to show the correlation of the two problems and the direction which the work is taking. The first is a theoretical review paper on genetic regulatory mecshanism by Jacob and Monod (1961) and the second is a short commentary by McClintock (1961) primarily concerned with position effects. Although Jacob and Monod supposed that the regulator substances (repressors) might be RNA at the time they wrote the above paper, other experiments very soon implicated proteins as the most likely candidates (Monod *et al.*, 1963). To date, the nature of these molecules is uncertain (see *Cold Spring Harbor Symp. Quant. Biol.*, 1963).

Another aspect of this problem of regulation in cells of higher forms has been opened up by the study of the effects of hormones on puffing patterns in salivary gland chromosomes (Beerman, 1961; Clever, 1962). Still another approach comes from studies of late replicating chromosomes in mammalian cells, particularly sex chromosomes, and the correlated suppression of genetic activity by an as yet unknown mechanism related to position effects (see reviews by Russell, 1961, 1963; Grumbach et al., 1963; Taylor, 1964).

REFERENCES

Baglioni, C. (1963). *In* "Molecular Genetics" (J. H. Taylor, ed.), Part 1, pp. 405–476. Academic Press, New York.

Beadle, G. W. (1950). *In* "Genetics in the 20th Century" (L. C. Dunn, ed.), pp. 221–239. Macmillan, New York.

Beadle, G. W. (1959). *Science* 129, 1715.

Beadle, G. W., and Tatum, E. L. (1941). *Proc. Natl. Acad. Sci. U. S.* 27, 499.

Beerman, W. (1961). *Chromosoma* 12, 1.

Clever, U. (1961). *Chromosoma* 12, 607.

Ephrussi, B. (1942). *Quart. Rev. Biol.* 17, 327.

Garrod, A. E. (1923). "Inborn Errors in Metabolism," 2nd ed. Oxford Univ. Press, London and New York.

Grumbach, M. M., Morishima, A., and Taylor, J. H. (1963). *Proc. Natl. Acad. Sci. U. S.* 49, 581.

Ingram, V. M. (1963). *In* "Genetics and Evolution," 165 pp. Columbia Univ. Press, New York.

Lawrence, W. J. C., and Price, J. R. (1940). *Biol. Rev. Cambridge Phil. Soc.* 15, 35.

Monod, J., Changeux, J., and Jacob, F. (1963). *J. Mol. Biol.* 6, 306.

Neel, J. V. (1949). *Science* 110, 64.

Onslow, M. W. (1925). "The Anthocyanin Pigments of Plants," 314 pp. Cambridge Univ. Press, London and New York.

Russell, L. B. (1961). *Science* 133, 1795.

Russell, L. B. (1963). *Science* 140, 976.

Taylor, J. H. (1964). *Symp. Intern. Soc. Cell Biol.* in press.

Tsugita, A., and Fraenkel-Conrat, H. (1963). *In* "Molecular Genetics" (J. H. Taylor, ed.), Part 1, pp. 477–520. Academic Press, New York.

Wagner, R. P., and Mitchell, H. K. (1955). "Genetics and Metabolism," 1st ed. Wiley, New York.

Wagner, R. P., and Mitchell, H. K. (1964). "Genetics and Metabolism," 2nd ed. Wiley, New York.

Wilson, E. B. (1900). "The Cell in Development and Inheritance," 2nd ed., pp. 430–431. Macmillan, New York.

Reprinted from the Proceedings of the NATIONAL ACADEMY OF SCIENCES,
Vol. 27, No. 11, pp. 499–506. November, 1941

GENETIC CONTROL OF BIOCHEMICAL REACTIONS IN NEUROSPORA*

BY G. W. BEADLE AND E. L. TATUM

BIOLOGICAL DEPARTMENT, STANFORD UNIVERSITY

Communicated October 8, 1941

From the standpoint of physiological genetics the development and functioning of an organism consist essentially of an integrated system of chemical reactions controlled in some manner by genes. It is entirely tenable to suppose that these genes which are themselves a part of the system, control or regulate specific reactions in the system either by acting directly as enzymes or by determining the specificities of enzymes.[1] Since the components of such a system are likely to be interrelated in complex ways, and since the synthesis of the parts of individual genes are presumably dependent on the functioning of other genes, it would appear that there must exist orders of directness of gene control ranging from simple one-to-one relations to relations of great complexity. In investigating the rôles of genes, the physiological geneticist usually attempts to determine the physiological and biochemical bases of already known hereditary traits. This approach, as made in the study of anthocyanin pigments in plants,[2] the fermentation of sugars by yeasts[3] and a number of other instances,[4] has established that many biochemical reactions are in fact controlled in specific ways by specific genes. Furthermore, investigations of this type tend to support the assumption that gene and enzyme specificities are of the same order.[5] There are, however, a number of limitations inherent in this approach. Perhaps the most serious of these is that the investigator must in general confine himself to a study of non-lethal heritable characters. Such characters are likely to involve more or less non-essential so-called "terminal" reactions.[5] The selection of these for genetic study was perhaps responsible for the now rapidly disappearing belief that genes are concerned only with the control of "superficial" characters. A second difficulty, not unrelated to the first, is that the standard approach to the problem implies the use of characters with visible manifestations. Many such characters involve morphological variations, and these are likely to be based on systems of biochemical reactions so complex as to make analysis exceedingly difficult.

Considerations such as those just outlined have led us to investigate

TABLE 1

Growth of Pyridoxinless Strain of *N. sitophila* on Liquid Medium Containing Inorganic Salts,[9] 1% Sucrose, and 0.004 Microgram Biotin per Cc. Temperature 25°C. Growth Period, 6 Days from Inoculation with Conidia

MICROGRAMS B_6 PER 25 CC. MEDIUM	STRAIN	DRY WEIGHT MYCELIA, MG.
0	Normal	76.7
0	Pyridoxinless	1.0
0.01	"	4.2
0.03	"	5.7
0.1	"	13.7
0.3	"	25.5
1.0	"	81.1
3.0	"	81.1
10.0	"	65.4
30.0	"	82.4

the general problem of the genetic control of developmental and metabolic reactions by reversing the ordinary procedure and, instead of attempting to work out the chemical bases of known genetic characters, to set out to determine if and how genes control known biochemical reactions. The ascomycete *Neurospora* offers many advantages for such an approach and is well suited to genetic studies.[6] Accordingly, our program has been built around this organism. The procedure is based on the assumption that x-ray treatment will induce mutations in genes concerned with the control of known specific chemical reactions. If the organism must be able to carry out a certain chemical reaction to survive on a given medium, a mutant unable to do this will obviously be lethal on this medium. Such a mutant can be maintained and studied, however, if it will grow on a medium to which has been added the essential product of the genetically blocked reaction. The experimental procedure based on this reasoning can best be illustrated by considering a hypothetical example. Normal strains of *Neurospora crassa* are able to use sucrose as a carbon source, and are therefore able to carry out the specific and enzymatically controlled

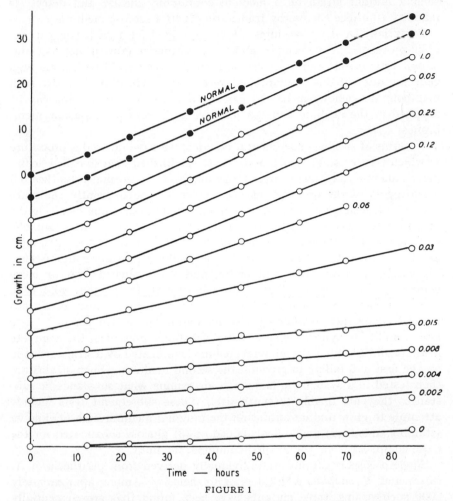

FIGURE 1

Growth of normal (top two curves) and pyridoxinless (remaining curves) strains of *Neurospora sitophila* in horizontal tubes. The scale on the ordinate is shifted a fixed amount for each successive curve in the series. The figures at the right of each curve indicate concentration of pyridoxine (B_6) in micrograms per 25 cc. medium.

reaction involved in the hydrolysis of this sugar. Assuming this reaction to be genetically controlled, it should be possible to induce a gene to mutate to a condition such that the organism could no longer carry out sucrose hydrolysis. A strain carrying this mutant would then be unable to grow on a medium containing sucrose as a sole carbon source but should be able to grow on a medium containing some other normally utilizable carbon source. In other words, it should be possible to establish and maintain such a mutant strain on a medium containing glucose and detect its inability to utilize sucrose by transferring it to a sucrose medium.

Essentially similar procedures can be developed for a great many metabolic processes. For example, ability to synthesize growth factors (vitamins), amino acids and other essential substances should be lost through gene mutation if our assumptions are correct. Theoretically, any such metabolic deficiency can be "by-passed" if the substance lacking can be supplied in the medium and can pass cell walls and protoplasmic membranes.

In terms of specific experimental practice, we have devised a procedure in which x-rayed single-spore cultures are established on a so-called "complete" medium, i.e., one containing as many of the normally synthesized constituents of the organism as is practicable. Subsequently these are tested by transferring them to a "minimal" medium, i.e., one requiring the organism to carry on all the essential syntheses of which it is capable. In practice the complete medium is made up of agar, inorganic salts, malt extract, yeast extract and glucose. The minimal medium contains agar (optional), inorganic salts and biotin, and a disaccharide, fat or more complex carbon source. Biotin, the one growth factor that wild type *Neurospora* strains cannot synthesize,[7] is supplied in the form of a commercial concentrate containing 100 micrograms of biotin per cc.[8] Any loss of ability to synthesize an essential substance present in the complete medium and absent in the minimal medium is indicated by a strain growing on the first and failing to grow on the second medium. Such strains are then tested in a systematic manner to determine what substance or substances they are unable to synthesize. These subsequent tests include attempts to grow mutant strains on the minimal medium with (1) known vitamins added, (2) amino acids added or (3) glucose substituted for the more complex carbon source of the minimal medium.

Single ascospore strains are individually derived from perithecia of *N. crassa* and *N. sitophila* x-rayed prior to meiosis. Among approximately 2000 such strains, three mutants have been found that grow essentially normally on the complete medium and scarcely at all on the minimal medium with sucrose as the carbon source. One of these strains (*N. sitophila*) proved to be unable to synthesize vitamin B₆ (pyridoxine). A second strain (*N. sitophila*) turned out to be unable to synthesize vitamin B₁ (thiamine). Additional tests show that this strain is able to synthesize the pyrimidine half of the B₁ molecule but not the thiazole half. If thiazole alone is added to the minimal medium, the strain grows essentially normally. A third strain (*N. crassa*) has been found to be unable to synthesize para-aminobenzoic acid. This mutant strain appears to be entirely normal when grown on the minimal medium to which *p*-amino-benzoic acid has been added. Only in the case of the "pyridoxinless" strain has an analysis of the inheritance of the induced metabolic defect been investigated. For this reason detailed accounts of the thiamine-deficient and *p*-aminobenzoic acid-deficient strains will be deferred.

Qualitative studies indicate clearly that the pyridoxinless mutant, grown on a medium containing one microgram or more of synthetic vitamin B_6 hydrochloride per 25 cc. of medium, closely approaches in rate and characteristics of growth normal strains grown on a similar medium with

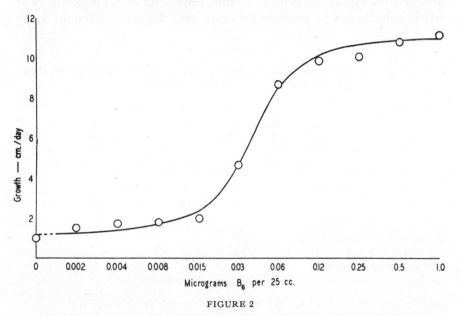

FIGURE 2

The relation between growth rate (cm./day) and vitamin B_6 concentration.

no B_6. Lower concentrations of B_6 give intermediate growth rates. A preliminary investigation of the quantitative dependence of growth of the mutant on vitamin B_6 in the medium gave the results summarized in table 1. Additional experiments have given results essentially similar but in only approximate quantitative agreement with those of table 1. It is clear that additional study of the details of culture conditions is necessary before rate of weight increase of this mutant can be used as an accurate assay for vitamin B_6.

It has been found that the progression of the frontier of mycelia of *Neurospora* along a horizontal glass culture tube half filled with an agar medium provides a convenient method of investigating the quantitative effects of growth factors. Tubes of about 13 mm. inside diameter and about 40 cm. in length are used. Segments of about 5 cm. at the two ends are turned up at an angle of about 45°. Agar medium is poured in so as to fill the tube about half full and is allowed to set with the main segment of the tube in a horizontal position. The turned up ends of the tube are stoppered with cotton plugs. Inoculations are made at one end of the agar surface and the position of the advancing front recorded at convenient intervals. The frontier formed by the advancing mycelia is remarkably well defined, and there is no difficulty in determining its position to within a millimeter or less. Progression along such tubes is strictly linear with time and the rate is independent of tube length (up to 1.5 meters). The rate is not changed by reducing the inside tube diameter to 9 mm., or by

TABLE 2

RESULTS OF CLASSIFYING SINGLE ASCOSPORE CULTURES FROM THE CROSS OF PYRIDOXINLESS AND NORMAL *N. sitophila*

ASCUS NUMBER	1	2	3	4	5	6	7	8
17	—	*pdx*	*pdx*	*pdx*	*N*	*N*	*N*	—
18	—	—	*N*	*N*	—	—	*pdx*	*pdx*
19	—	*pdx*	—	—	—	—	—	*N*
20	—	—	*N*	—	—	—	—	*pdx*
22	—	—	*N*	—	—	—	—	—
23	—	*	*	*	*N*	*N*	*pdx*	*pdx*
24	*N*	*N*	*N*	*N*	*pdx*	*pdx*	*pdx*	*pdx*

N, normal growth on B_6-free medium. *pdx*, slight growth on B_6-free medium. Failure of ascospore germination indicated by dash.

* Spores 2, 3 and 4 isolated but positions confused. Of these, two germinated and both proved to be mutants.

sealing one or both ends. It therefore appears that gas diffusion is in no way limiting in such tubes.

The results of growing the pyridoxinless strain in horizontal tubes in which the agar medium contained varying amounts of B_6 are shown graphically in figures 1 and 2. Rate of progression is clearly a function of vitamin B_6 concentration in the medium.[10] It is likewise evident that there is no significant difference in rate between the mutant supplied with B_6 and the normal strain growing on a medium without this vitamin. These results are consistent with the assumption that the primary physiological difference between pyridoxinless and normal strains is the inability of the former to carry out the synthesis of vitamin B_6. There is certainly more than one step in this synthesis and accordingly the gene differential involved is presumably concerned with only one specific step in the biosynthesis of vitamin B_6.

In order to ascertain the inheritance of the pyridoxinless character, crosses between normal and mutant strains were made. The techniques for hybridization and ascospore isolation have been worked out and described by Dodge, and by Lindegren.[6] The ascospores from 24 asci of the cross were isolated and their positions in the asci recorded. For some unknown reason, most of these failed to germinate. From seven asci, however, one or more spores germinated. These were grown on a medium containing glucose, malt-extract and yeast extract, and in this they all grew normally. The normal and mutant cultures were differentiated by growing them on a B_6 deficient medium. On this medium the mutant cultures grew very little, while the non-mutant ones grew normally. The results are summarized in table 2. It is clear from these rather limited data that this inability to synthesize vitamins B_6 is transmitted as it should be if it were differentiated from normal by a single gene.

The preliminary results summarized above appear to us to indicate that the approach outlined may offer considerable promise as a method of learning more about how genes regulate development and function. For example, it should be possible, by finding a number of mutants unable to carry out a particular step in a given synthesis, to determine whether only one gene is ordinarily concerned with the immediate regulation of a given specific chemical reaction.

It is evident, from the standpoints of biochemistry and physiology, that the method outlined is of value as a technique for discovering additional substances of physiological significance. Since the complete medium used can be made up with yeast extract or with an extract of normal *Neurospora*, it is evident that if, through mutation, there is lost the ability to synthesize an essential substance, a test strain is thereby made available for use in isolating the substance. It may, of course, be a substance not previously known to be essential for the growth of any organism. Thus we may expect to discover new vitamins, and in the same way, it should be possible to discover additional essential amino acids if such exist. We have, in fact, found a mutant strain that is able to grow on a medium containing Difco yeast extract but unable to grow on any of the synthetic media we have so far tested. Evidently some growth factor present in yeast and as yet unknown to us is essential for *Neurospora*.

Summary.—A procedure is outlined by which, using *Neurospora*, one can discover and maintain x-ray induced mutant strains which are characterized by their inability to carry out specific biochemical processes.

Following this method, three mutant strains have been established. In one of these the ability to synthesize vitamin B_6 has been wholly or largely lost. In a second the ability to synthesize the thiazole half of the vitamin B_1 molecule is absent, and in the third para-aminobenzoic acid is not synthesized. It is therefore clear that all of these substances are essential growth factors for *Neurospora*.[11]

Growth of the pyridoxinless mutant (a mutant unable to synthesize vitamin B_6) is a function of the B_6 content of the medium on which it is grown. A method is described for measuring the growth by following linear progression of the mycelia along a horizontal tube half filled with an agar medium.

Inability to synthesize vitamin B_6 is apparently differentiated by a single gene from the ability of the organism to elaborate this essential growth substance.

NOTE: Since the manuscript of this paper was sent to press it has been established that inability to synthesize both thiazole and *p*-aminobenzoic acid are also inherited as though differentiated from normal by single genes.

* Work supported in part by a grant from the Rockefeller Foundation. The authors are indebted to Doctors B. O. Dodge, C. C. Lindegren and W. S. Malloch for stocks and for advice on techniques, and to Miss Caryl Parker for technical assistance.

[1] The possibility that genes may act through the mediation of enzymes has been suggested by several authors. See Troland, L. T., *Amer. Nat.*, **51**, 321–350 (1917); Wright, S., *Genetics*, **12**, 530–569 (1927); and Haldane, J. B. S., in *Perspectives in Biochemistry*, Cambridge Univ. Press, pp. 1–10 (1937), for discussions and references.

[2] Onslow, Scott-Moncrieff and others, see review by Lawrence, W. J. C., and Price, J. R., *Biol. Rev.*, **15**, 35–58 (1940).

[3] Winge, O., and Laustsen, O., *Compt. rend. Lab. Carlsberg, Serie physiol.*, **22**, 337–352 (1939).

[4] See Goldschmidt, R., *Physiological Genetics*, McGraw-Hill, pp. 1–375 (1939), and Beadle, G. W., and Tatum, E. L., *Amer. Nat.*, **75**, 107–116 (1941) for discussion and references.

[5] See Sturtevant, A. H., and Beadle, G. W., *An Introduction to Genetics*, Saunders, pp. 1–391 (1931), and Beadle, G. W., and Tatum, E. L., loc. cit., footnote 4.

[6] Dodge, B. O., *Jour. Agric. Res.*, **35**, 289–305 (1927), and Lindegren, C. C., *Bull. Torrey Bot. Club*, **59**, 85–102 (1932).

[7] In so far as we have carried them, our investigations on the vitamin requirements of *Neurospora* corroborate those of Butler, E. T., Robbins, W. J., and Dodge, B. O., *Science*, **94**, 262–263 (1941).

[8] The biotin concentrate used was obtained from the S. M. A. Corporation, Chagrin Falls, Ohio.

[9] Throughout our work with *Neurospora*, we have used as a salt mixture the one designated number 3 by Fries, N., *Symbolae Bot. Upsalienses*, Vol. 3, No. 2, 1–188 (1938). This has the following composition: NH_4 tartrate, 5 g.; NH_4NO_3, 1 g.; KH_2PO_4, 1 g.; $MgSO_4 \cdot 7H_2O$, 0.5 g.; NaCl, 0.1 g.; $CaCl_2$, 0.1 g.; $FeCl_3$, 10 drops 1% solution; H_2O, 1 l. The tartrate cannot be used as a carbon source by *Neurospora*

[10] It is planned to investigate further the possibility of using the growth of *Neurospora* strains in the described tubes as a basis of vitamin assay, but it should be emphasized that such additional investigation is essential in order to determine the reproducibility and reliability of the method.

[11] The inference that the three vitamins mentioned are essential for the growth of normal strains is supported by the fact that an extract of the normal strain will serve as a source of vitamin for each of the mutant strains.

VI

GENES AND THE CHEMISTRY OF THE ORGANISM

By G. W. Beadle

California Institute of Technology

GENES are units of inheritance. They are found arranged linearly in exceedingly minute, filamentous structures, known as chromosomes, present in the nuclei of the cells from which the bodies of most organisms are constructed. The mechanism by which the chromosomes and their genes are passed on to successive cell generations is well known. So, too, are the methods by which they are transmitted from one sexual generation to the next. We are less familiar with genes from the standpoint of their material composition and of their precise function in controlling developmental and functional processes. It is primarily with these latter attributes of the gene that the present discussion is concerned.

GENIC CONTROL OF AMINO ACID METABOLISM IN MAN

As an illustration of gene activity I shall refer to several human traits. Unless you are familiar with the details of medicine or biochemistry, these traits are not likely to be known to you, because they do not affect the individual in a visible manner. They have to do with the way in which certain amino acids are utilized in the body. Amino acids are organic compounds which serve as building blocks in the elaboration of proteins, for example, muscle fibers. All organisms require twenty or more varieties of these important substances. Some of these must be obtained in our food in the form of plant or animal proteins, which we tear down into their component parts and then rebuild into our own specific types of proteins. One of the amino acids which must be acquired in this way is phenylalanine. Man is able to oxidize this compound to tyrosine, another variety of amino acid, as shown in Figure 51. Phenylalanine is called an "indis-pensable" amino acid because it must be present in our food supply. Tyrosine, on the other hand, is known as a "dispensable" amino acid because, having phenylalanine, the organism can make its own tyrosine and, therefore, is not dependent on its presence in the diet. Actually, both are essential components of our pro-teins and a part of our supply of these two amino acids is used in this way (Fig. 51).

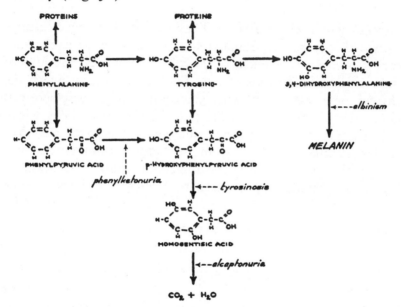

FIG. 51. Phenylalanine tyrosine metabolism in man showing relation of inherited defects to specific chemical reactions. (Based on Haldane [9] .)

Man is able to oxidize tyrosine still further to give 3, 4-dihydroxyphenylalanine, known to biologists under the ab-breviated name "dopa." Dopa serves as a precursor of the pig-ment melanin that gives color to our skin, hair, and eyes. Genes are active agents in the conversion of dopa to melanin. We know this because, if an individual receives a certain gene in defective or inactive form from each parent, he fails to produce melanin and becomes an albino with snow-white hair, light skin that will not tan, and pink eyes. The normal form of this particular gene evidently is significant in the elaboration of melanin. How this is accomplished chemically we are unable to say because we do not know the formula of melanin or how it is formed from dopa.

In our bodies both phenylalanine and tyrosine can have their amino groups (NH_2) replaced by oxygen atoms to give their keto acid analogues (Fig. 51). In much the same way that phenylalanine is oxidized to tyrosine, phenylpyruvic acid is oxidized to para-hydroxyphenylpyruvic acid. In normal individuals, this latter substance is finally broken down through a series of chemical reactions to carbon dioxide and water (Fig. 51). One of the intermediates in this breakdown is homogentisic acid (2, 5-dihydroxyphenylacetic acid, also known as alcapton). Homogentisic acid is of particular interest genetically because there are certain rare individuals who cannot break it down and who, therefore, accumulate it in the blood and excrete it in the urine. These individuals differ from normal persons in having both of a pair of genes defective. In other words, inability to decompose homogentisic acid is a simple mendelian recessive character, the presence of which may be revealed by the fact that the urine of such individuals turns dark on exposure to air. This darkening is due to the presence of the black, oxidized homogentisic acid. The abnormality is known as "alcaptonuria" and persons manifesting it are called "alcaptonurics" [8, 9].

Our knowledge of alcaptonuria indicates that the normal form of a particular gene is necessary for the breakdown of homogentisic acid. Furthermore, it is known that alcaptonurics lack an enzyme (organic catalyst), found in the blood of normal persons, which accelerates the conversion of homogentisic acid to the next compound in the series, probably acetoacetic acid. The normal gene, therefore, appears necessary for the formation of the enzyme. If the gene is defective, the enzyme is not present in active form, and the breakdown of homogentisic acid is not promoted. Since the individual apparently has no other way to dispose of it, the accumulated intermediate is excreted in the urine. We shall return later to a further consideration of this relationship between gene and enzyme.

There has been recorded in medical and biochemical literature an account of a man who was unable to convert para-hydroxyphenylpyruvic acid to the next compound in the break-down series (probably 2, 5-dihydroxyphenylpyruvic acid, not shown in Figure 51). Instead of degrading this substance, this individual excreted it in large amounts in the urine. The name "tyrosinosis" has been applied to this abnormality. Nothing, however, is known about its inheritance, since only one individual manifesting it has been found. This situation demonstrates that man is not a favorable organism for genetic studies —his life cycle is too long and he doesn't arrange his marriages for the convenience of geneticists. By analogy one might guess that tyrosinosis, like alcaptonuria, is a simple recessive heritable trait. But this must remain uncertain until more examples of it are found.

In some respects, the most interesting abnormality of phenyl-alanine-tyrosine metabolism known is "phenylketonuria." This, too, is a recessive trait, although there is some evidence that carriers of it—individuals with one member of the revelant gene pair normal and the other defective—are not completely normal. Metabolically, phenylketonurics are characterized by inability to oxidize phenylpyruvic acid (a phenyl-keto-acid) to the corresponding para-hydroxyphenylpyruvic acid. Consequently, phenylpyruvic acid accumulates and is excreted in the urine. Individuals who excrete this substance rather than breaking it down are invariably mentally defective. They are usually classified as idiots or imbeciles. It is evident that the ability to oxidize phenylpyruvic acid is necessary for normal functioning of the central nervous system. Whether the relation between the chemical reaction and rational thinking is direct or indirect we do not know. It may be that accumulated phenylpyruvic acid is harmful. On the other hand, the reaction per se may be essential for the higher orders of thought.

The relationship of the gene to phenylalanine-tyrosine metabolism just discussed and illustrated in Figure 51 suggests two generalizations. The first is that genes in some way control or direct specific chemical reactions. If both representatives of a given gene are defective, a specific chemical reaction fails to take place. The knowledge about alcaptonuria hints that gene control is indirect—that actually the gene determines whether or not a catalyst specific to the chemical reaction (an enzyme) is present in active form. We shall return to this point. The second generalization indicated is that, if the organism cannot handle a chemical compound in the usual way, the compound is disposed of by some alternative route—urinary excretion in the above examples. Biochemists have utilized these inherited abnormalities in phenylalanine-tyrosine metabolism to determine the exact chemical course of the process. For example, it is known that homogentisic acid comes from phenylalanine because, when extra amounts of this amino acid are fed to alcaptonurics, a corresponding increase in homogentisic acid is found. Normal individuals, on the other hand, are quite capable of handling extra amounts of phenylalanine. The same procedure has been used to determine what other chemicals are involved in the process. Homogentisic acid would be most difficult to identify as an intermediate in the degradation of phenylalanine and tyrosine if only normal persons were available for study, for such individuals do not accumulate a sufficient amount of homogentisic acid for chemical identification. As soon as any is produced it is further modified. In alcaptonurics this conversion is not possible. Therefore, individuals in which reactions are genetically blocked are useful in helping us qualitatively to identify intermediates in a system of reactions.

Since man is inherently unfavorable for either genetic or biochemical investigations, our knowledge concerning the genic control of phenylalanine and tyrosine metabolism is unusual. The relationship between genes and chemical characteristics, similar in principle, is known in several other organisms, many of them more appropriate for study than is man. But the independent development of the sciences of biochemistry and of genetics has unfortunately led to the use of different experimental animals and plants. Biochemistry emphasizes man because we are men, and rats because they are similar to man in many ways. On the other hand, genetics has made the vinegar fly, *Drosophila*, and Indian corn, *Zea mays*, its classical experimental material, because they have convenient life cycles and are easy to grow under controlled conditions.

Maximum progress in understanding the chemical activity of the gene demands that an organism be studied both genetically and biochemically, and this, of course, suggests that an organism as favorable as possible for both kinds of study should be selected. A few years ago Dr. E. L. Tatum and the writer [5] decided that the red bread mold *Neurospora* was such an organism. Dodge [6] and Lindegren [12] in their extensive studies had already shown this fungus to be particularly favorable for genetic study. You may regard the jump from man to a bread mold as a large one. Actually, in terms of many of the basic properties of protoplasm, this is not true. The bread mold needs amino acids just as man does, and it uses them for much the same purposes. It differs from us only in its ability to make them from simple materials, whereas man must obtain them ready made in the diet. Many other substances, which will be discussed, are required by both man and bread mold.

GENIC CONTROL OF METABOLISM IN *NEUROSPORA CRASSA*

Neurospora crassa, the preferred species in our work, is a mold that grows in tropical or semitropical regions [2]. It produces great masses of brilliant, orange-red asexual spores. As indicated by its common name, *Neurospora* grows on bread. It is not a common mold in temperate climates but it may occasionally infest bakeries. It is a heterothallic fungus, although molds of the two sexes are not visibly different. One can tell the sex of an individual only by putting it with another individual of a known sex for observation. If nothing happens, they are of the same sex. If fusion and formation of fruiting bodies takes place, they are of opposite sex. The bread mold differs from man in having in each of its cell nuclei only one set of chromosomes and genes instead of two. In this respect it corresponds to our gametes—eggs and sperms. The double condition, corresponding to the fertilized egg in man in having a set of chromosomes from each parent, is limited in *Neurospora* to a single cell generation. Because the stage of the organism ordinarily observed has nuclei with single sets of chromosomes, *Neurospora* is relatively simple genetically. There is no need to worry about dominance and recessiveness—there is only one representative of each gene in each nucleus. The mendelian ratio usually observed is, therefore, the basic one-to-one, such as we would find in our own gametes if we could detect ratios there, rather than the derived and more familiar three-to-one ratio so often observed in higher organisms.

In addition to a sexual reproductive cycle, *Neurospora* multiplies profusely by vegetative means. Normal strains produce millions of microscopic orange spores called conidia which float about in the air and multiply the mold wherever conditions are favorable for growth. These asexual spores correspond genetically to cuttings of an apple tree or runners of a strawberry; they multiply the individual without genetic change. This is a big advantage in biochemical work, since it enables us to grow an unlimited amount of any one individual.

The life cycle of the common heterothallic species of *Neurospora crassa* and *sitophila*, is shown diagrammatically in Figure 52.

Neurospora grows readily in pure culture on a relatively simple medium [3]. Its basic requirements for growth and reproduction are (1) a source of energy and carbon, (2) a suitable source of nitrogen, such as nitrates or ammonium salts, (3) inorganic salts supplying phosphate, sulfur, potassium, calcium, iron, and several other elements, and (4) biotin, a recently discovered member of the B-group of vitamins. From these basic materials it makes everything that it requires for normal development and functioning. Since the mature mold contains at least nine vitamins of the B-group in addition to the biotin supplied it, it is obvious that it is capable of synthesizing them. In the same way, since its proteins contain some 20 or more amino acids, we know that it has the chemical machinery with which to build its own supply of these organic acids. The mold can also manufacture yellow pigments—precursors of vitamin A in the animal—nucleic acids, which are made up of purine and pyrimidine build-

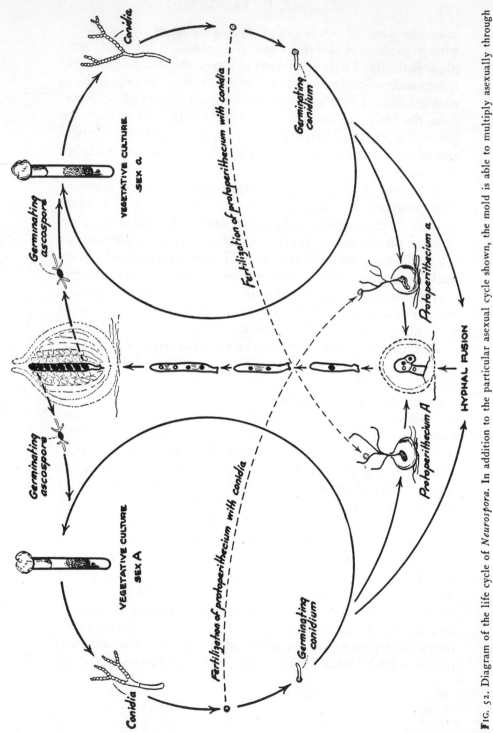

FIG. 52. Diagram of the life cycle of *Neurospora*. In addition to the particular asexual cycle shown, the mold is able to multiply asexually through microconidia and by means of fragments of the mycelium.

ing blocks, and a host of other compounds essential for its normal metabolism.

If it is true that genes are active in controlling the chemical reactions by which organisms function, it should be possible to modify the genes of the mold in such a way that it could no longer make all of the substances it requires from the materials supplied in a simple medium. We know from studies on *Drosophila*, corn, and other forms, that genes can be inactivated by various types of radiation—X rays, ultraviolet radiation, and neutrons. Treatments with these agents may either destroy genes completely or merely cripple them so that they no longer function normally [15]. In either event we can deduce from the change brought about in the organism the role of the gene in its normal condition. If in the manufacture of vitamin B-1 certain genes are essential, then destruction or inactivation of one of these genes should render the mold incapable of making this essential substance and, consequently, dependent on an external source, as we are.

In translating these theoretical considerations into experimental practice we follow the procedure illustrated in Figure 53. Conidia of a normal strain are irradiated with X rays, ultraviolet, or neutrons. They are then added to a normal culture of the opposite sex. Fusion occurs and fruiting bodies are formed. These contain many spore sacs in each of which there are produced eight black, ellipsoidal, sexual spores known as ascospores (literally "sac spores"). From one fruiting body a single ascospore is taken. This is placed on a medium in a culture tube and germinated. If the treatment of the conidia inactivated a gene concerned with the synthesis of vitamin B-1, there is a chance that the ascospore we select may carry this gene in the modified form. In this event, the mold arising from the spore will be unable to grow unless B-1 is supplied in the medium. To meet this contingency, we add some pure B-1 to the basic medium. But we cannot as yet aim beams of radiation at particular genes. Consequently, if we do produce a change that inactivates some one gene, it may not be one concerned with B-1 synthesis, but instead a gene that is essential for the synthesis of vitamin B-2 or any other compound. It is apparent, therefore, that if we want to save the maximum number of mutant types that cannot make biologically essential chemical compounds, the basal medium must be supplemented with all the known vitamins, all the known amino acids, and all other known compounds that are essential to the development and functioning of the mold. As a matter of fact, a gene concerned with the synthesis of an unknown substance, for instance a vitamin, is just as likely to be inactivated as one concerned with the formation of a known compound. If strains with such genes inactivated are to be saved, unknown as well as known substances must be added to the medium. At first thought this would seem to be impossible—how can a substance be added when it is unidentified? But it is not difficult to do this, since the mold normally makes everything it needs from the ingredients of the basal medium. The mold is ground, a crude extract made, and the extract added to the medium. Actually, there are commercial products, such as yeast extract, available which are essentially the same as such a *Neurospora* extract. By adding them the mold is supplied with substances the chemical nature of which is unknown.

A mold strain with one of the genes necessary for vitamin B-1 synthesis inactivated will now grow normally on the supplemented medium. This is fine, but a further test is needed to show that it requires B-1 from an external source. This test can be made by transferring conidia to a culture tube containing the unsupplemented basal medium. If the strain of mold cannot make B-1, growth will not occur. But failure of growth on "minimal" medium would also result if the strain were no longer capable of making any vitamin, any essential amino acid, or any other necessary substance. So growth on "complete" medium and absence of growth on minimal medium indicates merely a loss of ability to synthesize something present in the complete but not in the minimal medium. What the specific missing substance is must be determined by a systematic set of tests.

Before describing these tests it should be pointed out that when ascospores from fruiting bodies, one parent of which was treated with X rays or ultraviolet rays, are grown on complete medium, only about one or two per hundred give rise to "biochemical" mutant strains. An additional few per hundred give strains that are morphologically modified. These of course have their metabolism modified too, but the chance of finding out in just what way is so small that they are not investigated. The 1 or 2 per cent that give cultures growing on complete but not on minimal medium are investigated further.

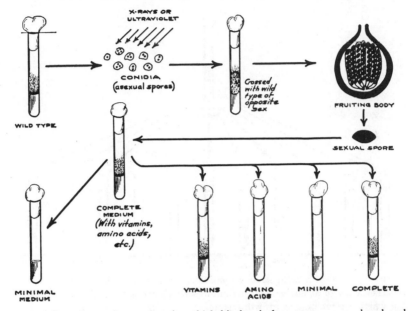

FIG. 53. Experimental procedure by which biochemical mutants are produced and detected in *Neurospora*.

Taking a particular modified strain that cannot grow on the minimal medium, asexual transfers are made to a series of tubes containing minimal medium supplemented with known substances. These are usually done in sets of four as indicated in Figure 53. The supplements are as follows:

Tube 1. Minimal plus known vitamins.
    2. Minimal plus known amino acids.
    3. Minimal (control).
    4. Complete (control).

The third and fourth tubes are controls to see that the mold shows the same behavior as that observed in the first tests. Strains usually fall into three groups when tested on these media. These are as follows:

1. Growth on vitamins but not on amino acids.
2. Growth on amino acids but not on vitamins.
3. No growth on vitamins and none on amino acids.

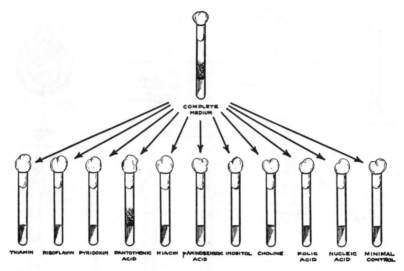

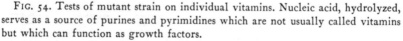

FIG. 54. Tests of mutant strain on individual vitamins. Nucleic acid, hydrolyzed, serves as a source of purines and pyrimidines which are not usually called vitamins but which can function as growth factors.

Behavior one suggests that the mold has lost the ability to make one or more of the known vitamins. If the second result is observed, the mold has lost the ability to make one or more of the amino acids. If the third result is obtained, some substance other than known amino acids or vitamins is needed. This may be a known chemical or one that remains to be discovered.

The strain chosen for illustration in Figure 53 grows on vitamins but not on amino acids. The next set of tests indicated include observations on the ability of the mold to grow on media supplemented with individual known vitamins, shown in Figure

54. It is evident that this particular strain grows only if pantothenic acid is supplied. We therefore conclude that the metabolic defect concerns the synthesis of pantothenic acid.

So far everything has been according to theory. But it is not yet known that transformation of the normal strain into one unable to make its own supply of pantothenic acid had anything to do with a gene. Genes are defined as units of inheritance. In order to tell whether the new strain differs from the old one in

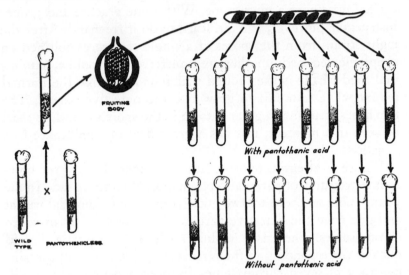

FIG. 55. Scheme by which the inheritance of a mutant type is determined. Transfers from medium supplemented with pantothenic acid to minimal medium are made by using conidia.

a gene, it must therefore be determined in an experimental test whether it differs in one unit of inheritance. This is done by crossing the new strain with an original strain of the opposite sex (Fig. 55). The two strains are merely put together in a tube on a suitable medium. They fuse and produce fruiting bodies containing sacs of eight spores. From the nuclear cycle, which will be explained shortly, and the principles of genetics it is known that if the two strains differ by one gene the spore sacs will contain ascospores of two kinds. One kind will give rise to strains like the normal parent that will be able to grow on a medium containing no pantothenic acid. The other type will be like the defective parent and will produce strains that require pantothenic acid for normal growth. To be sure we do not lose the defective strains, we grow the spores from individual sacs on a medium containing pantothenic acid. The eight spores from a sac are removed singly in the order in which they occur in the sac and planted individually. Since each spore is only approximately $\frac{1}{1000}$ of an inch long, this is a rather delicate operation carried out under a microscope. With some practice and proper instruction, however, one can learn to do it freehand. After the eight strains from the spores of a single sac are established on supplemented medium, they are transferred, by conidia, to minimal medium. It is then found that four grow like the normal parent while four fail to grow like the defective parent. The two types occur in a regular pattern in the spore sac and, as shall be seen in a moment, this has a great deal of significance to a geneticist.

Figure 56 attempts to make clear the genetic basis of the four-four segregation of parental types in individual spore sacs. In the young spore sac there are two nuclei, one from the normal parent and one from the defective parent. Each carries a set of seven chromosomes. These two haploid nuclei fuse to give a diploid nucleus corresponding to the fertilized egg in man and containing a set of seven chromosomes from each parent—14 in all. Since each of the members of a set is unique, there are seven pairs of chromosomes in the fusion nucleus. Unlike the nucleus of the human egg, the double nucleus in *Neurospora* immediately undergoes the meiotic divisions by which the chromosome number is again reduced to the single number. The course of these divisions is essentially similar to that of the corresponding divisions in most plants and animals. We know the chromosome number and the details of the meiotic divisions in *Neurospora crassa* as a result of recent work of Dr. Barbara McClintock [12 a]. In the course of the first meiotic division corresponding chromosomes pair side by side. In one of the members of one pair the normal parent contributes the normal form of a gene concerned with the synthesis of pantothenic acid. We indicate this with a plus sign. In a corresponding position in the other member of this pair of chromosomes is a defective form of the same gene contributed by the defective parent. This is indicated with a *p*, symbolic of its relation to pantothenic acid synthesis. In the diagram of chromosome behavior only the pair of

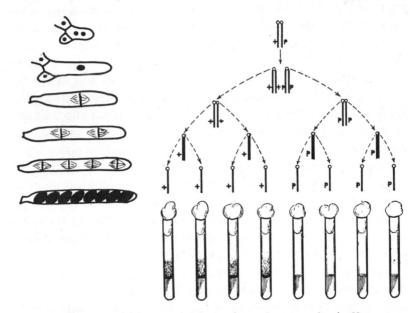

FIG. 56. Nuclear and chromosomal basis of genetic segregation in *Neurospora*. Corresponding nuclear and chromosomal stages are arranged on approximately the same horizontal position in the chart. The chromosomal basis of "first-division segregation" is shown.

chromosomes carrying the genes concerned with pantothenic acid synthesis are shown. In each spore sac six other pairs of chromosomes are, of course, acting similarly.

Following pairing, the chromosomes divide longitudinally except at one point. This one point is the so-called centromere— the point at which a chromosome becomes attached to a spindle fiber during cell division. With chromosome division each of the two forms of the gene we are talking about reproduces. Since sister chromosomes are attached to a single centromere, it follows that when this centromere is pulled to one of the poles of the spindle during the first meiotic division, either two plus genes or two defective genes will be pulled with it. Thus one of the two resulting daughter nuclei will carry two normal genes while the other will carry the two defective counterparts. In the second meiotic division the centromeres divide but the remaining parts of the chromosomes do not. One of the nuclei in this division produces two daughters carrying normal genes while the other produces daughters in which there are defective genes. At this point it is important to understand that the spindles formed during cell division are rigid structures and that they are large in relation to the spore sac. Consequently, the spindles lie in tandem in the spore sac and the nuclei do not slip past one another. This means that two of the four primary products of meiosis at one end of the spore sac will carry normal genes while those at the other end carry defective ones.

A third division takes place in each spore sac. This is an ordinary mitotic division in which each chromosome divides longitudinally throughout its length. The four meiotic products are duplicated in this division. Each of the eight nuclei resulting from the third division is included in an ascospore. Because of the special arrangements described (Fig. 56), four spores at one end will carry normal genes and will give strains of mold able to synthesize pantothenic acid while the remaining four will carry defective genes and will give mold strains dependent on an external supply of this B-vitamin.

An alternative arrangement of the two spore types is possible. The basis of this is indicated in Figure 57. During the origin of the tetrad stage of the first meiotic division, exchanges of corresponding segments of pair chromosomes occur. Since at any one position in a chromosome tetrad only two of the four chromosomes undergo this exchange, there results a cross-shaped structure known cytologically as a chiasma. If no chiasma falls between the pantothenic acid gene pair and the centromere of the chromosome in which they are carried, the segregation just described will result—two groups of four spores with respect to pantothenic acid requirement. On the other hand, if such a chiasma does fall between the segregating gene and its centro-

mere, the result will be that diagramed in Figure 57. Segregation does not occur until the second division and the final arrangement of spores is in alternating pairs with respect to their
genetic constitution. There is a simple relation between the position of the segregating gene pair in the chromosome and the
occurrence of chiasmata between it and the centromere. If the

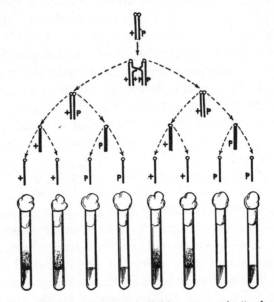

FIG. 57. Chromosomal basis of "second division segregation" of pantothenicless
mutant type.

gene pair is close to the centromere, there will be little chance
for a chiasma to fall between it and its centromere, while if it is
far away, the chance will be greater. For short distances, the
relation is one of direct proportionality. As a consequence we can
use frequency of second division segregation in *Neurospora* as a
measure of distance of the segregating gene from the centromere [12]. The principle involved here is used in the construction of chromosome maps in all organisms, but its application is
simpler in *Neurospora* than in most others.

    As can be seen from the mechanism of gene transmission in
the bread mold, there must be four spores like each parent in

each spore sac if there is a single gene difference between the two parents. The one-to-one ratio is entirely mechanical. If all spores are taken there can be no sampling error and as a consequence no statistical analysis is necessary. If this simple relationship is repeatedly observed in the fruiting bodies from a cross such as that between normal and pantothenic-defective strains, it is convincing evidence of the unitary nature of the difference between them. In other words, the modified strain differs from the original one by something that behaves as a single hereditary unit, or gene. From the standpoint of classical genetics alone, a gene never means more than this. The strain that cannot make its own pantothenic acid differs from the original strain by one gene, according to this criterion. Consequently the conclusion that the treatment modified a gene normally concerned in some essential step in the synthesis of this particular chemical substance is justified.

If many ascospores are tested in this manner, strains are found, among the 1 or 2 per cent of biochemical mutants, that cannot make other B-group vitamins, amino acids, or other compounds. At Stanford tests of this kind have been made on some 80,000 spores and, among the strains derived from them, many are deficient in their ability to carry out essential syntheses. There are so many that their genetical and biochemical analysis is by no means complete. But of those tested so far the great majority lack the ability to make only one compound and thus differ from the original wild type by single genes. These studies constitute gratifying support of our original assumption that genes in general act by controlling specific chemical reactions.

As a sample of the kinds of compounds, the syntheses of which are interrupted in particular mutant strains, Figure 58 shows the tentative positions in the chromosomes of a number of the genes that have been investigated in this manner. Relative distances of genes from the centromeres of the chromosomes in which they are carried are determined by the method already described. Whether two separate genes are carried in the same chromosome pair or in two different ones is indicated by whether they segregate dependently or independently in crosses in which both genes are segregating. It should be emphasized that the map positions indicated are only approximate, and that, because of selection of particular genes and particular chromosomes for study, the genes involved do not constitute a random sample. It is seen that genes having to do with the syntheses of many different compounds are represented. Still others are

FIG. 58. Tentative chromosome map of *Neurospora crassa* showing positions of certain genes concerned with the synthesis of known chemical compounds. Distances shown are only approximate. In many instances an alternative sequence of closely linked genes has not been excluded.

known that have not yet been located on the chromosome maps.

Omitting biotin, which the original mold cannot make, genes having to do with the vitamins B-1, B-2, B-6, niacin, pantothenic acid, *p*-aminobenzoic acid, inositol, and choline, have been modified [11]. Genes active in the elaboration of the amino acids arginine, isoleucine, leucine, lysine, methionine, phenylalanine, proline, threonine, tryptophane, and valine have been identified through their mutation [11]. Others are known which concern the synthesis of purines and pyrimidines—components of nucleic acid [11].

The list of compounds that *Neurospora* can be made to require from an external source is remarkably similar to a list of chemicals that we cannot make and require in our food supply. It is clear, therefore, that the substances the bread mold needs in its metabolism are very much the same as those we need. The difference is only an apparent one and results from the fact that bread mold makes them whereas we let some other organism make many of them for us. By inactivating the right genes the bread mold can be made very similar to man in its nutritional requirements.

The comparison of our synthetic abilities with those of the bread mold is not flattering to us, and in one sense we are quite defective. If B-1 were not supplied in our diet, we would be in a bad way indeed. But since in our normal environment there is an adequate supply of B-1 in our food, in this setting man is not defective. The human organism and the bread mold have evolved in different directions. Because it was no advantage to us to be able to synthesize vitamins and amino acids, we presumably lost the ability to do so through gene mutation some time in our distant evolutionary past. The bread mold, on the other hand, evidently finds it an advantage to carry out these synthetic processes and to be able to grow where the substances concerned are not obtainable in sufficient quantities.

A strain of *Neurospora* that cannot make a particular substance that it needs can be used to detect that substance both qualitatively and quantitatively. Thus if a strain that cannot synthesize B-1 is able to grow on a given medium, we know that that medium contains B-1 or something sufficiently closely related to substitute for it. Furthermore, through measuring the amount of growth that occurs we can determine, by comparison with the control on known quantities of B-1, the approximate amount of B-1 in the medium. Such methods of measuring vitamins and amino acids are known as bioassays. They are of importance because they often provide the basis by which vitamins are discovered and by which their subsequent isolation is accomplished. Even when chemical tests are available, bioassay methods are important because of their convenience, their ability to measure very small quantities, and their high specificity. In the past, naturally occurring organisms have been widely used for such bioassay procedures. The method of inducing specific metabolic defects in an organism opens up new possibilities in making bioassay organisms to order. Certain of the *Neurospora* mutant strains have already been put to use in this way [1]. But this has nothing to do with our original problem, the nature of gene action—it merely adds another to a long list of examples showing that useful applications may often come out of work that appears to have no practical value.

Our knowledge of the relationship between genes and chemical reactions can be put to use in another way. In much the same way as human individuals with heritable errors in phenylalanine-tyrosine metabolism have been used to work out the details of the processes involved, mutant strains of bread mold can be used to determine the details of its metabolism. An example of this is provided in the work of Srb and Horowitz [16] on strains of mold unable to make the amino acid arginine, and consequently requiring it, or some closely related compound, in the medium. They have studied seven different strains of this kind, each of which differs from the normal type of mold in one gene. But in each of these seven strains a different gene has been modified. This is known through genetic tests. The seven genes are located in seven different positions in the chromosomes. If a strain carrying one of them in defective form is crossed with a strain in which different gene is defective, it is possible to recover among the offspring types which carry the normal forms of both genes. This would not be possible if the defective genes in the two strains were the same.

Experiments on the nutritional requirements of the seven strains show that four of them will grow if supplied with any one of the three related amino acids—ornithine, citrulline, or arginine (Fig. 59). Two respond to citrulline or arginine, but not to ornithine. The seventh strain requires arginine and will not respond to either ornithine or citrulline. These results are interpreted in Figure 59. Gene 7 is concerned with the reaction by which citrulline is converted to arginine. If this gene is defective, the fungus must have arginine in its food supply. If either gene 5 or 6 is defective ornithine cannot be made into citrulline, and strains carrying either of those genes in defective form will grow on arginine or on citrulline, on the latter because it can be made into arginine. If any one of genes 1, 2, 3, or 4 is defective the mold cannot make ornithine. Because this is a precursor of citrulline, and citrulline a precursor of arginine, mold strains of this type are unable to complete the synthesis. If ornithine is supplied, the mold can complete the synthesis.

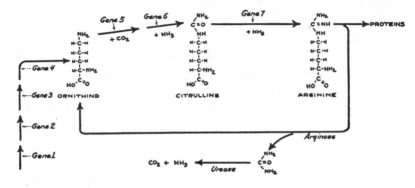

FIG. 59. Ornithine cycle in *Neurospora*. (Based on work of Srb and Horowitz [16].)

The cells of *Neurospora* contain the enzyme arginase which catalyzes the reaction by which arginine is split into a molecule of urea plus one of ornithine. The urea may be further degraded in the presence of the enzyme urease to carbon dioxide and ammonia. The regenerated ornithine is available for reconversion to arginine in normal strains. Thus it is seen that the process is cyclic. With each turn of the cycle, one molecule of urea is formed. It is interesting that this ornithine cycle in *Neurospora* is similar to the cycle in the mammalian liver postulated by Krebs and Henseleit. This is an additional indication that many of our basic metabolic processes resemble those of the bread mold.

Let us examine the ornithine cycle, as shown in Figure 59, to identify the role of the genes. The change of citrulline into arginine is a single chemical reaction and one gene is known that is concerned. Ornithine is changed to citrulline through two reactions, the addition of carbon dioxide and of ammonia. There are two genes known to control the two steps; presumably one normally directs the addition of carbon dioxide to give carbamino-ornithine, whereas the other controls the further step by which ammonia is added to give citrulline. Unfortunately, no one knows how ornithine is synthesized by *Neurospora* or any other organism. It is reasonable to suppose that there are at least several different reactions. Because instances exist in which there appears to be only one gene in charge of a reaction, it is logical to suppose that each of the four genes concerned with ornithine synthesis controls a different reaction. Actually, the assumption of a one-to-one correspondence between genes and reactions is consistent with the facts known about the ornithine cycle in *Neurospora*.

Before the analysis of arginine biosynthesis in *Neurospora* was made, ornithine and citrulline were known to be precursors of arginine in the mammal. This is unusual, for it is not known from what precursors organisms make other amino acids. Using the method of biochemical genetics Tatum and Bonner [21] have shown how tryptophane is made by *Neurospora*. This substance is another of the amino acids needed by all organisms as a part of their protoplasmic proteins. Man must get it in his food, but normal strains of *Neurospora* are able to synthesize it. Tatum and Bonner were able to show that this is done by combining indole and serine, as shown in Figure 60. Serine is itself an important amino acid. It can function in protein synthesis or it can become a part of tryptophane, which then enters protein molecules as a basic building block. Although it is not certain, it is assumed that all organisms that make tryptophane do so in essentially the same way as *Neurospora*. It has been possible to learn still more about the biosynthesis of tryptophane. Two mutant strains have been studied that cannot make indole. If supplied with this, they are able to combine it with serine, which they are able to make, and obtain their necessary supply of tryptophane. If the strain in which gene 2 is defective is grown in the presence of a small amount of tryptophane, the synthesis of 1-indole proceeds normally up to the last step. Because this cannot be taken, a precursor of indole is accumulated and excreted into the medium. The precursor was isolated and its chemical nature determined, which was that of anthranilic acid (ortho-aminobenzoic acid). We are therefore able to say that the biosynthesis of tryptophane in *Neurospora* involves the conversion of anthranilic acid to indole, followed by condensation with serine. The precise nature of the chemical step by which anthranilic acid is converted to indole is not yet known.

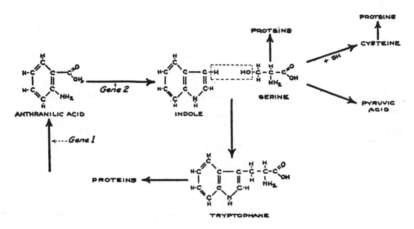

FIG. 60. Tryptophane synthesis in *Neurospora*. (Based on work of Tatum and Bonner [21].)

My colleagues, Dr. Horowitz, Dr. Bonner, and Mrs. Houlahan [10] are attempting to find out how choline is made in *Neurospora*. Choline is important to us in many ways. For example, it is a part of the acetylcholine molecule which is engaged in the transmission of nerve impulses. It is also a component of lecithin, a compound universally present in protoplasm and significant in surface phenomena. Finally, choline functions as a carrier of the methyl groups which we cannot make. They are important in the synthesis of compounds like methionine (Fig. 61). *Neurospora* uses choline for at least the last two indicated purposes. Its biosynthesis is interrupted if either of two genes is made defective through mutation (Fig. 61). If gene 2 is defective in a strain growing on a small amount of choline, a pre-

cursor of choline accumulates in the fungus mycelium and the
medium. If the precursor is supplied to a strain in which gene 1
is defective, it is made into choline. The chemical nature of this
precursor of choline has not yet been determined. When it has
been, the process of choline synthesis will be considerably clarified.

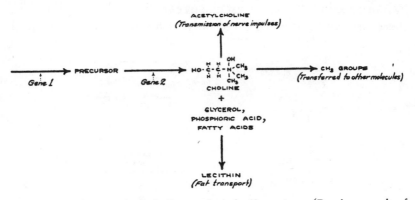

FIG. 61. Genetic control of choline synthesis in *Neurospora*. (Based on work of
Horowitz, Bonner, and Houlahan [10].)

Using biochemical genetics in an essentially similar way, Dr.
Bonner [4] is studying two genetically different mutant types
of *Neurospora* that cannot synthesize the vitamin niacin (Fig.
62). If a strain in which gene 2 is present in the mutant form
is grown under suitable conditions, a precursor of niacin is accumulated which can be used in place of niacin by a strain in
which gene 1 is defective. Again the chemical identification of
this precursor is not yet complete but the indications are clear
that the method is a most useful one.

Unfortunately, the identification of intermediates in biosynthetic processes by genetically blocking their normal utilization is not always so simple in practice as the examples might
suggest. Apparently, the intermediates are sometimes used up
by the organism in ways that are alternative to the normal path
of synthesis. Dr. Mitchell and Mrs. Houlahan [14] have investigated purine synthesis and have found a particular mutant strain
that cannot make adenine. Instead, it makes a purple pigment

that accumulates in the mold mycelium and in the culture medium. Another strain, also unable to make adenine, does not make the purple pigment and cannot use it to replace adenine as a growth factor. The tentative interpretation of this situation is given in Figure 63. It is assumed that a precursor of adenine, formed when gene 2 is defective, is converted to purple pigment by a process involving at least one irreversible reaction. There is, therefore, no simple and direct way of finding out the chemical

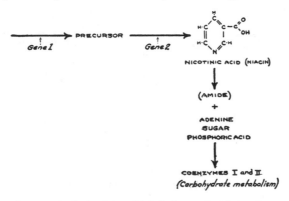

FIG. 62. Genetic control of nicotinic acid (niacin synthesis) in *Neurospora*. (Based on work of Bonner [4] .)

nature of the precursor. In the strain that makes purple pigment, the pigment is a substance not made by normal strains in detectable quantities. It appears that something has been added by inactivating a gene. In one sense this is true. Looked at in another way, however, the change is seen to consist merely in substituting purple pigment—for which the mold apparently has no use—for adenine, a compound that it must have. It is easy to imagine situations arising during the course of evolution in which the substitution of one end product of a synthetic chain for another might be of advantage to the organism. Man may have substituted other end products for at least some of the vitamins and amino acids that he can no longer synthesize and must consequently obtain in his food.

Among the mutant types that are able to grow on complete but cannot grow on minimal medium are some that do not grow on any of the known vitamins, amino acids, or other substances. It is possible that some of these have lost the ability to make substances, the biological significance of which has not yet been recognized. There are, however, alternative possibilities. Sometimes the conditions under which a mutant strain can utilize a substance necessary for growth are so restricted that the required substance is not identified in the preliminary tests. For example,

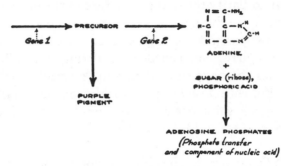

FIG. 63. Genetic control of adenine synthesis in *Neurospora*. (Based on work of Mitchell and Houlahan [14].)

Doermann [7] has shown that a strain unable to make lysine, responds to external lysine only if the arginine content of the medium is not too high. Another type requires the two related amino acids isoleucine and valine in a particular ratio. All possibilities of this type must be eliminated before the conclusion is justified that a "new" vitamin or amino acid is required. Final proof demands that the alleged new compound be chemically identified. No clear evidence for the existence of additional vitamins of the B-group or of amino acids other than those already known as protein constituents has been obtained in *Neurospora,* although not all of the mutant types appearing to require unknown substances have been analyzed in detail.

THE NATURE OF THE GENE

The reactions that are subject to control by genes are certainly of many kinds. Some of them, like those concerned with certain types of pigmentation, are of relatively minor importance to the organism. Others are of vital importance—the organism cannot exist in their absence unless their products are supplied already made. What is the nature of this gene control? Why is it that when a single gene is modified, a particular reaction fails to be carried out? Complete answers to questions of this kind require a knowledge of the structure of the gene as yet nonexistent. However, certain possibilities may be suggested that have some support.

One way to clarify the chemical nature of the gene is by direct chemical analysis. But because genes in pure form have not been isolated, this method cannot be used directly. Mirsky and Pollister [13] have succeeded in isolating the substance of chromosomes and have shown them to be largely nucleoprotein in nature. But chromosomes presumably contain a high proportion of nongenic substance and it is, therefore, possible that the genes differ chemically from the bulk of the chromosome material.

A second way of obtaining information as to the structure of genes involves an indirect measurement of their absorption spectra. As discussed above, ultraviolet radiation has the property of causing genes to mutate. Its efficiency in this respect is dependent on its wave length. If the mutation-producing efficiency per unit energy is plotted against wave length, a curve is obtained that is very similar to the curve of absorption of ultraviolet radiation by nucleic acid [17]. This parallelism strongly suggests that nucleic acid is a component of genes and that it is the component responsible for absorbing the energy producing mutational changes. While this is the simplest hypothesis, it is possible that the nucleic acid is extragenic and that it transfers the mutation-producing energy to the gene.

A third line of evidence involves analogy. Viruses and bacteriophages are self-duplicating units that have several important properties in common with genes [1, 18]. They have the property of self-duplication and, like genes, they multiply only in the living cell, presumably because only there do they find the necessary compounds out of which to construct more units like themselves. Both genes and viruses influence the metabolism of the organism. The properties responsible for this influence are subject to spontaneous change without the loss of the power of self-duplication—that is, both are subject to mutation. Although admittedly crude, estimates have been made of the sizes of genes. They appear to be of the same order of magnitude as tobacco mosaic virus, a medium-sized virus which can be measured directly under the electron microscope. With these several common properties, one might expect genes and viruses to be at least closely related chemically. Following Stanley's work on tobacco mosaic virus, several other viruses have been isolated in pure form. They are all nucleoproteins [1, 18] which increases our confidence in the conclusion suggested by independent evidence that genes, too, are nucleoproteins.

Even if the conclusion that genes are nucleoproteins were certain, there would still remain much to be learned about their chemistry, since there is an almost unlimited number of proteins and at least two types of nucleic acid.

In the process of reduplication genes and viruses must somehow direct the formation of new molecules like themselves—in the absence of old molecules, no new ones like them are found. This has suggested to geneticists and chemists that these self-duplicating particles act as master molecules or templets against which new particles like themselves are constructed [5, 9, 15, 22]. If they contain proteins, part of their reproduction must involve protein synthesis. If so, it would seem reasonable to suppose that nongenic proteins—the proteins of antigens, of enzymes, and of structural elements such as muscle fibers—are similarly built up under the direction of genes containing protein components of corresponding specificities. On this basis we would expect that the loss or modification of a particular gene would result in absence or modification of the corresponding nongenic protein. If this were an antigen protein, an antigenic modification would result. Many instances of genic control of antigen specificities are known, for example, the blood group antigens in man [19]. It is usual to find a one-to-one relation between genes and antigens. If the modified gene were concerned with an enzyme protein, one would expect the enzyme whose specificity corresponded to the particular protein to be absent or modified.

This, in turn, would result in the failure or modification of the chemical reaction normally catalyzed by the enzyme in question. This interpretation is in agreement with the observed correspondence between genes and chemical reactions.

However the process of gene multiplication is brought about —and there is little definite information to go on—the pieces out of which new genes are built must themselves be synthesized. The reactions by which these syntheses are accomplished will usually be enzymatically catalyzed and, on the assumptions outlined, under gene control. In other words, before any gene can reproduce, many other genes must have acted. This is only another way of concluding that the organism is not merely a bag of chemical reactions, but a complex and highly integrated system in which reactions are systematically related in both time and space. If one gene in the system is altered, one reaction will be modified. But, although this relation may be a relatively simple one, the subsequent consequences will usually be multitudinous. In fact, if all representatives of almost any gene in an organism are removed or replaced by a completely inactive form of the gene the chances are very great that the organism can no longer survive. If man were able to synthesize vitamin B-1 from simpler compounds and he lived on a diet free of this substance, a gene mutation could occur which would make the individual incapable of carrying out this synthesis. The primary effect of the gene change would be simple—inability to make B-1. But the final consequence would be death. Physiologically exactly the same thing happens when man, with his inability to synthesize B-1, is deprived of a dietary source of this vitamin. The initial event is simple—absence of B-1. But, again, changes of increasing complexity follow. These include inflammation of the nerves, muscular debility, rigidity of the limbs, often widespread edema, gradual wasting away, and, finally, death.

If the maximum possible understanding of what the organism is and what it does is to be obtained, it is clear that our approach must be made from many sides. In the present state of knowledge the chemist cannot understand what the organism does chemically without considering genes. Therefore, the methods of genetics, which are biological—not chemical, must supplement those of chemistry. In the same way, a biologist would be blind if he were to ignore chemistry in his attempts to understand how the organism is built and how it functions. Biochemical genetics represents an approach in which the coöperation of two disciplines is essential.

For References see p. 343.

CHAPTER VI

Genes and the Chemistry of the Organism by G. W. Beadle

1. BAWDEN, F. C. Plant viruses and virus diseases. Chronica Botanica Company, Waltham, Mass., 1943. 294 pp.
2. BEADLE, G. W. Genetics and metabolism in *Neurospora. Physiol. Rev.*, 25, 643–663, 1945.
3. —— and TATUM, E. L. Genetic control of biochemical reactions in *Neurospora. Proc. Nat. Acad. Sci.*, 27, 499–506, 1941.
4. BONNER, D. Unpublished work. Referred to in [11] and [20].
5. DELBRÜCK, M. A theory of autocatalytic synthesis of polypeptides and its application to the problem of chromosome reproduction. *Cold Spring Harbor Symp. Quant. Biol.*, 9, 122–124, 1941.
6. DODGE, B. O. Nuclear phenomena associated with heterothallism and homothallism in the ascomycete *Neurospora. Jour. Agr. Res.*, 35, 289–305, 1927.
7. DOERMANN, A. H. A lysineless mutant of *Neurospora* and its inhibition by arginine. *Arch. Biochem.*, 5, 373–384, 1944.
8. GARROD, A. E. Inborn errors of metabolism. 2d ed. Oxford University Press, London, 1923. 216 pp.
9. HALDANE, J. B. S. New paths in genetics. Harper & Bros., New York, 1942. 206 pp.
10. HOROWITZ, N. H., BONNER, D., and HOULAHAN, M. B. The utilization of choline analogues by cholineless mutants of *Neurospora. Jour. Biol. Chem.*, 159, 145–151, 1945.
11. —— BONNER, D., MITCHELL, H. K., TATUM, E. L., and BEADLE, G. W. Genic control of biochemical reactions in *Neurospora. Am. Naturalist*, 79, 304–317, 1945.
12. LINDEGREN, C. C. The use of fungi in modern genetical analysis. *Iowa State College Jour. Sci.*, 16, 271–290, 1942.
12a. McClintock, B. Neurospora. I. Preliminary observations of the chromosomes of *Neurospora crassa. Amer. Jour. Bul.*, 32, 671–678, 1945.
13. MIRSKY, A. E., and POLLISTER, A. W. Studies on the chemistry of chromatin. *Trans. New York Acad. Sci.*, Series II, 5, 190–198, 1943.
14. MITCHELL, H. K., and HOULAHAN, M. B. Unpublished, referred to in [11] and [20].
15. MULLER, H. J. Résumé and perspectives of the symposium on genes and chromosomes. *Cold Spring Harbor Symp. Quant. Biol.*, 9, 290–308, 1941.

16. SRB, A. M., and HOROWITZ, N. H. The ornithine cycle in *Neurospora* and its genetic control. *Jour. Biol. Chem.*, *154*, 129–139, 1944.

17. STADLER, L. J., and UBER, F. M. Genetic effects of ultraviolet radiation in maize IV. Comparisons of monochromatic radiations. *Genetics*, *27*, 84–118, 1942.

18. STANLEY, W. M. Chemical structure and the mutation of viruses. In: Virus diseases. Cornell University Press, Ithaca, N. Y., 1943.

19. STRANDSKOV, H. H. Physiological aspects of human genetics, five human blood characteristics. *Physiol. Rev.*, *24*, 445–446, 1944.

20. TATUM, E. L., and BEADLE, G. W. Biochemical genetics of *Neurospora*. *Annals Mo. Bot. Gard.*, *32*, 125–129, 1945.

21. —— and BONNER, D. Indole and serine in the biosynthesis and breakdown of tryptophane. *Proc. Nat. Acad. Sci.*, *30*, 30–37, 1944.

22. WRIGHT, S. Physiology of the gene. *Physiol. Rev.*, *21*, 487–527, 1941.

Reprinted from SCIENCE, November 25, 1949, Vol. 110, No. 2865, pages 543–548.

Sickle Cell Anemia, a Molecular Disease[1]

Linus Pauling, Harvey A. Itano,[2] S. J. Singer,[2] and Ibert C. Wells[3]

Gates and Crellin Laboratories of Chemistry,
California Institute of Technology, Pasadena, California[4]

THE ERYTHROCYTES of certain individuals possess the capacity to undergo reversible changes in shape in response to changes in the partial pressure of oxygen. When the oxygen pressure is lowered, these cells change their forms from the normal biconcave disk to crescent, holly wreath, and other forms. This process is known as sickling. About 8 percent of American Negroes possess this characteristic; usually they exhibit no pathological consequences ascribable to it. These people are said to have sicklemia, or sickle cell trait. However, about 1 in 40 (4) of these individuals whose cells are capable of sickling suffer from a severe chronic anemia resulting from excessive destruction of their erythrocytes; the term sickle cell anemia is applied to their condition.

The main observable difference between the erythrocytes of sickle cell trait and sickle cell anemia has been that a considerably greater reduction in the partial pressure of oxygen is required for a major fraction of the trait cells to sickle than for the anemia cells (11). Tests *in vivo* have demonstrated that between 30 and 60 percent of the erythrocytes in the venous circulation of sickle cell anemic individuals, but less than 1 percent of those in the venous circulation of sicklemic individuals, are normally sickled. Experiments *in vitro* indicate that under sufficiently low oxygen pressure, however, all the cells of both types assume the sickled form.

The evidence available at the time that our investigation was begun indicated that the process of sickling might be intimately associated with the state and the nature of the hemoglobin within the erythrocyte. Sickle cell erythrocytes in which the hemoglobin is combined with oxygen or carbon monoxide have the biconcave disk contour and are indistinguishable in

that form from normal erythrocytes. In this condition they are termed promeniscocytes. The hemoglobin appears to be uniformly distributed and randomly oriented within normal cells and promeniscocytes, and no birefringence is observed. Both types of cells are very flexible. If the oxygen or carbon monoxide is removed, however, transforming the hemoglobin to the uncombined state, the promeniscocytes undergo sickling. The hemoglobin within the sickled cells appears to aggregate into one or more foci, and the cell membranes collapse. The cells become birefringent (11) and quite rigid. The addition of oxygen or carbon monoxide to these cells reverses these phenomena. Thus the physical effects just described depend on the state of combination of the hemoglobin, and only secondarily, if at all, on the cell membrane. This conclusion is supported by the observation that sickled cells when lysed with water produce discoidal, rather than sickle-shaped, ghosts (10).

It was decided, therefore, to examine the physical and chemical properties of the hemoglobins of individuals with sicklemia and sickle cell anemia, and to compare them with the hemoglobin of normal individuals to determine whether any significant differences might be observed.

EXPERIMENTAL METHODS

The experimental work reported in this paper deals largely with an electrophoretic study of these hemoglobins. In the first phase of the investigation, which concerned the comparison of normal and sickle cell anemia hemoglobins, three types of experiments were performed: 1) with carbonmonoxyhemoglobins; 2) with uncombined ferrohemoglobins in the presence of dithionite ion, to prevent oxidation to methemoglobins; and 3) with carbonmonoxyhemoglobins in the presence of dithionite ion. The experiments of type 3 were performed and compared with those of type 1 in order to ascertain whether the dithionite ion itself causes any specific electrophoretic effect.

Samples of blood were obtained from sickle cell anemic individuals who had not been transfused within three months prior to the time of sampling. Stroma-free concentrated solutions of human adult hemoglobin were prepared by the method used by Drabkin (3). These solutions were diluted just before use with the

[1] This research was carried out with the aid of a grant from the United States Public Health Service. The authors are grateful to Professor Ray D. Owen, of the Biology Division of this Institute, for his helpful suggestions. We are indebted to Dr. Edward R. Evans, of Pasadena, Dr. Travis Winsor, of Los Angeles, and Dr. G. E. Burch, of the Tulane University School of Medicine, New Orleans, for their aid in obtaining the blood used in these experiments.
[2] U. S. Public Health Service postdoctoral fellow of the National Institutes of Health.
[3] Postdoctoral fellow of the Division of Medical Sciences of the National Research Council.
[4] Contribution No. 1333.

SELECTED PAPERS ON MOLECULAR GENETICS

appropriate buffer until the hemoglobin concentrations were close to 0.5 grams per 100 milliliters, and then were dialyzed against large volumes of these buffers for 12 to 24 hours at 4° C. The buffers for the experiments of types 2 and 3 were prepared by adding 300 ml of 0.1 ionic strength sodium dithionite solution to 3.5 liters of 0.1 ionic strength buffer. About 100 ml of 0.1 molar NaOH was then added to bring the pH of the buffer back to its original value. Ferrohemoglobin solutions were prepared by diluting the

concentrated solutions with this dithionite-containing buffer and dialyzing against it under a nitrogen atmosphere. The hemoglobin solutions for the experiments of type 3 were made up similarly, except that they were saturated with carbon monoxide after dilution and were dialyzed under a carbon monoxide atmosphere. The dialysis bags were kept in continuous motion in the buffers by means of a stirrer with a mercury seal to prevent the escape of the nitrogen and carbon monoxide gases.

The experiments were carried out in the modified Tiselius electrophoresis apparatus described by Swingle (14). Potential gradients of 4.8 to 8.4 volts per centimeter were employed, and the duration of the runs varied from 6 to 20 hours. The pH values of the buffers were measured after dialysis on samples which had come to room temperature.

RESULTS

The results indicate that a significant difference exists between the electrophoretic mobilities of hemoglobin derived from erythrocytes of normal individuals and from those of sickle cell anemic individuals. The two types of hemoglobin are particularly easily distinguished as the carbonmonoxy compounds at pH 6.9 in phosphate buffer of 0.1 ionic strength. In this buffer the sickle cell anemia carbonmonoxyhemoglobin moves as a positive ion, while the normal compound moves as a negative ion, and there is no detectable amount of one type present in the other.[4] The hemoglobin derived from erythrocytes of individuals with sicklemia, however, appears to be a mixture of the normal hemoglobin and sickle cell anemia hemoglobin in roughly equal proportions. Up to the present time the hemoglobins of 15 persons with sickle cell anemia, 8 persons with sicklemia, and 7 normal adults have been examined. The hemoglobins of normal adult white and negro individuals were found to be indistinguishable.

The mobility data obtained in phosphate buffers of 0.1 ionic strength and various values of pH are summarized in Figs. 1 and 2.[5]

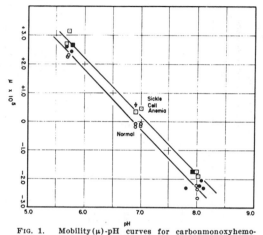

FIG. 1. Mobility(μ)-pH curves for carbonmonoxyhemoglobins in phosphate buffers of 0.1 ionic strength. The black circles and black squares denote the data for experiments performed with buffers containing dithionite ion. The open square designated by the arrow represents an average value of 10 experiments on the hemoglobin of different individuals with sickle cell anemia. The mobilities recorded in this graph are averages of the mobilities in the ascending and descending limbs.

[4] Occasionally small amounts (less than 5 percent of the total protein) of material with mobilities different from that of either kind of hemoglobin were observed in these uncrystallized hemoglobin preparations. According to the observations of Stern, Reiner, and Silber (12) a small amount of a component with a mobility smaller than that of oxyhemoglobin is present in human erythrocyte hemolyzates.

[5] The results obtained with carbonmonoxyhemoglobins with and without dithionite ion in the buffers indicate that the dithionite ion plays no significant role in the electrophoretic properties of the proteins. It is therefore of interest that ferrohemoglobin was found to have a lower isoelectric point in phosphate buffer than carbonmonoxyhemoglobin. Titration studies have indicated (5, 6) that oxyhemoglobin (similar in electrophoretic properties to the carbonmonoxy compound) has a lower isoelectric point than ferrohemoglobin in

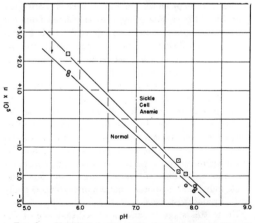

FIG. 2. Mobility(μ)-pH curves for ferrohemoglobins in phosphate buffers of 0.1 ionic strength containing dithionite ion. The mobilities recorded in the graph are averages of the mobilities in the ascending and descending limbs.

The isoelectric points are listed in Table 1. These results prove that the electrophoretic difference between normal hemoglobin and sickle cell anemia hemoglobin

TABLE 1

Isoelectric Points in Phosphate Buffer, $\mu = 0.1$

Compound	Normal	Sickle cell anemia	Difference
Carbonmonoxyhemoglobin	6.87	7.09	0.22
Ferrohemoglobin	6.68	6.91	0.23

exists in both ferrohemoglobin and carbonmonoxyhemoglobin. We have also performed several experiments in a buffer of 0.1 ionic strength and pH 6.52 containing 0.08 M NaCl, 0.02 M sodium cacodylate, and 0.0083 M cacodylic acid. In this buffer the average mobility of sickle cell anemia carbonmonoxyhemoglobin is 2.63×10^{-5}, and that of normal carbonmonoxyhemoglobin is 2.23×10^{-5} cm/sec per volt/cm.[6]

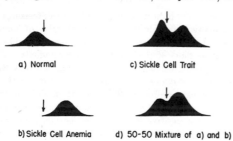

a) Normal

b) Sickle Cell Anemia

c) Sickle Cell Trait

d) 50-50 Mixture of a) and b)

FIG. 3. Longsworth scanning diagrams of carbonmonoxyhemoglobins in phosphate buffer of 0.1 ionic strength and pH 6.90 taken after 20 hours' electrophoresis at a potential gradient of 4.73 volts/cm.

These experiments with a buffer quite different from phosphate buffer demonstrate that the difference between the hemoglobins is essentially independent of the buffer ions.

Typical Longsworth scanning diagrams of experiments with normal, sickle cell anemia, and sicklemia carbonmonoxyhemoglobins, and with a mixture of the first two compounds, all in phosphate buffer of pH 6.90 and ionic strength 0.1, are reproduced in Fig. 3. It is apparent from this figure that the sicklemia material contains less than 50 percent of the anemia component. In order to determine this quantity accurately some experiments at a total protein concentra-

the absence of other ions. These results might be reconciled by assuming that the ferrous iron of ferrohemoglobin forms complexes with phosphate ions which cannot be formed when the iron is combined with oxygen or carbon monoxide. We propose to continue the study of this phenomenon.

[6] The mobility data show that in 0.1 ionic strength cacodylate buffers the isoelectric points of the hemoglobins are increased about 0.5 pH unit over their values in 0.1 ionic strength phosphate buffers. This effect is similar to that observed by Longsworth in his study of ovalbumin (7).

tion of 1 percent were performed with known mixtures of sickle cell anemia and normal carbonmonoxyhemoglobins in the cacodylate-sodium chloride buffer of 0.1 ionic strength and pH 6.52 described above. This buffer was chosen in order to minimize the anomalous electrophoretic effects observed in phosphate buffers (7). Since the two hemoglobins were incompletely resolved after 15 hours of electrophoresis under a potential gradient of 2.79 volts/cm, the method of Tiselius and Kabat (16) was employed to allocate the

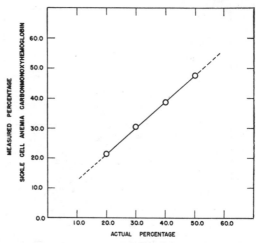

FIG. 4. The determination of the percent of sickle cell anemia carbonmonoxyhemoglobin in known mixtures of the protein with normal carbonmonoxyhemoglobin by means of electrophoretic analysis. The experiments were performed in a cacodylate sodium chloride buffer described in the text.

areas under the peaks in the electrophoresis diagrams to the two components. In Fig. 4 there is plotted the percent of the anemia component calculated from the areas so obtained against the percent of that component in the known mixtures. Similar experiments were performed with a solution in which the hemoglobins of 5 sicklemic individuals were pooled. The relative concentrations of the two hemoglobins were calculated from the electrophoresis diagrams, and the actual proportions were then determined from the plot of Fig. 4. A value of 39 percent for the amount of the sickle cell anemia component in the sicklemia hemoglobin was arrived at in this manner. From the experiments we have performed thus far it appears that this value does not vary greatly from one sicklemic individual to another, but a more extensive study of this point is required.

Up to this stage we have assumed that one of the two components of sicklemia hemoglobin is identical with sickle cell anemia hemoglobin and the other is identical with the normal compound. Aside from the genetic evidence which makes this assumption very probable (see the discussion section), electrophoresis experiments afford direct evidence that the assumption is valid. The experiments on the pooled sicklemia carbonmonoxyhemoglobin and the mixture containing 40 percent sickle cell anemia carbonmonoxyhemoglobin and 60 percent normal carbonmonoxyhemoglobin in the cacodylate-sodium chloride buffer described above were compared, and it was found that the mobilities of the respective components were essentially identical.[7] Furthermore, we have performed experiments in which normal hemoglobin was added to a sicklemia preparation and the mixture was then subjected to electrophoretic analysis. Upon examining the Longsworth scanning diagrams we found that the area under the peak corresponding to the normal component had increased by the amount expected, and that no indication of a new component could be discerned. Similar experiments on mixtures of sickle cell anemia hemoglobin and sicklemia preparations yielded similar results. These sensitive tests reveal that, at least electrophoretically, the two components in sicklemia hemoglobin are identifiable with sickle cell anemia hemoglobin and normal hemoglobin.

DISCUSSION

1) *On the Nature of the Difference between Sickle Cell Anemia Hemoglobin and Normal Hemoglobin*: Having found that the electrophoretic mobilities of sickle cell anemia hemoglobin and normal hemoglobin differ, we are left with the considerable problem of locating the cause of the difference. It is impossible to ascribe the difference to dissimilarities in the particle weights or shapes of the two hemoglobins in solution: a purely frictional effect would cause one species to move more slowly than the other throughout the entire pH range and would not produce a shift in the isoelectric point. Moreover, preliminary velocity ultracentrifuge[8] and free diffusion measurements indicate that the two hemoglobins have the same sedimentation and diffusion constants.

The most plausible hypothesis is that there is a difference in the number or kind of ionizable groups in the two hemoglobins. Let us assume that the only groups capable of forming ions which are present in carbonmonoxyhemoglobin are the carboxyl groups in the heme, and the carboxyl, imidazole, amino, phenolic hydroxyl, and guanidino groups in the globin. The number of ions nonspecifically adsorbed on the two proteins should be the same for the two hemoglobins

[7] The patterns were very slightly different in that the known mixture contained 1 percent more of the sickle cell anemia component than did the sickle cell trait material.

[8] We are indebted to Dr. M. Moskowitz, of the Chemistry Department, University of California at Berkeley, for performing the ultracentrifuge experiments for us.

under comparable conditions, and they may be neglected for our purposes. Our experiments indicate that the net number of positive charges (the total number of cationic groups minus the number of anionic groups) is greater for sickle cell anemia hemoglobin than for normal hemoglobin in the pH region near their isoelectric points.

According to titration data obtained by us, the acid-base titration curve of normal human carbonmonoxyhemoglobin is nearly linear in the neighborhood of the isoelectric point of the protein, and a change of one pH unit in the hemoglobin solution in this region is associated with a change in net charge on the hemoglobin molecule of about 13 charges per molecule. The same value was obtained by German and Wyman (5) with horse oxyhemoglobin. The difference in isoelectric points of the two hemoglobins under the conditions of our experiments is 0.23 for ferrohemoglobin and 0.22 for the carbonmonoxy compound. This difference corresponds to about 3 charges per molecule. With consideration of our experimental error, sickle cell anemia hemoglobin therefore has 2–4 more net positive charges per molecule than normal hemoglobin.

Studies have been initiated to elucidate the nature of this charge difference more precisely. Samples of porphyrin dimethyl esters have been prepared from normal hemoglobin and sickle cell anemia hemoglobin. These samples were shown to be identical by their x-ray powder photographs and by identity of their melting points and mixed melting point. A sample made from sicklemia hemoglobin was also found to have the same melting point. It is accordingly probable that normal and sickle cell anemia hemoglobin have different globins. Titration studies and amino acid analyses on the hemoglobins are also in progress.

2) *On the Nature of the Sickling Process*: In the introductory paragraphs we outlined the evidence which suggested that the hemoglobins in sickle cell anemia and sicklemia erythrocytes might be responsible for the sickling process. The fact that the hemoglobins in these cells have now been found to be different from that present in normal red blood cells makes it appear very probable that this is indeed so.

We can picture the mechanism of the sickling process in the following way. It is likely that it is the globins rather than the hemes of the two hemoglobins that are different. Let us propose that there is a surface region on the globin of the sickle cell anemia, hemoglobin molecule which is absent in the normal molecule and which has a configuration complementary to a different region of the surface of the hemoglobin molecule. This situation would be somewhat analogous to that which very probably exists in antigen-antibody reactions (9). The fact that sickling occurs only when the partial pressures of oxygen and carbon monoxide are low suggests that one of these sites is very near to the iron atom of one or more of the hemes, and that when the iron atom is combined with either one of these gases, the complementariness of the two structures is considerably diminished. Under the appropriate conditions, then, the sickle cell anemia hemoglobin molecules might be capable of interacting with one another at these sites sufficiently to cause at least a partial alignment of the molecules within the cell, resulting in the erythrocyte's becoming birefringent, and the cell membrane's being distorted to accommodate the now relatively rigid structures within its confines. The addition of oxygen or carbon monoxide to the cell might reverse these effects by disrupting some of the weak bonds between the hemoglobin molecules in favor of the bonds formed between gas molecules and iron atoms of the hemes.

Since all sicklemia erythrocytes behave more or less similarly, and all sickle at a sufficiently low oxygen pressure (11), it appears quite certain that normal hemoglobin and sickle cell anemia hemoglobin coexist within each sicklemia cell; otherwise there would be a mixture of normal and sickle cell anemia erythrocytes in sicklemia blood. We might expect that the normal hemoglobin molecules, lacking at least one type of complementary sité present on the sickle cell anemia molecules, and so being incapable of entering into the chains or three-dimensional frameworks formed by the latter, would interfere with the alignment of these molecules within the sicklemia erythrocyte. Lower oxygen pressures, freeing more of the complementary sites near the hemes, might be required before sufficiently large aggregates of sickle cell anemia hemoglobin molecules could form to cause sickling of the erythrocytes.

This is in accord with the observations of Sherman (11), which were mentioned in the introduction, that a large proportion of erythrocytes in the venous circulation of persons with sickle cell anemia are sickled, but that very few have assumed the sickle forms in the venous circulation of individuals with sicklemia. Presumably, then, the sickled cells in the blood of persons with sickle cell anemia cause thromboses, and their increased fragility exposes them to the action of reticulo endothelial cells which break them down, resulting in the anemia (1).

It appears, therefore, that while some of the details of this picture of the sickling process are as yet conjectural, the proposed mechanism is consistent with experimental observations at hand and offers a chemical and physical basis for many of them. Furthermore, if it is correct, it supplies a direct link between the existence of "defective" hemoglobin molecules and the pathological consequences of sickle cell disease.

3) *On the Genetics of Sickle Cell Disease*: A genetic basis for the capacity of erythrocytes to sickle was recognized early in the study of this disease (4). Taliaferro and Huck (15) suggested that a single dominant gene was involved, but the distinction between sicklemia and sickle cell anemia was not clearly understood at the time. The literature contains conflicting statements concerning the nature of the genetic mechanisms involved, but recently Neel (8) has reported an investigation which strongly indicates that the gene responsible for the sickling characteristic is in heterozygous condition in individuals with sicklemia, and homozygous in those with sickle cell anemia.

Our results had caused us to draw this inference before Neel's paper was published. The existence of normal hemoglobin and sickle cell anemia hemoglobin in roughly equal proportions in sicklemia hemoglobin preparations is obviously in complete accord with this hypothesis. In fact, if the mechanism proposed above to account for the sickling process is correct, we can identify the gene responsible for the sickling process with one of an alternative pair of alleles capable through some series of reactions of introducing the modification into the hemoglobin molecule that distinguishes sickle cell anemia hemoglobin from the normal protein.

The results of our investigation are compatible with a direct quantitative effect of this gene pair; in the chromosomes of a single nucleus of a normal adult somatic cell there is a complete absence of the sickle cell gene, while two doses of its allele are present; in the sicklemia somatic cell there exists one dose of each allele; and in the sickle cell anemia somatic cell there are two doses of the sickle cell gene, and a complete absence of its normal allele. Correspondingly, the erythrocytes of these individuals contain 100 percent normal hemoglobin, 40 percent sickle cell anemia hemoglobin and 60 percent normal hemoglobin, and 100 percent sickle cell anemia hemoglobin, respectively. This investigation reveals, therefore, a clear case of a change produced in a protein molecule by an allelic change in a single gene involved in synthesis.

The fact that sicklemia erythrocytes contain the two hemoglobins in the ratio 40:60 rather than 50:50 might be accounted for by a number of hypothetical schemes. For example, the two genes might compete for a common substrate in the synthesis of two different enzymes essential to the production of the two different hemoglobins. In this reaction, the sickle cell gene would be less efficient than its normal allele. Or, competition for a common substrate might occur at some later stage in the series of reactions leading to the synthesis of the two hemoglobins. Mechanisms of this sort are discussed in more elaborate detail by Stern (13).

The results obtained in the present study suggest that the erythrocytes of other hereditary hemolytic anemias be examined for the presence of abnormal hemoglobins. This we propose to do.

Based on a paper presented at the meeting of the National Academy of Sciences in Washington, D. C., in April, 1949, and at the meeting of the American Society of Biological Chemists in Detroit in April, 1949.

References

1. BOYD, W. *Textbook of pathology.* (3rd Ed.) Philadelphia : Lea and Febiger, 1938. P. 864.
2. DIGGS, L. W., AHMANN, C. F., and BIBB, J. *Ann. int. Med.,* 1933, **7**, 769.
3. DRABKIN, D. L. *J. biol. Chem.,* 1946, **164**, 703.
4. EMMEL, V. E. *Arch. int. Med.,* 1917, **20**, 586.
5. GERMAN, B. and WYMAN, J., JR. *J. biol. Chem.,* 1937, **117**, 533.
6. HASTINGS, A. B. *et al. J. biol. Chem.,* 1924, **60**, 89.
7. LONGSWORTH, L. G. *Ann. N. Y. Acad. Sci.,* 1941, **41**, 267.
8. NEEL, J. V. *Science,* 1949, **110**, 64.
9. PAULING, L., PRESSMAN, D., and CAMPBELL, D. H. *Physiol. Rev.,* 1943, **23**, 203.
10. PONDER, E. *Ann. N. Y. Acad. Sci.,* 1947, **48**, 579.
11. SHERMAN, I. J. *Bull. Johns Hopk. Hosp.,* 1940, **67**, 309.
12. STERN, K. G., REINER, M. and SILBER, R. H. *J. biol. Chem.,* 1945, **161**, 731.
13. STERN, C. *Science,* 1948, **108**, 615.
14. SWINGLE, S. M. *Rev. sci. Inst.,* 1947, **18**, 128.
15. TALIAFERRO, W. H. and HUCK, J. G. *Genetics,* 1923, **8**, 594.
16. TISELIUS, A. and KABAT, E. *J. exp. Med.,* 1939, **69**, 119.

Reprinted from COLD SPRING HARBOR SYMPOSIA
ON QUANTITATIVE BIOLOGY
Volume XVI, 1951
Made in United States of America

SOME RECENT STUDIES BEARING ON THE ONE GENE-ONE ENZYME HYPOTHESIS[1]

N. H. HOROWITZ AND URS LEUPOLD

Kerckhoff Laboratories of Biology, California Institute of Technology, Pasadena

The assumption that a given gene is involved, in a primary way, in the production of but a single enzyme has been implicit in most speculations on the nature of gene action since Cuénot's time. As a result of the investigations of the last ten years stemming from the discovery of nutritional mutants in *Neurospora* by Beadle and Tatum (1941), one is now in a position to scrutinize this supposition more closely than was previously possible. Specifically, we are in a better position to trace the consequences of the hypothesis and of its various alternatives, and to appraise the evidence which may have a bearing on it. In this paper we propose to examine some of the evidence, deriving from studies on *Neurospora*, and *E. coli*, which relates to this problem.

Before considering the experimental findings, it may be useful to define more explicitly the meaning of the one gene-one enzyme hypothesis. The concept is that of a gene whose sole activity aside from self-duplication is that of functioning in the synthesis of a particular enzyme or enzyme precursor. It is not thereby implied that genes at other loci may not also function directly in the formation of the enzyme. This is a completely independent problem with which we are not concerned here, and regarding which there is little evidence in *Neurospora* one way or the other; all that can be said with assurance is that if two or more genes do, in fact, cooperate in the production of a given enzyme, then their respective contributions must be different. Nor does the one gene-one enzyme hypothesis imply that the final phenotypic expression of a mutation is necessarily restricted to a particular structure or function of the organism. The ultimate effect of a mutation is the result of an enormous magnification of the

[1]The studies on *E. coli* reported in this paper were supported by a Grant-in-Aid from the American Cancer Society upon recommendation of the Committee on Growth of the National Research Council; by a grant from the Rockefeller Foundation; and by a contract between the Office of Naval Research, Department of the Navy and the California Institute of Technology (NR 164010).

initial gene change, brought about through a system of reactions which, originating at the gene rapidly branches out in various directions and coalesces with similar networks deriving from other loci to form a reticulum of as yet indeterminate extent and complexity. It is impossible to decide from the end-effects alone whether the gene has one or many primary functions, since on either assumption a complex pattern of effects is expected in most cases. In the biochemical mutants of *Neurospora* and other microorganisms, the end effects would, if they could be analysed, undoubtedly prove to be exceedingly numerous. A mutation which induces a deficiency of an amino acid, for example, must secondarily affect the synthesis of virtually every protein of the cell, and an exhaustive enumeration of the end effects might well include every structure and function of the organism.

It turns out, however, that it is possible in such a case to prevent the secondary damage and the consequent death of the mutant by supplying the lacking amino acid. When given a sufficient quantity of the amino acid the mutant becomes normal in growth rate, morphology, and fertility. It is difficult to escape the conclusion that the sole function of the gene in this case is to play some essential role in the synthesis of the amino acid. When biochemical analysis of the mutant is carried farther, it is discovered that the field of action of the gene is even more circumscribed than might have been supposed: it is restricted to sensibly a single chemical step of the synthesis. Apparently a single reaction is abolished in the mutant, while all others proceed normally. It is inferred that the role of the gene is to function in the synthesis of the enzyme which catalyses this reaction.

It has not yet been possible to analyse all, or even the majority, of the known *Neurospora* mutants in the detail we have just outlined, while in a few cases the analysis has been carried still farther by showing that the mutants are in fact lacking in particular enzymes (Mitchell and Lein, 1948;

[65]

Fincham, in press). Out of approximately 500 nutritional mutants which are, or have been, in the Pasadena collection, 84 per cent require single, known chemical substances for growth. The remaining 16 per cent have not responded to any of the individual substances tested, but do grow on complex media. It is very likely that many of the strains in this unanalysed group require individual compounds which have not been tested, others may have multiple requirements resulting from multiple mutations, while some may have multiple requirements resulting from the mutation of multifunctional genes.

The one gene-one enzyme hypothesis has been suggested as the simplest interpretation of the large class of mutants whose growth requirement is known to be satisfied by a single growth factor. Are there any grounds for suspecting that these mutants may not, in spite of appearances, represent mutations of unifunctional genes?

One basis for criticism of the one gene-one enzyme interpretation is the difficulty of excluding in every instance the alternative hypothesis that the given gene controls not one, but several sequential steps in the affected pathway. This interesting idea appears rather improbable, however, in view of the cumulative evidence from series of mutants which shows that each gene can be assigned to a particular step in a sequence of reactions; and it is virtually excluded in those cases where it has been possible, by enzyme studies, to define the reaction precisely.

A second ground for suspicion of the one gene-one enzyme interpretation rests on the fact that closer study of the mutants shows that they are not in all cases restored to a fully normal phenotype when supplied with the required growth substance. While all of the lethal consequences of the mutation are avoided, a residue of non-lethal effects may remain. In some cases, these residual effects are readily accounted for—partial sterility, for example, when the mutant carries a chromosomal rearrangement (McClintock, 1945). Others are not so easily understood. One of the commonest residual effects is a sensitivity toward certain natural substances—frequently amino acids. The first reported instance of this phenomenon was that described by Doermann (1944), who found that growth of all of the then known lysine-requiring mutants—a series involving at least three loci—is competitively inhibited by L-arginine in the medium. The growth of wild type *Neurospora* is not affected by arginine. Many similar cases are now known. A significant feature of this phenomenon is that the inhibition may, as in the case cited, extend to a whole class of genetically

different, but biochemically related mutants, indicating that the effect is not locus-specific but is inherent in the mechanism of utilization of the exogenously provided growth substance. A third residual effect which has been encountered is sterility in crosses in which both parents carry the same mutant allele. One interpretation is that in these cases the gene performs a specific function, possibly independent of its vegetative biochemical function, in connection with zygote formation or maturation. Some recent preliminary results which have been obtained in our laboratory by Mr. Henry Gershowitz, working with certain methionine-requiring strains, indicate, however, that the sterility can be overcome by supplementing the medium with a large quantity of the amino acid—at least twice as much as is required to produce optimal growth of vegetative cultures. This suggests that the sterility may result from a high metabolic requirement for the growth factor during the sexual process, or to a lowered permeability to it. A fourth, and relatively rare, residual effect is failure of the mutant to attain a normal growth rate. This also can characterize an entire class of mutants, as in a certain group of strains of the cysteine-methionine series now under investigation in our laboratory.

Everything considered, it is perhaps surprising that residual effects are not observed more frequently, since in no event is it possible, even in theory, to avoid all of the consequences of a mutation by supplying the deficient metabolite. The block in the synthetic pathway still remains, and it can have an influence quite apart from the effects of the nutritional deficiency. It has been shown in numerous instances that metabolic intermediates may accumulate behind the block, sometimes in spectacular quantities (for review, see Horowitz, 1950). It would be surprising if the presence of abnormal concentrations of metabolic intermediates in the cells did not at times produce deleterious side-effects. Actually, evidence has been obtained both in *Neurospora* (Bonner, 1946a) and in *E. coli* (Davis, 1950; Umbarger and Mueller, 1951) that accumulated intermediates may exert a lethal action by interfering with reactions in other metabolic pathways. This leads one to suspect that the so-called residual effects are to a large extent the irreparable side-effects of the primary block. (For further discussion, see Emerson, 1950.)

THE SELECTION PROBLEM

At the Cold Spring Harbor Symposium of 1946, Delbrück raised a question as to whether incompatibilities with the one gene-one enzyme hypothesis could be detected even if they occurred (see Discussion following paper by Bonner, 1946b). Delbrück's argument was based on the recognized fact that not all of the mutations which are produced can be detected by the methods usually employed for this purpose. Principally three classes of biochemical mutants are not recoverable: (1) those requiring a substance which is absent from the so-called "complete" medium used for recovering nutritional mutants, (2) those requiring a substance which is unable to diffuse into the cell, and (3) those requiring a substance which, though present and diffusible, is not utilized because of the inclusion in the medium of an inhibitor of the mutant in question. We shall refer to mutants which, for the above, or for any other reasons, are incapable of growing on complete medium as mutants which have lost an *indispensable function*. The point of Delbrück's argument was that if any gene has more than one primary function, it is likely that at least one of these is an indispensable function; in which case mutation of the gene would not be detected.

Now the validity of this argument depends on the relative frequency of indispensable functions. If this frequency is very high, then the probability of recovering a mutation of a gene with several primary functions will be very low. Thus, if 90 per cent of gene functions are indispensable, and if dispensable and indispensable functions are randomly distributed among the genes, then the probability of detecting a mutation in a gene with two primary functions is only one per cent. On the other hand, if the frequency of indispensable functions is low, then the chance of detecting multifunctional genes will be much better. The determination of the proportion of indispensable functions is thus critical for the one gene-one enzyme concept. The question is how this quantity is to be determined. It would seem almost by definition to be unknowable, in which case the one gene-one enzyme idea must be banished to the purgatory of untestable hypotheses, along with the proposition that a blue unicorn lives on the other side of the moon.

THE FREQUENCY OF INDISPENSABLE FUNCTIONS IN NEUROSPORA

What is needed is a method for detecting mutations which result in loss of an indispensable function and for comparing their frequency to that of mutations which cause loss of a dispensable function. It occurred to one of us (Horowitz, 1948, 1950) that the so-called "temperature mutants" of *Neurospora* might form the basis of such a method. Temperature mutants are a class

in which the mutant phenotype is fully expressed only in a particular temperature range. Generally, such mutants exhibit a growth factor requirement when cultured at $35°$, but grow in its absence at $25°$; in a few cases this relationship is reversed —i.e., the growth factor is required at the lower, but not at the higher, temperature. In three instances it has been found that particular temperature mutations behave as alleles of mutations of the usual, temperature-independent sort, and it seems not unlikely that this will be found to be generally true.

The usefulness of these mutants for the present problem is based on the expectation that the mutant will be recoverable in the temperature range within which it has no growth factor requirement, regardless af whether a dispensable or an indispensable function has been lost. This expectation is borne out by the fact that a group of temperature mutants which fails to grow on complete medium at the mutant temperature is, in fact, known. Of the 26 temperature mutants known in *Neurospora*, 12 are of this type, while 14 grow on complete medium in the temperature range within which they have a requirement. In other words, roughly one-half of these mutants has lost an indispensable function.

In using the temperature mutants as a sampling device it is assumed that genes controlling indispensable functions are just as likely to yield temperature alleles as those controlling dispensable functions. This assumption is supported by two considerations. In the first place, the two classes of functions are in no sense natural categories, but depend largely on the composition of the particular complete medium which is employed. There is thus no reason to assume that the genes governing these functions differ from one another in any fundamental way. In the second place, among the temperature mutants whose specific requirement is known there is no indication that any one kind of nutritional requirement is favored over others. Mutation to temperature alleles appears to occur at random among genes controlling known biochemical syntheses (Horowitz, 1950).

With the information that the frequency of indispensable gene functions constitutes approximately 50 per cent of the total, it becomes possible to estimate the intensity of the selection which operates against the detection of multifunctional genes. With a random distribution of functions, one-half of genes with a single function will be detectable by the usual methods, one-fourth of bifunctional genes, and, in general, $(\frac{1}{2})^n$ of n-functional genes. The original minimal estimate of 84 per cent of unifunctional genes, based on the observation that this fraction of the mutants responds to single growth substances can now be corrected. A sufficiently close approximation is given by neglecting genes with more than two functions, and we obtain 73 per cent as the corrected frequency of unifunctional genes:

$$\text{Observed frequency} = \frac{84}{84 + 16} = 0.84$$

$$\text{Corrected frequency} = \frac{84 \times 2}{84 \times 2 + 16 \times 4} = 0.73$$

The exact value is given by the first term of a Poisson distribution, and is equal to 0.71 (see Appendix).

This value is so high, that in spite of the uncertainties in its determination it may be regarded as strongly supporting the conclusion that at least the majority of genes controlling biosynthetic reactions in *Neurospora* are unifunctional. There are several obvious sources of uncertainty in the calculations. First, they should be based on the number of genetically different mutations, rather than on the total number of occurrences; this cannot be done at the present time. Second, the assumption was made that all of the unanalysed mutants, 16 per cent of the total, represent multifunctional genes; this is almost certainly incorrect and biases the calculations against the one gene–one enzyme theory. Finally, the number of temperature mutants is too small to give an accurate estimate of the frequency of indispensable functions. It is to the last point that we now turn.

The Frequency of Indispensable Functions in *E. coli*

It was clearly desirable to obtain a more reliable estimate of the frequency of indispensable functions, but to even double the existing number of temperature mutants in *Neurospora* would be a formidable operation. We therefore turned to *E. coli* K-12, with the expectation of recovering large numbers of temperature mutants by a modified penicillin technique (Davis, 1948; Lederberg and Zinder, 1948). Providentially, this method proved to be unsuited to our purpose: although temperature-independent mutants were obtained, the yield of temperature mutants was zero. This was a fortunate circumstance, since it forced us to adopt a more direct method, one which introduces fewer uncontrolled selective variables into the experiment than would the penicillin technique. The method is simply that of plating out U.V.-treated cells on minimal medium and incubating them for 48 hours at 40°. The plates are transferred to 25° for an additional 5 days, and the colonies which come up during this second period—so-called secondary colonies—are picked off and tested. This procedure was made feasible by a visual method devised by Dr. Leupold which makes it easier to detect a few secondary colonies on a plate containing hundreds of primary colonies. Altogether 161 temperature mutants were obtained by this method. Of these, only 37, or 23 per cent, were unable to grow on the *Neurospora* complete medium at 40° and therefore represent losses of indispensable functions. The statistics are shown in Table 1.

TABLE 1. STATISTICS OF *E. COLI* STUDY

No. of irradiated cells	1.7×10^9 (approx.)
No. of surviving cells	2.4×10^6 (approx.)
Secondary colonies isolated	2157
No. of temperature mutants	161
Type D40	124
Type I40	37

The remaining 124 mutants, those which grow on complete medium at 40°, were tested by the auxanographic method to determine their growth requirements. Seventy-nine per cent of these mutants were classifiable in this way. A variety of requirements was found (Table 2), indicating again that temperature mutation is random with respect to the classes of syntheses which can be affected. A number of substances are conspicuous by their absence from this list, notably tryptophane and p-aminobenzoic acid. It has not been excluded, however, that requirements for these substances are present among the mutants which were not classifiable in the auxanographic test.

Several other points of interest in connection with the *E. coli* study should be mentioned. These concern the selective forces operating in

TABLE 2. SYNTHESES KNOWN TO BE AFFECTED IN *E. COLI* TEMPERATURE MUTANTS

Amino Acids	Vitamins
Methionine	Biotin
Cystine	Thiamin
Arginine	Pyridoxin
Lysine	Nicotinamide
Histidine	Pantothenic acid
Leucine	
Isoleucine	
Valine	Nucleic Acid Constituents
Threonine	
Aminobutyrate	
Tyrosine	
Glycine	

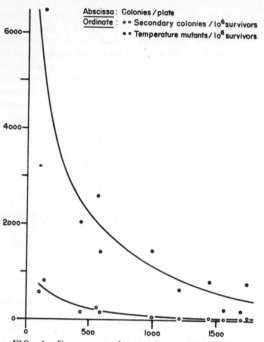

FIG. 1. Frequency of secondary colonies (solid circles) and of temperature mutants (open circles) per 10^6 survivors as functions of population density.

densely populated versus lightly populated Petri plates. It is obvious that in a method like this, in which there may be many hundred of colonies per (15 cm.) plate, we are not actually isolating the mutants in a minimal medium, but in a minimal medium plus or minus whatever the hundreds of wild type colonies add to or subtract from it. This is quite clearly shown in the relative yield of secondary colonies and temperature mutants per number of survivors. In our experiments the total number of colonies (i.e., survivors) per plate varied from 100 to 1,700. In sparsely populated plates the relative yield of both secondary colonies and temperature mutants was much higher than in densely populated plates. In Figure 1 the numbers of secondary colonies and temperature mutants per million survivors are plotted against the total number of colonies per plate. At the lowest densities, with populations of the order of 100 colonies per plate, yields of 3,400 and 6,500 secondary colonies per million survivors have been recorded. At higher densities, the yield decreases systematically and rapidly, reaching values between 200 and 800 secondary colonies per million survivors at population densities of 1,200 to 1,700 colonies per plate. The yield of temperature mutants per million survivors

is roughly one-tenth that of all secondary colonies, and it exhibits the same systematic trend. The difference between these two curves expresses the fact that approximately 90 per cent of the secondary colonies are wild types which, for one reason or another, started to grow late; partially blocked, slowly growing biochemical mutants; and completely blocked biochemical mutants which have been fed "syntrophically" by the wild types. Figure 2 shows that the composition of the population of secondary colonies is also influenced by the population density. It is seen that the yield of temperature mutants per hundred secondary colonies decreases with increasing densities, indicating that the yield of temperature mutants decreases even more rapidly than does the yield of secondary colonies in general.

At least three selective forces are at work in these populations: (1) competition for food, (2) probably more important, mutual inhibition by-products of metabolism, and (3) superimposed on these but acting in the opposite direction, cross-feeding, or syntrophism, the mutual exchange of essential growth factors. The first two mechanisms are probably mainly responsible for the rapid decrease in the yield of secondary colonies with increasing plate densities. Their intensity is evidently quite remarkable. They are unspecific forces, however, and cannot be expected to influence systematically the relative frequencies of the two types of temperature mutants which we set out to find. The third influence, cross-

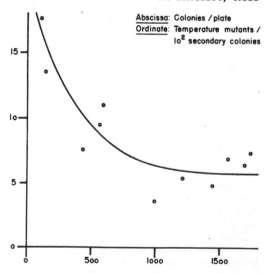

FIG. 2. Frequency of temperature mutants per hundred secondary colonies as a function of population density.

feeding, is much more dangerous in this respect, although its direction and intensity are difficult to predict. The effect of cross-feeding on the selective isolation of the two kinds of temperature mutants depends on both the quantity and quality of the output of growth factors by wild type *E. coli*. For example, let us assume that

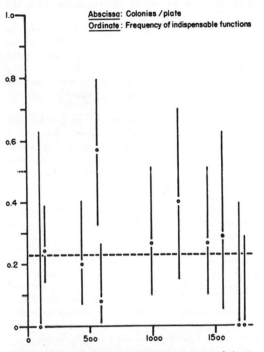

FIG. 3. Frequency of temperature mutants of the indispensable class as a function of population density. Vertical lines show the range within which the experimental points would be expected to fall in 95 per cent of similar experiments. The broken line shows the weighted mean of the distribution.

the growth factor excretion by the wild type is qualitatively similar to the composition of complete medium. Large amounts of such enrichment would tend to support the growth of temperature mutants which had lost a dispensable function, up to the point of visible colony formation, and would thus remove them from the isolation procedure. On the other hand, smaller quantities of the same enrichment might give these same mutants an advantage in the struggle for survival during the first 48 hours at the mutant temperature and during the second period at the lower temperature when they begin to grow against the heavy competition of established wild type colonies. The actual situation would be far more

complex, in that the sign and magnitude of the selection would differ from mutant to mutant.

In spite of the indisputable occurrence of cross-feeding on the plates, however, it can be said that no systematic selection favoring either of the two classes of temperature mutants is deducible from our data. In Figure 3 is plotted the fraction of temperature mutants which were found to belong to the indispensable class, together with the ranges within which the values would be expected to fall in 95 per cent of trials, against the population density. With the exception of one experiment, the data are consistent with the assumption that these are random samples drawn from a homogeneous population of temperature mutants in which the frequency of mutants of the indispensable class is between 20 and 25 per cent. In short, with the exception of a single experiment in the middle range of population densities, there is no indication that population density influences the relative frequencies of the two classes of temperature mutants: the various selective forces appear to affect both classes equally.

We may summarize the *E. coli* results, then, by saying that the frequency of indispensable functions, as revealed by the temperature mutant method, is even lower than was indicated by the less extensive series of temperature mutants in *Neurospora*. Actually, the two results—46 per cent of indispensable functions in *Neurospora*, compared to 23 per cent in *E. coli*—are not very different, considering the great differences in the respective organisms. The intensity of the selection which opposes the recovery of multifunctional genes in the usual screening procedures is thus of a rather low order and is incapable of accounting for the fact that the genes detected by these procedures appear to be preponderantly of the unifunctional type.

CONCLUSION

In concluding this paper, we should like to make some brief observations on the significance of the low frequency of indispensable functions and the one gene-one enzyme hypothesis.

Our results indicate that the effect of most lethal mutations in *Neurospora* and *E. coli* is to block the synthesis of metabolites which are replaceable by nutritional means; that is to say, of low molecular weight substances such as might be expected to diffuse into the cell and of which the complete medium is chiefly, if not exclusively, composed. This situation appears to contrast markedly with that encountered in *Drosophila*, where lethal mutations, as well as visibles, result in irreplaceable losses, frequently organ-specific in character. In some measure this may reflect fundamental biological differences between *Drosophila* and *Neurospora* or *E. coli*, but also, and to an indeterminate extent, it reflects the differences in methodological approach to these organisms. It would not be surprising to find that non-diffusible products play a more important role in the development of a highly differentiated organism like *Drosophila* than in relatively undifferentiated ones like *Neurospora* and *E. coli*. But on the other hand, it must be recognized that the methods of *Drosophila* culture are such as virtually to exclude the possibility of detecting nutritional mutants even if they occur.

The results we have obtained from the microorganisms suggest that in the great majority of cases the metabolic function of the gene is to produce an enzyme which catalyzes the formation of a low molecular weight product. If there exists a large class of enzymes whose function is other than this, we must conclude either that they are not individually essential to survival, or else that they are independent of the genes for their production. There is a strong suggestion in this result that the mechanism of biosynthesis of large molecules, especially proteins, is not an enzymatic mechanism in the usual sense. That is to say, the protein molecule may not be built, cathedral-like, by a process of accretion; but rather may be made directly from the amino acids or their simple derivatives by a single catalyst.

It is interesting to note that such a mechanism provides a simple explanation of another essential feature of our findings; namely, the mutual independence of the pathways of synthesis of different enzymes. On the hypothesis of growth by accretion of peptide fragments it seems unlikely that a one gene-one enzyme relationship could be found, even if it existed, since loss or modification of any peptide fragment would be expected to result in loss or modification of a particular group of enzymes; namely, those which contain this fragment in their structures. Unless the fragment could be introduced into the cells, the result would be the frequent occurrence of multiple unrelated biochemical deficiencies among the mutants. This has not been found. We find considerable appeal in the notion that the proposed mechanism of enzyme synthesis may underlie the results we have obtained.

SUMMARY

The one gene-one enzyme hypothesis is supported by the following evidence:

The great majority, at least 84 per cent, of the known nutritional mutants of *Neurospora* require single chemical substances as essential growth factors. Provision of the essential factor results in a normal phenotype in most cases; where a fully normal phenotype is not attained, the evidence indicates that this is to be accounted for on the basis of secondary effects unrelated to the mode of gene action.

Biochemical analysis of the mutants has indicated in many instances that the effect of the mutation is to block sensibly a single step in the pathway of synthesis of the growth factor. In a few cases it has been possible to show that the mutants are lacking in the specific enzyme involved.

The question of whether the known biochemical mutants are a highly selected sample from which multifunctional mutants are excluded by virtue of the screening procedure employed has been attacked by the temperature mutant method. Evidence has been presented which indicates that this method makes possible the recovery of mutants without regard to the nature of the induced biochemical deficiency or the composition of the (complete) medium.

Application of this method has shown that the proportion of biochemical mutants not recoverable by the usual screening tests may be less than 50 per cent in *Neurospora* and less than 25 per cent in *E. coli*. It is calculated that this rate of loss does not produce a sufficiently intense selection of unifunctional mutations to account for the high frequency of such mutations actually found.

Finally, it is suggested that the results can be simply accounted for on the hypothesis that the synthesis of a protein molecule is accomplished by a single catalyst working directly on the constituent amino acids or their simple derivatives.

APPENDIX

The corrected value of the frequency of unifunctional genes can be computed from a Poisson distribution as follows:

Assume that each gene has one function to begin with and that there is in addition a number of functions, m, randomly distributed among the genes. The fraction i of all gene functions is indispensable. Letting

$$n = \text{the number of genes}$$

Then $n + m =$ the number of gene functions,

$m/n = c =$ the mean number of additional functions per gene,

And $ic =$ the mean number of indispensable additional functions per gene.

The fraction of genes with no additional functions —i.e., unifunctional—is then given by e^{-c}, the first term of a Poisson distribution. Of these, the fraction $(1-i)$ are recoverable. The fraction of recoverable unifunctional genes is therefore

$$P_a = (1-i)e^{-c}$$

Similarly, the fraction of all genes, unifunctional and multifunctional, which can be recovered is

$$P_{a+b} = (1-i)e^{-ic}$$

The frequency of unifunctional genes among those recovered is therefore

$$P_a/P_{a+b} = e^{-c(1-i)}$$

Equating this expression to the observed value, 0.84, and substituting 0.5 for i, one finds c = 0.34. The corrected frequency of unifunctional genes is then $e^{-0.34} = 0.71$.

REFERENCES

BEADLE, G. W. and TATUM, E. L., 1941, Genetic control of biochemical reactions in *Neurospora*. Proc. Nat. Acad. Sci. Wash. 27: 499–506.

BONNER, D., 1946a, Further studies of mutant strains of *Neurospora* requiring isoleucine and valine. J. Biol. Chem. 166: 545–554.

1946b, Biochemical mutations in *Neurospora*. Cold Spr. Harbor Symposium Quant. Biol. 11: 14–24.

DAVIS, B. D., 1948, Isolation of biochemically deficient mutants of bacteria by penicillin. J. Amer. Chem. Soc. 70: 4267.

1950, Studies on nutritionally deficient bacterial mutants isolated by means of penicillin. Experientia 6: 41–50.

DOERMANN, A. H., 1944, A lysineless mutant of *Neurospora* and its inhibition by arginine. Arch. Biochem. 5: 373–383.

EMERSON, S., 1950, Competitive reactions and antagonisms in the biosynthesis of amino acids by *Neurospora*. Cold Spr. Harbor Symposium Quant. Biol. 14: 40–48.

FINCHAM, J. R. S., J. Gen. Microbiol., in press.

HOROWITZ, N. H., 1948, The one gene-one enzyme hypothesis. Genetics 33: 612–613.

1950, Biochemical genetics of *Neurospora*. Advances in Genetics 3: 33–71.

LEDERBERG, J. and ZINDER, N., 1948, Concentration of biochemical mutants of bacteria with penicillin. J. Amer. Chem. Soc. 70: 4267.

MITCHELL, H. K. and LEIN, J., 1948, A *Neurospora* mutant deficient in the enzymatic synthesis of tryptophan. J. Biol. Chem. 175: 481–482.

UMBARGER, H. E. and MUELLER, J. H., 1951, Isoleucine and valine metabolism of *Escherichia coli*. I. Growth studies on amino acid-deficient mutants. J. Biol. Chem. 189: 277–285.

DISCUSSION

EPHRUSSI: I should like to know what you consider to be convincing evidence that there is genic control of protein synthesis at all?

HOROWITZ: In *Neurospora*, at least two cases are known in which gene mutations lead to deficiency of specific enzymes. These are the tryptophane synthesizing enzyme worked on by Mitchell and Lein and the glutamic dehydrogenase studied by Fincham. If these cases merely involved loss of specific cofactors then it might be expected that the activity of mutant extracts would be restored to some extent by mixing them with extracts from normal cells. This experiment has been performed, and, if I am not mistaken, gave negative results with both enzymes. Similar evidence probably exists in other organisms.

It is more difficult to obtain data bearing on the question of whether genes actually function in the synthesis of the polypeptide chain, or only impress a particular folding on prefabricated protein molecules. The most important evidence is that which Pauling and co-workers have obtained in connection with the electrophoretic mobilities of sickle-cell anemia hemoglobin and normal hemoglobin. They show that these hemoglobins differ by 3 or 4 positive charges in the globin part of the molecule. The most likely interpretation is that the proteins differ in the number or kind of ionizable groups. Thus it appears probable that the sickle cell anemia mutation results in the production of a protein of altered composition.

MAAS: In answer to Dr. Ephrussi's question I would like to mention some recent experiments which indicate that a biochemical mutation can affect synthesis of an enzyme protein. The biochemical reaction under investigation was the coupling of β-alanine and pantoic acid through a peptidic linkage to form pantothenate in *E. coli*. Two types of mutants blocked at this reaction were obtained: an absolute one which requires pantothenate at all temperatures, and another which requires it only above 32°. Acetone dried powder of the wild type readily yielded stable and highly active cell-free preparations of the coupling enzyme. In contrast, no enzyme activity was found in extracts of the absolute mutant; the system was sensitive enough to detect 1/2000 of the usual wild type activity. From the temperature sensitive mutant active but extremely heat labile extracts were obtained. Extraction had to be carried out in the cold and activity measured at 15°C, since at 25°C the enzyme is rapidly and irreversibly inactivated. These results, in accordance with the one gene: one enzyme hypothesis, show the enzymatic activity of the cell-free extracts of the several strains to parallel their growth behavior.

In this connection, I would like to point out that a previous apparent exception to this parallelism has now been clarified. Wagner had found pantothenate synthesizing enzyme activity in extracts of two *Neurospora* mutants whose growth requirements under ordinary conditions implied absence of this enzyme. However, he has shown recently (Genetics *35*, 697, 1950) that under appropriate conditions the mutants can grow without pantothenate and can synthesize pantothenate as rapidly as the wild type. As in Dr. Bonner's tryptophane/niacin mutants the biochemical block is incomplete; it is therefore not surprising to find enzyme activity in the extracts.

DAVIS: Supplementing the demonstrations by Pauling and by Maas that mutation can result in the production of a qualitatively altered protein, I should like to present evidence that an enzyme of altered specificity is present in a drug-resistant mutant.

The argument is based on the following facts. In *E. coli* p-nitrobenzoic acid (PNBA) is a simultaneous competitor of two metabolites, p-hydroxybenzoic acid (POB) and p-aminobenzoic acid (PABA). In the presence of an excess of PABA, PNBA inhibits growth only by competition with POB; mutants resistant to this PNBA/POB inhibition are readily obtained. Similarly, in the presence of POB, mutants resistant to PNBA/PABA inhibition can be obtained. These two types of mutants show no cross resistance with each other. This observation excludes decreased permeability or increased destruction of the drug as the mechanism of resistance. Furthermore, resistance to a sulfonamide (e.g., sulfathiazole) competing with PABA is quite different from resistance to PNBA/PABA. Similarly, resistance to a sulfonamide analogue of POB does not entail resistance to PNBA/POB. These observations exclude mechanisms that could not distinguish different analogues of a metabolite, such as increased concentration of the metabolite antagonizing the drug, increased efficiency of utilization of the product of this metabolite, or an alternative metabolic pathway bypassing the metabolite. Furthermore, if we assume that both sulfonamide and PNBA inhibit by direct competition with the corresponding metabolite at the same enzyme surface, the specificity of the resistance to each type of inhibitor could not be explained by an increased concentration of the enzyme. If this assumption is correct, and unless some other explanation is being overlooked, these results appear to imply a specific change in the enzyme: i.e., an alteration in configuration that results in decreased affinity for the inhibitor in comparison with the metabolite. The type of alterations required in the present case can readily be visualized since the sulfonamide analogues differ

from the metabolite at the 1-position of the ring, and PNBA at the 4-position (see diagram).

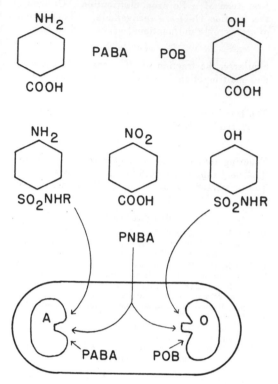

FOX: I should like to relate some observations which have a bearing on Dr. Muller's question regarding antigens, or Dr. Ephrussi's question regarding the role of genes in protein synthesis, and at the same time on the mechanism of protein synthesis proposed by Dr. Horowitz. In *Neurospora crassa*, the two mating types of strain 15,300 are distinct antigenically, each possessing an antigenic component not possessed by the other. These antigens are proteins, and chemical fractionation indicates that their specificity is not haptenic (?) in nature but resides in the protein itself. Genetic analysis of this difference, so far as it has gone, indicates that at least two, but probably more, loci are concerned with the production of these specific antigens. The data do not exclude the possibility that the mating-type locus is one of those concerned. We have here a case where genes are demonstrated to be involved in protein synthesis, and which, since more than one locus is concerned, would seem to argue against the single-step hypothesis of protein synthesis.

VILLEE: Many of the enzymes whose substrate specificities have been studied biochemically have been shown to be not completely specific for a single substrate but rather specific for a certain type of reaction; they will catalyze reactions involving any one of a class of compounds with a common reactive group. Have any biochemical mutants been obtained in which the enzyme involved has been shown to be the catalyst for a type of reaction rather than for one involving a single specific substrate as most of these stepwise gene-controlled syntheses appear to be?

(Question answered by Horowitz that he didn't know of any. Lederberg then cited a lactose mutant discovered in *E. coli* in which the enzyme involved was a general B-D-galactosidase.)

I think Dr. Horowitz's conclusion that his results suggest that protein synthesis is accomplished by a single step with a single catalyst working directly on amino acids is perhaps an unwarranted extrapolation from the data. His data show that there are still a considerable fraction of mutants for indispensable functions, some of which may be for protein synthesis. I would like to cite some evidence bearing on this obtained by Drs. Anfinsen and Steinberg at Harvard. They incubated minced chick oviduct in a saline medium containing $C^{14}O_2$. After a three or five hour incubation period, the synthesis was stopped and the ovalbumin was extracted, purified, and finally crystallized with added carrier. Then, using the *B. subtilis* enzyme discovered by Linderstrøm-Lang which splits off a hexapeptide from ovalbumin, leaving a distinctly different, crystallizable protein called plakalbumin, the radio-active ovalbumin was split into peptide and plakalbumin parts. When aspartic acid was isolated from the two parts, the specific activity of the peptide aspartic was twice that of the plakalbumin aspartic. This suggests that the ovalbumin molecule is not put together in one fell swoop by the accumulation of amino acids against some sort of template, but rather that the molecule is assembled bit by bit. More recent experiments show that a similar relation is true for the alanine isolated from the two parts of the ovalbumin molecule.

HOROWITZ: The *E. coli* experiment indicates that less than 25 per cent of temperature dependent lethals involve loss of indispensable functions. Preliminary experiments of Dr. Leupold have already shown that some of these mutants actually require low-molecular weight substances present in the complete medium; they appear in the indispensable class because their growth is inhibited

by other substances in this medium. Still other mutants may require small molecules which are absent from the medium. The point is that the fraction of mutants whose requirement is for large molecules is even smaller than the fraction which have lost indispensable functions. It should be mentioned that the enzymatic synthesis of peptides with special metabolic functions—for example, glutathione—is not excluded by our hypothesis. I agree that our suggestion is an extrapolation, but not an unwarranted one, since it accounts for our results in a straightforward way. For the present it is to be regarded as a working hypothesis and nothing more.

In connection with the interesting experiment by Anfinsen and Steinberg, cited by Villee, I wonder if exchange at certain preferred or exposed sites of the ovalbumin molecule was excluded.

(Dr. Villee stated that he thought exchange was excluded.)

WALLACE: Your tests were made on the survivors that were but 1/1000 of the original population. Aren't you disturbed by the fact that you know nothing about the other 999 in every 1000?

HOROWITZ: Every reasonable precaution was taken to insure that the temperature mutants isolated represented a random sample of those present immediately following the irradiation. After our experiments had been begun, however, Weigle and Delbrück discovered a mechanism which might lead to selective killing by ultraviolet in cultures of *E. coli* K-12. They found that ultraviolet induces lysis of K-12 by activating the phage lambda which, as shown by Mrs. Lederberg, is carried in a latent form by K-12. It seemed possible, therefore, that the survivors in our experiments had been selected on the basis of non-lysogenicity. With this in mind, our mutants have been tested by Dr. Margaret Lieb, and only five of them were found to be non-lysogenic. It appears unlikely that lysogenicity was an important factor in determining the types of temperature mutants recovered.

Another point raised by the finding of Weigle and Delbrück concerns the actual genetic effectiveness of the U.V. dose used in our experiments. It seems probable from the results of these workers that induced lysis was a major cause of death of the irradiated cells, in which case the mutagenic effectiveness of the irradiation would have been considerably less than might be inferred from the high mortality. It is quite possible that a large fraction of our mutants were, in fact, of spontaneous origin.

(Reprinted from Nature, Vol. 178, pp. 792–794, October 13, 1956)

A SPECIFIC CHEMICAL DIFFERENCE BETWEEN THE GLOBINS OF NORMAL HUMAN AND SICKLE-CELL ANÆMIA HÆMOGLOBIN

By Dr. V. M. INGRAM

Medical Research Council Unit for the Study of the Molecular Structure of Biological Systems, Cavendish Laboratory, University of Cambridge

A NEW and rapid technique of characterizing the chemical properties of a protein in considerable detail has been devised ; by its application a specific difference is found in the sequence of amino-acid residues of normal and sickle-cell hæmoglobin. This difference appears to be confined to one small section of one of the polypeptide chains.

Of all the abnormal human hæmoglobins, the one that has been most intensively studied is hæmoglobin S from patients with sickle-cell anæmia. In 1949 Pauling and his collaborators[1] demonstrated by electrophoretic experiments that at neutral pH the hæmoglobin S molecule has a net charge which is more positive by three units compared with the normal molecule, hæmoglobin A. It has since been suggested[2] that this difference is really due to hæmoglobin S having fewer free carboxyl groups than does hæmoglobin A. It is also known that in the reduced state the abnormal protein has a much lower solubility[3]. However, careful determinations of the amino-acid composition of the two proteins[4,5] did not show any significant differences between them within the accuracy of the methods employed. Comparison of the N-terminal[6] and C-terminal[7] amino-acids and of the sulphydryl groups[8] was equally disappointing. On this evidence alone, it is not possible to decide whether the difference between the proteins, which is in any event small, lies in the amino-acid sequences of the polypeptide chains or whether it lies in the folding of these chains leading to a masking of some amino-acid side-chains.

Hæmoglobin is still too large a molecule for detailed analysis of amino-acid sequence. However, it was thought that if a rapid method could be found of characterizing the chemical properties of the peptides in a tryptic digest, then perhaps a replacement of even a single residue for another might be detected without elaborate analysis.

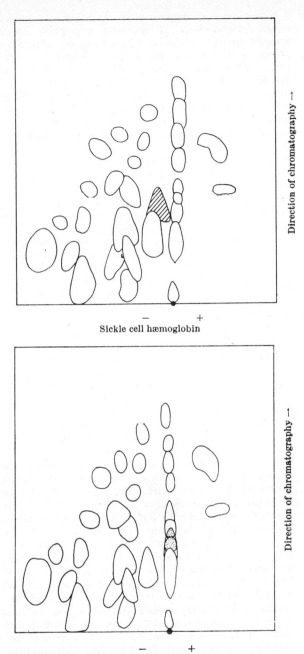

Direction of chromatography →

−   +

Sickle cell hæmoglobin

Direction of chromatography →

−   +

Normal hæmoglobin

Fig. 1. 'Finger prints' of human normal and sickle-cell hæmoglobins. Electrophoresis at pH 6·4, chromatography with n-butyl
alcohol/acetic acid/water (3 : 1 : 1). The shaded and the stippled
spots are those belonging to the peptide showing the difference

2

The action of trypsin on proteins is at present the most reliable way of splitting a peptide chain at specific peptide bonds. The enzyme attacks only those bonds which are derived from the carboxyl group of the amino-acids lysine and arginine. There are about sixty of these in the hæmoglobin A and S molecules[5], but since it is expected[9] that each molecule is composed of two identical half-molecules, the number of peptides obtained by the action of trypsin should be about thirty, with an average chain-length of ten amino-acids. Small differences in the two proteins will result in small changes in one or more of these peptides. These should be detectable when the mixture is examined by a two-dimensional combination of paper electrophoresis and paper chromatography. It was decided to call the resulting chromatogram the 'finger print' of the protein.

To prepare such a 'finger print', samples of purified[10] hæmoglobins A and S were denatured by heat at 90° C. for 4 min. and digested with trypsin (2 per cent by weight) at pH 8 and 37° C. for 43 hr. Aliquots of these digests (equivalent to 3 mgm. of protein) were placed on large sheets of Whatman No. 3 MM paper between glass plates and subjected to electrophoresis[11] in pyridine/acetic acid at pH 6·4 for 150 min. at 16 V./cm. The paper was then dried. Ascending chromatography with n-butyl alcohol/acetic acid/water (3 : 1 : 1) and development of the peptide spots with ninhydrin produced the chromatograms shown in the tracings of Fig. 1. When the papers were run strictly in parallel, reproducibility was often good enough to superimpose the spots belonging to similar peptides in the two chromatograms.

The 'finger prints' show approximately thirty peptide spots, as was expected from the amino-acid composition. This confirms the view that the human hæmoglobin molecule consists of two identical half-molecules and not of four identical sub-units each carrying one of the four hæme groups. The same number of peptides was found for both hæmoglobins, as was to be expected from their containing the same number of lysine and arginine residues. Most of the peptides are well resolved, and appear to be similar in the two proteins. However, there is one peptide spot clearly visible in the digest of hæmoglobin S which is not obvious in the hæmoglobin A 'finger print'. In the tracing it has been marked by shading. Apart from its position, this peptide is characterized by its orange-colour reaction with ninhydrin. Close inspection of the 'finger print' of hæmoglobin A shows the outline of an orange peptide spot in the 'back-bone' of neutral peptides which are

3

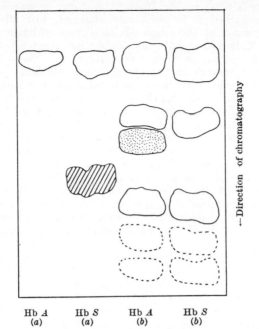

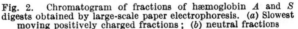

—Direction of chromatography→

| Hb A | Hb S | Hb A | Hb S |
| (a) | (a) | (b) | (b) |

Fig. 2. Chromatogram of fractions of hæmoglobin A and S digests obtained by large-scale paper electrophoresis. (a) Slowest moving positively charged fractions ; (b) neutral fractions

not separated by electrophoresis. This spot, which has been stippled in the tracing, is not present in the neutral fraction of the digested hæmoglobin S. However, the neutral peptides are not really well separated by this two-dimensional technique.

Accordingly, larger amounts of the digests from both hæmoglobins were run in one direction only, using the electrophoretic conditions described earlier. Many bands were obtained. Both the band of neutral peptides and the slowest of the positively charged bands were eluted in each case, but separately. The eluted peptide mixtures were subjected to descending chromatography with n-butyl alcohol/acetic acid/ water (4 : 1 : 5). Fig. 2 is a tracing of the chromatogram obtained showing the behaviour of the 'extra' or 'sickle cell' peptide in the two digests. This confirms that there is a particular peptide in the neutral fraction of the hæmoglobin A digest, which in the hæmoglobin S digest is shifted to the slowest positively charged zone. In addition, the R_F value of the hæmoglobin A peptide in the chromatographic solvent is lower than that of the analogous peptide derived from hæmoglobin S.

Summarizing the results of the electrophoretic and chromatographic examination, it can be seen that

4

there is one peptide among the thirty or so which in hæmoglobin S is positively charged, but which is uncharged at the same pH in digests of hæmoglobin A. This agrees with the higher net positive charge[1] of the parent protein, hæmoglobin S. There is also a small change in the chromatographic behaviour of the peptide. On the other hand, corresponding pairs of all the other peptides show similar behaviour in these separating systems and therefore probably have similar constitutions.

One can now answer at least partly the question put earlier, and say that there is a difference in the amino-acid sequence in one small part of one of the polypeptide chains. This is particularly interesting in view of the genetic evidence[12] that the formation of hæmoglobin S is due to a mutation in a single gene. It remains to be seen exactly how large a portion of the chains is affected and how the sequences differ.

Full details of these experiments will be reported elsewhere. I am indebted to Dr. A. C. Allison (Oxford) and Dr. G. Seaman (Cambridge) for supplying samples of hæmoglobin S and blood from patients with homozygous sickle-cell anæmia ; and I acknowledge the encouragement and interest shown by Dr. M. F. Perutz, and the expert assistance of Mrs. Leslie Barnett and Miss Rita Prior.

[1] Pauling, L., Itano, H. A., Singer, S. J., and Wells, I. C., *Science*, **110**, 543 (1949).

[2] Scheinberg, I. H., Harris, R. S., and Spitzer, J. L., *Proc. U.S. Nat. Acad. Sci.*, **40**, 777 (1954).

[3] Perutz, M. F., and Mitchison, J. M., *Nature*, **166**, 677 (1950).

[4] Schroeder, W. A., Kay, L. M., and Wells, I. C., *J. Biol. Chem.*, **187**, 221 (1950).

[5] Huisman, T. H. J., Jonxis, J. H. P., and van der Schaaf, P. C., *Nature*, **175**, 902 (1955).

[6] Porter, R. R., and Sanger, F., *Biochem. J.*, **42**, 287 (1948). Havinga, E., *Proc. U.S. Nat. Acad. Sci.*, **39**, 59 (1953). Huisman, T. H. J., and Drinkwaard, H., *Biochim. Biophys. Acta*, **18**, 588 (1955).

[7] Huisman, T. H. J., and Dozy, A., *Biochim. Biophys. Acta*, **20**, 400 (1956).

[8] Hommes, F. A., Santema-Drinkwaard, J., and Huisman, T. H. J., *Biochim. Biophys. Acta*, **20**. 564 (1956). Ingram, V. M. (in preparation).

[9] Perutz, M. F., Liquori, A. M., and Eirich, F., *Nature*, **167**, 929 (1951).

[10] Ingram, V. M., *Biochem. J.*, **59**, 653 (1955).

[11] Michl, H., *Monatsh. Chem.*, **82**, 489 (1951).

[12] Neel, J. V., *Science*, **110**, 64 (1949).

ABNORMAL HUMAN HAEMOGLOBINS

IV. THE CHEMICAL DIFFERENCE BETWEEN
NORMAL HUMAN HAEMOGLOBIN AND HAEMOGLOBIN C

J. A. HUNT[*] AND V. M. INGRAM[**]

*Molecular Biology Unit of the Medical Research Council, Cavendish Laboratory,
University of Cambridge, (Great Britain)*

(Received February 1st, 1960)

SUMMARY

Tryptic digests of normal human haemoglobin and of haemoglobin C contain a peptide fragment (peptide 4) which apparently alone of all the peptides has a different chemical structure in the two haemoglobins. These peptides have been degraded and their amino acid sequences have been determined in the two cases. The sole alteration is the replacement of a glutamic acid residue of normal haemoglobin by lysine in haemoglobin C.

INTRODUCTION

Human haemoglobin has been shown to consist of two identical halves[1]. The globin of the human haemoglobin molecule comprises two pairs of identical polypeptide chains[2-3]. The abnormal human haemoglobin, sickle cell haemoglobin (S), was found by INGRAM[4-6] to differ from normal human haemoglobin (A) by one amino acid in each of one pair of identical polypeptide chains, that is, by one amino acid in the half molecule. We have investigated the abnormal human haemoglobin C in a similar manner, and find that it also differs from haemoglobin A by one amino acid in the half molecule. The same glutamic acid residue of haemoglobin A which is replaced by valine in haemoglobin S, has been replaced by lysine[7] in haemoglobin C. The genetic implications of this change have been dealt with previously[7].

Haemoglobin C was discovered by ITANO AND NEEL[8] together with haemoglobin S in an individual suffering from a mild form of sickle cell anaemia. The techniques employed included electrophoresis on paper and in solution where haemoglobins S and C are easily distinguishable from each other and from haemoglobin A.

Individuals have been found who are homozygous for the haemoglobin C gene and who have virtually only haemoglobin C in their erythrocytes. Family studies on other patients have indicated that they are heterozygous for the haemoglobin C

Abbreviations: DNP, dinitrophenyl; PTC, phenylthiocarbamyl; PTH, phenylthiohydantoin.
* Present address: Chemical Department, Carlsberg Laboratory, Copenhagen, (Denmark).
** Present address: Division of Biochemistry, Department of Biology, Massachusetts Institute of Technology, Cambridge, Mass., (U.S.A.).

gene and the genes for either haemoglobins A, S or the thalassaemia syndrome[9]. The haemoglobin C gene is found mostly among people of negroid descent[9], but one case of the homozygous haemoglobin C disease has been reported in a Sicilian[10]. As in the case of haemoglobin S, the mutation producing haemoglobin C is inherited as a single gene[9]. From the examination of families having the genes for both haemoglobin S and haemoglobin C, RANNEY[11] has concluded that the genes for haemoglobins S and C are allelic or closely linked; that is to say they occupy the same or closely linked loci in the chromosome (see also refs. 12, 13).

Haemoglobin C has fewer net negative charges[14] than both haemoglobins A and S. This can be demonstrated both by moving boundary and paper electrophoresis under acid (pH 6.5) and alkaline (pH 8.6) conditions. ITANO[14] calculated that at pH 8.6 the haemoglobin C molecule (mol. wt.: 66,700) has about two net negative charges fewer than haemoglobin S, and that the haemoglobin S molecule has about two net negative charges fewer than haemoglobin A. On the other hand, SCHEINBERG[15] examined the relative mobilities of haemoglobins A, S and C by paper electrophoresis over a wide pH range. He concluded that haemoglobin C has between five and eight carboxyl groups fewer per molecule than haemoglobin A. We have found[7] that there is a charge difference between haemoglobins A and C caused by the substitution of two amino groups for two carboxyl groups in the molecule. These are the only charge differences in the molecules so far detected.

ITANO[16] reported that reduced haemoglobin C has a higher solubility than reduced haemoglobin A in 2.4 M phosphate solutions, but HUISMAN et al.[17] find that carbonmonoxy-haemoglobin C is less soluble than carbonmonoxy-haemoglobin A and that the reduced haemoglobins A and C have about the same solubility in salt solutions. These findings might suggest that there is more than one type of haemoglobin C (just as there is more than one type[18] of haemoglobin D); however, we have examined three samples of haemoglobin C from unrelated negro patients and all have the same structure as far as can be determined by our methods.

Amino acid analyses of haemoglobins A and C have shown only small and statistically insignificant differences in their compositions[14], except that HUISMAN reported an increase in the lysine content of haemoglobin C, as would be expected from our findings. On the other hand, he did not observe a corresponding fall in the number of glutamic acid residues. Other differences between the two haemoglobins, reported by HUISMAN in the same paper, have not so far been substantiated by us.

The present paper deals with the comparison of the tryptic digests of haemoglobins A and C, the chymotryptic digests of their trypsin resistant "cores", and the structural analyses of the peptides in the haemoglobin A and C trypsin digests which were found to differ.

MATERIALS AND METHODS

Haemoglobin

The method of preparation of the haemoglobin solutions was the same as previously described by INGRAM[5], except that the haemolysates were centrifuged after dialysis. Three different samples of haemoglobin C, from persons known to be homozygous for the haemoglobin C gene, and two samples of haemoglobin A were used. One of the samples of haemoglobin C was a solution of the pure haemoglobin in aqueous glycerine and was dialysed and centrifuged as usual. Paper electrophoresis in 0.06 M veronal buffer at pH 8.6 showed haemoglobin C migrating as a single band with a lower mobility than both haemoglobins A and S. No other components were visible in this test.

Digestion

Tryptic digestion of the heat denatured haemoglobin and chymotryptic digestion of the trypsin resistant core were performed in a "pH stat" as previously described[5,6].

Electrophoresis

Pyridine acetate buffers at pH 6.4 and 3.6, using AnalaR grade pyridine–glacial acetic acid–water (25 : 1 : 225) and (1 : 10 : 90), respectively, were used for one dimensional paper electrophoretic separation of the peptides as described by INGRAM[5]. "*Fingerprints*" of the resulting peptide mixtures of haemoglobins A and C were performed "in parallel" as previously described[5].

For better resolution of peptide mixtures, the tryptic and chymotryptic digests were subjected to electrophoresis on Whatman No. 3MM paper at pH 6.4 at 20 V/cm for 1.5 h. The peptide bands were located by a 0.025 % ninhydrin in water-saturated *n*-butanol spray followed by heating at 100° for about 5 min; they were then cut out and eluted with 20 % acetic acid. The bands from haemoglobin A and C digests so obtained were next run in parallel by descending chromatography[19] with *n*-butanol–acetic acid–water (4 : 1 : 5) on Whatman No. 1 paper or by paper electrophoresis at pH 3.6.

End group analysis of peptides

1-fluoro-2,4-dinitrobenzene as 5 % solution in alcohol was added to the peptide dissolved in 1 % aqueous trimethylamine, as described by SANGER AND THOMPSON[20] for the dinitrophenylation of peptides. The DNP amino acids were determined by a modification of LEVY's two dimensional paper chromatographic system[21]. The first solvent was replaced by the *tert.*-amyl alcohol solvent saturated with the pH 6 phthalate buffer of BLACKBURN AND LOWTHER[22].

EDMAN stepwise degradation was performed by coupling the peptide with phenylisothiocyanate in the triethylamine buffer described by SJÖQUIST[23]. The phenylisothiocyanate was a commercial grade, redistilled *in vacuo*; the triethylamine was redistilled from a commercial grade, but the acetone used was of AnalaR grade and was not further purified. The PTC peptide was cyclised to the PTH of the N-terminal amino acid either in acetic acid saturated with HCl, as described SJÖQUIST[23] or in 3 N HCl (ref. 24). The PTH amino acid was extracted with ethyl acetate from acid or neutralized solutions, as indicated (Table IIb). When acetic acid had been used for cyclisation, the reaction mixture was first diluted with water before extraction. In order to identify the PTH amino acid, the amino acid was regenerated by heating[25, 26] the PTH amino acid in concentrated HI (M.A.R.) for 4 h at 140°. The amino acid was then identified by using the two dimensional chromatographic system[27] of REDFIELD. The first (methanolic) solvent had been replaced by *n*-butanol–acetic acid–water (3 : 1 : 1). This system will be referred to as the "butanol–acetic acid: REDFIELD 2" system.

Qualitative amino acid analyses of peptides eluted from paper chromatograms were performed by hydrolysis of the peptides in hard glass capillary tubes for 14 h at 120° in constant boiling HCl which had been twice glass distilled from stannous chloride. This was followed by two dimensional chromatography in the REDFIELD system[27].

Quantitative amino acid analyses were performed in the following way. The peptides were hydrolysed as described above, and the hydrolysates chromatographed on a multisheet frame on 20 × 20 cm squares of Whatman No. 1 paper using the "butanol–acetic acid: REDFIELD 2" system. The papers were allowed to dry overnight in a fume cupboard. After development in the second dimension, the papers were dried in a Kodak film drying cabinet for 30–60 min and then steamed for 10 min to remove the excess diethylamine. The ninhydrin colour of the amino acids was developed by dipping the papers in a 5 % solution of ninhydrin in acetone which contained 5 % by volume of a 0.05 M phosphate solution (pH 7.2) (ref. 28) and by heating the papers at 65° for 22 min[29]. The spots were cut out with a razor blade and the ninhydrin colour eluted in 4-ml aliquots of 71 % ethanol. The O.D. of each spot so eluted was found by using a 1-cm cuvette in a Unicam SP 500 spectrophotometer at 575 mμ against a blank cut from one of the papers[29]. 10-μl aliquots of standard mixtures of amino acids of 2, 5, 8 and 10 mM strength were run with each determination. They contained lysine, histidine, glutamic acid, threonine, proline, valine and leucine. The amount of each amino acid in a peptide was found from the standard curves.

Partial acid hydrolysis was performed by incubation of the peptide in concentrated HCl (M.A.R.) at 37°.

Peptides T-4a and T-4b were purified by paper electrophoresis of the haemoglobin C tryptic digest at pH 6.4; peptide T-4a by electrophoresis of band 2 at pH 3.6, and peptide T-4b by paper electrophoresis of band 4 at pH 3.6 (see Fig. 4).

Tests for tryptophan and cysteine were performed by using the EHRLICH[30] and the platinic iodide[31] reagents respectively.

RESULTS AND DISCUSSION

Comparison of the haemoglobin A and C tryptic digests

The fingerprints of haemoglobin A and C digests (Fig. 1) show that in the neutral band of peptides the peptide T-4 of haemoglobin A, has been replaced in haemoglobin C by the neutral peptide T-4a. The more rigorous method of paper electrophoresis at pH 6.4 followed by chromatography (Fig. 2a and 2b) showed indeed that this was the only change in the neutral band (band 2), but in addition a new peptide (T-4b) was found in the positively charged band 4. Elution of this peptide from the chromatogram showed that it was mixed with other peptides and it was finally purified as described above.

The remaining peptides of the tryptic digests of haemoglobins A and C have been examined in the following ways: (a) By fingerprinting the digests in parallel locating the peptide spots by the 0.025 % ninhydrin spray, eluting each spot from each of two fingerprints and analysing qualitatively the amino acid composition of each and every peptide. (b) By parallel electrophoresis at pH 6.4 of the digests and parallel descending chromatography of the peptide bands (Fig. 2a and 2b). The peptides were located and qualitative amino acid analyses made as before.

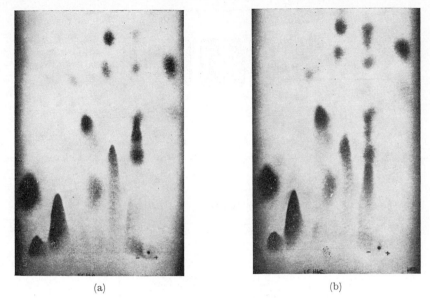

(a)   (b)

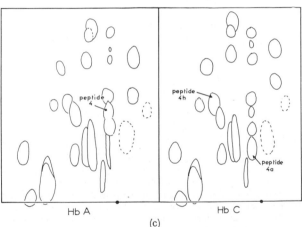

Hb A   Hb C

(c)

Fig. 1. Fingerprints of the trypsin digests of haemoglobins A and C. (a), Haemoglobin A; (b), Haemoglobin C; (c), Tracings showing the location of the changed peptides. The dotted lines indicate ninhydrin positive peptides which only become visible after heating.

No differences in amino acid composition, apart from the ones described in this paper, could be detected between the peptides in the tryptic digests of haemoglobins A and C.

Comparison of the chymotryptic digests of the trypsin resistant "cores" of haemoglobins A and C

Examination[6] of the "core" digests of haemoglobins A and C by fingerprinting revealed no differences in the patterns of the peptides.

Examination of the amino acid compositions of each peptide obtained by method 2 again revealed no differences between the two "cores" (Fig. 3).

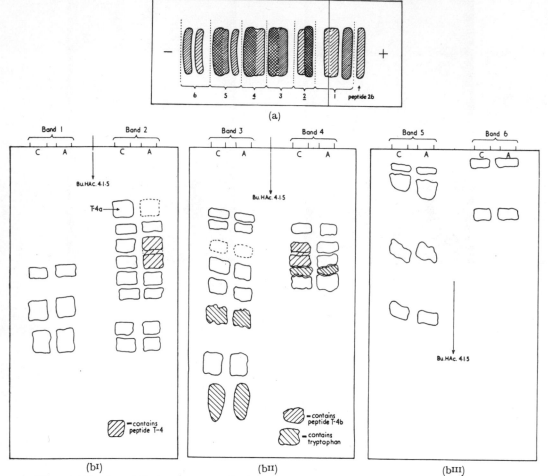

Fig. 2. (a) Tracing of the ionogram at pH 6.4 of the trypsin digest of haemoglobin A showing how the peptide bands were cut out for elution and subsequent fractionation. (Identical patterns were obtained from the trypsin digests of haemoglobin C). (b) Tracings of the peptide bands shown in Fig. 2 (a) after separation by chromatography in the *n*-butanol–acetic acid–water (4:1:5) system.

The amino acid sequence of haemoglobin A peptide T-4

The original sequence found by INGRAM[4,7] was shown to be incorrect by HUNT AND INGRAM[32], and HILL AND SCHWARTZ[33] and the corrected sequence is now:

val·his·leu·thr·pro·glu·glu·lys

Val, valine; his, histidine; leu, leucine; thr, threonine; pro, proline; glu, glutamic acid; lys, lysine. The γ-carboxyl groups of both glutamic acid residues are free and carry negative charges at neutral pH.

The amino acid sequence of haemoglobin C peptide T-4a (Fig. 1)

Equal amounts of glutamic acid and lysine were found by qualitative amino acid analysis of the peptide in the REDFIELD system as judged by eye. Tryptophan

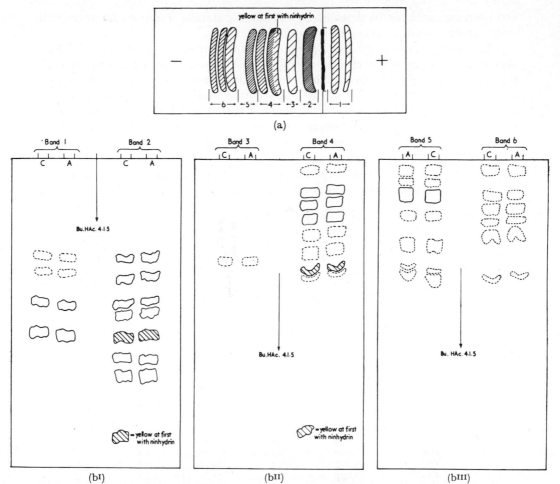

Fig. 3. (a) Tracing of the ionogram at pH 6.4 of the chymotrypsin digest of the trypsin-resistant "core" of haemoglobin (see Fig. 2(a)). (b) Tracings of the peptide bands shown in Fig. 3(a) separated by chromatography in the *n*-butanol–acetic acid–water (4:1:5) system.

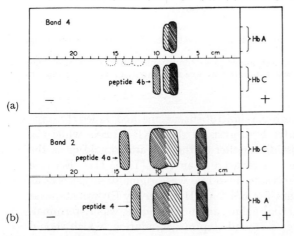

Fig. 4. (a) Tracing of the ionogram at pH 3.6 of the peptide band 2 from Fig. 2(a) of haemoglobins A and C run side by side to show the absence of the peptide A T-4 and the presence of the peptide C T-4a in haemoglobin C. (b) Tracing of the ionogram at pH 3.6 of the peptide band 4 from figure 2(1) of haemoglobins A and C run side by side to show the presence of the peptide C T-4b in haemoglobin C.

and cysteine could not be detected by the specific staining reactions for these two amino acids. No other amino acids were present.

End group analysis by the 1-fluoro-2,4-dinitrobenzene method yielded DNP-glutamic acid, identified by chromatography in the *tert.*-amyl alcohol–pH 6 phthalate system. It was the only ether soluble product after hydrolysis of the DNP-peptide T-4a. The acid soluble portion of the DNP-peptide contained only ε-DNP-lysine as determined by chromatography in the REDFIELD system[27]. Using the EDMAN stepwise degradation method[23], glutamic acid was again found to be N-terminal by hydrolysis of the PTH-amino acid in concentrated HI. The residue of the peptide after hydrolysis contained only lysine.

Thus the amino acid sequence of peptide T-4a must be glutamyl-lysine. This is in agreement with the known specificity of trypsin.

The amino acid sequence of haemoglobin C peptide T-4b

Qualitative amino acid analysis of peptide T-4b showed that the peptide contained histidine, leucine, lysine, proline, threonine and valine, while the specific staining reactions for tryptophan and cysteine were negative. Quantitative amino acid analysis using the "butanol–acetic acid, REDFIELD 2" system showed that the amino acids were present in equimolar quantities (Table I).

TABLE I

AMINO ACID ANALYSIS OF HAEMOGLOBIN C PEPTIDE T-4b

	Time of hydrolysis			
	18 h		*14 h*	
	μmoles found	*μmoles/μmoles Peptide**	*μmoles found*	*μmoles/μmoles Peptide**
Lys	0.024	1.0	0.057	1.0
His	0.020	0.9	0.061	1.1
Thr	0.027	1.2	0.045	0.8
Pro**	(0.02)	(1)	(0.05)	(1)
Val	0.020	0.9	0.054	1.0
Leu	0.023	1.1	0.065	1.2
Mean	0.023		0.056	

* Based on the mean value of μmoles of amino acid obtained in each experiment (omitting proline).
** Since the O.D. of proline is not great enough under these conditions to give accurate values the amount of proline in each hydrolysate was estimated by eye in comparison with the known standards.

End group analysis by the 1-fluoro-2,4-dinitrobenzene method failed to give any ether soluble DNP-amino acid after hydrolysis of the DNP-peptide while the residue of the peptide contained no histidine, either as the free amino acid or as the imidazole-DNP derivative, and valine was reduced in amount (Table IIa). Because of the absence of histidine in the hydrolysate, histidine was originally suspected[7] as the N-terminal amino acid in the peptides T-4 and T-4b. However, by EDMAN stepwise degradation of the peptide it was found that valine, and not histidine, was N-terminal. No amino acid could be identified after a second step of degradation, which should

TABLE II

END GROUP ANALYSIS OF PEPTIDE T-4b

a   By dinitrophenylation

	Lys	His	Thr	Pro	Val	Leu
Before dinitrophenylation	+++	++	++	++	+++	++++
After dinitrophenylation*	++	—	+++	++	++	++++

Lysine was determined as its ε-DNP derivative*

b   By EDMAN *stepwise degradation*

	Lys	His	Thr	Pro	Val	Leu	α-amino butyric acid
Before degradation	+	+	+	+	+	+±	—
1st step extract from an acid solution	±	—	—	—	++	—	—
2nd step extract from an acid solution	—	—	—	—	±	—	—
extract from neutral solution**	—	—	—	—	—	—	—
3rd step extract from acid solution	±	—	—	—	—	++	±
4th step extract from acid solution	—	—	—	—	—	+	+

* *a*-Amino butyric acid is probably formed by the reduction of PTH-threonine during hydrolysis with hydriodic acid.

** Attempt to find PTH-histidine (see text).

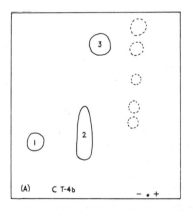

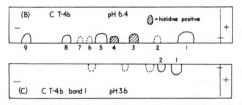

Fig. 5. (a) Tracing of the fingerprint of the partial acid hydrolysate of the haemoglobin C T-4b peptide. (b) Tracing of the ionogram at pH 6.4 of the partial acid hydrolysate of the haemoglobin C T-4b peptide. (c) Tracing of the ionogram at pH 3.6 of band 1 from Fig. 5(b).

TABLE III

PARTIAL ACID HYDROLYSIS OF PEPTIDE T-4b

a   40 h partial acid hydrolysate separated by Fingerprinting (Fig. 5a)

Peptide	Lys	His	Thr	Pro	Val	Leu
A-1	?	—	—	—	—	—
A-2	+++	—	+++	+++	—	—
A-3	—	++	—	—	++	+++

b   90 h partial acid hydrolysate separated by paper electrophoresis at pH 6.4 (Fig. 5b)

Peptide	Lys	His	Thr	Pro	Val	Leu
B-3	—	+++	—	—	+++	++++
B-4	±	++	±	±	++	—
B-5	+++	—	+++	+++	—	—
B-8	+	—	—	+	—	—
B-9	++	—	—	—	—	—

c   Band B-1 separated by paper electrophoresis at pH 3.6 (Fig. 5c)

Peptide	Lys	His	Thr	Pro	Val	Leu	Remarks
C-1	—	—	++	±	++	+++	Probably free amino acids
C-2	—	—	++	++	—	—	

TABLE IV

END GROUP ANALYSIS OF THE FRAGMENTS FROM PEPTIDE T-4b

a   By dinitrophenylation

Peptide B-3	His	Val	Leu	DPN amino acid
Residue after dinitrophenylation	—	+	++	None

Peptide B-5	Lys	Thr	Pro	DPN amino acid
Residue after dinitrophenylation	++	±	++	Threonine

Lysine was determined as the ε-DNP derivative

b   By EDMAN stepwise degradation

Peptide B-3	His	Val	Leu
Before degradation	++	++	+++
1st step			
extract from acid solution	±	++	±
extract from neutral solution	—	—	—
2nd step			
extract from acid solution	—	±	±
extract from neutral solution	—	—	—
3rd step			
extract from acid solution	—	—	+
Unhydrolysed residue	—	—	—

have given histidine, but leucine was found on the third step, as shown in Table IIb. The reason for this behaviour is not yet clear.

Partial acid hydrolysis of the peptide T-4b, derived from about 40 mg of haemoglobin, in concentrated HCl at 37° for 40 h, followed by separation of the peptide fragments obtained by fingerprinting, gave two main peptides, A-2 and A-3 (Fig. 5a). The qualitative amino acid analyses of these fragments are shown in Table IIIa. Hydrolysis of the peptide under the same conditions but for 90 h gave more fragments which were readily separated by paper electrophoresis at pH 6.4 and 3.6 (Fig. 5b and 5c). The qualitative amino acid analyses of some of these peptide fragments is shown in Table IIIb. Both peptides B-3 and B-5 were dinitrophenylated; B-3 gave no DNP amino acid and the residue contained no histidine and less valine than leucine as is shown in Table IVa. B-5 gave DNP-threonine in the ethereal extract and the residue of the hydrolysed DNP-peptide contained proline and lysine as shown in Table IVa. Three steps of the EDMAN degradation were performed on the peptide B-3 yielding valine for the first step, nothing for the second step and leucine for the third step, while the unhydrolysed residue contained no amino acids (Table IVb).

From these results the sequence of peptide T-4b can be constructed in the following way:

Composition	$val_1 his_1 leu_1 thr_1 pro_1 lys_1$
EDMAN degradation	val– ? –leu–(thr, pro, lys)
Partial acid hydrolysis	
A-2	(thr, pro, lys)
A-3	(val, his, leu)
B-3	val–his–leu.
B-4	(val, his)
B-5	thr–(pro, lys)
B-8	(pro, lys)
C-2	(thr, pro)
Sequence	val·his·leu·thr·pro·lys

Assuming that the T-4a peptide is joined to the C-terminal end of peptide T-4b then the sequence of the peptide in haemoglobin C equivalent to T-4 is:

val·his·leu·thr·pro·lys·glu·lys,

compared with peptide T-4 in haemoglobin A:

val·his·leu·thr·pro·glu·glu·lys

and peptide T-4 in haemoglobin S:

val·his·leu·thr·pro·val·glu·lys

It can be seen that there is a single amino acid change in haemoglobin C of a glutamic acid to a lysine in exactly the same place as the glutamic acid to valine change in haemoglobin S. These are the only differences so far detected by us in the haemoglobin half-molecule, and so are likely to represent the whole of the charge difference between the haemoglobins. Thus haemoglobin C has two less carboxyl groups and two additional amino groups per molecule, a total of four less negative charges per molecule of mol. wt. 66,700 than in haemoglobin A. SCHEINBERG[15] had estimated that the charge difference was due to five or six fewer carboxyl groups. He came to this conclusion because he was unable to detect a difference in electrophoretic mobility at low pH between molecules of haemoglobin A and C with positive charges of about 110 and 112. It is unlikely that his method would be sensitive enough.

One of the most striking differences in the properties of haemoglobins A, S and C are their solubilities in the deoxygenated form. Since the only detectable differences in the molecules so far found are the amino acid substitutions, it is quite likely that these cause the difference in the solubilities. Conceivably the charge differences affect the pattern of charges on the surface of the molecules, so as to alter the aggregation of the molecules under conditions of high salt concentrations, either facilitating or hindering precipitation. This suggested mechanism will have to serve until the detailed three dimensional structure of haemoglobin is known and understood. The fact that haemoglobin C is able to replace haemoglobin S up to 50 % without inhibiting the gelling of the reduced haemoglobin S solution, while haemoglobin A will only replace[34] up to 25 % of haemoglobin S, is still to be explained.

Both haemoglobins S and C are found close together in Africa, and it has been suggested by MOURANT[35] that the haemoglobin C mutation has arisen from the haemoglobin S mutation, although there is no evidence to support this theory. Genetically haemoglobins A, S and C are of great interest because they illustrate biochemically the effects of allelism. These results should also be viewed in conjunction with haemoglobin G (Neel). This haemoglobin has been found by HILL AND SCHWARTZ[33] to change in the same peptide T-4, but in this case it is the second glutamic acid residue which changes to a glycine.

The present experiments show not only that a gene mutation can affect just a single amino acid residue, but that individual mutations can alter the same amino acid in polypeptide chain in different ways.

ACKNOWLEDGEMENTS

We are grateful to Dr. H. LEHMANN, London, Dr. H. A. ITANO, Bethesda, Maryland, and Dr. I. H. SCHEINBERG, New York, for generously supplying the samples of haemoglobin C used in this investigation and for many stimulating discussions. We would also like to acknowledge the interest shown by Drs. M. F. PERUTZ, F.R.S., and F. H. C. CRICK, F.R.S., Cambridge.

One of us (J.A.H.) is grateful to the Medical Research Council for a scholarship.

REFERENCES

[1] M. F. PERUTZ, A. M. LIQUORI AND E. EIRICH, Nature, 167 (1951) 929.
[2] H. S. RHINESMITH, W. A. SCHROEDER AND L. PAULING, J. Am. Chem. Soc., 79 (1957) 4682.
[3] H. S. RHINESMITH, W. A. SCHROEDER AND N. MARTIN, J. Am. Chem. Soc., 80 (1958) 3358.
[4] V. M. INGRAM, Nature, 180 (1957) 326.
[5] V. M. INGRAM, Biochim. Biophys. Acta, 28 (1958) 539; 36 (1959) 402.
[6] J. A. HUNT AND V. M. INGRAM, Biochim. Biophys. Acta, 28 (1958) 546.
[7] J. A. HUNT AND V. M. INGRAM, Nature, 182 (1958) 1062.
[8] H. A. ITANO AND J. V. NEEL, Proc. Natl. Acad. Sci. U.S., 36 (1950) 613.
[9] W. W. ZUELZER, J. V. NEEL AND A. R. ROBINSON, Progr. Haematol., 1 (1956) 91.
[10] L. DIGGS, A. P. KRAUS, D. B. MORRISON AND L. P. RUDNICKI, Blood, 9 (1954) 1172.
[11] H. M. RANNEY, J. Clin. Invest., 33 (1954) 1364.
[12] J. V. NEEL, New Engl. J. Med., 256 (1957) 161.
[13] H. LEHMANN, Acta Genet., 6 (1956/7) 413.
[14] H. A. ITANO, Advances in Protein Chem., 12 (1957) 215.
[15] J. H. SCHEINBERG, Hemoglobin, Natl. Acad. Sci., Washington, 1958.

[16] H. A. ITANO, *Arch. Biochem. Biophys.*, 47 (1953) 148.
[17] T. H. J. HUISMAN, P. C. VAN DER SCHAAF AND A. VAN DER SAAR, *Blood*, 10 (1955) 1079.
[18] S. BENZER, V. M. INGRAM AND H. LEHMANN, *Nature*, 182 (1958) 852.
[19] S. M. PARTRIDGE, *Biochem. J.*, 42 (1948) 238.
[20] F. SANGER AND E. O. P. THOMPSON, *Biochem. J.*, 53 (1953) 353.
[21] A. L. LEVY, *Nature*, 174 (1954) 126.
[22] S. BLACKBURN AND A. G. LOWTHER, *Biochem. J.*, 48 (1951) 126.
[23] J. SJÖQUIST, *Arkiv Kemi*, 11 (1957) 129.
[24] H. FRAENKEL-CONRAT AND J. I. HARRIS, *J. Am. Chem. Soc.*, 76 (1954) 6058.
[25] G. SCHRAMM, G. BRAUNITZER AND J. W. SCHNEIDER, *Nature*, 76 (1955) 456.
[26] D. F. ELLIOT AND W. S. PEART, *Biochem. J.*, 65 (1957) 246.
[27] R. R. REDFIELD, *Biochim. Biophys. Acta*, 10 (1953) 344.
[28] V. M. INGRAM AND M. J. R. SALTON, *Biochim. Biophys. Acta*, 24 (1956) 9.
[29] R. E. KAY, D. C. HARRIS AND C. ENTENMAN, *Arch. Biochem. Biophys.*, 63 (1956) 14.
[30] I. SMITH, *Nature*, 171 (1951) 43.
[31] G. TOENNIES AND J. J. KOLB, *Anal. Chem.*, 23 (1951) 823.
[32] J. A. HUNT AND V. M. INGRAM, *Nature*, 184 (1959) 640.
[33] R. J. HILL AND H. C. SCHWARTZ, *Nature*, 184 (1959) 641.
[34] A. C. ALLISON, *Biochem. J.*, 65 (1957) 212.
[35] A. E. MOURANT, *The Distribution of Human Blood Groups*, Blackwell Oxford, 1954, p. 184.

Reprinted from COLD SPRING HARBOR SYMPOSIA ON QUANTITATIVE BIOLOGY
Volume XXVI, 1961
Printed in U.S.A.

The Effects of Mutation on the Composition and Properties of the A Protein of *Escherichia coli* Tryptophan Synthetase

CHARLES YANOFSKY, DONALD R. HELINSKI AND BARBARA D. MALING

Department of Biological Sciences, Stanford University, Stanford, California

INTRODUCTION

Only a little more than ten years ago the first case was described in which the mutationally induced loss of ability to catalyze a specific biochemical reaction was associated with the absence of the enzyme normally required for the reaction (Mitchell and Lein, 1948). More recently, it has been shown that mutational changes lead to many different types of enzyme alterations and that mutant proteins resembling the normal enzyme are often formed (Fincham, 1959; Yanofsky and St. Lawrence, 1960). With the development of techniques that can distinguish a mutant protein from the normal where the mutant protein differs by a single amino acid substitution (Ingram, 1958), it has become possible to study the effects of mutation in terms of alterations in the primary structure of specific proteins. Ingram and subsequent workers (Ingram, 1961) have, in fact, shown that several inherited abnormal forms of human hemoglobin differ from normal adult hemoglobin by single amino acid substitutions. Genetic methods have also been highly developed and now permit the mapping of mutational sites within genes and the ordering of these mutational sites with respect to one another. Furthermore, there is reason to believe that mutations often involve single nucleotide changes in DNA and that the smallest recombinable unit may be the nucleotide (Benzer, 1957; Benzer and Freese, 1958; Freese, 1959). These developments, plus advances in our understanding of the structure and composition of genetic material, have led to the hypothesis that the linear sequence of nucleotides in a DNA segment determines the linear sequence of amino acids in the corresponding protein. According to this concept the order of mutationally altered sites in a gene should correspond directly to the order of the positions at which amino acid substitutions occur in the corresponding mutant proteins. In view of the importance of this concept and the obvious way to examine it, several gene-protein systems are being studied at the present time as possible model test systems. Our recent work has been concerned with one of these systems, the A protein of the tryptophan synthetase of *Escherichia coli*, and the structural gene that controls its synthesis. The following report represents our present understanding of the effects of different types of mutations on this protein.

CHARACTERISTICS OF THE TRYPTOPHAN SYNTHETASE SYSTEM

The tryptophan synthetase system of *E. coli* consists of two protein components designated A and B (Crawford and Yanofsky, 1958; Yanofsky, 1959). These components may be separated by chromatography on ion exchange resins or by mild acidification, which precipitates only component B. Together these two proteins catalyze the following three reactions (Crawford and Yanofsky, 1958):

(1)   indole + L-serine → L-tryptophan

(2) indoleglycerol phosphate ⇌

indole + triose phosphate

(3) indoleglycerol phosphate + L-serine →

L-tryptophan + triose phosphate

Various lines of evidence suggest that reaction (3) is the physiologically important reaction and that free indole is not an intermediate in this reaction (Crawford and Yanofsky, 1958; Yanofsky and Rachmeler, 1958). Either component can be quantitatively assayed in any one of the three reactions in the presence of an excess of the second component. The three reactions have characteristic relative rates with either component limiting; these are given in Table 1. Component A in the absence of B has trace activity in reaction (2) and is inactive in the other two reactions. Component B is also slightly active by itself, but only in reaction (1). To obtain maximum reaction rates in any of the reactions, both components must combine with one another (Crawford and Yanofsky, 1958).

Wild-type strains of *E. coli* normally produce low levels of the A and B components of tryptophan synthetase. The A protein constitutes about 0.05 per cent of the extractable protein. Tryptophan auxotrophs, on the other hand, when grown on low levels of indole or tryptophan, produce approximately 20 to 50 times as much of these proteins (Yanofsky and Crawford, 1959). Presumably, repression is minimized when the endproduct level is low and, therefore, the mutants

11

TABLE 1. RELATIVE RATES OF THE TRYPTOPHAN
SYNTHETASE REACTIONS

Preparation	Reaction			
	In → Tryp	InGP → Tryp	InGP → In	In → InGP
Component A (excess B)	100*	43	3.4	2.6
Component B (excess A)	100*	40	3.2	2.7
Component A alone	<0.2	<0.02	—	.02
Component B alone	3	<.1	—	<.001

* The indole → tryptophan reaction arbitrarily set at
100. In = indole; InGP = indoleglycerol phosphate;
Tryp = tryptophan.

TABLE 2. AMINO ACID COMPOSITION OF THE
A PROTEIN

	moles/ mole protein		moles/ mole protein
Lysine	14	alanine	41
Histidine	4	valine	19
Arginine	12	methionine	5
Aspartic (+ amide)	24	isoleucine	20
Threonine	10	leucine	28
Serine	12	tyrosine	7
Glutamic (+ amide)	31	phenylalanine	12
Proline	20	cysteic (as cystine or cysteine)	3
Glycine	20	tryptophan	0

form higher levels of enzyme. Most of the other enzymes in the tryptophan pathway are also formed in
large amounts when auxotrophs are grown on limiting
levels of indole or tryptophan. The A protein can be
easily purified with good yields, the final steps involving chromatography on DEAE-cellulose and crystallization (Henning et al., in preparation). The purified
material is homogeneous electrophoretically and in the
ultracentrifuge. Sedimentation studies with highly purified A protein have led to an estimated molecular
weight of 29,500 (Henning et al., in preparation).
Amino acid analyses (Table 2) are consistent with
this figure and have shown that all the common amino
acids with the exception of tryptophan are present in
the A protein. It is interesting that a protein concerned with the biosynthesis of tryptophan lacks this
amino acid. The B protein of tryptophan synthetase
is relatively labile when highly purified and has not
been studied intensively.

Mutant strains with defects in the A or B protein
are readily detected as tryptophan auxotrophs (Yanofsky and Crawford, 1959) and may be isolated by
penicillin selection. Mutants with defective A proteins
respond to either indole or tryptophan since the B

protein they form can convert indole to tryptophan.
B mutants, on the other hand, grow only on tryptophan. Enzyme activity measurements with extracts of
the various A and B mutants permit the division of
the A and B mutants into two sub-groups (Yanofsky
and Crawford, 1959). Members of one of the sub-
groups form a protein which is enzymatically active
with the other normal component in one of the three
reactions, while members of the other sub-group do
not. All the altered B proteins (B mutants) are enzymatically inactive by themselves but will combine
with component A and catalyze the conversion of indoleglycerol phosphate to indole. Similarly, all the
mutationally altered A proteins, which are enzymatically inactive by themselves, combine with normal B;
and the complex converts indole to tryptophan. Immunological studies are consistent with these findings
—whenever an altered protein is detected enzymatically it can also be detected with the appropriate
antiserum (Yanofsky and Crawford, 1959). On the
other hand, mutants which lack any A or B activity
also lack a protein that will react with anti-A or anti-
B serum. Antibodies to the A or B protein are specific
for the corresponding protein.

The fact that all the altered A and B proteins are
enzymatically active with the normal second component is perhaps surprising, but is consistent with one
interpretation of the nature of the A-B interaction. It
is assumed that each of the proteins is primarily responsible for the catalysis of one of the reactions; A
catalyzing reaction (2), and B catalyzing reaction (1).
These are the same reactions which proceed at low
rates with each protein alone. It is further assumed
that each of the proteins activates the other with respect to the reaction the latter protein can perform
by itself. Thus the combination of normal or altered
B protein with normal A activates A in the indoleglycerol phosphate ⇌ indole reaction, while the combination of normal or altered A protein with B activates B in the indole → tryptophan reaction. This
activation can be visualized simply as alterations of
the surfaces of the two proteins as a result of association. Presumably, the new surface configuration created by the combination of the two normal proteins
permits catalysis of reaction (3). Considering the
types of mutants that have been obtained in the light
of this interpretation, one would conclude that mutations which affect the catalytic activity of either of
the proteins may not affect the ability to combine
with the other protein. One might expect to recover
some mutants in which one of the proteins is incapable
of combining with the second component. However,
if alterations affecting association do not affect activity, the inherent activity of the separate proteins
would probably permit limited growth in the absence
of tryptophan, assuming, as is likely, that such mutants would not be repressed.

Genetic studies using transducing phage Plkc have been performed with many ultraviolet-induced A and B mutants, and it appears that the A and B genes are located adjacent to one another on the *E. coli* chromosome (Yanofsky and Lennox, 1959; Yanofsky and Crawford, 1959). To date no mutant has been discovered which maps in one region and affects the other protein, but this possibility has not been rigorously examined. Several mutants with deletions including the A and B genes have been studied (Yanofsky and Lennox, 1959). As expected, these lack any enzymatically or immunologically detectable A or B protein (Yanofsky and Crawford, 1959).

Somewhat more extensive mapping has been performed with the A mutants and a cluster map of the strains that have been studied is shown in Fig. 1. The upper mutants form altered A proteins while the mutants on the lower half of the chart do not produce a detectable protein. The various mutants have been grouped into clusters, preliminary to final ordering of the mutationally altered sites. Each cluster includes those mutants that give less than 0.1 per cent recombination with one another in appropriate transduction tests. The total length of the A gene is about 2.5 map units (Maling and Yanofsky, 1961). Three-point tests are being performed to establish the order of the clusters and the order of the recombinable mutants within each cluster. Some of the A mutants give unexpectedly high recombination values, especially mutants A1 and A23 (and the others resembling A23).

To establish whether or not mutational changes which map in the same cluster represent repeat mutational events at the same site, transduction tests are carried out with *cys-tryp* double mutants as recipients (Maling and Yanofsky, 1961). The cysteine marker employed in these experiments is linked to the A region. The use of these double mutants as recipients eliminates reversion as a limiting factor in tests of genetic identity. This permits the detection of recombination frequencies down to a level where one might expect to distinguish between altered sites which are one or a few nucleotides apart. With this test it was shown that mutants A1, 3, 11, 26, 33, 37, 41, 45, and 48 do not recombine with one another and that the same is true for mutants A23, 24, 27, 28, 35, 36, and 53.

PROPERTIES OF THE MUTATIONALLY ALTERED A PROTEINS

Although quantitative enzymatic activity measurements and immunological tests failed to reveal significant differences between the altered A proteins (Maling and Yanofsky, 1961), differences were detected in other tests. The normal A protein is not precipitated when extracts are acidified to pH 4.0. The A proteins of six of the A mutants (A11, 26, 37, 41, 45, 48) were precipitated, but not inactivated, at this pH (Maling and Yanofsky, 1961). Apparently the mutational changes in these strains have affected both the solubility of the A proteins and their enzymatic activities. The A proteins of the other A mutants were not precipitated at pH 4.

Heat inactivation was also employed in an attempt to distinguish altered A proteins from one another (Maling and Yanofsky, 1961). The acid-precipitable A11 protein mentioned previously and the A protein from one other mutant, strain A34, were approximately as heat-sensitive as the normal A protein. On the other hand, the A proteins produced by seven other mutants (A23, 24, 27, 28, 35, 36, 53) were very labile to heating; only 5 to 15 per cent of the original A activity remained under conditions where 60 to 70 per cent of the wild-type A protein was stable to heating. In addition, there was one strain, A1, which formed a moderately heat-labile A protein. Three of the mutant proteins, those produced by strains A3, A33 and A46, were more stable to heating than the normal A protein. Various mixing experiments were performed with crude and partially purified preparations of the mutant A proteins, and in all cases the stability or lability seemed to be characteristic of the mutant protein itself and did not appear to be due to interactions with some other component of the preparation. Thus it is apparent that mutations in the A

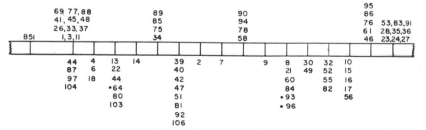

FIGURE 1. Cluster map of the A gene. The mutants listed on the upper half of the chart form altered A proteins while those on the lower half do not. The mutants marked • may form small amounts of A protein; they require further testing. Several of the clusters in the figure map close to one another, and three-point tests will be required to establish their relative order.

gene lead to the production of distinguishable altered A proteins.

Representatives of each of the different A protein types were examined in affinity tests to determine whether mutation affected the ability to combine with the B protein. In all cases the altered A protein had approximately the same affinity for the B protein as the normal A protein. This finding supports the interpretation mentioned previously that defective A proteins which are enzymatically active with the B protein are capable of combining with this protein.

One additional difference has been detected—of all the A mutants only strain A1 forms less A protein than B protein. Generally, the A-B ratio is between 1:1 and 2:1; in mutant A1 it is 1:2 (Maling and Yanofsky, 1961). Furthermore, this mutant forms much less A and B protein than any of the other mutants, although grown under the same conditions. It is apparent that the mutational change in strain A1 affects the rates of synthesis of the A and B proteins, as well as the structure of the A protein.

CORRELATION OF THE PROPERTIES OF ALTERED PROTEINS WITH THE GENETIC MAP

The map locations of the altered sites in the mutants discussed in the previous section are given in Fig. 1. All the mutants which form heat-labile proteins (A23 group) with approximately the same heat-lability map at the same site, at one end of the A region. Mutant A46 also maps at this end of the A region and forms an A protein which is slightly more heat-resistant than the normal A protein. At the other end of the A gene are located all the mutants (A11 group) which form acid-precipitable A proteins. In addition, two mutants, A3 and A33, which form heat-resistant proteins, and one mutant, A1, which forms a moderately heat-labile protein, map at the A11 site. Mutants A3 and A33 are clearly different from each other since A 3 reverts while A33 does not. Furthermore, a suppressor of A3 does not suppress A33.

The finding of four different mutant types, A1, A3, A11 and A33, which map at the same site is contrary to expectations. However, strain A33 does not revert; it may have mutational damage more extensive than a single nucleotide substitution. One mutant, strain A34, which maps near the A11 site, forms a protein which is indistinguishable from the normal protein in stability tests. Mutant A85 maps in the same cluster as A34 but grows slightly on minimal medium and thus must form a different type of altered A protein. Mutant A58 and other strains which map at or near the same site have not, as yet, been examined in stability tests; these mutants map somewhere near the center of the A gene. The mutational alterations which result in the absence of a detectable A protein are scattered throughout the A region.

It would appear from the limited sample analyzed to date that mutational alterations which lead to detectable altered proteins tend to be localized at the ends of the A gene. Whether this apparent localization has any meaning in terms of the function of the corresponding portions of the protein is, of course, not yet known. The genetic localization of mutant sites which lead to specific types of altered proteins has also been reported for the tryptophan synthetase of *Neurospora crassa* (Bonner, Suyama, and DeMoss, 1960).

Of the first 100 ultraviolet-induced A mutants which were isolated, only 32 formed an immunologically cross-reacting A protein. Most of the B mutants (38 out of 52), however, do form an altered B protein. Among the *Neurospora crassa* tryptophan synthetase mutants, 23 of the first 25 examined formed a detectable tryptophan synthetase-like protein (Suskind *et al.*, 1955; Rachmeler, 1960). The estimate of altered protein producers is probably low, and many of the mutants now classified as non-protein formers probably produce a protein which will be detected when more sensitive detection techniques are developed. These figures have some bearing on the type of genetic code employed in DNA. Most of the reasonable genetic codes that have been proposed predict that a large percentage of mutations will lead to nonsense coding units and consequently the absence of a specific protein (Crick *et al.*, 1957; Golomb *et al.*, 1958). Although the data quoted above is not corrected for repeat events at the same site, it would appear that in some genes nonsense mutations are much more infrequent than would be expected on the basis of any of these codes. Perhaps we should consider more seriously the possibility that several different nucleotide sequences code for each amino acid.

DOUBLE MUTANTS

Strains carrying more than one mutational alteration in the A gene have been prepared by transduction using the various A mutants described previously (Maling and Yanofsky, 1961). The identity of each double mutant was established by transduction experiments using phage grown on each of the single parental mutants. Double mutants were prepared between various strains, both of which formed altered proteins; only one of which formed A protein; and neither of which formed a detectable A protein. These double mutants were then examined for A protein in enzymatic and immunological tests. Only when both parents were capable of forming A protein was A protein detected in the corresponding double mutant (Table 3) (Maling and Yanofsky, 1961). Double mutant proteins sometimes showed the properties of both parental proteins. For example, a double mutant derived from a parental strain which formed an acid-precipitable A protein and a parental strain which formed a heat-labile protein, formed an A protein which was both heat-labile and acid-precipitable. Furthermore, this protein was as heat-labile and acid-precipitable as the A proteins of the parental strains. On the other hand, when double mutants were prepared between parental strains which formed a heat-resistant protein and a heat-labile protein, respectively, the A protein produced was heat-resistant. In several cases the heat-stability of the double mutant protein was intermediate to that of the two parental proteins and in one case (double mutant A1–34) the A protein formed was considerably more heat-labile than the A protein of either of the parental strains. It is clear that various types of interactions occur in proteins bearing two mutational alterations, leading in most cases to a protein phenotype which is distinguishable from that of either of the parental strains (Maling and Yanofsky, 1961). Quantitative immunological tests were performed with many of the double mutant proteins, and in some cases it appeared that the double mutant protein did not combine as well with anti-A serum as the normal A protein (Maling and Yanofsky, 1961). Since the A:B ratio is generally very low in extracts of such double mutants, it is also possible that this result is due to the presence of some enzymatically inactive A protein which can combine with antibody.

FINGERPRINTING STUDIES WITH MUTANT AND NORMAL A PROTEINS

Fingerprinting studies have been performed with many of the mutant A proteins (Helinski and Yanofsky, unpublished). A portion of a proteolytic digest of an A protein is pipetted on the corner of a sheet

TABLE 3. A-PROTEIN PRODUCTION BY DOUBLE MUTANTS

Parental Strains	Form A-Protein	
	Parental Strains	Double Mutant
1; 23	+; +	+
3; 23	+; +	+
11; 23	+; +	+
33; 23	+; +	+
34; 23	+; +	+
3; 46	+; +	+
11; 46	+; +	+
33; 46	+; +	+
34; 46	+; +	+
11; 17	+; −	−
14; 17	−; −	−
23; 13	+; −	−
46; 2	+; −	−
46; 14	+; −	−

TABLE 4. FINGERPRINTING RESULTS WITH MUTANT PROTEINS*

Protein Examined	Digest	Observation (compared with wild type)
A23	T, T + C	change in position of one peptide
A27	T, T + C	change in position of one peptide
A35	T, T + C	change in position of one peptide
A36	T, T + C	change in position of one peptide
A46	T, T + C, C	no change detected
A3	T, T + C, C	a possible change, not clear
A11	T + C, C	one additional peptide
A26	T + C, C	" " "
A33	T + C, C	" " "
A34	T, T + C, C	no change detected
A75	T, T + C, C	" " "

* Unpublished data of Helinski and Yanofsky. T = trypsin; C = chymotrypsin; T + C = trypsin + chymotrypsin.

of filter paper, chromatographed in one direction, dried, and then subjected to high voltage electrophoresis in the other direction. Tryptic digests of the A protein yield approximately 25 intense and clearly separated peptide spots by this method. Since there are 14 lysine and 12 arginine residues in the A protein, the number of peptides obtained is only slightly lower than the expected theoretical number, 27. The discrepancy is in part due to the fact that several tryptic peptides remain at the origin. The peptide pattern obtained with the wild-type A protein is highly reproducible and does not vary appreciably with the time of digestion. In addition to the 25 major peptide spots there are usually several minor peptide spots. These can be partly attributed to trace chymotrypsin activity generally associated with highly purified trypsin. Chymotrypsin or trypsin + chymotrypsin digests of the A proteins similarly give reproducible peptide patterns. We have routinely examined each mutant protein following digestion with trypsin alone, chymotrypsin alone, and trypsin + chymotrypsin. The mutant proteins that have been examined to date are listed in Table 4 along with the peptide pattern change observed, if any. The altered A proteins from four mutants which form a heat-labile A protein and map at the same site have been examined in these studies. All of these mutants show the same single peptide difference from the wild-type pattern when trypsin or trypsin + chymotrypsin peptide patterns are examined. This finding, in conjunction with other similarities between these mutants, suggests that they represent repeat identical mutational events at the same site. The particular peptide involved (T + C peptide) has been isolated and analyzed from two of these mutants and from the wild-type strain. The results of these analyses showed that the mutant peptides contained phenylalanine in addition to the nine amino acids that were present in the wild-type peptide (Helinski and Yanofsky, unpublished). The sequence of the N-terminal three amino acids has been determined for both mutant and normal peptides (Carlton, Helinski, and Yanofsky, unpublished) and is identical, with the exception that in the mutant peptide the extra phenylalanine is in the N-terminal position. Our interpretation of the presence of the extra phenylalanine in the mutant peptide is based in part on the results of total amino acid analyses of the wild-type and mutant proteins. These analyses indicated that the mutant protein contained one extra arginine, but it was not possible to say which amino acid, if any, was present in reduced amounts. This extra arginine in the mutant protein would be expected to give rise to an additional trypsin-sensitive bond in the peptide chain. Our current interpretation of these findings is that in the mutant protein this arginine is adjacent to the phenylalanine in the mutant peptide (on the N-terminal side), while in the wild-type protein there is an amino acid other than arginine in this position (see Fig. 2). Thus, when both proteins are treated with trypsin, cleavage occurs on the C-terminal side of the arginine in the mutant peptide, but there is no hydrolysis of the bond on the N-terminal side of the phenylalanine in the wild-type peptide. When chymotrypsin is added it will not attack the bond adjacent to phenylalanine in the mutant peptide because this amino acid has a free α-amino group, and the phenylalanine will remain in the mutant peptide. When the corresponding wild-type trypsin peptide is attacked by chymotrypsin, phenylalanine is not N-terminal; and the bond between phenylalanine and the next amino acid will be split. Further evidence that is consistent with this

interpretation is the finding that if the mutant protein is first treated with chymotrypsin and then with trypsin, the mutant peptide now appears at the same position as the wild-type peptide (Helinski and Yanofsky, unpublished). Studies are in progress to isolate the peptide on the N-terminal side of the mutant peptide and the corresponding peptide from the wild-type protein to determine the exact amino acid change. The other mutant which maps in this region, strain A46, forms a heat-resistant A protein. Digests of this protein do not show any peptide difference from the normal wild-type pattern. The peptide corresponding to the altered peptide in mutant A23 has been isolated from the mutant protein and found to have the same amino acid composition as the corresponding wild-type peptide.

The A proteins of two mutants which form acid-precipitable A proteins have been examined, and both mutant fingerprints contain one peptide in addition to those observed with the wild-type protein (Helinski and Yanofsky, unpublished). The heat-resistant proteins formed by mutants which map at the same site have also been examined, and the peptide pattern of one of these mutants has the identical change observed with the acid-precipitable proteins, that is, one extra peptide present in a chromatographically high position. Amino acid analyses have been performed on this extra peptide from both types of mutants, and the peptides have the same amino acid composition (Helinski and Yanofsky, unpublished). These results suggest that in both mutant types the amino acid change resulting in the appearance of this extra peptide probably was at the C-terminal position of the N-adjacent peptide. The other heat-resistant protein does not show any clear-cut peptide pattern difference from the wild-type pattern. Further studies with the acid-precipitable proteins and the heat-resistant protein which gives the extra peptide have shown that the same tryptic peptide fraction (obtained by paper electrophoresis) gives rise to the additional chymotrypsin peptide characteristic of these proteins. It appears likely, therefore, that amino acid changes have occurred at the same position in the A proteins of these two mutant types, giving different amino acids, each one of which adds a new chymotrypsin-sensitive bond in the protein (see Fig. 2). Total amino acid analyses of the A protein of one of these mutants (strain A33) showed the presence of an extra methionine residue. Since methionine bonds are often split by chymotrypsin, this may be the amino acid substituted or added in mutant A33. Two other mutants which were examined, strains A34 and A75, do not show any definite fingerprint differences.

It is clear from our fingerprinting studies, therefore, that although peptide pattern differences are often encountered, it is rare that a single amino acid substitution can be simply and unequivocally established.

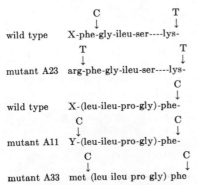

FIGURE 2. Interpretation of fingerprint differences. Trypsin is generally added first, then chymotrypsin. Bonds which should be split by trypsin or chymotrypsin are indicated by T and C, respectively.

Furthermore, in several of the mutants that have been analyzed, one would expect to find peptide differences in addition to those observed, if our interpretations of the nature of the amino acid changes are correct. It is also obvious that the fingerprinting technique will not detect all amino acid changes.

Fingerprinting analyses were carried out with double mutant proteins where the A protein of one or both of the parental types contributing to the double mutant strain showed a peptide pattern difference. These analyses were of particular importance since most of the double mutant proteins had different properties than the single mutant proteins. Thus it was possible to determine whether or not peptide pattern differences actually indicated the location of the primary structure alterations, or whether they reflected different stabilities of the altered proteins and corresponding differences in the degree or sites of digestion by proteolytic enzymes. The peptide patterns obtained with several of these double mutant proteins are shown in Fig. 3. In each case it was found that the peptide pattern differences characteristic of the proteins of both of the parental strains were pres-

ent in the double mutant protein fingerprints, with no additional changes. Thus it is clear that peptide patterns reflect the corresponding primary structure changes in the proteins examined.

Incidentally, double mutants have been extremely useful as sources of mutant peptides. For example, the A protein of mutant A23 is labile and very difficult to purify. The A protein of the double mutant A23-33 is very stable, purifies easily, and has both the A23 and A33 peptide alterations.

REVERSION STUDIES

Representatives of each of the various types of A mutants have been examined in reversion studies. Many of the mutants yield tryptophan-independent strains which grow more poorly than the wild-type strain in the absence of tryptophan, in addition to strains which are indistinguishable from the wild type. The slow-growing strains are either partial revertants, that is, strains in which the reversion occurred in the A gene, or suppressed mutants. Since partial revertants should be of considerable help in relating the genetic map to the protein map, an effort was made

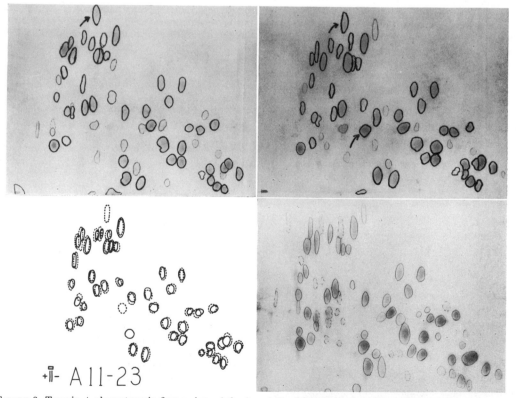

FIGURE 3. Trypsin + chymotrypsin fingerprints of the A protein of double mutants A11-46 (upper left), A23-33 (upper right), A11-23 (lower left, a tracing) and the wild-type A protein. On the A11-23 tracing the major wild-type peptides are outlined with a solid line and the A11-23 peptides with a dashed line.

TABLE 5. TESTS USED IN CLASSIFYING TRYPTOPHAN-INDEPENDENT COLONIES

Tryp⁺ types	Colony size	InG accum.	5 me-Tryp sensitivity	Whole cell TSase†	Specific A	Activity B	Ratio A/B	Genetic test
A	=WT	0	=WT	=WT	=WT	=WT	1:1–2:1	FR
B	=WT	0	>WT	=WT	?	?	?	FR
C	=WT	0	>WT	>WT	?	?	?	FR
D	<WT	+	>WT	>WT	>WT	>WT	=WT	PR
E	≪WT	+	≫WT	>WT	>WT	>WT	<WT	PR
F	<WT	+	≫WT	<WT	<WT	>WT	<WT	PR
G	<WT	+	>WT	>WT	>WT	>WT	=WT	su
H	<WT	+	>WT	<WT	<WT	>WT	<WT	su

InG = indole-3-glycerol. 5 me-Tryp = 5-methyl tryptophan.
FR = full revertant (indistinguishable from wild type in growth rate and accumulation behavior).
PR = partial revertant.
† = indole to tryptophan reaction measurements with cell suspensions.

to develop a number of different tests which would detect differences between partial revertant types derived from the same mutant. The tests employed (Allen and Yanofsky, unpublished), and the revertant and partial revertant types encountered, are listed in Table 5. Also included are the two most frequently encountered suppressor types. Since many of the tests described can be performed quantitatively, it is possible to distinguish different partial revertant types within each of the groups listed.

Unfortunately, the analysis of reversion is rather complex, as can be seen from the possibilities considered in Fig. 4. Reversion may affect the nucleotide substituted in the original mutation, or different nucleotides in the same coding unit, or a nucleotide in a different coding unit. These changes would be expected to lead to amino acid substitutions at the same position in the first two cases, and at a different position if the reversion were in a separate coding unit. Genetic tests should distinguish the last case from the other two, but probably would not readily distinguish between the first two possibilities. Second-step reversion experiments with base analogs as mutagens may be of help here. The use of analogs in single-step reversion experiments presumably adds some specificity to the reversion process and may also indicate the nucleotide change in the original mutational event.

The reversion patterns of many of the A mutants and the effect of 2-aminopurine on the reversion of these mutants are shown in Fig. 5. These studies are not as yet completed, and the types listed represent the minimum number of distinguishable revertants obtained from each mutant. The data presented indicates that 2-aminopurine increases the reversion rate of about one-half of the ultraviolet-induced A mutants that have been examined. In general, mainly the number of wild-type-like colonies is increased, although in one case (mutant A7) 2-aminopurine also increased the frequency of suppressor mutations. As yet, 2-aminopurine has not led to an increase in any partial revertant type. It should also be pointed out that of the cluster of mutants which map at the same site, A1, A3, A11 and A33, the reversion frequency of only A1 is increased by aminopurine. Presumably only this mutant, of the several at this site, was formed by a GC → AT transition (Bautz and Freese, 1960).

Four of the partial revertants have been studied

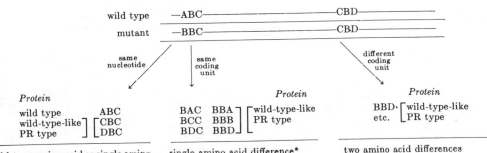

* Assuming that for each amino acid there is a unique nucleotide sequence.

FIGURE 4. Reversion analysis. Possible events at the nucleotide and amino acid levels.

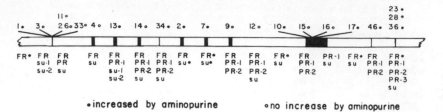

FIGURE 5. Reversion patterns of A mutants. Based on the work of Allen and Yanofsky, unpublished. FR = full revertant; PR = partial revertant.

more fully, and two of these have been examined by the fingerprinting method. Table 6 presents the results of enzymatic and immunological tests with the A proteins of these partial revertants. It is apparent that they are all abnormal. The A proteins in these strains are also distinguishable from the corresponding parental proteins in stability. This is shown in Fig. 6 where the results of heating experiments with the parental and partial revertant proteins are presented.

The A proteins from both A46 partial revertants were fingerprinted, and a single peptide difference was detected in tryptic + chymotryptic digests of the A protein of strain A46PR8 (Helinski and Yanofsky, unpublished). The mutant peptide contains one mole each of leucine, serine, and arginine, while the corresponding wild-type peptide contains these amino acids and, in addition, a second mole of leucine (Helinski and Yanofsky, unpublished). Whether there is one less amino acid in the partial revertant protein, or whether the amino acid replacing leucine is on the C-terminal end of the peptide adjacent to the mutant

peptide, is not as yet known. The amino acid compositions of the corresponding peptides from mutant A46 and the other partial revertant have also been determined, and both are identical to the wild-type peptide (Helinski and Yanofsky, unpublished). Clearly, therefore, the amino acid change associated with the reversion in A46PR8 is not in the peptide presumably altered in mutant A46. This would suggest that A46PR8 is a second-site revertant. Genetic tests have been performed to examine this possibility and have led to the recovery of mutant A46 from this partial revertant, confirming this expectation. It is apparent, therefore, that in strain A46PR8, interactions between different portions of the A protein molecule result in a catalytically effective protein, although the protein is very inefficient (see Table 6). Second-site reversion has also been detected in bacteriophage (Feynman, personal communication; Jinks, 1961).

SUPPRESSOR MUTATIONS

Since suppressor mutations by definition include all genetic changes which reverse the effects of mutational alterations at other loci, it is not surprising that they have been found to act in a variety of ways (Fincham, 1960; Yanofsky and St. Lawrence, 1960). Relatively few instances of suppression have been examined at the enzyme level, and as a result we know little of the effects of suppression on specific proteins. In one of the best analyzed cases of suppression it has been concluded that the effect is indirect and that it does

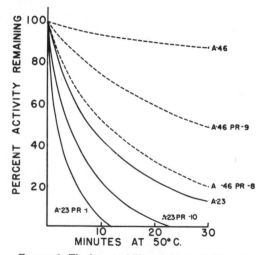

FIGURE 6. The heat stability of the A proteins from mutants A23 and A46 and their partial revertants.

TABLE 6. EXAMINATION OF THE A PROTEINS FROM PARTIAL REVERTANTS

Strain	A specific activity In → Tryp	Activity Ratio In → Tryp/ InGP → Tryp	Relative antibody inhibition
wild type	2.1	2.5	100%
A-23 PR-1	2.3	187	36%
A-23 PR-10	32	790	92%
A-46 PR-8	32	4200	92%
A-46 PR-9	95	4300	86%

not involve an alteration of the mutant protein (Suskind, 1957). Nevertheless, suppressor mutations remain a very interesting and important category since they represent the most obvious possible exception to the rule that the primary structure of a single polypeptide chain is determined by only one genic region.

In our recent studies on suppressor gene action (Brody and Yanofsky, in preparation) we have directed our attention to three questions. What are the normal functions of suppressor genes? Do suppressed mutants form specific proteins which differ from the corresponding mutant proteins? Does suppressor action occur before, during, or after the synthesis of specific proteins? In attempting to answer the first of these questions a large number of A mutants were examined (A1, 2, 3, 4, 7, 9, 10, 11, 12, 13, 14, 15, 17, 23, 33, 34, 46), only some of which were previously found to be suppressible. Suppressor mutations (and reversions) were induced in these strains by ultraviolet light, but instead of plating on the usual minimal medium, the irradiated suspensions were plated on a medium supplemented with all of the common amino acids except tryptophan, a mixture of B vitamins, and a nucleic acid hydrolysate. The *tryp⁺* colonies which appeared due to reversion or suppression were then replicated to minimal medium and the plates examined for colonies which could only grow on the supplemented medium. If suppressor genes are the genes controlling biosynthetic reactions involved in the synthesis of amino acids, vitamins, etc., one would expect to find that some of the suppressed mutants would be auxotrophs. No auxotrophs were found among the *tryp⁺* colonies although many of the colonies that appeared contained suppressed mutants (Brody and Yanofsky, in preparation). These findings suggest that most of the allele-specific suppressor genes that affect the different A mutants are concerned with cellular functions other than the biosynthesis of small molecules.

TABLE 7. THE ACTIVITY OF THE A PROTEINS FROM SUPPRESSED MUTANTS

Strain	A protein specific activity		InGP → Tryp In → Tryp per cent
	In → Tryp	InGP → Tryp	
wild type	2.5	1	40
A36	22	0	—
A36su	6	0.25	4.2
A3	35	0	—
A3su	44	0.19	0.44
A11	31	0	—
A11su	55	0.48	0.87

The second question has been examined with suppressed mutants derived from A mutants that form characteristically altered A proteins. If suppression affects the primary structure of the A protein, one might expect to find a suppressed A protein with properties different than those of the mutant A protein. If suppression affects only a fraction of the A protein molecules, then one might expect to find two types of A protein in a suppressed mutant, the A protein of the original unsuppressed mutant and another A protein species. Fortunately, as can be seen from the data presented in Table 7, extracts of the suppressed A mutants have a label which can be used to identify the suppressed mutant protein. Unlike the A proteins of the unsuppressed mutants, the A protein fraction of suppressed mutants is capable of a limited conversion of indoleglycerol phosphate to tryptophan in the presence of the normal B component. This activity accounts for the growth of suppressed mutants in the absence of tryptophan. The A protein fractions from the suppressed mutants listed are fully active in the indole to tryptophan reaction.

These findings lead to the question—does the slight activity in the indoleglycerol phosphate to tryptophan reaction indicate that all the A protein molecules are considerably less active in this reaction (as in the partial revertants), or is there a mixture of A protein types in the suppressed mutants? The answer to this question was obtained by following the loss of enzymatic activity in the two reactions under conditions that were known to inactivate the A protein of the unsuppressed parents. If the indoleglycerol phosphate to tryptophan activity of the suppressed mutants was associated with a small amount of a second A protein species, this activity might be expected to have different stability properties than the majority of the A protein in these extracts. The mutants selected for this study form A proteins with distinctive properties —one forms a heat-labile A protein (A36), another a heat-stable A protein (A3), and a third an acid-precipitable A protein (A11). When the A proteins from the various suppressed mutants were examined in stability tests, it was found that the indole to tryptophan activity was associated with an A protein type that had the same stability as the A protein of the original unsuppressed mutants. In all cases, however, the A protein bearing the indoleglycerol phosphate to tryptophan activity was inactivated at a different rate—a rate characteristic of the wild-type protein (Brody and Yanofsky, in preparation). Furthermore, it was also shown that after prolonged heating of the A protein fraction from A36su the remaining activity had the wild-type ratio of the two enzymatic activities. Thus it appears that each of the three suppressed mutants examined forms two A proteins, one with the physical characteristics of the A protein of the parental unsuppressed mutant, and the other with the physical properties of the wild-type A protein. In

I. BIOCHEMICAL GENETICS

other studies with two of these suppressed mutants it was possible to separate the two A proteins by chromatography on DEAE-cellulose columns (Crawford and Yanofsky, 1958; Brody and Yanofsky, in preparation). When enough of the wild-type-like component has been isolated, it will be examined in fingerprinting studies to determine if it actually has the wild-type primary structure.

Assuming that a small amount of wild-type protein is produced by the suppressed mutants, we are confronted with the problem of deciding whether this protein species is formed by a reaction between the mutant protein and some other cellular component or is synthesized with this configuration. Two approaches have been employed in attempting to answer this question. First, suppressor genes which affect altered sites at the ends of the A gene have been tested on other mutants that map close to these sites. If there is some exchange mechanism which operates at the ends of the A protein, one might expect these suppressors to be effective with many mutants altered at these ends. No cross-suppression was observed; the suppressors were allele-specific. Experiments were also performed in which the ratio of the activities in the two reactions, indole → tryptophan and indoleglycerol phosphate → tryptophan, was determined under conditions of tryptophan repression. It was reasoned that if suppression involves a bimolecular reaction between the mutant A protein and some cellular constituent, then lowering the concentration of the mutant A protein should increase the proportion of the wild-type-like A protein (especially since the data presented in Table 7 suggests that the mutant pro-

tein is in great excess). The results of these experiments showed that the characteristic ratio of the two activities in each of the three suppressed mutants examined was not appreciably affected by repression (Brody and Yanofsky, in preparation). Thus it would appear that these cases of suppression do not involve interactions between mutant proteins and other cellular constituents but probably reflect a limited synthesis of the wild-type-like protein.

A number of schemes have been considered as explanations for these observations, and those that we favor at this time are presented in Fig. 7. There is, of course, no direct experimental data as yet which supports any of the explanations given. They are offered within the framework of what seems reasonable on the basis of present knowledge. The possibilities under consideration assume that suppressor genes are either the genes that determine the primary structure of the amino acid-activating enzymes or the genes that determine the composition of sRNA's and thus their ability to combine with specific activating enzymes. In either case a suppressor mutation would cause a specificity change which would lead to a mistake in the attachment of a given amino acid to its sRNA. In the example cited the mutant protein would differ from the normal in having arginine at a position normally occupied by glycine. The suppressor mistake would involve the attachment of glycine to some of the sRNA molecules which are normally specific for arginine. This error could only occur infrequently, for it is almost certain that a high mistake level for any amino acid would be lethal. It is of interest in this regard that the suppressor genes we have studied

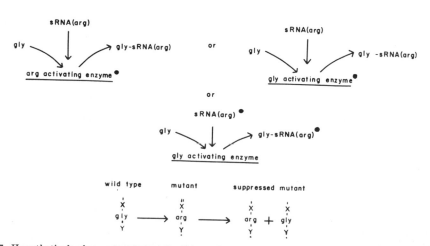

FIGURE 7. Hypothetical schemes to account for the results of the suppressor studies. ● = mutationally altered enzyme or sRNA. It is assumed that the altered enzyme or sRNA performs its normal function most of the time but can also make the above-mentioned mistakes.

never detectably alter more than 10% of the A protein molecules. Similar interpretations of suppression have been considered by other investigators (M. Lieb and L. Hertzenberg, personal communication; Benzer and Champe, 1961). Benzer and Champe have shown that different groups of T4rII mutants will grow in certain K-12(λ) strains of *E. coli* but not in others. This observation has been interpreted in much the same manner as we have interpreted suppressor mutations. Obviously, serious consideration of the possibilities offered depends on the demonstration that suppression does affect primary structure, and, hopefully, this will be decided in the near future.

CONCLUSIONS

The studies described in this paper demonstrate that mutational changes at several sites in the A gene lead to the formation of altered A proteins. Many of these altered A proteins are distinguishable from one another in addition to differing from the wild-type protein. Furthermore, distinguishable altered proteins are formed by several mutants which map at the same site. The altered A proteins produced by all of these strains were examined in peptide pattern studies, and a number of differences were detected. No more than a single peptide difference was observed with any of the mutant proteins, however, suggesting that in each case the mutational event led to a localized alteration in the primary structure of the A protein. Total amino acid analyses performed on most of the mutant proteins described here also indicate that the amino acid changes in the mutant proteins are slight indeed (Helinski and Yanofsky, unpublished). The peptide pattern studies performed with the double mutant proteins support the conclusion that primary structure alterations are localized and further show that the patterns obtained reflect the specific mutationally altered genetic sites which are combined in the double mutants. Together, the findings described leave no doubt that the A gene determines the primary structure of the A protein.

The number of mutants examined and the peptide alterations detected are insufficient to seriously test the concept of collinearity of amino acid sequence and nucleotide sequence. However, the fact that mutants A11 and A33 mapped at the same site and formed distinguishable A proteins which appeared to have amino acid changes in the same position certainly suggests that there is a correlation between the region on the genetic map at which a mutation occurs and the amino acid position that will be affected. The fact that several indistinguishable mutational changes at the same site lead to altered proteins with identical properties and with identical peptide pattern differences is also consistent with expectations.

In no case has it been possible as yet to demonstrate a single amino acid substitution in a mutant A protein. In most cases the amino acid changes in the mutant proteins examined result in a new point of cleavage by one of the proteolytic enzymes employed. This considerably complicates the analysis of the altered proteins. Our present data do not exclude the possibility that some of the altered A proteins differ from the normal by the addition or loss of a single amino acid rather than a substitution of an amino acid.

Reversion studies with selected A mutants have given a wealth of material for further study. The A proteins from two partial revertants derived from the same mutant were examined in peptide pattern studies, and one of them was found to have an amino acid change in a peptide which is unaltered in its composition in the original mutant. This finding suggests that the secondary mutational event in this strain occurred at a second site, a conclusion supported by genetic tests.

The suppressor studies demonstrate that suppression leads to the formation, in the suppressed mutants, of a small amount of a second A protein which resembles the wild-type A protein in several properties. It appears that this second protein is not formed by the interaction of the mutant protein with some other cell constituent but that its final structure is determined at the time of synthesis. Whether suppression does, in fact, restore the wild-type primary structure remains to be determined. If this is the case it will be interesting to test the explanations of suppressor gene action which were mentioned.

ACKNOWLEDGMENT

The work described in this paper was supported by grants from the National Science Foundation and the U. S. Public Health Service.

REFERENCES

BAUTZ, E., and E. FREESE. 1960. On the mutagenic effect of alkylating agents. Proc. Nat. Acad. Sci. U.S., *46*: 1585–1594.

BENZER, S. 1957. The elementary units of heredity. pp. 70–93. *A Symposium on the Chemical Basis of Heredity*. Baltimore: The Johns Hopkins Univ. Press.

BENZER, S., and S. P. CHAMPE. Modifications of *Escherichia coli* affecting the expression of specific phage mutations. Proc. Nat. Acad. Sci. U.S., in press.

BENZER, S., and E. FREESE. 1958. Induction of specific mutations with 5-bromouracil. Proc. Nat. Acad. Sci. U.S., *44*: 112–119.

BONNER, D. M., Y. SUYAMA, and J. A. DeMoss. 1960. Genetic fine structure and enzyme formation. Federation Proc., *19*: 926–930.

CRAWFORD, I. P., and C. YANOFSKY. 1958. On the separation of the tryptophan synthetase of *Escherichia coli* into two protein components. Proc. Nat. Acad. Sci. U. S., *44*: 1161–1170.

——, ——. 1959. The formation of a new enzymatically active protein as a result of suppression. Proc. Nat. Acad. Sci. U.S., *45*: 1280–1288.

CRICK, F. H. C., J. S. GRIFFITH, and L. E. ORGEL. 1957.

Codes without commas. Proc. Nat. Acad. Sci. U.S., *43*: 416–421.

FINCHAM, J. R. S. 1959. The biochemistry of genetic factors. Ann. Rev. Biochem., *28*: 343–364.

——. 1960. Genetically controlled differences in enzyme activity. Advances in Enzymology, *22*: 1–43.

FREESE, E. 1959. The difference between spontaneous and base-analogue induced mutations of phage T4. Proc. Nat. Acad. Sci. U. S., *45*: 622 633.

GOLOMB, S. W., L. R. WELCH, and M. DELBRÜCK. 1958. Construction and properties of comma-free codes. Kgl. Danske Videnskarb. Selskab, Biol. Medd., *23*: 1–34.

HENNING, U., D. R. HELINSKI, F. C. CHAO, and C. YANOFSKY. Manuscript in preparation.

INGRAM, V. 1958. Abnormal human haemoglobins. I. The comparison of normal human and sickel-cell haemoglobins by "fingerprinting." Biochim. Biophys. Acta, *28*: 539–545.

——. 1961. *Hemoglobin and Its Abnormalities.* Springfield, Illinois: Charles C. Thomas.

JINKS, J. L. 1961. Heredity, in press.

MALING, B., and C. YANOFSKY. 1961. The properties of altered proteins from mutants bearing one or two lesions in the same gene. Proc. Nat. Acad. Sci. U.S., *47*: 551–566.

MITCHELL, H. K., and J. LEIN. 1948. A *Neurospora* mutant deficient in the enzymatic synthesis of tryptophan. J. Biol. Chem., *175*: 481–482.

RACHMELER, M. 1960. A study of the normal and mutationally altered forms of the tryptophan synthetase of *Neurospora.* Ph.D. Dissertation, Western Reserve University, Cleveland, Ohio.

SUSKIND, S. R. 1957. Gene function and enzyme formation. pp. 123–129. *The Chemical Basis of Heredity.* Baltimore: The Johns Hopkins Univ. Press.

SUSKIND, S. R., C. YANOFSKY, and D. M. BONNER. 1955. Allelic strains of *Neurospora* lacking tryptophan synthetase: A preliminary immunochemical characterization. Proc. Nat. Acad. Sci. U.S., *41*: 577–582.

YANOFSKY, C. 1959. A second reaction catalyzed by the tryptophan synthetase of *Escherichia coli.* Biochim. Biophys. Acta, *31*: 409–416.

YANOFSKY, C., and I. P. CRAWFORD. 1959. The effects of deletions, point mutations, reversions and suppressor mutations on the two components of the tryptophan synthetase of *Escherichia coli.* Proc. Nat. Acad. Sci. U.S., *45*: 1016–1026.

YANOFSKY, C., and E. S. LENNOX. 1959. Transduction and recombination study of linkage relationships among the genes controlling tryptophan synthesis in *Escherichia coli.* Virology, *8*: 425–447.

YANOFSKY, C., and M. RACHMELER. 1958. The exclusion of free indole as an intermediate in the biosynthesis of tryptophan in *Neurospora crassa.* Biochim. Biophys. Acta, *28*: 640–641.

YANOFSKY, C., and P. ST. LAWRENCE. 1960. Gene action. Ann. Rev. Microbiol., *14*: 311–340.

DISCUSSION

ROTHMAN: Cyrus Levinthal, Alan Garen, and I have studied the alkaline phosphatase of *E. coli* with similar intent and approach as that described by Dr. Yanofsky. Over eighty mutants with no or reduced alkaline phosphatase activity (P—) have been isolated from an Hfr strain of *E. coli* K12 after mutagenesis with ultraviolet light (UV), X-rays, or ethyl methane sulfonate (EMS). (The EMS mutants were isolated by Dr. E. Lin.) Mapping by Hfr × F— crosses has shown all of these mutations to be located in a small locus (estimated as 0.01% of the *E. coli* linkage map) near the *lac* region. The mutants map at many different sites within this locus, since pairwise crosses among them give rise to various numbers of recombinants with full phosphatase activity (P+), which can be selected on plates containing β-glycerol phosphate as the phosphate source. A linkage map of the phosphatase locus has been constructed, normalizing the number of P+ recombinants to the number of zygotes which have received the phosphatase gene from both parents. The maximum recombination frequency between any pair of mutants found to date is 2×10^{-3}, and the minimum frequency greater than zero is 5×10^{-5}. For convenience in the ensuing discussion I shall refer to the value of 2×10^{-3} as the "gene length" although obviously there may be sites outside the present terminal sites which have not been detected, and perhaps can not be detected because mutations there do not result in changes in phenotype.

We have examined a number of P+ revertants from several sites to see whether the alkaline phosphatase made differs from the wild-type enzyme in spite of having comparable specific enzymatic activity. About half of the revertants examined make enzymes differing from the wild type in electrophoretic mobility (experiments by M. Bach and E. Signer) and in the "fingerprint" patterns of the tryptic peptides. These results demonstrate that alterations in the primary structure of the protein which do not drastically alter the enzymatic activity occur frequently. Such mutations in the forward direction are, of course, undetected.

One altered revertant (U24R3A), obtained upon UV treatment of a UV-induced mutant (U24), has been backcrossed to the wild type to determine the site of the reverse mutation relative to the site of the forward mutation. One P— colony was found among 350,000 progeny colonies examined. Since this value approximates the spontaneous mutation frequency, the result indicates reversion at or near the site of the original mutation (probably less than one three-hundredth of the "gene length" away). Two tryptic peptides (#8 and #17), and a third low-yield peptide (#41), are missing from the fingerprint of U24R3A. Peptide #17, composed of thirteen amino acids (one-thirtieth of the total polypeptide chain), has also been altered in mutant E26, which maps one-fortieth of the "gene length" away from U24. This finding, that closely linked mutations affect the same tryptic peptide, is in accord with the hypothesis of the collinearity of the genetic map and the polypeptide chain. The alteration of peptide #8 in U24R3A, but not in E26, may be explained without violating the collinearity hypothesis if peptide #8 is adjacent to #17, and the U24R3A mutations give rise to alterations at or very near the junction of the two. This point is under investigation.

We have also examined an EMS induced revertant (S6RS1) from an EMS induced mutant (S6) which maps at the same site as E26 but differs from it phenotypically. The backcross of this revertant to wild type gave rise to many colonies of mutant phenotype indicating that the reversion took place at a site distant from the forward mutation (about two-thirds of the "gene length" away). Genetic analysis of the mutant progeny revealed that half of them give no recombinants with S6 while the other half do, showing that a bacterium carrying the reversion alteration without the S6 alteration has a mutant phenotype. Fingerprints of S6RS1 show alterations in tryptic peptides #17 and #25. Semiquantitative amino acid analysis shows that one of the new peptides present in the S6RS1 fingerprint differs from peptide #25 by the substitution of a valine residue, probably for one of the four alanine residues present. The amino acid alteration in peptide #17 is not known yet. It is interesting that the combination of two alterations in the molecule, each of which alone destroys enzymatic activity, gives rise to an active enzyme. The data on this revertant is again in accord with the collinearity hypothesis if we assume that the change in peptide #25 is the result of the reverse mutation, and the change in #17 the result of the forward mutation. This assumption is being tested by fingerprinting the altered (inactive) phosphatase produced by mutant S6, which has been identified serologically.

SAGER: Do you have any information as yet about the location of your altered peptides in the polypeptide chain? I ask this question because I have been thinking about a model of gene action to be discussed later in this meeting in which part of the coding information is carried in an autonomously replicating RNA, rather than in DNA. Such coding information would be unavailable for random mutation, and consequently, the genetic map would be collinear only with a part of the protein. Amino acid substitutions induced by mutation would only be found in the segments of the protein coded by the DNA, and consequently would be found in clusters, rather than in a random distribution along the protein chain. Is there as yet any evidence bearing on this point?

YANOFSKY: No.

STRAUSS: The ideas of Dr. Yanofsky on the mechanism of suppressor action might be restricted to only a *class* of suppressor. We have been working with the non-specific suppressors of the methionine- or cystathionine-requiring *Neurospora* mutants. Both mutants blocked between cysteine and cystathionine,

and those blocked between cystathionine and homocysteine can be suppressed by this single suppressor. The mutants which are suppressed are leaky, that is, incorporate $S^{35}O_4$ into methionine. The one non-leaky mutant we have, blocked between cysteine and cystathionine, is not suppressed. We find that the two $\pm$ *su* strains we have obtained grow less well than the wild type on minimal medium, but they are completely restored by methionine or cysteine. Cysteine inhibits *ml su* strains but stimulates the $\pm su$. In this case, then, the suppressor mutation has (probably) resulted in a partial block in the synthesis of a small molecule—in this case the same molecule involved in the original mutation. I think this signifies, and I know Dr. Yanofsky agrees, that the class of suppressor mutations is really a new heterogeneous one. Certain suppresors can act via the interactions of small molecules.

YANOFSKY: I did not intend to imply that all suppressor genes act the same way. As Dr. Strauss knows, suppression includes a variety of effects which depend on the nature of the primary mutation. I am primarily interested in cases of suppression in which primary structure may be affected.

FINCHAM: If suppressor mutations act in the way you suggest, they should lead to heterogeneity in other proteins as well. Have you any evidence bearing on this?

YANOFSKY: We have not yet looked at other proteins but I agree that the mechanisms I have discussed would lead to heterogeneity in other proteins.

The fact that many suppressor genes have a deleterious effect on the growth of the wild-type strain is consistent with the expectation of general protein heterogeneity.

HOROWITZ: The A36 suppressor could be alternatively accounted for by assuming that the A36 mutation causes a fragment—a small peptide, say—to be attached to the A protein. The suppressor could then hydrolyze off the extra piece and restore the original protein. Would you comment on this possibility?

YANOFSKY: The amino acid composition of the A protein of mutant A36 is only slightly different from that of the wild-type protein so the hypothetical fragment could contain only a few amino acids at most. The peptide studies suggest that the amino acid change in the A36 A protein is on the N-terminal side of a peptide containing 10 amino acids. This peptide is not the N-terminal peptide, and, furthermore, the terminal three amino acids of the A36 A protein and the wild-type A protein are identical. Thus it is very unlikely that the A36 protein differs from the normal A protein by an additional peptide.

J. Mol. Biol. (1961) **3**, 318–356

REVIEW ARTICLE

Genetic Regulatory Mechanisms in the Synthesis of Proteins †

FRANÇOIS JACOB AND JACQUES MONOD

*Services de Génétique Microbienne et de Biochimie Cellulaire,
Institut Pasteur, Paris*

(*Received 28 December 1960*)

The synthesis of enzymes in bacteria follows a double genetic control. The so-called structural genes determine the molecular organization of the proteins. Other, functionally specialized, genetic determinants, called regulator and operator genes, control the rate of protein synthesis through the intermediacy of cytoplasmic components or repressors. The repressors can be either inactivated (induction) or activated (repression) by certain specific metabolites. This system of regulation appears to operate directly at the level of the synthesis by the gene of a short-lived intermediate, or messenger, which becomes associated with the ribosomes where protein synthesis takes place.

1. Introduction

According to its most widely accepted modern connotation, the word "gene" designates a DNA molecule whose specific self-replicating structure can, through mechanisms unknown, become translated into the specific structure of a polypeptide chain.

This concept of the "structural gene" accounts for the multiplicity, specificity and genetic stability of protein structures, and it implies that such structures are not controlled by environmental conditions or agents. It has been known for a long time, however, that the synthesis of individual proteins may be provoked or suppressed within a cell, under the influence of specific external agents, and more generally that the relative rates at which different proteins are synthesized may be profoundly altered, depending on external conditions. Moreover, it is evident from the study of many such effects that their operation is absolutely essential to the survival of the cell.

It has been suggested in the past that these effects might result from, and testify to, complementary contributions of genes on the one hand, and some chemical factors on the other in determining the final structure of proteins. This view, which contradicts at least partially the "structural gene" hypothesis, has found as yet no experimental support, and in the present paper we shall have occasion to consider briefly some of this negative evidence. Taking, at least provisionally, the structural gene hypothesis in its strictest form, let us assume that the DNA message contained within a gene is both necessary and sufficient to define the structure of a protein. The elective effects of agents other than the structural gene itself in promoting or suppressing the synthesis of a protein must then be described as operations which control the rate of transfer of structural information from gene to protein. Since it seems to be established

† This work has been aided by grants from the National Science Foundation, the Jane Coffin Childs Memorial Fund for Medical Research, and the Commissariat à l'Energie Atomique.

318

that proteins are synthesized in the cytoplasm, rather than directly at the genetic level, this transfer of structural information must involve a chemical intermediate synthesized by the genes. This hypothetical intermediate we shall call the structural messenger. The rate of information transfer, i.e. of protein synthesis, may then depend either upon the activity of the gene in synthesizing the messenger, or upon the activity of the messenger in synthesizing the protein. This simple picture helps to state the two problems with which we shall be concerned in the present paper. If a given agent specifically alters, positively or negatively, the rate of synthesis of a protein, we must ask:

(a) Whether the agent acts at the cytoplasmic level, by controlling the activity of the messenger, or at the genetic level, by controlling the synthesis of the messenger.

(b) Whether the specificity of the effect depends upon some feature of the information transferred from structural gene to protein, or upon some specialized controlling element, not represented in the structure of the protein, gene or messenger.

The first question is easy to state, if difficult to answer. The second may not appear so straightforward. It may be stated in a more general way, by asking whether the genome is composed exclusively of structural genes, or whether it also involves determinants which may control the rates of synthesis of proteins according to a given set of conditions, without determining the structure of any individual protein. Again it may not be evident that these two statements are equivalent. We hope to make their meaning clear and to show that they are indeed equivalent, when we consider experimental examples.

The best defined systems wherein the synthesis of a protein is seen to be controlled by specific agents are examples of enzymatic adaptation, this term being taken here to cover both enzyme induction, i.e. the formation of enzyme electively provoked by a substrate, and enzyme repression, i.e. the specific inhibition of enzyme formation brought about by a metabolite. Only a few inducible and repressible systems have been identified both biochemically and genetically to an extent which allows discussion of the questions in which we are interested here. In attempting to generalize, we will have to extrapolate from these few systems. Such generalization is greatly encouraged, however, by the fact that lysogenic systems, where phage protein synthesis might be presumed to obey entirely different rules, turn out to be analysable in closely similar terms. We shall therefore consider in succession certain inducible and repressible enzyme systems and lysogenic systems.

It might be best to state at the outset some of the main conclusions which we shall arrive at. These are:

(a) That the mechanisms of control in all these systems are negative, in the sense that they operate by inhibition rather than activation of protein synthesis.

(b) That in addition to the classical structural genes, these systems involve two other types of genetic determinants (regulator and operator) fulfilling specific functions in the control mechanisms.

(c) That the control mechanisms operate at the genetic level, i.e. by regulating the activity of structural genes.

2. Inducible and Repressible Enzyme Systems

(a) *The phenomenon of enzyme induction. General remarks*

It has been known for over 60 years (Duclaux, 1899; Dienert, 1900; Went, 1901) that certain enzymes of micro-organisms are formed only in the presence of their specific substrate. This effect, later named "enzymatic adaptation" by Karstrom (1938), has been the subject of a great deal of experimentation and speculation. For a long time, "enzymatic adaptation" was not clearly distinguished from the selection of spontaneous variants in growing populations, or it was suggested that enzymatic adaptation and selection represented *alternative* mechanisms for the acquisition of a "new" enzymatic property. Not until 1946 were adaptive enzyme systems shown to be controlled in bacteria by discrete, specific, stable, i.e. genetic, determinants (Monod & Audureau, 1946). A large number of inducible systems has been discovered and studied in bacteria. In fact, enzymes which attack exogeneous substrates are, as a general rule, inducible in these organisms. The phenomenon is far more difficult to study in tissues or cells of higher organisms, but its existence has been established quite clearly in many instances. Very often, if not again as a rule, the presence of a substrate induces the formation not of a single but of several enzymes, sequentially involved in its metabolism (Stanier, 1951).

Most of the fundamental characteristics of the induction effect have been established in the study of the "lactose" system of *Escherichia coli* (Monod & Cohn, 1952; Cohn, 1957; Monod, 1959) and may be summarized in a brief discussion of this system from the biochemical and physiological point of view. We shall return later to the genetic analysis of this system.

(b) *The lactose system of* Escherichia coli

Lactose and other β-galactosides are metabolized in *E. coli* (and certain other enteric bacteria) by the hydrolytic transglucosylase β-galactosidase. This enzyme was isolated from *E. coli* and later crystallized. Its specificity, activation by ions and transglucosylase *vs* hydrolase activity have been studied in great detail (*cf.* Cohn, 1957). We need only mention the properties that are significant for the present discussion. The enzyme is active exclusively on β-galactosides unsubstituted on the galactose ring. Activity and affinity are influenced by the nature of the aglycone moiety both being maximum when this radical is a relatively large, hydrophobic group. Substitution of sulfur for oxygen in the galactosidic linkage of the substrate abolishes hydrolytic activity completely, but the thiogalactosides retain about the same affinity for the enzyme site as the homologous oxygen compounds.

As isolated by present methods, β-galactosidase appears to form various polymers (mostly hexamers) of a fundamental unit with a molecular weight of 135,000. There is one end group (threonine) and also one enzyme site (as determined by equilibrium dialysis against thiogalactosides) per unit. It is uncertain whether the monomer is active as such, or exists *in vivo*. The hexameric molecule has a turnover number of 240,000 mol $\times$ min^{-1} at 28°C, pH 7·0 with *o*-nitrophenyl-β-D-galactoside as substrate and Na$^+$ (0·01 M) as activator.

There seems to exist only a single homogeneous β-galactosidase in *E. coli*, and this organism apparently cannot form any other enzyme capable of metabolizing lactose, as indicated by the fact that mutants that have lost β-galactosidase activity cannot grow on lactose as sole carbon source.

However, the possession of β-galactosidase activity is not sufficient to allow utilization of lactose by *intact E. coli* cells. Another component, distinct from β-galactosidase, is required to allow penetration of the substrate into the cell (Monod, 1956; Rickenberg, Cohen, Buttin & Monod, 1956; Cohen & Monod, 1957; Pardee, 1957; Képès, 1960). The presence and activity of this component is determined by measuring the rate of entry and/or the level of accumulation of radioactive thiogalactosides into intact cells. Analysis of this active permeation process shows that it obeys classical enzyme kinetics allowing determination of K_m and V_{max}. The specificity is high since the system is active only with galactosides (β or α), or thiogalactosides. The spectrum of apparent affinities ($1/K_m$) is very different from that of β-galactosidase. Since the permeation system, like β-galactosidase, is inducible (see below) its formation can be studied *in vivo*, and shown to be invariably associated with protein synthesis. By these criteria, there appears to be little doubt that this specific permeation system involves a specific protein (or proteins), formed upon induction, which has been called galactoside-permease. That this protein is distinct from and independent of β-galactosidase is shown by the fact that mutants that have lost β-galactosidase retain the capacity to concentrate galactosides, while mutants that have lost this capacity retain the power to synthesize galactosidase. The latter mutants (called cryptic) cannot however use lactose, since the intracellular galactosidase is apparently accessible exclusively *via* the specific permeation system.

Until quite recently, it had not proved possible to identify *in vitro* the inducible protein (or proteins) presumably responsible for galactoside-permease activity. During the past year, a protein characterized by the ability to carry out the reaction:

Ac. Coenzyme A + Thiogalactoside → 6-Acetylthiogalactoside + Coenzyme A

has been identified, and extensively purified from extracts of *E. coli* grown in presence of galactosides (Zabin, Képès & Monod, 1959). The function of this enzyme in the system is far from clear, since formation of a free covalent acetyl-compound is almost certainly not involved in the permeation process *in vivo*. On the other hand:

(a) mutants that have lost β-galactosidase and retained galactoside-permease, retain galactoside-acetylase;

(b) most mutants that have lost permease cannot form acetylase;

(c) permeaseless acetylaseless mutants which revert to the permease-positive condition simultaneously regain the ability to form acetylase.

These correlations strongly suggest that galactoside-acetylase is somehow involved in the permeation process, although its function *in vivo* is obscure, and it seems almost certain that other proteins (specific or not for this system) are involved. In any case, we are interested here not in the mechanisms of permeation, but in the control mechanisms which operate with β-galactosidase, galactoside-permease and galactoside-acetylase. The important point therefore is that, as we shall see, galactoside-acetylase invariably obeys the same controls as galactosidase.†

(c) Enzyme induction and protein synthesis

Wild type *E. coli* cells grown in the absence of a galactoside contain about 1 to 10 units of galactosidase per mg dry weight, that is, an average of 0·5 to 5 active molecules

† For reasons which will become apparent later it is important to consider whether there is any justification for the assumption that galactosidase and acetylase activities might be associated with the same fundamental protein unit. We should therefore point to the following observation:

(a) There are mutants which form gacatosidase and no acetylase, and *vice versa*.

(b) Purified acetylase is devoid of any detectable galactosidase activity.

(c) The specificity of the two enzymes is very different.

(d) The two enzymes are easily and completely separated by fractional precipitation.

(e) Acetylase is highly heat-resistant, under conditions where galactosidase is very labile.

(f) Anti-galactosidase serum does not precipitate acetylase; nor does anti-acetylase serum precipitate galactosidase.

There is therefore no ground for the contention that galactosidase and acetylase activities are associated with the same protein.

per cell or 0·15 to 1·5 molecules per nucleus. Bacteria grown in the presence of a suitable inducer contain an average of 10,000 units per mg dry weight. This is the induction effect.

A primary problem, to which much experimental work has been devoted, is whether this considerable increase in specific activity corresponds to the synthesis of entirely "new" enzyme molecules, or to the activation or conversion of pre-existing protein precursors. It has been established by a combination of immunological and isotopic methods that the enzyme formed upon induction:

(a) is distinct, as an antigen, from all the proteins present in uninduced cells (Cohn & Torriani, 1952);

(b) does not derive any significant fraction of its sulfur (Monod & Cohn, 1953; Hogness, Cohn & Monod, 1955) or carbon (Rotman & Spiegelman, 1954) from pre-existing proteins.

The inducer, therefore, brings about the complete *de novo* synthesis of enzyme molecules which are new by their specific structure as well as by the origin of their elements. The study of several other induced systems has fully confirmed this conclusion, which may by now be considered as part of the *definition* of the effect. We will use the term "induction" here as meaning "activation by inducer of enzyme-protein synthesis."

(d) *Kinetics of induction*

Accepting (still provisionally) the structural gene hypothesis, we may therefore consider that the inducer somehow accelerates the rate of information transfer from gene to protein. This it could do either by provoking the synthesis of the messenger or by activating the messenger. If the messenger were a *stable* structure, functioning as a catalytic template in protein synthesis, one would expect different kinetics of induction, depending on whether the inducer acted at the genetic or at the cyto-plasmic level.

The kinetics of galactosidase induction turn out to be remarkably simple when determined under proper experimental conditions (Monod, Pappenheimer & Cohen-Bazire, 1952; Herzenberg, 1959). Upon addition of a suitable inducer to a growing culture, enzyme activity increases at a rate proportional to the increase in total protein within the culture; i.e. a linear relation is obtained (Fig. 1) when total enzyme activity is plotted against mass of the culture. The slope of this line:

$$P = \frac{\Delta z}{\Delta M}$$

is the "differential rate of synthesis," which is taken by definition as the measure of the effect. Extrapolation to the origin indicates that enzyme formation begins about three minutes (at 37 °C) after addition of inducer (Pardee & Prestidge, 1961). Removal of the inducer (or addition of a specific anti-inducer, see below) results in cessation of enzyme synthesis within the same short time. The differential rate of synthesis varies with the concentration of inducer reaching a different saturation value for different inducers. The inducer therefore acts in a manner which is (kinetically) similar to that of a dissociable activator in an enzyme system: activation and inactivation follow very rapidly upon addition or removal of the activator.

The conclusion which can be drawn from these kinetics is a negative one: the inducer does not appear to activate the synthesis of a stable intermediate able to accumulate in the cell (Monod, 1956).

Similar kinetics of induction have been observed with most or all other systems which have been adequately studied (Halvorson, 1960) with the exception of penicillinase of *Bacillus cereus*. The well-known work of Pollock has shown that the synthesis of this enzyme continues for a long time, at a decreasing rate, after removal of inducer (penicillin) from the medium. This effect is apparently related to the fact that minute amounts of penicillin are retained irreversibly by the cells after transient exposure to the drug (Pollock, 1950). The unique behavior of this system therefore does not contradict the rule that induced synthesis stops when the inducer is removed from the cells. Using this system, Pollock & Perret (1951) were able to show that the inducer acts catalytically, in the sense that a cell may synthesize many more enzyme molecules than it has retained inducer molecules.

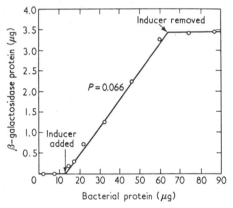

Fig. 1. Kinetics of induced enzyme synthesis. Differential plot expressing accumulation of β-galactosidase as a function of increase of mass of cells in a growing culture of *E. coli*. Since abscissa and ordinates are expressed in the same units (micrograms of protein) the slope of the straight line gives galactosidase as the fraction (*P*) of total protein synthesized in the presence of inducer. (After Cohn, 1957.)

(e) *Specificity of induction*

One of the most conspicuous features of the induction effect is its extreme specificity. As a general rule, only the substrate of an enzyme, or substances very closely allied to the normal substrate, are endowed with inducer activity towards this enzyme. This evidently suggests that a correlation between the molecular structure of the inducer and the structure of the catalytic center on the enzymes is *inherently* involved in the mechanism of induction. Two main types of hypotheses have been proposed to account for this correlation, and thereby for the mechanism of action of the inducer:

(a) The inducer serves as "partial template" in enzyme synthesis, molding as it were the catalytic center.

(b) The inducer acts by combining specifically with preformed enzyme (or "preenzyme"), thereby somehow accelerating the synthesis of further enzyme molecules.

It is not necessary to discuss these "classical" hypotheses in detail, because it seems to be established now that the correlation in question is in fact *not* inherent to the mechanism of induction.

Table 1 lists a number of compounds tested as inducers of galactosidase, and as substrates (or specific inhibitors) of the enzyme. It will be noted that:

(a) no compound that does not possess an intact unsubstituted galactosidic residue induces;

TABLE 1

Induction of galactosidase and galactoside-transacetylase by various galactosides

Compound	Concentrations	β-galactosidase			Galactoside-transacetylase	
		Induction value	V	$1/K_m$	Induction value	V/K_m
β-D-thiogalactosides						
(*iso*propyl)	10^{-4} M	100	0	140	100	80
(methyl)	10^{-4} M	78	0	7	74	30
	10^{-5} M	7·5	—	—	10	—
(phenyl)	10^{-3} M	<0·1	0	100	<1	100
(phenylethyl)	10^{-3} M	5	0	10,000	3	—
β-D-galactosides						
(lactose)	10^{-3} M	17	30	14	12	35
(phenyl)	10^{-3} M	15	100	100	11	—
α-D-galactoside						
(melibiose)	10^{-3} M	35	0	<0·1	37	<1
β-D-glucoside						
(phenyl)	10^{-3} M	<0·1	0	0	<1	50
(galactose)	10^{-3} M	<0·1	—	4	<1	<1
Methyl-β-D-thiogalactoside (10^{-4} M) + phenyl-β-D-thiogalactoside (10^{-3} M)		52	—	—	63	—

Columns "induction value" refer to specific activities developed by cultures of wild type *E. coli* K12 grown on glycerol as carbon source with each galactoside added at molar concentration stated. Values are given in percent of values obtained with *iso*propyl-thiogalactoside at 10^{-4} M (for which actual units were about 7,500 units of β-galactosidase and 300 units of galactoside-transacetylase per mg of bacteria). Column V refers to maximal substrate activity of each compound with respect to galactosidase. Values are given in percent of activity obtained with phenyl-galactoside. Column $1/K_m$ expresses affinity of each compound with respect to galactosidase. Values are given in percent of that observed with phenylgalactoside. In case of galactoside-trans-acetylase, only the relative values V/K_m are given since low affinity of this enzyme prevents independent determination of the constants. (Computed from Monod & Cohn, 1952; Monod *et al.*, 1952; Buttin, 1956; Zabin *et al.*, 1959; Képès *et al.*, unpublished results.)

(b) many compounds which are not substrates (such as the thiogalactosides) are excellent inducers (for instance *iso*propyl thiogalactoside);

(c) there is no correlation between affinity for the enzyme and capacity to induce (*cf*. thiophenylgalactoside and melibiose).

The possibility that the enzyme formed in response to different inducers may have somewhat different specific properties should also be considered, and has been rather thoroughly tested, with entirely negative results (Monod & Cohn, 1952).

There is therefore no quantitative correlation whatever between inducing capacity and the substrate activity or affinity parameters of the various galactosides tested. The fact remains, however, that only galactosides will induce galactosidase, whose binding site is complementary for the galactose ring-structure. The possibility that this correlation is a necessary requisite, or consequence, of the induction mechanism was therefore not completely excluded by the former results.

As we shall see later, certain mutants of the galactosidase structural gene (*z*) have been found to synthesize, in place of the normal enzyme, a protein which is identical to it by its immunological properties, while being completely devoid of any enzymatic activity. When tested by equilibrium dialysis, this inactive protein proved to have no measurable affinity for galactosides. In other words, it has lost the specific binding site. In diploids carrying both the normal and the mutated gene, both normal galactosidase and the inactive protein are formed, to a quantitatively similar extent, in the presence of different concentrations of inducer (Perrin, Jacob & Monod, 1960).

This finding, added to the sum of the preceding observations, appears to prove beyond reasonable doubt that the mechanism of induction does not imply any inherent correlation between the molecular structure of the inducer and the structure of the binding site of the enzyme.

On the other hand, there is complete correlation in the induction of galactosidase and acetylase. This is illustrated by Table 1 which shows not only that the same compounds are active or inactive as inducers of either enzyme, but that the relative amounts of galactosidase and acetylase synthesized in the presence of different inducers or at different concentrations of the same inducer are constant, even though the absolute amounts vary greatly. The remarkable qualitative and quantitative correlation in the induction of these two widely different enzyme proteins strongly suggests that the synthesis of both is directly governed by a common controlling element with which the inducer interacts. This interaction must, at some point, involve stereospecific binding of the inducer, since induction is sterically specific, and since certain galactosides which are devoid of any inducing activity act as competitive inhibitors of induction in the presence of active inducers (Monod, 1956; Herzenberg, 1959). This suggests that an enzyme, or some other protein, distinct from either galactosidase or acetylase, acts as "receptor" of the inducer. We shall return later to the difficult problem raised by the identification of this "induction receptor."

(f) *Enzyme repression*

While positive enzymatic adaptation, i.e. induction, has been known for over sixty years, negative adaptation, i.e. specific inhibition of enzyme synthesis, was discovered only in 1953, when it was found that the formation of the enzyme tryptophan-synthetase was inhibited selectively by tryptophan and certain tryptophan analogs (Monod & Cohen-Bazire, 1953). Soon afterwards, other examples of this effect were observed (Cohn, Cohen & Monod, 1953; Adelberg & Umbarger, 1953; Wijesundera &

Woods, 1953), and several systems were studied in detail in subsequent years (Gorini & Maas, 1957; Vogel, 1957a,b; Yates & Pardee, 1957; Magasanik, Magasanik & Neidhardt, 1959). These studies have revealed that the "repression" effect, as it was later named by Vogel (1957a,b), is very closely analogous, albeit symmetrically opposed, to the induction effect.

Enzyme repression, like induction, generally involves not a single but a sequence of enzymes active in successive metabolic steps. While inducibility is the rule for catabolic enzyme sequences responsible for the degradation of exogenous substances, repressibility is the rule for anabolic enzymes, involved in the synthesis of essential metabolites such as amino acids or nucleotides.[†] Repression, like induction, is highly specific, but while inducers generally are substrates (or analogs of substrates) of the sequence, the repressing metabolites generally are the product (or analogs of the product) of the sequence.

That the effect involves inhibition of enzyme *synthesis*, and not inhibition (directly or indirectly) of enzyme *activity* was apparent already in the first example studied (Monod & Cohen-Bazire, 1953), and has been proved conclusively by isotope incorporation experiments (Yates & Pardee, 1957). It is important to emphasize this point, because enzyme repression must not be confused with another effect variously called "feedback inhibition" or "retro-inhibition" which is equally frequent, and may occur in the same systems. This last effect, discovered by Novick & Szilard (in Novick, 1955), involves the inhibition of activity of an early enzyme in an anabolic sequence, by the ultimate product of the sequence (Yates & Pardee, 1956; Umbarger, 1956). We shall use "repression" exclusively to designate specific inhibition of enzyme *synthesis*.[‡]

(g) *Kinetics and specificity of repression*

The kinetics of enzyme synthesis provoked by "de-repression" are identical to the kinetics of induction (see Fig. 2). When wild type *E. coli* is grown in the presence of arginine, only traces of ornithine-carbamyltransferase are formed. As soon as arginine is removed from the growth medium, the differential rate of enzyme synthesis increases about 1,000 times and remains constant, until arginine is added again, when it immediately falls back to the repressed level. The repressing metabolite here acts (kinetically) as would a dissociable inhibitor in an enzyme system.

The specificity of repression poses some particularly significant problems. As a rule, the repressing metabolite of an anabolic sequence is the ultimate product of this sequence. For instance, L-arginine, to the exclusion of any other amino acid, represses the enzymes of the sequence involved in the biosynthesis of arginine. Arginine shows no specific affinity for the early enzymes in the sequence, such as, in particular, ornithine-carbamyltransferase. In this sense, arginine is a "gratuitous" repressing metabolite for this protein, just as galactosides are "gratuitous inducers" for the mutated (inactive) galactosidase. The possibility must be considered however that arginine may be converted back, through the sequence itself, to an intermediate product

---

[†] Certain enzymes which attack exogenous substrates are controlled by repression. Alkaline phosphatase (*E. coli*) is not induced by phosphate esters, but it is repressed by orthophosphate. Urease (*Pseudomonas*) is repressed by ammonia.

[‡] We should perhaps recall the well-known fact that glucose and other carbohydrates inhibit the synthesis of many *inducible* enzymes, attacking a variety of substrates (Dienert, 1900; Gale, 1943; Monod, 1942; Cohn & Horibata, 1959). It is probable that this non-specific "glucose effect" bears some relation to the repressive effect of specific metabolites, but the relationship is not clear (Neidhardt & Magasanik, 1956a,b). We shall not discuss the glucose effect in this paper.

or substrate of the enzyme. This has been excluded by Gorini & Maas (1957) who showed that, in mutants lacking one of the enzymes involved in later steps of the sequence, ornithine transcarbamylase is repressed by arginine to the same extent as in the wild type. Moreover, neither ornithine nor any other intermediate of the sequence is endowed with repressing activity in mutants which cannot convert the intermediate into arginine. It is quite clear therefore that the specificity of action of the repressing metabolite does not depend upon the specific configuration of the enzyme site.

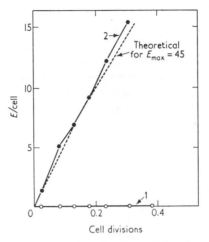

Fig. 2. Repression of ornithine-transcarbamylase by arginine. *E. coli* requiring both histidine and arginine were grown in a chemostat with 1 μg/ml. histidine + 6 μg/ml. arginine (curve 1) or with 10 μg/ml. histidine + 5 μg/ml. arginine (curve 2). Cultures are inoculated with washed cells taken from cultures growing exponentially in excess of arginine. The theoretical curve was calculated from the constant enzyme/cell value reached after 4 cell divisions. (After Gorini & Maas, 1958.)

The same conclusion is applicable to the enzymes of the histidine synthesizing pathway which are repressed in the presence of histidine, both in the wild type and in different mutants lacking one of the enzymes. The work of Ames & Garry (1959) has shown that the rates of synthesis of different enzymes in this sequence vary in *quantitatively* constant ratios under any set of medium conditions, and that the ratios are the same in various mutants lacking one of the enzymes and in the wild type. Here again, as in the case of the lactose system, the synthesis of widely different, albeit functionally related, enzymes appears to be controlled by a single common mechanism, with which the repressing metabolite specifically interacts.

In summary, repression and induction appear as closely similar effects, even if opposed in their results. Both control the rate of synthesis of enzyme proteins. Both are highly specific, but in neither case is the specificity related to the specificity of action (or binding) of the controlled enzyme. The kinetics of induction and repression are the same. Different functionally related enzymes are frequently co-induced or co-repressed, quantitatively to the same extent, by a single substrate or metabolite.

The remarkable similarity of induction and repression suggests that the two effects represent different manifestations of fundamentally similar mechanisms (Cohn & Monod, 1953; Monod, 1955; Vogel, 1957a, b; Pardee, Jacob & Monod, 1959; Szilard,

1960). This would imply either that in inducible systems the inducer acts as an antagonist of an internal repressor or that in repressible systems the repressing metabolite acts as an antagonist of an internal inducer. This is not an esoteric dilemma since it poses a very pertinent question, namely what would happen in an adaptive system of either type, when *both* the inducer and the repressor were eliminated? This, in fact, is the main question which we shall try to answer in the next section.

3. Regulator Genes

Since the specificity of induction or repression is not related to the structural specificity of the controlled enzymes, and since the rate of synthesis of different enzymes appears to be governed by a common element, this element is presumably not controlled or represented by the structural genes themselves. This inference, as we shall now see, is confirmed by the study of certain mutations which convert inducible or repressible systems into constitutive systems.

(a) *Phenotypes and genotypes in the lactose systems*

If this inference is correct, mutations which affect the controlling system should not behave as alleles of the structural genes. In order to test this prediction, the structural genes themselves must be identified. The most thoroughly investigated case is the lactose system of *E. coli*, to which we shall now return. Six phenotypically different classes of mutants have been observed in this system. For the time being, we shall consider only three of them which will be symbolized and defined as follows:

(1) Galactosidase mutations: $z^+ \rightleftharpoons z^-$ expressed as the loss of the capacity to synthesize active galactosidase (with or without induction).

(2) Permease mutations: $y^+ \rightleftharpoons y^-$ expressed as the loss of the capacity to form galactoside-permease. Most, but not all, mutants of this class simultaneously lose the capacity to synthesize active acetylase. We shall confine our discussion to the acetylaseless subclass.

(3) Constitutive mutations: $i^+ \rightleftharpoons i^-$ expressed as the ability to synthesize large amounts of galactosidase *and* acetylase in the absence of inducer (Monod, 1956; Rickenberg *et al.*, 1956; Pardee *et al.*, 1959).

The first two classes are specific for either galactosidase or acetylase: the galactosidaseless mutants form normal amounts of acetylase; conversely the acetylaseless mutants form normal amounts of galactosidase. In contrast, the constitutive mutations, of which over one hundred recurrences have been observed, invariably affect both the galactosidase and the permease (acetylase).† There are eight possible combinations of these phenotypes, and they have all been observed both in *E. coli* ML and K12.

The loci corresponding to a number of recurrences of each of the three mutant types have been mapped by recombination in *E. coli* K12. The map (Fig. 3) also

---

† The significance of this finding could be questioned since, in order to isolate constitutive mutants, one must of course use selective media, and this procedure might be supposed to favour double mutants, where the constitutivity of galactosidase and permease had arisen independently. It is possible, however, to select for $i^+ \rightarrow i^-$ mutants in organisms of type $i^+z^+y^-$, i.e. permeaseless. Fifty such mutants were isolated, giving rise to "constitutive cryptic" types $i^-z^+y^-$ from which, by reversion of y^-, fifty clones of constitutive $i^-z^+y^+$ were obtained. It was verified that in each of these fifty clones the permease was constitutive.

indicates the location of certain other mutations (*o* mutations) which will be discussed later. As may be seen, all these loci are confined to a very small segment of the chromosome, the *Lac* region. The extreme proximity of all these mutations raises the question whether they belong to a single or to several independent functional units. Such functional analysis requires that the biochemical expression of the various genetic structures be studied in heterozygous diploids. Until quite recently, only transient diploids were available in *E. coli*; the recent discovery of a new type of gene transfer in these bacteria (sexduction) has opened the possibility of obtaining stable clones which are diploid (or polyploid) for different small segments of the chromosome.

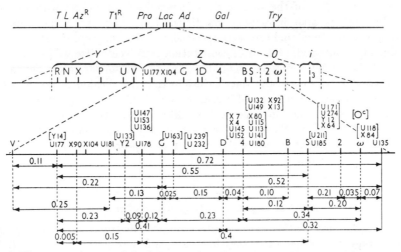

FIG. 3. Diagrammatic map of the lactose region of *E. coli* K12. The upper line represents the position of the *Lac* region with respect to other known markers. The middle line represents an enlargement of the *Lac* region with the four loci *y*, *z*, *o* and *i*. The lower line represents an enlargement of the *z* and *o* loci. Recombination frequencies (given at the bottom) are obtained in two factor crosses of the type $Hfr\ Lac_A^- ad^+ S^s \times F^- Lac_B^- ad^- S^r$, from the ratios "recombinants $Lac^+ ad^+ S^r$/ recombinants $ad^+ S^r$." The total length of the *z* gene may be estimated to be 0.7 map units, i.e. about 3,500 nucleotide pairs for about 1,000 amino acids in the monomer of β-galactosidase.

In this process, small fragments of the bacterial chromosome are incorporated into the sex factor, *F*. This new unit of replication is transmissible by conjugation, and is then added to the normal genome of the recipient bacterium which becomes diploid for the small chromosomal fragment. Among the units thus isolated, one carries the whole *Lac* region (Jacob & Adelberg, 1959; Jacob, Perrin, Sanchez & Monod, 1960). To symbolize the genetic structure of these diploids, the chromosomal alleles are written in the usual manner, while the alleles attached to the sex factor are preceded by the letter *F*.

Turning our attention to the behaviour of *z* and *y* mutant types, we may first note that diploids of structure $z^+ y^- / Fz^- y^+$ or $z^- y^+ / Fz^+ y^-$ are wild type, being able to ferment lactose, and forming normal amounts of both galactosidase and acetylase. This complete complementation between z^- and y^- mutants indicates that they belong to independent cistrons. Conversely, no complementation is observed between different y^- mutants, indicating that they all belong to a single cistron. No complementation is observed between most z^- mutants. Certain diploids of structure $z_a^- z_b^+ / Fz_a^+ z_b^-$ synthesize galactosidase in reduced amounts, but pairs of mutually non-complementing mutants overlap mutually complementing mutants, suggesting again that a single cistron is involved, as one might expect, since the monomer of galacto-sidase has a single N-terminal group. It should be recalled that intracistronic partial complementation has been observed in several cases (Giles, 1958), and has (tenta-tively) been explained as related to a polymeric state of the protein.

Mutations in the z gene affect the structure of galactosidase. This is shown by the fact that most of the z^- mutants synthesize, in place of active enzyme, a protein which is able to displace authentic (wild type) galactosidase from its combination with specific antibody (Perrin, Bussard & Monod, 1959). Among proteins synthesized by different z^- mutants (symbolized Cz_1, Cz_2, etc.) some give complete cross reactions (i.e. precipitate 100% of the specific antigalactosidase antibodies) with the serum used, while others give incomplete reactions. The different Cz proteins differ therefore, not only from wild type galactosidase, but also one from the other. Finally, as we already mentioned, diploids of constitution z^+/z_1^- synthesize wild type galacto-sidase and the modified protein simultaneously, and at similar rates (Perrin *et al.*, 1960). These observations justify the conclusions that the z region or cistron contains the structural information for β-galactosidase. Proof that mutations in the y region not only suppress but may in some cases modify the structure of acetylase has not been obtained as yet, but the assumption that the y region does represent, in part at least, the structural gene for the acetylase protein appears quite safe in view of the properties of the y mutants.

(b) *The i+ gene and its cytoplasmic product*

We now turn our attention to the constitutive (i^-) mutations. The most significant feature of these mutations is that they invariably affect simultaneously two different enzyme-proteins, each independently determined, as we have just seen, by different structural genes. In fact, most i^- mutants synthesize more galactosidase and acetylase than induced wild type cells, but it is quite remarkable that the *ratio* of galactosidase to acetylase is the same in the constitutive cells as in the induced wild type, strongly suggesting that the mechanism controlled by the i gene is the same as that with which the inducer interacts.

The study of double heterozygotes of structures: i^+z^-/Fi^-z^+ or i^-y^+/Fi^+y^- shows (Table 2, lines 4 and 5) that the inducible i^+ allele is dominant over the constitutive and that it is active in the *trans* position, with respect to both y^+ and z^+.

Therefore the i mutations belong to an independent cistron, governing the expres-sion of y and z *via* a cytoplasmic component. The dominance of the inducible over the constitutive allele means that the former corresponds to the active form of the i gene. This is confirmed by the fact that strains carrying a *deletion* of the *izy* region behave like i^- in diploids (Table 2, line 7). However, two different interpretations of the func-tion of the i^+ gene must be considered.

(a) The i^+ gene determines the synthesis of a repressor, inactive or absent in the i^- alleles.

(b) The i^+ gene determines the synthesis of an enzyme which destroys an inducer, produced by an independent pathway.

The first interpretation is the most straightforward, and it presents the great interest of implying that the fundamental mechanisms of control may be the same in inducible and repressible systems. Several lines of evidence indicate that it is the correct interpretation.

First, we may mention the fact that constitutive synthesis of β-galactosidase by $i^-z^+y^+$ types is not inhibited by thiophenyl-galactoside which has been shown (Cohn & Monod, 1953) to be a competitive inhibitor of induction by exogenous galactosides (see p. 325).

TABLE 2

Synthesis of galactosidase and galactoside-transacetylase by haploids and heterozygous diploids of regulator mutants

Strain No.	Genotype	Galactosidase		Galactoside-transacetylase	
		Non-induced	Induced	Non-induced	Induced
1	$i^+z^+y^+$	<0.1	100	<1	100
2	$i_6^- z^+y^+$	100	100	90	90
3	$i_3^- z^+y^+$	140	130	130	120
4	$i^+z_1^-y^+/Fi_3^-z^+y^+$	<1	240	1	270
5	$i_3^- z_1^-y^+/Fi^+z^+y_\overline{\text{U}}$	<1	280	<1	120
6	$i_3^- z_1^-y^+/Fi^-z^+y^+$	195	190	200	180
7	$\Delta_{izy}/Fi^-z^+y^+$	130	150	150	170
8	$i^s z^+y^+$	<0.1	<1	<1	<1
9	$i^s z^+y^+/Fi^+z^+y^+$	<0.1	2	<1	3

Bacteria are grown in glycerol as carbon source and induced, when stated, by *isopropyl*-thio-galactoside, 10^{-4} M. Values are given as a percentage of those observed with induced wild type (for absolute values, see legend of Table 1). Δ_{izy} refers to a deletion of the whole *Lac* region. It will be noted that organisms carrying the wild allele of one of the structural genes (z or y) on the F factor form more of the corresponding enzyme than the haploid. This is presumably due to the fact that several copies of the *F-Lac* unit are present per chromosome. In i^+/i^- heterozygotes, values observed with uninduced cells are sometimes higher than in the haploid control. This is due to the presence of a significant fraction of i^-/i^- homozygous recombinants in the population.

A direct and specific argument comes from the study of one particular mutant of the lactose system. This mutant (i^s) has lost the capacity to synthesize *both* galactosidase and permease. It is not a deletion because it recombines, giving *Lac*+ types, with all the z^- and y^- mutants. In crosses with z^-i^- organisms the progeny is *exclusively* i^- while in crosses with z^-i^+ it is *exclusively* i^+, indicating exceedingly close linkage of this mutation with the i region. Finally, in diploids of constitution i^s/i^+, i^s turns out to be *dominant*: the diploids cannot synthesize either galactosidase or acetylase (see Table 2, lines 8 and 9).

These unique properties appear exceedingly difficult to account for, except by the admittedly very specific hypothesis that mutant i^s is an allele of i where the *structure* of the repressor is such that it cannot be antagonized by the inducer any more. If this hypothesis is correct, one would expect that the i^s mutant could regain the ability to metabolize lactose, not only by reversion to wild type ($i^s \to i^+$) but also, and probably more frequently, by inactivation of the i gene, that is to say by achieving the constitutive condition ($i^s \rightarrow i^-$). Actually, Lac^+ "revertants" are very frequent in populations of mutant i^s, and 50% of these "revertants" are indeed constitutives of the i^- (recessive) type. (The other revertants are also constitutives, but of the o^c class which we shall mention later.) The properties of this remarkable mutant could evidently not be understood under the assumption that the i gene governs the synthesis of an inducer-destroying enzyme (Willson, Perrin, Jacob & Monod, 1961):

Accepting tentatively the conclusion that the i^+ gene governs the synthesis of an intracellular repressor, we may now consider the question of the presence of this substance in the cytoplasm, and of its chemical nature.

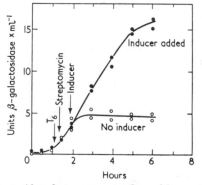

FIG. 4. Synthesis of β-galactosidase by merozygotes formed by conjugation between inducible, galactosidase-positive males and constitutive, galactosidase-negative females. Male ($Hfr\ i^+z^+T6^sS^s$) and female ($F^-\ i^-z^-T6^rS^r$) bacteria grown in a synthetic medium containing glycerol as carbon source are mixed in the same medium (time O) in the absence of inducer. In such a cross, the first zygotes which receive the Lac region from the males are formed from the 20th min. The rate of enzyme synthesis is determined from enzyme activity measurement on the whole population, to which streptomycin and phage T6 are added at times indicated by arrows to block further formation of recombinants and induction of the male parents. It may be seen that in the absence of inducer enzyme synthesis stops about 60 to 80 min after penetration of the first z^+i^+ segment but is resumed by addition of inducer (From Pardee $et\ al$, 1959).

Important indications on this question have been obtained by studying the kinetics and conditions of expression of the i^+ and z^+ genes when they are introduced into the cytoplasm of cells bearing the inactive (z^- and i^-) alleles. The sexual transfer of the Lac segment from male to female cells provides an adequate experimental system for such studies. It should be recalled that conjugation in $E.\ coli$ involves essentially the transfer of a male chromosome (or chromosome segment) to the female cell. This transfer is oriented, always beginning at one extremity of the chromosome, and it is progressive, each chromosome segment entering into the recipient cell at a fairly precise time following inception of conjugation in a given mating pair (Wollman & Jacob, 1959). The conjugation does not appear to involve any significant cytoplasmic mixing, so that the zygotes inherit virtually all their cytoplasm from the female cell, receiving only a chromosome or chromosome segment from the male. In order to study galactosidase synthesis by the zygotes, conditions must be set up such that the unmated parents cannot form the enzymes. This is the case when mating between inducible galactosidase-positive, streptomycin-sensitive males ($\male\ z^+i^+Sm^s$) and constitutive, galactosidase-negative, streptomycin-resistant females ($\female z^-i^-Sm^r$) is performed in presence of streptomycin (Sm), since: (i) the male cells which are sensitive to Sm cannot synthesize enzyme in its presence; (ii) the female cells are genetically incompetent; (iii) the vast majority of the zygotes which receive the z^+ gene, do not become streptomycin sensitive (because the $\widetilde{Sm}^s$ gene is transferred only to a small proportion of them, and at a very late time). The results of such an experiment, performed in the absence of inducer, are shown in Fig. 4. It is seen that galactosidase synthesis starts almost immediately following actual entry of the z^+ gene. We shall return later to a more precise analysis of the expression of the z^+ gene. The important point to be stressed here is that during this initial period the zygotes behave like *constitutive* cells, synthesizing enzyme in the *absence* of inducer. Approximately sixty minutes later, however, the rate of galactosidase synthesis falls off to zero. If at that time inducer is added, the maximum rate of enzyme synthesis is resumed. We are, in other words, witnessing the conversion of the originally i^- phenotype of the zygote cell, into an i^+ phenotype. And this experiment clearly shows that the "inducible" state is associated with the presence, at a sufficient level, of a *cytoplasmic* substance synthesized under the control of the i^+ gene. (It may be pointed out that the use of a female strain carrying a *deletion* of the *Lac* region instead of the i^-z^- alleles gives the same results (Pardee *et al.*, 1959).)

If now 5-methyltryptophan is added to the mated cells a few minutes before entry of the z^+ gene, no galactosidase is formed because, as is well known, this compound inhibits tryptophan synthesis by retro-inhibition, and therefore blocks protein synthesis. If the repressor is a protein, or if it is formed by a specific enzyme, the synthesis of which is governed by the i^+ gene, its accumulation should also be blocked. If on the other hand the repressor is not a protein, and if its synthesis does not require the preliminary synthesis of a specific enzyme controlled by the i^+ gene, it may accumulate in presence of 5-methyltryptophan which is known (Gros, unpublished results) *not* to inhibit energy transfer or the synthesis of nucleic acids.

The results of Pardee & Prestige (1959) show that the repressor *does* accumulate under these conditions, since the addition of tryptophan 60 min after 5-methyl-tryptophan allows immediate and complete resumption of enzyme synthesis, *but only in the presence of inducer*; in other words, the cytoplasm of the zygote cells has been converted from the constitutive to the inducible state during the time that protein synthesis was blocked. This result has also been obtained using chloramphenicol as the agent for blocking protein synthesis, and it has been repeated using another system of gene transfer (Luria *et al.*, unpublished results).

This experiment leads to the conclusion that the repressor is not a protein, and this again excludes the hypothesis that the i^+ gene controls an inducer-destroying enzyme. We should like to stress the point that this conclusion does not imply that no enzyme is involved in the synthesis of the repressor, but that the enzymes which may be involved are *not* controlled by the i^+ gene. The experiments are negative, as far as the chemical nature of the repressor itself is concerned, since they only eliminate protein as a candidate. They do, however, invite the speculation that the repressor may be the primary product of the i^+ gene, and the further speculation that such a primary product may be a polyribonucleotide.

Before concluding this section, it should be pointed out that constitutive mutations have been found in several inducible systems; in fact wherever they have been searched for by adequate selective techniques (amylomaltase of *E. coli* (Cohen-Bazire & Jolit, 1953), penicillinase of *B. cereus* (Kogut, Pollock & Tridgell, 1956), glucuronidase of *E. coli* (F. Stoeber, unpublished results), galactokinase and galactose-transferase (Buttin, unpublished results)). That *any* inducible system should be potentially capable of giving rise to constitutive mutants, strongly indicates that such mutations occur, or at least can always occur, by a loss of function. In the case of the "galactose" system of *E. coli*, it has been found that the constitutive mutation is pleiotropic, affecting a sequence of three different enzymes (galactokinase, galactose-transferase, UDP-galactose epimerase), and occurs at a locus distinct from that of the corresponding structural genes (Buttin, unpublished results).

The main conclusions from the observations reviewed in this section may be summarized as defining a new type of gene, which we shall call a "regulator gene" (Jacob & Monod, 1959). A regulator gene does not contribute structural information to the proteins which it controls. The specific product of a regulator gene is a cytoplasmic substance, which inhibits information transfer from a structural gene (or genes) to protein. In contrast to the classical structural gene, a regulator gene may control the synthesis of several different proteins: the one-gene one-protein rule does not apply to it.

We have already pointed out the profound similarities between induction and repression which suggest that the two effects represent different manifestations of the same fundamental mechanism. If this is true, and if the above conclusions are valid, one expects to find that the genetic control of repressible systems also involves regulator genes.

(c) *Regulator genes in repressible systems*

The identification of constitutive or "de-repressed" mutants of several repressible systems has fulfilled this expectation. For the selection of such mutants, certain analogs of the normal repressing metabolite may be used as specific selective agents, because they cannot substitute for the metabolite, except as repressing metabolites. For instance, 5-methyltryptophan does not substitute for tryptophan in protein synthesis (Munier, unpublished results), but it represses the enzymes of the tryptophan-synthesizing sequence (Monod & Cohen-Bazire, 1953). Normal wild type *E. coli* does not grow in the presence of 5-methyltryptophan. Fully resistant stable mutants arise, however, a large fraction of which turn out to be constitutive for the tryptophan system.[†] The properties of these organisms indicate that they arise by mutation of a regulator gene R_T (Cohen & Jacob, 1959). In these mutants tryptophan-synthetase as well as at least two of the enzymes involved in previous steps in the sequence are formed at the same rate irrespective of the presence of tryptophan, while in the wild type all these enzymes are strongly repressed. Actually the mutants form more of the enzymes in the presence of tryptophan, than does the wild type in its absence (just as i^-z^+ mutants form more galactosidase in the absence of inducer than the wild type does at saturating concentration of inducer). The capacity of the mutants to concentrate tryptophan from the medium is not impaired, nor is their tryptophanase activity increased. The loss of sensitivity to tryptophan as repressing metabolite cannot therefore be attributed to its destruction by, or exclusion from, the cells, and can only reflect the breakdown of the control system itself. Several recurrences of the R_T mutation have been mapped. They are all located in the same small section of the chromosome, at a large distance from the cluster of genes which was shown by Yanofsky & Lennox (1959) to synthesize the different enzymes of the sequence. One of these genes (comprising two cistrons) has been very clearly identified by the work of Yanofsky (1960) as the structural gene for tryptophan synthetase, and it is a safe assumption that the other genes in this cluster determine the structure of the preceding

† Resistance to 5-methyltryptophan may also arise by other mechanisms in which we are not interested here.

enzymes in the sequence. The R_T gene therefore controls the rate of synthesis of several different proteins without, however, determining their structure. It can only do so *via* a cytoplasmic intermediate, since it is located quite far from the structural genes. To complete its characterization as a regulator gene, it should be verified that the constitutive (R_T^-) allele corresponds to the inactive state of the gene (or gene product), i.e. is recessive. Stable heterozygotes have not been available in this case, but the transient (sexual) heterozygotes of a cross $\male R_T^- \times \female R_T^+$ are sensitive to 5-methyltryptophan, indicating that the repressible allele is dominant (Cohen & Jacob, 1959).

In the arginine-synthesizing sequence there are some seven enzymes, simultaneously repressible by arginine (Vogel, 1957*a,b*; Gorini & Maas, 1958). The specific (i.e. probably structural) genes which control these enzymes are dispersed at various loci on the chromosome. Mutants resistant to canavanine have been obtained, in which several (perhaps all) of these enzymes are simultaneously de-repressed. These mutations occur at a locus (near Sm^r) which is widely separated from the loci corresponding (probably) to the structural genes. The dominance relationships have not been analysed (Gorini, unpublished results; Maas, Lavallé, Wiame & Jacob, unpublished results).

The case of alkaline phosphatase is particularly interesting because the structural gene corresponding to this protein is well identified by the demonstration that various mutations at this locus result in the synthesis of altered phosphatase (Levinthal, 1959). The synthesis of this enzyme is repressed by orthophosphate (Torriani, 1960). Constitutive mutants which synthesize large amounts of enzyme in the presence of orthophosphate have been isolated. They occur at two loci, neither of which is allelic to the structural gene, and the constitutive enzyme is identical, by all tests, to the wild type (repressible) enzyme. The constitutive alleles for both of the two loci have been shown to be recessive with respect to wild type. Conversely, mutations in the structural (P) gene do not affect the regulatory mechanism, since the altered (inactive) enzyme formed by mutants of the P gene is repressed in the presence of orthophosphate to the same extent as the wild type enzyme (Echols, Garen, Garen & Torriani, 1961).

(d) *The interaction of repressors, inducers and co-repressors*

The sum of these observations leaves little doubt that repression, like induction, is controlled by specialized regulator genes, which operate by a basically similar mechanism in both types of systems, namely by governing the synthesis of an intracellular substance which inhibits information transfer from structural genes to protein.

It is evident therefore that the metabolites (such as tryptophan, arginine, orthophosphate) which inhibit enzyme synthesis in repressible systems are not active by themselves, but only by virtue of an interaction with a repressor synthesized under the control of a regulator gene. Their action is best described as an activation of the genetically controlled repression system. In order to avoid confusion of words, we shall speak of repressing metabolites as "co-repressors" reserving the name "repressors" (or apo-repressors) for the cytoplasmic products of the regulator genes.

The nature of the interaction between repressor and co-repressor (in repressible systems) or inducer (in inducible systems) poses a particularly difficult problem. As a purely formal description, one may think of inducers as antagonists, and of co-repressors as activators, of the repressor. A variety of chemical models can be imagined to account for such antagonistic or activating interactions. We shall not go into these speculations since there is at present no evidence to support or eliminate any particular model. But it must be pointed out that, in any model, the structural specificity of inducers or co-repressors must be accounted for, and can be accounted for, only by the assumption that a stereospecific receptor is involved in the interaction. The fact that the repressor is apparently not a protein then raises a serious difficulty since the capacity to form stereospecific complexes with small molecules appears to be a privilege of proteins. If a protein, perhaps an enzyme, is responsible for the specificity, the structure of this protein is presumably determined by a structual gene and mutation in this gene would result in loss of the capacity to be induced (or repressed). Such mutants, which would have precisely predictable properties (they would be pleiotropic, recessive, and they would be complemented by mutants of the other structural genes) have not been encountered in the lactose system, while the possibility that the controlled enzymes themselves (galactosidase or acetylase) play the role of "induction enzyme" is excluded.

It is conceivable that, in the repressible systems which synthesize amino acids, this role is played by enzymes simultaneously responsible for essential functions (e.g. the activating enzymes) whose loss would be lethal, but this seems hardly conceivable in the case of most inducible systems. One possibility which is not excluded by these observations is that the repressor itself synthesizes the "induction protein" and remains thereafter associated with it. Genetic inactivation of the induction enzyme would then be associated with structural alterations of the repressor itself and would generally be expressed as constitutive mutations of the regulator gene.† This possibility is mentioned here only as an illustration of the dilemma which we have briefly analysed, and whose solution will depend upon the chemical identification of the repressor.

(e) *Regulator genes and immunity in temperate phage systems*

One of the most conspicuous examples of the fact that certain genes may be either allowed to express their potentialities, or specifically prohibited from doing so, is the phenomenon of immunity in temperate phage systems (*cf.* Lwoff, 1953; Jacob, 1954; Jacob & Wollman, 1957; Bertani, 1958; Jacob, 1960).

The genetic material of the so-called temperate phages can exist in one of two states within the host cell:

(1) In the *vegetative state*, the phage genome multiplies autonomously. This process, during which all the phage components are synthesized, culminates in the production of infectious phage particles which are released by lysis of the host cell.

(2) In the *prophage state*, the genetic material of the phage is attached to a specific site of the bacterial chromosome in such a way that both genetic elements replicate as a single unit. The host cell is said to be "lysogenic." As long as the phage genome remains in the prophage state, phage particles are not produced. For lysogenic bacteria to produce phage, the genetic material of the phage must undergo a transition from the prophage to the vegetative state. During normal growth of lysogenic bacteria, this event is exceedingly rare. With certain types of prophages, however, the transition can be induced in the whole population by exposure of the culture to u.v. light,

† Such a model could account for the properties of the i^s (dominant) mutant of the regulator gene in the lactose system, by the assumption that in this mutant the repressor remains active, while having lost the capacity to form its associated induction protein.

X-rays or various compounds known to alter DNA metabolism (Lwoff, Siminovitch & Kjeldgaard, 1950; Lwoff, 1953; Jacob, 1954).

The study of "defective" phage genomes, in which a mutation has altered one of the steps required for the production of phage particles, indicates the existence of at least two distinct groups of viral functions, both of which are related to the capacity of synthesizing specific proteins (Jacob, Fuerst & Wollman, 1957). Some "early" functions appear as a pre-requisite for the vegetative multiplication of the phage genome and, at least in virulent phages of the T-even series, it is now known that they correspond to the synthesis of a series of new enzymes (Flaks & Cohen, 1959; Kornberg, Zimmerman, Kornberg & Josse, 1959). A group of "late" functions correspond to the synthesis of the structural proteins which constitute the phage coat. The expression of these different viral functions appears to be in some way co-ordinated by a sequential process, since defective mutations affecting some of the early functions may also result in the loss of the capacity to perform several later steps of phage multiplication (Jacob et al., 1957).

In contrast, the viral functions are not expressed in the prophage state and the protein constituents of the phage coat cannot be detected within lysogenic bacteria. In addition, lysogenic bacteria exhibit the remarkable property of being specifically *immune* to the very type of phage particles whose genome is already present in the cell as prophage. When lysogenic cells are infected with homologous phage particles, these particles absorb onto the cells and inject their genetic material, but the cell survives. The injected genetic material does not express its viral functions: it is unable to initiate the synthesis of the protein components of the coat and to multiply vegetatively. It remains inert and is diluted out in the course of bacterial multiplication (Bertani, 1953; Jacob, 1954).

The inhibition of phage-gene functions in lysogenic bacteria therefore applies not only to the prophage, but also to additional homologous phage genomes. It depends only upon the presence of the prophage (and not upon a permanent alteration, provoked by the prophage, of bacterial genes) since loss of the prophage is both necessary and sufficient to make the bacteria sensitive again.

Two kinds of interpretation may be considered to account for these "immunity" relationships:

(a) The prophage occupies and blocks a *chromosomal* site of the host, specifically required in some way for the vegetative multiplication of the homologous phage.

(b) The prophage produces a *cytoplasmic* inhibitor preventing the completion of some reactions (presumably the synthesis of a particular protein) necessary for the initiation of vegetative multiplication.

A decision between these alternative hypotheses may be reached through the study of persistent diploids, heterozygous for the character lysogeny. A sex factor has been isolated which has incorporated a segment of the bacterial chromosome carrying the genes which control galactose fermentation, *Gal*, and the site of attachment of prophage, λ. Diploid heterozygotes with the structure $Gal^- \lambda^-/F\ Gal^+.\lambda^+$ or $Gal^- \lambda^+/F\ Gal^+\ \lambda^-$ are immune against superinfection with phage λ, a result which shows that "immunity" is dominant over "non-immunity" and has a cytoplasmic expression (Jacob, Schaeffer & Wollman, 1960).

The study of transient zygotes formed during conjugation between lysogenic (λ^+) and non-lysogenic (λ^-) cells leads to the same conclusion. In crosses $\male\lambda^+ \times \female\lambda^-$, the transfer of the prophage carried by the male chromosome into the non-immune recipient results in transition to the vegetative state: multiplication of the phage occurs in the zygotes, which are lysed and release phage particles. This phenomenon is known as "zygotic induction" (Jacob & Wollman, 1956). In the *reverse* cross $\male\lambda^- \times \female\lambda^+$, however, *no zygotic induction occurs*. The transfer of the "non-lysogenic" character carried by the male chromosome into the immune recipient does not bring about the development of the prophage and the zygotes are immune against super-infection with phage λ.

The opposite results obtained in reciprocal crosses of lysogenic by non-lysogenic male and female cells are entirely analogous to the observations made with the lactose system in reciprocal crosses of inducible by non-inducible cells. In both cases, it is evident that the decisive factor is the origin of the *cytoplasm* of the zygote, and the conclusion is inescapable, that the immunity of lysogenic bacteria is due to a cytoplasmic constituent, in the presence of which the viral genes cannot become expressed (Jacob, 1960).

The same two hypotheses which we have already considered for the interpretation of the product of the regulator gene in the lactose system, apply to the cytoplasmic inhibitor insuring immunity in lysogenic bacteria.

(a) The inhibitor is a specific repressor which prevents the synthesis of some early protein(s) required for the initiation of vegetative multiplication.

(b) The inhibitor is an enzyme which destroys a metabolite, normally synthesized by the non-lysogenic cell and specifically required for the vegetative multiplication of the phage.

Several lines of evidence argue against the second hypothesis (Jacob & Campbell, 1959; Jacob, 1960). First, for a given strain of bacteria, many temperate phages are known, each of which exhibits a different immunity pattern. According to the second hypothesis, each of these phages would specifically require for vegetative multiplication a different metabolite normally produced by the non-lysogenic cells, an assumption which appears extremely unlikely. The second argument stems from the fact that, like the repressor of the lactose system, the inhibitor responsible for immunity is synthesized in the presence of chloramphenicol, i.e. in the absence of protein synthesis: when crosses $\male\lambda^+ \times \female\lambda^-$ are performed in the presence of chloramphenicol, no zygotic induction occurs and the prophage is found to segregate normally among recombinants.

In order to explain immunity in lysogenic bacteria, we are led therefore to the same type of interpretation as in the case of adaptive enzyme systems. According to this interpretation, the prophage controls a cytoplasmic repressor, which inhibits specifically the synthesis of one (or several) protein(s) necessary for the initiation of vegetative multiplication. In this model, the introduction of the genetic material of the phage into a non-lysogenic cell, whether by infection or by conjugation, results in a "race" between the synthesis of the specific repressor and that of the early proteins required for vegetative multiplication. The fate of the host-cell, survival with lysogenization or lysis as a result of phage multiplication, depends upon whether the synthesis of the repressor or that of the protein is favoured. Changes in the cultural conditions favoring the synthesis of the repressor such as infection at low temperature, or in the presence of chloramphenicol, would favor lysogenization and *vice versa*. The phenomenon of induction by u.v. light could then be understood, for instance, in the following way: exposure of inducible lysogenic bacteria to u.v. light or X-rays would transiently disturb the regulation system, for example by preventing further synthesis of the repressor. If the repressor is unstable, its concentration inside the cell would decrease and reach a level low enough to allow the synthesis of the early proteins. Thus the vegetative multiplication would be irreversibly initiated.

The similarity between lysogenic systems and adaptive systems is further strengthened by the genetic analysis of immunity. Schematically, the genome of phage λ appears to involve two parts (see Fig. 5): a small central segment, the C region, contains a few determinants which control various functions involved in lysogenization (Kaiser, 1957); the rest of the linkage group contains determinants which govern the "viral functions," i.e. presumably the structural genes corresponding to the different phage proteins. Certain strains of temperate phages which exhibit different immunity patterns are able nevertheless to undergo genetic recombination. The specific immunity pattern segregates in such crosses, proving to be controlled by a small segment "im" of the C region (Kaiser & Jacob, 1957). In other words, a prophage contains in its C region a small segment "im" which controls the synthesis of a specific repressor, active on the phage genome carrying a homologous "im" segment.

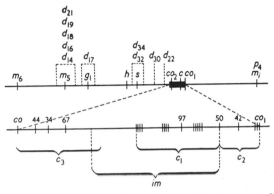

Fig. 5. Diagrammatic representation of the linkage group of the temperate bacteriophage λ. The upper diagram represents the linear arrangement of markers. Symbols refer to various plaque size, plaque type and host-range markers. Symbols d refer to various defective mutations. The C region represented by a thicker line is enlarged in the lower diagram. The figures correspond to various C mutations. The C region can be subdivided into three functional units, C_1, C_2 and C_3; the segment controlling immunity is designated im.

In the "im" region, two types of mutations arise, whose properties are extremely similar to those of the different mutations affecting the regulator genes of adaptive enzyme systems.

(1) Some mutations ($C_I^+ \rightarrow C_I$) result in the complete loss of the capacity for lysogenization in single infection. All the C_I mutations are located in a cluster, in a small part of the "im" segment, and they behave as belonging to a single cistron in complementation tests.

In mixed infections with both C_I and C_I^+ phages, double lysogenic clones carrying both C_I and C_I^+ prophages can be recovered. In such clones, single lysogenic cells segregate, which carry the C^+ type alone but never the C_I type alone. These findings indicate that the wild allele is dominant over the mutant C_I alleles and is cytoplasmically expressed, repressing the mutant genome into the prophage state. The properties of the C_I mutations are therefore similar to those of the recessive constitutive mutations of adaptive systems. The evidence suggests that the C_I locus controls the synthesis of the repressor responsible for immunity, and that the C_I mutations correspond to inactivation of this locus, or of its product.

(2) A mutation ($ind^+\rightarrow ind^-$) has been found which results in the loss of the inducible property of the prophage, i.e. of its capacity to multiply vegetatively upon exposure of lysogenic bacteria to u.v. light, X-rays or chemical inducers. This mutation is located in the C_I segment. The mutant allele ind^- is dominant over the wild allele ind^+ since double lysogenic $\lambda ind^+/\lambda ind^-$ or diploid heterozygotes of structure $Gal^-\lambda ind^+/F\ Gal^+\lambda ind^-$ or $Gal^-\lambda ind^-/F\ Gal^+\lambda ind^+$ are all non-inducible. In addition, the mutant λind^- exhibits a unique property. If lysogenic bacteria K12 (λ^+) carrying a wild type prophage are exposed to u.v. light, the whole population lyses and releases phage. Infection of such cells with λind^- mutants, either before or immediately after irradiation, completely inhibits phage production and lysis.

The properties of the ind^- mutant appear in every respect similar to those of the previously described mutant i^s of the lactose system. The unique properties of the ind^- mutants can be explained only by the same type of hypothesis, namely that the mutation ind^- affects, quantitatively or qualitatively, the synthesis of the repressor in such a way that more repressor or a more efficient repressor is produced. If this assumption as well as the hypothesis that the C_I mutation results in the loss of the capacity to produce an active repressor, are correct, the double mutants $C_I ind^-$ should have lost the capacity of inhibiting phage multiplication upon infection of wild type lysogenic cells. This is actually what is observed. It is evident that the properties of the ind^- mutant cannot be accounted for by the assumption that the C_I locus controls the synthesis of a metabolite-destroying enzyme (Jacob & Campbell, 1959).

In summary, the analysis of lysogenic systems reveals that the expression of the viral genes in these systems is controlled by a cytoplasmic repressor substance, whose synthesis is governed by one particular "regulator" gene, belonging to the viral genome. The identity of the proteins whose synthesis is thus repressed is not established, but it seems highly probable that they are "early" enzymes which initiate the whole process of vegetative multiplication. With the (important) limitation that they are sensitive to entirely different types of inducing conditions, the phage repression systems appear entirely comparable to the systems involved in enzymatic adaptation.

4. The Operator and the Operon

(a) *The operator as site of action of the repressor*

In the preceding section we have discussed the evidence which shows that the transfer of information from structural genes to protein is controlled by specific repressors synthesized by specialized regulator genes. We must now consider the next problem, which is the site and mode of action of the repressor.

In regard to this problem, the most important property of the repressor is its characteristic pleiotropic specificity of action. In the lactose system of *E. coli*, the repressor is both *highly specific* since mutations of the i gene do not affect any other system, and *pleiotropic* since both galactosidase and acetylase are affected simultaneously and quantitatively to the same extent, by such mutations.

The specificity of operation of the repressor implies that it acts by forming a stereo-specific combination with a constituent of the system possessing the proper (complementary) molecular configuration. Furthermore, it must be assumed that the flow of information from gene to protein is interrupted when this element is combined with the repressor. This controlling element we shall call the *"operator"* (Jacob & Monod, 1959). We should perhaps call attention to the fact that, once the existence of a specific repressor is considered as established, the existence of an operator element defined as above follows necessarily. Our problem, therefore, is not whether an operator exists, but where (and how) it intervenes in the system of information transfer.

An important prediction follows immediately from the preceding considerations. Under any hypothesis concerning the nature of the operator, its specific complementary configuration must be genetically determined; therefore it could be affected by mutations which would alter or abolish its specific affinity for the repressor, without necessarily impairing its activity as initiator of information-transfer. Such mutations would result in *constitutive* synthesis of the protein or proteins. These mutations would define an "operator locus" which should be genetically distinct from the regulator gene (i.e. its mutations should not behave as alleles of the regulator); the most distinctive predictable property of such mutants would be that the constitutive allele should be *dominant* over the wild type since, again under virtually any hypothesis, the presence in a diploid cell of repressor-sensitive operators would not prevent the operation of repressor-insensitive operators.

(b) *Constitutive operator mutations*

Constitutive mutants possessing the properties predicted above have so far been found in two repressor-controlled systems, namely the phage λ and *Lac* system of *E. coli*.

In the case of phage λ, these mutants are characterized, and can be easily selected, by the fact that they develop vegetatively in immune bacteria, lysogenic for the wild type. This characteristic property means that these mutants (*v*) are *insensitive* to the repressor present in lysogenic cells. When, in fact, lysogenic cells are infected with these mutant particles, the development of the wild type prophage is induced, and the resulting phage population is a mixture of *v* and v^+ particles. This is expected, since presumably the initiation of prophage development depends only on the formation of one or a few "early" enzyme-proteins, which are supplied by the virulent particle (Jacob & Wollman, 1953).

In the *Lac* system, dominant constitutive (o^c) mutants have been isolated by selecting for constitutivity in cells diploid for the *Lac* region, thus virtually eliminating the recessive (i^-) constitutive mutants (Jacob *et al.*, 1960a). By recombination, the o^c mutations can be mapped in the *Lac* region, between the i and the z loci, the order being (*Pro*) *yzoi* (*Ad*) (see Fig. 3). Some of the properties of these mutants are summarized in Table 3. To begin with, let us consider only the effects of this mutation on galactosidase synthesis. It will be noted that in the absence of inducer, these organisms synthesize 10 to 20% of the amount of galactosidase synthesized by i^- mutants, i.e. about 100 to 200 times more than uninduced wild type cells (Table 3, lines 3 and 7). In the presence of inducer, they synthesize maximal amounts of enzyme. They are therefore only partially constitutive (except however under conditions of starvation, when they form maximum amounts of galactosidase in the absence of inducer (Brown, unpublished results)). The essential point however is that the enzyme is synthesized constitutively by diploid cells of constitution o^c/o^+ (see Table 3). The o^c allele therefore is "dominant."

If the constitutivity of the o^c mutant results from a loss of sensitivity of the operator to the repressor, the o^c organisms should also be insensitive to the presence of the altered repressor synthesized by the i^s (dominant) allele of the i^+ gene (see page 331). That this is indeed the case, as shown by the constitutive behavior of diploids with the constitution $i^s o^+/F i^+ o^c$ (see Table 3, line 12), is a very strong confirmation of the interpretation of the effects of *both* mutations (i^s and o^c). In addition, and as one would expect according to this interpretation, o^c mutants frequently arise as lactose positive "revertants" in populations of i^s cells (see p. 332).

TABLE 3

*Synthesis of galactosidase, cross-reacting material (CRM), and galactoside-transacetylase
by haploid and heterozygous diploid operator mutants*

Strain No.	Genotype	Galactosidase		Cross-reacting material	
		Non-induced	Induced	Non-induced	Induced
1	o^+z^+	<0·1	100	—	—
2	$o^+z^+/Fo^+z_1^-$	<0·1	105	<1	310
3	$o^c z^+$	15	90	—	—
4	$o^+z^+/Fo^c z_1$	<0·1	90	30	180
5	$o^+z_1^-/Fo^c z^+$	90	250	<1	85

Strain No.	Genotype	Galactosidase		Galactoside-transacetylase	
		Non-Induced	Induced	Non-induced	Induced
6	$o^+z^+y^+$	<0·1	100	<1	100
7	$o^c z^+y^+$	25	95	15	110
8	$o^+z^+y_U^-/Fo^c z^+y^+$	70	220	50	160
9	$o^+z_1^- y^+/Fo^c z^+y_U^-$	180	440	<1	220
10	$i^+ o_{84}^\circ z^+y^+$	<0·1	<0·1	<1	<1
11	$i^+ o_{84}^\circ z^+y^+/Fi^- o^+z^+y^+$	1	260	2	240
12	$i^s o^+z^+y^+/Fi^+ o^c z^+y^+$	190	210	150	200

Bacteria are grown in glycerol as carbon source and induced when stated, with *iso*propyl-thiogalactoside, 10^{-4} M. Values of galactosidase and acetylase are given as a percentage of those observed with induced wild type. Values of CRM are expressed as antigenic equivalents of galactosidase. Note that the proteins corresponding to the alleles carried by the sex factor are often produced in greater amount than that observed with induced haploid wild type. This is presumably due to the existence of several copies of the *F-Lac* factor per chromosome. In o^c mutants, haploid or diploid, the absolute values of enzymes produced, especially in the non-induced cultures varies greatly from day to day depending on the conditions of the cultures.

We therefore conclude that the $o^+ \rightarrow o^c$ mutations correspond to a modification of the specific, repressor-accepting, structure of the operator. This identifies the operator locus, i.e. the genetic segment responsible for the structure of the operator, but not the operator itself.

(c) *The operon*

Turning now to this problem, we note that the o^c mutation (like the i^- mutation) is pleiotropic: it affects simultaneously and quantitatively to the same extent, the synthesis of galactosidase and acetylase (see Table 3, lines 7 and 8). The structure of the operator, or operators, which controls the synthesis of the two proteins, therefore, is controlled by a single determinant.†

Two alternative interpretations of this situation must be considered:

(a) A single operator controls an *integral* property of the z-y genetic segment, or of its cytoplasmic product.

(b) The specific product of the operator locus is able to associate in the cytoplasm, with the products of the z and y cistrons, and thereby governs the expression of both structural genes.

The second interpretation implies that mutations of the operator locus should behave as belonging to a cistron *independent* of both the z and y cistrons. The first interpretation requires, on the contrary, that these mutations behave functionally as if they *belonged to both cistrons simultaneously*. These alternative interpretations can therefore be distinguished without reference to any particular physical model of operator action by testing for the *trans* effect of o alleles, that is to say for the constitutive *vs* inducible expression of the two structural genes in o^+/o^c diploids, heterozygous for one or both of these structural genes.

The results obtained with diploids of various structures are shown in Table 3. We may first note that in diploids of constitution $o^+z^+/F o^c z_1^-$ or $o^+z_1^-/F o^c z^+$ (lines 4 and 5), both the normal galactosidase produced by the z^+ allele and the altered protein (CRM) produced by the z_1^- allele are formed in the presence of inducer, while in the *absence* of inducer, *only the protein corresponding to the z allele in position cis to the o^c is produced*. The o^c therefore has no effect on the z allele in position *trans*. Or putting it otherwise: the expression of the z allele attached to an o^+ remains fully repressor-sensitive even in the presence of an o^c in position *trans*. The o locus might be said to behave as belonging to the same cistron as the z markers. But as we know already, the o^c mutation is equally effective towards the acetylase which belongs to a cistron independent of z, and not adjacent to the operator locus. The results shown in Table 3, lines 8 and 9, confirm that the $o \rightarrow y$ relationship is the same as the $o \rightarrow z$ relationship, that is, the effect of the o^c allele extends *exclusively* to the y allele in the *cis* position. For instance, in the diploid $o^+z^-y^+/F o^c z^+ y_U^-$ the galactosidase is constitutive and the acetylase is inducible, while in the diploid $o^+z^+y_U^-/F o^c z^+ y^+$ both enzymes are constitutive.

These observations, predicted by the first interpretation, are incompatible with the second and lead to the conclusion that the operator governs an integral property of the genetic segment *ozy*, or of its cytoplasmic product (Jacob *et al.*, 1960a; Képès, Monod & Jacob, 1961).

This leads to another prediction. Certain mutations of the o segment could modify the operator in such a way as to inactivate the whole *ozy* segment resulting in the loss of the capacity to synthesize *both* galactosidase and permease.

These "o^o" mutants would be *recessive* to o^+ or o^c, and they would *not* be complemented either by $o^+z^+y^-$ or by $o^+z^-y^+$ mutants. Several point-mutants, possessing

† Let us recall again that no *non-pleiotropic* constitutive mutants of any type have been isolated in this system, in spite of systematic screening for such mutants.

precisely these properties, have been isolated (Jacob *et al.*, 1960*a*). They all map very closely to *o*ᶜ, as expected (see Fig. 3). It is interesting to note that in these mutants the *i*⁺ gene is functional (Table 3, line 11), which shows clearly, not only that the *i* and *o* mutants are not alleles, but that the *o* segment, while governing the expression of the *z* and *y* genes, does not affect the expression of the regulator gene.

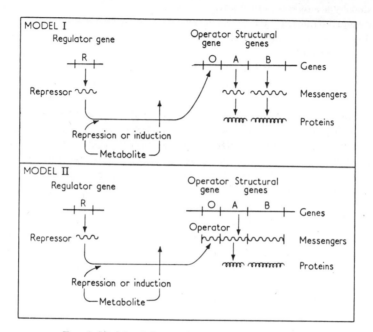

Fɪɢ. 6. Models of the regulation of protein synthesis.

In conclusion, the integral or *co-ordinate* expression of the *ozy* genetic segment signifies that the operator, which controls this expression, is and remains attached (see Fig. 6):

(a) either to the genes themselves (Fig. 6, I),

(b) or to the cytoplasmic messenger of the linked *z* and *y* genes which must then be assumed to form a single, integral, particle corresponding to the structure of the whole *ozy* segment, and functioning as a whole (Fig. 6, II).

In the former case, *the operator would in fact be identical with the o locus* and it would govern directly the activity of the genes, i.e. the synthesis of the structural messengers.

Both of these models are compatible with the observations which we have discussed so far. We shall return in the next section to the question whether the operator, i.e. the site of specific interaction with the repressor, is genetic or cytoplasmic. In either case, the *ozy* segment, although containing at least two independent structural genes, governing two independent proteins, behaves as a *unit* in the transfer of information. This *genetic unit of co-ordinate expression* we shall call the "operon" (Jacob *et al.*, 1960*a*).

The existence of such a unit of genetic expression is proved so far only in the case of the *Lac* segment. As we have already seen, the *v* mutants of phage λ, while illustrating the existence of an operator in this system, do not define an operon (because the number and the functions of the structural genes controlled by this operator are unknown). However, many observations hitherto unexplained by or even conflicting with classical genetic theory, are immediately accounted for by the operon theory. It is well known that, in bacteria, the genes governing the synthesis of different enzymes sequentially involved in a metabolic pathway are often found to be extremely closely linked, forming a cluster (Demerec, 1956). Various not very convincing speculations have been advanced to account for this obvious correlation of genetic structure and biochemical function (see Pontecorvo, 1958). Since it is now established that simultaneous induction or repression also generally prevails in such metabolic sequences, it seems very likely that the gene clusters represent units of co-ordinate expression, i.e. operons.

We have already mentioned the fact that two inducible enzymes sequentially involved in the metabolism of galactose by *E. coli*, galactokinase and UDP-galactose-transferase, are simultaneously induced by galactose, or by the gratuitous inducer D-fucose (Buttin, 1961). The genes which control specifically the synthesis of these enzymes, i.e. presumably the structural genes, are closely linked, forming a cluster on the *E. coli* chromosome. (Kalckar, Kurahashi & Jordan, 1959; Lederberg, 1960; Yarmolinsky & Wiesmeyer, 1960; Adler, unpublished results.) Certain point-mutations which occur in this chromosome segment abolish the capacity to synthesize both enzymes. These pleiotropic loss mutations are not complemented by any one of the specific (structural) loss mutations, an observation which is in apparent direct conflict with the one-gene one-enzyme hypothesis. These relationships are explained and the conflict is resolved if it is assumed that the linked structural genes constitute an operon controlled by a single operator and that the pleiotropic mutations are mutations of the operator locus.

We have also already discussed the system of simultaneous repression which controls the synthesis of the enzymes involved in histidine synthesis in *Salmonella*. This system involves eight or nine reaction steps. The enzymes which catalyse five of these reactions have been identified. The genes which individually determine these enzymes form a closely linked cluster on the *Salmonella* chromosome. Mutations in each of these genes result in a loss of capacity to synthesize a single enzyme; however, certain mutations at one end of the cluster abolish the capacity to synthesize all the enzymes simultaneously, and these mutations are not complemented by any one of the specific mutations (Ames, Garry & Herzenberg, 1960; Hartman, Loper & Serman, 1960). It will be recalled that the relative rates of synthesis of different enzymes in this sequence are constant under any set of conditions (see p. 327). All these remarkable findings are explained if it is assumed that this cluster of genes constitutes an operon, controlled by an operator associated with the *g* cistron.

The rule that genes controlling metabolically sequential enzymes constitute genetic clusters does not apply, in general, to organisms other than bacteria (Pontecorvo, 1958). Nor does it apply to all bacterial systems, even where simultaneous repression is known to occur and to be controlled by a single regulator gene, as is apparently the case for the enzymes of arginine biosynthesis. In such cases, it must be supposed that several identical or similar operator loci are responsible for sensitivity to repressor of each of the independent information-transfer systems.

It is clear that when an operator controls the expression of only a single structural cistron, the concept of the operon does not apply, and in fact there are no conceivable genetic-biochemical tests which could identify the operator-controlling genetic segment as distinct from the structural cistron itself.† One may therefore wonder whether it will be possible experimentally to extend this concept to dispersed (as opposed to clustered) genetic systems. It should be remarked at this point that many enzyme proteins are apparently made up of two (or more) different polypeptide chains. It is tempting to predict that such proteins will often be found to be controlled by two (or more) adjacent and co-ordinated structural cistrons, forming an operon.

5. The Kinetics of Expression of Structural Genes, and the Nature of the Structural Message

The problem we want to discuss in this section is whether the repressor-operator system functions at the genetic level by governing the *synthesis* of the structural message or at the cytoplasmic level, by controlling the protein-synthesizing *activity* of the messenger (see Fig. 6). These two conceivable models we shall designate respectively as the "genetic operator model" and the "cytoplasmic operator model."

The existence of units of co-ordinate expression involving several structural genes appears in fact difficult to reconcile with the cytoplasmic operator model, if only because of the size that the cytoplasmic unit would have to attain. If we assume that the message is a polyribonucleotide and take a coding ratio of 3, the "unit message" corresponding to an operon governing the synthesis of three proteins of average (monomeric) molecular weight 60,000 would have a molecular weight about 1.8×10^6; we have seen that operons including up to 8 structural cistrons may in fact exist. On the other hand, RNA fractions of *E. coli* and other cells do not appear to include polyribonucleotide molecules of molecular weight exceeding 10^6.

This difficulty is probably not insuperable; and this type of argument, given the present state of our knowledge, cannot be considered to eliminate the cytoplasmic operator model, even less to establish the validity of the genetic model. However, it seems more profitable tentatively to adopt the genetic model and to see whether some of the more specific predictions which it implies are experimentally verified.

The most immediate and also perhaps the most striking of these implications is that the structural message must be carried by a very short-lived intermediate both rapidly formed and rapidly destroyed during the process of information transfer. This is required by the kinetics of induction. As we have seen, the addition of inducer, or the removal of co-repressor, provokes the synthesis of enzyme at maximum rate within a matter of a few minutes, while the removal of inducer, or the addition of co-repressor interrupts the synthesis within an equally short time. Such kinetics are incompatible with the assumption that the repressor-operator interaction controls the rate of synthesis of *stable* enzyme-forming templates (Monod, 1956, 1958). Therefore, if the genetic operator model is valid, one should expect the kinetics of structural gene expression to be *essentially the same* as the kinetics of induction: injection of a "new" gene into an otherwise competent cell should result in virtually immediate synthesis of the corresponding protein at maximum rate; while removal of the gene should be attended by concomitant cessation of synthesis.

† It should be pointed out that the operational distinction between the operator locus and the structural cistron to which it is directly adjacent rests exclusively on the fact that the operator mutations affect the synthesis of several proteins governed by linked cistrons. This does not exclude the possibility that the operator locus is actually *part* of the structural cistron to which it is "adjacent." If it were so, one might expect certain constitutive operator mutations to involve an alteration of the structure of the protein governed by the "adjacent" cistron. The evidence available at present is insufficient to confirm or eliminate this assumption.

(a) *Kinetics of expression of the galactosidase structural gene*

Additions and removals of genes to and from cells are somewhat more difficult to perform than additions or removals of inducer. However, it can be done. Gene injection without cytoplasmic mixing occurs in the conjugation of *Hfr* male and *F⁻* female *E. coli*. In a mixed male and female population the individual pairs do not all mate at the same time, but the distribution of times of injection of a *given* gene can be rather accurately determined by proper genetic methods. The injection of the z^+ (galactosidase) gene from male cells into galactosidase-negative (z^-) female cells is rapidly followed by enzyme synthesis within zygotes (cf. p. 332). When the rate of enzyme synthesis in the population is expressed as a function of time, taking into

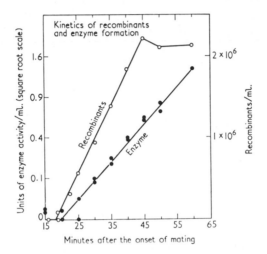

FIG. 7. Kinetics of enzyme production by merozygotes formed by conjugation between inducible galactosidase-positive males and constitutive galactosidase-negative females. Conditions are such that only the zygotes can form enzyme. Increase in the number of z^+ containing zygotes is determined by counting recombinants on adequate selective medium. Formation of enzyme is followed by enzyme activity measurements on the total population. It is seen that the enzyme increases linearly with the square of time. Since the zygote population increases linearly with time, it is apparent that the rate of enzyme synthesis per zygote is constant from the time of penetration of the z^+ gene. (From Riley *et al.*, 1960.)

account the increase with time of the number of z^+ containing zygotes, it is found (see Fig. 7):

(1) that enzyme synthesis begins within two minutes of the penetration of the z^+ gene;

(2) that the rate per zygote is constant and maximum over at least the first 40 min following penetration (Riley, Pardee, Jacob & Monod, 1960).

These observations indicate that the structural messenger is very rapidly formed by the z^+ gene, and does not accumulate. This could be interpreted in one of two ways:

(a) the structural messenger is a short-lived intermediate;

(b) the structural messenger is stable, but the gene rapidly forms a limited number of messenger molecules, and thereafter stops functioning.

If the second assumption is correct, removal of the gene after the inception of enzyme synthesis should not prevent the synthesis from continuing. This possibility is tested by the "removal" experiment, which is performed by loading the male chromosome with ^{32}P before injection. Following injection (into unlabelled female cells), ample time (25 min) is allowed for expression of the z^+ gene, before the zygotes are frozen to allow ^{32}P decay for various lengths of time. The rate of galactosidase synthesis by the population is determined immediately after thawing. It is found to decrease sharply as a function of the fraction of ^{32}P atoms decayed. If a longer period of time (110 min) is allowed for expression before freezing, no decrease in either enzyme-forming capacity or in viability of the z^+ marker are observed. This is to be expected, since by that time most of the z^+ genes would have replicated, and this observation provides an internal control showing that no indirect effects of ^{32}P disintegrations are involved.

This experiment therefore indicates that even after the z^+ gene has become expressed its integrity is required for enzyme synthesis to continue, as expected if the messenger molecule is a short-lived intermediate (Riley *et al.*, 1960).

The interpretation of both the injection and the removal experiment rests on the assumption that the observed effects are not due to (stable) cytoplasmic messenger molecules introduced with the genetic material, during conjugation. As we have already noted, there is strong evidence that no cytoplasmic transfer, even of small molecules, occurs during conjugation. Furthermore, if the assumption were made that enzyme synthesis in the zygotes is due to pre-formed messenger molecules rather than to the activity of the gene, it would be exceedingly difficult to account for both (a) the very precise coincidence in time between inception of enzyme synthesis and entry of the gene (in the injection experiment) and (b) the parallel behaviour of enzyme-forming capacity and genetic viability of the z^+ gene (in the removal experiment).

These experiments therefore appear to show that the kinetics of expression of a structural gene are entirely similar to the kinetics of induction-repression, as expected if the operator controls the activity of the gene in the synthesis of a short-lived messenger, rather than the activity of a ready-made (stable) messenger molecule in synthesizing protein.

It is interesting at this point to recall the fact that infection of *E. coli* with virulent (ϕII, T2, T4) phage is attended within 2 to 4 minutes by inhibition of *bacterial* protein synthesis, including in particular β-galactosidase (Cohen, 1949; Monod & Wollman, 1947; Benzer, 1953). It is known on the other hand that phage-infection results in rapid visible lysis of bacterial nuclei, while no major destruction of pre-formed bacterial RNA appears to occur (Luria & Human, 1950). It seems very probable that the inhibition of specific bacterial protein synthesis by virulent phage is due essentially to the depolymerization of bacterial DNA, and this conclusion also implies that the integrity of bacterial genes is required for continued synthesis of bacterial protein. In confirmation of this interpretation, it may be noted that infection of *E. coli* by phage λ, which does not result in destruction of bacterial nuclei, allows β-galactosidase synthesis to continue almost to the time of lysis (Siminovitch & Jacob, 1952).

(b) *Structural effects of base analogs*

An entirely different type of experiment also leads to the conclusion that the structural messenger is a short-lived intermediate and suggests, furthermore, that this intermediate is a ribonucleotide. It is known that certain purine and pyrimidine analogs are incorporated by bacterial cells into ribo- and deoxyribonucleotides, and it has been found that the synthesis of protein, or of some proteins, may be inhibited in the presence of certain of these analogs. One of the mechanisms by which these effects could be explained may be that certain analogs are incorporated into the structural messenger. If so, one might hope to observe that the molecular structure of specific proteins formed in the presence of an analog is modified. It has in fact been found that the molecular properties of β-galactosidase and of alkaline phosphatase synthesized by *E. coli* in the presence of 5-fluorouracil (5FU) are strikingly altered. In the case of β-galactosidase, the ratio of enzyme activity to antigenic valency is decreased by 80%. In the case of alkaline phosphatase, the rate of thermal inactivation (of this normally highly heat-resistant protein) is greatly increased (Naono & Gros, 1960*a,b*; Bussard, Naono, Gros & Monod, 1960).

It can safely be assumed that such an effect cannot result from the mere presence of 5FU in the cells, and must reflect incorporation of the analog into a constituent involved in some way in the information transfer system. Whatever the identity of this constituent may be, the kinetics of the effect must in turn reflect the kinetics of 5FU incorporation into this constituent. The most remarkable feature of the 5FU effect is that it is almost immediate, in the sense that abnormal enzyme is synthesized almost from the time of addition of the analog, and that the degree of abnormality of the molecular population thereafter synthesized does not increase with time. For instance, in the case of galactosidase abnormal enzyme is synthesized within 5 min of addition of the analog, and the ratio of enzyme activity to antigenic valency remains constant thereafter. In the case of alkaline phosphatase, the thermal inactivation curve of the abnormal protein synthesized in the presence of 5FU is monomolecular, showing the molecular population to be *homogeneously* abnormal rather than made up of a mixture of normal and abnormal molecules. It is clear that if the constituent responsible for this effect were stable, one would expect the population of molecules made in the presence of 5FU to be heterogeneous, and the fraction of abnorma molecules to increase progressively. It follows that the responsible constituent must be formed, and also must decay, very rapidly.

Now it should be noted that, besides the structural gene-synthesized messenger, the information transfer system probably involves other constituents responsible for the correct translation of the message, such as for instance the RNA fractions involved in amino acid transfer. The 5FU effect could be due to incorporation into one of these fractions rather than to incorporation into the messenger itself. However, the convergence of the results of the different experiments discussed above strongly suggests that the 5FU effect does reflect a high rate of turnover of the messenger itself.

(c) *Messenger RNA*

Accepting tentatively these conclusions, let us then consider what properties would be required of a cellular constituent, to allow its identification with the structural messenger. These qualifications based on general assumptions, and on the results discussed above, would be as follows:

(1) The "candidate" should be a polynucleotide.

(2) The fraction would presumably be very heterogeneous with respect to molecular weight. However, assuming a coding ratio of 3, the average molecular weight would not be lower than 5×10^5.

(3) It should have a base composition reflecting the base composition of DNA.

(4) It should, at least temporarily or under certain conditions, be found associated with ribosomes, since there are good reasons to believe that ribosomes are the seat of protein synthesis.

(5) It should have a very high rate of turnover and in particular it should saturate with 5FU within less than about 3 min.

It is immediately evident that none of the more classically recognized cellular RNA fractions meets these very restrictive qualifications. Ribosomal RNA, frequently assumed to represent the "template" in protein synthesis, is remarkably homogeneous in molecular weight. Its base composition is similar in different species, and does not reflect the variations in base ratios found in DNA. Moreover it appears to be entirely stable in growing cells (Davern & Meselson, 1960). It incorporates 5FU only in proportion to net increase.

Transfer RNA, or (sRNA) does not reflect DNA in base composition. Its average molecular weight is much lower than the 5×10^5 required for the messenger. Except perhaps for the terminal adenine and cytidine, its rate of incorporation of bases, including in particular 5FU, is not higher than that of ribosomal RNA.

However, a small fraction of RNA, first observed by Volkin & Astrachan (1957) in phage infected *E. coli*, and recently found to exist also in normal yeasts (Yčas & Vincent, 1960) and coli (Gros, *et al.*, 1961), does seem to meet all the qualifications listed above.

This fraction (which we shall designate "messenger RNA" or M-RNA) amounts to only about 3% of the total RNA; it can be separated from other RNA fractions by column fractionation or sedimentation (Fig. 8). Its average sedimentation velocity coefficient is 13, corresponding to a minimum molecular weight of 3×10^5, but since the molecules are presumably far from spherical, the molecular weight is probably much higher. The rate of incorporation of ^{32}P, uracil or 5FU into this fraction is extremely rapid: half saturation is observed in less than 30 sec, indicating a rate of synthesis several hundred times faster than any other RNA fraction. Its half life is also very short, as shown by the disappearance of radioactivity from this fraction in pre-labelled cells. At high concentrations of Mg^{2+} (0·005 M) the fraction tends to associate with the 70s ribosomal particles, while at lower Mg^{2+} concentrations it sediments independently of the ribosomal particles (Gros *et al.*, 1961).

The striking fact, discovered by Volkin & Astrachan, that the base-composition of this fraction in T2-infected cells reflects the base composition of *phage* (rather than bacterial) DNA, had led to the suggestion that it served as a precursor of phage DNA The agreement between the properties of this fraction and the properties of a short-lived structural messenger suggests that, in phage infected cells as well as in normal cells, this fraction served in fact in the transfer of genetic information from phage DNA to the protein synthesizing centers. This assumption implies that the same protein-forming centers which, in uninfected cells, synthesize bacterial protein, also serve in infected cells to synthesize phage protein according to the new structural information provided by phage DNA, *via* M-RNA. This interpretation is strongly supported by recent observations made with T4 infected *E. coli*. (Brenner, Jacob & Meselson, 1961).

Uninfected cells of *E. coli* were grown in the presence of ^{15}N. They were then infected and resuspended in ^{14}N medium. Following infection, they were exposed to short pulses of ^{32}P or ^{35}S, and the ribosomes were analysed in density gradients. It was found:

(1) that no detectable amounts of ribosomal RNA were synthesized after infection;

(2) labelled M-RNA formed *after* infection became associated with unlabelled ribosomal particles formed *before* infection;

(3) newly formed (i.e. phage-determined) protein, identified by its ^{35}S content, was found associated with the 70s particles before it appeared in the soluble protein fraction.

These observations strongly suggest that phage protein is synthesized by *bacterial* ribosomes formed before infection and associated with *phage-determined* M-RNA. Since the structural information for phage protein could not reside in the bacterial ribosomes, it must be provided by the M-RNA fraction.

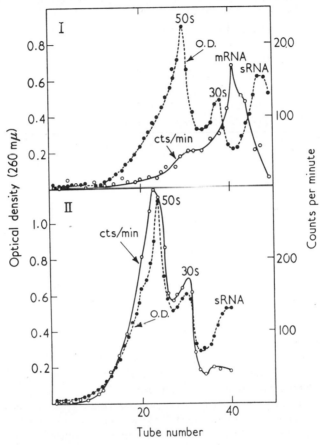

FIG. 8. Incorporation and turnover of uracil in messenger RNA. *E. coli* growing exponentially in broth were incubated for 5 sec with [14C]-uracil. The bacteria were centrifuged, washed and resuspended in the original volume of the same medium containing 100-fold excess of [12C]-uracil. Half the bacteria were then harvested and frozen (I) and the remainder were incubated for 15 min at 37°C (II) prior to harvesting and freezing. The frozen samples were ground with alumina and extracted with tris buffer (2-amino-2 hydroxymethylpropane-1:3-diol) containing 10^{-4}M-Mg, treated with DNase and applied to a sucrose gradient. After 3 hr, sequential samples were taken for determination of radioactivity and absorption at 260 mμ. It may be seen (part I) that after 5 sec, M-RNA is the only labelled fraction, and that subsequently (part II) uracil incorporated into M-RNA is entirely renewed. (From Gros *et al.*, 1961.)

Finally, the recent experiments of Lamfrom (1961) independently repeated by Kruh, Rosa, Dreyfus & Schapira (1961) have shown directly that species specificity in the synthesis of haemoglobin is determined by a "soluble" RNA-containing fraction rather than by the ribosomal fraction. Lamfrom used reconstructed systems, containing ribosomes from one species (rabbit) and soluble fractions from another (sheep) and found that the haemoglobin formed *in vitro* by these systems belonged in part to the type characteristic of the species used to prepare the *soluble* fraction. It is not, of course, positively proved that *inter-specific* differences in haemoglobin structure are gene-determined rather than cytoplasmic, but the assumption seems safe enough. In any case, Lamfrom's experiment proves beyond doubt that the ribosomes cannot be considered to determine entirely (if at all) the specific structure of proteins.

We had stated the problem to be discussed in this section as the choice between the genetic operator model and the cytoplasmic operator model. The adoption of the genetic operator model implies, as we have seen, some very distinctive and specific predictions concerning the behaviour of the intermediate responsible for the transfer of information from gene to protein. These predictions appear to be borne out by a considerable body of evidence which leads actually to a tentative identification of the intermediate in question with one particular RNA fraction. Even if this identification is confirmed by direct experiments, it will remain to be proved, also by direct experiments, that the synthesis of this "M-RNA" fraction is controlled at the genetic level by the repressor-operator interaction.

6. Conclusion

A convenient method of summarizing the conclusions derived in the preceding sections of this paper will be to organize them into a model designed to embody the main elements which we were led to recognize as playing a specific role in the control of protein synthesis; namely, the structural, regulator and operator genes, the operon, and the cytoplasmic repressor. Such a model could be as follows:

The molecular structure of proteins is determined by specific elements, the *structural genes*. These act by forming a cytoplasmic "transcript" of themselves, the structural messenger, which in turn synthesizes the protein. The synthesis of the messenger by the structural gene is a sequential replicative process, which can be initiated only at certain points on the DNA strand, and the cytoplasmic transcription of several, linked, structural genes may depend upon a single initiating point or *operator*. The genes whose activity is thus co-ordinated form an *operon*.

The operator tends to combine (by virtue of possessing a particular base sequence) specifically and reversibly with a certain (RNA) fraction possessing the proper (complementary) sequence. This combination blocks the initiation of cytoplasmic transcription and therefore the formation of the messenger by the structural genes in the whole operon. The specific "repressor" (RNA?), acting with a given operator, is synthesized by a *regulator gene*.

The repressor in certain systems (inducible enzyme systems) tends to combine specifically with certain specific small molecules. The combined repressor has no affinity for the operator, and the combination therefore results in *activation of the operon*.

In other systems (repressible enzyme systems) the repressor by itself is inactive (i.e. it has no affinity for the operator) and is activated only by combining with certain specific small molecules. The combination therefore leads to *inhibition of the operon*.

The structural messenger is an unstable molecule, which is destroyed in the process of information transfer. The rate of messenger synthesis, therefore, in turn controls the rate of protein synthesis.

This model was meant to summarize and express conveniently the properties of the different factors which play a specific role in the control of protein synthesis. In order concretely to represent the functions of these different factors, we have had to introduce some purely speculative assumptions. Let us clearly discriminate the experimentally established conclusions from the speculations:

(1) The most firmly grounded of these conclusions is the existence of *regulator* genes, which control the rate of information-transfer from *structural* genes to proteins, without contributing any information to the proteins themselves. Let us briefly recall the evidence on this point: mutations in the structural gene, which are reflected as alterations of the protein, do not alter the regulatory mechanism. Mutations that alter the regulatory mechanism do not alter the protein and do not map in the structural genes. Structural genes obey the one-gene one-protein principle, while regulator genes may affect the synthesis of several different proteins.

(2) That the regulator gene acts *via* a specific cytoplasmic substance whose effect is to *inhibit* the expression of the structural genes, is equally clearly established by the *trans* effect of the gene, by the different properties exhibited by genetically identical zygotes depending upon the origin of their cytoplasm, and by the fact that absence of the regulator gene, or of its product, results in uncontrolled synthesis of the protein at maximum rates.

(3) That the product of the regulator gene acts directly as a *repressor* (rather than indirectly, as antagonist of an endogenous inducer or other activator) is proved in the case of the *Lac* system (and of the λ lysogenic systems) by the properties of the dominant mutants of the regulator.

(4) The chemical identification of the repressor as an RNA fraction is a logical assumption based only on the *negative* evidence which indicates that it is not a protein.

(5) The existence of an operator, defined as the site of action of the repressor, is deduced from the existence and specificity of action of the repressor. The identification of the operator with the genetic segment which controls sensitivity to the repressor, is strongly suggested by the observation that a *single* operator gene may control the expression of *several adjacent structural genes*, that is to say, by the demonstration of the *operon* as a co-ordinated unit of genetic expression.

The assumption that the operator represents an initiating point for the cytoplasmic transcription of several structural genes is a pure speculation, meant only as an illustration of the fact that the operator controls an integral property of the group of linked genes which form an operon. There is at present no evidence on which to base any assumption on the molecular mechanisms of the operator.

(6) The assumptions made regarding the interaction of the repressor with inducers or co-repressors are among the weakest and vaguest in the model. The idea that specific coupling of inducers to the repressor could result in inactivation of the repressor appears reasonable enough, but it raises a difficulty which we have already pointed out. Since this reaction between repressor and inducer must be stereospecific (for both) it should presumably require a specific enzyme; yet no evidence, genetic or biochemical, has been found for such an enzyme.

(7) The property attributed to the structural messenger of being an unstable intermediate is one of the most specific and novel implications of this scheme; it is required, let us recall, by the kinetics of induction, once the assumption is made that the control systems operate at the genetic level. This leads to a new concept of the mechanism of information transfer, where the protein synthesizing centers (ribosomes) play the role of non-specific constituents which can synthesize different proteins, according to specific instructions which they receive from the genes through M-RNA. The already fairly impressive body of evidence, kinetic and analytical, which supports

this new interpretation of information transfer, is of great interest in itself, even if some of the other assumptions included in the scheme turn out to be incorrect.

These conclusions apply strictly to the bacterial systems from which they were derived; but the fact that adaptive enzyme systems of both types (inducible and repressible) and phage systems appear to obey the same fundamental mechanisms of control, involving the same essential elements, argues strongly for the generality of what may be called "repressive genetic regulation" of protein synthesis.

One is led to wonder whether all or most structural genes (i.e. the synthesis of most proteins) are submitted to repressive regulation. In bacteria, virtually all the enzyme systems which have been adequately studied have proved sensitive to inductive or repressive effects. The old idea that such effects are characteristic only of "non-essential" enzymes is certainly incorrect (although, of course, these effects can be detected only under conditions, natural or artificial, such that the system under study is at least partially non-essential (gratuitous). The results of mutations which abolish the control (such as constitutive mutations) illustrate its physiological importance. Constitutive mutants of the lactose system synthesize 6 to 7% of all their proteins as β-galactosidase. In constitutive mutants of the phosphatase system, 5 to 6% of the total protein is phosphatase. Similar figures have been obtained with other constitutive mutants. It is clear that the cells could not survive the breakdown of more than two or three of the control systems which keep in pace the synthesis of enzyme proteins.

The occurrence of inductive and repressive effects in tissues of higher organisms has been observed in many instances, although it has not proved possible so far to analyse any of these systems in detail (the main difficulty being the creation of controlled conditions of gratuity). It has repeatedly been pointed out that enzymatic adaptation, as studied in micro-organisms, offers a valuable model for the interpretation of biochemical co-ordination within tissues and between organs in higher organisms. The demonstration that adaptive effects in micro-organisms are primarily negative (repressive), that they are controlled by functionally specialized genes and operate at the genetic level, would seem greatly to widen the possibilities of interpretation. The fundamental problem of chemical physiology and of embryology is to understand why tissue cells do not all express, all the time, all the potentialities inherent in their genome. The survival of the organism requires that many, and, in some tissues most, of these potentialities be unexpressed, that is to say *repressed*. Malignancy is adequately described as a breakdown of one or several growth controlling systems, and the genetic origin of this breakdown can hardly be doubted.

According to the strictly structural concept, the genome is considered as a mosaic of independent molecular blue-prints for the building of individual cellular constituents. In the execution of these plans, however, co-ordination is evidently of absolute survival value. The discovery of regulator and operator genes, and of repressive regulation of the activity of structural genes, reveals that the genome contains not only a series of blue-prints, but a co-ordinated program of protein synthesis and the means of controlling its execution.

REFERENCES

Adelberg, E. A. & Umbarger, H. E. (1953). *J. Biol. Chem.* **205**, 475.
Ames, B. N. & Garry, B. (1959). *Proc. Nat. Acad. Sci., Wash.* **45**, 1453.
Ames, B. N., Garry, B. & Herzenberg, L. A. (1960). *J. Gen. Microbiol.* **22**, 369.
Benzer, S. (1953). *Biochim. biophys. Acta*, **11**, 383.
Bertani, G. (1953). *Cold. Spr. Harb. Symp. Quant. Biol.* **18**, 65.

Bertani, G. (1958). *Advanc. Virus Res.* **5**, 151.

Brenner, S., Jacob, F. & Meselson, M. (1961). *Nature*, **190**, 576.

Bussard, A., Naono, S., Gros, F. & Monod, J. (1960). *C. R. Acad. Sci., Paris*, **250**, 4049.

Buttin, G. (1956). Diplôme Et. Sup., Paris.

Buttin, G. (1961). *C. R. Acad. Sci., Paris*, in the press.

Cohen, G. N. & Jacob, F. (1959). *C. R. Acad. Sci., Paris*, **248**, 3490.

Cohen, G. N. & Monod, J. (1957). *Bact. Rev.* **21**, 169.

Cohen, S. S. (1949). *Bact. Rev.* **13**, 1.

Cohen-Bazire, G. & Jolit, M. (1953). *Ann. Inst. Pasteur*, **84**, 1.

Cohn, M. (1957). *Bact. Rev.* **21**, 140.

Cohn, M., Cohen, G. N. & Monod, J. (1953). *C. R. Acad. Sci., Paris*, **236**, 746.

Cohn, M. & Horibata, K. (1959). *J. Bact.* **78**, 624.

Cohn, M. & Monod, J. (1953). In *Adaptation in Micro-organisms*, p. 132. Cambridge University Press.

Cohn, M. & Torriani, A. M. (1952). *J. Immunol.* **69**, 471.

Davern, C. I. & Meselson, M. (1960). *J. Mol. Biol.* **2**, 153.

Demerec, M. (1956). *Cold Spr. Harb. Symp. Quant. Biol.* **21**, 113.

Dienert, F. (1900). *Ann. Inst. Pasteur*, **14**, 139.

Duclaux, E. (1899). *Traité de Microbiologie*. Paris: Masson et Cie.

Echols, H., Garen, A., Garen, S. & Torriani, A. M. (1961). *J. Mol. Biol.*, in the press.

Flaks, J. G. & Cohen, S. S. (1959). *J. Biol. Chem.* **234**, 1501.

Gale, E. F. (1943). *Bact. Rev.* **7**, 139.

Giles, N. H. (1958). *Proc. Xth Intern. Cong. Genetics*, Montreal, **1**, 261.

Gorini, L. & Maas, W. K. (1957). *Biochim. biophys. Acta*, **25**, 208.

Gorini, L. & Maas, W. K. (1958). In *The Chemical Basis of Development*, p. 469. Baltimore: Johns Hopkins Press.

Gros, F., Hiatt, H., Gilbert, W., Kurland, C. G., Risebrough, R. W. & Watson, J. D. (1961). *Nature*, **190**, 581.

Halvorson, H. O. (1960). *Advanc. Enzymol.* in the press.

Hartman, P. E., Loper, J. C. & Serman, D. (1960). *J. Gen. Microbiol.* **22**, 323.

Herzenberg, L. (1959). *Biochim. biophys. Acta*, **31**, 525.

Hogness, D. S., Cohn, M. & Monod, J. (1955). *Biochim. biophys. Acta*, **16**, 99.

Jacob, F. (1954). *Les Bactéries Lysogènes et la Notion de Provirus*. Paris: Masson et Cie.

Jacob, F. (1960). *Harvey Lectures*, 1958–1959, series **54**, 1.

Jacob, F. & Adelberg, E. A. (1959). *C.R. Acad. Sci., Paris*, **249**, 189.

Jacob, F. & Campbell, A. (1959). *C.R. Acad. Sci., Paris*, **248**, 3219.

Jacob, F., Fuerst, C. R. & Wollman, E. L. (1957). *Ann. Inst. Pasteur*, **93**, 724.

Jacob, F. & Monod, J. (1959). *C.R. Acad. Sci., Paris*, **249**, 1282.

Jacob, F., Perrin, D., Sanchez, C. & Monod, J. (1960a). *C.R. Acad. Sci., Paris*, **250**, 1727.

Jacob, F., Schaeffer, P. & Wollman, E. L. (1960b). In *Microbial Genetics*, Xth Symposium of the Society for General Microbiology, p. 67.

Jacob, F. & Wollman, E. L. (1953). *Cold Spr. Harb. Symp. Quant. Biol.* **18**, 101.

Jacob, F. & Wollman, E. L. (1956). *Ann. Inst. Pasteur*, **91**, 486.

Jacob, F. & Wollman, E. L. (1957). In *The Chemical Basis of Heredity*, p. 468. Baltimore: Johns Hopkins Press.

Kaiser, A. D. (1957). *Virology*, **3**, 42.

Kaiser, A. D. & Jacob, F. (1957). *Virology*, **4**, 509.

Kalckar, H. M., Kurahashi, K. & Jordan, E. (1959). *Proc. Nat. Acad. Sci., Wash.* **45**, 1776.

Karstrom, H. (1938). *Ergebn. Enzymforsch.* **7**, 350.

Képès, A. (1960). *Biochim. biophys. Acta*, **40**, 70.

Képès, A., Monod, J. & Jacob, F. (1961). In preparation.

Kogut, M., Pollock, M. & Tridgell, E. J. (1956). *Biochem. J.* **62**, 391.

Kornberg, A., Zimmerman, S. B., Kornberg, S. R. & Josse, J. (1959). *Proc. Nat. Acad. Sci., Wash.* **45**, 772.

Kruh, J., Rosa, J., Dreyfus, J.-C. & Schapira, G. (1961). *Biochim. biophys. Acta*, in the press.

Lamfrom, H. (1961). *J. Mol. Biol.* **3**, 241.

Lederberg, E. (1960). In *Microbial Genetics*, The Xth Symposium of the Society of General Microbiology, p. 115.

Levinthal, C. (1959). In *Structure and Function of Genetic Elements*, Brookhaven Symposia in Biology, p. 76.

Luria, S. E. & Human, M. L. (1950). *J. Bact.* **59**, 551.

Lwoff, A. (1953). *Bact. Rev.* **17**, 269.

Lwoff, A., Siminovitch, L. & Kjeldgaard, N. (1950). *Ann. Inst. Pasteur*, **79**, 815.

Magasanik, B., Magasanik, A. K. & Neidhardt, F. C. (1959). In *A Ciba Symposium on the Regulation of Cell Metabolism*, p. 334. London: Churchill.

Monod, J. (1942). *Recherches sur la Croissance des Cultures Bactériennes*. Paris: Hermann.

—— 1955). *Exp. Ann. Biochim. Méd.* série XVII, p. 195. Paris: Masson et Cie.

Monod, J. (1956). In *Units of Biological Structure and Function*, p. 7. New York: Academic Press.

Monod, J. (1958). *Rec. Trav. Chim. des Pays-Bas*, **77**, 569.

Monod, J. (1959). *Angew. Chem.* **71**, 685.

Monod, J. & Audureau, A. (1946). *Ann. Inst. Pasteur*, **72**, 868.

Monod, J. & Cohen-Bazire, G. (1953). *C.R. Acad. Sci., Paris*, **236**, 530.

Monod, J. & Cohn, M. (1952). *Advanc. Enzymol.* **13**, 67.

Monod, J. & Cohn, M. (1953). In *Symposium on Microbial Metabolism*. VIth Intern. Cong. of Microbiol., Rome, p. 42.

Monod, J., Pappenheimer, A. M. & Cohen-Bazire, G. (1952), *Biochim. biophys. Acta*, **9**, 648.

Monod, J. & Wollman, E. L. (1947). *Ann. Inst. Pasteur*, **73**, 937.

Naono, S. & Gros, F. (1960a). *C.R. Acad. Sci., Paris*, **250**, 3527.

Naono, S. & Gros, F. (1960b). *C.R. Acad. Sci., Paris*, **250**, 3889.

Neidhardt, F. C. & Magasanik, B. (1956a). *Nature*, **178**, 801.

Neidhardt, F. C. & Magasanik, B. (1956b). *Biochim. biophys. Acta*, **21**, 324.

Novick, A. & Szilard, L., in Novick, A. (1955). *Ann. Rev. Microbiol.* **9**, 97.

Pardee, A. B. (1957). *J. Bact.* **73**, 376.

Pardee, A. B., Jacob, F. & Monod, J. (1959). *J. Mol. Biol.* **1**, 165.

Pardee, A. B. & Prestidge, L. S. (1959). *Biochim. biophys. Acta*, **36**, 545.

Pardee, A. B. & Prestidge, L. S. (1961). In preparation.

Perrin, D., Bussard, A. & Monod, J. (1959). *C.R. Acad. Sci., Paris*, **249**, 778.

Perrin, D., Jacob, F. & Monod, J. (1960). *C.R. Acad. Sci., Paris*, **250**, 155.

Pollock, M. (1950). *Brit. J. Exp. Pathol.* **4**, 739.

Pollock, M. & Perret, J. C. (1951). *Brit. J. Exp. Pathol.* **5**, 387.

Pontecorvo, G. (1958). *Trends in Genetic Analysis*. New York: Columbia University Press.

Rickenberg, H. V., Cohen, G. N., Buttin, G. & Monod, J. (1956). *Ann. Inst. Pasteur*, **91**, 829.

Riley, M., Pardee, A. B., Jacob, F. & Monod, J. (1960). *J. Mol. Biol.* **2**, 216.

Rotman, B. & Spiegelman, S. (1954). *J. Bact.* **68**, 419.

Siminovitch, L. & Jacob, F. (1952). *Ann. Inst. Pasteur*, **83**, 745.

Stanier, R. Y. (1951). *Ann. Rev. Microbiol.* **5**, 35.

Szilard, L. (1960). *Proc. Nat. Acad. Sci., Wash.* **46**, 277.

Torriani, A. M. (1960). *Biochim. biophys. Acta*, **38**, 460.

Umbarger, H. E. (1956). *Science*, **123**, 848.

Vogel, H. J. (1957a). *Proc. Nat. Acad. Sci., Wash.* **43**, 491.

Vogel, H. J. (1957b). In *The Chemical Basis of Heredity*, p. 276. Baltimore: Johns Hopkins Press.

Volkin, E. & Astrachan, L. (1957). In *The Chemical Basis of Heredity*, p. 686. Baltimore: Johns Hopkins Press.

Went, F. C. (1901). *J. Wiss. Bot.* **36**, 611.

Wijesundora, S. & Woods, D. D. (1953). *Biochem. J.* **55**, viii.

Willson, C., Perrin, D., Jacob, F. & Monod, J. (1961). In preparation.

Wollman, E. L. & Jacob, F. (1959). *La Sexualité des Bactéries*. Paris: Masson et Cie.

Yanofsky, C. (1960). *Bact. Rev.* **24**, 221.

Yanofsky, C. & Lennox, E. S. (1959). *Virology*, **8**, 425.

Yarmolinsky, M. B. & Wiesmeyer, H. (1960). *Proc. Nat. Acad. Sci., Wash.* in the press.

Yates, R. A. & Pardee, A. B. (1956). *J. Biol. Chem.* **221**, 757.

Yates, R. A. & Pardee, A. B. (1957). *J. Biol. Chem.* **227**, 677.

Yčas, M. & Vincent, W. S. (1960). *Proc. Nat. Acad. Sci., Wash.* **46**, 804.

Zabin, I., Képès, A. & Monod, J. (1959). *Biochem. Biophys. Res. Comm.* **1**, 289.

PRINTED IN GREAT BRITAIN AT THE UNIVERSITY PRESS ABERDEEN

THE
AMERICAN NATURALIST

Vol. XCV   September–October, 1961   No. 884

SOME PARALLELS BETWEEN GENE CONTROL SYSTEMS IN MAIZE AND IN BACTERIA

BARBARA McCLINTOCK

Department of Genetics, Carnegie Institution of Washington,
Cold Spring Harbor, New York

It has been realized for some time that, although the gene is necessary for expression of a certain phenotype, it may not in itself be sufficient for such expression and mechanisms may exist that control its action. Genetic systems that serve this purpose in maize were recognized some years ago, and studies conducted with a number of them have been reported (for references, see Brink, 1958, 1960; McClintock, 1956a and b; Peterson, 1960). Without adequate confirmation of similar systems in other organisms, it could be considered that the systems in maize may not reflect a type of control of gene action that is common to organisms in general. Recently, however, genetic systems that control gene action have been discovered in bacteria (Jacob and Monod, 1959, 1961; Jacob et al., 1960) and it is now apparent that a relationship may exist between the bacterial and the maize control systems. The bacterial control systems, described by Jacob et al., are composed of two genetic elements, each distinct from the "structural" gene. One of them, designated the "operator," is located adjacent to the structural gene (or sequence of structural genes) and controls its activation. The structural gene, when activated, is responsible for the production of a particular sequence of amino acids and thus for the specificity of a protein. The second element of this system, termed the "regulator," may be located close to the structural gene, or it may be located elsewhere in the bacterial chromosome. The regulator is responsible for the production of a repressor substance—not a protein—that appears in the cytoplasm. The operator element responds in some yet unknown manner to changes in degree of effective action of the repressor substance by "turning on" or "turning off" the action of the structural gene in accordance with such changes. Each operator-regulator system is specific, in that an operator will respond only to the specific product of the regulator of its system.

In maize likewise, some of the control systems are composed, basically, of two elements. One is closely associated with the structural gene and directly controls its action; it may be likened to the operator element in bacteria. The other element may be located near the first or may be independently located in the chromosome complement. It establishes the conditions

265

to which the gene-associated element responds, a particular change in these conditions being reflected in a particular change in action of the gene, and thus is comparable to the regulator element in bacteria. In maize, as in bacteria, each "operator-regulator" system is quite specific: an "operator" element will respond only to the particular "regulator" element of its own system.

Several different two-element control systems, each operating independently of the others, have been identified in maize. These were discovered, originally, because the elements belonging to each were transposed from one location to another in the chromosome complement without losing their individual identities in the process. It was found that the gene-associated element of a system can leave the locus of one gene and become associated with that of another. After such an association is established, the action of the gene comes under the control of the system to which the gene-associated element belongs. It has been possible, therefore, to examine the mode of operation of a particular control system at a number of different gene loci and, conversely, to examine the operation of different control systems at the same gene locus. It should be emphasized that, although transposition of controlling elements in maize made it possible to recognize their presence in the chromosome complement and to study the mode of operation of the component elements of a system, transposition does not necessarily characterize the behavior of a controlling element. An element previously exhibiting transposition may become fixed in location. If it is the gene-associated element that becomes fixed, the action of the gene will then be permanently under the control of the system to which that element belongs. Examples will be considered in this report.

Jacob (Jacob, 1960; Jacob, Schaeffer and Wollman, 1960) and Richter (1961) have postulated that controlling elements in maize may be comparable to episomes in bacteria. Recent evidence (Buttin, Jacob and Monod, 1960; Yarmolinsky and Wiesmeyer, 1960) about the manner in which a phage particle may control the action of bacterial genes in the neighborhood of its attachment to the bacterial chromosome lends support to this interpretation. In a lysogenic bacterium, induction of phage by ultraviolet light or by chemical treatment releases inhibition of gene action not only in phage genes that are concerned with initiating vegetative replication but also in genes of the bacterial chromosome in the neighborhood of phage attachment. This effect resembles that which occurs in maize when a controlling element at the locus of a gene is removed by the transposition mechanism. A change in action of the gene accompanies this removal.

Notwithstanding the analogies that may be drawn between controlling elements in maize and episomes in bacteria, it now appears to the author that control systems in maize also resemble the operator-regulator systems of control of gene action in bacteria, as outlined above. In maize, as in bacteria, the controlling element (the "operator") at the locus of the structural gene responds to altered activities of the second element (the "regulator") of the system by inducing modification in action of the structural gene. In maize, the response of the "operator" element to change in effective action of the "regulator" element results in controlled types of change in action of the structural gene, and many such changes are accompanied by removal of the "operator" element from the locus. In other cases, however, the "operator" element is not removed from the locus. It responds merely by "turning on" or "turning off" the action of the structural gene. When this occurs, the maize systems resemble the operator-regulator systems in bacteria.

The control system composed of the elements Dissociation (Ds) and Activator (Ac) was the first of those in maize to be explored extensively. Its mode of operation was examined at a number of different gene loci (McClintock, 1953). This system was studied intensively because it was possible to identify readily both the "operator" element, Ds, and the "regulator" element, Ac. In several cases $(bz^{m-4}, sh^m, c^{m-1})$ the proximal or distal position of Ds with respect to the components of the structural gene could also be determined. With some other two element systems, the regulator element is readily identifiable but the presence of the operator element at the gene locus often must be assumed on the basis of the control that the regulator exerts on gene action. However, when adequate test methods are available, it is possible to confirm the presence of an operator element at the locus of the gene by means of crossover techniques which are capable of defining its location with respect to the components of the structural gene. This method has been used successfully to define the location of this element in the case where action of the structural gene, A_1, came under the control of the two-element system of which Dotted (Dt) is the regulator (Laughnan, 1955; Sarma, 1956, 1961).

This report will describe the mode of operation of the elements that compose a single control system in maize. It is not the purpose of the paper to present the evidence for the statements that will be made here but rather to indicate some of the resemblances between the systems in bacteria and those in maize. The Suppressor-mutator control system in maize has been chosen because it illustrates these resemblances more directly than do other examined systems in maize.

Five independent inceptions of control of gene action by the Suppressor-mutator (Spm) control system have been recognized in the Cold Spring Harbor cultures. Three of them occurred when the "operator" element of this system was inserted at the locus of A_1 in chromosome 3. These three cases are designated $a_1{}^{m-1}$, $a_1{}^{m-2}$, and $a_1{}^{m-5}$. The symbols $m-1$, $m-2$, and $m-5$ refer to the order in time of inception of control of gene action at A_1 by this system ($a_1{}^{m-3}$ and $a_1{}^{m-4}$ refer to inceptions of control of gene action at A_1 by the Ds-Ac control system). A fourth case occurred at the A_2 locus in chromosome 5 (designated $a_2{}^{m-1}$), and a fifth at the Wx locus in chromosome 9 (designated wx^{m-8}). (Both A_1 and A_2 are associated with anthocyanin pigment formation in plant and kernel. Wx is associated with production amylose in the pollen grain and in the endosperm of the kernel.) Two independently located elements are primarily responsible for control of gene action at $a_1{}^{m-1}$, $a_1{}^{m-5}$, $a_2{}^{m-1}$, and wx^{m-8}. One controlling element, com-

parable to the operator, resides at the locus of the gene and directly controls its type of action. The other element, comparable to the regulator, is
Spm, to which the "operator" element at the locus of the gene responds in
accordance with the type of activity of Spm and the changes in this activity.
Preliminary evidence suggests that Spm resides close to the A_1 locus in the
case of $a_1{}^{m-2}$. It is possible that here the "operator" and "regulator" elements of the system are located adjacent or close to each other. If this
proves to be true, $a_1{}^{m-2}$ will resemble in its organization and its behavior
one of the cases examined in studies of the Ds-Ac system. (See discussion
of bz^{m-2} in McClintock, 1956 c.)

Basically, the mode of control of gene action by the Spm system is relatively easy to comprehend. However, there are some conditions that complicate its analysis and so obscure its basic simplicity. They arise from
(1) alterations at the locus of the gene (termed "altered states" of the gene
locus), induced by the controlling element there residing, that modify subsequent expression of the gene, both in the presence and in the absence of
Spm; (2) modifications of Spm itself, expressed by altered degrees in
strength of its action, or by cyclically occurring change in phase of its activity—from active to inactive and back to active; and (3) the action of an
independently located, transposible Modifier element that alters the expression of some of the states of the gene locus in a predictable manner, but
only when Spm is also present and in its active phase. Each of these conditions will be considered in turn. The discussion will apply to those cases
in which the two elements that are basically concerned in control of gene
action are independently located, one being at the locus of the gene, the
other, Spm, being located elsewhere.

THE CLASS I AND CLASS II STATES OF A GENE LOCUS UNDER THE CONTROL OF THE Spm SYSTEM

There are two main categories of state, designated class I and class II.
Because the class II states behave in a simple manner, they will be considered first. In the presence of a fully active Spm, no gene action is expressed. If Spm is removed by somatic transposition, or by meiotic segregation, or if it enters its inactive phase in a cell of the plant or the kernel,
gene action is expressed. The degree of expression serves to distinguish
between different members of the class II states. An apparently full, or near
full gene expression characterizes some class II states whereas a much reduced expression characterizes others. With the class II states, Spm serves
as the "regulator" of action of the "structural" gene, causing it to be
"turned on" and "turned off" through the direct mediation of the "operator"
element residing at the locus of the "structural" gene. It should be emphasized that this turning on and turning off of gene action is not accompanied
by any modification that permanently alters the structure of the gene locus,
as may occur with the class I states. However, the class II states originate
from the class I states, which will now be described.

Because of the variety of expressions that may be produced by class I states, they appear to be far more complex than the class II states. Regardless of the degrees of difference in expression, all class I states exhibit the same basic pattern of behavior. With respect to any one gene under the control of the *Spm* system, all the many different class I states that have been isolated trace their origin to the class I state that was produced, initially, when the "operator" element became associated with the structural gene. Each class I state is distinguished not only by its behavior pattern in the presence of active *Spm*, but also by the type of gene action that it gives rise to in the absence of *Spm* (or in the presence of *Spm* in an inactive phase). When a fully active *Spm* is present, all gene action is suppressed until, in a cell of the plant or of the kernel, a modification is instigated at the locus of the gene by the "operator" element there residing. Each class I state is distinguished by a particular type of consequence of such modifications. There are two main consequences: production of a mutant, which is thereafter stable in the presence of active *Spm*; or production of a new state, either class I or class II. The time during development of a plant or kernel when these modifications occur, the number of cells in which they occur at any one stage in development, and the particular types of consequence, serve to characterize a particular class I state. For example, with some states, such modifications at the locus of the gene may occur early in development, but each state is distinguished from others by the type of consequence of these modifications. One such state may give rise to two main types of stable mutants, those that express high levels of gene action and those that give the null expression; and these two types of mutants are produced at constant relative rates. With another such state, the early-occurring mutations result only in mutants that express low levels of gene action. Some class I states give rise to many new states whereas others produce few new states.

There is a group of class I states characterized by the fact that all mutation-inducing events occur late in development of plant or kernel. The states in this group may be distinguished from one another by differences in the number of phenotypically distinguishable mutant areas that are produced, and also by the levels of gene action these mutant areas exhibit. These states are particularly useful for many studies. Mutation-inducing events occur so late in development that germinal mutations may not be encountered or are encountered only rarely. Thus, such states are preserved, unaltered, through generations of plants, even when *Spm* is present and fully active in the plants.

In the absence of *Spm* all but one of the many class I states that have been isolated express some degree of gene action. The level of action may be low with some states, intermediate with others, and even quite high with still others. As long as *Spm* is absent (or is present in its inactive phase), the particular type of gene action expressed by any one state is constant and may be maintained unaltered from generation to generation. Also, in the absence of an active *Spm*, any state behaves as a stable allele of any other state. However, no relation has been observed between the type of gene expression that a class I state exhibits in the absence of *Spm* and the types of mutation it produces in its presence.

If, in a plant having an active *Spm*, a different class I state is carried in each homologue, each state reacts to *Spm* in its own individual manner, and each may be recovered in the progeny, unaltered by its association in the same nucleus with the other state. Again, if two different gene loci, each under the control of the *Spm* system, are present in a plant or a kernel—for example, $a_2{}^{m-1}$ and wx^{m-8}—each responds to *Spm* in its own characteristic manner according to its state. It may be added, also, that in plants or kernels having two such states each state responds directly to a somatically occurring change in action of *Spm*. Each depicts this change in the expected manner, in accordance with its state (see below).

TYPES OF CHANGE IN *Spm*

Spm itself undergoes modification. After a modification has occurred, the *Spm* exhibiting it may be isolated and further examined. The modifications may result in one of several different types of change in *Spm* action or behavior. One type affects the time during development of the plant when transposition of *Spm* will occur. Some isolates of *Spm* undergo transposition mainly early in development. Others undergo transposition mainly late in development, with only an occasional occurrence in young tissues. Several isolates have been obtained that rarely undergo transposition at times during development that will result in the appearance of gametes in which *Spm* occupies a new location in the chromosome complement; and one isolate has not yet given any evidence of transposition.

One conspicuous type of change undergone by *Spm* results in a weakening of its capacity to effect mutation with the class I states of those gene loci that have come under the control of the *Spm* system. The designation Spm^w is used to symbolize this type of alteration of *Spm* (McClintock, 1957). In this section, the symbol Spm^s will henceforth be used to designate an *Spm* expressing full activity. A newly arising Spm^w may be recognized readily. With the class I states, its presence is made evident by a pronounced delay in time of occurrence of mutation at the locus of the gene, and also in a pronounced reduction in frequency of occurrence of such mutation. If the class I state is one that gives only late-occurring mutations with Spm^s, then with Spm^w only a few very late-occurring mutations will be produced, and sometimes none at all. If the class I state is one that gives many early-occurring mutations with Spm^s, then Spm^w will delay the time of occurrence of mutation until the late stages of development of a tissue. Only small areas exhibiting the mutant phenotype will appear in plant and kernel. The response of any one class I state to any one isolate of Spm^w is quite predictable.

Each Spm^w arises from an Spm^s as the consequence of a single event occurring within a cell. If it takes place early in plant development, all the cells producing an ear of the plant may be descendants of the cell in which it occurred, and thus all carry the newly produced Spm^w. Or, the descendent cells may contribute only to a part of the ear, and the newly produced Spm^w be evident only in the kernels within a sector derived from these cells. In either case, the Spm^w may be isolated from those kernels that carry it. There are different types of Spm^w, distinguishable from each other by several criteria. They differ in degree of weakening of the capacity to induce mutation at the loci of genes controlled by the Spm system, in frequency of occurrence of transposition and the time of its occurrence during development, and in stability of the Spm^w expression. In the last-named respect, differences between Spm^w isolates of independent origin are conspicuous. Some isolates are highly stable whereas others undergo frequent return to Spm^s. It is again evident that change in action of Spm, this time from Spm^w to Spm^s, is effected by a single event occurring in an individual cell.

If both an Spm^w and an Spm^s are present in the same plant, Spm^s is dominant. However, the Spm^w in such plants may be recovered in their progeny, with its type of action unaltered by previous association in the same nucleus with Spm^s.

It should be emphasized that no modifications resulting in mutation or change in state will occur at the locus of a gene that is under the control of the Spm system (that is, with the class I states of the gene locus), unless all gene action has first been suppressed by Spm in the ancestor cells, whether by Spm^w or by Spm^s. In other words, suppression of gene action by Spm must precede the mutation-inducing event. This fact is especially well illustrated in plants that have an Spm element that is undergoing change in phase of its activity during the development of plant or kernel, as described in the next section.

CYCLICALLY OCCURRING REVERSALS OF PHASE OF ACTIVITY OF Spm

One of the most interesting and theoretically important types of expression of Spm consists in the sequentially occurring reversals in phase of its activity—from active to inactive and back to active (McClintock, 1958, 1959). Each such change in phase results from an event occurring in an individual cell of the plant or kernel. The effect produced by the change is then exhibited in the descendants of this cell, if either a class I or a class II state of a gene locus under the control of this Spm system is also present to register it. Following such a reversal of phase, the duration of the particular phase may be long, continuing unaltered through many cell or even plant generations, or it may be short, reversal occurring again in a number of cells only a relatively few cell generations removed from that which initiated the preceding phase. Control of duration of a particular phase appears to be associated with the event that produces the particular reversal of phase. By selective methods it has been possible to isolate Spm displaying either a long duration of an active phase or a long duration of an inactive phase.

The phenotypes appearing in mature plants and kernels as the consequence of phase reversal of *Spm* may be very complex. The degree of complexity depends on the state of a gene locus that is present in the plant or
kernel, on the number of reversals of phase of *Spm* that occur, and also on
the times of their occurrence during development of a tissue. If an inactive
Spm is present, initially, in a plant or kernel, along with either a class I or
a class II state of a gene locus, no evidence of the presence of this *Spm*
will appear in either the plant or the kernel unless reversal of phase occurs
in one or more cells during development. After *Spm* is reactivated in an individual cell, its presence is revealed in the descendants of that cell. When
a class II state is used as the indicator, reactivation of *Spm* is made evident by suppression of gene action in these cells. Should subsequent reversal of phase occur in some of the descendent cells, then gene action will
be evidenced in their descendent cells. With the class II states, then, reversals of phase of activity of *Spm* merely effect a "turning on" and "turning off" of gene action; and with the class II states of those gene loci that
are associated with the production of anthocyanin pigment, both in plant and
in kernel, the alternating cycles of phase of activity of *Spm* are registered
with great clarity. No pigment appears in cells in which *Spm* is in its active
phase, and pigment appears in those cells in which it is in its inactive
phase. It may be pointed out here that the type of control of gene action,
just described, resembles that associated with phase variation in Salmonella
in which the system of chromosomal elements responsible for control of gene
action likewise has been identified (Lederberg and Iino, 1956; Iino and
Lederberg, 1957, 1958; Iino, 1959, 1960).

The response of the class I states to reversal of phase of activity of *Spm*
is basically the same as that of the class II states, but the types of phenotypic expression of the gene and the various different patterns of expression
that may appear in an individual plant or kernel can be very complex. This
is because mutation-inducing events may occur at the gene locus in some
cells when their *Spm* is in its active phase. The pattern of mutant areas
that may appear in a sector of the plant or kernel, after a change in phase of
Spm from inactive to active, will depend upon the developmental stage of the
tissue when the reversal occurs. An example will illustrate this. If a plant
or kernel starts development with an active *Spm* having a long duration of
the active phase, and also a class I state of the gene locus that responds
to it by producing a number of early-occurring mutations, then large areas,
each exhibiting a mutant phenotype, will be present in the mature plant or
kernel. Each such area reflects an early-occurring "operator"-induced modification at the locus of the gene. If, however, development commences with
Spm in its inactive phase, no mutations may occur at the gene locus having
this class I state unless and until a reversal of phase of activity of *Spm* occurs. If reversal takes place in a cell rather late in the development of a
tissue, suppression of gene action will be effected in the descendants of
that cell. However, mutation-inducing events may occur in some of these
descendent cells and, by necessity, all these mutations will arise in cells

of a tissue that is approaching maturity. Consequently, the areas that can exhibit a mutant phenotype must be small. In other words, the size of the mutant areas will depend upon the stage of development of a tissue when *Spm* reverts to its active phase. It is evident, then, that complex and often irregular patterns of gene expression may be exhibited by a plant or by a kernel carrying a particular class I state when its *Spm* is undergoing frequent reversal of phase of activity. Different patterns of gene expression may be observed in different areas of the same plant or kernel. These patterns reflect the time of occurrence of reversal of phase of activity of *Spm* and also the number of such reversals.

Evidence has been obtained to indicate that inactivation of *Spm*, as described above, is not associated with a complete blocking of its functional capacity but rather with some change affecting its mode of functioning, such as an altered form of its product. This was made evident, initially, in plants and kernels having an inactive *Spm* characterized by a long duration of inactivity, and also an active *Spm* undergoing frequent reversal of phase during development. If only the latter *Spm* were present, a class II state would register each reversal of phase by showing no evidence of gene action in those cells in which it was active and by exhibiting gene action in those cells in which it was inactive. When two active *Spm* elements are present, initially, a class II state registers reversal of phase only when it occurs to both *Spm* elements, either simultaneously in an individual cell, or successively (that is, affecting one *Spm* in one cell and the other *Spm* in a descendant of that cell). Thus, in either plant or kernel, both the number and the size of areas exhibiting gene action will differ according to the number of active *Spm* elements that were present initially. From these patterns, it is often possible to deduce the number of *Spm* elements that are present in a plant or kernel.

It was anticipated that combination of an inactive *Spm*, having a long duration of the inactive phase, with an initially active *Spm* in a plant or kernel carrying a class II state would give rise to a phenotype resembling that produced when only one active *Spm* is present initially. This assumption proved to be incorrect. Instead, it was found that this combination produced a phenotype resembling the one that appears when two active *Spm* elements are initially present in a plant or when three active *Spm* elements are initially present in a kernel. However, the pattern produced by the areas that exhibit gene action (no active *Spm* in them) is much more uniform, and this is particularly well illustrated in the aleurone layer of kernels whose endosperms receive two inactive *Spm* elements from the female parent and one initially active *Spm* from the male parent. All areas exhibiting gene action are small, and they are evenly distributed over the aleurone layer. That this pattern is not produced by reversal of phase of the inactive *Spm*, brought about by association in the same nucleus with an active *Spm*, is made evident when progeny of plants having an initially active *Spm* and the described inactive *Spm* are examined. The inactive *Spm* is recovered with its phase quite unaltered. Also, it appears in the expected proportions of the progeny in accordance with the type of testcross that has been made to determine this. In order to be certain that the inactive *Spm* appearing in the progeny was the same as that which had been combined with the active *Spm* in the zygote produced from the initial cross, the relative locations of the two *Spm* elements in the chromosome complement had to be known in advance of the initial cross. Also, the location of each had to be determined in the individual progeny.

A number of tests had been made to observe the effects produced on either the class I or the class II states by bringing together in a zygote nucleus, or in a primary endosperm nucleus, an inactive and an active *Spm*. The effects produced in all such tests conformed with that described above. The inactive *Spm* proved not to be totally inactive, although it was quite ineffective by itself. This evidence does not preclude the possibility or the probability that some modifications of *Spm* may result in its total inactivation.

THE MODIFIER ELEMENT IN THE *Spm* SYSTEM

A transposible element that serves to increase the frequency of occurrence of mutation-inducing events with some of the class I states of a_1^{m-1} first appeared in only one of many a_1^{m-1}, *Spm*-carrying kernels on an ear and on only one of several ears produced by an a_1^{m-1}/a_1, *Spm*-carrying plant. This kernel exhibited a marked increase in mutation frequency in comparison with that exhibited by the other a_1^{m-1}, *Spm*-carrying kernels on the ear. The class I state of a_1^{m-1} that was present in the ear-bearing plant was one that undergoes only late-occurring mutations in the presence of an active *Spm*. No change in this state had been observed to occur in many tests conducted with it over a number of plant generations. The presence of a Modifier element, which was responsible for the marked increase in mutation frequency in the exceptional kernel, was revealed in tests conducted with the plant derived from this kernel. Subsequently, the effects produced by this Modifier on the expression of other class I states of a_1^{m-1} were investigated. Study of its effects was confined to a_1^{m-1}, but the results allow the following conclusions to be drawn:

(1) The presence of the Modifier can be detected only when *Spm* also is present in the chromosome complement and only when it is in its active phase. Under these circumstances, the Modifier effects a marked increase in frequency of mutation to stable alleles with some of the class I states, but does not modify the time of occurrence of such mutation. Also, the rate of increase in frequency of mutation is proportional to that produced by the state in the absence of the Modifier. However, if the state is one that produces very many mutations with *Spm* alone, the Modifier does not effect a measurable increase in mutation rate (McClintock, 1958).

(2) When the Modifier is present, the same phenotype is produced with *Spm*^{w} as with *Spm*^{s}. Thus, plants and kernels that have only *Spm*^{w} and the Modifier are not distinguishable in phenotype from those that have *Spm*^{s} and the Modifier. However, the presence of either one or the other type of *Spm* may be determined by means of progeny tests. Individuals carrying *Spm* but

no Modifier appear in the progeny, and the type of *Spm* in them is made evident.

(3) The Modifier element is transposible. A number of early-occurring transpositions of it were detected. Its transposition to and away from locations in the chromosome complement close to marked gene loci were examined (McClintock, 1958).

The Modifier element acts as if it could complement both the "regulator" element, *Spm*, and the element of this system that is at the locus of the gene. It complements *Spm* in that in its presence a weakly acting *Spm* (Spm^w) is as effective as a fully active *Spm* (Spm^s). It complements the element at the A_1 locus in that in its presence a class I state that gives relatively few mutations with Spm^s alone can mimic another state that gives many more mutations with Spm^s alone.

DISCUSSION AND SUMMARY

Although the mode of operation of the *Spm* system of control of gene action, as outlined above, may appear to be complex, it is evident, nevertheless, that the diverse gene expressions that it may produce stem from one basic mechanism of action and response of the component elements of the system. The action of the *Spm* element resembles that of the regulator "gene" in bacteria. It may well be that *Spm* produces a specific repressor substance to which the element of the system at the locus of the gene, the "operator" element, responds by "turning off" gene action. Suppression of gene action requires the presence of this operator element at the locus of the gene. No suppression occurs when an operator element belonging to another system is present at the gene locus, or when the specific operator element of this system is transposed away from the gene locus. In other words, if *Spm* produces a specific repressor substance, then the operator element at the locus of the gene responds only to this specific repressor and to no other. The same principle would apply to all the two-element control systems investigated so far in maize; and in this respect they resemble the two-element control systems in bacteria.

In bacteria, both the operator and the regulator element undergo mutation. The mutations arise from single events, and some of them are reversible. The same applies to the controlling elements in maize. Each can undergo mutation, and each such mutation is produced by a single event. Also, some of them are reversible.

In bacteria, most of the control systems that are subject to analysis effect control of production of specific enzymes in response to certain changes in the cellular environment. A "turning on" and "turning off" of gene action constitute an efficient means of control of production of enzymes in response to changes in intracellular environment. Mutations, such as those that occur with the class I states described above, would effect a differentiation. Some of them could be lethal or could result in competitive disadvantage for unicellular organisms. In higher organisms, such mutations, occurring in somatic tissues, need not be lethal or disadvantageous and, indeed, may be required. Specific types of mutation occurring at given times during development and produced by a control system, such as the *Spm* system, may effect tissue differentiation along certain paths. However, as emphasized above, the *Spm* system can operate in either way—in a manner similar to that exhibited in bacteria, or in a manner that accomplishes a permanent and specific type of change in gene action.

The class II states of gene loci under the control of the *Spm* system best illustrate the similarities in mode of operation of the bacterial and the maize systems. The "operator" element is fixed in location. No transpositions of it away from the gene locus occur, nor does it effect mutation at the gene locus. Its behavior is much the same as that of the operator "gene" in bacteria. If *Spm* produces a specific repressor substance, then the operator element responds to this by "turning off" gene action. If the repressor substance is not produced, or if its structure is modified by mutations that occur to *Spm*, then gene action is "turned on." A class II state, with its operator element fixed in position and an *Spm* element that also is fixed in position, gives rise to a system of control of gene action in maize that simulates in its mode of operation some of the described systems in bacteria. As stated earlier, cases of effective fixation of *Spm* at a specific locus have been found.

Study of the *Spm* system has shown that a relatively simple system of control of gene action may be derived from one that originally expressed a seemingly complex pattern of such control and it may be no coincidence that this simple system resembles those recently discovered in bacteria and in phage. It is expected that such a basic mechanism of control of gene action will be operative in all organisms. In higher organisms, lack of means of identifying the components of a control system of this type may be responsible for delay in recognition of their general prevalence, even though there is much genetic and cytological evidence to indicate that control systems do exist. It is anticipated, however, that control systems exhibiting more complex levels of integration will be found in the higher organisms.

LITERATURE CITED

Brink, R. A., 1958, Mutable loci and development of the organism. J. Cellular Comp. Physiol. (Suppl. 1): 169–196.

— 1960, Paramutation and chromosome organization. Quart. Rev. Biol. 35: 120–137.

Buttin, G., F. Jacob and J. Monod, 1960, Synthèse constitutive de galacto-kinase consécutive au développment des bactériophage λ chez *Escherichia coli* K 12. Compt. rend. 250: 2471–2473.

Jacob, F., 1960, Genetic control of viral function. The Harvey Lectures, Ser. 54: 1–39.

Jacob, F., and J. Monod, 1959, Gènes de structure et gènes de régulation dans la biosynthèse des protéins. Compt. rend. 249: 1282–1284.

— 1961, Genetic regulatory mechanisms in the synthesis of proteins. J. Mol. Biol. 2: 318–356.

Jacob, F., D. Perrin, C. Sanchez and J. Monod, 1960, L'opéron: groupe de gènes à expression coordonnée par un opérateur. Compt. rend. 250: 1727–1729.

Jacob, F., P. Schaeffer and E. L. Wollman, 1960, Episomic elements in bacteria. Tenth Symp. Soc. Gen. Microbiol.: 67–91.

Iino, T., 1959, Curly flagellar mutants in Salmonella. Natl. Inst. Genet. (Japan) Ann. Rept. 9: 95.

1960, Unequal recombination in Salmonella. Natl. Inst. Genet. (Japan) Ann. Rept. 10: 112–113.

Iino, T., and J. Lederberg, 1957a, Transductional analysis of phase variation in Salmonella. Natl. Inst. Genet. (Japan) Ann. Rept. 7: 89–91.

1957b, An analysis of monophase variation in Salmonella. Genetics 42: 378.

1958, Transductional analysis of monophasic types of Salmonella. Natl. Inst. Genet. (Japan) Ann. Rept. 8: 101–102.

Laughnan, J. R., 1955, Structural and functional bases for the action of the A alleles in maize. Am. Naturalist 89: 91–103.

Lederberg, J., and T. Iino, 1956, Phase variation in Salmonella. Genetics 41: 743–757.

McClintock, B., 1953, Induction of instability at selected loci in maize. Genetics 38: 579–599.

1956a, Intranuclear systems controlling gene action and mutation. Brookhaven Symp. Biol. 8: 58–74.

1956b, Controlling elements and the gene. Cold Spring Harbor Symp. Quant. Biol. 21: 197–216.

1956c, Mutation in maize. Carnegie Inst. Wash. Yrb. No. 55: 323–332.

1957, Genetic and cytological studies of maize. Carnegie Inst. Wash. Yrb. No. 56: 393–401.

1958, The Suppressor-mutator system of control of gene action in maize. Carnegie Inst. Wash. Yrb. No. 57: 415–429.

1959, Genetic and cytological studies of maize. Carnegie Inst. Wash. Yrb. No. 58: 452–456.

Peterson, P. A., 1960, The pale green mutable system in maize. Genetics 45: 115–133.

Richter, A., 1961, Attachment of wild type F factor to a specific chromosomal region in a variant strain of *Escherichia coli* K 12: The phenomenon of episomic alternation. Genet. Res. 2 (in press).

Sarma, M. S., 1959, A test of the mutational hypothesis for the origin of the noncrossover alpha derivatives from A^b:P and A^b:Ec. Maize Genet. Cooperation News Letter 33: 44-48.

1961, Colorless components of the A^b:Ec and A^b:P complexes in maize. Maize Genet. Cooperation News Letter 35: 47–50.

Yarmolinsky, M. B., and H. Wiesmeyer, 1960, Regulation of coliphage *lambda* of the expression of the capacity to synthesize a sequence of host enzymes. Proc. Natl. Acad. Sci. U.S. 46: 1626–1645.

SECTION II
The Nature of Genetic Material

Introduction

The idea that nucleic acid is the physical basis of inheritance is not new. Before 1900, as a result of the work of Miescher (1896), Kossel (1896), and Mathews (1897), the chromatin of sperm nuclei (in fishes and sea urchins) was shown to be composed of a salt of nucleinic acid (nucleic acid) with histone or protamine. Miescher's analysis gave 60.56% nucleic acid and 35.56% protamine for salmon spermatozoa, and Kossel's analysis showed herring sperm chromatin to be over 63% nucleic acid combined with a protamine called clupein. Mathews reported the chromatin in sea urchin sperm to be a compound of nucleic acid and a histone, "arbacin." Kossel also found that chromatin (nuclein) derived from thymus gland and leucocytes is largely a histone salt of nucleic acid. True nucleinic acid (now called DNA) found in chromatin was already distinguished from pseudo-nucleinic acid (now called RNA) known to occur characteristically in the cytoplasm, where no true nucleinic acid was found.

To get an idea of the evaluation of a leading biologist of the period, I quote again from Wilson's 1900 edition of "The Cell in Development and Inheritance" (pp. 358–359). "The periodic changes of staining-capacity undergone by the chromatin during the cycle of cell-life, taken in connection with the researches of physiological chemists on the chemical composition and staining-reactions of the nuclein series, indicate that the phosphorus-rich substance known as *nucleinic acid* plays a leading part in the constructive process. During the vegetative phases of the cell this substance is combined with a large amount of the albumin radicles histon, protamin, and related substances, and probably in part with albumin itself, to form nuclein. During the mitotic or reproductive processes this combination appears to be dissolved, the albuminous elements being in large part split off, leaving the substance of the chromosomes with a high percentage of nucleinic acid, as is shown by direct analysis of the sperm-nucleus and is indicated by staining-reactions of chromosomes. There is, therefore, considerable ground for the hypothesis that in a chemical sense this substance is the most essential nuclear element handed on from cell to cell, whether by cell division or by fertilization; and that it may be a primary factor in the constructive processes of the nucleus and through these be indirectly concerned with those of the cytoplasm."

Wilson also points out that the spermatozoon is as potent in inheritance as the ovum even though the former contributes an amount of cytoplasm which is an infinitesimal fraction of that supplied by the ovum. However, his optomistic evaluation of the role of nucleic acid was forgotten or largely ignored during the next fifty years. Perhaps this may be attributed to the chemists whose analyses indicated that the nucleic acids were simpler substances than the proteins and most likely composed of simple, repeating tetranucleotide units. By the time Wilson wrote his third edition of "The Cell in Development and Heredity" published in 1925, he expressed the prevalent view that the proteinaceous component was of most importance in cellular inheritance and that the nucleic acid was variable and transitory. Certainly the widely held view among geneticists, as well as biochemists, was that biological specificity resided in proteins and many were reluctant to accept the evidence that DNA was genetic material even after Avery *et al.* [(1944), see first paper in this section] provided good evidence that it was the transforming principle. We find statements such as those by Caspersson and Schultz (1938) to the effect that the DNA is probably concerned with gene reproduction, but few if any were willing to suggest that it formed the physical basis of inheritance. It is remarkable that a volume ("Genetics in the 20th Century," edited by L. C. Dunn, 1951) summarizing the progress of genetics during its first fifty years (1900–1950) mentions the work of Avery, MacLeod, and McCarty only in one paper and in this instance spends considerably more space pointing out why DNA might not be the active principle than in describing the experiments which supported the hypothesis that DNA is the genetic material.

The achievements and growth of the new science of genetics in the first fifty years of this century was indeed a record of which its mentors could be proud. However, there is little evidence that many of them could foresee the events of the next decade. Their ranks were to be invaded by chemists, physicists, microbiologists and a new breed of biologists who had begun to think of themselves as molecular biologists. Many of these intruders had little knowledge or appreciation of the details of what would soon be called classical genetics, but they came with enthusiasm and a bagful of techniques to ask and solve the most fundamental question of all time—what is life? The question had been phrased many times, but Erwin Schrödinger's little book (1945) of that title was typical of the kind of questioning which appealed to a new generation who thought they saw the means to answer. They selected the simplest biological systems, learned quickly the pertinent details, cut through the morass of entangling facts to ask simple questions and came to expect quick solutions. Of course, like most surprise attacks the evidence of their presence had been evident long before to discerning observers (see the paper by Schrader, 1948). Wendel Stanley's (1935a,b) isolation and crystallization of tobacco mosiac virus (TMV) was not only a signal achievement, but a forecast of events to come. However, it would be years before the role of the two components of TMV, RNA and protein, would be fully understood [Fraenkel-Conrat and Singer (1957), last paper in this section].

The discovery by Griffith in 1928, that heat-killed bacteria injected in a mouse could confer their virulence on another related type of *Pneumococcus* growing *in vivo*, initiated a series of experiments which resulted in the demonstration of the same type of transformation *in vitro* (Dawson and Sia, 1931; Alloway, 1933). The investigations finally culminated in the isolation and characterization of the transforming principle. The report of these results by Avery, MacLeod, and McCarty is reprinted as the first paper in this section. Although it would be several years before these results would cease to be questioned as a special case or due to the minute amounts of contaminating proteins, attention was turned to the chemistry of nucleic acids. In addition the long neglected work begun by Miescher, Kossel, Altmann, and others in the last quarter of the century would be reviewed and expanded. The second paper in our selection (Pollister and Mirsky, 1946) is an example. A milder method for isolating highly polymerized DNA was devised and there was an attempt to account for all of the components of the sperm heads of trout. The best estimate indicated that 90% of the dry mass was DNA and protamine, but this left what might be a significant fraction unaccounted for. If one were willing to discount the role of the major fraction of material contributed by the sperm, it was still possible that genetic specificity resided in an unidentified protein component. Further work by Mirsky and Ris (1947, 1949) on isolated chromosomes or chromatin threads emphasized the possible role of a protein fraction, which they called residual protein, because it was not soluble in molar sodium chloride.

Other evidence that DNA was the genetic component was its slow metabolic turnover as measured in isotopic incorporation studies (Hammarsten and Hevesy, 1946) and its constancy per genome. Papers by Boivin, Vendrely, and Vendrely (the third one reprinted in this section) and another by Mirsky and Ris (1949) pointed out the constancy by comparing the amount of DNA in sperm nuclei and somatic cell nuclei. In addition when the amount of DNA per nucleus from a species was compared at different stages of the cell division cycle (Swift, 1950a,b), the amount varied in the manner predicted if a doubling occurred prior to each division and the DNA present was equally distributed to the two daughter nuclei. The second of Swift's papers (1950b) on this subject is reprinted here as an example of the work in this area. More extensive reviews will be found by Swift (1955) and Walker (1956).

Work on the genetics of certain viruses (phages) which parasitize *Escherichia coli* had been developing under the leadership of Luria (1945), Delbruck (Luria and Delbruck, 1943), and Hershey (1946). Hershey and Chase [(1952), see fifth paper in this section] were able to demonstrate in a simple experiment utilizing the isotopic labeling techniques that nearly all of the protein was left outside the cell upon infection while the DNA was injected. This important paper is reprinted as the fifth paper in this section. Not only was this a clear demonstration of the importance of DNA in reproducing the whole phage, but the experiments came at a time when the molecular complexity of DNA could be better appreciated from the work on its chemistry (see the next section on the structure and replication of DNA).

The final paper in this section (Fraenkel-Conrat and Singer) demonstrates the role of RNA in genetic transmission in a most convincing way by means of elegant manipulations of macromolecules. This crowning achievement demonstrating the role of nucleic acid in genetic specificity, has at last brought us to a full turnabout—perhaps to a point where we discount too much the possible role of the protein component which accompanies the DNA in sperm nuclei.

REFERENCES

Alloway, J. L. (1933). *J. Exptl. Med.* **57,** 265.

Casperson, T., and Schultz, J. (1938). *Nature* **142,** 294.

Dawson, M. H., and Sia, R. H. P. (1931). *J. Exptl. Med.* **54,** 681.

Dunn, L. C., ed. (1951). "Genetics in the 20th Century." Macmillan, New York.

Griffith, F. (1928). *J. Hyg.* **27,** 113.

Hammarsten, E., and Hevesy, G. (1946). *Acta Physiol. Scand.* **11,** 335.

Hershey, A. D. (1946). *Cold Spring Harbor Symp. Quant. Biol.* **11,** 67.

Kossel, A. (1896). *Z. Physiol. Chem.* **22,** 176.

Luria, S. E. (1945). *Ann. Missouri Bot. Garden* **32,** 235.

Luria, S. E., and Delbruck, M. (1943). *Genetics* **28,** 491.

Mathews, A. P. (1897). *Z. Physiol. Chem.* **23,** 45.

Miescher, F. (1896). *Arch. Exptl. Pathol. Pharmakol.* **37,** 100.

Mirsky, A. E., and Ris, H. (1947). *J. Gen. Physiol.* **31,** 7.

Mirsky, A. E., and Ris, H. (1949). *Nature* **163,** 666.

Schrader, F. (1948). *Science* **107,** 155.

Schrödinger, E. (1945). "What is Life?," 91 pp. Cambridge Univ. Press, London and New York.

Stanley, W. M. (1935a). *Science* **81,** 644.

Stanley, W. M. (1935b). *Phytopathology* **26,** 305.

Swift, H. (1950a). *Physiol. Zool.* **23,** 169.

Swift, H. (1950b). *Proc. Natl. Acad. Sci. U. S.* **36,** 643.

Swift, H. (1955). *In* "The Nucleic Acids" (E. Chargaff and J. N. Davidson, eds.), Vol. II, pp. 51–92. Academic Press, New York.

Walker, P. M. B. (1956). *In* "Physical Techniques in Biological Research" (G. Oster and A. W. Pollister, eds.), Vol. III, pp. 401–487. Academic Press, New York.

Wilson, E. B. (1900). "The Cell in Development and Inheritance." Macmillan, New York.

Wilson, E. B. (1925). "The Cell in Development and Heredity," 3rd ed. Macmillan, New York.

[Reprinted from THE JOURNAL OF EXPERIMENTAL MEDICINE, February 1, 1944, Vol. 79, No. 2, pp. 137–158]

STUDIES ON THE CHEMICAL NATURE OF THE SUBSTANCE INDUCING TRANSFORMATION OF PNEUMOCOCCAL TYPES

INDUCTION OF TRANSFORMATION BY A DESOXYRIBONUCLEIC ACID FRACTION ISOLATED FROM PNEUMOCOCCUS TYPE III

BY OSWALD T. AVERY, M.D., COLIN M. MACLEOD, M.D., AND MACLYN McCARTY,* M.D.

(*From the Hospital of The Rockefeller Institute for Medical Research*)

PLATE 1

(Received for publication, November 1, 1943)

Biologists have long attempted by chemical means to induce in higher organisms predictable and specific changes which thereafter could be transmitted in series as hereditary characters. Among microörganisms the most striking example of inheritable and specific alterations in cell structure and function that can be experimentally induced and are reproducible under well defined and adequately controlled conditions is the transformation of specific types of Pneumococcus. This phenomenon was first described by Griffith (1) who succeeded in transforming an attenuated and non-encapsulated (R) variant derived from one specific type into fully encapsulated and virulent (S) cells of a heterologous specific type. A typical instance will suffice to illustrate the techniques originally used and serve to indicate the wide variety of transformations that are possible within the limits of this bacterial species.

Griffith found that mice injected subcutaneously with a small amount of a living R culture derived from Pneumococcus Type II together with a large inoculum of heat-killed Type III (S) cells frequently succumbed to infection, and that the heart's blood of these animals yielded Type III pneumococci in pure culture. The fact that the R strain was avirulent and incapable by itself of causing fatal bacteremia and the additional fact that the heated suspension of Type III cells contained no viable organisms brought convincing evidence that the R forms growing under these conditions had newly acquired the capsular structure and biological specificity of Type III pneumococci.

The original observations of Griffith were later confirmed by Neufeld and Levinthal (2), and by Baurhenn (3) abroad, and by Dawson (4) in this laboratory. Subsequently Dawson and Sia (5) succeeded in inducing transformation *in vitro*. This they accomplished by growing R cells in a fluid medium containing anti-R serum and heat-killed encapsulated S cells. They showed that in the test tube as in the animal body transformation can be selectively induced, depending on the type specificity of the S cells used in the reaction system. Later, Alloway (6) was able to cause

---

* Work done in part as Fellow in the Medical Sciences of the National Research Council.

specific transformation *in vitro* using sterile extracts of S cells from which all formed elements and cellular debris had been removed by Berkefeld filtration. He thus showed that crude extracts containing active transforming material in soluble form are as effective in inducing specific transformation as are the intact cells from which the extracts were prepared.

Another example of transformation which is analogous to the interconvertibility of pneumococcal types lies in the field of viruses. Berry and Dedrick (7) succeeded in changing the virus of rabbit fibroma (Shope) into that of infectious myxoma (Sanarelli). These investigators inoculated rabbits with a mixture of active fibroma virus together with a suspension of heat-inactivated myxoma virus and produced in the animals the symptoms and pathological lesions characteristic of infectious myxomatosis. On subsequent animal passage the transformed virus was transmissible and induced myxomatous infection typical of the naturally occurring disease. Later Berry (8) was successful in inducing the same transformation using a heat-inactivated suspension of washed elementary bodies of myxoma virus. In the case of these viruses the methods employed were similar in principle to those used by Griffith in the transformation of pneumococcal types. These observations have subsequently been confirmed by other investigators (9).

The present paper is concerned with a more detailed analysis of the phenomenon of transformation of specific types of Pneumococcus. The major interest has centered in attempts to isolate the active principle from crude bacterial extracts and to identify if possible its chemical nature or at least to characterize it sufficiently to place it in a general group of known chemical substances. For purposes of study, the typical example of transformation chosen as a working model was the one with which we have had most experience and which consequently seemed best suited for analysis. This particular example represents the transformation of a non-encapsulated R variant of Pneumococcus Type II to Pneumococcus Type III.

EXPERIMENTAL

Transformation of pneumococcal types *in vitro* requires that certain cultural conditions be fulfilled before it is possible to demonstrate the reaction even in the presence of a potent extract. Not only must the broth medium be optimal for growth but it must be supplemented by the addition of serum or serous fluid known to possess certain special properties. Moreover, the R variant, as will be shown later, must be in the reactive phase in which it has the capacity to respond to the transforming stimulus. For purposes of convenience these several components as combined in the transforming test will be referred to as the *reaction system*. Each constituent of this system presented problems which required clarification before it was possible to obtain consistent and reproducible results. The various components of the system will be described in the following order: (1) nutrient broth, (2) serum or serous fluid, (3) strain of R Pneumococcus, and (4) extraction, purification, and chemical nature of the transforming principle.

1. Nutrient Broth.—Beef heart infusion broth containing 1 per cent neopeptone with no added dextrose and adjusted to an initial pH of 7.6–7.8 is used as the basic medium. Individual lots of broth show marked and unpredictable variations in the property of supporting transformation. It has been found, however, that charcoal adsorption, according to the method described by MacLeod and Mirick (10) for removal of sulfonamide inhibitors, eliminates to a large extent these variations; consequently this procedure is used as routine in the preparation of consistently effective broth for titrating the transforming activity of extracts.

2. Serum or Serous Fluid.—In the first successful experiments on the induction of transformation *in vitro*, Dawson and Sia (5) found that it was essential to add serum to the medium. Anti-R pneumococcal rabbit serum was used because of the observation that reversion of an R pneumococcus to the homologous S form can be induced by growth in a medium containing anti-R serum. Alloway (6) later found that ascitic or chest fluid and normal swine serum, all of which contain R antibodies, are capable of replacing antipneumococcal rabbit serum in the reaction system. Some form of serum is essential, and to our knowledge transformation *in vitro* has never been effected in the absence of serum or serous fluid.

In the present study human pleural or ascitic fluid has been used almost exclusively. It became apparent, however, that the effectiveness of different lots of serum varied and that the differences observed were not necessarily dependent upon the content of R antibodies, since many sera of high titer were found to be incapable of supporting transformation. This fact suggested that factors other than R antibodies are involved.

It has been found that sera from various animal species, irrespective of their immune properties, contain an enzyme capable of destroying the transforming principle in potent extracts. The nature of this enzyme and the specific substrate on which it acts will be referred to later in this paper. This enzyme is inactivated by heating the serum at 60°–65°C., and sera heated at temperatures known to destroy the enzyme are often rendered effective in the transforming system. Further analysis has shown that certain sera in which R antibodies are present and in which the enzyme has been inactivated may nevertheless fail to support transformation. This fact suggests that still another factor in the serum is essential. The content of this factor varies in different sera, and at present its identity is unknown.

There are at present no criteria which can be used as a guide in the selection of suitable sera or serous fluids except that of actually testing their capacity to support transformation. Fortunately, the requisite properties are stable and remain unimpaired over long periods of time; and sera that have been stored in the refrigerator for many months have been found on retesting to have lost little or none of their original effectiveness in supporting transformation.

The recognition of these various factors in serum and their rôle in the reaction system has greatly facilitated the standardization of the cultural conditions required for obtaining consistent and reproducible results.

3. The R Strain (R36A).—The unencapsulated R strain used in the present study was derived from a virulent "S" culture of Pneumococcus Type II. It will be recalled that irrespective of type derivation all "R" variants of Pneumococcus are characterized by the lack of capsule formation and the consequent loss of both type specificity and the capacity to produce infection in the animal body. The designation of these variants as R forms has been used to refer merely to the fact that on artificial media the colony surface is "rough" in contrast to the smooth, glistening surface of colonies of encapsulated S cells.

The R strain referred to above as R36A was derived by growing the parent S culture of Pneumococcus Type II in broth containing Type II antipneumococcus rabbit serum for 36 serial passages and isolating the variant thus induced. The strain R36A has lost all the specific and distinguishing characteristics of the parent S organisms and consists only of attenuated and non-encapsulated R variants. The change S → R is often a reversible one provided the R cells are not too far "degraded." The reversion of the R form to its original specific type can frequently be accomplished by successive animal passages or by repeated serial subculture in anti-R serum. When reversion occurs under these conditions, however, the R culture invariably reverts to the encapsulated form of the same specific type as that from which it was derived (11). Strain R36A has become relatively fixed in the R phase and has never spontaneously reverted to the Type II S form. Moreover, repeated attempts to cause it to revert under the conditions just mentioned have in all instances been unsuccessful.

The reversible conversion of S⇌R within the limits of a single type is quite different from the transformation of one specific type of Pneumococcus into another specific type through the R form. Transformation of types has never been observed to occur spontaneously and has been induced experimentally only by the special techniques outlined earlier in this paper. Under these conditions, the enzymatic synthesis of a chemically and immunologically different capsular polysaccharide is specifically oriented and selectively determined by the specific type of S cells used as source of the transforming agent.

In the course of the present study it was noted that the stock culture of R36 on serial transfers in blood broth undergoes spontaneous dissociation giving rise to a number of other R variants which can be distinguished one from another by colony form. The significance of this in the present instance lies in the fact that of four different variants isolated from the parent R culture only one (R36A) is susceptible to the transforming action of potent extracts, while the others fail to respond and are wholly inactive in this regard. The fact that differences exist in the responsiveness of different R variants to the same specific stimulus emphasizes the care that must be exercised in the selection of a suitable R variant for use in experiments on transformation. The capacity of this R strain (R36A) to respond to a variety of different transforming agents is shown by the readiness with which it can be transformed to Types I, III, VI, or XIV, as well as to its original type (Type II), to which, as pointed out, it has never spontaneously reverted.

Although the significance of the following fact will become apparent later on, it must be mentioned here that pneumococcal cells possess an enzyme capable of destroying the activity of the transforming principle. Indeed, this enzyme has been found to be present and highly active in the autolysates of a number of different strains. The fact that this intracellular enzyme is released during autolysis may explain, in part at least, the observation of Dawson and Sia (5) that it is essential in bringing about transformation in the test tube to use a small inoculum of young and actively growing R cells. The irregularity of the results and often the failure to induce transformation when large inocula are used may be attributable to the release from autolyzing cells of an amount of this enzyme sufficient to destroy the transforming principle in the reaction system.

In order to obtain consistent and reproducible results, two facts must be borne in mind: first, that an R culture can undergo spontaneous dissociation and give rise to other variants which have lost the capacity to respond to the transforming stimulus; and secondly, that pneumococcal cells contain an intracellular enzyme which when released destroys the activity of the transforming principle. Consequently, it is important to select a responsive strain and to prevent as far as possible the destructive changes associated with autolysis.

Method of Titration of Transforming Activity.—In the isolation and purification of the active principle from crude extracts of pneumococcal cells it is desirable to have a method for determining quantitatively the transforming activity of various fractions.

The experimental procedure used is as follows: Sterilization of the material to be tested for activity is accomplished by the use of alcohol since it has been found that this reagent has no effect on activity. A measured volume of extract is precipitated in a sterile centrifuge tube by the addition of 4 to 5 volumes of absolute ethyl alcohol, and the mixture is allowed to stand 8 or more hours in the refrigerator in order to effect sterilization. The alcohol precipitated material is centrifuged, the supernatant discarded, and the tube containing the precipitate is allowed to drain for a few minutes in the inverted position to remove excess alcohol. The mouth of the tube is then carefully flamed and a dry, sterile cotton plug is inserted. The precipitate is redissolved in the original volume of saline. Sterilization of active material by this technique has invariably proved effective. This procedure avoids the loss of active substance which may occur when the solution is passed through a Berkefeld filter or is heated at the high temperatures required for sterilization.

To the charcoal-adsorbed broth described above is added 10 per cent of the sterile ascitic or pleural fluid which has previously been heated at 60°C. for 30 minutes, in order to destroy the enzyme known to inactivate the transforming principle. The enriched medium is distributed under aseptic conditions in 2.0 cc. amounts in sterile tubes measuring 15 × 100 mm. The sterilized extract is diluted serially in saline neutralized to pH 7.2–7.6 by addition of 0.1 N NaOH, or it may be similarly diluted in M/40 phosphate buffer, pH 7.4. 0.2 cc. of each dilution is added to at least 3 or 4 tubes of the serum medium. The tubes are then seeded with a 5 to 8 hour blood broth culture of R36A. 0.05 cc. of a 10^{-4} dilution of this culture is added to each tube, and the cultures are incubated at 37°C. for 18 to 24 hours.

The anti-R properties of the serum in the medium cause the R cells to agglutinate during growth, and clumps of the agglutinated cells settle to the bottom of the tube leaving a clear supernatant. When transformation occurs, the encapsulated S cells, not being affected by these antibodies, grow diffusely throughout the medium. On the other hand, in the absence of transformation the supernatant remains clear, and only sedimented growth of R organisms occurs. This difference in the character of growth makes it possible by inspection alone to distinguish tentatively between positive and negative results. As routine all the cultures are plated on blood agar for confirmation and further bacteriological identification. Since the extracts used in the present study were derived from Pneumococcus Type III, the differentiation between the colonies of the original R organism and those of the transformed S cells is especially striking, the latter being large, glistening, mucoid colonies typical of Pneumococcus Type III. Figs. 1 and 2 illustrate these differences in colony form.

A typical protocol of a titration of the transforming activity of a highly purified preparation is given in Table IV.

Preparative Methods

Source Material.—In the present investigation a stock laboratory strain of Pneumococcus Type III (A66) has been used as source material for obtaining the active principle. Mass cultures of these organisms are grown in 50 to 75 liter lots of plain beef heart infusion broth. After 16 to 18 hours' incubation at 37°C. the bacterial cells are collected in a steam-driven sterilizable Sharples centrifuge. The centrifuge is equipped with cooling coils immersed in ice water so that the culture fluid is thoroughly chilled before flowing into the machine. This procedure retards autolysis during the course of centrifugation. The sedimented bacteria are removed from the collecting cylinder and resuspended in approximately 150 cc. of chilled saline (0.85 per cent NaCl), and care is taken that all clumps are thoroughly emulsified. The glass vessel containing the thick, creamy suspension of cells is immersed in a water bath, and the temperature of the suspension rapidly raised to 65°C. During the heating process the material is constantly stirred, and the temperature maintained at 65°C. for 30 minutes. Heating at this temperature inactivates the intracellular enzyme known to destroy the transforming principle.

Extraction of Heat-Killed Cells.—Although various procedures have been used, only that which has been found most satisfactory will be described here. The heat-killed cells are washed with saline 3 times. The chief value of the washing process is to remove a large excess of capsular polysaccharide together with much of the protein, ribonucleic acid, and somatic "C" polysaccharide. Quantitative titrations of transforming activity have shown that not more than 10 to 15 per cent of the active material is lost in the washing, a loss which is small in comparison to the amount of inert substances which are removed by this procedure.

After the final washing, the cells are extracted in 150 cc. of saline containing sodium desoxycholate in final concentration of 0.5 per cent by shaking the mixture mechanically 30 to 60 minutes. The cells are separated by centrifugation, and the extraction process is repeated 2 or 3 times. The desoxycholate extracts prepared in this manner are clear and colorless. These extracts are combined and precipitated by the addition of 3 to 4 volumes of absolute ethyl alcohol. The sodium desoxycholate being soluble in alcohol remains in the supernatant and is thus removed at this step. The precipitate forms a fibrous mass which floats to the surface of the alcohol and can be removed directly by lifting it out with a spatula. The excess alcohol is drained from the precipitate which is then redissolved in about 50 cc. of saline. The solution obtained is usually viscous, opalescent, and somewhat cloudy.

Deproteinization and Removal of Capsular Polysaccharide.—The solution is then deproteinized by the chloroform method described by Sevag (12). The procedure is repeated 2 or 3 times until the solution becomes clear. After this preliminary treatment the material is reprecipitated in 3 to 4 volumes of alcohol. The precipitate obtained is dissolved in a larger volume of saline (150 cc.) to which is added 3 to 5 mg. of a purified preparation of the bacterial enzyme capable of hydrolyzing the Type III capsular polysaccharide (13). The mixture is incubated at 37°C., and the destruction of the capsular polysaccharide is determined by serological tests with Type III antibody solution prepared by dissociation of immune precipitate according to the method described by Liu and Wu (14). The advantages of using the antibody solution for this purpose are that it does not react with other serologically active substances in the extract and that it selectively detects the presence of the capsular polysaccharide in dilutions as high as 1:6,000,000. The enzymatic breakdown of the polysaccharide is usually complete within 4 to 6 hours, as evidenced by the loss of serological reactivity. The digest is then precipitated in 3 to 4 volumes of ethyl alcohol, and the precipitate is redissolved in 50 cc. of saline. Deproteinization by the chloroform process is again used to remove the added enzyme protein and remaining traces of pneumococcal protein. The procedure is repeated until no further film of protein-chloroform gel is visible at the interface.

Alcohol Fractionation.—Following deproteinization and enzymatic digestion of the capsular polysaccharide, the material is repeatedly fractionated in ethyl alcohol as follows. Absolute ethyl alcohol is added dropwise to the solution with constant stirring. At a critical concentration varying from 0.8 to 1.0 volume of alcohol the active material separates out in the form of fibrous strands that wind themselves around the stirring rod. This precipitate is removed on the rod and washed in a 50 per cent mixture of alcohol and saline. Although the bulk of active material is removed by fractionation at the critical concentration, a small but appreciable amount remains in solution. However, upon increasing the concentration of alcohol to 3 volumes, the residual fraction is thrown down together with inert material in the form of a flocculent precipitate. This flocculent precipitate is taken up in a small volume of saline (5 to 10 cc.) and the solution again fractionated by the addition of 0.8 to 1.0 volume of alcohol. Additional fibrous material is obtained which is combined with that recovered from the original solution. Alcoholic fractionation is repeated 4 to 5 times. The yield of fibrous material obtained by this method varies from 10 to 25 mg. per 75 liters of culture and represents the major portion of active material present in the original crude extract.

Effect of Temperature.—As a routine procedure all steps in purification were carried out at room temperature unless specifically stated otherwise. Because of the theoretical advantage of working at low temperature in the preparation of biologically active material, the purification of one lot (preparation 44) was carried out in the cold. In this instance all the above procedures with the exception of desoxycholate extraction and enzyme treatment were conducted in a cold room maintained at 0–4°C. This preparation proved to have significantly higher activity than did material similarly prepared at room temperature.

Desoxycholate extraction of the heat-killed cells at low temperature is less efficient and yields smaller amounts of the active fraction. It has been demonstrated that higher temperatures facilitate extraction of the active principle, although activity is best preserved at low temperatures.

Analysis of Purified Transforming Material

General Properties.—Saline solutions containing 0.5 to 1.0 mg. per cc. of the purified substance are colorless and clear in diffuse light. However, in strong transmitted light the solution is not entirely clear and when stirred exhibits a silky sheen. Solutions at these concentrations are highly viscous.

Purified material dissolved in physiological salt solution and stored at 2–4°C. retains its activity in undiminished titer for at least 3 months. However, when dissolved in distilled water, it rapidly decreases in activity and becomes completely inert within a few days. Saline solutions stored in the frozen state in a CO_2 ice box (−70°C.) retain full potency for several months. Similarly, material precipitated from saline solution by alcohol and stored under the supernatant remains active over a long period of time. Partially purified material can be preserved by drying from the frozen state in the lyophile apparatus. However, when the same procedure is used for the preservation of the highly purified substance, it is found that the material undergoes changes resulting in decrease in solubility and loss of activity.

The activity of the transforming principle in crude extracts withstands heating for 30 to 60 minutes at 65°C. Highly purified preparations of active material are less stable, and some loss of activity occurs at this temperature. A quantitative study of the effect of heating purified material at higher temperatures has not as yet been made. Alloway (6), using crude extracts prepared from Type III pneumococcal cells, found that occasionally activity could still be demonstrated after 10 minutes' exposure in the water bath to temperatures as high as 90°C.

The procedures mentioned above were carried out with solutions adjusted to neutral reaction, since it has been shown that hydrogen ion concentrations in the acid range result in progressive loss of activity. Inactivation occurs rapidly at pH 5 and below.

Qualitative Chemical Tests.—The purified material in concentrated solution gives negative biuret and Millon tests. These tests have been done directly on dry material with negative results. The Dische diphenylamine reaction for desoxyribonucleic acid is strongly positive. The orcinol test (Bial) for ribonucleic acid is weakly positive. However, it has been found that in similar concentrations pure preparations of desoxyribonucleic acid of animal origin prepared by different methods give a Bial reaction of corresponding intensity.

Although no specific tests for the presence of lipid in the purified material have been made, it has been found that crude material can be repeatedly extracted with alcohol and ether at $-12°C$. without loss of activity. In addition, as will be noted in the preparative procedures, repeated alcohol precipitation and treatment with chloroform result in no decrease in biological activity.

Elementary Chemical Analysis.[1]—Four purified preparations were analyzed for content of nitrogen, phosphorus, carbon, and hydrogen. The results are presented in Table I. The nitrogen-phosphorus ratios vary from 1.58 to 1.75 with an average value of 1.67 which is in close agreement with that calculated

TABLE I

Elementary Chemical Analysis of Purified Preparations of the Transforming Substance

Preparation No.	Carbon	Hydrogen	Nitrogen	Phosphorus	N/P ratio
	per cent	*per cent*	*per cent*	*per cent*	
37	34.27	3.89	14.21	8.57	1.66
38B	—	—	15.93	9.09	1.75
42	35.50	3.76	15.36	9.04	1.69
44	—	—	13.40	8.45	1.58
Theory for sodium desoxyribonucleate.....	34.20	3.21	15.32	9.05	1.69

on the basis of the theoretical structure of sodium desoxyribonucleate (tetranucleotide). The analytical figures by themselves do not establish that the substance isolated is a pure chemical entity. However, on the basis of the nitrogen-phosphorus ratio, it would appear that little protein or other substances containing nitrogen or phosphorus are present as impurities since if they were this ratio would be considerably altered.

Enzymatic Analysis.—Various crude and crystalline enzymes[2] have been tested for their capacity to destroy the biological activity of potent bacterial extracts. Extracts buffered at the optimal pH, to which were added crystalline trypsin and chymotrypsin or combinations of both, suffered no loss in activity following treatment with these enzymes. Pepsin could not be tested because

[1] The elementary chemical analyses were made by Dr. A. Elek of The Rockefeller Institute.

[2] The authors are indebted to Dr. John H. Northrop and Dr. M. Kunitz of The Rockefeller Institute for Medical Research, Princeton, N. J., for the samples of crystalline trypsin, chymotrypsin, and ribonuclease used in this work.

extracts are rapidly inactivated at the low pH required for its use. Prolonged treatment with crystalline ribonuclease under optimal conditions caused no demonstrable decrease in transforming activity. The fact that trypsin, chymotrypsin, and ribonuclease had no effect on the transforming principle is further evidence that this substance is not ribonucleic acid or a protein susceptible to the action of tryptic enzymes.

In addition to the crystalline enzymes, sera and preparations of enzymes obtained from the organs of various animals were tested to determine their effect on transforming activity. Certain of these were found to be capable of completely destroying biological activity. The various enzyme preparations tested included highly active phosphatases obtained from rabbit bone by the method of Martland and Robison (15) and from swine kidney as described by

TABLE II

The Inactivation of Transforming Principle by Crude Enzyme Preparations

Crude enzyme preparations	Enzymatic activity			
	Phosphatase	Tributyrin esterase	Depolymerase for desoxyribonucleate	Inactivation of transforming principle
Dog intestinal mucosa....................	+	+	+	+
Rabbit bone phosphatase.................	+	+	−	−
Swine kidney "	+	−	−	−
Pneumococcus autolysates................	−	+	+	+
Normal dog and rabbit serum............	+	+	+	+

H. and E. Albers (16). In addition, a preparation made from the intestinal mucosa of dogs by Levene and Dillon (17) and containing a polynucleotidase for thymus nucleic acid was used. Pneumococcal autolysates and a commercial preparation of pancreatin were also tested. The alkaline phosphatase activity of these preparations was determined by their action on β-glycerophosphate and phenyl phosphate, and the esterase activity by their capacity to split tributyrin. Since the highly purified transforming material isolated from pneumococcal extracts was found to contain desoxyribonucleic acid, these same enzymes were tested for depolymerase activity on known samples of desoxyribonucleic acid isolated by Mirsky[3] from fish sperm and mammalian tissues. The results are summarized in Table II in which the phosphatase, esterase, and nucleodepolymerase activity of these enzymes is compared with their capacity to destroy the transforming principle. Analysis of these results shows that irrespective of the presence of phosphatase or esterase only those

[3] The authors express their thanks to Dr. A. E. Mirsky of the Hospital of The Rockefeller Institute for these preparations of desoxyribonucleic acid.

preparations shown to contain an enzyme capable of depolymerizing authentic samples of desoxyribonucleic acid were found to inactivate the transforming principle.

Greenstein and Jenrette (18) have shown that tissue extracts, as well as the milk and serum of several mammalian species, contain an enzyme system which causes depolymerization of desoxyribonucleic acid. To this enzyme system Greenstein has later given the name desoxyribonucleodepolymerase (19). These investigators determined depolymerase activity by following the reduction in viscosity of solutions of sodium desoxyribonucleate. The nucleate and enzyme were mixed in the viscosimeter and viscosity measurements made at intervals during incubation at 30°C. In the present study this method was used in the measurement of depolymerase activity except that incubation was carried out at 37°C. and, in addition to the reduction of viscosity, the action of the enzyme was further tested by the progressive decrease in acid precipitability of the nucleate during enzymatic breakdown.

The effect of fresh normal dog and rabbit serum on the activity of the transforming substance is shown in the following experiment.

Sera obtained from a normal dog and normal rabbit were diluted with an equal volume of physiological saline. The diluted serum was divided into three equal portions. One part was heated at 65°C. for 30 minutes, another at 60°C. for 30 minutes, and the third was used unheated as control. A partially purified preparation of transforming material which had previously been dried in the lyophile apparatus was dissolved in saline in a concentration of 3.7 mg. per cc. 1.0 cc. of this solution was mixed with 0.5 cc. of the various samples of heated and unheated diluted sera, and the mixtures at pH 7.4 were incubated at 37°C. for 2 hours. After the serum had been allowed to act on the transforming material for this period, all tubes were heated at 65°C. for 30 minutes to stop enzymatic action. Serial dilutions were then made in saline and tested in triplicate for transforming activity according to the procedure described under Method of titration. The results given in Table III illustrate the differential heat inactivation of the enzymes in dog and rabbit serum which destroy the transforming principle.

From the data presented in Table III it is evident that both dog and rabbit serum in the unheated state are capable of completely destroying transforming activity. On the other hand, when samples of dog serum which have been heated either at 60°C. or at 65°C. for 30 minutes are used, there is no loss of transforming activity. Thus, in this species the serum enzyme responsible for destruction of the transforming principle is completely inactivated at 60°C. In contrast to these results, exposure to 65°C. for 30 minutes was required for complete destruction of the corresponding enzyme in rabbit serum.

The same samples of dog and rabbit serum used in the preceding experiment were also tested for their depolymerase activity on a preparation of sodium desoxyribonucleate isolated by Mirsky from shad sperm.

A highly viscous solution of the nucleate in distilled water in a concentration of 1 mg. per cc. was used. 1.0 cc. amounts of heated and unheated sera diluted in saline as shown in the preceding protocol were mixed in Ostwald viscosimeters with 4.0 cc.

TABLE III

Differential Heat Inactivation of Enzymes in Dog and Rabbit Serum Which Destroy the Transforming Substance

	Heat treatment of serum	Dilution*	Triplicate tests					
			1		2		3	
			Diffuse growth	Colony form	Diffuse growth	Colony form	Diffuse growth	Colony form
Dog serum	Unheated	Undiluted	−	R only	−	R only	−	R only
		1:5	−	R "	−	R "	−	R "
		1:25	−	R "	−	R "	−	R "
	60°C. for 30 min.	Undiluted	+	SIII	+	SIII	+	SIII
		1:5	+	SIII	+	SIII	+	SIII
		1:25	+	SIII	+	SIII	+	SIII
	65°C. for 30 min.	Undiluted	+	SIII	+	SIII	+	SIII
		1:5	+	SIII	+	SIII	+	SIII
		1:25	+	SIII	+	SIII	+	SIII
Rabbit serum	Unheated	Undiluted	−	R only	−	R only	−	R only
		1:5	−	R "	−	R "	−	R "
		1:25	−	R "	−	R "	−	R "
	60°C. for 30 min.	Undiluted	−	R only	−	R only	−	R only
		1:5	−	R "	−	R "	−	R "
		1:25	−	R "	−	R "	−	R "
	65°C. for 30 min.	Undiluted	+	SIII	+	SIII	+	SIII
		1:5	+	SIII	+	SIII	+	SIII
		1:25	+	SIII	+	SIII	+	SIII
Control (no serum)	None	Undiluted	+	SIII	+	SIII	+	SIII
		1:5	+	SIII	+	SIII	+	SIII
		1:25	+	SIII	+	SIII	+	SIII

* Dilution of the digest mixture of serum and transforming substance.

of the aqueous solution of the nucleate. Determinations of viscosity were made immediately and at intervals over a period of 24 hours during incubation at 37°C.

The results of this experiment are graphically presented in Chart 1. In the case of unheated serum of both dog and rabbit, the viscosity fell to that of water in 5 to 7 hours. Dog serum heated at 60°C. for 30 minutes brought about no significant reduction in viscosity after 22 hours.   On the other hand, heating rabbit serum at 60°C. merely reduced the rate of depolymerase action, and after 24 hours the viscosity was brought to the same level as with the unheated serum.   Heating at 65°C., however, completely destoyed the rabbit serum depolymerase.

Thus, in the case of dog and rabbit sera there is a striking parallelism between the temperature of inactivation of the depolymerase and that of the enzyme which destroys the activity of the transforming principle.   The fact that this difference in temperature of inactivation is not merely a general property of all enzymes in the sera is evident from experiments on the heat inactivation of

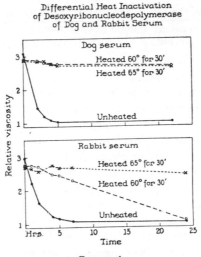

CHART 1

tributyrin esterase in the same samples of serum.   In the latter instance, the results are the reverse of those observed with depolymerase since the esterase of rabbit serum is almost completely inactivated at 60°C. while that in dog serum is only slightly affected by exposure to this temperature.

Of a number of substances tested for their capacity to inhibit the action of the enzyme known to destroy the transforming principle, only sodium fluoride has been found to have a significant inhibitory effect.   Regardless of whether this enzyme is derived from pneumococcal cells, dog intestinal mucosa, pancreatin, or normal sera its activity is inhibited by fluoride.   Similarly it has been found that fluoride in the same concentration also inhibits the enzymatic depolymerization of desoxyribonucleic acid.

The fact that transforming activity is destroyed only by those preparations containing depolymerase for desoxyribonucleic acid and the further fact that in both instances the enzymes concerned are inactivated at the same temperature and inhibited by fluoride provide additional evidence for the belief that the active principle is a nucleic acid of the desoxyribose type.

Serological Analysis.—In the course of chemical isolation of the active material it was found that as crude extracts were purified, their serological activity in Type III antiserum progressively decreased without corresponding loss in biological activity. Solutions of the highly purified substance itself gave only faint trace reactions in precipitin tests with high titer Type III antipneumococcus rabbit serum.[4] It is well known that pneumococcal protein can be detected by serological methods in dilutions as high as 1:50,000 and the capsular as well as the somatic polysaccharide in dilutions of at least 1:5,000,000. In view of these facts, the loss of serological reactivity indicates that these cell constituents have been almost completely removed from the final preparations. The fact that the transforming substance in purified state exhibits little or no serological reactivity is in striking contrast to its biological specificity in inducing pneumococcal transformation.

Physicochemical Studies.[5]—A purified and active preparation of the transforming substance (preparation 44) was examined in the analytical ultracentrigue. The material gave a single and unusually sharp boundary indicating that the substance was homogeneous and that the molecules were uniform in size and very asymmetric. Biological activity was found to be sedimented at the same rate as the optically observed boundary, showing that activity could not be due to the presence of an entity much different in size. The molecular weight cannot be accurately determined until measurements of the diffusion constant and partial specific volume have been made. However, Tennent and Vilbrandt (20) have determined the diffusion constant of several preparations of thymus nucleic acid the sedimentation rate of which is in close agreement with the values observed in the present study. Assuming that the asymmetry of the molecules is the same in both instances, it is estimated that the molecular weight of the pneumococcal preparation is of the order of 500,000.

Examination of the same active preparation was carried out by electrophoresis in the Tiselius apparatus and revealed only a single electrophoretic component of relatively high mobility comparable to that of a nucleic acid. Transforming activity was associated with the fast moving component giving the

[4] The Type III antipneumococcus rabbit serum employed in this study was furnished through the courtesy of Dr. Jules T. Freund, Bureau of Laboratories, Department of Health, City of New York.

[5] Studies on sedimentation in the ultracentrifuge were carried out by Dr. A. Rothen; the electrophoretic analyses were made by Dr. T. Shedlovsky; and the ultraviolet absorption curves by Dr. G. I. Lavin. The authors gratefully acknowledge their indebtedness to these members of the staff of The Rockefeller Institute.

optically visible boundary.   Thus in both the electrical and centrifugal fields, the behavior of the purified substance is consistent with the concept that biological activity is a property of the highly polymerized nucleic acid.

Ultraviolet absorption curves showed maxima in the region of 2600 Å and minima in the region of 2350 Å.   These findings are characteristic of nucleic acids.

Quantitative Determination of Biological Activity.—In its highly purified state the material as isolated has been found to be capable of inducing transformation in amounts ranging from 0.02 to 0.003 μg.   Preparation 44, the purification of which was carried out at low temperature and which had a nitrogen-phosphorus

TABLE IV

Titration of Transforming Activity of Preparation 44

Transforming principle Preparation 44*		Quadruplicate tests							
		1		2		3		4	
Dilution	Amount added	Diffuse growth	Colony form	Diffuse growth	Colony form	Diffuse growth	Colony form	Diffuse growth	Colony form
	μg.								
10^{-2}	1.0	+	SIII	+	SIII	+	SIII	+	SIII
$10^{-2.5}$	0.3	+	SIII	+	SIII	+	SIII	+	SIII
10^{-3}	0.1	+	SIII	+	SIII	+	SIII	+	SIII
$10^{-3.5}$	0.03	+	SIII	+	SIII	+	SIII	+	SIII
10^{-4}	0.01	+	SIII	+	SIII	+	SIII	+	SIII
$10^{-4.5}$	0.003	−	R only	+	SIII	−	R only	+	SIII
10^{-5}	0.001	−	R "	−	R only	−	R "	−	R only
Control	None	−	R "	−	R "	−	R "	−	R "

* Solution from which dilutions were made contained 0.5 mg. per cc. of purified material. 0.2 cc. of each dilution added to quadruplicate tubes containing 2.0 cc. of standard serum broth.   0.05 cc. of a 10^{-4} dilution of a blood broth culture of R36A is added to each tube.

ratio of 1.58, exhibited high transforming activity.   Titration of the activity of this preparation is given in Table IV.

A solution containing 0.5 mg. per cc. was serially diluted as shown in the protocol. 0.2 cc. of each of these dilutions was added to quadruplicate tubes containing 2.0 cc. of standard serum broth.   All tubes were then inoculated with 0.05 cc. of a 10^{-4} dilution of a 5 to 8 hour blood broth culture of R36A.   Transforming activity was determined by the procedure described under Method of titration.

The data presented in Table IV show that on the basis of dry weight 0.003 μg. of the active material brought about transformation.   Since the reaction system containing the 0.003 μg. has a volume of 2.25 cc., this represents a final concentration of the purified substance of 1 part in 600,000,000.

DISCUSSION

The present study deals with the results of an attempt to determine the chemical nature of the substance inducing specific transformation of pneumococcal types. A desoxyribonucleic acid fraction has been isolated from Type III pneumococci which is capable of transforming unencapsulated R variants derived from Pneumococcus Type II into fully encapsulated Type III cells. Thompson and Dubos (21) have isolated from pneumococci a nucleic acid of the ribose type. So far as the writers are aware, however, a nucleic acid of the desoxyribose type has not heretofore been recovered from pneumococci nor has specific transformation been experimentally induced *in vitro* by a chemically defined substance.

Although the observations are limited to a single example, they acquire broader significance from the work of earlier investigators who demonstrated the interconvertibility of various pneumococcal types and showed that the specificity of the changes induced is in each instance determined by the particular type of encapsulated cells used to evoke the reaction. From the point of view of the phenomenon in general, therefore, it is of special interest that in the example studied, highly purified and protein-free material consisting largely, if not exclusively, of desoxyribonucleic acid is capable of stimulating unencapsulated R variants of Pneumococcus Type II to produce a capsular polysaccharide identical in type specificity with that of the cells from which the inducing substance was isolated. Equally striking is the fact that the substance evoking the reaction and the capsular substance produced in response to it are chemically distinct, each belonging to a wholly different class of chemical compounds.

The inducing substance, on the basis of its chemical and physical properties, appears to be a highly polymerized and viscous form of sodium desoxyribonucleate. On the other hand, the Type III capsular substance, the synthesis of which is evoked by this transforming agent, consists chiefly of a non-nitrogenous polysaccharide constituted of glucose-glucuronic acid units linked in glycosidic union (22). The presence of the newly formed capsule containing this type-specific polysaccharide confers on the transformed cells all the distinguishing characteristics of Pneumococcus Type III. Thus, it is evident that the inducing substance and the substance produced in turn are chemically distinct and biologically specific in their action and that both are requisite in determining the type specificity of the cell of which they form a part.

The experimental data presented in this paper strongly suggest that nucleic acids, at least those of the desoxyribose type, possess different specificities as evidenced by the selective action of the transforming principle. Indeed, the possibility of the existence of specific differences in biological behavior of nucleic acids has previously been suggested (23, 24) but has never been experimentally demonstrated owing in part at least to the lack of suitable biological methods.

The techniques used in the study of transformation appear to afford a sensitive means of testing the validity of this hypothesis, and the results thus far obtained add supporting evidence in favor of this point of view.

If it is ultimately proved beyond reasonable doubt that the transforming activity of the material described is actually an inherent property of the nucleic acid, one must still account on a chemical basis for the biological specificity of its action. At first glance, immunological methods would appear to offer the ideal means of determining the differential specificity of this group of biologically important substances. Although the constituent units and general pattern of the nucleic acid molecule have been defined, there is as yet relatively little known of the possible effect that subtle differences in molecular configuration may exert on the biological specificity of these substances. However, since nucleic acids free or combined with histones or protamines are not known to function antigenically, one would not anticipate that such differences would be revealed by immunological techniques. Consequently, it is perhaps not surprising that highly purified and protein-free preparations of desoxyribonucleic acid, although extremely active in inducing transformation, showed only faint trace reactions in precipitin tests with potent Type III antipneumococcus rabbit sera.

From these limited observations it would be unwise to draw any conclusion concerning the immunological significance of the nucleic acids until further knowledge on this phase of the problem is available. Recent observations by Lackman and his collaborators (25) have shown that nucleic acids of both the yeast and thymus type derived from hemolytic streptococci and from animal and plant sources precipitate with certain antipneumococcal sera. The reactions varied with different lots of immune serum and occurred more frequently in antipneumococcal horse serum than in corresponding sera of immune rabbits. The irregularity and broad cross reactions encountered led these investigators to express some doubt as to the immunological significance of the results. Unless special immunochemical methods can be devised similar to those so successfully used in demonstrating the serological specificity of simple non-antigenic substances, it appears that the techniques employed in the study of transformation are the only ones available at present for testing possible differences in the biological behavior of nucleic acids.

Admittedly there are many phases of the problem of transformation that require further study and many questions that remain unanswered largely because of technical difficulties. For example, it would be of interest to know the relation between rate of reaction and concentration of the transforming substance; the proportion of cells transformed to those that remain unaffected in the reaction system. However, from a bacteriological point of view, numerical estimations based on colony counts might prove more misleading than enlightening because of the aggregation and sedimentation of the R cells agglutinated by the antiserum in the medium. Attempts to induce transformation in suspensions of resting cells held under conditions inhibiting growth and multiplication have thus far proved unsuccessful, and it seems probable that transformation occurs only during active reproduction of the cells. Important in this connection is the fact that the R cells, as well as those that have undergone transformation, presumably also all other variants and types of pneumococci, contain an intracellular enzyme which is released during autolysis and in the free state is capable of rapidly and completely destroying the activity of the transforming agent. It would appear, therefore, that during the logarithmic phase of growth when cell division is most active and autolysis least apparent, the cultural conditions are optimal for the maintenance of the balance between maximal reactivity of the R cell and minimal destruction of the transforming agent through the release of autolytic ferments.

In the present state of knowledge any interpretation of the mechanism involved in transformation must of necessity be purely theoretical. The biochemical events underlying the phenomenon suggest that the transforming principle interacts with the R cell giving rise to a coordinated series of enzymatic reactions that culminate in the synthesis of the Type III capsular antigen. The experimental findings have clearly demonstrated that the induced alterations are not random changes but are predictable, always corresponding in type specificity to that of the encapsulated cells from which the transforming substance was isolated. Once transformation has occurred, the newly acquired characteristics are thereafter transmitted in series through innumerable transfers in artificial media without any further addition of the transforming agent. Moreover, from the transformed cells themselves, a substance of identical activity can again be recovered in amounts far in excess of that originally added to induce the change. It is evident, therefore, that not only is the capsular material reproduced in successive generations but that the primary factor, which controls the occurrence and specificity of capsular development, is also reduplicated in the daughter cells. The induced changes are not temporary modifications but are permanent alterations which persist provided the cultural conditions are favorable for the maintenance of capsule formation. The transformed cells can be readily distinguished from the parent R forms not alone by serological reactions but by the presence of a newly formed and visible capsule which is the immunological unit of type specificity and the accessory structure essential in determining the infective capacity of the microorganism in the animal body.

It is particularly significant in the case of pneumococci that the experimentally induced alterations are definitely correlated with the development of a new morphological structure and the consequent acquisition of new antigenic and invasive properties. Equally if not more significant is the fact that these changes are predictable, type-specific, and heritable.

Various hypotheses have been advanced in explanation of the nature of the changes induced. In his original description of the phenomenon Griffith (1) suggested that the dead bacteria in the inoculum might furnish some specific protein that serves as a "pabulum" and enables the R form to manufacture a capsular carbohydrate.

More recently the phenomenon has been interpreted from a genetic point of view (26, 27). The inducing substance has been likened to a gene, and the capsular antigen which is produced in response to it has been regarded as a gene product. In discussing the phenomenon of transformation Dobzhansky (27) has stated that "If this transformation is described as a genetic mutation—and it is difficult to avoid so describing it—we are dealing with authentic cases of induction of specific mutations by specific treatments. . . ."

Another interpretation of the phenomenon has been suggested by Stanley (28) who has drawn the analogy between the activity of the transforming agent and that of a virus. On the other hand, Murphy (29) has compared the causative agents of fowl tumors with the transforming principle of Pneumococcus. He has suggested that both these groups of agents be termed "transmissible mutagens" in order to differentiate them from the virus group. Whatever may prove to be the correct interpretation, these differences in viewpoint indicate the implications of the phenomenon of transformation in relation to similar problems in the fields of genetics, virology, and cancer research.

It is, of course, possible that the biological activity of the substance described is not an inherent property of the nucleic acid but is due to minute amounts of some other substance adsorbed to it or so intimately associated with it as to escape detection. If, however, the biologically active substance isolated in highly purified form as the sodium salt of desoxyribonucleic acid actually proves to be the transforming principle, as the available evidence strongly suggests, then nucleic acids of this type must be regarded not merely as structurally important but as functionally active in determining the biochemical activities and specific characteristics of pneumococcal cells. Assuming that the sodium desoxyribonucleate and the active principle are one and the same substance, then the transformation described represents a change that is chemically induced and specifically directed by a known chemical compound. If the results of the present study on the chemical nature of the transforming principle are confirmed, then nucleic acids must be regarded as possessing biological specificity the chemical basis of which is as yet undetermined.

SUMMARY

1. From Type III pneumococci a biologically active fraction has been isolated in highly purified form which in exceedingly minute amounts is capable under appropriate cultural conditions of inducing the transformation of unencapsulated R variants of Pneumococcus Type II into fully encapsulated cells of the

same specific type as that of the heat-killed microorganisms from which the inducing material was recovered.

2. Methods for the isolation and purification of the active transforming material are described.

3. The data obtained by chemical, enzymatic, and serological analyses together with the results of preliminary studies by electrophoresis, ultracentrifugation, and ultraviolet spectroscopy indicate that, within the limits of the methods, the active fraction contains no demonstrable protein, unbound lipid, or serologically reactive polysaccharide and consists principally, if not solely, of a highly polymerized, viscous form of desoxyribonucleic acid.

4. Evidence is presented that the chemically induced alterations in cellular structure and function are predictable, type-specific, and transmissible in series. The various hypotheses that have been advanced concerning the nature of these changes are reviewed.

CONCLUSION

The evidence presented supports the belief that a nucleic acid of the desoxyribose type is the fundamental unit of the transforming principle of Pneumococcus Type III.

BIBLIOGRAPHY

1. Griffith, F., *J. Hyg.*, Cambridge, Eng., 1928, **27,** 113.
2. Neufeld, F., and Levinthal, W., *Z. Immunitätsforsch.*, 1928, **55,** 324.
3. Baurhenn, W., *Centr. Bakt., 1. Abt., Orig.*, 1932, **126,** 68.
4. Dawson, M. H., *J. Exp. Med.*, 1930, **51,** 123.
5. Dawson, M. H., and Sia, R. H. P., *J. Exp. Med.*, 1931, **54,** 681.
6. Alloway, J. L., *J. Exp. Med.*, 1932, **55,** 91; 1933, **57,** 265.
7. Berry, G. P., and Dedrick, H. M., *J. Bact.*, 1936, **31,** 50.
8. Berry, G. P., *Arch. Path.*, 1937, **24,** 533.
9. Hurst, E. W., *Brit. J. Exp. Path.*, 1937, **18,** 23. Hoffstadt, R. E., and Pilcher, K. S., *J. Infect. Dis.*, 1941, **68,** 67. Gardner, R. E., and Hyde, R. R., *J. Infect. Dis.*, 1942, **71,** 47. Houlihan, R. B., *Proc. Soc. Exp. Biol. and Med.*, 1942, **51,** 259.
10. MacLeod, C. M., and Mirick, G. S., *J. Bact.*, 1942, **44,** 277.
11. Dawson, M. H., *J. Exp. Med.*, 1928, **47,** 577; 1930, **51,** 99.
12. Sevag, M. G., *Biochem. Z.*, 1934, **273,** 419. Sevag, M. G., Lackman, D. B., and Smolens, J., *J. Biol. Chem.*, 1938, **124,** 425.
13. Dubos, R. J., and Avery, O. T., *J. Exp. Med.*, 1931, **54,** 51. Dubos, R. J., and Bauer, J. H., *J. Exp. Med.*, 1935, **62,** 271.
14. Liu, S., and Wu, H., *Chinese J. Physiol.*, 1938, **13,** 449.
15. Martland, M., and Robison, R., *Biochem. J.*, 1929, **23,** 237.
16. Albers, H., and Albers, E., *Z. physiol. Chem.*, 1935, **232,** 189.
17. Levene, P. A., and Dillon, R. T., *J. Biol. Chem.*, 1933, **96,** 461.
18. Greenstein, J. P., and Jenrette, W. Y., *J. Nat. Cancer Inst.*, 1940, **1,** 845.

19. Greenstein, J. P., *J. Nat. Cancer Inst.*, 1943, **4,** 55.
20. Tennent, H. G., and Vilbrandt, C. F., *J. Am. Chem. Soc.*, 1943, **65,** 424.
21. Thompson, R. H. S., and Dubos, R. J., *J. Biol. Chem.*, 1938, **125,** 65.
22. Reeves, R. E., and Goebel, W. F., *J. Biol. Chem.*, 1941, **139,** 511.
23. Schultz, J., in Genes and chromosomes. Structure and organization, Cold Spring Harbor symposia on quantitative biology, Cold Spring Harbor, Long Island Biological Association, 1941, **9,** 55.
24. Mirsky, A. E., in Advances in enzymology and related subjects of biochemistry, (F. F. Nord and C. H. Werkman, editors), New York, Interscience Publishers, Inc., 1943, **3,** 1.
25. Lackman, D., Mudd, S., Scvag, M. G., Smolens, J., and Wiener, M., *J. Immunol.*, 1941, **40,** 1.
26. Gortner, R. A., Outlines of biochemistry, New York, Wiley, 2nd edition, 1938, 547.
27. Dobzhansky, T., Genetics and the origin of the species, New York, Columbia University Press, 1941, 47.
28. Stanley, W. M., in Doerr, R., and Hallauer, C., Handbuch der Virusforschung, Vienna, Julius Springer, 1938, **1,** 491.
29. Murphy, J. B., *Tr. Assn. Am. Physn.*, 1931, **46,** 182; *Bull. Johns Hopkins Hosp.*, 1935, **56,** 1.

THE JOURNAL OF EXPERIMENTAL MEDICINE VOL. 79   PLATE 1

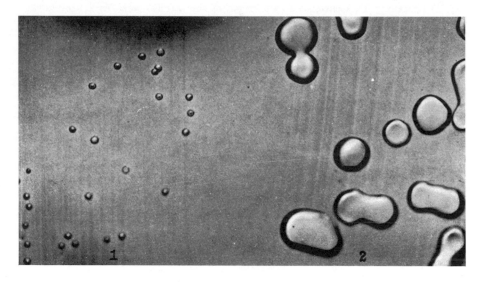

(Avery *et al.*: Transformation of pneumococcal types)

EXPLANATION OF PLATE 1

The photograph was made by Mr. Joseph B. Haulenbeek.

FIG. 1. Colonies of the R variant (R36A) derived from Pneumococcus Type II. Plated on blood agar from a culture grown in serum broth in the absence of the transforming substance. ×3.5.

FIG. 2. Colonies on blood agar of the same cells after induction of transformation during growth in the same medium with the addition of active transforming principle isolated from Type III pneumococci. The smooth, glistening, mucoid colonies shown are characteristic of Pneumococcus Type III and readily distinguishable from the small, rough colonies of the parent R strain illustrated in Fig. 1. ×3.5.

[Reprinted from THE JOURNAL OF GENERAL PHYSIOLOGY, November 20, 1946, Vol. 30, No. 2, pp. 101–116]

THE NUCLEOPROTAMINE OF TROUT SPERM

BY A. W. POLLISTER AND A. E. MIRSKY

(*From the Department of Zoology, Columbia University, and the Laboratories of The Rockefeller Institute for Medical Research, New York*)

PLATES 1 and 2

(Received for publication, June 20, 1946)

Constituents of the cell nucleus were extracted and isolated for the first time by Miescher (1). Sperm was the material used in most of Miescher's classical investigations on nuclear constituents; and in the long series of subsequent investigations on sperm, by Kossel (2) and his numerous associates, by Steudel (3), and finally by Rasmussen and Linderstrøm-Lang (4), the methods of extraction were essentially the same as those used by Miescher. These methods involved the use of such strong acid and alkali that the nuclear materials were drastically changed in the course of extraction. We have extracted nuclear constituents from sperm by a far milder procedure. In this paper we describe our method of extraction, some of the properties of the extracted material, and at the same time the cytological changes wrought by the extractant. At one stage in the extraction the highly condensed sperm nucleus changes so that it shows a striking resemblance to a resting nucleus or early prophase, thread-like chromosomes now being clearly visible.

Sperm was selected by Miescher as a material for study of the cell nucleus because the sperm cell contains relatively little cytoplasm, and the sperm of fish was used because this is available in such large quantities. In practically all of his work Miescher used salmon sperm; other workers have frequently used herring sperm. Two of the constituents of the sperm nucleus are a basic protein and nucleic acid. The basic proteins in salmon and herring sperm are protamines, proteins having a nitrogen content of 31.6 per cent, and 89.2 per cent of this is in the form of one basic amino acid, arginine. Protamine was extracted by treating sperm with 0.2 N HCl. The residue remaining after acid extraction still contained all the nucleic acid and this was later extracted with sodium hydroxide. Within the nucleus, protamine and nucleic acid are combined. They are separated by the hydrochloric acid used to extract protamine. It is possible that protamine is altered by treatment with 0.2 N HCl, but this is not known because protamine has never been prepared by a mild procedure. It is also possible that nucleic acid is modified by the treatment first with hydrochloric acid and then with sodium hydroxide.

We have found that both nucleic acid and protamine can be extracted by a neutral 1 M solution of NaCl.

101

Material.—For our work neither fresh salmon nor herring sperm were available. The trout (*Salmo fario*, the brown trout) is a member of the same genus as the Atlantic salmon (*Salmo salar*), and trout sperm was available.[1] A disadvantage of this material is that one is obliged to work with relatively small quantities. For one preparation Rasmussen and Linderstrøm-Lang used 20 kilos of herring testes; no more than 20 gm. of trout sperm were available to us at one time. A considerable advantage of working with trout sperm is that the material is obtained by stripping live fish, so that all of the sperm is ripe and therefore relatively uniform in composition; other investigators have worked with excised testes which, even in the breeding season, may contain some immature sperm. While stripping the trout, care is taken that no feces become mixed with the sperm. Within 2 hours after being collected the sperm were in the laboratory and while being transported they were packed in ice. All the experiments to be described, unless otherwise noted, were done in a cold room kept between 0 and 1°C. Most of our work has been on trout sperm, but, as will be mentioned later, we have also used the sperm of other animals—the shad, key-hole limpet, fresh-water clam, sea urchin, frog, fowl, and bull.

Extraction.—Before extraction the trout sperm are washed to free them of the small quantities of intercellular material present. The wash fluid contains in 1000 ml.; 7.8 gm. NaCl, 0.664 gm. KCl, and 0.687 gm. K_2SO_4 (5). After stirring, the sperm suspension is centrifuged at 5000 R.P.M. for 15 minutes. The supernatant is water-clear.

The washed sperm are extracted with 1 M NaCl, final concentration after mixing. On adding salt solution, the sperm mass immediately becomes sticky and gelatinous, so that it appears at first as if the cells were merely swelling. It is necessary to add a large volume of solution and to stir vigorously in a Waring mixer before it becomes apparent that the cells are breaking up as their contents pass into solution. For a mass of sperm with a dry weight of 900 mg. the volume of the extraction mixture should be about 500 ml. Even so, the mixture is quite viscous. After vigorous stirring the mixture is centrifuged at 12,000 R.P.M. for 60 minutes. A perfectly clear, viscous supernatant and a scanty residue are obtained. The material extracted from the sperm is precipitated by pouring the supernatant into 6 volumes of water. The precipitate is in the form of long fibrous strands, so fibrous that they can easily be wound around a rod and, if the rod has a crook at its lower end, the fibers can be transferred to another vessel while still clinging to the rod. If the fibers are not twisted around a rod they soon settle and after the supernatant is decanted much fluid can be pressed from the fibrous mass. The fibrous precipitate redissolves in 1 M NaCl. Vigorous stirring shortens the time needed to dissolve the precipitate. The solution is as viscous as it was when the material was initally extracted from the sperm. Any suspended particles are removed by centrifugation and the dissolved material is then reprecipitated by pouring the solution into 6 volumes of water. The precipitate has the same fibrous character as when first formed. The fibrous material

---

[1] Trout sperm was obtained from the New York State Fish Hatchery at Cold Spring Harbor, Long Island, and from the New Jersey State Hatchery at Hacketts-town. We are much indebted to the superintendents of these hatcheries, Mr. Stanley Walters and Mr. C. O. Hayford.

is soluble in 1 M NaCl and insoluble in 0.14 M NaCl and, because of these properties can easily be reprecipitated and redissolved any number of times.   Dissolved in 1 M NaCl it keeps well without any preservative at 0°.

A fibrous nucleoprotein has also been extracted in 1 M NaCl from the sperm of another fish, the shad.   From the sperm of the sea urchin, key-hole limpet, and fresh-water clam no nucleoprotein was extractable with 1 M NaCl.   With 2 M NaCl, however, there was no difficulty extracting fibrous nucleoproteins from these sperm.   From frog and mouse testes nucleoproteins were extracted with 1 M NaCl.   No nucleoproteins could be extracted from bull sperm (obtained by centrifuging bull semen) with either 1 M or 2 M NaCl.   It would be interesting to know the nature of the change that occurs in the maturation of mammalian sperm that prevents extraction of nucleoproteins with concentrated salt solutions.

Composition.—For analytical purposes the whole trout sperm and the fibrous precipitate prepared from it are washed first with 65 per cent alcohol to remove salt, then with hot 95 per cent alcohol, and finally with ether.   The dehydrated preparations are dried at 106°.   Phosphorus (6) and nitrogen (7) analyses give the following results:

Material	Phosphorus content	Nitrogen
	per cent	*per cent*
Trout whole sperm.....................	5.02	18.2
Trout whole sperm.....................	5.04	18.33
Nucleoprotein.........................	5.93	18.1
Nucleoprotein.........................	6.14	18.4

This is the elementary composition that would be expected of a nucleoprotamine.   If it is assumed (and it will be shown below that this assumption is justified) that all of the phosphorus is in the form of nucleic acid, it can be calculated that the substance joined to the nucleic acid has a nitrogen content of somewhat more than 25 per cent, a value high for any protein other than a protamine.   And there can be little doubt that the fibrous material extracted from trout sperm consists largely if not entirely of nucleoprotamine, for the quantity obtained from trout sperm is of about the same order as the quantity of protamine and nucleic acid extracted from salmon sperm by Miescher; the fibrous material forms 81.6 per cent of the whole trout sperm and the amounts of protamine and nucleic acid in salmon sperm as reckoned by Miescher account for 81 per cent of the weight of the sperm head.   This comparison does not exclude the possibility that there is some other protein in addition to protamine in the fibrous material.   But no other protein can in fact be detected in this material.   One of the characteristics of a protein such as salmine (the protamine of salmon sperm) is its lack of tyrosine, tryptophane, and certain other amino acids. The Millon reaction, an exceedingly sensitive test for tyrosine and furthermore a test with which nucleic acid does not interfere, is altogether negative when applied either to purified salmine or to the fibrous material derived from trout sperm.

There are other indications, to be described more fully below, that the fibrous nucleoprotamine contains no other protein than protamine. If an aqueous solution of protein is shaken with a chloroform-octyl alcohol mixture a layer of protein soon appears at the interface, and as the shaking is continued, more and more of the dissolved protein accumulates at the interface (8). When a solution of nucleohistone is shaken in this way nearly all of the histone gradually accumulates at the interface, nucleic acid remaining dissolved in the aqueous phase. On shaking a nucleoprotamine with a chloroform-octyl alcohol mixture, it is found that very little material appears at the interface even after prolonged shaking. This is to be expected because it is known that a protamine does not spread at the surface of water. The experiment also shows that the fibrous nucleoprotamine contains no considerable quantity of protein that does spread at the surface of water.

The presence of nucleic acid in the nucleoprotamine is demonstrated at once by the ultraviolet absorption spectrum; and from the magnitude of the extinction coefficient at 2600 A. u. the quantity of nucleic acid present can be estimated. In Text-fig. 1 are shown absorption spectra in the ultraviolet of a sample of thymus nucleic acid (prepared by a procedure which will be described in another paper) and of trout nucleoprotamine. It is apparent that the nucleoprotamine has the characteristic nucleic acid absorption spectrum and that when concentrations of material are expressed in terms of phosphorus contents, that the absorption coefficients at the position of maximum absorption (2600 A. u.) are the same for nucleic acid and nucleoprotamine. This means that all of the phosphorus in the fibrous nucleoprotamine is in the form of nucleic acid. As seen in Text-fig. 1, the absorption curves of nucleic acid and nucleoprotamine differ only at wave-lengths below 2440 A. u. Below this wave-length the effect of protamine absorption can be seen.

All of the nucleic acid in the nucleoprotamine is of the desoxyribose type. This can be demonstrated by use of the Dische diphenylamine reagent (9). The intensity of blue color given by the nucleoprotamine is precisely the same as that given by a quantity of desoxyribose nucleic acid (prepared from the thymus) with an equivalent phosphorus content.

Separation of Nucleoprotein into Its Component Parts.—To separate nucleic acid from protamine it was found, to our great surprise, that dialysis suffices. Dialysis against water is ineffective because the nucleoprotamine complex precipitates and remains combined within the cellophane membrane, as the sodium chloride in which it is dissolved is removed. But if the solution of nucleoprotamine in 1 M NaCl is dialyzed not against water, but against 1 M NaCl, protamine slowly passes through the cellophane membrane leaving nucleic acid behind.   Even when dialysis takes place in a rocking dialyzer in which the fluid inside the cellophane membrane is constantly stirred and the outer fluid is frequently changed the removal of protamine proceeds very slowly. The process can be followed by nitrogen and phosphorus analyses on the solution within the membrane.   At the outset the nitrogen:phosphorus

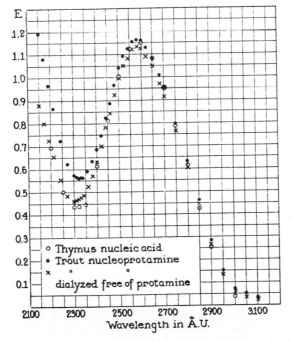

TEXT-FIG. 1. Absorption spectra in the ultraviolet of thymus nucleic acid, trout nucleoprotamine, and trout nucleoprotamine dialyzed free of protamine.   In each solution the concentration of phosphorus is 0.005 mg. per ml.

ratio is 3.45 and as protamine passes through the membrane the ratio drops. After 2 days the nitrogen:phosphorus ratio is 2.40, after 4 days it is 2.08, and after 15 days 1.72.

At the same time that the nitrogen content of the solution within the membrane drops the phosphorus content remains unchanged.   In one experiment, for example the solution put into the cellophane tube had 0.092 mg. P per ml. and after 10 days' dialysis it had 0.093 mg. P per ml.   The unchanged phosphorus content shows that no nucleic acid passes through the cellophane membrane.   Two other observations also show that all the nucleic acid is

retained by the membrane: the desoxyribose content of the solution, as estimated by the diphenylamine reaction remains unchanged; and the ultraviolet
extinction coefficient at 2600 A. u. remains constant.

After dialysis the nucleic acid is precipitated by pouring the solution into 5 volumes
of alcohol. A fibrous precipitate is obtained. The fibers are washed quickly in
65 per cent alcohol to remove adhering sodium chloride, and then after washing with
alcohol and ether, are dried in a vacuum. Phosphorus content 8.97 per cent; nitrogen
14.47 per cent. The nitrogen:phosphorus ratio is 1.72. This composition is close
to the theoretical for the sodium salt of desoxyribose nucleic acid: 9.28 per cent P;
15.58 per cent N; and a nitrogen:phosphorus ratio of 1.68.

Removal of protamine from nucleoprotamine causes no significant change
in the originally high viscosity of a nucleoprotamine solution. Measurements
in an Ostwald viscosimeter show that the relative viscosity in 1 M NaCl of a
nucleoprotamine solution containing 0.052 mg. P per ml. is 2.85; after a prolonged dialysis in which all the protamine is lost the phosphorus content is
0.051 mg. P per ml. and the relative viscosity is 2.80. The high viscosity of
nucleoprotamine solutions is obviously due entirely to the nucleic acid component of the complex and it is clear that the nucleic acid must be highly
polymerized.

Removal of protamine from a nucleoprotamine complex by dialysis in presence of 1 M NaCl shows that the components of the complex readily dissociate
in 1 M NaCl. The fact that protamine has no influence on the viscosity of
nucleic acid in 1 M NaCl strongly suggests that dissociation is in fact complete.

Solubility of the nucleoprotamine complex is, on the other hand, much
influenced by presence of protamine. The nucleoprotamine, though soluble
in 1 M NaCl is insoluble in distilled water and in physiological saline (0.14 M
NaCl). After removal of protamine the nucleic acid is soluble under all of
these conditions. These observations on solubility show clearly that in low
concentrations of salt protamine and nucleic acid are firmly combined. Increasing the salt concentration dissolves the complex because dissociation
occurs. Within the sperm cell the electrolyte concentration is low and consequently protamine and nucleic acid combine to form an insoluble complex;
extraction with M NaCl is effective because in the presence of so much salt the
complex dissociates. In a recent paper on "The enzymatic degradation of
thymus nucleohistone," Cohen (10) repeats on somewhat different material
many of our experiments (which we have briefly mentioned in earlier publications (11)) on the nucleoprotamine complex and comes to essentially the same
conclusion concerning the effects of M NaCl.

The dissociating effect of sodium chloride on the nucleoprotamine complex
was clearly foreshadowed by Miescher. He found that when 10 per cent
sodium chloride is added to the complex formed by adding protamine to

nucleic acid, the insoluble complex swells. (When this experiment is done with a nucleic acid preparation that has not been degraded, as Miescher's was, the complex dissolves.) And he discovered that when sodium chloride is added to sperm defatted by extraction with alcohol and ether that they too swell. In the clear saline fluid in which the gel-like clumps are suspended considerable quantities of dissolved protamine were detected. This fluid contained no nucleic acid, Miescher said, or only traces of it. As more salt solution was added, more protamine went into solution, but there was never more than a fraction of the total present. When the gel with its surrounding fluid was poured into a large volume of water and shaken for a moment the clumps contracted and combined with all the protamine in the surrounding fluid, so that not even a trace of dissolved protamine could be found. Our experiments show that if the sperm had not been treated previously with alcohol and ether practically all of the protamine, and the nucleic acid as well, would have been dissolved by the concentrated sodium chloride and that the dissociated components would recombine and precipitate on addition of water.

The nucleic acid isolated from salmon sperm by Miescher and his successors has the same elementary composition as has the nucleic acid that we have prepared from trout sperm. The difference between the two preparations can, however, be perceived at once in their appearance even when dry; the older preparations are powders whereas our preparation consists of fibers. The fibers dissolve readily in water to form a viscous solution which exhibits birefringence of flow; the powder dissolves only on addition of a little alkali to form a solution hardly more viscous than water and not birefringent. These observations show clearly that the strong acid and alkali used in the older preparations depolymerize the nucleic acid. And the alteration produced goes beyond depolymerization; the desoxyribose nucleic acid has been changed to some extent. The intensity of blue color given in the diphenylamine reaction by the depolymerized nucleic acid is considerably less than that given by an equivalent quantity of polymerized nucleic acid.[2]

The highly polymerized nucleic acid prepared from sperm resembles the nucleic acid prepared from the thymus gland by the Bang-Hammarsten method (12). In this procedure the material is extracted with water and so a drastic depolymerization is avoided. Extraction with water is altogether ineffective when applied to trout sperm. It is of interest to note that Miescher himself came very close to discovering that nucleoprotamine can be extracted from salmon sperm by a 1 M solution of sodium chloride. He noticed (page 63) in his first experiments on salmon sperm in 1874 that when sperm are treated with concentrated salt solutions they are immediately transformed into "transparent, slimy lumps of jelly" and that at the same time the sperm heads swell

---

[2] These experiments will be described in another paper.

and disappear.   He did not pursue the matter, fearful apparently of the slimy mass he had produced.

The protamine that diffuses through the cellophane membrane has not yet been collected and studied.   Rasmussen and Linderstrøm-Lang (4) have shown that the equivalent weight of the protamine clupein determined by electrometric titration lies between 4000 and 4100.   This determination was on clupein prepared by acid extraction.   Our observations show that a protamine preparation that has not been exposed to such drastic treatment has a very low molecular weight, low enough to allow the protamine to pass through a cellophane membrane.   It is therefore probable that the equivalent weight determined by Rasmussen and Linderstrøm-Lang is the molecular weight of the intact protamine.

Composition of the Sperm Nucleus.—There is such a large quantity of nucleoprotamine in the sperm head that the question arises of how much other material there is in this part of the sperm.   Miescher was the first to consider this problem and it has fascinated all later workers who have approached it. The composition of the sperm head is of great interest because this portion of the sperm is very nearly a bare nucleus, the surrounding cytoplasm being so scanty.   The nucleus, in turn, consists almost entirely of chromatin so that a study of the composition of the sperm head is virtually a study of the composition of chromatin.

We have attempted to determine the relative volumes of major morphological constituents of the salmonid spermatozoon for comparison with the amount of the nucleoprotamine fraction.   These measurements have been made on sperm of the rainbow trout, *Salmo irideus*.   The photographs upon which the measurements were based were made with sealed drops of unwashed and unfixed spermatozoa, which were stained with crystal violet (0.05 per cent in normal saline).   Comparison of these photographs with those of unstained spermatozoa mounted in seminal fluid indicate that the crystal violet staining causes no measureable change of volume.

Study of the sperm head by critical focusing and by observation of heads as they are rotated by flow makes it clear that the head is a symmetrical bell-shaped body.   In cross-section the head is approximately an ellipse.   There are three profiles which are significant to a determination of its volume: first, the view directly on end, from which it is learned that the head is a symmetrical ellipse at all focal levels, and from which also one can accurately determine the principal axes of the ellipse where these are maximal; second and third are the widest and narrowest, full length profiles.   At any point along the principal axis of the head the latter two profiles will give the major and minor axes of the elliptical cross-section of that level.   Profile one is a check on the correctness of the identification of the two longitudinal profiles, for the points of greatest widths of the latter coincide (as they should) with the lengths of the two axes (32.0 mm. and 26.0 mm. respectively) when the focus is at the level of greatest cross-sectional area. Another check on the determination of the longitudinal profiles comes from measurements of sperm heads that are oriented at random. These should approach, but not exceed, the measurements of the full length profiles; that is, the vertical (longitudinal) axis should approach 37.0 mm. and the horizontal axis, at greatest width, of any single sperm head on the photographs should lie between 32.0 mm. and 26.0 mm. Caliper measurements of photographs of 34 sperms agree with this expectation. The mean maximum width of the 34.0 specimens was 29.6 mm. which is not far from 29.0, the calculated mean between 32.0 and 26.0 mm.

From the three profiles described above the volume of the nucleus was determined as follows:[3] Photomicrographs of the three profiles were enlarged to 11,400 diameters. By strong transmitted light these enlarged profiles were projected, without change of magnification, onto a millimeter graph paper, on which outlines of one-half profiles were traced. Caliper measurements of the profiles on the photographs were compared with the tracing to check the accuracy of the latter. These measurements were made to the *middle* of the blurred marginal diffraction band. We have never actually obtained longitudinal profiles in which both sides were in perfect focus at all points along the margin, but checking by comparison with the cross-section profile and by comparison with various oblique views indicates that the side in good focus in several of the best profiles has not been appreciably distorted by the slight cant of the head shown by the softer focus of the opposite side of the profile; and that, therefore, the half of the profile on the better focus side of the central axis is fairly close to a perfect one-half profile. A whole sperm head diagram was constructed from two of these half-profiles. Since the calculations involve only one-half the total width at any one level, a good half profile is all that is needed. The actual volume calculations are made from the longitudinal profiles as follows: the total length of the enlarged head was 37.0 mm. (corresponding to an actual length of 3.25μ). This is considered to be a series of 37 elliptical cylinders of 1 mm. height and with axes greatest (from the widest profile) and least (from the narrowest profile). The volume of the total head is obtained by adding together the volumes of the 37 cylinders. The total volume of the head we have thus determined as 15,743 mm.[3] For nuclear volume this figure is too high; for there is a central cone of cytoplasm projecting into the base of the nucleus the volume of which is determined from the profiles to be 291 mm.[3] The real nuclear volume then is 15,452 mm.[3] From this figure determined from the photographs the actual nuclear volume is calculated to be $10.430\mu^3$.

Next to the nucleus the principal piece of the tail is the largest part of the

[3] We are indebted to Dr. K. J. Arnold for suggesting this method of determining the nuclear volume.

spermatozoon. On the accuracy of the determination of its volume, then, rests the chief value of any determination of volume of the nucleus relative to the whole cell. The tail is considerably less than 1.0 micron in diameter, and although it appears to be of equal width from any profile, it can only be said to be cylindrical within the limits imposed by the resolution of the microscope, which in the case of so small an object leaves considerable room for variation. The determination of the length of the sperm principal piece offers no special difficulty. Photographs, at magnification × 11,400, of six complete principal pieces ranged from 339 mm. to 364 mm., with the mean at 347.7 mm. (corresponding to an actual length of 30.5 μ).

Measuring to the middle of the marginal diffraction images, the diameter of the tail is 5.0 mm. Calculating the tail volume as that of a cylinder of height 347.7 mm. and radius 2.5 mm., we reach a figure of 6824 mm.^{3}. In the

TABLE I

Part of sperm	Volume at ×11,400	Actual volume	Total sperm volume
	mm.^{3}	μ^3	per cent
Nucleus..........................	15,452	10.430	66.92
Tail..............................	6,824	4.606	29.55
Nebenkern.......................	524	0.354	2.27
Cone in head.....................	291	0.196	1.26
Total sperm volume...............	23,091	15.586	100.00

suspended spermatozoa the nebenkern is an approximately spherical body, the diameter of which, on the photographs, is about 10 mm. Calculated as a sphere its volume is 524 mm.^{3}. The measurements of the volumes of parts of the salmonid spermatozoon are summarized in Table I. Significant in connection with our analytical studies of the nucleoprotein content of these spermatozoa are the relative volumes of sperm "head" (or nucleus plus cone) and "tail" (or principal piece plus middle piece). The former is 68.2 per cent of the total sperm, the latter 31.8 per cent. From our analyses it appears that the fat-free content of the sperm heads makes up 89.6 per cent of the total weight of the sperm, see page 113. The remaining 10.4 per cent of the total weight of the spermatozoon must include the total lipoid of all parts plus the non-lipoidal content of the "tail." It appears, then, that 31.8 per cent of the volume of the spermatozoon can constitute at most 10.4 per cent of the dry weight. This low specific gravity of the non-nuclear parts of the sperm is not unexpected, in view of the reported high water and lipoid content of mitochondria (13) (of which the nebenkern is constituted), and of the high lipoid content which Schmiedeberg (1) found in isolated tails of the Atlantic salmon sperm.

In his final work on the composition of the sperm nucleus, Miescher's procedure was first to remove the tail and midpiece from the head by washing the sperm with water. The suspension of sperm nuclei was extracted with alcohol and ether and so converted into a white powder. From a weighed quantity of the powder protamine was extracted with hydrochloric acid and finally isolated and weighed. The nucleic acid content of the residue left after acid treatment was computed by assuming that all of the phosphorus present in the residue was in the form of nucleic acid. In Miescher's experiments the sum of the isolated protamine plus the computed nucleic acid accounted for 81 per cent of the sperm nuclear material.

With 1 M NaCl nucleoprotamine can be extracted from water-washed sperm cells, and there is no difficulty in gathering the extracted material. In this way it would be possible to compute what part of the sperm nucleus consists of nucleoprotamine, if one could be confident that a water-washed sperm cell is actually a sperm nucleus.

There are two reasons for caution in considering a water-washed sperm cell to be equivalent to a sperm nucleus: first, it is possible that some of the material removed by washing may be derived from the sperm nucleus; and secondly, careful microscopic examination of water-washed sperm shows that by no means all of the sperm tails have been washed away.

A more reliable method of finding what part of the sperm nucleus consists of nucleoprotamine would be to extract intact sperm cells with 1 M NaCl and refer the quantity of extracted nucleoprotamine not to the whole sperm mass but to the mass of nuclear material only. For this purpose it is necessary to know: (1) that the nucleoprotamine extracted is derived from the nucleus only; (2) that practically all of the nucleoprotamine is extracted by 1 M NaCl, and (3) what fraction of the sperm cell is occupied by the nucleus. These three problems will now be considered.

It has long been realized that one cannot account for more than a small part of the nucleic acid and protamine which may be extracted from suspensions of salmonid sperms unless one assumes that there has been material extracted from the nucleus. From our cytological study of the effect of strong saline upon the spermatozoa it is clear that probably the whole nucleoprotamine fraction comes from the nucleus. Even after long treatment with 1 M NaCl the sperm tails are unaltered; the heads (nuclei), however, swell and apparently become completely dissolved immediately upon exposure to the sodium chloride.

The following simple experiment demonstrates the effect of salt solution on the spermatozoa. A small drop of sperm suspension (Figs. 1–3) and another of 2 M NaCl are placed a few millimeters apart on a cover-slip, which has a small amount of vaseline around its edge, except at one point. A slide is brought in contact with the vaseline and is then inverted carrying the cover-slip. Pressure on the edges of the cover-slip seals the preparation except at one point; and further pressure flattens the drops until they come in contact with one another.   The seal is then completed by adding vaseline at the point which has served as an air escape valve during the flattening of the drops. Since this technique has involved no vigorous stirring of the drops of salt solution and sperm suspension, there is a sodium chloride gradient across the latter.   The sperms farthest from the concentrated salt are quite unaltered.   By contrast, the spermatozoa adjacent to the salt drop are represented only by a mass of sperm tails (Fig. 6).

In areas between these two extremes one finds a whole sequence of stages in swelling and solution of the highly condensed sperm nuclei.   As the salt content rises the nuclei first become swollen, with little change of shape (Fig. 4).   With further increase in size (to approximately four times the original volume) the nucleus becomes a sphere, which internally shows a most striking resemblance to a resting nucleus (Fig. 8)— or rather more to an early prophase, for it has none of the heterochromatic masses which are so characteristic of most resting nuclei.   At any one focal plane the nucleus appears at first sight granular, but focussing quickly shows that the granules are actually the endwise views of threads.   This observation is confirmed by the next events, for upon further swelling (e.g. to about 12 times the size of the sperm head) the nuclear membrane breaks down; and in place of the nucleus an entangled mass of threads, the chromosomes, then lies at the anterior end of the sperm tail.   Release of the chromosomes occurs with dramatic speed; and they actually spring out of the nucleus and writhe about as if they were so many steel springs which had been compressed within the nuclear membrane.   The threads appear somewhat more slender than those first seen within the swelling nucleus; and when isolated it can be seen that the released threads have the form of loose helices.   There is good reason, therefore, to regard them as the chromonemata.   When the salt content of the medium continues to rise a stage is soon reached where the chromosomes are no longer visible (Fig. 5).

These interesting structural changes in the sperm nucleus proceed quite rapidly when the cells are in a region of rising salt concentration.   However, if sperms are placed for some time in various salt strengths below 1.0 M, the sequence of nuclear changes becomes arrested at one particular stage for each concentration.   In 0.8 M NaCl the nuclei are finally slightly swollen, but never become spherical.   The spherical nucleus, with chromosomes visible within it, is reached in 0.9 M NaCl.   The final swelling and disappearance take place only when the salt concentration is very nearly 1.0 M.

Cytological examination shows that the residue which sediments after 1 M NaCl extraction consists largely of sperm tails.   The mitochondrial body, or nebenkern, likewise is not dissolved by the sodium chloride.   Nucleus, tail, and mitochondrial body make up practically the total volume of the salmonid sperm.   The cytological observations indicate that, of these, only the nucleus contributes to the 1 M NaCl extract, and that this contribution is all, or nearly all, of the nuclear substance.

Practically complete extraction of nucleoprotamine can be accomplished with 1 M NaCl.   The residue remaining after extraction gives only a faint Feulgen reaction, indicating that all but traces of desoxyribose nucleic acid have been extracted.   The low phosphorus content of the residue is further evidence that practically all the desoxyribose nucleic acid has been extracted. The residue represents less than 20 per cent of the sperm mass and its phosphorus content is only 0.35 per cent, to be compared with the 5.03 per cent P content of the whole sperm.   And the residue contains little, if any, protamine, for the residue has only 13.1 per cent N, as against the 18.2 per cent of the whole sperm.

Being able to extract practically all of the nucleoprotamine from a known mass of sperm, our next problem is to determine what fraction of that mass consists of nuclei.   This can be accomplished by washing a suspension of sperm with dilute citric acid, for the treatment removes tails and midpieces leaving a suspension of clean nuclei (as shown in Fig. 7).   We used citric acid to isolate the sperm nucleus because we had previously found this technique effective in isolating the nuclei of liver, kidney, thymus, and other cells.   The use of citric acid to remove cytoplasm and leave the nuclei of tissue cells was introduced by Crossmon (15) and Stoneburg (16), but the equivalent of citric acid had been used many years earlier by Miescher.   He found that dilute acetic acid removes the tail and midpiece of the salmon sperm, and there can be little doubt that in using citric acid we are simply replacing acetic acid with another weak acid.   After treating sperm with citric acid (and the same holds for acetic acid) the nucleoprotamine is changed so that it is no longer readily extracted by 1 M NaCl.   Because of this, our procedure is to take a suspension of trout sperm, determine at once the mass of dried sperm material per cubic centimeter, and then divide the suspension into two parts: from one of these nucleoprotamine is extracted with 1 M NaCl, isolated, dried, and weighed; the other part of the suspension is treated with citric acid and the isolated nuclei are dried and weighed.   In these experiments preparations are carefully washed with alcohol and ether before being dried, so that all the results obtained refer to lipid-free material.   The quantity of nucleoprotamine isolated is 81.5 per cent of the mass of the sperm.   The nucleus is found to be 89 per cent of the mass of the sperm cell, and nucleoprotamine accounts, therefore, for 91 per cent of the mass of the nucleus.

The trout sperm used in this experiment were centrifuged and washed once with 500 cc. of the saline mentioned above and then brought to a volume of 200 cc.   Of this two 10 cc. samples were taken for dry weight determinations.   The weights were 103.0 mg. and 103.4 mg., so that 1 cc. of the sperm suspension contained 10.34 mg. of sperm substance.   For determination of the nuclear mass 80 cc. of the suspension (containing 825.6 mg. sperm) were taken.   The sperm were washed three times with 0.2 per cent citric acid, 500 cc. being used for each washing.   The sperm heads were washed with 65 per cent alcohol, hot 95 per cent alcohol, and ether.   Dry weight was 740 mg. or 89.6 per cent of the sperm mass.   Nucleoprotamine was extracted from two samples of the whole sperm suspension.   In one case 30 cc. of the suspension (containing 309.6 mg. sperm) were taken.   To this were added 30 cc. of 2 M NaCl and

190 cc. of 1 M NaCl. To another sample of the sperm suspension consisting of 70 cc. (containing 722.4 mg. sperm) were added 70 cc. of 2 M NaCl and 160 cc. 1 M NaCl. These mixtures were stirred in the Waring blendor for a few minutes, stirred overnight with an ordinary mechanical stirrer, and then before being centrifuged they were again placed in the Waring blendor. Centrifugation was for 60 minutes at 12,000 R.P.M. The supernatants were almost water-clear. Of the first sample 225 cc. of the supernatant were taken and of the second 250 cc. were taken. These fluids were added to 6 volumes of water. The fibrous precipitates were carefully collected, washed with 65 per cent alcohol, hot 95 per cent alcohol, ether, dried, and weighed: first sample, 227.8 mg. or 81.7 per cent of the sperm used; second sample, 491.8 mg. or 81.5 per cent of sperm used.

There are two sources of error in estimating the nucleoprotamine content of the trout sperm nucleus. In extracting and isolating nucleoprotamine a small quantity is lost. Another error may be introduced when tail and midpiece are separated from the sperm by citric acid, for some material other than nucleoprotamine may be removed from the nucleus at the same time. This would make the nucleus appear to be smaller than it actually is, and so render the estimate of the nuclear content of nucleoprotamine higher than it should be. The two errors would, accordingly, tend to balance each other.

The estimate of 91 per cent for the nucleoprotamine content of the trout sperm nucleus is considerably higher than Miescher's estimate of 81 per cent, made by an entirely different, and less direct, method. In this method protamine is extracted with dilute HCl, and the extraction is far from complete. This difficulty was recognized by Schmideberg, who edited Miescher's papers, and he attempted to compute how much protamine failed to be extracted, but the assumptions introduced in making this correction are unsatisfactory. High as the nucleoprotamine content of the trout sperm nucleus is, the remaining nuclear constituents are not negligible quantitatively. We have already isolated one other nuclear constituent. It will be described in another paper.

SUMMARY

The nucleoprotamine of trout sperm can be extracted completely with 1 M sodium chloride. On reducing the salt concentration to 0.14 M, physiological saline, the nucleoprotamine precipitates in long, fibrous strands. When the nucleoprotamine, dissolved in M NaCl, is dialyzed all the protamine diffuses through the membrane leaving behind highly polymerized, protein-free desoxyribose nucleic acid. The nucleoprotamine constitutes 91 per cent of the lipid-free mass of the sperm nucleus. While nucleoprotamine is being extracted by M NaCl a stage is reached at which the sperm chromosomes are clearly visible.

BIBLIOGRAPHY

1. Miescher, F., Die Histochemischen und Physiologischen Arbeiten, Leipzig, F. C. W. Vogel, 1897.
2. Kossel, A., The Protamines and Histones, New York, Longmans, Green and Co., 1928.
3. Steudel, H., *Z. physiol. Chem.*, 1913, **83,** 72.
4. Rasmussen, K. E., *Compt.-rend. trav. Lab. Carlsberg*, 1934, **20,** No. 6.
   Rasmussen, K. E., and Linderstrøm-Lang, K., *Compt.-rend. trav. Lab. Carlsberg*, 1935, **20,** No. 10.
5. Schlenk, W., and Kahmann, H., *Biochem. Z.*, 1938, **295,** 283.
6. Allen, R. J. L., *Biochem. J.*, 1940, **34,** 858.
7. Koch, F. C., and McMeekin, T. L., *J. Am. Chem. Soc.*, 1924, **46,** 2066.
8. Sevag, M. G., Lackman, D. B., and Smolens, J., *J. Biol. Chem.*, 1938, **124,** 425.
9. Dische, Z., *Mikrochemie*, 1930, **8,** 4.
10. Cohen, S. S., *J. Biol. Chem.*, 1945, **158,** 255.
11. Mirsky, A. E., and Pollister, A. W., *Proc. Nat. Acad. Sc.*, 1942, **28,** 344.
12. Hammarsten, E., *Biochem. Z.*, 1924, **144,** 383.
13. Bensley, R. R., and Hoerr, N. L., *Anat. Rec.*, 1934, **60,** 251, 449.
14. Crossmon, G., *Science*, 1937, **85,** 250.
15. Stoneburg, C. A., *J. Biol. Chem.*, 1939, **129,** 189.

EXPLANATION OF PLATES

PLATE 1

All figures are photomicrographs of unfixed salmonid spermatozoa, stained with crystal violet. Figs. 1 to 7 are *Salmo fario*. Fig. 8 is from *Salmo irideus*. All figures are magnified × 1960. The illumination was the 5460 Å line from an H4 Mercury arc lampisolated by Wratten Filter No. 62.

Figs. 1 to 3. Various views of normal spermatozoa, showing the three conspicuous morphological features. The nucleus is in the shape of a bell, ellipsoidal in cross-section: the narrowest profile is on the right in Fig. 3, while two of the three complete sperms of Fig. 2 are oriented with the nucleus in nearly its widest profile. The mitochondrial body, nebenkern, is a small approximately spherical structure at the broad base, or posterior end, of the nucleus. The tail is a filament approximately 11 times the length of the head.

FIG. 4. Spermatozoon from an area where the salt concentration was just high enough (approximately 0.8 M) to cause the first step in swelling.

FIG. 5. The same sperm as Fig. 4, 40 minutes later, when the salt concentration had risen because of diffusion from the 2 M droplet (to 1 M or higher), and the nucleus had dissolved.

FIG. 6. From a region adjacent to the 2 M NaCl droplet. The sperm nuclei have disappeared, leaving tails only. (The mitochondrial bodies also remain, but they are not shown here since they have become detached and have floated upward to the lower surface of the cover-slip.)

FIG. 7. Isolated nuclei, after citric acid treatment has dissolved the sperm tails.

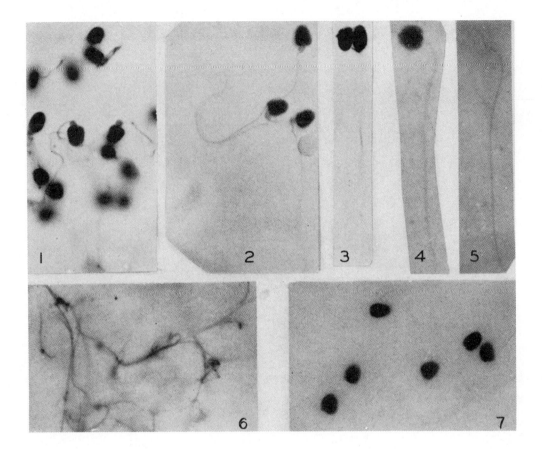

(Pollister and Mirsky: Nucleoprotamine of trout sperm)

II. THE NATURE OF GENETIC MATERIAL

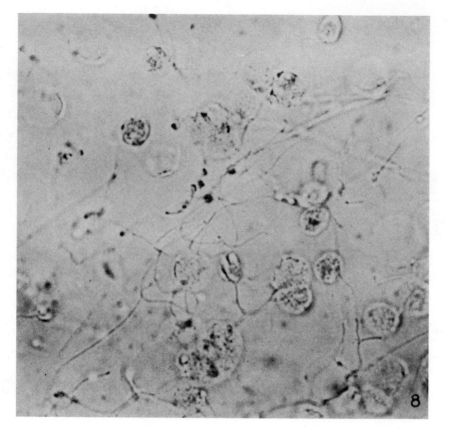

(Pollister and Mirsky: Nucleoprotamine of trout sperm)

PLATE 2

FIG. 8. Sperm nuclei in a zone where the NaCl concentration is approaching 1 M. The nuclei have all become spherical.   In the less swollen nuclei the chromosomes may be seen.

INSTITUT DE FRANCE.

ACADÉMIE DES SCIENCES.

(Extrait des *Comptes rendus des séances de l'Académie des Sciences*, t. 226, p. 1061-1063, séance du 31 mars 1948.)

BIOCHIMIE DE L'HÉRÉDITÉ. — *L'acide désoxyribonucléique du noyau cellulaire, dépositaire des caractères héréditaires; arguments d'ordre analytique.* Note (*) de MM. André Boivin, Roger Vendrely et Mme Colette Vendrely.

Nous avons exposé antérieurement (1) comment l'analyse du phénomène des mutations (*dirigées*) chez les bactéries, par des principes actifs de nature désoxyribonucléique, conduit à faire de l'acide désoxyribonucléique du noyau cellulaire le dépositaire des caractères héréditaires de l'espèce. Chaque gêne aurait pour constituant essentiel une macromolécule d'un acide désoxyribonucléique particulier. S'il en va bien ainsi, chez une même espèce vivante la quantité absolue d'acide désoxyribonucléique doit être la même pour tous les noyaux de toutes les cellules, à l'exception des gamètes (haploïdes) qui doivent en contenir deux fois moins. Nous avons entrepris de soumettre cette hypothèse au contrôle de l'expérience, en opérant sur des noyaux isolés provenant de cellules animales, et nous rapportons ici nos premier résultats.

TECHNIQUES EMPLOYÉES : 1° *Isolement des noyaux.* — Nous inspirant spécialement des ravaux de Stoneburg, nous avons eu recours au broyage des tissus en présence d'acide citrique (M/3), suivi de centrifugations différentielles répétées à basse température. Cela nous a permis d'obtenir des grammes de noyaux, absolument débarrassés de tous débris cellulaires.

2° *Numération des noyaux.* — Nous avons utilisé une *cellule* servant à compter les globules sanguins.

3° *Dosage de l'acide désoxyribonucléique dans les noyaux.* — Nous avons commence

---

(*) Seance du 22 mars 1948.
(1) A. Boivin, R. Vendrely et Y. Lehoult, *Comptes rendus*, 221, 1945, p. 646; A. Boivin, *Cold Spring Harbor Symp. quant. Biol.*, 12, 1947, p. 7; A. Boivin, R. Tulasne et R. Vendrely, *Comptes rendus*, 225, 1947, p. 703.

par priver les noyaux de leur acido-soluble par de l'acide trichloracétique froid, puis en avons retiré l'acide nucléique total par de l'acide trichloracétique chaud (selon Schneider), pour le doser par les purines qu'il libère à l'hydrolyse; nous en avons retranché l'acide ribonucléique estimé colorimétriquement (suivant von Euler) dans l'extrait trichloracétique obtenu à chaud. Nous avons contrôlé nos résultats, d'une part par une séparation de l'acide désoxyribonucléique à la soude (selon Schmidt et Thannhauser), suivie du dosage de cet acide par les purines, d'autre part par une évaluation colorimétrique (suivant Dische) du désoxyribose contenu dans l'extrait trichloracétique obtenu à chaud. Ces diverses méthodes ont fourni des résultats concordants. Un calcul aisé nous a permis ensuite de rapporter les données analytiques à un seul noyau.

Nous avons opéré sur des noyaux isolés du foie, du pancréas, du rein et du thymus provenant de veaux. Il s'agit là d'organes différant largement les uns des autres tant par la taille que par le degré de colorabilité de leurs noyaux et qui, au surplus, présentent des richesses fort diverses en acide désoxyribonucléique (le thymus est, par exemple, 10 à 20 fois plus riche que le foie, à l'unité de poids d'organe total). Certains de ces organes (foie, thymus) ne livrent guère qu'une seule catégorie de noyaux; d'autres (pancréas, rein) en livrent plusieurs en mélange. Or chose remarquable, lorsqu'on recherche la teneur absolue d'un noyau en acide désoxyribonucléique, on trouve très sensiblement la même valeur d'un organe à l'autre et d'un individu à l'autre, soit en moyenne $6,5 \times 10^{-6} \gamma$, avec des écarts ne dépassant pas 10 % et qu'expliquent largement les erreurs d'origine analytique. Nous avons opéré, d'autre part, sur des spermatozoïdes de taureaux et avons trouvé alors une teneur de $3,4 \times 10^{-6} \gamma$, c'est-à-dire très approximativement la moitié de celle qui répond aux organes.

Les noyaux isolés renferment une quantité d'acide désoxyribonucléique se situant autour de 25 à 30 % de leur poids sec. Ils sont par contre très pauvres en acide ribonucléique (par exemple $0,3$ à $0,5 \times 10^{-6} \gamma$ par noyau, soit environ 20 fois moins que d'acide désoxyribonucléique). Mais nous nous sommes aperçus que l'acide citrique, à la concentration utilisée par nous, solubilise largement les ribonucléoprotéines s'il laisse insolubles les désoxyribonucléoprotéines. D'autre part, il a l'avantage d'inhiber totalement l'action des désoxyribonucléases (mais non des ribonucléases) éventuellement présentes.

Nous nous proposons d'étendre progressivement ces recherches à d'autres espèces animales : autres Mammifères (y compris l'Homme), Oiseaux, Vertébrés inférieurs et Invertébrés. Il sera intéressant de rechercher, sur du matériel approprié (gamètes d'échinodermes, par exemple) si, dans une même espèce, les ovules et les spermatozoïdes ont vraiment le même contenu en acide désoxyribonucléique. Les tissus végétaux et les microorganismes retiendront également notre attention. Nous pouvons déjà dire que chez les Bactéries (chez le Colibacille en particulier) le noyau bactérien, dont le diamètre est de l'ordre du demi-micron, renferme une quantité d'acide désoxyribonucléique de l'ordre de $10^{-8} \gamma$, au lieu de $10^{-6} \gamma$ chez les bovidés. A la suite de ses expériences d'irradiation, D. E. Lea (²) évalue à quelques centaines le nombre des gènes chez les bactéries. Si l'on admet qu'il existe une proportionnalité, au moins grossière, entre la teneur d'un noyau en acide désoxyribonucléique et le nombre de ses gènes, cela conduit à plusieurs dizaines de milliers de gènes pour les bovidés, résultat tout à fait plausible. D'autre part, compte tenu de la valeur du nombre d'Avogadro fournie par les physiciens, des observations de Lea et des nôtres, on peut calculer la masse moléculaire du gène désoxyribonucléique bactérien; on arrive à un ordre de grandeur de 10 000 000, fort acceptable. Nous pensons que l'analyse du noyau à travers la série des êtres vivants ne pourra manquer d'apporter des données vraiment intéressantes concernant la biochimie de l'hérédité.

⁄ (²) *Actions of Radiations on living Cells*, 1947, New-York.

GAUTHIER-VILLARS, IMPRIMEUR-LIBRAIRE DES COMPTES RENDUS DES SÉANCES DE L'ACADÉMIE DES SCIENCES
129069-48   Paris. — Quai des Grands-Augustins, 55.

II. THE NATURE OF GENETIC MATERIAL

Reprinted from the Proceedings of the NATIONAL ACADEMY OF SCIENCES,
Vol. 36, No. 11, pp. 643–654.   November, 1950

THE CONSTANCY OF DESOXYRIBOSE NUCLEIC ACID IN PLANT NUCLEI*

By HEWSON SWIFT

DEPARTMENT OF ZOOLOGY, THE UNIVERSITY OF CHICAGO

Communicated by Carl R. Moore, August 11, 1950

For a number of years considerable interest has been centered in the role of nucleic acids in cellular processes.   Recently desoxyribose nucleic acid (DNA) has been shown to possess interesting characteristics that have led several workers to consider it an essential component of the gene.[1-3] DNA is probably a universal constituent of plant and animal nuclei.   Its low turnover rate to radioactive phosphorus and nitrogen, in non-dividing tissues, is evidence for a chemical stability considerably greater than that of other cell components.[4, 5]   Moreover, recent analytic data on the actual amounts of DNA within nuclei have suggested that it possesses a quantitative stability as well.

Computations on the amount of DNA per nucleus have been made in two ways.   Chemical analyses of large numbers of cells, with the number present estimated by sample counts, have given the average amount of

DNA, per nucleus, for many thousand cells. Light absorption measurements made through a microscope have, on the other hand, yielded data on individual nuclei. Both methods involve technical difficulties and are open to certain criticisms. Nevertheless both biochemical[1, 2, 6] and microscopic[3, 7, 8] measurements by a number of different investigators have supported the concept first proposed by Boivin, Vendrely and Vendrely[1] that within the tissues of an organism the actual amount of DNA per nucleus is apparently constant.

Boivin, *et al.*, have considered that all somatic cells of an animal possess the same amount of DNA, with the gametes containing half this value. A number of discrepancies from this simple relation have been reported. Although some of these may be attributable to errors in the analytical techniques employed, at least two processes obviously involve naturally occurring variations. Ris and Mirsky[7] first showed that DNA classes with the ratio $1:2:4$ occur in the rat liver associated with polyploid nuclei. It was later found[3] that such DNA classes, apparently associated with polyploidy and polyteny, occur in a variety of animal tissues. Variation of another type occurs in association with the mitotic cycle. Since DNA in several animal tissues has been found to increase in interphase preceding cell division to twice the diploid amount, interphase nuclei of dividing tissues may contain anywhere from two to four times the amount found in the haploid sperm.[3] These variations in the amounts of DNA, associated with mitosis or DNA classes, cannot be considered in disagreement with the basic tenets of Boivin's theory. It is clear that, at least in many different animal tissues, the amount of DNA per nucleus is under rather definite quantitative restrictions. Interphase nuclei of non-dividing tissues, with a few possible exceptions, have been found to contain an amount of DNA approximately 2, 4, 8, etc., times that found in the gametes. A haploid amount of DNA has been found in sperm,[1, 2] spermatids[3, 9, 10] and male and female pronuclei.[8] In general these estimates of the nucleic acids in cells are at present accurate to 10 or 20%. The question of how precisely the quantitative relations are obeyed must await more accurate techniques.

The quantitative behavior of DNA in plant tissues has as yet received little attention. Schrader and Leuchtenberger[11] have recently shown that the amount of DNA varies from tissue to tissue in Tradescantia. The data presented, although they clearly show that the amount of DNA is different in different tissues, are not extensive enough to demonstrate the type of variability. Does DNA tend to occur in the well-marked constant units found for a number of animal tissues, or, as might be inferred from the work of Schrader and Leuchtenberger, does it fail to follow any definite quantitative pattern? The present work was primarily designed to answer this question.

Material and Methods.—Two plant species have been studied in detail and two others briefly. Plants of *Tradescantia paludosa* were kindly provided by Dr. J. M. Beal of the University of Chicago. Corn plants (*Zea mays*) were obtained from several sources, particularly commercial Golden Bantam, and three strains from the collection of Dr. M. M. Rhoades of the University of Illinois. Plants of *T. canaliculata* were collected in the Chicago region, and cultivated plants of *T. "virginiana,"* differing slightly from the typical native form, came from a Chicago garden. All material was fixed in neutral 50% formalin (one part of the stock 40% formaldehyde solution to one part of distilled water, with calcium carbonate added) immediately after removal from the plant. Pieces were small, with the smallest dimension rarely exceeding 1 mm., and buds were opened to permit rapid pentration. Fixation was for at least three hours. Material was thoroughly washed, sectioned in paraffin, and stained with the Feulgen reagent for one hour after an hydrolysis in normal hydrochloric acid of 14 minutes at 60°C. In the present study, wherever possible, all tissues to be compared were mounted together on the same slide, and where this was not done, a section of tissue previously studied was mounted beside the unknown. Control sections in five of the eight slide series studied gave essentially similar values. In the remaining three the Feulgen intensity of the control sections were slightly below that usually obtained, and all values from these series were consequently raised.

The amount of Feulgen dye in individual nuclei was estimated by photometric determinations made through a microscope. The technique was approximately as described previously[3, 12] with the following exceptions: Essentially monochromatic light was isolated by a Beckman spectrophotometer with a slit width of 0.1 or 0.03 mm. Measurements were made with a Leitz achromatic-aplanatic condenser, N.A. 1.4, a 90 × Leitz 2-mm. oil immersion apochromatic objective, N.A. 1.32, and a 20 × Bausch and Lomb coated hyperplane ocular, containing an iris diaphragm to minimize distortion from internal reflection. The microscope image, enlarged 1000 times, was projected on a field diaphragm, which allowed an area 2, 3, 4 or 5 mm. in diameter, taken in the center of the nuclear image to fall on the phototube. Measurements were made with a battery-powered 1P21 electron multiplier phototube, with output leads connected to a Farrand type B control unit and a Rubicon galvanometer. Measurements of corn tissues were made at the absorption peak of the Feulgen dye, 560 mμ. Tradescantia nuclei at this wave-length were too dark to measure accurately, and consequently were measured considerably off the maximum absorption, at 615 mμ. The extinction at this wave-length was about 22% of that at 560 mμ.

Photometric determinations of biological material are subject to a variety of technical variables [3] The most important of these in the present work were probably caused by the irregular distribution of the stainable components in the nucleus and inaccuracies in estimating nuclear volume. A strong formalin fixative, where rapid penetration is aided by using small pieces of tissue, tends to keep the chromatin in its natural extended state. Where the nuclei measured were markedly irregular, e.g., in meiotic diakinesis, measured values tended to be low. The apparatus was calibrated

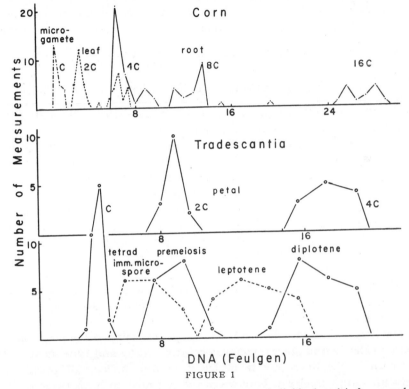

DNA (Feulgen)

FIGURE 1

Distribution of DNA (Feulgen) measurements on individual nuclei of corn and Tradescantia tissues. The amount of DNA is shown in arbitrary units. *Upper graph:* Corn microgamete nuclei from pollen grains (dashed lines), leaf nuclei (dotted lines) and nuclei from corn root zone of elongation (solid lines). *Middle graph:* Tradescantia petal nuclei from mature flower. *Lower graph:* Stages in Tradescantia pollen formation from developing anthers, showing measurements on premeiosis (preleptotene), leptotene, diplotene, tetrad and immature microspore stages.

as previously, and the non-specific light loss was found to be negligible by measuring unhydrolyzed controls.

The advisability of using the Feulgen reaction for quantitative microphotometric determinations of DNA has been discussed by a number of workers. It is now generally agreed that, where staining procedures are properly carried out, the Feulgen reaction can give an accurate relative estimate of the DNA in nuclei.[3, 7, 10]   Since the actual intensity of the dye produced can be markedly altered by such factors as the type of fixative used, size of the tissue fixed and slight changes in hydrolysis conditions no attempt has been made here to convert the data presented into absolute amounts of DNA.   All values are given in the arbitrary units used elsewhere.[3, 8]   The measured extinction (E) of a central region 2 to 5 microns in diameter of an uncut nucleus has been multiplied by the squared radius of the measured area (C^2) and divided by the fraction (F) of the total nuclear volume included in the measured region.   Units $= \dfrac{EC^2}{F}$, where $F = \dfrac{R^3 - (R^2 - C^2)^{1/2}}{R^3}$, and R is the radius of the nucleus.   Markedly aspherical nuclei were not measured.   Where nuclei were slightly ellipsoid, R was taken as the mean of major and minor axes.

Results.—(A) Non-Dividing Tissues: Photometric measurements made on tissues where mitoses were uncommon tended to fall in certain well-marked classes.   Means of these classes fit in the series $1:2:4:8:16:32$. The distributions of measured values from corn leaf and root, and Tradescantia petal are shown in figure 1.   Means for all measurements are given in tables 1 and 2.   The values are expressed as the total number of dye molecules per nucleus, in arbitrary units, and thus constitute a relative estimate of the DNA in nuclei.   In similar tissues the arbitrary units are about 2.5 times higher for Tradescantia than for corn.   Since the Tradescantia tissues were measured at a wave-length giving only about 22% of maximum extinction, these nuclei contain approximately 10 times the DNA found in corn.

The lowest values for Tradescantia have been found in the young microspore nuclei (tetrad stage), young generative nuclei and tube nuclei; and for corn in the microgamete nuclei of mature pollen, all presumably haploid.   Most nuclei in both species were found to have twice ($2C$) or four times ($4C$) the haploid amount.   Nuclei falling in class $8C$ have been found in Tradescantia stamen hairs, corn root and root cap and in the scutellum nuclei of the corn kernel.   In the root and scutellum $16C$ nuclei also occur.   In a few tissues, i.e., the root cap and zone of elongation in corn, and in the mature stamen hairs in Tradescantia, class $2C$ nuclei are rare and almost all nuclei belong to the higher classes.   In young stamen hairs, however, class $2C$ cells are common.   Measurements on the aleurone and endosperm of the corn kernel, tissues long known to be triploid through the joining of one microgamete with the $2N$ endosperm nucleus, fell in the series $3:6:12:24$.   Most aleurone nuclei in the kernels studied fell in class $6C$.   Endosperm nuclei were measured in young ears, since those of the mature kernel are highly irregular.   The smaller classes tended to be peripheral.

In the corn root zone of elongation most nuclei fell in classes $4C$ and $8C$. However, in certain rows of cells forming the major vessels of the root, larger classes (up to $32C$) were found.　When all the nuclei in such a vessel were measured in order from the root tip back to about $1500\,\mu$ from the tip,

TABLE 1

AVERAGE AMOUNTS OF DNA (FEULGEN) PER NUCLEUS IN VARIOUS TISSUES OF CORN
(*Zea mays*)

CELL TYPE	DNA CLASS	DNA IN ARBITRARY UNITS	STANDARD ERROR	NO. MEASURED
Microgamete nucleus (interphase)	C	1.6^a	0.06	22
Leaf				
(interphase)	$2C$	3.4^a	0.05	23
	$2C \rightarrow 4C$	4.8^a	..	1
	$4C$	6.6^a	0.12	19
(prophase)	$4C$	6.9	0.12	10
(telophase)	$2C$	3.2	0.09	12
Root cap (interphase)	$4C$	6.9	0.12	15
	$8C$	12.6	0.33	22
Root elongation zone (interphase)	$4C$	6.6^a	0.06	29
	$4C \rightarrow 8C$	8.7^a	..	6
	$8C$	12.5^a	0.27	19
	$8C \rightarrow 16C$	20.2^a	..	2
	$16C$	26.1^a	0.45	17
	$16C \rightarrow 32C$	33.8	..	2
	$32C$	49.0	..	6
Root meristem				
(interphase)	$2C \rightarrow 4C$	5.4^a	0.21	36
(prophase)	$4C$	6.4^a	0.09	15
(telophase)	$2C$	3.2^a	0.05	20
Embryo (interphase)	$2C$	3.6	0.07	15
	$4C$	7.1	0.13	15
Scutellum (interphase)	$2C$	3.3	0.09	20
	$4C$	6.4	0.11	40
	$8C$	12.6	0.24	15
	$16C$	26.2	..	5
Aleurone (interphase)	$3C$	4.8	0.07	15
	$6C$	10.1	0.20	40
	$12C$	20.5	0.60	15
Endosperm (interphase)	$3C$	5.0	0.06	15
	$6C$	9.3	0.14	17
	$12C$	19.1	0.60	16
	$24C$	38.0	1.20	10

[a] Data graphed in figure 1 or figure 2.

all classes from $4C$ to 16 or $32C$ were usually represented, in ascending order. From 6 to 12 nuclei have been found together from each class, and between these groups anywhere from 0 to 6 intermediate values have been obtained It is thus likely that these large vessel cells, while remaining in interphase undergo a periodic DNA doubling.　Values from a few such series are combined in figure 1 and table 1; in table 1 only values falling outside the expected interclass variability have been considered as intermediate. More work on this process is in progress.

Only one intermediate value has been obtained from leaf tissue in more than 150 measurements, and this came from the leaf base where a few mitoses were present. In the differentiated leaf, where cell division is absent, no intermediates have been found. It seems probable that intermediate amounts occur only when cells are synthesizing DNA for cell division (see below) or periodic DNA doubling.

(*B*) *Dividing Tissues:* The quantitative changes in DNA during the mitotic cycle were studied in corn root and leaf meristem, and in the root

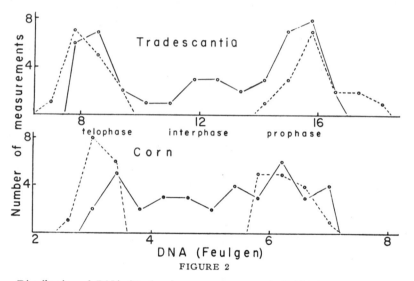

FIGURE 2

Distribution of DNA (Feulgen) measurements on individual nuclei from the root meristem of corn and Tradescantia. The amount of DNA is shown in arbitrary units. Interphase nuclei (solid lines), prophase nuclei (dotted lines at right), and telophase nuclei (dotted lines at left).

meristem and sporogenous tissue of Tradescantia. In all these tissues the process was essentially the same, paralleling that described previously for animals.[3] Where mitotic figures were common, measurements on interphase nuclei scattered widely between classes 2C and 4C (Fig. 2). Prophase values fell in 4C and telophases in 2C. Late prophase, metaphase and anaphase cells were too irregular to measure, but the behavior of DNA in these stages can easily be inferred. Apparently DNA increases during interphase to double the common diploid amount, reaching the 4C value at or before the visible beginning of prophase. During prophase and metaphase probably no DNA is synthesized. The 4C amount is then cut in two at anaphase, and the telophase nuclei each possess the $2C$ value. In the tissues studied no $8C$ or $16C$ prophase stages have been found, although

TABLE 2

AVERAGE AMOUNTS OF DNA (FEULGEN) PER NUCLEUS IN VARIOUS TISSUES OF *Tradescantia paludosa*

CELL TYPE	DNA CLASS	DNA IN ARBITRARY UNITS	STANDARD ERROR	NO. MEASURED
Leaf (interphase)	$2C$	8.5	0.07	20
Root meristem				
(interphase)	$2C \rightarrow 4C$	13.1^a	0.47	30
(prophase)	$4C$	16.2^a	0.29	15
(telophase)	$2C$	8.3^a	0.16	15
Tapetum (interphase)	$2C$	8.5	0.10	33
	$4C$	16.4	0.36	14
Petal (interphase)	$2C$	8.6^a	0.13	15
	$4C$	16.9^a	0.27	15
Stamen hairs (interphase)	$2C$	8.5	0.26	10
	$4C$	16.6	0.26	21
	$8C$	33.6	0.65	15
Sporogenous tissue				
(interphase)	$2C \rightarrow 4C$	13.1	1.00	15
(prophase)	$4C$	16.0	0.24	15
(telophase)	$2C$	8.1	0.19	15
Microspore mother cells				
(preleptotene)	$2C$	8.7^a	0.20	15
(leptotene)	$2C \rightarrow 4C$	12.6^a	0.39	15
(leptotene)	$2C \rightarrow 4C$	13.0	0.54	20
(zygotene)	$4C$	16.1	0.20	20
(pachytene)	$4C$	16.8	0.39	15
(diplotene)	$4C$	16.9^a	0.28	20
(diakinesis)	$4C$	16.3	0.25	20
Microspores				
(tetrad stage)	C	4.4^a	0.04	30
(early interphase)	C	4.0	0.10	20
(late interphase)	$C \rightarrow 2C$	5.9	0.34	10
(late interphase)	$C \rightarrow 2C$	7.4^a	0.24	25
(prophase)	$2C$	9.2	0.20	15
Pollen tube nuclei				
(early interphase)	C	4.2	0.09	15
(late interphase)	C	4.1	0.07	27
Generative nuclei				
(early interphase)	C	4.3	0.11	14
(late interphase)	$2C$	8.5	0.08	16

^{a} Data graphed in figure 1 or figure 2.

their occurrence might be expected in connection with the division of $4C$ or $8C$ nuclei. In the corn root zone of elongation where most interphase nuclei fall in class $4C$, cells apparently proceed directly into a $4C$ prophase without DNA synthesis, the $4C$ level then being restored in the following interphase. In the stamen hairs of Tradescantia most cell division was found to take place in developing buds, where $2C$ nuclei were common, following the usual pattern. No division stages were seen in the $4C$ or $8C$ nuclei from mature flowers.

(*C*) *Meiosis:* The behavior of DNA during pollen formation was studied only in Tradescantia, since the chromosomal material during most meiotic stages of corn was found too irregular for measurement. Anthers of Tradescantia, when first differentiated, are filled with rapidly dividing sporogenous cells. Measurements of these cells, in young anthers, tended to follow the pattern found in other dividing tissues (table 2). Prophases fell in $4C$, telophases in $2C$, and interphases were scattered in between. The beginning of meiosis is marked by general cessation of mitotic activity in the anther, except at the periphery. The nuclei measured in this pre-leptotene resting stage, before the thread-like chromosome structure becomes apparent, fell in class $2C$. During the subsequent leptotene, microspore mother cells were found to increase in amount of DNA so that measurements on this stage were intermediate between $2C$ and $4C$ (Fig. 1). The next stage measured was late zygotene, where only a few unpaired strands were visible. In these cells the DNA had approximately doubled ($4C$), and throughout the rest of the meiotic prophase no further increase was found. Immediately after the second maturation division, while still in the tetrad stage, the microspore nuclei fell in class C. Measurements on microspores from three later stages of development indicate that a comparatively long period ensues during which the microspore contains the class C amount, followed by a fairly rapid increase prior to mitosis. Data for microspores from one anther, intermediate between C and $2C$, are graphed in figure 1. At early prophase of the microspore division nuclei fall in class $2C$ and are divided into tube and generative nuclei, each with the class C amount. Some time before anthesis the generative nucleus increases to $2C$, but the tube nucleus remains at the C amount. In the mature pollen most generative nuclei become very elongate and are thus impossible to measure, but a few continue to be spheroidal, and in these the DNA can be determined. The two microgamete nuclei resulting from division of the generative nucleus were not measured in Tradescantia, but the microgamete nuclei were studied in corn and fell in class C (Fig. 1 and table 1).

The course of DNA in Tradescantia meiosis can thus be outlined briefly as follows: The earliest microspore mother cells fall in class $2C$, increasing during leptotene and possibly also during zygotene to $4C$ for the remaining stages of the meiotic prophase. The four tetrad nuclei resulting from the maturation divisions each have the C amount, increasing to $2C$ before the microspore mitosis. This division results in class C tube and generative nuclei, the latter increasing to $2C$ before anthesis. The generative nucleus apparently divides to form two haploid (C) microgamete nuclei.

(*D*) *Strain and Species Differences:* As mentioned above, nuclei of *Tradescantia paludosa* contain about ten times the DNA found in corn nuclei of the same class. The amount of DNA in *T. paludosa* leaf nuclei was compared with that found in two other closely related Tradescantia species (table 3). Both species have a haploid chromosome number of 12, twice that of *T. paludosa*, and thus it is not surprising to find the diploid nuclei contain about twice the DNA. Interspecific variation in amounts of DNA has been reported for animals and is not unexpected in view of the deletions, duplications, polysomaty, etc., considered to accompany evolution. On the same basis one would also expect the amount of DNA per nucleus might differ to some extent in various strains of the same species. To test this possibility similar tissues from two corn strains, differing in amount of heterochromatin, were mounted together and measured. Strain *A* (table 3) contained several *B* chromosomes and knobs, and the interphase nuclei showed the chromocenters associated with them.[13] Strain *B* had no *B* chromosomes and contained only a small amount of

TABLE 3

AVERAGE AMOUNTS OF DNA (FEULGEN) PER NUCLEUS IN TISSUES OF TWO STRAINS OF CORN AND THREE SPECIES OF TRADESCANTIA

	LEAF			ROOT		
	DNA IN ARBITRARY UNITS	STANDARD ERROR	NO. MEASURED	DNA IN ARBITRARY UNITS	STANDARD ERROR	NO. MEASURED
Corn strain A B	6.4	0.12	15	6.6	0.08	15
Corn strain B A	7.2	0.10	15	7.4	0.12	15
T. paludosa	8.5	0.08	25			
T. "virginiana"	16.8	0.20	25			
T. canaliculata	16.1	0.18	25			

heterochromatin on chromosome 6. Class 4*C* nuclei, from root and leaf, showed a difference in DNA between strains of about 10%.

Discussion.—The data presented indicate that DNA follows quantitative restrictions of the same general type reported for animal tissues. Three points may be stressed: (1) The amount per nucleus shows a marked step-like occurrence. (2) There is a duplication with mitosis and a reduction with meiosis. (3) Since species and strains have characteristic amounts of DNA it is apparent that the quantities involved are directly associated with the genotype. At least for the present these factors seem best interpreted by considering DNA as a component of the gene.

A considerable amount of recent cytological evidence has accumulated that points to the occurrence of "supernumerary chromonemal reproductions" as they have been called by Lorz[14] in numerous plant tissues. In several instances chromosomes have been described as 2, 4 or 8 stranded (polytene).[15,16] Endomitotic cycles, such as those described in the tapetum of Spinacia[17] or tomato,[18] are known to cause doubling of the chromosome number, and where differentiated resting nuclei have been stimulated to divide by auxins[19] or other treatment, polyploid nuclei with 2, 4, 8, etc., times the diploid chromosome number have been found. As pointed out by Schrader and Leuchtenberger it seems likely that the occurrence of varying amounts of DNA is associated with such factors.

The nuclei measured in the course of the present work naturally represent an extremely small sample. Nevertheless it is interesting that so few intermediate values have been found in non-dividing tissues. This would seem to indicate that the "endomitotic" processes, during which DNA doubling occurs, are comparatively rapid, and that unsynchronized chromonemal reproductions of the type seen in Rhoeo[19] are rare in the tissues studied. They may be more common in the older nuclei, which are often too irregular to measure.

The conclusion seems unavoidable, from both cytological and photometric evidence, that many, and in some tissues most, cells typically contain multiple chromonemal sets. The role played by these cells in the economy of the organism can at present only be conjectured. By analogy with the situation in autopolyploid plants one might expect the physiological balance to be altered. It has often been suggested that endomitotic gene doubling is associated with differentiation.[20, 21] However, in Tradescantia stamen hairs, as well as in some mammalian tissues, the higher classes do not appear until differentiation is completed.

Summary.—Photometric determinations on individual Feulgen-stained corn and Tradescantia nuclei support the view that DNA occurs in well-marked units characteristic of the strain or species. Nuclei with 2, 4, 8, 16 or 32 times the haploid (microgamete) value occur. Preceding mitosis DNA increases in interphase to twice the dipoloid amount. In meiosis the DNA is reduced, so that the microgamete contains half the diploid value.

* Aided by a grant from the Dr. Wallace C. and Clara A. Abbott Memorial Fund of The University of Chicago.

[1] Boivin, A., Vendrely, R., and Vendrely, C., *C. R. Acad. Sci.*, Paris, **226**, 1061–1063 (1948).

[2] Mirsky, A. E., and Ris, H., *Nature*, **163**, 666–667 (1949).

[3] Swift, H. H., *Physiol. Zool.*, **23**, 169–198 (1950).

[4] Brues, A., Tracy, M. M., and Cohn, W. E., *J. Biol. Chem.*, **155**, 619–633 (1944).

[5] Brown, G. B., *Cold Spring Harbor Symp. Quant. Biol.*, **13**, 43–51 (1948).

[6] Vendrely, R., and Vendrely, C., *Experientia*, **4**, 434–436 (1948).

[7] Ris, H., and Mirsky, A. E., *J. Gen. Physiol.*, **33**, 125–145 (1949).

[8] Alfert, M. (in press) (1950).

[9] Lison, L., and Pasteels, J., *Compt. rend. soc. biol.*, **143**, 1607–1608 (1949).

[10] Pasteels, J., and Lison, L., *C. R. Acad. Sci.*, Paris, **230**, 780–782 (1950).

[11] Schrader, F., and Leuchtenberger, C., Proc. Natl. Acad. Sci., **35**, 464–468 (1949).

[12] Pollister, A. W., and Ris, H., *Cold Spring Harbor Symp. Quant. Biol.*, **12**, 147–157 (1947).

[13] Morgan, D. T., *J. Hered.*, **34**, 194–198 (1943).
[14] Lorz, A. P., *Bot. Rev.*, **13**, 597–624 (1947).
[15] Kaufmann, B. P., *Ibid.*, **14**, 57–126 (1948).
[16] Duncan, R. E., *J. Hered.* (in press) (1950).
[17] Witkus, E. R., *Am. J. Bot.*, **32**, 326–330 (1945).
[18] Brown, S. W., *Ibid.*, **36**, 703–716 (1949).
[19] Huskins, G. L., and Steinitz, L. M., *J. Hered.*, **39**, 66 77 (1948).
[20] Jacobi, W., *Zeitschr. mikr.-anat. Forsch.*, **38**, 161–240 (1935).
[21] Huskins, G. L., *Am. Nat.*, **81**, 401–434 (1947).

II. THE NATURE OF GENETIC MATERIAL

[Reprinted from THE JOURNAL OF GENERAL PHYSIOLOGY, September 20, 1952,
Vol. 36, No. 1, pp. 39–56]
Printed in U.S.A.

INDEPENDENT FUNCTIONS OF VIRAL PROTEIN AND NUCLEIC ACID IN GROWTH OF BACTERIOPHAGE*

BY A. D. HERSHEY AND MARTHA CHASE

(*From the Department of Genetics, Carnegie Institution of Washington, Cold Spring
Harbor, Long Island*)

(Received for publication, April 9, 1952)

The work of Doermann (1948), Doermann and Dissosway (1949), and Anderson and Doermann (1952) has shown that bacteriophages T2, T3, and T4 multiply in the bacterial cell in a non-infective form. The same is true of the phage carried by certain lysogenic bacteria (Lwoff and Gutmann, 1950). Little else is known about the vegetative phase of these viruses. The experiments reported in this paper show that one of the first steps in the growth of T2 is the release from its protein coat of the nucleic acid of the virus particle, after which the bulk of the sulfur-containing protein has no further function.

Materials and Methods.—Phage T2 means in this paper the variety called T2H (Hershey, 1946); T2*h* means one of the host range mutants of T2; UV-phage means phage irradiated with ultraviolet light from a germicidal lamp (General Electric Co.) to a fractional survival of 10^{-5}.

Sensitive bacteria means a strain (H) of *Escherichia coli* sensitive to T2 and its *h* mutant; resistant bacteria B/2 means a strain resistant to T2 but sensitive to its *h* mutant; resistant bacteria B/2*h* means a strain resistant to both. These bacteria do not adsorb the phages to which they are resistant.

"Salt-poor" broth contains per liter 10 gm. bacto-peptone, 1 gm. glucose, and 1 gm. NaCl. "Broth" contains, in addition, 3 gm. bacto-beef extract and 4 gm. NaCl.

Glycerol-lactate medium contains per liter 70 mM sodium lactate, 4 gm. glycerol, 5 gm. NaCl, 2 gm. KCl, 1 gm. NH$_4$Cl, 1 mM MgCl$_2$, 0.1 mM CaCl$_2$, 0.01 gm. gelatin, 10 mg. P (as orthophosphate), and 10 mg. S (as MgSO$_4$), at pH 7.0.

Adsorption medium contains per liter 4 gm. NaCl, 5 gm. K$_2$SO$_4$, 1.5 gm. KH$_2$PO$_4$, 3.0 gm. Na$_2$HPO$_4$, 1 mM MgSO$_4$, 0.1 mM CaCl$_2$, and 0.01 gm. gelatin, at pH 7.0.

Veronal buffer contains per liter 1 gm. sodium diethylbarbiturate, 3 mM MgSO$_4$, and 1 gm. gelatin, at pH 8.0.

The HCN referred to in this paper consists of molar sodium cyanide solution neutralized when needed with phosphoric acid.

---

* This investigation was supported in part by a research grant from the National Microbiological Institute of the National Institutes of Health, Public Health Service. Radioactive isotopes were supplied by the Oak Ridge National Laboratory on allocation from the Isotopes Division, United States Atomic Energy Commission.

39

Adsorption of isotope to bacteria was usually measured by mixing the sample in adsorption medium with bacteria from 18 hour broth cultures previously heated to 70°C. for 10 minutes and washed with adsorption medium. The mixtures were warmed for 5 minutes at 37°C., diluted with water, and centrifuged. Assays were made of both sediment and supernatant fractions.

Precipitation of isotope with antiserum was measured by mixing the sample in 0.5 per cent saline with about 10^{11} per ml. of non-radioactive phage and slightly more than the least quantity of antiphage serum (final dilution 1:160) that would cause visible precipitation. The mixture was centrifuged after 2 hours at 37°C.

Tests with DNase (desoxyribonuclease) were performed by warming samples diluted in veronal buffer for 15 minutes at 37°C. with 0.1 mg. per ml. of crystalline enzyme (Worthington Biochemical Laboratory).

Acid-soluble isotope was measured after the chilled sample had been precipitated with 5 per cent trichloroacetic acid in the presence of 1 mg./ml. of serum albumin, and centrifuged.

In all fractionations involving centrifugation, the sediments were not washed, and contained about 5 per cent of the supernatant. Both fractions were assayed.

Radioactivity was measured by means of an end-window Geiger counter, using dried samples sufficiently small to avoid losses by self-absorption. For absolute measurements, reference solutions of P^{32} obtained from the National Bureau of Standards, as well as a permanent simulated standard, were used. For absolute measurements of S^{35} we relied on the assays (±20 per cent) furnished by the supplier of the isotope (Oak Ridge National Laboratory).

Glycerol-lactate medium was chosen to permit growth of bacteria without undesirable pH changes at low concentrations of phosphorus and sulfur, and proved useful also for certain experiments described in this paper. 18-hour cultures of sensitive bacteria grown in this medium contain about 2×10^9 cells per ml., which grow exponentially without lag or change in light-scattering per cell when subcultured in the same medium from either large or small seedings. The generation time is 1.5 hours at 37°C. The cells are smaller than those grown in broth. T2 shows a latent period of 22 to 25 minutes in this medium. The phage yield obtained by lysis with cyanide and UV-phage (described in context) is one per bacterium at 15 minutes and 16 per bacterium at 25 minutes. The final burst size in diluted cultures is 30 to 40 per bacterium, reached at 50 minutes. At 2×10^8 cells per ml., the culture lyses slowly, and yields 140 phage per bacterium. The growth of both bacteria and phage in this medium is as reproducible as that in broth.

For the preparation of radioactive phage, P^{32} of specific activity 0.5 mc./mg. or S^{35} of specific activity 8.0 mc./mg. was incorporated into glycerol-lactate medium, in which bacteria were allowed to grow at least 4 hours before seeding with phage. After infection with phage, the culture was aerated overnight, and the radioactive phage was isolated by three cycles of alternate slow (2000 G) and fast (12,000 G) centrifugation in adsorption medium. The suspensions were stored at a concentration not exceeding 4 μc./ml.

Preparations of this kind contain 1.0 to 3.0 $\times$ 10^{-12} μg. S and 2.5 to 3.5 $\times$ 10^{-11} μg. P per viable phage particle. Occasional preparations containing excessive amounts of sulfur can be improved by absorption with heat-killed bacteria that do not adsorb the phage. The radiochemical purity of the preparations is somewhat uncertain, owing to the possible presence of inactive phage particles and empty phage membranes. The presence in our preparations of sulfur (about 20 per cent) that is precipitated by antiphage serum (Table I) and either adsorbed by bacteria resistant to phage, or not adsorbed by bacteria sensitive to phage (Table VII), indicates contamination by membrane material. Contaminants of bacterial origin are probably negligible for present purposes as indicated by the data given in Table I. For proof that our principal findings reflect genuine properties of viable phage particles, we rely on some experiments with inactivated phage cited at the conclusion of this paper.

The Chemical Morphology of Resting Phage Particles.—Anderson (1949) found that bacteriophage T2 could be inactivated by suspending the particles in high concentrations of sodium chloride, and rapidly diluting the suspension with water. The inactivated phage was visible in electron micrographs as tadpole-shaped "ghosts." Since no inactivation occurred if the dilution was slow

TABLE I

Composition of Ghosts and Solution of Plasmolyzed Phage

Per cent of isotope]	Whole phage labeled with		Plasmolyzed phage labeled with	
	P^{32}	S^{35}	P^{32}	S^{35}
Acid-soluble..............................	—	—	1	—
Acid-soluble after treatment with DNase.......	1	1	80	1
Adsorbed to sensitive bacteria................	85	90	2	90
Precipitated by antiphage...................	90	99	5	97

he attributed the inactivation to osmotic shock, and inferred that the particles possessed an osmotic membrane. Herriott (1951) found that osmotic shock released into solution the DNA (desoxypentose nucleic acid) of the phage particle, and that the ghosts could adsorb to bacteria and lyse them. He pointed out that this was a beginning toward the identification of viral functions with viral substances.

We have plasmolyzed isotopically labeled T2 by suspending the phage (10^{11} per ml.) in 3 M sodium chloride for 5 minutes at room temperature, and rapidly pouring into the suspension 40 volumes of distilled water. The plasmolyzed phage, containing not more than 2 per cent survivors, was then analyzed for phosphorus and sulfur in the several ways shown in Table I. The results confirm and extend previous findings as follows:—

1. Plasmolysis separates phage T2 into ghosts containing nearly all the sulfur and a solution containing nearly all the DNA of the intact particles.

2. The ghosts contain the principal antigens of the phage particle detectable by our antiserum. The DNA is released as the free acid, or possibly linked to sulfur-free, apparently non-antigenic substances.

3. The ghosts are specifically adsorbed to phage-susceptible bacteria; the DNA is not.

4. The ghosts represent protein coats that surround the DNA of the intact particles, react with antiserum, protect the DNA from DNase (desoxyribonuclease), and carry the organ of attachment to bacteria.

5. The effects noted are due to osmotic shock, because phage suspended in salt and diluted slowly is not inactivated, and its DNA is not exposed to DNase.

TABLE II

Sensitization of Phage DNA to DNase by Adsorption to Bacteria

Phage adsorbed to		Phage labeled with	Non-sedimentable isotope, per cent	
			After DNase	No DNase
Live bacteria		S^{35}	2	1
" "		P^{32}	8	7
Bacteria heated before infection		S^{35}	15	11
" " " "		P^{32}	76	13
Bacteria heated after infection		S^{35}	12	14
" " " "		P^{32}	66	23
Heated unadsorbed phage: acid-soluble P^{32}	70°	P^{32}	5	
	80°	P^{32}	13	
	90°	P^{32}	81	
	100°	P^{32}	88	

Phage adsorbed to bacteria for 5 minutes at 37°C. in adsorption medium, followed by washing.

Bacteria heated for 10 minutes at 80°C. in adsorption medium (before infection) or in veronal buffer (after infection).

Unadsorbed phage heated in veronal buffer, treated with DNase, and precipitated with trichloroacetic acid.

All samples fractionated by centrifuging 10 minutes at 1300 G.

Sensitization of Phage DNA to DNase by Adsorption to Bacteria.—The structure of the resting phage particle described above suggests at once the possibility that multiplication of virus is preceded by the alteration or removal of the protective coats of the particles. This change might be expected to show itself as a sensitization of the phage DNA to DNase. The experiments described in Table II show that this happens. The results may be summarized as follows:—

1. Phage DNA becomes largely sensitive to DNase after adsorption to heat-killed bacteria.

2. The same is true of the DNA of phage adsorbed to live bacteria, and then

heated to 80°C. for 10 minutes, at which temperature unadsorbed phage is not sensitized to DNase.

3. The DNA of phage adsorbed to unheated bacteria is resistant to DNase, presumably because it is protected by cell structures impervious to the enzyme.

Graham and collaborators (personal communication) were the first to discover the sensitization of phage DNA to DNase by adsorption to heat-killed bacteria.

The DNA in infected cells is also made accessible to DNase by alternate freezing and thawing (followed by formaldehyde fixation to inactivate cellular enzymes), and to some extent by formaldehyde fixation alone, as illustrated by the following experiment.

Bacteria were grown in broth to 5×10^7 cells per ml., centrifuged, resuspended in adsorption medium, and infected with about two P^{32}-labeled phage per bacterium. After 5 minutes for adsorption, the suspension was diluted with water containing per liter 1.0 mM $MgSO_4$, 0.1 mM $CaCl_2$, and 10 mg. gelatin, and recentrifuged. The cells were resuspended in the fluid last mentioned at a concentration of 5×10^8 per ml. This suspension was frozen at $-15°C$. and thawed with a minimum of warming, three times in succession. Immediately after the third thawing, the cells were fixed by the addition of 0.5 per cent (v/v) of formalin (35 per cent HCHO). After 30 minutes at room temperature, the suspension was dialyzed free from formaldehyde and centrifuged at 2200 G for 15 minutes. Samples of P^{32}-labeled phage, frozen-thawed, fixed, and dialyzed, and of infected cells fixed only and dialyzed, were carried along as controls.

The analysis of these materials, given in Table III, shows that the effect of freezing and thawing is to make the intracellular DNA labile to DNase, without, however, causing much of it to leach out of the cells. Freezing and thawing and formaldehyde fixation have a negligible effect on unadsorbed phage, and formaldehyde fixation alone has only a mild effect on infected cells.

Both sensitization of the intracellular P^{32} to DNase, and its failure to leach out of the cells, are constant features of experiments of this type, independently of visible lysis. In the experiment just described, the frozen suspension cleared during the period of dialysis. Phase-contrast microscopy showed that the cells consisted largely of empty membranes, many apparently broken. In another experiment, samples of infected bacteria from a culture in salt-poor broth were repeatedly frozen and thawed at various times during the latent period of phage growth, fixed with formaldehyde, and then washed in the centrifuge. Clearing and microscopic lysis occurred only in suspensions frozen during the second half of the latent period, and occurred during the first or second thawing. In this case the lysed cells consisted wholly of intact cell membranes, appearing empty except for a few small, rather characteristic refractile bodies apparently attached to the cell walls. The behavior of intracellular P^{32} toward DNase, in either the lysed or unlysed cells, was not significantly different from that shown in Table III, and the content of P^{32} was only slightly less after lysis. The phage liberated during freezing and thawing was also titrated in this experiment. The lysis occurred without appreciable liberation of phage in suspensions frozen up to and including the 16th minute, and the 20 minute sample yielded only five per bacterium. Another sample of the culture formalinized at 30 minutes, and centrifuged without freezing, contained 66 per cent of the P^{32} in non-sedimentable form. The yield of extracellular phage at 30 minutes was 108 per bacterium, and the sedimented material consisted largely of formless debris but contained also many apparently intact cell membranes.

TABLE III

Sensitization of Intracellular Phage to DNase by Freezing, Thawing, and Fixation with Formaldehyde

	Unadsorbed phage frozen, thawed, fixed	Infected cells frozen, thawed, fixed	Infected cells fixed only
Low speed sediment fraction			
Total P^{32}...............................	—	71	86
Acid-soluble................................	—	0	0.5
Acid-soluble after DNase....................	—	59	28
Low speed supernatant fraction			
Total P^{32}...............................	—	29	14
Acid-soluble................................	1	0.8	0.4
Acid-soluble after DNase....................	11	21	5.5

The figures express per cent of total P^{32} in the original phage, or its adsorbed fraction.

We draw the following conclusions from the experiments in which cells infected with P^{32}-labeled phage are subjected to freezing and thawing.

1. Phage DNA becomes sensitive to DNAse after adsorption to bacteria in buffer under conditions in which no known growth process occurs (Benzer, 1952; Dulbecco, 1952).

2. The cell membrane can be made permeable to DNase under conditions that do not permit the escape of either the intracellular P^{32} or the bulk of the cell contents.

3. Even if the cells lyse as a result of freezing and thawing, permitting escape of other cell constituents, most of the P^{32} derived from phage remains inside the cell membranes, as do the mature phage progeny.

4. The intracellular P^{32} derived from phage is largely freed during spontaneous lysis accompanied by phage liberation.

We interpret these facts to mean that intracellular DNA derived from phage is not merely DNA in solution, but is part of an organized structure at all times during the latent period.

Liberation of DNA from Phage Particles by Adsorption to Bacterial Fragments.—The sensitization of phage DNA to specific depolymerase by adsorption to bacteria might mean that adsorption is followed by the ejection of the phage DNA from its protective coat. The following experiment shows that this is in fact what happens when phage attaches to fragmented bacterial cells.

TABLE IV

Release of DNA from Phage Adsorbed to Bacterial Debris

	Phage labeled with	
	S^{35}	P^{32}
Sediment fraction		
Surviving phage	16	22
Total isotope	87	55
Acid-soluble isotope	0	2
Acid-soluble after DNase	2	29
Supernatant fraction		
Surviving phage	5	5
Total isotope	13	45
Acid-soluble isotope	0.8	0.5
Acid-soluble after DNase	0.8	39

S^{35}- and P^{32}-labeled T2 were mixed with identical samples of bacterial debris in adsorption medium and warmed for 30 minutes at 37°C. The mixtures were then centrifuged for 15 minutes at 2200 G, and the sediment and supernatant fractions were analyzed separately. The results are expressed as per cent of input phage or isotope.

Bacterial debris was prepared by infecting cells in adsorption medium with four particles of T2 per bacterium, and transferring the cells to salt-poor broth at 37°C. The culture was aerated for 60 minutes, M/50 HCN was added, and incubation continued for 30 minutes longer. At this time the yield of extracellular phage was 400 particles per bacterium, which remained unadsorbed because of the low concentration of electrolytes. The debris from the lysed cells was washed by centrifugation at 1700 G, and resuspended in adsorption medium at a concentration equivalent to 3×10^9 lysed cells per ml. It consisted largely of collapsed and fragmented cell membranes. The adsorption of radioactive phage to this material is described in Table IV. The following facts should be noted.

1. The unadsorbed fraction contained only 5 per cent of the original phage particles in infective form, and only 13 per cent of the total sulfur. (Much of this sulfur must be the material that is not adsorbable to whole bacteria.)

2. About 80 per cent of the phage was inactivated. Most of the sulfur of this phage, as well as most of the surviving phage, was found in the sediment fraction.

3. The supernatant fraction contained 40 per cent of the total phage DNA (in a form labile to DNase) in addition to the DNA of the unadsorbed surviving phage. The labile DNA amounted to about half of the DNA of the inactivated phage particles, whose sulfur sedimented with the bacterial debris.

4. Most of the sedimentable DNA could be accounted for either as surviving phage, or as DNA labile to DNase, the latter amounting to about half the DNA of the inactivated particles.

Experiments of this kind are unsatisfactory in one respect: one cannot tell whether the liberated DNA represents all the DNA of some of the inactivated particles, or only part of it.

Similar results were obtained when bacteria (strain B) were lysed by large amounts of UV-killed phage T2 or T4 and then tested with P^{32}-labeled T2 and T4. The chief point of interest in this experiment is that bacterial debris saturated with UV-killed T2 adsorbs T4 better than T2, and debris saturated with T4 adsorbs T2 better than T4. As in the preceding experiment, some of the adsorbed phage was not inactivated and some of the DNA of the inactivated phage was not released from the debris.

These experiments show that some of the cell receptors for T2 are different from some of the cell receptors for T4, and that phage attaching to these specific receptors is inactivated by the same mechanism as phage attaching to unselected receptors. This mechanism is evidently an active one, and not merely the blocking of sites of attachment to bacteria.

Removal of Phage Coats from Infected Bacteria.—Anderson (1951) has obtained electron micrographs indicating that phage T2 attaches to bacteria by its tail. If this precarious attachment is preserved during the progress of the infection, and if the conclusions reached above are correct, it ought to be a simple matter to break the empty phage membranes off the infected bacteria, leaving the phage DNA inside the cells.

The following experiments show that this is readily accomplished by strong shearing forces applied to suspensions of infected cells, and further that infected cells from which 80 per cent of the sulfur of the parent virus has been removed remain capable of yielding phage progeny.

Broth-grown bacteria were infected with S^{35}- or P^{32}-labeled phage in adsorption medium, the unadsorbed material was removed by centrifugation, and the cells were resuspended in water containing per liter 1 mM $MgSO_4$, 0.1 mM $CaCl_2$, and 0.1 gm. gelatin. This suspension was spun in a Waring blendor (semimicro size) at 10,000 R.P.M. The suspension was cooled briefly in ice water at the end of each 60 second running period. Samples were removed at intervals, titrated (through antiphage serum) to measure the number of bacteria capable of yielding phage, and centrifuged to measure the proportion of isotope released from the cells.

The results of one experiment with each isotope are shown in Fig. 1. The data for S^{35} and survival of infected bacteria come from the same experiment, in which the ratio of added phage to bacteria was 0.28, and the concentrations

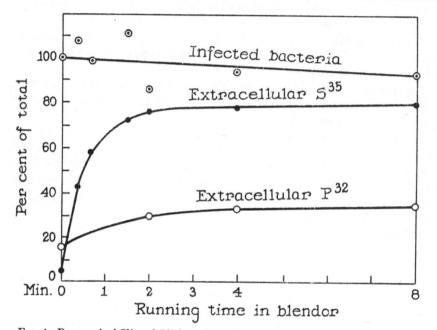

FIG. 1. Removal of S^{35} and P^{32} from bacteria infected with radioactive phage, and survival of the infected bacteria, during agitation in a Waring blendor.

of bacteria were 2.5×10^8 per ml. infected, and 9.7×10^8 per ml. total, by direct titration. The experiment with P^{32}-labeled phage was very similar. In connection with these results, it should be recalled that Anderson (1949) found that adsorption of phage to bacteria could be prevented by rapid stirring of the suspension.

At higher ratios of infection, considerable amounts of phage sulfur elute from the cells spontaneously under the conditions of these experiments, though the elution of P^{32} and the survival of infected cells are not affected by multiplicity of infection (Table V). This shows that there is a cooperative action among phage particles in producing alterations of the bacterial membrane which weaken the attachment of the phage. The cellular changes detected in this way may be related to those responsible for the release of bacterial components from infected bacteria (Prater, 1951; Price, 1952).

A variant of the preceding experiments was designed to test bacteria at a later stage in the growth of phage. For this purpose infected cells were aerated in broth for 5 or 15 minutes, fixed by the addition of 0.5 per cent (v/v) commercial formalin, centrifuged, resuspended in 0.1 per cent formalin in water, and subsequently handled as described above. The results were very similar to those already presented, except that the release of P^{32} from the cells was slightly less, and titrations of infected cells could not be made.

The S^{35}-labeled material detached from infected cells in the manner described possesses the following properties. It is sedimented at 12,000 G, though less completely than intact phage particles. It is completely precipitated by

TABLE V

Effect of Multiplicity of Infection on Elution of Phage Membranes from Infected Bacteria

Running time in blendor	Multiplicity of infection	P^{32}-labeled phage		S^{35}-labeled phage	
		Isotope eluted	Infected bacteria surviving	Isotope eluted	Infected bacteria surviving
min.		*per cent*	*per cent*	*per cent*	*per cent*
0	0.6	10	120	16	101
2.5	0.6	21	82	81	78
0	6.0	13	89	46	90
2.5	6.0	24	86	82	85

The infected bacteria were suspended at 10^9 cells per ml. in water containing per liter 1 mM $MgSO_4$, 0.1 mM $CaCl_2$, and 0.1 gm. gelatin. Samples were withdrawn for assay of extracellular isotope and infected bacteria before and after agitating the suspension. In either case the cells spent about 15 minutes at room temperature in the eluting fluid.

antiphage serum in the presence of whole phage carrier. 40 to 50 per cent of it readsorbs to sensitive bacteria, almost independently of bacterial concentration between 2×10^8 and 10^9 cells per ml., in 5 minutes at 37°C. The adsorption is not very specific: 10 to 25 per cent adsorbs to phage-resistant bacteria under the same conditions. The adsorption requires salt, and for this reason the efficient removal of S^{35} from infected bacteria can be accomplished only in a fluid poor in electrolytes.

The results of these experiments may be summarized as follows:—

1. 75 to 80 per cent of the phage sulfur can be stripped from infected cells by violent agitation of the suspension. At high multiplicity of infection, nearly 50 per cent elutes spontaneously. The properties of the S^{35}-labeled material show that it consists of more or less intact phage membranes, most of which have lost the ability to attach specifically to bacteria.

2. The release of sulfur is accompanied by the release of only 21 to 35 per

cent of the phage phosphorus, half of which is given up without any mechanical agitation.

3. The treatment does not cause any appreciable inactivation of intracellular phage.

4. These facts show that the bulk of the phage sulfur remains at the cell surface during infection, and takes no part in the multiplication of intracellular phage. The bulk of the phage DNA, on the other hand, enters the cell soon after adsorption of phage to bacteria.

Transfer of Sulfur and Phosphorus from Parental Phage to Progeny.—We have concluded above that the bulk of the sulfur-containing protein of the resting phage particle takes no part in the multiplication of phage, and in fact does not enter the cell. It follows that little or no sulfur should be transferred from parental phage to progeny. The experiments described below show that this expectation is correct, and that the maximal transfer is of the order 1 per cent

Bacteria were grown in glycerol-lactate medium overnight and subcultured in the same medium for 2 hours at 37°C. with aeration, the size of seeding being adjusted nephelometrically to yield 2×10^8 cells per ml. in the subculture. These bacteria were sedimented, resuspended in adsorption medium at a concentration of 10^9 cells per ml., and infected with S^{35}-labeled phage T2. After 5 minutes at 37°C., the suspension was diluted with 2 volumes of water and resedimented to remove unadsorbed phage (5 to 10 per cent by titer) and S^{35} (about 15 per cent). The cells were next suspended in glycerol-lactate medium at a concentration of 2×10^8 per ml. and aerated at 37°C. Growth of phage was terminated at the desired time by adding in rapid succession 0.02 mM HCN and 2×10^{11} UV-killed phage per ml. of culture. The cyanide stops the maturation of intracellular phage (Doermann, 1948), and the UV-killed phage minimizes losses of phage progeny by adsorption to bacterial debris, and promotes the lysis of bacteria (Maaløe and Watson, 1951). As mentioned in another connection, and also noted in these experiments, the lysing phage must be closely related to the phage undergoing multiplication (*e.g.*, T2H, its *h* mutant, or T2L, but not T4 or T6, in this instance) in order to prevent inactivation of progeny by adsorption to bacterial debris.

To obtain what we shall call the maximal yield of phage, the lysing phage was added 25 minutes after placing the infected cells in the culture medium, and the cyanide was added at the end of the 2nd hour. Under these conditions, lysis of infected cells occurs rather slowly.

Aeration was interrupted when the cyanide was added, and the cultures were left overnight at 37°C. The lysates were then fractionated by centrifugation into an initial low speed sediment (2500 *G* for 20 minutes), a high speed supernatant (12,000 *G* for 30 minutes), a second low speed sediment obtained by recentrifuging in adsorption medium the resuspended high speed sediment, and the clarified high speed sediment.

The distribution of S^{35} and phage among fractions obtained from three cultures of this kind is shown in Table VI. The results are typical (except for the excessively good recoveries of phage and S^{35}) of lysates in broth as well as lysates in glycerol-lactate medium.

The striking result of this experiment is that the distribution of S^{35} among the fractions is the same for early lysates that do not contain phage progeny, and later ones that do. This suggests that little or no S^{35} is contained in the mature phage progeny. Further fractionation by adsorption to bacteria confirms this suggestion.

Adsorption mixtures prepared for this purpose contained about 5×10^9 heat-killed bacteria (70°C. for 10 minutes) from 18 hour broth cultures, and

TABLE VI

Per Cent Distributions of Phage and S^{35} among Centrifugally Separated Fractions of Lysates after Infection with S^{35}-Labeled T2

Fraction	Lysis at $t = 0$ S^{35}	Lysis at $t = 10$ S^{35}	Maximal yield	
			S^{35}	Phage
1st low speed sediment	79	81	82	19
2nd " " "	2.4	2.1	2.8	14
High speed "	8.6	6.9	7.1	61
" " supernatant	10	10	7.5	7.0
Recovery	100	100	96	100

Infection with S^{35}-labeled T2, 0.8 particles per bacterium. Lysing phage UV-killed *h* mutant of T2. Phage yields per infected bacterium: <0.1 after lysis at $t = 0$; 0.12 at $t = 10$; maximal yield 29. Recovery of S^{35} means per cent of adsorbed input recovered in the four fractions; recovery of phage means per cent of total phage yield (by plaque count before fractionation) recovered by titration of fractions.

about 10^{11} phage (UV-killed lysing phage plus test phage), per ml. of adsorption medium. After warming to 37°C. for 5 minutes, the mixtures were diluted with 2 volumes of water, and centrifuged. Assays were made from supernatants and from unwashed resuspended sediments.

The results of tests of adsorption of S^{35} and phage to bacteria (H) adsorbing both T2 progeny and *h*-mutant lysing phage, to bacteria (B/2) adsorbing lysing phage only, and to bacteria (B/2*h*) adsorbing neither, are shown in Table VII, together with parallel tests of authentic S^{35}-labeled phage.

The adsorption tests show that the S^{35} present in the seed phage is adsorbed with the specificity of the phage, but that S^{35} present in lysates of bacteria infected with this phage shows a more complicated behavior. It is strongly adsorbed to bacteria adsorbing both progeny and lysing phage. It is weakly adsorbed to bacteria adsorbing neither. It is moderately well adsorbed to bacteria adsorbing lysing phage but not phage progeny. The latter test shows that the S^{35} is not contained in the phage progeny, and explains the fact that the S^{35} in early lysates not containing progeny behaves in the same way.

The specificity of the adsorption of S^{35}-labeled material contaminating the phage progeny is evidently due to the lysing phage, which is also adsorbed much more strongly to strain H than to B/2, as shown both by the visible reduction in Tyndall scattering (due to the lysing phage) in the supernatants of the test mixtures, and by independent measurements. This conclusion is further confirmed by the following facts.

TABLE VII

Adsorption Tests with Uniformly S^{35}-Labeled Phage and with Products of Their Growth in Non-Radioactive Medium

Adsorbing bacteria	Per cent adsorbed				
	Uniformly labeled S^{35} phage		Products of lysis at $t = 10$	Phage progeny (Maximal yield)	
	+ UV-h	No UV-h			
	S^{35}	S^{35}	S^{35}	S^{35}	Phage
Sensitive (H).....................	84	86	79	78	96
Resistant (B/2)...................	15	11	46	49	10
Resistant (B/2h)................	13	12	29	28	8

The uniformly labeled phage and the products of their growth are respectively the seed phage and the high speed sediment fractions from the experiment shown in Table VI.

The uniformly labeled phage is tested at a low ratio of phage to bacteria: +UV-h means with added UV-killed h mutant in equal concentration to that present in the other test materials.

The adsorption of phage is measured by plaque counts of supernatants, and also sediments in the case of the resistant bacteria, in the usual way.

1. If bacteria are infected with S^{35} phage, and then lysed near the midpoint of the latent period with cyanide alone (in salt-poor broth, to prevent readsorption of S^{35} to bacterial debris), the high speed sediment fraction contains S^{35} that is adsorbed weakly and non-specifically to bacteria.

2. If the lysing phage and the S^{35}-labeled infecting phage are the same (T2), or if the culture in salt-poor broth is allowed to lyse spontaneously (so that the yield of progeny is large), the S^{35} in the high speed sediment fraction is adsorbed with the specificity of the phage progeny (except for a weak non-specific adsorption). This is illustrated in Table VII by the adsorption to H and B/2h.

It should be noted that a phage progeny grown from S^{35}-labeled phage and containing a larger or smaller amount of contaminating radioactivity could not be distinguished by any known method from authentic S^{35}-labeled phage, except that a small amount of the contaminant could be removed by adsorption to bacteria resistant to the phage. In addition to the properties already mentioned, the contaminating S^{35} is completely precipitated with the phage by antiserum, and cannot be appreciably separated from the phage by further fractional sedimentation, at either high or low concentrations of electrolyte. On the other hand, the chemical contamination from this source would be very small in favorable circumstances, because the progeny of a single phage particle are numerous and the contaminant is evidently derived from the parents.

The properties of the S^{35}-labeled contaminant show that it consists of the remains of the coats of the parental phage particles, presumably identical with the material that can be removed from unlysed cells in the Waring blendor. The fact that it undergoes little chemical change is not surprising since it probably never enters the infected cell.

The properties described explain a mistaken preliminary report (Hershey *et al.*, 1951) of the transfer of S^{35} from parental to progeny phage.

It should be added that experiments identical to those shown in Tables VI and VII, but starting from phage labeled with P^{32}, show that phosphorus is transferred from parental to progeny phage to the extent of 30 per cent at yields of about 30 phage per infected bacterium, and that the P^{32} in prematurely lysed cultures is almost entirely non-sedimentable, becoming, in fact, acid-soluble on aging.

Similar measures of the transfer of P^{32} have been published by Putnam and Kozloff (1950) and others. Watson and Maaløe (1952) summarize this work, and report equal transfer (nearly 50 per cent) of phosphorus and adenine.

A Progeny of S^{35}-Labeled Phage Nearly Free from the Parental Label.—The following experiment shows clearly that the obligatory transfer of parental sulfur to offspring phage is less than 1 per cent, and probably considerably less. In this experiment, the phage yield from infected bacteria from which the S^{35}-labeled phage coats had been stripped in the Waring blendor was assayed directly for S^{35}.

Sensitive bacteria grown in broth were infected with five particles of S^{35}-labeled phage per bacterium, the high ratio of infection being necessary for purposes of assay. The infected bacteria were freed from unadsorbed phage and suspended in water containing per liter 1 mM $MgSO_4$, 0.1 mM $CaCl_2$, and 0.1 gm. gelatin. A sample of this suspension was agitated for 2.5 minutes in the Waring blendor, and centrifuged to remove the extracellular S^{35}. A second sample not run in the blendor was centrifuged at the same time. The cells from both samples were resuspended in warm salt-poor broth at a concentration of 10^8 bacteria per ml., and aerated for 80 minutes. The cultures were then lysed by the addition of 0.02 mM HCN, 2×10^{11} UV-killed T2, and 6 mg. NaCl per ml. of culture. The addition of salt at this point causes S^{35} that would otherwise be eluted (Hershey *et al.*, 1951) to remain attached to the bacterial debris. The lysates were fractionated and assayed as described previously, with the results shown in Table VIII.

The data show that stripping reduces more or less proportionately the S^{35}-content of all fractions. In particular, the S^{35}-content of the fraction containing most of the phage progeny is reduced from nearly 10 per cent to less than 1 per cent of the initially adsorbed isotope. This experiment shows that the bulk of the S^{35} appearing in all lysate fractions is derived from the remains of the coats of the parental phage particles.

Properties of Phage Inactivated by Formaldehyde.—Phage T2 warmed for 1 hour at 37°C. in adsorption medium containing 0.1 per cent (*v/v*) commercial formalin (35 per cent HCHO), and then dialyzed free from formalde-

TABLE VIII

Lysates of Bacteria Infected with S^{35}-Labeled T2 and Stripped in the Waring Blendor

Per cent of adsorbed S^{35} or of phage yield:	Cells stripped		Cells not stripped	
	S^{35}	Phage	S^{35}	Phage
Eluted in blendor fluid........................	86	—	39	—
1st low-speed sediment........................	3.8	9.3	31	13
2nd " " "	(0.2)	11	2.7	11
High-speed "	(0.7)	58	9.4	89
" " supernatant........................	(2.0)	1.1	(1.7)	1.6
Recovery........................	93	79	84	115

All the input bacteria were recovered in assays of infected cells made during the latent period of both cultures. The phage yields were 270 (stripped cells) and 200 per bacterium, assayed before fractionation. Figures in parentheses were obtained from counting rates close to background.

hyde, shows a reduction in plaque titer by a factor 1000 or more. Inactivated phage of this kind possesses the following properties.

1. It is adsorbed to sensitive bacteria (as measured by either S^{35} or P^{32} labels), to the extent of about 70 per cent.

2. The adsorbed phage kills bacteria with an efficiency of about 35 per cent compared with the original phage stock.

3. The DNA of the inactive particles is resistant to DNase, but is made sensitive by osmotic shock.

4. The DNA of the inactive particles is not sensitized to DNase by adsorption to heat-killed bacteria, nor is it released into solution by adsorption to bacterial debris.

5. 70 per cent of the adsorbed phage DNA can be detached from infected cells spun in the Waring blendor. The detached DNA is almost entirely resistant to DNase.

These properties show that T2 inactivated by formaldehyde is largely incapable of injecting its DNA into the cells to which it attaches. Its behavior in the experiments outlined gives strong support to our interpretation of the corresponding experiments with active phage.

DISCUSSION

We have shown that when a particle of bacteriophage T2 attaches to a bacterial cell, most of the phage DNA enters the cell, and a residue containing at least 80 per cent of the sulfur-containing protein of the phage remains at the cell surface. This residue consists of the material forming the protective membrane of the resting phage particle, and it plays no further role in infection after the attachment of phage to bacterium.

These facts leave in question the possible function of the 20 per cent of sulfur-containing protein that may or may not enter the cell. We find that little or none of it is incorporated into the progeny of the infecting particle, and that at least part of it consists of additional material resembling the residue that can be shown to remain extracellular. Phosphorus and adenine (Watson and Maaløe, 1952) derived from the DNA of the infecting particle, on the other hand, are transferred to the phage progeny to a considerable and equal extent. We infer that sulfur-containing protein has no function in phage multiplication, and that DNA has some function.

It must be recalled that the following questions remain unanswered. (1) Does any sulfur-free phage material other than DNA enter the cell? (2) If so, is it transferred to the phage progeny? (3) Is the transfer of phosphorus (or hypothetical other substance) to progeny direct—that is, does it remain at all times in a form specifically identifiable as phage substance—or indirect?

Our experiments show clearly that a physical separation of the phage T2 into genetic and non-genetic parts is possible. A corresponding functional separation is seen in the partial independence of phenotype and genotype in the same phage (Novick and Szilard, 1951; Hershey et al., 1951). The chemical identification of the genetic part must wait, however, until some of the questions asked above have been answered.

Two facts of significance for the immunologic method of attack on problems of viral growth should be emphasized here. First, the principal antigen of the infecting particles of phage T2 persists unchanged in infected cells. Second, it remains attached to the bacterial debris resulting from lysis of the cells. These possibilities seem to have been overlooked in a study by Rountree (1951) of viral antigens during the growth of phage T5.

SUMMARY

1. Osmotic shock disrupts particles of phage T2 into material containing nearly all the phage sulfur in a form precipitable by antiphage serum, and capable of specific adsorption to bacteria. It releases into solution nearly all

the phage DNA in a form not precipitable by antiserum and not adsorbable to bacteria. The sulfur-containing protein of the phage particle evidently makes up a membrane that protects the phage DNA from DNase, comprises the sole or principal antigenic material, and is responsible for attachment of the virus to bacteria.

2. Adsorption of T2 to heat-killed bacteria, and heating or alternate freezing and thawing of infected cells, sensitize the DNA of the adsorbed phage to DNase. These treatments have little or no sensitizing effect on unadsorbed phage. Neither heating nor freezing and thawing releases the phage DNA from infected cells, although other cell constituents can be extracted by these methods. These facts suggest that the phage DNA forms part of an organized intracellular structure throughout the period of phage growth.

3. Adsorption of phage T2 to bacterial debris causes part of the phage DNA to appear in solution, leaving the phage sulfur attached to the debris. Another part of the phage DNA, corresponding roughly to the remaining half of the DNA of the inactivated phage, remains attached to the debris but can be separated from it by DNase. Phage T4 behaves similarly, although the two phages can be shown to attach to different combining sites. The inactivation of phage by bacterial debris is evidently accompanied by the rupture of the viral membrane.

4. Suspensions of infected cells agitated in a Waring blendor release 75 per cent of the phage sulfur and only 15 per cent of the phage phosphorus to the solution as a result of the applied shearing force. The cells remain capable of yielding phage progeny.

5. The facts stated show that most of the phage sulfur remains at the cell surface and most of the phage DNA enters the cell on infection. Whether sulfur-free material other than DNA enters the cell has not been determined. The properties of the sulfur-containing residue identify it as essentially unchanged membranes of the phage particles. All types of evidence show that the passage of phage DNA into the cell occurs in non-nutrient medium under conditions in which other known steps in viral growth do not occur.

6. The phage progeny yielded by bacteria infected with phage labeled with radioactive sulfur contain less than 1 per cent of the parental radioactivity. The progeny of phage particles labeled with radioactive phosphorus contain 30 per cent or more of the parental phosphorus.

7. Phage inactivated by dilute formaldehyde is capable of adsorbing to bacteria, but does not release its DNA to the cell. This shows that the interaction between phage and bacterium resulting in release of the phage DNA from its protective membrane depends on labile components of the phage particle. By contrast, the components of the bacterium essential to this interaction are remarkably stable. The nature of the interaction is otherwise unknown.

8. The sulfur-containing protein of resting phage particles is confined to a

protective coat that is responsible for the adsorption to bacteria, and functions as an instrument for the injection of the phage DNA into the cell. This protein probably has no function in the growth of intracellular phage. The DNA has some function. Further chemical inferences should not be drawn from the experiments presented.

REFERENCES

Anderson, T. F., 1949, The reactions of bacterial viruses with their host cells, *Bot. Rev.*, **15**, 464.

Anderson, T. F., 1951, *Tr. New York Acad. Sc.*, **13**, 130.

Anderson, T. F., and Doermann, A. H., 1952, *J. Gen. Physiol.*, **35**, 657.

Benzer, S., 1952, *J. Bact.*, **63**, 59.

Doermann, A. H., 1948, *Carnegie Institution of Washington Yearbook, No. 47*, 176.

Doermann, A. H., and Dissosway, C., 1949, *Carnegie Institution of Washington Year-book, No. 48*, 170.

Dulbecco, R., 1952, *J. Bact.*, **63**, 209.

Herriott, R. M., 1951, *J. Bact.*, **61**, 752.

Hershey, A. D., 1946, *Genetics*, **31**, 620.

Hershey, A. D., Roesel, C., Chase, M., and Forman, S., 1951, *Carnegie Institution of Washington Yearbook, No. 50*, 195.

Lwoff, A., and Gutmann, A., 1950, *Ann. Inst. Pasteur*, **78**, 711.

Maaløe, O., and Watson, J. D., 1951, *Proc. Nat. Acad. Sc.*, **37**, 507.

Novick, A., and Szilard, L., 1951, *Science*, **113**, 34.

Prater, C. D., 1951, Thesis, University of Pennsylvania.

Price, W. H., 1952, *J. Gen. Physiol.*, **35**, 409.

Putnam, F. W., and Kozloff, L., 1950, *J. Biol. Chem.*, **182**, 243.

Rountree, P. M., 1951, *Brit. J. Exp. Path.*, **32**, 341.

Watson, J. D., and Maaløe, O., 1952, *Acta path. et microbiol. scand.*, in press.

VIRUS RECONSTITUTION

II. COMBINATION OF PROTEIN AND NUCLEIC ACID
FROM DIFFERENT STRAINS*

H. FRAENKEL-CONRAT AND B. SINGER

The Virus Laboratory, University of California, Berkeley, Calif. (U.S.A.)

The *in vitro* formation of typical TMV particles from small molecular fractions of virus protein and virus nucleic acid has been described[1], as well as the finding that some infectivity similar in nature to that of the original virus was restored in this process. These studies have now been extended to various strains of TMV. Of particular significance, both from a theoretical and a potentially practical standpoint, appeared the incorporation into one virus particle of protein and nucleic acid originating from different strains of the virus. This has been achieved with various combinations of nucleic acid from 4 different strains and of protein from 3 strains. The biological and immunological characteristics of such mixed virus preparations have supplied what appears to be incontrovertible evidence that the infectivity of the reconstituted virus is actually a property of the newly formed virus particles. The biological and chemical nature of the progeny of a number of preparations of virus reconstituted from one or two strains has been studied. Some of the conclusions have been described in a preliminary note[2].

METHODS AND MATERIALS

Virus preparations and fractions

The different strains of TMV were the same as used in earlier studies from this laboratory[3,4]. All virus preparations were isolated by differential centrifugation. Nucleic acid was prepared from these strains by a slight modification[5] of the detergent method previously used[1]. About 90 % of the experiments yielded preparations of biologically active nucleic acid, stable for periods up to several months, if stored at —60°.

For the preparation of native protein, the virus was degraded at 3° and at pH 10.0 to 10.5[1]. Recently 2-amino-2-methylpropanol-1 and ethanolamine have been suggested as advantageous buffers for that purpose**. After dialysis for 16 hours of a 1 % solution of virus (20–50 ml) against 1000 ml of an 0.1 % solution of the amine adjusted with HCl to pH 10.5, degradation was almost complete, as indicated by the small amount of material sedimented upon ultracentrifugation (1 hour at 40,000 with refrigeration). The clear supernate was brought to 0.28 saturation with ammonium sulfate and centrifuged. The precipitated protein was redissolved in water, freed from small amounts of material precipitating at low ammonium sulfate concentrations, and the bulk of the protein reprecipitated between about 0.15 and 0.25 salt saturation. The nature and the amount of material in each fraction was ascertained spectrophotometrically. The final protein precipitate generally showed a sharp maximum at 280 mμ and an R-value (max/min) of 2.2 to 2.4, and of 2.4 to 2.5 after dialysis. A contamination with 0.1 % nucleic acid decreased this ratio

---

* Aided by a grant from the National Foundation for Infantile Paralysis, and by a grant from the Rockefeller Foundation.
** Unpublished results of P. E. AND M. NEWMARK.

References p. 548.

by 0.1. After thorough dialysis in the cold, the protein solutions were adjusted to pH 8.0, and subjected to ultracentrifugation (2 hours, 40,000 r.p.m., refrigerated). The marked tendency of the protein solutions to spoilage could be counteracted by storing them in the frozen state. Lyophilization caused some denaturation and decreased their suitability for reconstitution.

The preparation of protein from the masked strain was possible by the same method. Protein from the ribgrass strain (HR) could be prepared only with considerable difficulty and in poorer yield. A lower pH was required for splitting (9.8–10), because of the great tendency of this protein to become denatured by alkali. From the YA strain no native protein could be isolated, probably for the same reason.

Antisera

The rabbit antisera and γ-globulin fractions were kindly prepared and placed at our disposal by Dr. R. C. BACKUS and Mrs. G. PEREZ-MENDEZ. The sera were prepared in customary manner by biweekly intramuscular injections of about 1 mg of TMV or HR with mineral oil and aquaphor as adjuvants. After 3 weeks the rabbits were bled and then injected intermittently and bled weekly.

The γ-globulin fraction was separated as the trailing component in the analytical electrophoresis cell.

The efficacy of the antisera was tested by means of precipitin and neutralization tests. As an example of the latter, 1 ml of an 0.01 % solution (0.075 M sodium chloride) of TMV or HR virus was treated for 16 hours at 3° with varying amounts of the homologous or heterologous antiserum. Of the homologous sera 0.01 to 0.025 ml were required to reduce the infectivity of the virus (100 γ) by a factor of 5 or 10, as indicated by the number of lesions produced, after suitable dilution, by the usual assay procedure. There was, however, considerable cross reaction in the case of both the unfractionated serum and the γ-globulin fraction, particularly between anti-TMV sera and the HR virus. To decrease this hetero-specificity, the antisera were treated with varying amounts of the heterologous virus (0.16–4.0 mg/ml), and ultracentrifuged after several hours. Anti-HR sera and γ-globulins were thus obtained which had very little if any effect on TMV while reducing the infectivity of HR by about 95 %. From anti-TMV sera no similarly selective antibody could be isolated. Repeated pretreatment with great amounts of HR virus removed all antibody activity from the solutions. Serum preparations cross-absorbed with less HR reduced the infectivity of TMV by about 97 %, and that of HR to a somewhat variable extent, averaging 44 %. Fortunately the latter antibody preparations were quite adequate to permit clear-cut serological identification of the two virus strains (Table I).

TABLE I

NEUTRALIZATION AND CROSSREACTION OF VIRUS STRAINS AND ANTISERA

Anti-serum		Percentage neutralization of infectivity* of	
Type	ml/mg virus	HR	TMV
Anti-HR-Serum**	0.1	90	0
Anti-HR-γ-globulin**	4	95	15
Anti-HR-γ-globulin	0.4	87	0
Anti-TMV-γ-globulin I**	4	62	97
Anti-TMV-γ-globulin II**	8	26	98

* Average of 2–8 experiments, each tested on about 8 half leaves at levels giving about 20 lesions per half leaf.
** Cross-absorbed with heterologous virus.

Analytical methods

For amino acid analysis, virus preparations (about 6 mg in 0.2–0.4 ml) were mixed with 2 ml of twice-redistilled constant boiling HCl, sealed *in vacuo*, and heated to 108° for 16 hours. After repeated evaporation of the acid in a desiccator, the hydrolysates were taken up in a 50-fold amount of water (50 γ per mg virus). Aliquots were chromatographed one-dimensionally on paper for the detection and analysis of histidine, methionine, tyrosine, and arginine by a recently described technique[6]. Another aliquot (1 mg) was dinitrophenylated for complete amino acid analysis, in principle according to LEVY[7]. The correction factors for the recovery of the amino acids as DNP-derivatives have been reinvestigated, and several were found to differ from those

References p. 548.

obtained two years ago under seemingly similar conditions[8]. Since only comparative data were required, hydrolyses for varying time periods were not carried out, and the analyses were not corrected for destruction of acid-sensitive amino acids during hydrolysis. Di-DNP-Cystine was almost absent, and not accounted for by a corresponding amount of DNP-cysteic acid. For histidine, methionine, tyrosine and arginine the results of the DNP-analyses were not readily reproducible, and the colorimetric analyses after chromatographic separation[6] were regarded as more reliable.

Tryptophane was determined, in conjunction with tyrosine on unhydrolyzed protein preparations by the spectrophotometric method as applied by BEAVAN AND HOLIDAY[9]. The tyrosine values were generally in good accord with those obtained by colorimetry[6]. The results of the amino acid analyses for TMV and HR are listed on Table II together with those available from the literature.

TABLE II

COMPARISON OF AMINO-ACID COMPOSITION OF TMV AND HR WITH VALUES IN THE LITERATURE*

	TMV				HR		
	Present methods	Microbiol.	Average**	Ion-exchange column***	Present methods	Microbiol.	Average**
Glycine	2.3	1.8	2.5	2.1	2.7	1.6	1.3	1.7	1.5
Valine	9.6	9.2	10.9	10.1	9.1	5.9	6.3	7.3	6.8
Alanine	6.5	5.1	7.4	6.3	7.9	8.5	6.4	9.2	7.8
Leucine + Isoleucine	14.2	15.9	13.9	14.9	15.1	12.2	15.2	13.1	14.2
Proline	5.0	5.8	5.5	5.7	6.3	5.0	5.8	5.5	5.7
Serine	9.0	7.3	9.1	8.2	8.7	8.1	5.7	7.2	6.5
Threonine	8.9	9.9	11.9	10.9	10.5	7.2	8.2	9.8	9.0
Lysine	1.9	1.5	1.4	1.5		2.4	1.5	1.4	1.5
Arginine	9.5	9.8	9.7	9.8		8.9	9.8	9.7	9.8
Histidine	0.0	0.0	0.0	0.0	0.0	0.7	0.7	0.7	0.7
Phenylalanine	7.2	8.4	8.2	8.3	7.6	5.3	5.4	5.3	5.4
Tyrosine	4.1	3.8	3.7	3.8	4.2	6.3	6.7	6.6	6.7
Tryptophan	2.8§	2.1	1.9	2.0		2.2	1.4	1.4	1.4
Methionine	0.0	0.0	0.0	0.0	0.0	2.0	2.2	2.2	2.2
Glutamic acid	12.4	11.3	11.0	11.2	13.5	16.4	15.5	15.1	15.3
Aspartic acid	13.8	13.5	11.9	12.8	14.5	15.0	12.6	11.2	11.9
	107.2	105.4	108.1			106.9	104.7	107.4	

* All values expressed as g of amino acid per 100 g virus, not corrected for destruction during hydrolysis. It must be noted, however, that the values of FRASER AND NEWMARK are percentages of the material recovered from the ion-exchange column. Cysteine (about 0.6%) was not determined, nor listed.

** The two sets of analyses for TMV published by KNIGHT[3] and by BLACK AND KNIGHT[11] are listed, as well as the average. In the case of HR, the second column represents the expected values, had HR been again analyzed in 1953 and shown changes parallel to those observed wth TMV

*** FRASER AND NEWMARK[10].

§ The possibility of different protein fractions differing in their tryptophan content is still under investigation (2.6–3.2%). See footnote on p. 547.

RESULTS

Reconstitution of virus from common TMV protein and nucleic acid

The technique generally used for reconstitution was as follows: To 1–10 mg of protein (0.5–1.0% solution of pH 8) was added one tenth the amount of nucleic acid, and 3 M pH 6 acetate (10 γ per ml reaction mixture). Phosphate buffer (pH 6.8 M, 50 γ per ml) has also often been used and has at times given higher yields of active virus. Below pH 5.0 and above pH 8.5 little or no active virus was formed. The solutions

References p. 548.

were held at room temperature at least for the first few hours. Aliquots of the reaction mixture, which rapidly gets opalescent, were diluted for assay after various time periods, *e.g.*, 15 minutes, 1 hour, 20 hours. Upon assay, maximal activity was sometimes found after the short reaction periods, but more generally maximal activity was obtained after 20 hours. Activity has also occasionally been observed to decrease or disappear from reaction mixtures. Many of these experiments, however, were performed before the intrinsic infectivity of the nucleic acid, and its instability in the assay medium[5], were recognized, and these experiments are being repeated with due regard to the properties of the two types of infectious agents. When ribonuclease is added at various time intervals to inactivate any free nucleic acid, the infectivity is a true measure of the extent of reconstitution. It appears that at room temperature reaction is quite rapid in phosphate and proceeds to the same point in 24 hours in acetate (Fig. 1).

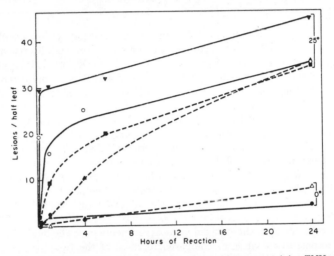

Fig. 1. Rate of reconstitution of active virus in reaction mixtures containing TMV protein (1 %), nucleic acid (0.1 %) and buffer. All samples are treated with ribonuclease (10 λ 0.1 % per ml, 16 hours) prior to assay, to inactivate any uncombined nucleic acid. Solid lines are results obtained with pH 7 phosphate (0.05 M), broken lines are for pH 6 acetate (0.03 M). Experiment I ($\blacktriangledown$, $\blacksquare$) yielded higher activity and was assayed at a protein concentration of 5 γ/ml. The final activity reached indicated a yield of about 5 %. Experiment II (O, ●, ▲, △) was assayed at 25 γ/ml.

Considerable effort has been put into establishing the extent of contamination, if any, of the protein and nucleic acid fractions with undegraded virus. The protein preparations usually gave no lesions when tested at 1–5 mg/ml, or at 100- to 500-fold levels of those at which reconstituted preparations gave 20–50 lesions per half leaf. That contaminating TMV would be pathogenic under these conditions was shown when TMV (0.1–0.5 γ/ml) added to the protein (1–5 mg/ml) gave 10–50% of the expected lesions. Assays of typical protein preparations by Dr. W. Takahashi with a particularly sensitive assay technique suggested the presence of less than 0.0001 % virus.

A similar search for contaminating virus in nucleic acid preparations has led to

References p. 548.

II. THE NATURE OF GENETIC MATERIAL   233

the discovery that the nucleic acid *per se* is infectious[2, 5*]. It was shown also that contaminating virus can be removed very effectively by ultracentrifugation of nucleic acid preparations. Upon repeated ultracentrifugation rod-like particles most of which are usually shorter than 300 mμ may at times be sedimented from such solutions. Their appearance seems to be favored by the presence of salts, and is probably due to reconstitution involving traces of contaminating protein. These findings have rendered definitive proof for the absence of the last traces of contaminating virus from the nucleic acid both less crucially important and more difficult. In view of the much higher yields in activity obtained in some recent reconstitution experiments, such hypothetical "last traces" become progressively more irrelevant. Furthermore, the experiments with strain mixtures to be described below have definitely shown that the activity in reconstitution experiments is inherent in newly formed particles, and cannot be attributed to undegraded virus particles.

Mixed strains

The viruses employed were common TMV, and the masked (M), yellow aucuba (YA) and Holmes ribgrass (HR) strains[3]. Active virus rods were successfully reconstituted from (1) TMV-nucleic acid and M-protein, (2) M-nucleic acid and TMV-protein, (3) YA-nucleic acid and TMV-protein, (4) YA-nucleic acid and M-protein, (5) HR-nucleic acid and TMV-protein, (6) TMV-nucleic acid and HR-protein and (7) HR-nucleic acid and M-protein. The infectivity of these mixed virus preparations was within the same range as that obtained for TMV-nucleic acid + TMV-protein. This was surprising in the case of the HR strain, because the original virus showed only 5% of the activity of TMV on a weight basis (to be referred to as specific infectivity, henceforth). The lesser infectivity of HR seems to be due to the protein component, however, since HR nucleic acid was found to be as infectious as TMV nucleic acid. It has in this case been possible to obtain a reconstituted preparation showing a fourfold higher specific infectivity than that of the original virus supplying the nucleic acid, the HR strain (mixed virus of type 5 above, to be referred to as M.V. HR/TMV).

Of greatest interest in these mixed virus experiments were the biological properties of the reconstituted virus, as compared to those of the two "parent" strains. When each of the reaction products was tested on *N. tabacum* and on *N. sylvestris*, it gave in every case the same symptoms as did the original strain supplying the nucleic acid. Thus in Turkish tobacco, M.V. TMV/M and TMV/HR gave a green mosaic disease, M.V. M/TMV produced virus without visible symptoms, M.V. YA/TMV and YA/M gave a yellow mosaic disease and M.V. HR/TMV and HR/M gave typical ringspot lesions[**]. These findings strongly suggest that the nucleic acid is the genetic determinant in TMV, and related strains, playing the same decisive role which DNA seems to play in the bacteriophages.

In striking contrast to the nature of the infection which is determined by the nucleic acid component, the serological characteristics of mixed virus preparations resemble those of the protein component. When anti-TMV serum or its γ-globulin

---

[*] The same conclusion was reached independently by A. GIERER AND G. SCHRAMM, *Nature*, 177 (1956) 702.
[**] The difference between HR- and TMV-like virus is also quite evident from the size of the local lesions on *N. glutinosa*. The differentiation of TMV and M on the one side, and HR and YA on the other is based on the type of response obtained in *N. sylvestris*.

References p. 548.

TABLE III

NEUTRALIZATION OF INFECTIVITY OF TMV, HR, AND THE TWO MIXED VIRUS PREPARATIONS DERIVED FROM THESE[*]

Assay level (γ/ml)	TMV 0.17	HR 1.7	HR/TMV** 0.44	TMV/HR** 22	TMV and		HR and		HR TMV 0.45	TMV/HR 9.7
					TMV Prot. 0.11	HR Prot. 0.11	TMV Prot. 1.7	HR Prot. 1.7		
Untreated	22	21	19	29	30	28	37	56	22	14
+ Anti-TMV γ-globulin	0.9	8.0	3.6	11	0.2	0.8	17	33	1	9
+ Anti-HR γ-globulin	23	1.1	16	2.9	6	3	2	4	11	3

[*] All figures in the table represent average number of lesions per half leaf on *N. glutinosa* plants. Most assays were performed 2 or 3 times on 8 or 10 half leaves per sample.

Two experiments selected out of about 30 are listed, all of which showed the same phenomenon though some were less complete, others showed more cross reaction. Of TMV and HR 5 γ were used, of the mixed virus preparations 20–30 γ; of the γ-globulin fractions, pretreated with the heterologous virus (see EXPERIMENTAL) 10 or 20 λ were used, and the final volume of the reaction mixtures was 0.3 ml. When protein was added to the reaction mixture, 25 γ was used. Combinations showing specific neutralization have been printed in italics.

** HR/TMV represents mixed virus prepared from HR-nucleic acid and TMV-protein; TMV/HR represents the virus prepared from TMV-nucleic acid and HR-protein.

(see METHODS AND MATERIALS) was added to the two preparations, it neutralized M.V. HR/TMV to a similar extent as it did TMV, but had little effect on M.V. TMV/HR. Anti-HR serum, on the other hand, neutralized M.V. TMV/HR much more effectively than it did M.V. HR/TMV (Table III). At the same time, and in the same assays, the nature of the lesions clearly showed that the latter was of HR character, while M.V. TMV/HR was of TMV character. Control experiments in which the neutralisability of the two viruses by anti-sera was tested in the presence of excess homologous or heterologous protein confirmed the validity of the experimental procedure. Thus there appears to be no doubt that the activity appearing in reaction mixtures containing HR-nucleic acid and TMV-protein is due to a particle containing a genetically determining HR-nucleic acid core, and an immunologically determining TMV-protein coat. No alternate explanations seem able to explain the observed facts. Thus reconstitution of infectious virus particles from two chemical components appears to be definitely established.

Nature of the progeny of mixed virus

The finding that TMV-nucleic acid will combine with HR-protein, and vice versa, is particularly surprising in view of the great differences between the proteins of these two strains. It appears from KNIGHT's analyses[3], as confirmed by us, that only 2 to 4 amino acids occur in the same amounts in HR and TMV. Histidine and methionine are completely absent from all strains that have been investigated by KNIGHT, with the exception of HR. An important functional property of the virus proteins probably resides in their specific tendency to aggregate in a superhelical array around, if they are present, nucleic acid strands. In view of the exchangeability of different virus proteins, as observed in the present experiments, one must conclude that this activity is dependent only upon a few suitably situated key sites surrounded by nonspecific areas.

References p. 548.

In view of the marked difference in amino acid composition of TMV and HR, the mixed virus preparations obtained from these two were of particular interest and value in establishing the nature of the progeny of reconstituted virus. Paper chromatographic comparison of the hydrolysates of TMV, HR, and the progeny of the two mixed virus preparations has clearly demonstrated the presence of about 0.7% histidine and about 2% methionine in HR and the progeny of M.V. HR/TMV, and the absence of these amino acids from TMV and the progeny of M.V. TMV/HR. Complete amino acid analyses were then carried out for these 4 types of preparations (see Table IV). The first impression, based on the presence or absence of histidine and methionine was generally confirmed by these analyses. The protein of each progeny closely resembled that of the virus supplying the nucleic acid to the mixed virus from which it was derived. Only very minor differences were noted (less than 10% of the content in any one amino acid). However, in the case of glycine, that small difference was observed in 8 separate hydrolysates of 5 different progeny preparations from M.V. HR/TMV as compared to HR, and a small difference in the lysine contents between these has been observed almost as consistently. Yet these differences are too small to be regarded as more than a suggestion that the protein component may slightly influence the genetic message transferred by the nucleic acid.

TABLE IV

COMPARISON OF AMINO ACID COMPOSITION OF HR AND TMV WITH PROGENY OF EXPERIMENTAL PREPARATIONS[*]

	HR	Progeny of HR/TMV	TMV	Progeny of TMV/HR	Mutant strain from TMV-nucleic acid
Glycine	1.6	*1.8*	2.3	2.3	2.5
Alanine	8.5	8.5	6.5	6.9	5.5
Valine	5.9	6.3	9.6	9.0	9.6
Leucine + Isoleucine	12.2	12.2	14.2	14.3	13.0
Proline	5.0	5.1	5.0	5.1	4.3
Serine	8.1	8.1	9.0	8.8	7.8
Threonine	7.2	7.5	8.9	8.9	8.8
Lysine	2.4	2.3	1.9	1.8	2.1
Arginine	8.9	8.5	9.5	9.7	7.6
Histidine	0.70	0.70	0.0	0.0	0.0
Phenylalanine	5.3	5.4	7.2	7.1	6.8
Tyrosine	6.3	6.2	4.1	4.3	*5.4*
Tryptophan	2.2	2.2	2.8	2.6	2.7
Methionine	2.0	2.2	0.0	0.0	0.6
Glutamic acid	16.4	17.3	12.4	12.1	12.4
Aspartic acid	15.0	14.8	13.8	14.2	15.5

[*] All values expressed as g of amino acid per 100 g virus.
Values are not corrected for destruction during hydrolysis.
The first 2 columns represent averages of 8 hydrolysates each; the next three columns averages of 3 hydrolysates each.
Seemingly significant differences have been printed in italics.

It must further be noted that the observed differences are definitely less than one amino acid residue per subunit, and their acceptance requires the assumption that not all subunits can be identical. This assumption appears also required to explain the tryptophan content of TMV which is close to 2.5 residues per 18,000 molecular weight subunit. That value was obtained both by a chemical method[8], and by

References p. 548.

spectrophotometry both in 0.1 N sodium hydroxide and at neutral pH[8,9*], and appears definitely more probable than the lower value obtained by microbiological methods.

Another difference between HR and the progeny of M.V. HR/TMV is shown by the specific infectivity, which has been higher for many of the latter preparations than the highest obtained for any HR sample (20–45% *vs* 12%).

The significance of these differences between the original virus strains and the M.V. preparations will be dependent on whether they recur in successive progeny preparations. This seems to be the case for the specific infectivities, but as yet no sufficient number of amino acid analyses have been completed with successive single-lesion progeny preparations to warrant any definite conclusions in this regard. At the present time, one can only conclude from all this work that the nucleic acid of each strain has the ability to provoke the synthesis, within the host cell, of new virus protein very similar to, if not identical with, its own homologous protein; and that it retains this ability even when packaged, *in vitro*, in the protein of another strain.

Heritable modifications

In observing the plant-pathogenic nature, and the protein composition of the progeny from single lesions of many preparations of mixed virus or of isolated nucleic acids, a marked variation was noted in at least one instance. This apparent mutant was characterized by differences in both disease symptomatology and amino acid composition of progeny virus (Table IV). Its appearance may be regarded as indicative of the labilisation of the genetic material through chemical exposure and manipulation, since no similar variations have been observed from single lesion propagation of the original virus strains. In contrast to other instances where genetically more labile variants were observed, this mutant strain has continued to produce a striking necrotic disease in Turkish tobacco through several passages and isolations, including the separation of its nucleic acid and protein.

ACKNOWLEDGEMENTS

The authors wish to thank Professors W. M. STANLEY and R. C. WILLIAMS for their stimulating and encouraging interest in this work, and Professor C. A. KNIGHT for his help and advice in the assay and differentiation of TMV strains. The untiring assistance of Miss SUE VELDEE in the assays of virus infectivity is also gratefully acknowledged.

SUMMARY

1. A method of preparation of native protein from TMV and other strains has been described.
2. The reconstitution of virus particles from protein and nucleic acid of different strains has yielded very active preparations, one of which showed higher infectivity than one of its parent strains.

---

* The spectrum of TMV protein (1 mg/ml) differs markedly in shape from that of an *ad hoc* mixture of the amino acids contributing to its absorption (30 γ tryptophan, 40 γ tyrosine, 65 γ phenylalanine, 7 γ cysteine, and 1.0 mg triglycine per ml). However, the maximum, though at 282 and 278 mμ respectively, is the same (O.D. = 1.25). When solutions of protein and amino acids were prepared in 67% acetic acid, the O.D.'s were the same and the spectra very much more similar in shape (maxima at 279 and 278 mμ, respectively).

References p. 548.

3. The nature of the disease provoked by mixed virus preparations resembled in each case that characteristic of the virus supplying the nucleic acid.

4. The chemical nature of the progeny of mixed virus preparations also closely resembled that of the virus supplying the nucleic acid, although the significance of minor differences in amino acid composition has not yet been established.

5. In contrast to these properties the serological characteristics of mixed virus preparations were those of the virus supplying the protein.

6. The dual nature of the activity of reconstituted virus particles has thus been clearly demonstrated.

7. Variants or mutants of different biological and chemical properties have occurred randomly in the course of this work, and are regarded as indications of a labilisation of the genetic material through chemical manipulation.

REFERENCES

[1] H. FRAENKEL-CONRAT AND R. C. WILLIAMS, *Proc. Natl. Acad. Sci. U.S.*, 41 (1955) 690.
[2] H. FRAENKEL-CONRAT, *J. Am. Chem. Soc.*, 78 (1956) 882.
[3] C. A. KNIGHT, *J. Biol. Chem.*, 171 (1947) 297.
[4] C. I. NIU AND H. FRAENKEL-CONRAT, *Arch. Biochem. Biophys.*, 59 (1955) 538.
[5] H. FRAENKEL-CONRAT, B. SINGER AND R. C. WILLIAMS, *Biochim. Biophys. Acta*, 25 (1957) (in the press); see also: *Symposium on the Chemical Basis of Heredity, McCollum Pratt Institute, Johns Hopkins University, Baltimore*, June 1956.
[6] H. FRAENKEL-CONRAT AND B. SINGER, *Arch. Biochem. Biophys.*, (in the press).
[7] A. L. LEVY, *Nature*, 174 (1954) 126.
[8] H. FRAENKEL-CONRAT AND B. SINGER, *Arch. Biochem. Biophys.*, 60 (1956) 64.
[9] G. H. BEAVAN AND E. R. HOLIDAY, *Advances in Prot. Chem.*, 7 (1952) 320.
[10] D. FRASER AND P. NEWMARK, *J. Am. Chem. Soc.*, 78 (1956) 1588.
[11] F. L. BLACK AND C. A. KNIGHT, *J. Biol. Chem.*, 202 (1953) 51.

Received January 17th, 1957

SECTION III

DNA Structure and Replication

Introduction

Although the chemistry of nucleic acids had not kept pace with that of the proteins in the first half of the century, we do not wish to leave the impression that the field was completely neglected. The work began by Miescher, Kossel, Mathews, and others in the latter part of the nineteenth century, was summarized in monographs by Kossel in 1928 on the protamines and histones and by Levene and Bass (1931) on nucleic acids. Feulgen, the German chemist, had discovered the color reaction specific for the deoxy-sugars and later showed how it could be applied to histological preparations (Feulgen and Rossenbeck, 1924) to reveal the intracellular location of DNA. However, it was only after the discovery of the nature of transforming principle, that the activity in this area showed much evidence of a revolution. Improvements in the new technique of chromatography and the discovery and purification of specific enzymes to degrade nucleic acids (Kunitz, 1940, 1948) were, of course, necessary preliminary steps to much progress. We have selected Chargaff's paper on the chemical specificity of nucleic acids to lead off this section. He and his students were major contributors to the rapid advances, but the achievements and the persons involved cannot be reviewed here [for details see Chargaff and Davidson's "Nucleic Acids" in 3 volumes (1955, 1960) or Davidson's "Biochemistry of the Nucleic Acids" (1960) for a briefer summary].

Coincident with the work on the constituents of nucleic acids and the nature of the chemical bonds involved, progress was being made on the analysis of macromolecular structure by means of X-ray diffraction. The early work was brought to the attention of geneticists by Astbury (1939, 1945) who made significant contributions in applying the technique to biological materials. The later developments are so well known that a detailed account is hardly necessary. We have selected for reprinting three papers by Watson and Crick and two by Wilkins and his collaborators which are already well known to most biologists and chemists.

Although the template hypothesis for control of macromolecular synthesis and replication goes back many years, its general acceptance came only when specific testable models were proposed. One of the long-standing objections to such models for replication was that the template should produce a mirror image or complement rather than an identical copy. Models based on crystallization patterns and the "lock and key" fitting of complementary surfaces were most commonly used. Astbury (1939) had pointed out the similarity in the spacings of the nucleotide residues in nucleic acid, particularly DNA, and the amino acid residues in a polypeptide chain. This suggested a complementary structure which might have the properties required by templates, but no specific model was proposed. Haurowitz (1950) presented a rather detailed scheme for the replication or synthesis of a polypeptide chain based on the crystallization concept. The product in this instance was proposed to be identical to the template. However, these models could not be tested at the time and although geneticists maintained an active interest in the subject little else could be done. The extent of this interest and the real need for a specific working model is illustrated by events of 1953. By this time the experiments on transformation in *Pneumococcus* (Hotchkiss, 1951, Ephrussi-Taylor, 1951) had convinced most geneticists that DNA carried genetic specificity. The experiments of Hershey and Chase (1952) showing that only the DNA component of bacteriophage entered the host cell strongly supported this concept. The suggestions of Casperson and Schultz and Brachet that RNA was involved in protein synthesis because it was abundant in rapidly growing cells and cells which secrete protein had begun to have an effect on the design of experiments and models for synthesis of macromolecules. In short geneticists and some biochemists, who had been caught up in the enthusiasm that pervaded the field, were ready for a specific testable model. Watson and Crick provided one in the late spring of 1953 at the meetings of the *Cold Spring Harbor Symposium on Quantitative Biology* (see fifth paper in this section). While their molecular model had been published in *Nature* shortly before, its impact was most dramatic when presented to this receptive gathering. Probably the authors themselves were unprepared for the enthusiastic response which the genetic implications of the proposed structure would bring. Other models of DNA structure had been proposed shortly before; for example, one by Pauling consisted of three helically wound polynucleotide chains and another placed the bases on the periphery of a two-stranded chain. However, the simplicity of the new model and its proposed mechanism for replication appealed to geneticists, in particular. Chargaff's observation on the equivalence of the bases in which adenine equaled thymine and guanine equaled cytosine was rationalized by the new model. The X-ray diffraction studies of Wilkins and his colleagues on the spacings in fibers of DNA contributed important data for constructing the model and, of course, without the accumulated information on the nature of the chemical bonds involved, their distances and angles, and the most likely tautomeric state of the bases, a precise model could not have been constructed. Nevertheless, the invention required a combination of genius and luck which seldom meet at the appropriate time. Tests for the replication scheme proposed were not immediately available, but would soon be devised.

The discovery by Grunberg-Manago and Ochoa (1955) that an enzyme extract of *Azotobacter agilis* catalyzed the polymerization of nucleoside 5'-diphosphates into polyribonucleotides opened the way to a study of nucleic acid synthesis in cell-free systems. Unfortunately for the new hypotheses of macro-molecular synthesis, this system did not appear to take directions from a template. However, Arthur Kornberg, a former colleague of Ochoa, soon reported success with an extract from *Escherichia coli* which synthesized a DNA-like polymer (the seventh paper in this section). This system apparently did require a DNA primer. Early evidence indicated that the primer might be acting as a template, for the base ratio of primer and product were very similar. This system would eventually have an important role in supplying proof for the Watson-Crick scheme for DNA replication, but in the meantime other support-ing evidence was presented.

The simplest and clearest results came from a study of segregation of DNA labeled with radioactive or heavy isotopes during synthesis *in vivo*. The Watson-Crick model and the proposed scheme of replication predicted molecules which would be composed of one new polynucleotide chain and one original chain after each replication. This feature might be tested by observing the segregation of DNA in dividing nuclei (Plaut and Mazia, 1956) or better still in individual chromosomes (Taylor, 1956). Taylor who had been impressed by the potentiali-ties of high resolution autoradiography with tritium, the as yet little used radio-isotope of hydrogen, joined Philip S. Woods, a former colleague, and Walter L. Hughes at Brookhaven in the summer of 1956. The objective was to label the nucleoside, thymidine, known to be a selective intermediate for DNA synthesis (Friedkin *et al.*, 1956) and to use it to observe segregation of DNA in chromo-somes following their replication. Results were obtained in time to make a few photographs and to present the results to the Genetics Society which was meeting with the AIBS at Storrs, Connecticut in late August. The results which were in accord with the Watson-Crick scheme for replication became quickly known to geneticists around the world. This was aided in part by an International Sym-posium on Genetics being held in Japan where the participants learned of the experiments although the results were too recent to be included in the program. The first written report (Taylor *et al.*, 1957) did not appear until January 1957. Although the results were consistent with the proposed hypothesis, it soon became clear that without more detailed knowledge of chromosome organiza-tion, one could not be sure that the DNA duplex really separated during replica-tion. The multi-stranded chromosome model of classical cytology used in the first paper could hardly be in accord with the experimental results on the segregation of tritium-labeled DNA. Experiments were designed to test the idea that a chromosome might consist of a single duplex of DNA (Taylor, 1958). The results reported in the eighth paper of this section (Taylor, 1959) supported this concept, but results reported on the replication of DNA in *E. coli* by Meselson and Stahl (1958) made it almost certain. In addition, these experi-ments (described in the ninth paper in this section) proved that a semiconserva-tive scheme of replication was operating at the molecular level. The results appeared difficult to reconcile with any other model or scheme of replication.

The cell-free system developed by Kornberg and his colleagues had shown the mechanism of DNA synthesis and now it provided strong evidence from a nearest neighbor analysis that the product was produced by synthesis in which each strand of a double helix acted as a template for a daughter strand with complementary bases and reverse polarity (Josse *et al.*, 1961). A summary of this work which is too extensive to cover in detail is given in the tenth paper in this section (Kornberg, 1960).

The final evidence supporting the Watson-Crick scheme is presented in the eleventh and twelfth papers in the section. An elegant technique for preparing the whole DNA complement of phages and even *E. coli*, devised by Cairns (1961, 1963), shows not only that the DNA double helix is reproduced semiconservatively, but that replication proceeds in a sequential fashion from one point on an *E. coli* chromosome which can exist as a ring.

Finally the work on the mutagenic effects of base analogs supports the Watson-Crick scheme for replication. Both *in vivo* [Freese (1959), the thirteenth paper reprinted in this section] and in the cell-free system (Bessman, 1963), the substitution of base analogs follows the prediction made on the basis of the model.

REFERENCES

Astbury, W. T. (1939). *Proc. 7th Intern. Congr. Genet. Edinburgh, 1938*, pp. 49–51.

Astbury, W. T. (1945). *In* "Essays on Growth and Form" (Clark Le Gros and Medawar, eds.), p. 249. Oxford Univ. Press, London and New York.

Bessman, M. J. (1963). *In* "Molecular Genetics" (J. H. Taylor, ed.), Part 1, pp. 1–64. Academic Press, New York.

Chargaff, E., and Davidson, J. N., eds. (1955, 1960). "The Nucleic Acids," 3 vols. Academic Press, New York.

Davidson, J. N. (1960). "Biochemistry of the Nucleic Acids," 4th ed. Wiley, New York.

Ephrussi-Taylor, H. (1951). *Cold Spring Harbor Symp. Quant. Biol.* 16, 445.

Feulgen, R., and Rossenbeck, H. (1924). *Z. Physiol. Chem.* 135, 203.

Friedkin, M., Tilson, D., and Roberts, D. (1956). *J. Biol. Chem.* 220, 627.

Grunberg-Manago, M., and Ochoa, S. (1955). *J. Am. Chem. Soc.* 77, 3165.

Haurowitz, F. (1950). "Chemistry and Biology of Proteins," 374 pp. Academic Press, New York.

Hershey, A. D., and Chase, M. (1952). *J. Gen. Physiol.* 36, 39.

Hotchkiss, R. D. (1951). *Cold Spring Harbor Symp. Quant. Biol.* 16, 457.

Josse, J., Kaiser, A. D., and Kornberg, A. (1961). *J. Biol. Chem.* 236, 864.

Kossel, A. (1928). "The Protamines and Histones," Longmans, Green and Co., London and New York.

Kunitz, M. (1940). *J. Gen. Physiol.* 24, 15.

Kunitz, M. (1948). *Science* 108, 19.

Levene, P. A., and Bass, L. W. (1931). "Nucleic Acids," Chem. Catalog Co., New York.

Plaut, W. S., and Mazia, D. (1956). *J. Biophys. Biochem. Cytol.* 2, 573.

Taylor, J. H. (1956). *In* "Physical Techniques in Biological Research" (G. Oster and A. W. Pollister, eds.), Vol. III, pp. 545–576. Academic Press, New York.

Taylor, J. H. (1958). *Genetics* 43, 515.

Taylor, J. H. (1959). *Proc. 10th Intern. Congr. Genet. Montreal, 1958*, 1, 63.

Taylor, J. H., Woods, P. S., and Hughes, W. L. (1957). *Proc. Natl. Acad. Sci. U. S.* 43, 122.

Troland, L. T. (1917). *Am. Naturalist* 51, 321.

Separatum

EXPERIENTIA VOL. VI/6, 1950 · pp. 201–209

BIRKHÄUSER PUBLISHERS, BASEL/SWITZERLAND

Chemical Specificity of Nucleic Acids and Mechanism of their Enzymatic Degradation[1]

By Erwin Chargaff[2], New York, N.Y.

I. *Introduction*

The last few years have witnessed an enormous revival in interest for the chemical and biological properties of nucleic acids, which are components essential for the life of all cells. This is not particularly surprising, as the chemistry of nucleic acids represents one of the remaining major unsolved problems in biochemistry. It is not easy to say what provided the impulse for this rather sudden rebirth. Was it the fundamental work of E. Hammarsten[3] on the highly polymerized desoxyribonucleic acid of calf thymus? Or did it come from the biological side, for instance the experiments of Brachet[4] and Caspersson[5]? Or was it the very important research of Avery[6] and his collaborators on the transformation of pneumococcal types that started the avalanche?

It is, of course, completely senseless to formulate a hierarchy of cellular constituents and to single out certain compounds as more important than others. The economy of the living cell probably knows no conspicuous waste; proteins and nucleic acids, lipids and polysaccharides, all have the same importance. But one observation may be offered. It is impossible to write the history of the cell without considering its geography; and we cannot do this without attention to what may be called the chronology of the cell, i. e. the sequence in which the cellular constituents are laid down and in which they develop from each other. If this is done, nucleic acids will be found pretty much at the beginning. An attempt to say more leads directly into empty speculations in which almost no field

abounds more than the chemistry of the cell. Since an ounze of proof still weighs more than a pound of prediction, the important genetical functions, ascribed —probably quite rightly—to the nucleic acids by many workers, will not be discussed here. Terms such as "template" or "matrix" or "reduplication" will not be found in this lecture.

II. *Identity and Diversity in High Molecular Cell Constituents*

The determination of the constitution of a complicated compound, composed of many molecules of a number of organic substances, evidently requires the exact knowledge of the nature and proportion of all constituents. This is true for nucleic acids as much as for proteins or polysaccharides. It is, furthermore, clear that the value of such constitutional determinations will depend upon the development of suitable methods of hydrolysis. Otherwise, substances representing an association of many chemical individuals can be described in a qualitative fashion only; precise decisions as to structure remain impossible. When our laboratory, more than four years ago, embarked upon the study of nucleic acids, we became aware of this difficulty immediately.

The state of the nucleic acid problem at that time found its classical expression in Levene's monograph[1]. (A number of shorter reviews, indicative of the development of our conceptions concerning the chemistry of nucleic acids, should also be mentioned[2].) The old tetranucleotide hypothesis—it should never have been called a theory—was still dominant; and this was characteristic of the enormous sway that the organic chemistry of small molecules held over biochemistry. I should like to illustrate what I mean by one example. If in the investigation of a disaccharide consisting of two different hexoses we isolate 0·8 mole of one sugar and 0·7 mole of the other, this will be sufficient for the

[1] This article is based on a series of lectures given before the Chemical Societies of Zürich and Basle (June 29th and 30th, 1949), the Société de chimie biologique at Paris, and the Universities of Uppsala, Stockholm, and Milan.

[2] Department of Biochemistry, College of Physicians and Surgeons, Columbia University, New York. The author wishes to thank the *John Simon Guggenheim Memorial Foundation* for making possible his stay in Europe. The experimental work has been supported by a research grant from the *United States Public Health Service*.

[3] E. Hammarsten, Biochem. Z. *144*, 383 (1924).

[4] J. Brachet in *Nucleic Acid*, Symposia Soc. Exp. Biol. No. 1 (Cambridge University Press, 1947), p. 207. Cp. J. Brachet, in *Nucleic Acids and Nucleoproteins*, Cold Spring Harbor Symp. Quant. Biol. *12*, 18. (Cold Spring Harbor, N.Y., 1947).

[5] T. Caspersson, in *Nucleic Acid*, Symp. Soc. Exp. Biol., No. 1 (Cambridge University Press, 1947), p. 127.

[6] O. T. Avery, C. M. MacLeod, and M. McCarty, J. Exp. Med. *79*, 137 (1944).

[1] P. A. Levene and L. W. Bass, Nucleic Acids (Chemical Catalog Co., New York, 1931).

[2] H. Bredereck, Fortschritte der Chemie organischer Naturstoffe *1*, 121 (1938). – F. G. Fischer, Naturwissensch. *30*, 377 (1942). – R. S. Tipson, Adv. Carbohydrate Chem. *1*, 193 (1945). – J. M. Gulland, G. R. Barker, and D. O. Jordan, Ann. Rev. Biochem. *14*, 175 (1945). – E. Chargaff and E. Vischer, Ann. Rev. Biochem. *17*, 201 (1948). – F. Schlenk, Adv. Enzymol. *9*, 455 (1949).

recognition of the composition of the substance, provided its molecular weight is known. The deviation of the analytical results from simple, integral proportions is without importance in that case. But this will not hold for high-molecular compounds in which variations in the proportions of their several components often will provide the sole indication of the occurrence of different compounds.

In attempting to formulate the problem with some exaggeration one could say: The validity of the identification of a substance by the methods of classical organic chemistry ends with the mixed melting point. When we deal with the extremely complex compounds of cellular origin, such as nucleic acids, proteins, or polysaccharides, a chemical comparison aiming at the determination of identity or difference must be based on the nature and the proportions of their constituents, on the sequence in which these constituents are arranged in the molecule, and on the type and the position of the linkages that hold them together. The smaller the number of components of such a high-molecular compound is, the greater is the difficulty of a decision. The occurrence of a very large number of different proteins was recognized early; no one to my knowledge ever attempted to postulate a protein as a compound composed of equimolar proportions of 18 or 20 different amino acids. In addition, immunological investigations contributed very much to the recognition of the multiplicity of proteins. A decision between identity and difference becomes much more difficult when, as is the case with the nucleic acids, only few primary components are encountered. And when we finally come to high polymers, consisting of one component only, e. g. glycogen or starch, the characterization of the chemical specificity of such a compound becomes a very complicated and laborious task.

While, therefore, the formulation of the tetranucleotide conception appeared explainable on historical grounds, it lacked an adequate experimental basis, especially as regards "thymonucleic acid". Although only two nucleic acids, the desoxyribose nucleic acid of calf thymus and the ribose nucleic acid of yeast, had been examined analytically in some detail, all conclusions derived from the study of these substances were immediately extended to the entire realm of nature; a jump of a boldness that should astound a circus acrobat. This went so far that in some publications the starting material for the so-called "thymonucleic acid" was not even mentioned or that it was not thymus at all, as may sometimes be gathered from the context, but, for instance, fish sperm or spleen. The animal species that had furnished the starting material often remained unspecified.

Now the question arises: How different must complicated substances be, before we can recognize their difference? In the multiformity of its appearances nature can be primitive and it can be subtle. It is

primitive in creating in a cell, such as the tubercle bacillus, a host of novel compounds, new fatty acids, alcohols, etc., that are nowhere else encountered. There, the recognition of chemical peculiarities is relatively easy. But in the case of the proteins and nucleic acids, I believe, nature has acted most subtly; and the task facing us is much more difficult. There is nothing more dangerous in the natural sciences than to look for harmony, order, regularity, before the proper level is reached. The harmony of cellular life may well appear chaotic to us. The disgust for the amorphous, the ostensibly anomalous—an interesting problem in the psychology of science—has produced many theories that shrank gradually to hypotheses and then vanished.

We must realize that minute changes in the nucleic acid, e. g. the disappearance of one guanine molecule out of a hundred, could produce far-reaching changes in the geometry of the conjugated nucleoprotein; and it is not impossible that rearrangements of this type are among the causes of the occurrence of mutations[1].

The molecular weight of the pentose nucleic acids, especially of those from animal tissue cells, is not yet known; and the problem of their preparation and homogeneity still is in a very sad state. But that the desoxypentose nucleic acids, prepared under as mild conditions as possible and with the avoidance of enzymatic degradation, represent fibrous structures of high molecular weight, has often been demonstrated. No agreement has as yet been achieved on the order of magnitude of the molecular weight, since the interpretation of physical measurements of largely asymmetric molecules still presents very great difficulties. But regardless of whether the desoxyribonucleic acid of calf thymus is considered as consisting of elementary units of about 35,000 which tend to associate to larger structures[2] or whether it is regarded as a true macromolecule of a molecular weight around 820,000[3], the fact remains that the desoxypentose nucleic acids are high-molecular substances which in size resemble, or even surpass, the proteins. It is quite possible that there exists a critical range of molecular weights above which two different cells will prove unable to synthesize completely identical substances. The enormous number of diverse proteins may be cited as an example. *Duo non faciunt idem* is, with respect to cellular chemistry, perhaps an improved version of the old proverb.

III. Purpose

We started in our work from the assumption that the nucleic acids were complicated and intricate high-

---

[1] For additional remarks on this problem, compare E. Chargaff, in *Nucleic Acids and Nucleoproteins*, Cold Spring Harbor Symp. Quant. Biol., *12*, 28 (Cold Spring Harbor, N.Y., 1947).
[2] E. Hammarsten, Acta med. Scand., Suppl. *196*, 634 (1947). – G. Jungner, I. Jungner, and L.-G. Allgén, Nature *163*, 849 (1949).
[3] R. Cecil and A. G. Ogston, J. Chem. Soc. 1382 (1948).

polymers, comparable in this respect to the proteins, and that the determination of their structures and their structural differences would require the development of methods suitable for the precise analysis of all constituents of nucleic acids prepared from a large number of different cell types. These methods had to permit the study of minute amounts, since it was clear that much of the material would not be readily available. The procedures developed in our laboratory make it indeed possible to perform a complete constituent analysis on 2 to 3 mg of nucleic acid, and this in six parallel determinations.

The basis of the procedure is the partition chromatography on filter paper. When we started our experiments, only the qualitative application to amino acids was known[1]. But it was obvious that the high and specific absorption in the ultraviolet of the purines and pyrimidines could form the basis of a quantitative ultra-micro method, if proper procedures for the hydrolysis of the nucleic acids and for the sharp separation of the hydrolysis products could be found.

IV. *Preparation of the Analytical Material*

If preparations of desoxypentose nucleic acids are to be subjected to a structural analysis, the extent of their contamination with pentose nucleic acid must not exceed 2 to 3%. The reason will later be made clearer; but I should like to mention here that all desoxypentose nucleic acids of animal origin studied by us so far were invariably found to contain much more adenine than guanine. The reverse appears to be true for the animal pentose nucleic acids: in them guanine preponderates. A mixture of approximately equal parts of both nucleic acids from the same tissue, therefore, would yield analytical figures that would correspond, at least as regards the purines, to roughly equimolar proportions. Should the complete purification — sometimes an extremely difficult task — prove impossible in certain cases, one could think of subjecting preparations of both types of nucleic acid from the same tissue specimen to analysis and of correcting the respective results in this manner. This, however, is an undesirable device and was employed only in some of the preparations from liver which will be mentioned later.

It is, furthermore, essential that the isolation of the nucleic acids be conducted in such a manner as to exclude their degradation by enzymes, acid or alkali. In order to inhibit the desoxyribonucleases which require magnesium[2], the preparation of the desoxypentose nucleic acids was carried out in the presence of citrate ions[3]. It would take us here too far to

describe in detail the methods employed in our laboratory for the preparation of the desoxypentose nucleic acids from animal tissues. They represent in general a combination of many procedures, as described recently for the isolation of yeast desoxyribonucleic acid[1]. In this manner, the desoxypentose nucleic acids of thymus, spleen, liver, and also yeast were prepared. The corresponding compound from tubercle bacilli was isolated *via* the nucleoprotein[2]. The procedures leading to the preparation of desoxypentose nucleic acid from human sperm will soon be published[3]. All desoxypentose nucleic acids used in the analytical studies were prepared as the sodium salts (in one case the potassium salt was used); they were free of protein, highly polymerized, and formed extremely viscous solutions in water. They were homogeneous electrophoretically and showed a high degree of monodispersity in the ultracentrifuge.

The procedure for the preparation of pentose nucleic acids from animal tissues resembled, in its first stages, the method of Clarke and Schryver[4]. The details of the isolation procedures and related experiments on yeast ribonucleic acid are as yet unpublished. Commercial preparations of yeast ribonucleic acid also were examined following purification. As has been mentioned before, the entire problem of the preparation and homogeneity of the pentose nucleic acids, and even of the occurrence of only one type of pentose nucleic acid in the cell, urgently requires re-examination.

V. *Separation and Estimation of Purines and Pyrimidines*

Owing to the very unpleasant solubility and polar characteristics of the purines, the discovery of suitable solvent systems and the development of methods for their quantitative separation and estimation[5] presented a rather difficult problem in the solution of which Dr. Ernst Vischer had an outstanding part. The pyrimidines proved somewhat easier to handle. The choice of the solvent system for the chromatographic separation of purines and pyrimidines will, of course, vary with the particular problem. The efficiency of different solvent systems in effecting separation is illustrated schematically in Fig. 1. Two of the solvent systems listed there are suitable for the separation of the purines found in nucleic acids, i. e. adenine and guanine, namely (1) n-butanol, morpholine, diethylene glycol, water (column 5 in Fig. 1); and (2) n-butanol, diethylene glycol, water in a NH_3 atmosphere (column 11). The second system listed proved particularly

[1] R. Consden, A. H. Gordon, and A. J. P. Martin, Biochem. J. *38*, 224 (1944).
[2] F. G. Fischer, I. Böttger, and H. Lehmann-Echternacht, Z. physiol. Chem. *271*, 246 (1941).
[3] M. McCarty, J. Gen. Physiol. *29*, 123 (1946).

[1] E. Chargaff and S. Zamenhof, J. Biol. Chem. *173*, 327 (1948).
[2] E. Chargaff and H. F. Saidel, J. Biol. Chem. *177*, 417 (1949).
[3] S. Zamenhof, L. B. Shettles, and E. Chargaff, Nature (in press).
[4] G. Clarke and S. B. Schryver, Biochem. J. *11*, 319 (1917).
[5] E. Vischer and E. Chargaff, J. Biol. Chem. *168*, 781 (1947); *176*, 703 (1948).

III. DNA STRUCTURE AND REPLICATION

convenient. The separation of the pyrimidines is carried out in aqueous butanol (column 1).

Following the separation, the location of the various adsorption zones on the paper must be demonstrated. Our first attempts to bring this about in ultraviolet light were unsuccessful, probably because of inadequate filtration of the light emitted by the lamp then at our disposal. For this reason, the expedient was

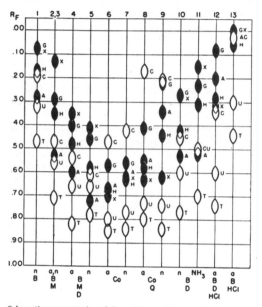

Schematic representation of the position on the paper chromatogram of the purines and pyrimidines following the separation of a mixture. *A* adenine, *G* guanine, *H* hypoxanthine, *X* xanthine, *U* uracil, *C* cytosine, *T* thymine. The conditions under which the separations were performed are indicated at the bottom, *a* acidic, *n* neutral, *B* n-butanol, *M* morpholine, *D* diethylene glycol, *Co* collidine, *Q* quinoline.

(Taken from E. VISCHER and E. CHARGAFF, J. Biol. Chem. *176*, 704 [1948].)

used of fixing the separated purines or pyrimidines on the paper as mercury complexes which then were made visible by their conversion to mercuric sulfide. The papers thus developed served as guide strips for the removal of the corresponding zones from untreated chromatograms that were then extracted and analyzed in the ultraviolet spectrophotometer. The development of the separated bases as mercury derivatives has, however, now become unnecessary, except for the preservation of permanent records, since there has for some time been available commercially an ultraviolet lamp emitting short wave ultraviolet ("Mineralight", Ultraviolet Products Corp., Los Angeles, California). With the help of this lamp it is now easy to demonstrate directly the position of the separated purines and pyrimidines (and also of nucleosides and nucleo-

tides[1]) which appear as dark absorption shadows on the background of the fluorescing filter paper and can be cut apart accordingly. (We are greatly indebted to Dr. C. E. CARTER, Oak Ridge National Laboratory, who drew our attention to this instrument[2].)

The extracts of the separated compounds are then studied in the ultraviolet spectrophotometer. The measurement of complete absorption spectra permits the determination of the purity of the solutions and at the same time the quantitative estimation of their contents. The details of the procedures employed have been published[3]. In this manner, adenine, guanine, uracil, cytosine, and thymine (and also hypoxanthine, xanthine, and 5-methylcytosine[4]) can be determined quantitatively in amounts of 2–40 γ. The precision of the method is ±4% for the purines and even better for the pyrimidines, if the averages of a large series of determinations are considered. In individual estimations the accuracy is about ±6%.

Procedures very similar in principle served in our laboratory for the separation and estimation of the ribonucleosides uridine and cytidine and for the separation of desoxyribothymidine from thymine. Methods for the separation and quantitative determination of the ribonucleotides in an aqueous ammonium isobutyrate-isobutyric acid system have likewise been developed[5].

VI. Methods of Hydrolysis

It has long been known that the purines can be split off completely by a relatively mild acid hydrolysis of the nucleic acids. This could be confirmed in our laboratory in a more rigorous manner by the demonstration that heating at 100° for 1 hour in N sulfuric acid effects the quantitative liberation of adenine and guanine from adenylic and guanylic acids respectively[6]. The liberation of the pyrimidines, however, requires much more energetic methods of cleavage. Heating at high temperatures with strong mineral acid under pressure is usually resorted to. To what extent these procedures brought about the destruction of the pyrimidines, could not be ascertained previously owing to the lack of suitable analytical procedures. The experiments summarized in Table I, which are quoted from a recent paper[6], show that the extremely robust cleavage methods with mineral acids usually employed must have led to a very considerable degradation of cytosine to uracil. Uracil and also thymine are much more resistant. For this reason, we turned to

[1] E. CHARGAFF, B. MAGASANIK, R. DONIGER, and E. VISCHER, J. Amer. Chem. Soc. *71*, 1513 (1949).
[2] A similar arrangement was recently described by E. R. HOLIDAY and E. A. JOHNSON, Nature *163*, 216 (1949).
[3] E. VISCHER and E. CHARGAFF, J. Biol. Chem. *176*, 703 (1948).
[4] J. KREAM and E. CHARGAFF, unpublished experiments.
[5] E. VISCHER, B. MAGASANIK, and E. CHARGAFF, Federation Proc. *8*, 263 (1949). – E. CHARGAFF, B. MAGASANIK, R. DONIGER, and E. VISCHER, J. Amer. Chem. Soc. *71*, 1513 (1949).
[6] E. VISCHER and E. CHARGAFF, J. Biol. Chem. *176*, 715 (1948).

Table I

Resistance of pyrimidines to treatment with strong acid. A mixture of pyrimidines of known concentration was dissolved in the acids indicated below and heated at 175° in a bomb tube. The concentration shifts of the individual pyrimidines were determined through a comparison of the recoveries of separated pyrimidines before and after the heating of the mixture.

Experiment No.	Acid	Heating time min.	Concentration shift, per cent of starting concentration		
			Uracil	Cytosine	Thymine
1	HCl (10%)	90	+62	−63	+3
2	10 N HCOOH +	60	+ 3	− 5	0
3	N HCl (1:1)	120	+24	−19	0
4	HCOOH (98 to 100%)	60	0	− 1	−2
5		120	0	+ 2	+1

the hydrolysis of the pyrimidine nucleotides by means of concentrated formic acid. For the liberation of the purines N sulfuric acid (100°, 1 hour) is employed; for the liberation of the pyrimidines, the purines are first precipitated as the hydrochlorides by treatment with dry HCl gas in methanol and the remaining pyrimidine nucleotides cleaved under pressure with concentrated formic acid (175°, 2 hours). This procedure proved particularly suitable for the investigation of the desoxypentose nucleic acids. For the study of the composition of pentose nucleic acids a different procedure, making use of the separation of the ribonucleotides, was developed more recently, which will be mentioned later.

VII. *Composition of Desoxypentose Nucleic Acids*

It should be stated at the beginning of this discussion that the studies conducted thus far have yielded no indication of the occurrence in the nucleic acids examined in our laboratory of unusual nitrogenous constituents. In all desoxypentose nucleic acids investigated by us the purines were adenine and guanine, the pyrimidines cytosine and thymine. The occurrence in minute amounts of other bases, e.g. 5-methylcytosine, can, however, not yet be excluded. In the pentose nucleic acids uracil occurred instead of thymine.

A survey of the composition of desoxyribose nucleic acid extracted from several organs of the ox is provided

Table II [1]

Composition of desoxyribonucleic acid of ox (in moles of nitrogenous constituent per mole of P).

Constituent	Thymus			Spleen		Liver
	Prep.1	Prep.2	Prep.3	Prep.1	Prep.2	
Adenine ..	0·26	0·28	0·30	0·25	0·26	0·26
Guanine ..	0·21	0·24	0·22	0·20	0·21	0·20
Cytosine ..	0·16	0·18	0·17	0·15	0·17	
Thymine ..	0·25	0·24	0·25	0·24	0·24	
Recovery ..	0·88	0·94	0·94	0·84	0·88	

[1] From E. Chargaff, E. Vischer, R. Doniger, C. Green, and F. Misani, J. Biol. Chem. *177*, 405 (1949); and unpublished results.

in Table II. The molar proportions reported in each case represent averages of several hydrolysis experiments. The composition of desoxypentose nucleic acids from human tissues is similarly illustrated in Table III. The preparations from human liver were obtained from a pathological specimen in which it was possible, thanks to the kind cooperation of M. Faber, to separate portions of unaffected hepatic tissue from carcinomatous tissue consisting of metastases from the sigmoid colon, previous to the isolation of the nucleic acids[1].

Table III [2]

Composition of desoxypentose nucleic acid of man (in moles of nitrogenous constituent per mole of P).

Constituent	Sperm		Thymus	Liver	
	Prep.1	Prep.2		Normal	Carcinoma
Adenine ...	0·29	0·27	0·28	0·27	0·27
Guanine ...	0·18	0·17	0·19	0·19	0·18
Cytosine ...	0·18	0·18	0·16		0·15
Thymine ...	0·31	0·30	0·28		0·27
Recovery ...	0·96	0·92	0·91		0·87

In order to show examples far removed from mammalian organs, the composition of two desoxyribonucleic acids of microbial origin, namely from yeast[3] and from avian tubercle bacilli[4], is summarized in Table IV.

Table IV [5]

Composition of two microbial desoxyribonucleic acids.

Constituent	Yeast		Avian tubercle bacilli
	Prep. 1	Prep. 2	
Adenine	0·24	0·30	0·12
Guanine	0·14	0·18	0·28
Cytosine	0·13	0·15	0·26
Thymine	0·25	0·29	0·11
Recovery	0·76	0·92	0·77

The very far-reaching differences in the composition of desoxypentose nucleic acids of different species are best illustrated by a comparison of the ratios of adenine to guanine and of thymine to cytosine as given in Table V. It will be seen that in all cases where enough material for statistical analysis was available highly significant differences were found. The analytical figures on which Table V is based were derived by comparing the ratios found for individual nucleic acid hydrolysates of one species regardless of the organ from which the preparation was isolated. This procedure assumes that there is no organ specificity with

[1] Unpublished experiments.
[2] From E. Chargaff, S. Zamenhof, and C. Green, Nature (in press); and unpublished results.
[3] E. Chargaff and S. Zamenhof, J. Biol. Chem. *173*, 327 (1948).
[4] E. Chargaff and H. F. Saidel, J. Biol. Chem. *177*, 417 (1949).
[5] From E. Vischer, S. Zamenhof, and E. Chargaff, J. Biol. Chem. *177*, 429 (1949); and unpublished results.

III. DNA STRUCTURE AND REPLICATION   249

Table V
Molar proportions of purines and pyrimidines in desoxypentose nucleic acids from different species.

Species	Number of different organs	Number of different preparations	Adenine/Guanine			Thymine/Cytosine		
			Number of hydrolyses[3]	Mean ratio	Standard error	Number of hydrolyses[3]	Mean ratio	Standard error
Ox[1]	3	7	20	1·29	0·013	6	1·43	0·03
Man[2]	2	3	6	1·56	0·008	5	1·75	0·03
Yeast.	1	2	3	1·72	0·02	2	1·9	
Avian tubercles bacillus	1	1	2	0·4		1	0·4	

[1] Preparations from thymus, spleen, and liver served for the purine determinations, the first two organs for the estimation of pyrimidines.

[2] Preparations from spermatozoa and thymus were analysed.
[3] In each hydrolysis between 12 and 24 determinations of individual purines and pyrimidines were performed.

respect to the composition of desoxypentose nucleic acids of the same species. That this appears indeed to be the case may be gathered from Tables II and III and even better from Table VI where the average purine and pyrimidine ratios in individual tissues of the same species are compared. That the isolation of nucleic acids did not entail an appreciable fractionation is shown by the finding that when whole defatted human spermatozoa, after being washed with cold 10% trichloroacetic acid, were analyzed, the same ratios of adenine to guanine and of thymine to cytosine were found as are reported in Tables V and VI. It should also be mentioned that all preparations, with the exception of those from human liver, were derived from pooled starting material representing a number, and in the case of human spermatozoa a very large number, of individuals.

Table VI
Molar proportions of purines and pyrimidines in desoxypentose nucleic acids from different organs of one species.

Species	Organ	Adenine/ Guanine	Thymine/ Cytosine
Ox	Thymus	1·3	1·4
	Spleen	1·2	1·5
	Liver	1·3	
Man	Thymus	1·5	1·8
	Sperm	1·6	1·7
	Liver (normal)	1·5	1·8
	Liver (carcinoma)	1·5	1·8

The desoxypentose nucleic acids extracted from different species thus appear to be different substances or mixtures of closely related substances of a composition constant for different organs of the same species and characteristic of the species.

The results serve to disprove the tetranucleotide hypothesis. It is, however, noteworthy—whether this is more than accidental, cannot yet be said—that in all desoxypentose nucleic acids examined thus far the molar ratios of total purines to total pyrimidines, and also of adenine to thymine and of guanine to cytosine, were not far from 1.

VIII. Composition of Pentose Nucleic Acids

Here a sharp distinction must be drawn between the prototype of all pentose nucleic acid investigations—the ribonucleic acid of yeast—and the pentose nucleic acids of animal cells. Nothing is known as yet about bacterial pentose nucleic acids. In view of the incompleteness of our information on the homogeneity of pentose nucleic acids, which I have stressed before, I feel that the analytical results on these preparations do not command the same degree of confidence as do those obtained for the desoxypentose nucleic acids.

Table VIII[1]
Composition of pentose nucleic acids from animal tissues.

Constituent	Calf liver	Ox liver	Sheep liver	Pig liver	Pig pancreas
Guanylic acid . . .	16·3	14·7	16·7	16·2	22·5
Adenylic acid . . .	10	10	10	10	10
Cytidylic acid . . .	11·1	10·9	13·4	16·1	9·8
Uridylic acid . . .	5·3	6·6	5·6	7·7	4·6
Purines : pyrimidines	1·6	1·4	1·4	1·1	2·5

Three procedures, to which reference is made in Tables VII and VIII, were employed in our laboratory for the analysis of pentose nucleic acids. In *Procedure 1*, the pentose nucleic acid was hydrolysed to the nucleotide stage with alkali, at p_H 13·5 and 30°, and the nucleotides, following adjustment to about p_H 5, separated by chromatography with aqueous ammonium isobutyrate-isobutyric acid as the solvent. Under these conditions, guanylic acid shares its position on the chromatogram with uridylic acid; but it is possible to determine the concentrations of the two components in the eluates by simultaneous equations based on the ultraviolet absorption of the pure nucleotides[2]. The very good recoveries of nucleotides obtained in terms of both nucleic acid phosphorus and nitrogen show the cleavage by mild alkali treatment of pentose nucleic acids to be practically quantitative.—In

[1] Unpublished results.
[2] E. VISCHER, B. MAGASANIK, and E. CHARGAFF, Federation Proc. 8, 263 (1949). — E. CHARGAFF, B. MAGASANIK, R. DONIGER, and E. VISCHER, J. Amer. Chem. Soc. 71, 1513 (1949).

Table VII [1]

Composition of yeast ribonucleic acid (in moles of nitrogenous constituent per mole of P).

Constituent	Preparation 1			Preparation 2			Preparation 3		
	Procedure 1	Procedure 2	Procedure 3	Procedure 1	Procedure 2	Procedure 3	Procedure 1	Procedure 2	Procedure 3
Adenylic acid	0·29	0·26	0·26	0·27		0·24	0·25	0·23	0·24
Guanylic acid	0·28	0·29	0·26	0·25		0·25	0·26	0·28	0·26
Cytidylic acid	0·18	0·17	0·24	0·20			0·21	0·21	
Uridylic acid	0·20	0·20	0·08	0·18	0·19		0·20	0·25	
Recovery	0·95	0·92	0·84	0·90			0·92	0·97	

[1] From E. VISCHER and E. CHARGAFF, J. Biol. Chem. *176*, 715 (1948). – E. CHARGAFF, B. MAGASANIK, R. DONIGER, and E. VISCHER, J. Amer. Chem. Soc. *71*, 1513 (1949); and unpublished results.

Procedure 2, the purines are first liberated by gaseous HCl in dry methanol and the evaporation residue of the reaction mixture is adjusted to p_H 13·5 and then treated as in Procedure 1. In this manner, uridylic and cytidylic acids, adenine and guanine are separated and determined on one chromatogram.—The determinations of free purines and pyrimidines in acid hydrolysates of pentose nucleic acids, following the methods outlined before for the desoxypentose nucleic acids, are listed as *Procedure 3*. It will be seen that it is mainly uracil which in this procedure escapes quantitative determination. This is due to the extreme refractoriness of uridylic acid to complete hydrolysis by acids, a large portion remaining partially unsplit as the nucleoside uridine. As matters stand now, I consider the values for purines yielded by Procedures 1 and 3 and those for pyrimidines found by Procedures 1 and 2 as quite reliable.

A survey of the composition of yeast ribonucleic acid is provided in Table VII. Preparations 1 and 2, listed in this table, were commercial preparations that had been purified in our laboratory and had been subjected to dialysis; Preparation 3 was isolated from baker's yeast by B. MAGASANIK in this laboratory by procedures similar to those used for the preparation of pentose nucleic acids from animal tissues and had not been dialyzed. It will be seen that the results are quite constant and not very far from the proportions required by the presence of equimolar quantities of all four nitrogenous constituents.

An entirely different picture, however, was encountered when the composition of pentose nucleic acids from animal cells was investigated. A preliminary summary of the results, in all cases obtained by *Procedure 1*, is given in Table VIII. Here guanylic acid was the preponderating nucleotide followed, in this order, by cytidylic and adenylic acids; uridylic acid definitely was a minor constituent. This was true not only of the ribonucleic acid of pancreas which has been known to be rich in guanine[1], but also of all pentose

[1] E. HAMMARSTEN, Z. physiol. Ch. *109*, 141 (1920). – P. A. LEVENE and E. JORPES, J. Biol. Chem. *86*, 389 (1930). – E. JORPES, Biochem. J. *28*, 2102 (1934).

nucleic acids isolated by us from the livers of three different species (Table VIII).

In the absence of a truly reliable standard method for the isolation of a pentose nucleic acid from animal tissue, generalizations are not yet permitted; but it would appear that pentose nucleic acids from the same organ of different species are more similar to each other, at least in certain respects (e. g. the ratio of guanine to adenine), than are those from different organs of the same species. (Compare the pentose nucleic acids from the liver and the pancreas of pig in Table VIII.)

IX. *Sugar Components*

It is deplorable that such designations as desoxyribose and ribose nucleic acids continue to be used as if they were generic terms. Even the "thymus nucleic acid of fish sperm" is encountered in the literature. As a matter of fact, only in a few cases have the sugars been identified, namely, d-2-desoxyribose as a constituent of the guanine and thymine nucleosides of the desoxypentose nucleic acid from calf thymus, D-ribose as a constituent of the pentose nucleic acids from yeast, pancreas, and sheep liver.

Since the quantities of novel nucleic acids usually will be insufficient for the direct isolation of their sugar components, we attempted to employ the very sensitive procedure of the filter paper chromatography of sugars[1] for the study of the sugars isolated from minute quantities of nucleic acids. It goes without saying that identifications based on behavior in adsorption or partition are by no means as convincing as the actual isolation, but they will at least permit a tentative classification of new nucleic acids. Thus far the pentose nucleic acids of pig pancreas[2] and of the avian tubercle bacillus[3] have been shown to contain ribose, the desoxypentose nucleic acids of ox spleen[4],

[1] S. M. PARTRIDGE, Nature *158*, 270 (1946). – S. M. PARTRIDGE and R. G. WESTALL, Biochem. J. *42*, 238 (1948). – E. CHARGAFF, C. LEVINE, and C. GREEN, J. Biol. Chem. *175*, 67 (1948).
[2] E. VISCHER and E. CHARGAFF, J. Biol. Chem. *176*, 715 (1948).
[3] E. VISCHER, S. ZAMENHOF, and E. CHARGAFF, J. Biol. Chem. *177*, 429 (1949).
[4] E. CHARGAFF, E. VISCHER, R. DONIGER, C. GREEN, and F. MISANI, J. Biol. Chem. *177*, 405 (1949).

III. DNA STRUCTURE AND REPLICATION

yeast and avian tubercle bacilli[1] desoxyribose. It would seem that the free play with respect to the variability of components that nature permits itself is extremely restricted, where nucleic acids are concerned.

X. *Depolymerizing Enzymes*

Enzymes capable of bringing about the depolymerization of both types of nucleic acids have long been known; but it is only during the last decade that crystalline ribonuclease[2] and desoxyribonuclease[3] from pancreas have become available thanks to the work of KUNITZ. Important work on the latter enzyme was also done by MCCARTY[4].

Table IX [5]

Enzymatic degradation of calf thymus desoxyribonucleic acid.

	Digestion *hours*	Dialysis *hours*	Distribution of fractions % of original	Composition of fractions (molar proportions)			
				Adenine Guanine	Thymine Cytosine	Adenine Cytosine	Pyrimidines Purines
Original	0	0	100	1·2	1·3	1·6	1·2
Dialysate . . .	6	6	53	1·2	1·2	1·2	1·0
Dialysis residue	24	72	7	1·6	2·2	3·8	2·0

We were, of course, interested in applying the chromatographic micromethods for the determination of nucleic acid constituents to studies of enzymatic reaction mechanisms for which they are particularly suited. The action of crystalline desoxyribonuclease on calf thymus desoxyribonucleic acid resulted in the production of a large proportion of dialyzable fragments (53 per cent of the total after 6 hours digestion), without liberation of ammonia or inorganic phosphate. But even after extended digestion there remained a non-dialyzable core whose composition showed a significant divergence from both the original nucleic acid and the bulk of the dialyzate[6]. The preliminary findings summarized in Table IX indicate a considerable increase in the molar proportions of adenine to guanine and especially to cytosine, of thymine to cytosine, and of purines to pyrimidines. This shows that the dissymmetry in the distribution of constituents, found in the original nucleic acid (Table II), is intensified in the core. The most plausible explanations of this interesting phenomenon, the study of which is being continued, are that the preparations consisted of more than one desoxypentose nucleic acid or that the nucleic contained in its chain clusters of nucleotides

(relatively richer in adenine and thymine) that were distinguished from the bulk of the molecule by greater resistance to enzymatic disintegration.

In this connection another study, carried out in collaboration with S. ZAMENHOF, should be mentioned briefly that dealt with the desoxypentose nuclease of yeast cells[1]. This investigation afforded a possibility of exploring the mechanisms by which an enzyme concerned with the disintegration of desoxypentose nucleic acid is controlled in the cell. Our starting point again was the question of the specificity of desoxypentose nucleic acids; but the results were entirely unexpected. Since we had available a number of nucleic acids from different sources, we wanted to study a pair of desoxypentose nucleic acids as distant from each other as possible, namely that of the ox and that of yeast, and to investigate the action on them of the two desoxypentose nucleases from the same cellular sources. The desoxyribonuclease of ox pancreas has been thoroughly investigated, as was mentioned before. Nothing was known, however, regarding the existence of a yeast desoxypentose nuclease.

It was found that fresh salt extracts of crushed cells contained such an enzyme in a largely inhibited state, due to the presence of a specific inhibitor protein. This inhibitor specifically inhibited the desoxypentose nuclease from yeast, but not that from other sources, such as pancreas. The yeast enzyme depolymerized the desoxyribose nucleic acids of yeast and of calf thymus, which differ chemically, as I have emphasized before, at about the same rate. In other words, the enzyme apparently exhibited inhibitor specificity, but not substrate specificity. It is very inviting to assume that such relations between specific inhibitor and enzyme, in some ways reminiscent of immunological reactions, are of more general biological significance. In any event, a better understanding of such systems will permit an insight into the delicate mechanisms through which the cell manages the economy of its life, through which it maintains its own continuity and protects itself against agents striving to transform it.

XI. *Concluding Remarks*

Generalizations in science are both necessary and hazardous; they carry a semblance of finality which conceals their essentially provisional character; they drive forward, as they retard; they add, but they also take away. Keeping in mind all these reservations, we arrive at the following conclusions. The desoxypentose nucleic acids from animal and microbial cells contain varying proportions of the same four nitrogenous constituents, namely, adenine, guanine, cytosine, thymine. Their composition appears to be characteristic of the species, but not of the tissue, from which

[1] E. VISCHER, S. ZAMENHOF, and E. CHARGAFF, J. Biol. Chem. *177*, 429 (1949).

[2] M. KUNITZ, J. Gen. Physiol. *24*, 15 (1940).

[3] M. KUNITZ, Science *108*, 19 (1948).

[4] M. MCCARTY, J. Gen. Physiol. *29*, 123 (1946).

[5] From S. ZAMENHOF and E. CHARGAFF, J. Biol. Chem. *178*, 531 (1949).

[6] S. ZAMENHOF and E. CHARGAFF, J. Biol. Chem. *178*, 531 (1949).

[1] S. ZAMENHOF and E. CHARGAFF, Science *108*, 628 (1948); J. Biol. Chem. *180*, 727 (1949).

they are derived. The presumption, therefore, is that there exists an enormous number of structurally different nucleic acids; a number, certainly much larger than the analytical methods available to us at present can reveal.

It cannot yet be decided, whether what we call the desoxypentose nucleic acid of a given species is one chemical individual, representative of the species as a whole, or whether it consists of a mixture of closely related substances, in which case the constancy of its composition merely is a statistical expression of the unchanged state of the cell. The latter may be the case if, as appears probable, the highly polymerized desoxypentose nucleic acids form an essential part of the hereditary processes; but it will be understood from what I said at the beginning that a decision as to the identity of natural high polymers often still is beyond the means at our disposal. This will be particularly true of substances that differ from each other only in the sequence, not in the proportion, of their constituents. The number of possible nucleic acids having the same analytical composition is truly enormous. For example, the number of combinations exhibiting the same molar proportions of individual purines and pyrimidines as the desoxyribonucleic acid of the ox is more than 10^{56}, if the nucleic acid is assumed to consist of only 100 nucleotides; if it consists of 2,500 nucleotides, which probably is much nearer the truth, then the number of possible "isomers" is not far from 10^{1500}.

Moreover, desoxypentose nucleic acids from different species differ in their chemical composition, as I have shown before; and I think there will be no objection to the statement that, as far as chemical possibilities go, they could very well serve as one of the agents, or possibly as the agent, concerned with the transmission of inherited properties. It would be gratifying if one could say—but this is for the moment no more than an unfounded speculation—that just as the desoxypentose nucleic acids of the nucleus are species–specific and concerned with the maintenance of the species, the pentose nucleic acids of the cytoplasm are organ-specific and involved in the important task of differentiation.

I should not want to close without thanking my colleagues who have taken part in the work discussed here; they are, in alphabetical order, Miss R. Doniger, Mrs. C. Green, Dr. B. Magasanik, Dr. E. Vischer, and Dr. S. Zamenhof.

Zusammenfassung

Die Betrachtung der Nukleinsäuren, sowohl der Desoxypentosen als der Pentosen enthaltenden Verbindungen, als organische Makromoleküle macht eine Auseinandersetzung mit den Problemen notwendig, welche sich auf die Bestimmung von Identität oder Verschiedenheit solcher aus verschiedenen Zellen isolierten hochpolymeren Substanzen beziehen. Dies führt zu einer kritischen Besprechung der sicherlich nicht haltbaren Tetranukleotidhypothese und zur Formulierung eines Arbeitsprogramms für die Aufklärung der Zusammensetzung individueller Nukleinsäuren.

Die mikrochromatographischen und spektrophotometrischen Methoden zur Trennung und quantitativen Bestimmung der stickstoffhaltigen Nukleinsäurebestandteile werden kurz geschildert. Sie ermöglichen die quantitative Analyse der Purine Adenin, Guanin, Hypoxanthin und Xanthin und der Pyrimidine Cytosin, Uracil und Thymin im Bereiche von 2 bis 40 γ. An die Beschreibung der Verfahren zur Isolierung der als Analysenmaterial dienenden hochpolymerisierten Nukleinsäurepräparate aus verschiedenen Zellen schließt sich eine Besprechung der Hydrolysen- und Analysenmethoden, die auf sehr geringe Nukleinsäuremengen (2 bis 3 mg) anwendbar sind.

Alle bis jetzt untersuchten Desoxypentosenukleinsäuren enthielten 2-Desoxyribose als Zucker und Adenin, Guanin, Cytosin und Thymin als Stickstoffkomponenten in für die betreffende Zelle konstanten, von der Tetranukleotidhypothese weit abweichenden Proportionen. Ihre Zusammensetzung ist spezifisch für die Spezies, die als Ausgangsmaterial dient, jedoch nicht für das Ausgangsgewebe. Weit auseinanderliegende Arten, wie z. B. Säugetiere gegenüber Mikroorganismen, enthalten völlig verschieden zusammengesetzte Desoxypentosenukleinsäuren. In manchen Fällen lassen sich jedoch auch bei näherliegenden Nukleinsäuren, z. B. denen des Ochsen und des Menschen, ins Gewicht fallende Verschiedenheiten aufzeigen. Die Untersuchung der Pentosenukleinsäuren, die auf einer quantitativen Bestimmung der sie zusammensetzenden Mononukleotide beruht, ist noch nicht so weit gediehen. Es hat vorläufig gezeigt, daß sich die Verbindungen aus Säugetiergewebe von denen aus Hefe durch einen relativ sehr hohen Gehalt an Guanylsäure unterscheiden, und hat Anhaltspunkte dafür gegeben, daß die Pentosenukleinsäuren eher organ- als spezies-spezifisch sind.

Als Beispiele für den Beitrag, den die Untersuchung enzymatischer Reaktionsmechanismen zum Problem der chemischen Spezifität der Nukleinsäuren leisten kann, werden schließlich Versuche mit der kristallisierten Desoxyribonuklease aus Pankreas und mit einer durch interessante Hemmungsstoffspezifität ausgezeichneten Desoxypentosenukease aus Hefe geschildert. Zum Abschluß werden einige der Probleme gestreift, die sich aus der hier nachgewiesenen Existenz vieler verschiedener Nukleinsäuren ergeben.

14 Exper.

III. DNA STRUCTURE AND REPLICATION

253

(*Reprinted from Nature*, Vol. 171, p. 737, April 25, 1953)

MOLECULAR STRUCTURE OF NUCLEIC ACIDS

A Structure for Deoxyribose Nucleic Acid

WE wish to suggest a structure for the salt of deoxyribose nucleic acid (D.N.A.). This structure has novel features which are of considerable biological interest.

A structure for nucleic acid has already been proposed by Pauling and Corey[1]. They kindly made their manuscript available to us in advance of publication. Their model consists of three intertwined chains, with the phosphates near the fibre axis, and the bases on the outside. In our opinion, this structure is unsatisfactory for two reasons: (1) We believe that the material which gives the X-ray diagrams is the salt, not the free acid. Without the acidic hydrogen atoms it is not clear what forces would hold the structure together, especially as the negatively charged phosphates near the axis will repel each other. (2) Some of the van der Waals distances appear to be too small.

Another three-chain structure has also been suggested by Fraser (in the press). In his model the phosphates are on the outside and the bases on the inside, linked together by hydrogen bonds. This structure as described is rather ill-defined, and for this reason we shall not comment on it.

We wish to put forward a radically different structure for the salt of deoxyribose nucleic acid. This structure has two helical chains each coiled round the same axis (see diagram). We have made the usual chemical assumptions, namely, that each chain consists of phosphate di-ester groups joining β-D-deoxyribofuranose residues with 3′,5′ linkages. The two chains (but not their bases) are related by a dyad perpendicular to the fibre axis. Both chains follow right-handed helices, but owing to the dyad the sequences of the atoms in the two chains run in opposite directions. Each chain loosely resembles Furberg's[2] model No. 1; that is, the bases are on the inside of the helix and the phosphates on the outside. The configuration of the sugar and the atoms near it is close to Furberg's 'standard configuration', the sugar being roughly perpendicular to the attached base. There is a residue on each chain every 3·4 A. in the z-direction. We have assumed an angle of 36° between adjacent residues in the same

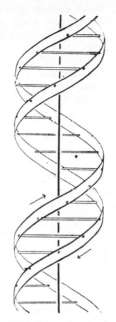

This figure is purely diagrammatic. The two ribbons symbolize the two phosphate—sugar chains, and the horizontal rods the pairs of bases holding the chains together. The vertical line marks the fibre axis

chain, so that the structure repeats after 10 residues on each chain, that is, after 34 A. The distance of a phosphorus atom from the fibre axis is 10 A. As the phosphates are on the outside, cations have easy access to them.

The structure is an open one, and its water content is rather high. At lower water contents we would expect the bases to tilt so that the structure could become more compact.

The novel feature of the structure is the manner in which the two chains are held together by the purine and pyrimidine bases. The planes of the bases are perpendicular to the fibre axis. They are joined together in pairs, a single base from one chain being hydrogen-bonded to a single base from the other chain, so that the two lie side by side with identical z-co-ordinates. One of the pair must be a purine and the other a pyrimidine for bonding to occur. The hydrogen bonds are made as follows : purine position 1 to pyrimidine position 1 ; purine position 6 to pyrimidine position 6.

If it is assumed that the bases only occur in the structure in the most plausible tautomeric forms

2

(that is, with the keto rather than the enol configurations) it is found that only specific pairs of bases can bond together. These pairs are : adenine (purine) with thymine (pyrimidine), and guanine (purine) with cytosine (pyrimidine).

In other words, if an adenine forms one member of a pair, on either chain, then on these assumptions the other member must be thymine ; similarly for guanine and cytosine. The sequence of bases on a single chain does not appear to be restricted in any way. However, if only specific pairs of bases can be formed, it follows that if the sequence of bases on one chain is given, then the sequence on the other chain is automatically determined.

It has been found experimentally[3,4] that the ratio of the amounts of adenine to thymine, and the ratio of guanine to cytosine, are always very close to unity for deoxyribose nucleic acid.

It is probably impossible to build this structure with a ribose sugar in place of the deoxyribose, as the extra oxygen atom would make too close a van der Waals contact.

The previously published X-ray data[5,6] on deoxyribose nucleic acid are insufficient for a rigorous test of our structure. So far as we can tell, it is roughly compatible with the experimental data, but it must be regarded as unproved until it has been checked against more exact results. Some of these are given in the following communications. We were not aware of the details of the results presented there when we devised our structure, which rests mainly though not entirely on published experimental data and stereochemical arguments.

It has not escaped our notice that the specific pairing we have postulated immediately suggests a possible copying mechanism for the genetic material.

Full details of the structure, including the conditions assumed in building it, together with a set of co-ordinates for the atoms, will be published elsewhere.

We are much indebted to Dr. Jerry Donohue for constant advice and criticism, especially on interatomic distances. We have also been stimulated by a knowledge of the general nature of the unpublished experimental results and ideas of Dr. M. H. F. Wilkins, Dr. R. E. Franklin and their co-workers at King's College, London. One of us (J. D. W.) has been aided by a fellowship from the National Foundation for Infantile Paralysis.

J. D. Watson
F. H. C. Crick

Medical Research Council Unit for the
Study of the Molecular Structure of
Biological Systems,
Cavendish Laboratory, Cambridge.
April 2.

3

[1] Pauling, L., and Corey, R. B., *Nature*, **171**, 346 (1953) ; *Proc. U.S. Nat. Acad. Sci.*, **39**, 84 (1953).

[2] Furberg, S., *Acta Chem. Scand.*, **6**, 634 (1952).

[3] Chargaff, E., for references see Zamenhof, S., Brawerman, G., and Chargaff, E., *Biochim. et Biophys. Acta*, **9**, 402 (1952).

[4] Wyatt, G. R., *J. Gen. Physiol.*, **36**, 201 (1952).

[5] Astbury, W. T., Symp. Soc. Exp. Biol. 1, Nucleic Acid, 66 (Camb. Univ. Press, 1947).

[6] Wilkins, M. H. F., and Randall, J. T., *Biochim. et Biophys. Acta*, **10**, 192 (1953).

Molecular Structure of Deoxypentose Nucleic Acids

WHILE the biological properties of deoxypentose nucleic acid suggest a molecular structure containing great complexity, X-ray diffraction studies described here (cf. Astbury[1]) show the basic molecular configuration has great simplicity. The purpose of this communication is to describe, in a preliminary way, some of the experimental evidence for the polynucleotide chain configuration being helical, and existing in this form when in the natural state. A fuller account of the work will be published shortly.

The structure of deoxypentose nucleic acid is the same in all species (although the nitrogen base ratios alter considerably) in nucleoprotein, extracted or in cells, and in purified nucleate. The same linear group of polynucleotide chains may pack together parallel in different ways to give crystalline[1-3], semi-crystalline or paracrystalline material. In all cases the X-ray diffraction photograph consists of two regions, one determined largely by the regular spacing of nucleotides along the chain, and the other by the longer spacings of the chain configuration. The sequence of different nitrogen bases along the chain is not made visible.

Oriented paracrystalline deoxypentose nucleic acid ('structure *B*' in the following communication by Franklin and Gosling) gives a fibre diagram as shown in Fig. 1 (cf. ref. 4). Astbury suggested that the strong 3·4-A. reflexion corresponded to the internucleotide repeat along the fibre axis. The ~ 34 A. layer lines, however, are not due to a repeat of a polynucleotide composition, but to the chain configuration repeat, which causes strong diffraction as the nucleotide chains have higher density than the interstitial water. The absence of reflexions on or near the meridian immediately suggests a helical structure with axis parallel to fibre length.

Diffraction by Helices

It may be shown[5] (also Stokes, unpublished) that the intensity distribution in the diffraction pattern of a series of points equally spaced along a helix is given by the squares of Bessel functions. A uniform continuous helix gives a series of layer lines of spacing

4

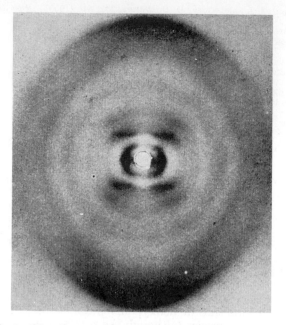

Fig. 1. Fibre diagram of deoxypentose nucleic acid from *B. coli*.
Fibre axis vertical

corresponding to the helix pitch, the intensity distribution along the nth layer line being proportional to the square of J_n, the nth order Bessel function. A straight line may be drawn approximately through the innermost maxima of each Bessel function and the origin. The angle this line makes with the equator is roughly equal to the angle between an element of the helix and the helix axis. If a unit repeats n times along the helix there will be a meridional reflexion (J_0^2) on the nth layer line. The helical configuration produces side-bands on this fundamental frequency, the effect[5] being to reproduce the intensity distribution about the origin around the new origin, on the nth layer line, corresponding to C in Fig. 2.

We will now briefly analyse in physical terms some of the effects of the shape and size of the repeat unit or nucleotide on the diffraction pattern. First, if the nucleotide consists of a unit having circular symmetry about an axis parallel to the helix axis, the whole diffraction pattern is modified by the form factor of the nucleotide. Second, if the nucleotide consists of a series of points on a radius at right-angles to the helix axis, the phases of radiation scattered by the helices of different diameter passing through each point are the same. Summation of the corresponding Bessel functions gives reinforcement for the inner-

5

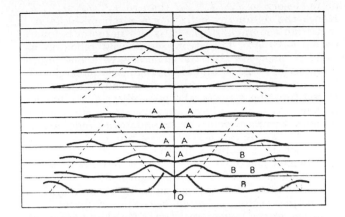

Fig. 2. Diffraction pattern of system of helices corresponding to structure of deoxypentose nucleic acid. The squares of Bessel functions are plotted about 0 on the equator and on the first, second, third and fifth layer lines for half of the nucleotide mass at 20 A. diameter and remainder distributed along a radius, the mass at a given radius being proportional to the radius. About C on the tenth layer line similar functions are plotted for an outer diameter cf 12 A.

most maxima and, in general, owing to phase difference, cancellation of all other maxima. Such a system of helices (corresponding to a spiral staircase with the core removed) diffracts mainly over a limited angular range, behaving, in fact, like a periodic arrangement of flat plates inclined at a fixed angle to the axis. Third, if the nucleotide is extended as an arc of a circle in a plane at right-angles to the helix axis, and with centre at the axis, the intensity of the system of Bessel function layer-line streaks emanating from the origin is modified owing to the phase differences of radiation from the helices drawn through each point on the nucleotide. The form factor is that of the series of points in which the helices intersect a plane drawn through the helix axis. This part of the diffraction pattern is then repeated as a whole with origin at C (Fig. 2). Hence this aspect of nucleotide shape affects the central and peripheral regions of each layer line differently.

Interpretation of the X-Ray Photograph

It must first be decided whether the structure consists of essentially one helix giving an intensity distribution along the layer lines corresponding to $J_1, J_2, J_3 \ldots$, or two similar co-axial helices of twice the above size and relatively displaced along the axis a distance equal to half the pitch giving $J_2, J_4, J_6 \ldots$, or three helices, etc. Examination of the width of the layer-line streaks suggests the intensities correspond

6

more closely to $J_1{}^2$, $J_2{}^2$, $J_3{}^2$ than to $J_2{}^2$, $J_4{}^2$, $J_6{}^2$ . . . Hence the dominant helix has a pitch of ~ 34 A., and, from the angle of the helix, its diameter is found to be ~ 20 A. The strong equatorial reflexion at ~ 17 A. suggests that the helices have a maximum diameter of ~ 20 A. and are hexagonally packed with little interpenetration. Apart from the width of the Bessel function streaks, the possibility of the helices having twice the above dimensions is also made unlikely by the absence of an equatorial reflexion at ~ 34 A. To obtain a reasonable number of nucleo- tides per unit volume in the fibre, two or three intertwined coaxial helices are required, there being ten nucleotides on one turn of each helix.

The absence of reflexions on or near the meridian (an empty region AAA on Fig. 2) is a direct con- sequence of the helical structure. On the photograph there is also a relatively empty region on and near the equator, corresponding to region BBB on Fig. 2. As discussed above, this absence of secondary Bessel function maxima can be produced by a radial dis- tribution of the nucleotide shape. To make the layer-line streaks sufficiently narrow, it is necessary to place a large fraction of the nucleotide mass at ~ 20 A. diameter. In Fig. 2 the squares of Bessel functions are plotted for half the mass at 20 A. diameter, and the rest distributed along a radius, the mass at a given radius being proportional to the radius.

On the zero layer line there appears to be a marked $J_{10}{}^2$, and on the first, second and third layer lines, $J_9{}^2 + J_{11}{}^2$, $J_8{}^2 + J_{12}{}^2$, etc., respectively. This means that, in projection on a plane at right-angles to the fibre axis, the outer part of the nucleotide is relatively concentrated, giving rise to high-density regions spaced $c.$ 6 A. apart around the circumference of a circle of 20 A. diameter. On the fifth layer line two J_5 functions overlap and produce a strong reflexion. On the sixth, seventh and eighth layer lines the maxima correspond to a helix of diameter ~ 12 A. Apparently it is only the central region of the helix structure which is well divided by the 3·4-A. spacing, the outer parts of the nucleotide overlapping to form a con- tinuous helix. This suggests the presence of nitrogen bases arranged like a pile of pennies[1] in the central regions of the helical system.

There is a marked absence of reflexions on layer lines beyond the tenth. Disorientation in the specimen will cause more extension along the layer lines of the Bessel function streaks on the eleventh, twelfth ·and thirteenth layer lines than on the ninth, eighth and seventh. For this reason the reflexions on the higher- order layer lines will be less readily visible. The form

7

factor of the nucleotide is also probably causing diminution of intensity in this region. Tilting of the nitrogen bases could have such an effect.

Reflexions on the equator are rather inadequate for determination of the radial distribution of density in the helical system. There are, however, indications that a high-density shell, as suggested above, occurs at diameter ~ 20 A.

The material is apparently not completely para-crystalline, as sharp spots appear in the central region of the second layer line, indicating a partial degree of order of the helical units relative to one another in the direction of the helix axis. Photographs similar to Fig. 1 have been obtained from sodium nucleate from calf and pig thymus, wheat germ, herring sperm, human tissue and T_2 bacteriophage. The most marked correspondence with Fig. 2 is shown by the exceptional photograph obtained by our colleagues, R. E. Franklin and R. G. Gosling, from calf thymus deoxypentose nucleate (see following communication).

It must be stressed that some of the above discussion is not without ambiguity, but in general there appears to be reasonable agreement between the experimental data and the kind of model described by Watson and Crick (see also preceding communication).

It is interesting to note that if there are ten phosphate groups arranged on each helix of diameter 20 A. and pitch 34 A., the phosphate ester backbone chain is in an almost fully extended state. Hence, when sodium nucleate fibres are stretched[3], the helix is evidently extended in length like a spiral spring in tension.

Structure *in vivo*

The biological significance of a two-chain nucleic acid unit has been noted (see preceding communication). The evidence that the helical structure discussed above does, in fact, exist in intact biological systems is briefly as follows :

Sperm heads. It may be shown that the intensity of the X-ray spectra from crystalline sperm heads is determined by the helical form-function in Fig. 2. Centrifuged trout semen give the same pattern as the dried and rehydrated or washed sperm heads used previously[6]. The sperm head fibre diagram is also given by extracted or synthetic[1] nucleoprotamine or extracted calf thymus nucleohistone.

Bacteriophage. Centrifuged wet pellets of T_2 phage photographed with X-rays while sealed in a cell with mica windows give a diffraction pattern containing the main features of paracrystalline sodium nucleate

8

as distinct from that of crystalline nucleoprotein. This confirms current ideas of phage structure.

Transforming principle (in collaboration with H. Ephrussi-Taylor). Active deoxypentose nucleate allowed to dry at ∼ 60 per cent humidity has the same crystalline structure as certain samples[3] of sodium thymonucleate.

We wish to thank Prof. J. T. Randall for encouragement; Profs. E. Chargaff, R. Signer, J. A. V. Butler and Drs. J. D. Watson, J. D. Smith, L. Hamilton, J. C. White and G. R. Wyatt for supplying material without which this work would have been impossible; also Drs. J. D. Watson and Mr. F. H. C. Crick for stimulation, and our colleagues R. E. Franklin, R. G. Gosling, G. L. Brown and W. E. Seeds for discussion. One of us (H. R. W.) wishes to acknowledge the award of a University of Wales Fellowship.

M. H. F. Wilkins

Medical Research Council Biophysics
     Research Unit,

A. R. Stokes
H. R. Wilson

Wheatstone Physics Laboratory,
   King's College, London.
     April 2.

[1] Astbury, W. T., Symp. Soc. Exp. Biol., 1, Nucleic Acid (Cambridge Univ. Press, 1947).

[2] Riley, D. P., and Oster, G., *Biochim. et Biophys. Acta*, **7**, 526 (1951).

[3] Wilkins, M. H. F., Gosling, R. G., and Seeds, W. E., *Nature*, **167**, 759 (1951).

[4] Astbury, W. T., and Bell, F. O., Cold Spring Harb. Symp. Quant. Biol., **6**, 109 (1938).

[5] Cochran, W., Crick, F. H. C., and Vand, V., *Acta Cryst.*, **5**, 581 (1952).

[6] Wilkins, M. H. F., and Randall, J. T., *Biochim. et Biophys. Acta*, **10**, 192 (1953).

(Reprinted from Nature, Vol. 171, p. 964, May 30, 1953)

GENETICAL IMPLICATIONS OF THE STRUCTURE OF DEOXYRIBONUCLEIC ACID

By J. D. WATSON and F. H. C. CRICK

Medical Research Council Unit for the Study of the Molecular Structure of Biological Systems, Cavendish Laboratory, Cambridge

THE importance of deoxyribonucleic acid (DNA) within living cells is undisputed. It is found in all dividing cells, largely if not entirely in the nucleus, where it is an essential constituent of the chromosomes. Many lines of evidence indicate that it is the carrier of a part of (if not all) the genetic specificity of the chromosomes and thus of the gene itself.

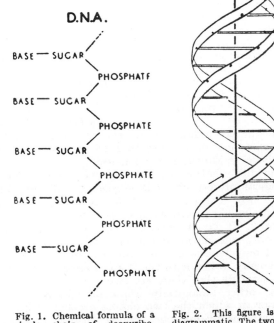

Fig. 1. Chemical formula of a single chain of deoxyribonucleic acid

Fig. 2. This figure is purely diagrammatic. The two ribbons symbolize the two phosphate-sugar chains, and the horizontal rods the pairs of bases holding the chains together. The vertical line marks the fibre axis

Until now, however, no evidence has been presented to show how it might carry out the essential operation required of a genetic material, that of exact self-duplication.

We have recently proposed a structure[1] for the salt of deoxyribonucleic acid which, if correct, immediately suggests a mechanism for its self-duplication. X-ray evidence obtained by the workers at King's College, London[2], and presented at the same time, gives qualitative support to our structure and is incompatible with all previously proposed structures[3]. Though the structure will not be completely proved until a more extensive comparison has been made with the X-ray data, we now feel sufficient confidence in its general correctness to discuss its genetical implications. In doing so we are assuming that fibres of the salt of deoxyribonucleic acid are not artefacts arising in the method of preparation, since it has been shown by Wilkins and his co-workers that similar X-ray patterns are obtained from both the isolated fibres and certain intact biological materials such as sperm head and bacteriophage particles[3,4].

The chemical formula of deoxyribonucleic acid is now well established. The molecule is a very long chain, the backbone of which consists of a regular alternation of sugar and phosphate groups, as shown in Fig. 1. To each sugar is attached a nitrogenous base, which can be of four different types. (We have considered 5-methyl cytosine to be equivalent to cytosine, since either can fit equally well into our structure.) Two of the possible bases—adenine and guanine—are purines, and the other two—thymine and cytosine—are pyrimidines. So far as is known, the sequence of bases along the chain is irregular. The monomer unit, consisting of phosphate, sugar and base, is known as a nucleotide.

The first feature of our structure which is of biological interest is that it consists not of one chain, but of two. These two chains are both coiled around a common fibre axis, as is shown diagrammatically in Fig. 2. It has often been assumed that since there was only one chain in the chemical formula there would only be one in the structural unit. However, the density, taken with the X-ray evidence[2], suggests very strongly that there are two.

The other biologically important feature is the manner in which the two chains are held together. This is done by hydrogen bonds between the bases, as shown schematically in Fig. 3. The bases are joined together in pairs, a single base from one chain being hydrogen-bonded to a single base from the

2

other. The important point is that only certain pairs
of bases will fit into the structure. One member of a
pair must be a purine and the other a pyrimidine in
order to bridge between the two chains. If a pair
consisted of two purines, for example, there would
not be room for it.

We believe that the bases will be present almost
entirely in their most probable tautomeric forms. If
this is true, the conditions for forming hydrogen
bonds are more restrictive, and the only pairs of
bases possible are :

adenine with thymine ;
guanine with cytosine.

The way in which these are joined together is shown
in Figs. 4 and 5. A given pair can be either way
round. Adenine, for example, can occur on either
chain ; but when it does, its partner on the other
chain must always be thymine.

This pairing is strongly supported by the recent
analytical results[5], which show that for all sources
of deoxyribonucleic acid examined the amount of
adenine is close to the amount of thymine, and the
amount of guanine close to the amount of cytosine,
although the cross-ratio (the ratio of adenine to
guanine) can vary from one source to another.
Indeed, if the sequence of bases on one chain is
irregular, it is difficult to explain these analytical
results except by the sort of pairing we have
suggested.

The phosphate-sugar backbone of our model is
completely regular, but any sequence of the pairs of

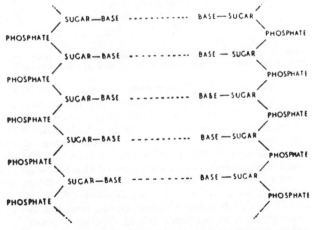

Fig. 3. Chemical formula of a pair of deoxyribonucleic acid
chains. The hydrogen bonding is symbolized by dotted lines

3

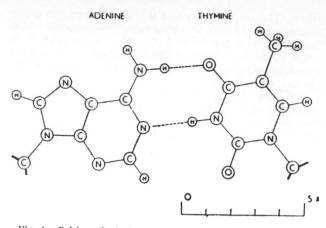

ADENINE   THYMINE

Fig. 4. Pairing of adenine and thymine. Hydrogen bonds are shown dotted. One carbon atom of each sugar is shown

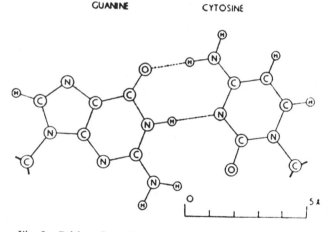

GUANINE   CYTOSINE

Fig. 5. Pairing of guanine and cytosine. Hydrogen bonds are shown dotted. One carbon atom of each sugar is shown

bases can fit into the structure. It follows that in a long molecule many different permutations are possible, and it therefore seems likely that the precise sequence of the bases is the code which carries the genetical information. If the actual order of the bases on one of the pair of chains were given, one could write down the exact order of the bases on the other one, because of the specific pairing. Thus one chain is, as it were, the complement of the other, and it is this feature which suggests how the deoxyribonucleic acid molecule might duplicate itself.

Previous discussions of self-duplication have usually involved the concept of a template, or mould. Either

4

the template was supposed to copy itself directly or it was to produce a 'negative', which in its turn was to act as a template and produce the original 'positive' once again. In no case has it been explained in detail how it would do this in terms of atoms and molecules.

Now our model for deoxyribonucleic acid is, in effect, a *pair* of templates, each of which is complementary to the other. We imagine that prior to duplication the hydrogen bonds are broken, and the two chains unwind and separate. Each chain then acts as a template for the formation on to itself of a new companion chain, so that eventually we shall have *two* pairs of chains, where we only had one before. Moreover, the sequence of the pairs of bases will have been duplicated exactly.

A study of our model suggests that this duplication could be done most simply if the single chain (or the relevant portion of it) takes up the helical configuration. We imagine that at this stage in the life of the cell, free nucleotides, strictly polynucleotide precursors, are available in quantity. From time to time the base of a free nucleotide will join up by hydrogen bonds to one of the bases on the chain already formed. We now postulate that the polymerization of these monomers to form a new chain is only possible if the resulting chain can form the proposed structure. This is plausible, because steric reasons would not allow nucleotides 'crystallized' on to the first chain to approach one another in such a way that they could be joined together into a new chain, unless they were those nucleotides which were necessary to form our structure. Whether a special enzyme is required to carry out the polymerization, or whether the single helical chain already formed acts effectively as an enzyme, remains to be seen.

Since the two chains in our model are intertwined, it is essential for them to untwist if they are to separate. As they make one complete turn around each other in 34 A., there will be about 150 turns per million molecular weight, so that whatever the precise structure of the chromosome a considerable amount of uncoiling would be necessary. It is well known from microscopic observation that much coiling and uncoiling occurs during mitosis, and though this is on a much larger scale it probably reflects similar processes on a molecular level. Although it is difficult at the moment to see how these processes occur without everything getting tangled, we do not feel that this objection will be insuperable.

Our structure, as described[1], is an open one. There is room between the pair of polynucleotide chains

5

(see Fig. 2) for a polypeptide chain to wind around the same helical axis. It may be significant that the distance between adjacent phosphorus atoms, 7·1 A., is close to the repeat of a fully extended polypeptide chain. We think it probable that in the sperm head, and in artificial nucleoproteins, the polypeptide chain occupies this position. The relative weakness of the second layer-line in the published X-ray pictures[3a,4] is crudely compatible with such an idea. The function of the protein might well be to control the coiling and uncoiling, to assist in holding a single polynucleotide chain in a helical configuration, or some other non-specific function.

Our model suggests possible explanations for a number of other phenomena. For example, spontaneous mutation may be due to a base occasionally occurring in one of its less likely tautomeric forms. Again, the pairing between homologous chromosomes at meiosis may depend on pairing between specific bases. We shall discuss these ideas in detail elsewhere.

For the moment, the general scheme we have proposed for the reproduction of deoxyribonucleic acid must be regarded as speculative. Even if it is correct, it is clear from what we have said that much remains to be discovered before the picture of genetic duplication can be described in detail. What are the polynucleotide precursors ? What makes the pair of chains unwind and separate ? What is the precise role of the protein ? Is the chromosome one long pair of deoxyribonucleic acid chains, or does it consist of patches of the acid joined together by protein ?

Despite these uncertainties we feel that our proposed structure for deoxyribonucleic acid may help to solve one of the fundamental biological problems— the molecular basis of the template needed for genetic replication. The hypothesis we are suggesting is that the template is the pattern of bases formed by one chain of the deoxyribonucleic acid and that the gene contains a complementary pair of such templates.

One of us (J. D. W.) has been aided by a fellowship from the National Foundation for Infantile Paralysis (U.S.A.).

[1] Watson, J. D., and Crick, F. H. C., *Nature*, **171**, 737 (1953).
[2] Wilkins, M. H. F., Stokes, A. R., and Wilson, H. R., *Nature*, **171**, 738 (1953). Franklin, R. E., and Gosling, R. G., *Nature*, **171**, 740 (1953).
[3] (a) Astbury, W. T., Symp. No. 1 Soc. Exp. Biol., 66 (1947). (b) Furberg, S., *Acta Chem. Scand.*, **6**, 634 (1952). (c) Pauling, L., and Corey, R. B., *Nature*, **171**, 346 (1953) ; *Proc. U.S. Nat. Acad. Sci.*, **39**, 84 (1953). (d) Fraser, R. D. B. (in preparation).
[4] Wilkins, M. H. F., and Randall, J. T., *Biochim. et Biophys. Acta*, **10**, 192 (1953).
[5] Chargaff, E., for references see Zamenhof, S., Brawerman, G., and Chargaff, E., *Biochim. et Biophys. Acta*, **9**, 402 (1952). Wyatt, G. R., *J. Gen. Physiol.*, **36**, 201 (1952).

THE STRUCTURE OF DNA

J. D. WATSON[1] AND F. H. C. CRICK
Cavendish Laboratory, Cambridge, England
(Contribution to the Discussion of Provirus.)

It would be superfluous at a Symposium on Viruses to introduce a paper on the structure of DNA with a discussion on its importance to the problem of virus reproduction. Instead we shall not only assume that DNA is important, but in addition that it is the carrier of the genetic specificity of the virus (for argument, see Hershey, this volume) and thus must possess in some sense the capacity for exact self-duplication. In this paper we shall describe a structure for DNA which suggests a mechanism for its self-duplication and allows us to propose, for the first time, a detailed hypothesis on the atomic level for the self-reproduction of genetic material.

We first discuss the chemical and physical-chemical data which show that DNA is a long fibrous molecule. Next we explain why crystallographic evidence suggests that the structural unit of DNA consists not of one but of two polynucleotide chains. We then discuss a stereochemical model which we believe satisfactorily accounts for both the chemical and crystallographic data. In conclusion we suggest some obvious genetic implications of the proposed structure. A preliminary account of some of these data has already appeared in Nature (Watson and Crick, 1953a, 1953b).

I. EVIDENCE FOR THE FIBROUS NATURE OF DNA

The basic chemical formula of DNA is now well established. As shown in Figure 1 it consists of a very long chain, the backbone of which is made up of alternate sugar and phosphate groups, joined together in regular 3' 5' phosphate di-ester linkages. To each sugar is attached a nitrogenous base, only four different kinds of which are commonly found in DNA. Two of these—adenine and guanine—are purines, and the other two—thymine and cytosine—are pyrimidines. A fifth base, 5-methyl cytosine, occurs in smaller amounts in certain organisms, and a sixth, 5-hydroxy-methyl-cytosine, is found instead of cytosine in the T even phages (Wyatt and Cohen, 1952).

It should be noted that the chain is unbranched, a consequence of the regular internucleotide linkage. On the other hand the sequence of the different nucleotides is, as far as can be ascertained, completely irregular. Thus, DNA has some features which are regular, and some which are irregular.

A similar conception of the DNA molecule as a long thin fiber is obtained from physico-chemical analysis involving sedimentation, diffusion, light scattering, and viscosity measurements. These techniques indicate that DNA is a very asymmetrical structure approximately 20 A wide and many thousands of angstroms long. Estimates of its molecular weight currently center between 5×10^6 and 10^7 (approximately 3×10^4 nucleotides). Surprisingly each of these measurements tend to suggest that the DNA is relatively rigid, a puzzling finding in view of the large number of single bonds (5 per nucleotide) in the phosphate-sugar back-

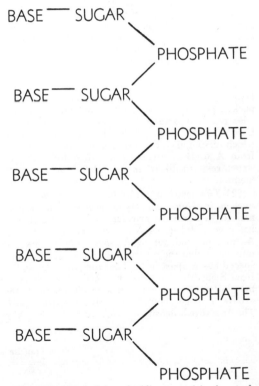

FIGURE 1. Chemical formula (diagrammatic) of a single chain of desoxyribonucleic acid.

[1] Aided by a Fellowship from the National Foundation for Infantile Paralysis.

bone. Recently these indirect inferences have been confirmed by electron microscopy. Employing high resolution techniques both Williams (1952) and Kahler *et al.* (1953) have observed, in preparations of DNA, very long thin fibers with a uniform width of approximately 15-20 A.

II. EVIDENCE FOR THE EXISTENCE OF TWO CHEMICAL CHAINS IN THE FIBER

This evidence comes mainly from X-ray studies. The material used is the sodium salt of DNA (usually from calf thymus) which has been extracted, purified, and drawn into fibers. These fibers are highly birefringent, show marked ultraviolet and infrared dichroism (Wilkins *et al.*, 1951; Fraser and Fraser, 1951), and give good X-ray fiber diagrams. From a preliminary study of these, Wilkins, Franklin and their co-workers at King's College, London (Wilkins *et al.*, 1953; Franklin and Gosling 1953a, b and c) have been able to draw certain general conclusions about the structure of DNA. Two important facts emerge from their work. They are:

(1) *Two distinct forms of DNA exist.* Firstly a crystalline form, Structure A, (Figure 2) which occurs at about 75 per cent relative humidity and contains approximately 30 per cent water. At higher humidities the fibers take up more water, increase in length by about 30 per cent and assume Structure B (Figure 3). This is a less ordered form than Structure A, and appears to be paracrystalline; that is, the individual molecules are all packed parallel to one another, but are not otherwise regularly arranged in space. In Table 1, we have tabulated some of the characteristic features which distinguish the two forms. The transition from A to B is reversible and therefore the two structures are likely to be related in a simple manner.

(2) *The crystallographic unit contains two polynucleotide chains.* The argument is crystallographic and so will only be given in outline. Structure B has a very strong 3.4 A reflexion on the meridian. As first pointed out by Astbury (1947), this can only mean that the nucleotides in it occur in groups spaced 3.4 A apart in the fiber direction. On going from Structure B to Structure A the fiber shortens by about 30 per cent. Thus in Structure A the groups must be about 2.5 per cent A apart axially. The measured density of Structure A, (Franklin

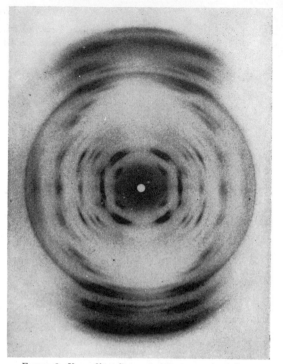

FIGURE 2. X-ray fiber diagram of Structure A of desoxyribonucleic acid. (H. M. F. Wilkins and H. R. Wilson, unpub.)

and Gosling, 1953c) together with the cell dimensions, shows that there must be *two* nucleotides in each such group. Thus it is very probable that the crystallographic unit consists of two distinct polynucleotide chains. Final proof of this can only come from a complete solution of the structure.

Structure A has a pseudo-hexagonal lattice, in which the lattice points are 22 A apart. This distance roughly corresponds with the diameter of fibers seen in the electron microscope, bearing in mind that the latter are quite dry. Thus it is probable that the crystallographic unit and the fiber are the one and the same.

III. DESCRIPTION OF THE PROPOSED STRUCTURE

Two conclusions might profitably be drawn from the above data. Firstly, the structure of DNA is

TABLE 1.
(From Franklin and Gosling, 1953a, b and c)

	Degree of orientation	Repeat distance along fiber axis	Location of first equatorial spacing	Water content	Number of nucleotides within unit cell
Structure A	Crystalline	28 A	18 A	30%	22-24
Structure B	Paracrystalline	34 A	22-24 A	> 30%	20 (?)

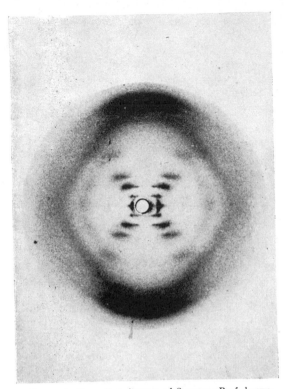

structure is a well-defined one and all bond distances and angles, including van der Waal distances, are stereochemically acceptable.

The essential element of the structure is the manner in which the two chains are held together by hydrogen bonds between the bases. The bases are perpendicular to the fiber axis and joined together in pairs. The pairing arrangement is very specific, and only certain pairs of bases will fit into the structure. The basic reason for this is that we have assumed that the backbone of each polynucleotide chain is in the form of a regular helix. Thus, irrespective of which bases are present, the glucosidic bonds (which join sugar and base) are arranged in a regular manner in space. In particular, any two glucosidic bonds (one from each chain)

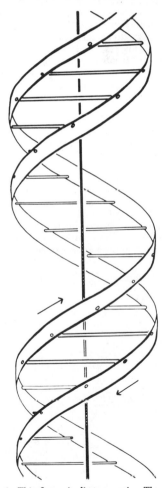

FIGURE 4. This figure is diagrammatic. The two ribbons symbolize the two phosphate-sugar chains and the horizontal rods. The paths of bases holding the chain together. The vertical line marks the fiber axis.

regular enough to form a three dimensional crystal. This is in spite of the fact that its component chains may have an irregular sequence of purine and pyrimidine nucleotides. Secondly, as the structure contains two chains, these chains must be regularly arranged in relation to each other.

To account for these findings, we have proposed (Watson and Crick, 1953a) a structure in which the two chains are coiled round a common axis and joined together by hydrogen bonds between the nucleotide bases (see Figure 4). Both chains follow right handed helices, but the sequences of the atoms in the phosphate-sugar backbones run in opposite directions and so are related by a dyad perpendicular to the helix axis. The phosphates and sugar groups are on the outside of the helix whilst the bases are on the inside. The distance of a phosphorus atom from the fiber axis is 10 A. We have built our model to correspond to Structure B, which the X-ray data show to have a repeat distance of 34 A in the fiber direction and a very strong reflexion of spacing 3.4 A on the meridian of the X-ray pattern. To fit these observations our structure has a nucleotide on each chain every 3.4 A in the fiber direction, and makes one complete turn after 10 such intervals, i.e., after 34 A. Our which are attached to a bonded pair of bases, must always occur at a fixed distance apart due to the regularity of the two backbones to which they are joined. The result is that one member of a pair of bases must always be a purine, and the other a pyrimidine, in order to bridge between the two chains. If a pair consisted of two purines, for example, there would not be room for it; if of two pyrimidines they would be too far apart to form hydrogen bonds.

In theory a base can exist in a number of tautomeric forms, differing in the exact positions at which its hydrogen atoms are attached. However, under physiological conditions one particular form of each base is much more probable than any of the others. If we make the assumption that the favored forms always occur, then the pairing requirements are even more restrictive. Adenine can only pair with thymine, and guanine only with cytosine (or 5-methyl-cytosine, or 5-hydroxy-methyl-cytosine). This pairing is shown in detail in Figures 5 and 6. If adenine tried to pair with cytosine it could not form hydrogen bonds, since there would be two hydrogens near one of the bonding positions, and none at the other, instead of one in each.

A given pair can be either way round. Adenine, for example, can occur on either chain, but when it does its partner on the other chain must always be thymine. This is possible because the two glucoside bonds of a pair (see Figures 5 and 6) are symmetrically related to each other, and thus occur in the same positions if the pair is turned over.

It should be emphasized that since each base can form hydrogen bonds at a number of points one can pair up *isolated* nucleotides in a large variety of ways. *Specific* pairing of bases can only be obtained by imposing some restriction, and in our

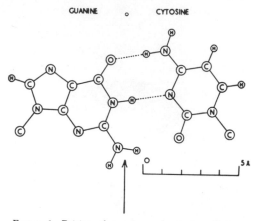

FIGURE 6. Pairing of guanine and cytosine. Hydrogen bonds are shown dotted. One carbon atom of each sugar is shown.

case it is in a direct consequence of the postulated regularity of the phosphate-sugar backbone.

It should further be emphasized that whatever pair of bases occurs at one particular point in the DNA structure, no restriction is imposed on the neighboring pairs, and any *sequence* of pairs can occur. This is because all the bases are flat, and since they are stacked roughly one above another like a pile of pennies, it makes no difference which pair is neighbor to which.

Though any sequence of bases can fit into our structure, the necessity for specific pairing demands a definite relationship between the sequences on the two chains. That is, if we knew the actual order of the bases on one chain, we could automatically write down the order on the other. *Our structure therefore consists of two chains, each of which is the complement of the other.*

IV. EVIDENCE IN FAVOR OF THE COMPLEMENTARY MODEL

The experimental evidence available to us now offers strong support to our model though we should emphasize that, as yet, it has not been proved correct. The evidence in its favor is of three types:

(1) The general appearance of the X-ray picture strongly suggests that the basic structure is helical (Wilkins *et al.*, 1953; Franklin and Gosling, 1953a). If we postulate that a helix is present, we immediately are able to deduce from the X-ray pattern of Structure B (Figure 3), that its pitch is 34 A and its diameter approximately 20 A. Moreover, the pattern suggests a high concentration of atoms on the circumference of the helix, in accord with our model which places the phosphate sugar backbone on the outside. The photograph also indicates that the two polynucleotide chains are not

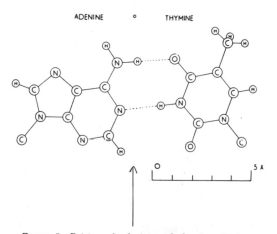

FIGURE 5. Pairing of adenine and thymine. Hydrogen bonds are shown dotted. One carbon atom of each sugar is shown.

spaced equally along the fiber axis, but are probably displaced from each other by about three-eighths of the fiber axis period, an inference again in qualitative agreement with our model.

The interpretation of the X-ray pattern of Structure A (the crystalline form) is less obvious. This form does not give a meridional reflexion at 3.4 A, but instead (Figure 2) gives a series of reflexions around 25° off the meridian at spacings between 3 A and 4 A. This suggests to us that in this form the bases are no longer perpendicular to the fiber axis, but are tilted about 25° from the perpendicular position in a way that allows the fiber to contract 30 per cent and reduces the longitudinal translation of each nucleotide to about 2.5 A. It should be noted that the X-ray pattern of Structure A is much more detailed than that of Structure B and so if correctly interpreted, can yield more precise information about DNA. Any proposed model for DNA must be capable of forming either Structure A or Structure B and so it remains imperative for our very tentative interpretation of Structure A to be confirmed.

(2) The anomolous titration curves of undegraded DNA with acids and bases strongly suggests that hydrogen bond formation is a characteristic aspect of DNA structure. When a solution of DNA is initially treated with acids or bases, no groups are titratable at first between pH 5 and pH 11.0, but outside these limits a rapid ionization occurs (Gulland and Jordan, 1947; Jordan, 1951). On back titration, however, either with acid from pH 12 or with alkali from pH 2½, a different titration curve is obtained indicating that the titratable groups are more accessible to acids and bases than is the untreated solution. Accompanying the initial release of groups at pH 11.5 and in the range pH 3.5 to pH 4.5 is a marked fall in the viscosity and the disappearance of strong flow birefringence. While this decrease was originally thought to be caused by a reversible depolymerization (Vilbrandt and Tennent, 1943), it has been shown by Gulland, Jordan and Taylor (1947) that this is unlikely as no increase was observed in the amount of secondary phosphoryl groups. Instead these authors suggested that some of the groups of the bases formed hydrogen bonds between different bases. They were unable to decide whether the hydrogen bonds linked bases in the same or in adjacent structural units. The fact that most of the ionizable groups are originally inaccessible to acids and bases is more easily explained if the hydrogen bonds are between bases within the same structural unit. This point would definitely be established if it were shown that the shape of the initial titration curve was the same at very low DNA concentrations, when the interaction between neighboring structural units is small.

(3) The analytical data on the relative proportion of the various bases show that the amount of adenine is close to that of thymine, and the amount of guanine close to the amount of cytosine + 5-methyl cytosine, although the ratio of adenine to guanine can vary from one source to another (Chargaff, 1951; Wyatt, 1952). In fact as the techniques for estimation of the bases improve, the ratios of adenine to thymine, and guanine to cytosine + 5-methyl cytosine appear to grow very close to unity. This is a most striking result, especially as the sequence of bases on a given chain is likely to be irregular, and suggests a structure involving paired bases. In fact, we believe the analytical data offer the most important evidence so far available in support of our model, since they specifically support the biologically interesting feature, the presence of complementary chains.

We thus believe that the present experimental evidence justifies the working hypothesis that the essential features of our model are correct and allows us to consider its genetic possibilities.

V. GENETICAL IMPLICATIONS OF THE COMPLEMENTARY MODEL

As a preliminary we should state that the DNA fibers from which the X-ray diffraction patterns were obtained are not artifacts arising in the method of preparation. In the first place, Wilkins and his co-workers (see Wilkins *et al.*, 1953) have shown that X-ray patterns similar to those from the isolated fibers can be obtained from certain intact biological materials such as sperm head and bacteriophage particles. Secondly, our postulated model is so extremely specific that we find it impossible to believe that it could be formed during the isolation from living cells.

A genetic material must in some way fulfil two functions. It must duplicate itself, and it must exert a highly specific influence on the cell. Our model for DNA suggests a simple mechanism for the first process, but at the moment we cannot see how it carries out the second one. We believe, however, that its specificity is expressed by the precise sequence of the pairs of bases. The backbone of our model is highly regular, and the sequence is the only feature which can carry the genetical information. It should not be thought that because in our structure the bases are on the "inside," they would be unable to come into contact with other molecules. Owing to the open nature of our structure they are in fact fairly accessible.

A MECHANISM FOR DNA REPLICATION

The complementary nature of our structure suggests how it duplicates itself. It is difficult to imagine how like attracts like, and it has been suggested (see Pauling and Delbrück, 1940; Friedrich-Freksa, 1940; and Muller, 1947) that self duplication may involve the union of each part with an opposite or complementary part. In these discussions it has generally been suggested that protein and nucleic acid are complementary to each other and that self replication involves the alternate syntheses of these two components. We should like to propose instead that the specificity of DNA self replication is accomplished without recourse to specific protein synthesis and that each of our complementary DNA chains serves as a template or mould for the formation onto itself of a new companion chain.

For this to occur the hydrogen bonds linking the complementary chains must break and the two chains unwind and separate. It seems likely that the single chain (or the relevant part of it) might itself assume the helical form and serve as a mould onto which free nucleotides (strictly polynucleotide precursors) can attach themselves by forming hydrogen bonds. We propose that polymerization of the precursors to form a new chain only occurs if the resulting chain forms the proposed structure. This is plausible because steric reasons would not allow monomers "crystallized" onto the first chain to approach one another in such a way that they could be joined together in a new chain, unless they were those monomers which could fit into our structure. It is not obvious to us whether a special enzyme would be required to carry out the polymerization or whether the existing single helical chain could act effectively as an enzyme.

DIFFICULTIES IN THE REPLICATION SCHEME

While this scheme appears intriguing, it nevertheless raises a number of difficulties, none of which, however, do we regard as insuperable. The first difficulty is that our structure does not differentiate between cytosine and 5-methyl cytosine, and therefore during replication the specificity in sequence involving these bases would not be perpetuated. The amount of 5-methyl cytosine varies considerably from one species to another, though it is usually rather small or absent. The present experimental results (Wyatt, 1952) suggest that each species has a characteristic amount. They also show that the sum of the two cytosines is more nearly equal to the amount of guanine than is the amount of cytosine by itself. It may well be that the difference between the two cytosines is not functionally significant. This interpretation would be considerably strengthened if it proved possible to change the amount of 5-methyl cytosine in the DNA of an organism without altering its genetical make-up.

The occurrence of 5-hydroxy-methyl-cytosine in the T even phages (Wyatt and Cohen, 1952) presents no such difficulty, since it completely replaces cytosine, and its amount in the DNA is close to that of guanine.

The second main objection to our scheme is that it completely ignores the role of the basic protamines and histones, proteins known to be combined with DNA in most living organisms. This was done for two reasons. Firstly, we can formulate a scheme of DNA reproduction involving it alone and so

from the viewpoint of simplicity it seems better to believe (at least at present) that the genetic specificity is never passed through a protein intermediary. Secondly, we know almost nothing about the structural features of protamines and histones. Our only clue is the finding of Astbury (1947) and of Wilkins and Randall (1953) that the X-ray pattern of nucleoprotamine is very similar to that of DNA alone. This suggests that the protein component, or at least some of it, also assumes a helical form and in view of the very open nature of our model, we suspect that protein forms a third helical chain between the pair of polynucleotide chains (see Figure 4). As yet nothing is known about the function of the protein; perhaps it controls the coiling and uncoiling and perhaps it assists in holding the single polynucleotide chains in a helical configuration.

The third difficulty involves the necessity for the two complementary chains to unwind in order to serve as a template for a new chain. This is a very fundamental difficulty when the two chains are interlaced as in our model. The two main ways in which a pair of helices can be coiled together have been called plectonemic coiling and paranemic coiling. These terms have been used by cytologists to describe the coiling of chromosomes (Huskins, 1941; for a review see Manton, 1950). The type of coiling found in our model (see Figure 4) is called plectonemic. Paranemic coiling is found when two separate helices are brought to lie side by side and then pushed together so that their axes roughly coincide. Though one may start with two regular helices the process of pushing them together necessarily distorts them. It is impossible to have paranemic coiling with two regular simple helices going round the same axis. This point can only be clearly grasped by studying models.

There is of course no difficulty in "unwinding" a *single* chain of DNA coiled into a helix, since a polynucleotide chain has so many single bonds about which rotation is possible. The difficulty occurs when one has a pair of simple helices with a common axis. The difficulty is a topological one and cannot be surmounted by simple manipulation. Apart from breaking the chains there are only two sorts of ways to separate two chains coiled plectonemically. In the first, one takes hold of one end of one chain, and the other end of the other, and simply pulls in the axial direction. The two chains slip over each other, and finish up separate and end to end. It seems to us highly unlikely that this occurs in this case, and we shall not consider it further. In the second way the two chains must be directly untwisted. When this has been done they are separate and side by side. The number of turns necessary to untwist them completely is equal to the number of turns of one of the chains round the common axis. For our structure this comes to one turn every 34 A, and thus about 150 turns per million molecular weight of DNA, that is per 5000

A of our structure. The problem of uncoiling falls into two parts:

(1) How many turns must be made, and how is tangling avoided?

(2) What are the physical or chemical forces which produce it?

For the moment we shall be mainly discussing the first of these. It is not easy to decide what is the uninterrupted length of functionally active DNA. As a lower limit we may take the molecular weight of the DNA after isolation, say fifty thousand A in length and having about 1000 turns. This is only a lower limit as there is evidence suggesting a breakage of the DNA fiber during the process of extraction. The upper limit might be the total amount of DNA in a virus or in the case of a higher organism, the total amount of DNA in a chromosome. For T2 this upper limit is approximately 800,000 A which corresponds to 20,000 turns, while in the higher organisms this upper limit may sometimes be 1000 fold higher.

The difficulty might be more simple to resolve if successive parts of a chromosome coiled in opposite directions. The most obvious way would be to have both right and left handed DNA helices in sequence but this seems unlikely as we have only been able to build our model in the right handed sense. Another possibility might be that the long strands of right handed DNA are joined together by compensating strands of left handed polypeptide helices. The merits of this proposition are difficult to assess, but the fact that the phage DNA does not seem to be linked to protein makes it rather unattractive.

The untwisting process would be less complicated if replication started at the ends as soon as the chains began to separate. This mechanism would produce a new two-strand structure without requiring at any time a free single-strand stage. In this way the danger of tangling would be considerably decreased as the two-strand structure is much more rigid than a single strand and would resist attempts to coil around its neighbors. Once the replicating process is started the presence, at the growing end of the pair, of double-stranded structures might facilitate the breaking of hydrogen bonds in the original unduplicated section and allow replication to proceed in a zipper-like fashion.

It is also possible that one chain of a pair occasionally breaks under the strain of twisting. The polynucleotide chain remaining intact could then release the accumulated twist by rotation about single bonds and following this, the broken ends, being still in close proximity, might rejoin.

It is clear that, in spite of the tentative suggestions we have just made, the difficulty of untwisting is a formidable one, and it is therefore worthwhile re-examining why we postulate plectonemic coiling, and not paranemic coiling in which the two helical threads are not intertwined, but merely in close apposition to each other. Our answer is that with paranemic coiling, the specific pairing of bases would not allow the successive residues of each helix to be in equivalent orientation with regard to the helical axis. This is a possibility we strongly oppose as it implies that a large number of stereochemical alternatives for the sugar-phosphate backbone are possible, an inference at variance to our finding, with stereochemical models (Crick and Watson, 1953) that the position of the sugar-phosphate group is rather restrictive and cannot be subject to the large variability necessary for paranemic coiling. Moreover, such a model would not lead to specific pairing of the bases, since this only follows if the glucosidic links are arranged regularly in space. We therefore believe that if a helical structure is present, the relationship between the helices will be plectonemic.

We should ask, however, whether there might not be another complementary structure which maintains the necessary regularity but which is not helical. One such structure can, in fact, be imagined. It would consist of a ribbon-like arrangement in which again the two chains are joined together by specific pairs of bases, located 3.4 A above each other, but in which the sugar-phosphate backbone instead of forming a helix, runs in a straight line at an angle approximately 30° off the line formed by the pair of bases. While this ribbon-like structure would give many of the features of the X-ray diagram of Structure B, we are unable to define precisely how it should pack in a macroscopic fiber, and why in particular it should give a strong equatorial reflexion at 20-24 A. We are thus not enthusiastic about this model though we should emphasize that it has not yet been disproved.

Independent of the details of our model, there are two geometrical problems which *any* model for DNA must face. Both involve the necessity for some form of super folding process and can be illustrated with bacteriophage. Firstly, the total length of the DNA within T2 is about 8×10^5 A. As its DNA is thought (Siegal and Singer, 1953) to have the same very large M.W. as that from other sources, it must bend back and forth many times in order to fit into the phage head of diameter 800 A. Secondly, the DNA must replicate itself without getting tangled. Approximately 500 phage particles can be synthesized within a single bacterium of average dimensions $10^4 \times 10^4 \times 2 \times 10^4$ A. The total length of the newly produced DNA is some 4×10^8 A, all of which we believe was at some interval in contact with its parental template. Whatever the precise mechanism of replication we suspect the most reasonable way to avoid tangling is to have the DNA fold up into a compact bundle as it is formed.

A POSSIBLE MECHANISM FOR NATURAL MUTATION

In our duplication scheme, the specificity of replication is achieved by means of specific pairing between purine and pyrimidine bases; adenine with thymine, and guanine with one of the cytosines. This specificity results from our assumption that each of the bases possesses one tautomeric form which is very much more stable than any of the other possibilities. The fact that a compound is tautomeric, however, means that the hydrogen atoms can occasionally change their locations. It seems plausible to us that a spontaneous mutation, which as implied earlier we imagine to be a change in the sequence of bases, is due to a base occurring very occasionally in one of the less likely tautomeric forms, at the moment when the complementary chain is being formed. For example, while adenine will normally pair with thymine, if there is a tautomeric shift of one of its hydrogen atoms it can pair with cytosine (Figure 7). The next time pairing occurs, the adenine (having resumed its more usual tautomeric form) will pair with thymine, but the cytosine will pair with guanine, and so a change in the sequence of bases will have occurred. It would be of interest to know the precise difference in free energy between the various tautomeric forms under physiological conditions.

GENERAL CONCLUSION

The proof or disproof of our structure will have to come from further crystallographic analysis, a task we hope will be accomplished soon. It would be surprising to us, however, if the idea of complementary chains turns out to be wrong. This feature was initially postulated by us to account for the crystallographic regularity and it seems to us unlikely that its obvious connection with self replication is a matter of chance. On the other hand the plectonemic coiling is, superficially at least, biologically unattractive and so demands precise crystallographic proof. In any case the evidence for both the model and the suggested replication scheme will be strengthened if it can be shown unambiguously that the genetic specificity is carried by DNA alone, and, on the molecular side, how the structure could exert a specific influence on the cell.

REFERENCES

ASTBURY, W. T., 1947, X-Ray Studies of nucleic acids in tissues. Sym. Soc. Exp. Biol. 1:66-76.

CHARGAFF, E., 1951, Structure and function of nucleic acids as cell constituents. Fed. Proc. 10:654-659.

CRICK, F. H. C., and WATSON, J. D., 1953, Manuscript in preparation.

FRANKLIN, R. E., and GOSLING, R., 1953a, Molecular configuration in sodium thymonucleate. Nature, Lond. 171:740-741.

—— 1953b, Fiber diagrams of sodium thymonucleate. I. The influence of water content. Acta Cryst., Camb. (in press).

—— 1953c, The structure of sodium thymonucleate fibers. II. The cylindrically symmetrical Patterson Function. Acta Cryst., Camb. (in press).

FRASER, M. S., and FRASER, R. D. B., 1951, Evidence on the structure of desoxyribonucleic acid from measurements with polarized infra-red radiation. Nature, Lond. 167:760-761.

FRIEDRICH-FREKSA, H., 1940, Bei der Chromosomen Konjugation wirksame Krafte und ihre Bedeutung für die identische Verdopplung von Nucleoproteinen. Naturwissenshaften 28:376-379.

GULLAND, J. M., and JORDAN, D. O., 1946, The macromolecular behavior of nucleic acids. Sym. Soc. Exp. Biol. 1: 56-65.

GULLAND, J. M., JORDAN, D. O., and TAYLOR, H. F. W., 1947, Electrometric titration of the acidic and basic groups of the desoxypentose nucleic acid of calf thymus. J. Chem. Soc. 1131-1141.

HUSKINS, C. L., 1941, The coiling of chromonemata. Cold Spr. Harb. Symp. Quant. Biol. 9:13-18.

JORDAN, D. O., 1951, Physiochemical properties of the nucleic acids. Prog. Biophys. 2:51-89.

KAHLER, H., and LLOYD, B. J., 1953, The electron microscopy of sodium desoxyribonucleate. Biochim. Biophys. Acta 10:355-359.

MANTON, I., 1950, The spiral structure of chromosomes. Biol. Rev. 25:486-508.

MULLER, H. J., 1947, The Gene. Proc. Roy. Soc. Lond. Ser. B. 134:1-37.

PAULING, L., and DEDBRÜCK, M., 1940, The nature of the intermolecular forces operative in biological processes. Science 92:77-79.

SIEGAL, A., and SINGER, S. J., 1953, The preparation and properties of desoxypentosenucleic acid. Biochim. Biophys. Acta 10:311-319.

VILBRANDT, C. F., and TENNENT, H. G., 1943, The effect of

ADENINE   **THYMINE**

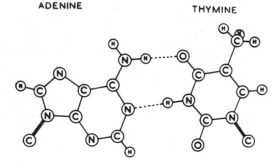

ADENINE   **CYTOSINE**

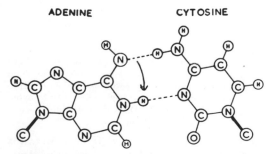

FIGURE. 7. Pairing arrangements of adenine before (above) and after (below) it has undergone a tautomeric shift.

pH changes upon some properties of sodium thymo-nucleate solutions. J. Amer. Chem. Soc. 63:1806-1809.

WATSON, J. D., and CRICK, F. H. C., 1953a, A structure for desoxyribose nucleic acids. Nature, Lond. 171:737-738. 1953b, Genetical implications of the structure of desoxyribose nucleic acid. Nature, Lond. (in press).

WILKINS, M. H. F., GOSLING, R. G., and SEEDS, W. E., 1951, Physical studies of nucleic acids—nucleic acid: an extensible molecule. Nature, Lond. 167:759 760.

WILKINS, M. H. F., and RANDALL, J. T., 1953, Crystallinity in sperm-heads: molecular structure of nucleoprotein in vivo. Biochim. Biophys. Acta 10:192 (1953).

WILKINS, M. H. F., STOKES, A. R., and WILSON, H. R., 1953, Molecular structure of desoxypentose nucleic acids. Nature, Lond. 171:738-740.

WILLIAMS, R. C., 1952, Electron microscopy of sodium desoxyribonucleate by use of a new freeze-drying method. Biochim. Biophys. Acta 9:237-239.

WYATT, G. R., 1952, Specificity in the composition of nucleic acids. In "The Chemistry and Physiology of the Nucleus," pp. 201-213, N. Y. Academic Press.

WYATT, G. R., and COHEN, S. S., 1952, A new pyrimidine base from bacteriophage nucleic acid. Nature, Lond. 170:1072.

III. DNA STRUCTURE AND REPLICATION

Reprinted from COLD SPRING HARBOR SYMPOSIA ON QUANTITATIVE BIOLOGY
Volume XXI, 1956
Printed in U.S.A.

Physical Studies of the Molecular Structure of Deoxyribose Nucleic Acid and Nucleoprotein

M. H. F. WILKINS

Medical Research Council, Biophysics Research Unit, King's College, London

INTRODUCTION

It may be useful at this time to consider how much we know about DNA structure and how much we do not know. It is about six years since clear X-ray diffraction photographs of DNA were first obtained, and three years since Watson and Crick (1953) built their molecular model of DNA (then described by Watson at the Symposium here), and proposed a hypothesis to explain how DNA molecules could be replicated *in vivo*. We have now much data to show that their general idea for the structure is correct, but evidence bearing on the biological hypothesis is somewhat conflicting. It seems necessary to stress that correctness of the structure does not imply correctness of the biological hypothesis. In the next decade we can expect that an increasing number of molecular structures will appear and become part of biology, and, as the derivation of such structures is not easily understood by biologists, it may be of interest to discuss the background for the finding of the DNA molecular configuration and use it to illustrate the nature of the methods employed.

THE ROLE OF MOLECULAR MODELS IN THE DETERMINATION OF MOLECULAR STRUCTURES

The X-ray photographs taken in our laboratory (Wilkins *et al.*, 1953; Franklin and Gosling, 1953) followed the earlier work of Astbury (1947) and provided the means of determining the 3-dimensional molecular configuration of the DNA molecule; in particular, it was clear at an early stage in our work that the molecule was very likely to have a helical configuration, and Astbury had pointed out that the nucleotides were probably arranged like "a pile of pennies." This kind of physical approach, however, would be of little use without the fundamental chemical knowledge which was built up at about the same time and made clear the system of covalent bonds linking the chemical groups in DNA (in other words, the chemists determined the structure in a chemical sense) and also gave information about the weaker links—the hydrogen bonds. Physico-chemical techniques also gave helpful information: they demonstrated the thread-like shape of the molecule and the arrangement of the bases at right angles to its length. What X-ray diffraction did

was to indicate the arrangement in space of the chemical groups in the molecular thread. It is very convenient (and probably genetically necessary) that the DNA molecule has a well-defined and in some ways simple configuration which stays intact during extraction from living things, and thus may then be studied by physical methods.

It is probably worth stressing that X-ray diffraction, for most molecules which are not very small, is the only technique which can establish their configuration; on the other hand, only very rarely can it be used to determine the chemical structure of such molecules before this has been achieved by chemical methods. But when a small molecule is being studied, X-ray diffraction may be used by itself to determine the position, size, and weight of the atoms in the molecule. The extent to which it is profitable to combine stereochemical methods with the X-ray technique increases with the complexity of the molecules studied.

To find the structure of very large molecules it is necessary to know the form of the small chemical groups of which it is composed. The structures of these groups are found by studying crystals of simple compounds. Molecular models are then built using inter-atomic distances and arrangements already known to occur in crystals, and a search is made for a structure which would give a diffraction pattern similar to that observed with X-rays. The structure can be established only by close combination of model-building and X-ray diffraction.

THE BACKGROUND OF THE WATSON AND CRICK MOLECULAR MODEL

The more important information available as a guide in the building of the Watson and Crick model was as follows. The covalent linkages in the polynucleotide chain were firmly established and knowledge of the dimensions and shapes of the chemical groups was fairly complete. X-ray diffraction data gave the main dimensions of the helix and provided important suggestions about its internal structure (*e.g.* the "pile of pennies") and showed that the molecule was almost certainly composed of more than one polynucleotide chain. The equalities found in the base analyses suggested that the bases occurred in pairs, and titration studies showed that the bases were probably

75

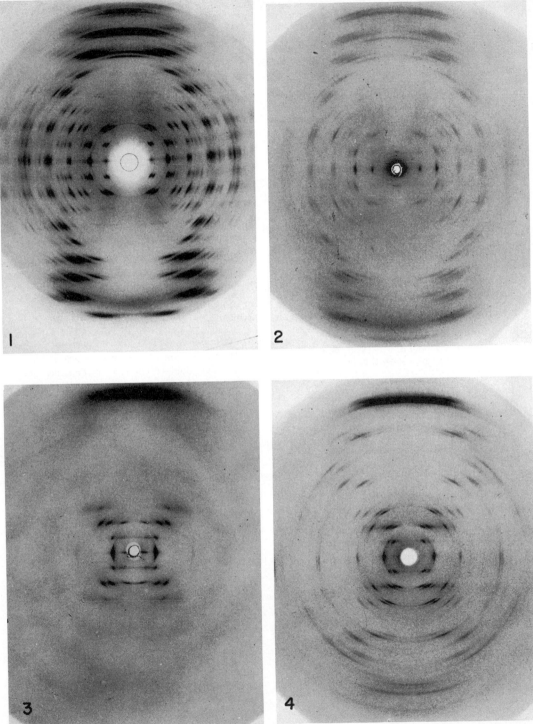

Figures 1–4

III. DNA STRUCTURE AND REPLICATION

joined by hydrogen bonds. The difficulty about DNA structure was that a regular helix had to be built from four nucleotides of different shape and size. This paradox was resolved by Watson and Crick. They made the important assumption that the number of polynucleotide chains in the molecule was two; and they so arranged the hydrogen bonds between the bases that they achieved the elegant result of having two pairs of bases such that in both pairs the bonds joining the base to the sugar ring were the same distance apart and inclined to each other at the same angle and were symmetrically arranged. This symmetry and equivalence made it possible to build a helical molecule with the sugar and phosphate portions regularly arranged but with any complicated sequence of bases along the length of the molecule.

Although many of the dimensions of the model were indicated by X-ray diffraction data, the precise dimensions and much of the internal configuration of the structure were largely derived by the actual process of building the model so that it conformed with available stereochemical data. It may be seen therefore, that the structure was somewhat hypothetical insofar as it was not derived entirely or directly from experiment (Crick and Watson, 1954). In fact, calculation of the diffraction pattern produced by the structure showed that it did not agree adequately with detailed X-ray data, and it remained to be shown that a molecular model of this type could be built which would agree well with the data.

REFINED STRUCTURE FOR DNA

1. Use of the Lithium Salt of DNA

About a year ago we described a modified structure (Feughelman et al., 1955) which was in satisfactory agreement with the experimental data, the main modification being to place the nitrogen bases closer to the helix axis than in the Watson and Crick model and to reduce the diameter of the helix. Since then more rigorous proof of the correctness of the structure has become possible; first, because more accurate X-ray data have been obtained, and second, because models have been built using new stereochemical data.

The unpublished X-ray diffraction and model-

FIGURE 1. X-ray diffraction pattern of Na DNA in the A configuration at 75% relative humidity. The sharp spots indicate a high degree of crystallinity.
FIGURE 2. X-ray diffraction pattern of Rb DNA in the A configuration at 75% relative humidity. The inner spots on the first and second layer-lines are weaker than in Na DNA, and a spot not present in Na DNA is visible at the centre of the first layer-line.
FIGURE 3. X-ray diffraction photograph of Na DNA in the B configuration at 92% relative humidity. Spots are visible near the centre of the pattern only; this indicates crystallinity is imperfect. The spots are clearer than those obtained in another specimen (Fig. 5).
FIGURE 4. X-ray diffraction photograph of Li DNA in the B configuration at 66% relative humidity. The sharp spots in all parts of the pattern indicate a high degree of crystallinity.

building results which I will describe are the joint work of Dr. W. E. Seeds, Dr. H. R. Wilson, Mr. R. Langridge, Mr. C. W. Hooper and myself at King's College, London, in collaboration with Dr. L. D. Hamilton and Dr. R. K. Barclay of the Sloan-Kettering Institute, New York, who supplied new materials. The earlier X-ray pictures of the sodium salt of DNA (e.g. Fig. 5) in the B configuration (Fig. 9), although fairly sharp, were still sufficiently diffuse to make really reliable measurements of the diffracted X-ray intensity impossible. The new lithium salt of DNA made by L. D. Hamilton crystallizes in the B configuration and the X-ray photograph consists of sharply defined spots (Fig. 4) which may be measured accurately. Another advantage of the lithium salt is that the lithium ion scatters about three times less X rays than the sodium ion and may be ignored in the calculation of the diffracted intensities from the molecular model. When sodium is used, the possibility of appreciable error exists because the position of the metal ion in the structure is uncertain. The new stereochemical data used in building the model consists of bond lengths and angles in a phosphate di-ester (dibenzyl-phosphoric acid) (Dunitz and Rollett, 1956) and the configuration of thymidine (Huber, 1956).

The micro-crystals in the fibre of Li DNA are orthorhombic and, at about 66 per cent relative humidity, the unit cell dimensions are: a. 22.8 Å; b. 31.7 Å; c. 33.6 Å. The axes of the helical molecules are in the direction which is parallel to the fibre axis, and two DNA molecules pass through the unit cell, one molecule being displaced relative to the other along its axis by one third of the helix pitch length. The distance between centres of the molecules which make contact on the same level is 22.8 Å, but where the contact is between molecules at different levels, the distance is as small as 19.1 Å.

Model building confirms that the molecules are in contact, and that displacement of the molecules by one third of the pitch length allows them (on account of being double and not single helices) to come more closely in contact than when on the same level. There are exactly ten nucleotide pairs in the molecule per turn of the helix. As the symmetry of the lattice may reflect the symmetry of the molecule, one expects tenfold helices to pack in orthorhombic manner if crystallization is perfect. Crystallization of the B configuration in a hexagonal form (Feughelman et al., 1955) is necessarily imperfect.

The correspondence between diffraction intensities calculated from the model and as observed is satisfactory and is shown in Figure 10, and the configuration of the molecule is shown in Figure 11. (This configuration still requires some refining but the actual structure cannot be very different from it.) The sugar ring has the O atom ~ ¼ Å

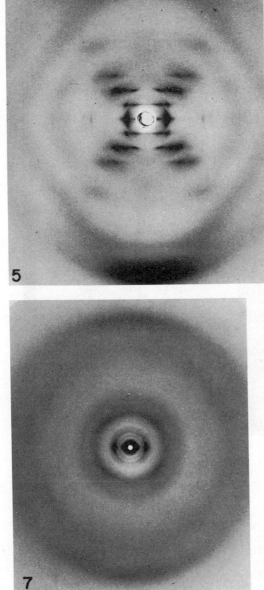

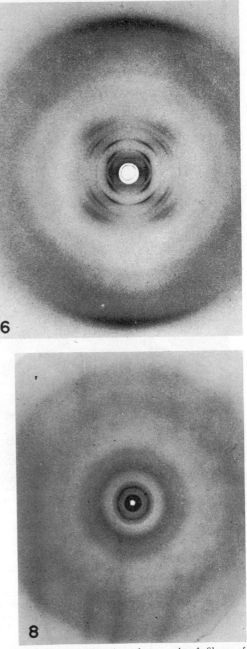

FIGURE 5. X-ray diffraction photograph of fibres of Na DNA in B configuration. Crystallinity is not well defined.

FIGURE 7. X-ray photograph of fibres of nucleohistone extracted from calf thymus. The diagonal cross pattern characteristic of the DNA helix is visible and the 2nd and 3rd layer-lines can be distinguished. The first layer-line is not visible.

FIGURE 6. X-ray diffraction photograph of fibres of oriented *Sepia* sperm. The pattern resembles that of DNA (*e.g.* Fig. 5) except that the first layer-line (see Fig. 18) is stronger.

FIGURE 8. X-ray photograph of intact sperm heads of *Arbacia*. The pattern is unoriented but otherwise is indistinguishable from that of extracted nucleohistone.

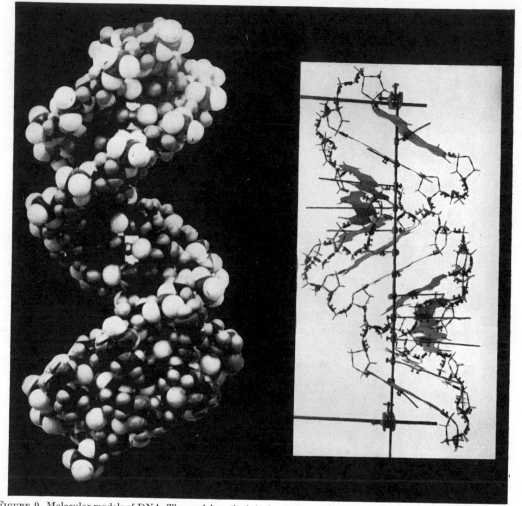

FIGURE 9. Molecular models of DNA. The model on the left shows the molecule in the B configuration and the shape and size of the atoms. On the lower groove of the model a polyarginine group has been added to show how protamine can combine compactly with DNA. The model on the right shows the molecule in the A configuration; this type of model made with wire is the kind mainly used in this research—the centres of atoms occur at the junctions in the wires and the nitrogen base-pairs are represented by metal plates; interatomic distances may be measured accurately.

out-of-plane but this value could be altered if the bond-angles and lengths in the phosphate-ester chain were adjusted slightly. The distances between atoms in contact are about the same as in previous models (Feughelman *et al.*, 1955) and the diffraction pattern was calculated from the model by the same procedure as before.

2. Use of Sodium and Rubidium Salts of DNA

The certainty with which the correctness of a molecular structure may be established is increased when the molecule can be studied in more

than one configuration. Fortunately this is possible with DNA. The sodium salt crystallizes with the helical molecules in the A configuration (Fig. 9) where the attractive forces between the ions have caused the helix to shrink in length and eleven nucleotide pairs are packed in one turn of the helix and the planes of the nitrogen bases become tilted at $\sim 70°$ to the helix axis. As eleven is an odd number the crystal form is monoclinic; there is one molecule passing through the unit cell. The dimensions of the unit cell at ~ 75 per cent relative humidity are: a. 21.9 Å; b. 40.4 Å;

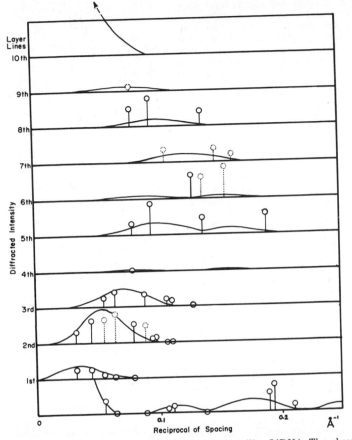

FIGURE 10. Observed and calculated intensities of diffraction for crystalline LiDNA. The observed intensities are shown by circles (the values for full circles are more reliable than for dotted circles); the smooth curve is calculated from the model. The curve on the 10th layer-line rises to a higd level off the diagram and the corresponding very strong observed intensities are not shown.

c. 28.4 Å; β. 97.15°. In the crystallites the molecules are arranged in contact and are at slightly different levels to allow closest approach. The correspondence between calculated and observed intensities of diffraction is satisfactory and is shown in Figure 12. It is only possible to obtain this correspondence if the sodium ions are placed in certain positions near the phosphate groups. These particular positions are not stereochemically unique and it is very desirable to confirm their correctness. This may be achieved by making use of the sodium, potassium, and rubidium salts of DNA which were prepared by L. D. Hamilton and R. K. Barclay. These salts are isomorphous and, as the effective X-ray scattering from the rubidium ion is about 3.5 times that of sodium, the intensities of the spots on the X-ray picture change greatly when sodium is replaced by

rubidium. The calculated and observed intensities agree very satisfactorily, all the large changes being accounted for (see Fig. 13).

INEXACT FIT OF OBSERVED AND CALCULATED DIFFRACTION INTENSITIES

Certain parts of the DNA X-ray diffraction pattern are determined by the basic characteristics of the molecular structure and are not affected much by changes in structural details. If the structure is to be established it is necessary that observed and calculated intensities of diffraction agree well in these regions. Such agreement exists. The first significant region is in the centre of the pattern on the first four-layer-lines where the strong diffraction defines the main shape and dimension of the helix. The other important region is on the tenth layer-line on the B pattern, and on the sixth, seventh and eighth layer-lines on the A pattern, where the strong diffraction defines the way the nitrogen bases are piled on top of one another. Agreement may be poor for other parts of the pattern but this does not matter for the diffraction in those parts is determined by details of configuration. We cannot expect to predict these details because we do not know accurately the correct values to use for many bond lengths and angles, nor can we predict the detailed arrangement of the water molecules surrounding the DNA.

THE LIMITATIONS IN KNOWLEDGE OF DNA STRUCTURE OBTAINED BY X-RAY DIFFRACTION

All the atoms in a fibre of DNA diffract X rays, and if the structure in the molecule is repeated periodically and if the molecules are packed regularly side-by-side (*i.e.* the arrangement is crystalline), the energy of the diffracted waves is concentrated in certain directions, and spots appear on the X-ray photograph. Regular double-helix molecules packed irregularly in the fibre will produce diffuse rings on the photograph; distorted molecules will produce even more diffuse rings. Such diffuse rings will not show clearly on the photograph and are not amenable to study. Our attention has been concentrated on the crystalline portions of the fibre. We now know that these regions consist of double-helix molecules, but we also know that density and water content measurement combined with X-ray diffraction gives a value of $\sim$2.5 for the number of polynucleotide chains in the molecule with the B configuration. Such discrepancy occurs in the study of fibres and is explained by postulating the existence in the fibre of non-crystalline regions where the molecules are packed more closely than in the crystalline parts. Existence of these amorphous regions, which probably constitute half or more of the fibre, is also required to explain infra-red dichroism measurements as well as the measurements, made by Dr. Harold Wyckoff, of mechanical properties of DNA fibres. (I would like to say here that Dr. Wyckoff, has single-handed, in unpublished work, paralleled much of the earlier X-ray studies on DNA carried out by our team.)

If X-ray diffraction has told us nothing of the amorphous regions in the DNA fibre, the question arises as to whether molecules with structure other than the double helix might exist in these regions. However, it is unlikely that other structures exist to any great extent, because analysis of whole fibres shows unity ratios of base content, and absence of non-hydrogen-bonded bases, and a non-double helix structure which satisfies these analyses and hydrogen-bonding conditions is not easily conceived.

Measurement of the ratio of amorphous to crystalline material in DNA fibres is difficult and unreliable; hence we have made no attempt to

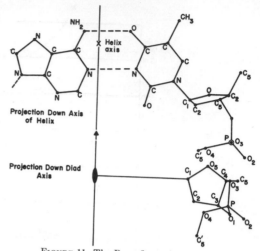

FIGURE 11. The B configuration of DNA.

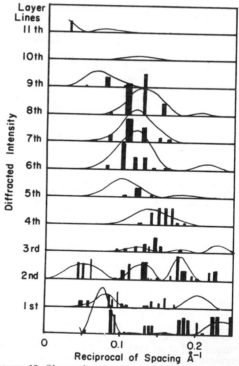

FIGURE 12. Observed and calculated intensities of diffraction for crystalline Na DNA. The observed intensities are shown by the heights of the black rectangles and the smooth curve is calculated from the model.

find how this ratio varies with the type of cell from which the DNA is prepared. However, we have found no difference in X-ray photographs of DNA isolated from rapidly and slowly dividing

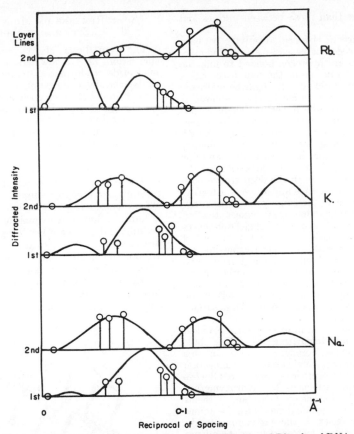

FIGURE 13. The difference of intensity of diffraction in isomorphous Na, K, and Rb salts of DNA. The smooth curve is calculated from the model; observed intensities are shown by circles. The main differences as the mass of the ion is increased are: On the first layer-line the first point on the left becomes of appreciable intensity only for Rb, and the second pair of points decreases almost to zero; on the second layer-line, the ratio of the first two peaks changes considerably.

cells, that is, with a high and low rate of DNA turnover, and from cells with high and low rates of protein synthesis.

Apart from lack of knowledge of the amorphous material, information about the molecules in the crystalline regions is also limited. We cannot exclude the possibility that there are occasional branches or breaks in the molecule. All we know is that the molecule is on the average a regular helix for about 20 turns (i.e. molecular weight ~ 70,000). We do not know whether the molecule is regular over a greater length; the diffraction provides no evidence about discontinuities placed farther apart than about 20 turns.

THE DNA MOLECULE CONSIDERED AS A TEMPLATE

In considering how DNA might act as a template, the sugar and phosphate part of the mole-cule are not of primary interest as they are regularly arranged; also it is quite likely that there are few breaks or branches in the poly-nucleotide chain, and therefore, one expects all specificity to be mainly associated with the nitrogen bases. These, in the B configuration which exists *in vivo*, lie fairly well exposed to outside influence, at the bottom of the 2 helical grooves on the molecule (Fig. 9). The surface of these grooves is fairly smooth, for example, interchange of a purine by a pyrimidine or a hydrogen atom by a methyl or amino group causes a difference in position of the bottom of the groove of 1.5 Å or less. Hence, from a space-filling point of view, the template character of DNA is not very marked. In particular, DNA does not look like a template for amino acids because the volume differences between amino acids are larger than those between purines and pyrimidines.

The difference in chemical reactivity between the various nitrogen bases is also small. The more reactive groups are hydrogen-bonded to link the bases in pairs. Only one of the four bases has a free amino group (and even it might be hydrogen bonded); this is on guanine in the shallower of the two grooves on the molecule. There is also little difference between the number of hydrogen-bonding sites on the two pairs of bases, though the positions of these sites differ. In the shallow groove both base-pairs have two sites, and the guanine-cytosine pair has an extra site on the amino group of guanine. In the deep groove both base-pairs have three sites and there is a methyl group on thymine in the same position as a hydrogen on cytosine. One may expect to find template action expressed in the slight differences of shape of the bases and exact positions of hydrogen-bonding sites. It is clearly possible for a suitably-shaped molecule to be held firmly, and with a high degree of specificity, in either of the grooves on DNA, by the combined effect of the pattern of hydrogen bonds and the total action of van der Waals forces acting over a large surface area in the grooves.

Polynucleotides would in principle possess ideal characteristics for templating to DNA; but, although polypeptides appear unlikely in this role, there are other possibilities in this connection which should not altogether be forgotten. Glucose has been found attached to hydroxymethyl cytosine in T2 bacteriophage DNA and it seems possible that other groups may also be found attached to the bases. If these attachments are labile, much attached matter may exist and yet remain undetected because it has been removed during purification. The presence of the unknown groups would of course enormously increase the templating possibilities of DNA, and Crick (1956) has suggested that specific templates might exist which link DNA and amino acids. In any case, as Chargaff (1955) has pointed out, it would be a mistake to let acceptance of ideas of DNA structure discourage further analytical research.

Hypothesis Concerning Replication of DNA Molecules

The Watson and Crick hypothesis about DNA replication has shown a kind of way biological processes may be interpreted in terms of precise molecular structure and is of much significance for this reason if for none other. Several experimental studies are in progress in an attempt to find if the hypothesis is correct or not, and at the moment the situation is not clear: Drs. Plaut and Mazia have results on plant cells, and different kinds of studies on bacteriophages have been carried out by Dr. Levinthal, Dr. Stent and Dr. Hershey.

Some Remarks on Molecular-Model Schemes in Biology

The hypothesis of Watson-Crick, and the suggestion of Gamow (1954) that groups of nucleotides could act as templates for 20 amino acids considered relevant to protein synthesis, have stimulated much speculation about molecular biology. Some schemes published have begun by being based on sound stereochemical ideas but, when these ideas were found unsuitable for the scheme, they were modified in a way stereochemically unlikely or impossible. It should be recognized that the work of Watson and Crick is seriously regarded because in it they adhered carefully to accepted stereochemical standards. When considering molecular model schemes, accurate 3-dimensional molecular models should be built and, among other things, the interatomic distances should be measured to make sure they are not too small. Molecular model building is a precise and often tedious discipline and need not be the fanciful expression of half-formed ideas. Most X-ray crystallographers are competent to advise those interested in these matters.

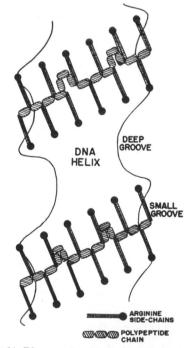

DNA HELIX

DEEP GROOVE

SMALL GROOVE

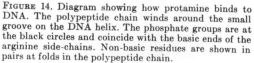

ARGININE SIDE-CHAINS

POLYPEPTIDE CHAIN

Figure 14. Diagram showing how protamine binds to DNA. The polypeptide chain winds around the small groove on the DNA helix. The phosphate groups are at the black circles and coincide with the basic ends of the arginine side-chains. Non-basic residues are shown in pairs at folds in the polypeptide chain.

STRUCTURE OF DEOXYRIBOSE NUCLEOPROTEINS

Nucleoprotamine

We hope that a study of the structure of nucleoproteins can cast light on the functional relationship of nucleic acids and proteins. The simplest basic protein to combine with DNA is protamine, and the mode of combination is known with a fair degree of certainty (Feughelman *et al.*, 1955). The polypeptide chain in nucleoprotamine is in a fully-extended form and winds helically around the DNA molecule and over, or in, the small groove on it (Fig. 14). The side-chains reach out from the polypeptide chain at about right-angles so that, on alternate sides, their basic end-groups can combine with the phosphate groups of the DNA. One-third of the residues in protamines are non-basic and these residues probably occur at folds in the polypeptide chain so that all the basic groups are able to combine with phosphates. A single residue cannot form a fold, but two together can; sequence analysis shows that the non-basic residues do in fact occur in pairs and not singly (Felix *et al.*, 1956). However, we do not know yet whether the folds point inwards towards the nitrogen bases or outwards.

It would seem that the possibility of folding can be large in basic proteins. The X-ray photographs (Fig. 15) of complexes of DNA with protamine and with polylysine (supplied by Prof. Katchalski) show no significant difference from those with lysine-rich histone (70 per cent non-basic residues) supplied by Dr. Mirsky and from naturally occurring nucleoprotein in sperm heads of *Sepia* or of *Loligo* which contain proteins with 70 per cent non-basic residues (Hamer, 1955) (see also Fig. 16). Molecular model-building

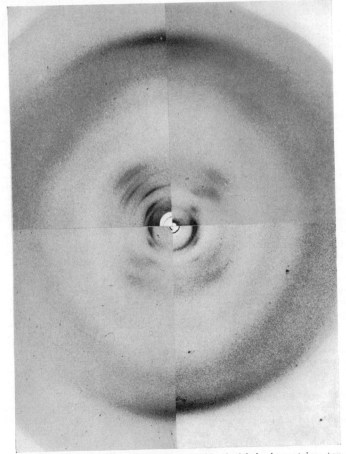

FIGURE 15. Comparison of the X-ray photographs of DNA combined with basic proteins: top left, intact oriented *Sepia* sperm; top right, DNA recipitated with lysine-rich histone; bottom left, nucleoprotamine extracted from *Salma trutta* sperm; bottom right, DNA precipitated with protamine.

shows that the polypeptide chain can fit snugly into the small groove on the DNA molecule (Fig. 9). We have also confirmed, more thoroughly than in earlier experiments, that the X-ray picture from *Loligo* sperm heads is not the result of artifact. Dr. D. B. Carlisle of the Marine Biological Laboratory at Plymouth supplied us with live spermatophores from a large species of *Loligo*. We obtained in four hours, from an intact spermatophore (enclosed in a mica cell to prevent drying) X-ray photographs which showed all the features previously observed using dried fibres of sperm.

Nucleohistone

Nucleoprotamines have been found in sperm heads (of many species but not all) and not in nuclei of other kinds of cell. The genetic material in sperm heads is probably in an inert state, being stored before beginning its genetical function in the egg. We have studied nucleoprotamine because it appeared to be the simplest combination of DNA and protein. The structure of nucleoprotein in cells which are growing, differentiating, or synthesizing protein might be more directly connected with dynamic relations between DNA and protein. In such cells—at least in higher organisms—DNA is, in the chromosomes, somehow in association with histone, non-basic protein, and possibly RNA. We thought the molecular structure of chromosomes in a functional state might be too complex to respond to direct study. Certain cells, for example, thymocytes and fowl erythrocytes, have nuclei which consist largely of nucleohistone and contain a minimum of non-basic protein and RNA. We thought these nuclei might have a simpler structure than those containing more non-basic protein and we have therefore, begun our work on these nuclei although the biological activity of erythrocyte nuclei may be low.

We have found that substantially the same X-ray diffraction photograph is obtained from calf thymus and from fowl erythrocyte nuclei, *Arbacia* sperm heads (Fig. 8) (which contain a basic protein which resembles histone more than protamine; Hamer, 1955) and calf thymus nucleohistone extracted with water (Fig. 7). (We are grateful to Dr. G. L. Brown of our laboratory for providing most of the extracted materials.) Evidently nucleohistone has a characteristic molecular morphology which may be preserved intact during extraction. Extracted material, or a jelly of coalesced nuclei, may be stretched into fibres in which the thread-like molecules tend to lie parallel to the length of the fibre. The X-ray photographs obtained from such fibres (Fig. 7) are, apart from orientation, the same as those from the unoriented material. The picture is not so well defined as when DNA or nucleoprotamine is used, but it is clear that much of the DNA in nucleohistone exists in its usual helical configu-

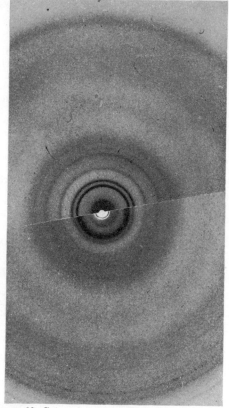

FIGURE 16. Comparison of the X-ray diffraction photographs of sperm heads of *Salvelinus* containing nucleoprotamine and *Loligo* (non-oriented) containing a nucleoprotein with a higher proportion of non-basic amino acids. The rings are less clearly defined in the photograph of *Salvelinus* and this means that the arrangement of the molecules is more disordered than in *Loligo*; otherwise no difference is apparent. (*Salvelinus* and *Salmo* sperm were kindly supplied by Prof. K. Felix.)

ration. Because nucleoprotamine consists of a polypeptide wrapped around the small groove on the DNA molecule, the first layer-line (Fig.17 and 18) of the nucleoprotamine X-ray diagram is stronger compared to the second layer-line than is the case for DNA alone. This strong first layer-line does not appear on the X-ray pictures of nucleohistone fibres, and it therefore seems that histone is not combined with DNA in the same way as in nucleoprotamine. An arrangement of histone which would be compatible with the relative intensities of the layer-lines is that in which histone polypeptide chains are wrapped around both grooves (Fig. 19) on the DNA molecule. We can eliminate also the possibility that all protein in the nucleohistone specimens is equally distributed between the DNA molecules

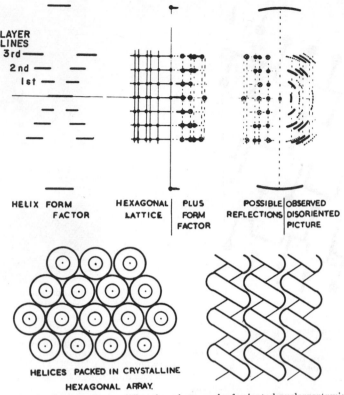

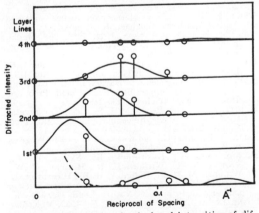

FIGURE 17. Diagrams showing how the X-ray diffraction photograph of oriented nucleoprotamine in sperm heads is produced. The diffraction spots (or reflections) occur where the crystal lattice points superimpose on the calculated diffraction (or form-factor). The molecules in the specimen are slightly disoriented and as a result the X-ray spots are enlarged into arcs of circles.

FIGURE 18. Observed and calculated intensities of diffraction from nucleoprotamine. The observed intensities are shown by circles and the smooth curve is calculated from the model. The dotted part of the curve and the observed point on it have been reduced in height 10 times.

and wrapped around them; for if this were so, the X-ray spacings at right angles to the fibre length would, in partly dried specimens, be larger than those observed. These spacings increase when the fibres are wetted, until a value of ~38 Å is reached. The molecules are then disoriented, possibly owing to coiling of the chromonemata which had been straightened out in the stretched fibres. The 38 Å spacing is also observed in unfixed nuclei (Fig. 20) and even in whole thymocyte cells. It appears likely, that in the living interphase nucleus, nucleoprotein molecules lie parallel and equally spaced in groups of at least several dozen. The 38 Å spacing would correspond to a distance of 45 A between centres of the molecules if they are packed hexagonally. In one direction at least, the molecules are only about 25 Å across, and hence, in the living nucleus there is a space of about 20 A, filled largely with water, between adjacent molecules. Possibly this space is necessary to enable large molecules to move between the nucleoprotein threads.

III. DNA STRUCTURE AND REPLICATION

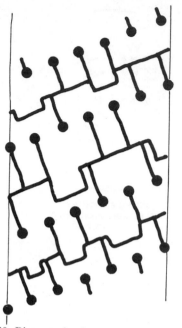

FIGURE 19. Diagram showing a possible way histone might bind to DNA. The black circles show the position of the phosphate groups on the DNA helix; the lines trace the polypeptide chain, the folds in it, and the side-chains of arginine and lysine.

There is, on the X-ray photographs of the various kinds of nucleohistone mentioned, a strong X-ray spacing at about 60 Å (Fig. 21). In fibres this spacing is at right angles to their length. We have not yet eliminated the possibility that the spacing corresponds to a periodicity in lipid associated with the nucleohistone, but this appears rather unlikely in view of the fact that the spacing is also observed in nucleohistone which has been purified by precipitation from aqueous solution with 0.14 Molar sodium chloride. If it is assumed that all the spacings arise from one kind of nucleoprotein, they could be explained by the idea that DNA molecules occur in pairs joined together by protein. Such an interpretation is, however, at the moment very uncertain. The nucleohistone we study is known to contain many different proteins, some described as histone and others not. The fractionation and study of these components has only begun, and until much more is known of the chemistry of the nucleus, it is unlikely that physical studies by methods such as X-ray diffraction will yield results which can be interpreted without ambiguity. It is, however, clear that the interphase nucleus is largely composed of fine threads containing one or two DNA molecules, and that these threads lie parallel, packed together in groups. It seems probable that X-ray diffraction is here showing us the ultimate fibrillar structure of polytenic chromosomes.

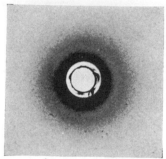

FIGURE 20. The 38 Å ring in the X-ray diffraction photograph of unfixed nuclei from fowl erythrocytes.

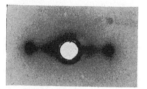

FIGURE 21. The 60 Å diffraction spots in the X-ray picture of oriented extracted calf thymus nucleohistone.

ACKNOWLEDGMENTS

I am most grateful to my colleagues at King's for help in preparing the illustrations for this paper and to Dr. L. D. Hamilton for help with the manuscript.

REFERENCES

ASTBURY, W. T., 1947, X-ray studies on nucleic acids. Symp. Soc. Exp. Biol. *1:* 66–76.

CHARGAFF, E., 1955, Isolation and composition of the deoxypentose nucleic acids and of the corresponding nucleoproteins. In: The Nucleic Acids, New York, Academic Press, Vol. 1. Chapter 10: 307–368.

CRICK, F. H. C., 1956, Conference on nucleic acids and protein synthesis, Biochem. J. (in press).

CRICK, F. H. C., and WATSON, J. D., 1954, The complementary structure of deoxyribosenucleic acid. Proc. Roy. Soc. *223:* 80–96.

DALY, M. M., and MIRSKY, A. E., 1955, Histones with high lysine content. J. Gen. Physiol. *38:* 405–413.

DOTY, P., 1956, The characterization, denaturation and degradation of desoxyribose nucleic acid. Proc. 3rd Intern. Congr. Biochem.: 135–139.

DUNITZ, J. D., AND ROLLETT, J. S., 1956, The crystal structure of dibenzylphosphoric acid. Acta. cryst. Camb. *9:* 327–334.

FELIX, K. FISCHER, H., and KREKELS, A., 1956, Progress in Biophysics. London, Pergamon Press, p. 1.

FEUGHELMAN, M., LANGRIDGE, R., SEEDS, W. E., STOKES, A. R., WILSON, H. R., HOOPER, C. W., WILKINS, M. H. F., BARCLAY, R. K., HAMILTON, L. D., 1955, Molecular structure of deoxyribose nucleic acid and nucleoprotein. Nature, Lond. *175:* 834–836.

FRANKLIN, R. E., and GOSLING, R. G., 1953, Molecular configuration in sodium thymonucleate. Nature, Lond. *171:* 740–741.

GAMOW, G., 1954. Possible relation between deoxyribonucleic acid and protein structure. Nature, Lond. *173:* 318.

HAMER, D., 1955, The composition of the basic proteins of echinoderm sperm. Biol. Bull., Wood's Hole *10:* 35–39.

HUBER, M., 1956, Acta. cryst. Camb. (in press).
WATSON, J. D., and CRICK, F. H. C., 1953, A structure
    for deoxyribose nucleic acids. Nature, Lond. *171:*
    737–738.
    1953, Genetical implications of the structure of deoxy-
    ribose nucleic acid. Nature, Lond. *171:* 964.
WILKINS, M. H. F., STOKES, A. R., and WILSON, H. R.,
    1953, Molecular structure of desoxypentose nucleic
    acids. Nature, Lond. *171:* 738–740.

DISCUSSION

PLAINE: You have stated that the structure of
the DNA molecule *is* continuous. From their
analysis of terminal phosphate groups, Dekker
and Schachman concluded that the structure
consisted of interrupted strands, with the breaks
occurring about every fifty nucleotides but being
staggered in the two chains of the molecule. Such
an interrupted-two-strand structure might be
more flexible than a continuous one and might
possibly be more applicable for explaining some
of the genetic and cytogenetic phenomena. Would
you please explain why you object to, or what is
wrong with, the interpretation of the interrupted
structure?

WILKINS: Until recently there existed much
evidence from dye-binding and titration studies

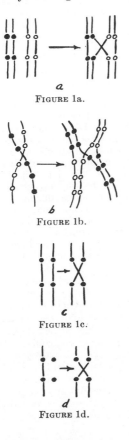

FIGURE 1a.

FIGURE 1b.

FIGURE 1c.

FIGURE 1d.

which indicated that there was in DNA one
secondary phosphoryl group per 20–30 nucleotides
(*e.g.* Peacocke, 1955). It was suggested that these
phosphoryl groups were at the ends of branches
attached to the main polynucleotide chains.

Dekker and Schachman (1954) preferred to
interpret their results in terms of breaks in the
phosphate-ester chains in the double-helix DNA
molecule, and they produced experimental evidence to show that, when the hydrogen bonds
linking the chains in the double-helix molecule
were broken by heating, the molecular weight of
DNA fell to that of 20–30 nucleotides. However,
Doty and Rice (1955) have shown that when
hydrogen bonds in DNA are broken by heat or
low pH, the molecular weight is unaltered. It is
not clear to me to what extent differences of
conditions of heating in the two sets of experiments or differences in initial intactness of the
DNA explain the disagreement in these results.
However, Peacocke (1956), one of the main
workers studying the question of secondary
phosphoryl groups in DNA, now claims that
neither dye-binding nor titration experiments
give evidence of secondary phosphoryl groups. It
appears therefore, that there is not much reason
for supposing that the suggestion of Dekker and
Schachman is correct. Furthermore, it seems
rather unlikely that the regularity and rigidity
of the double-helix molecule would be preserved
when breaks occur in the phosphate-ester chain
for, at such breaks, the helix would be held intact
only by van der Waals forces. (Refs.: Dekker, C.
A., and Schachman, H. K., 1954, Proc. Nat.
Acad. Sci. Wash. *40:* 894–909; Doty, P., and
Rice, S. A., 1955, Biochim. Biophys. Acta *16:*
446–448; Peacocke, A. R., 1955, La Ricerca Sci.,
Suppl. Simp. Intern. Chim. Macromol., Oct. 1954,
and 1956, J. Chem. Soc. in press.)

WEINSTEIN: I wonder whether Dr. Wilkins
would care to say anything about the relation
between the structure of DNA or of other substances in the chromosomes and crossing over.

The classical theory of crossing over, which goes
back to Janssens and Morgan, implies, from a
chemical point of view, that connections between
atoms in the same chromatid are replaced by connections between atoms in different chromatids.
(Fig. 1a). The necessity for such a change is avoided
in Belling's theory, because some of the new genes
are formed on one of the old chromatids and some
on the other, as the two old chromatids lie across
each other (Fig. 1b). But the avoidance is only
for crossovers between homologous strands; because to account for 3-strand (progressive) and
4-strand (digressive) crossovers, Belling's theory
must be modified to allow exchanges to occur
between sister chromatids. A sister exchange, if
it occurs after the new genes have become linked
in a chain, implies a change of two bonds. (See
fig. 1c.) If, when it occurs, the new genes are not
yet linked in a chain, there is only one longitudinal

bond to be altered. (See fig. 1d.) Therefore the genetic evidence implies that at least in some cases of crossing over, connections between old genes are replaced by connections between old and new genes; and we might expect some indication of this in the chemistry of the chromosomes. WILKINS: The only substance about which we know much in chromosomes is DNA and hence it would seem best to confine speculations to this substance. There is, of course, no difficulty in envisaging a supply of energy in the cell sufficient to cause polynucleotide or polypeptide chains to break and afterwards to reform in other ways which might then give rise to recombination. It is not easy, however, to suggest a scheme for recombination which arises naturally from the structure of DNA. Most theories would involve the idea that crossing over and replication took place simultaneously, but in higher organisms it is uncertain whether crossing over occurs during DNA synthesis or afterwards when chiasmata formation is observed. It seems likely that crossing over in higher organisms differs from that in bacteriophage. Possibly this difference is due to bacteriophage processes probably taking place on a molecular level, whereas the chromosomes of higher organisms have a more complicated organization (e.g., contain many strands). In such chromosomes the molecular changes may be substantially the same as in bacteriophages, but the expression of these changes may appear different. The first problem in devising a molecular theory is to find a mechanism for homologous pairing. No one appears to have obtained a really satisfactory solution in terms of DNA molecules only, but I understand that this question will be discussed at the Symposium on the Chemical Basis of Heredity, about to take place at the Johns Hopkins University.

I would like to mention here some points which are relevant to Dr. Weinstein's question insofar as they illustrate the kind of difficulty which arises in speculation about the molecular processes in biology. (These points have arisen at this Symposium out of discussion with Dr. Levinthal, Dr. Stent and others; while I make no claim to these ideas, I may be responsible for any errors involved.)

First, let us consider one of the main objections to the Watson and Crick hypothesis of DNA replication. The argument is that, if the hydrogen bonds between the two polynucleotide chains in a DNA molecule are broken, the two parts cannot easily separate because they are intertwined. Unwinding of the two chains is considered to be an unlikely process because of interaction between the chains. This argument, however, seems to involve the assumption that some unspecific process such as Brownian motion would unwind the chains. There is no difficulty in unwinding the chains if a directed process of separation begins at one end of the molecule and travels

along it. As an example of such a process, it has been suggested that, as the two chains separate, nucleotides condense on them to form two new DNA molecules. (It is necessary, of course, to explain why the reaction proceeds forwards and not backwards.) Thus, while duplication of the original molecule is taking place, the two new partly-formed molecules are joined to the portion of the original molecule which has not yet duplicated. The junction moves until the original molecule has split along its whole length and two complete separate new molecules have been formed. The helical molecular strands rotate about their axes during this duplication, but Dr. Levinthal has made a calculation which shows that the energy required to overcome the viscous forces involved is quite small. Many rather unsatisfying schemes for DNA replication have been suggested in order to avoid the difficulty of unwinding, and it seems that such schemes only deserve attention if it can be shown that the difficulty of unwinding really exists.

This kind of argument about the helical nature of DNA may be taken a stage farther by suggesting that the helical nature, rather than being an impediment, may in fact be of considerable help to the molecule in its functioning. Let us confine the discussion to DNA replication according to the Watson and Crick hypothesis. We know that the hydrogen bonds in DNA can be readily broken by heating, but the value of the activation energy of this process indicates that the bonds reform unless they are broken in about 15 consecutive base-pairs (Doty, 1956). Bond repair also seems to take place when ultraviolet light is absorbed by the bases. It seems likely that in vivo the hydrogen bonds in DNA may be breaking and reforming, a process like melting and solidifying. This conclusion is not surprising if we accept the idea that any templating actions of DNA, replication or otherwise, are determined primarily by hydrogen bonds to the nitrogen bases. If it is necessary at one stage during the templating process for the two molecular components to be held together, it is equally necessary for them soon afterwards to come apart freely. This might be easily achieved if the hydrogen bonds were close to their "melting point." If the phosphate-ester chains in the DNA molecule were straight, or consisted of adjacent and non-intertwined helices, the two chains might, on account of their flexible nature, begin accidentally to separate whenever the hydrogen bonds melted locally. The intertwined helical structure of DNA is semi-rigid because the configuration is determined not only by the hydrogen bonds pairing the bases, but also by van der Waals forces; and hence, the polynucleotide chains cannot separate locally unless a sufficiently large region of the hydrogen-bonding system is melted to enable the helical configuration in that region to become seriously disordered. However, as we have said above, if the bonds are broken at one end of the molecule, and systematic rearrangement of the bases prevents them from reforming, the two poly-nucleotide chains might be separated readily.

It has often been commented that, while much is known about the structure of DNA and of its biological activity, almost nothing is known of its biochemical activity. This absence of knowledge, however, is only to be expected if the activity of DNA consists of transient hydrogen bonding to highly specific substances.

ALFERT: Dr. Wilkins presented evidence that sperm protamines are attached to DNA in a manner different from that of histones found usually combined with DNA in somatic nuclei. A difference in the configuration of nucleoprotein complexes is also reflected in a particular cyto-chemical property of DNA, namely its relative basophilia in various types of nuclei. Lison (1955, Acta Histochem. *2:* 47) has recently shown that the basic dye-binding capacity of rat sperm nuclei greatly decreases during maturation of the sperm while the nuclear protein increases in basicity. By means of similar cytophotometric de-terminations of nuclear Feulgen/methyl green staining ratios on sections of guinea-pig testis we have obtained data in accord with those of Lison, also showing a substantial relative decrease in the basophilia of sperm DNA as compared to that of other nuclear types in the testis. While Lison postulates that the high arginine content of sperm protein is responsible for its ability to suppress the dye-binding capacity of DNA-phos-phate groups, the same cytochemical effect on DNA can apparently be produced in other systems by a very different mechanism: this is shown by the findings of Bloch and Godman (1956, J. Biophys. Biochem. Cytol. *1:* 531) which suggest that a partial staining inhibition of nuclear DNA in physiologically active somatic cells may be produced by its association with a non-basic protein fraction.

Reprinted from
Biochim. Bioph. Acta

Enzymic synthesis of deoxyribonucleic acid

We have reported[1] the conversion of ^{14}C-thymidine via a sequence of discrete enzymic steps to a product with the properties of DNA*.

$$\text{Thymidine} \xrightarrow{\text{ATP}} \text{T5P} \xrightarrow{\text{ATP}} \text{TTP} \xrightarrow{\text{ATP}} \text{"DNA"} \qquad (1)$$

The thymidine product is acid-insoluble, destroyed by DNAase, alkali-stable and resistant to RNAase. We have now extended these studies to include adenine, guanine and cytosine deoxynucleotides, and with partially purified enzymes from *E. coli* we have studied further the nature of the polymerization reaction.

^{32}P-labeled deoxynucleotides were prepared by enzymic digestion of DNA obtained from *E. coli* grown in a ^{32}P-containing medium; the nucleotides were then phosphorylated by a partially purified enzyme. The principal product of T5P phosphorylation was separated as a single component in an ion-exchange chromatogram and identified as TTP. The ratios of thymidine:acid-labile P:total P were 1.00:2.03:3.08. Enzymic formation of the di- and triphosphates of deoxyadenosine and the pyrimidine deoxyribonucleosides has been observed[2] and the presence of pyrimidine deoxyribonucleoside polyphosphates in thymus extracts has been reported[3].

Polymerization of TTP requires ATP, a heat-stable DNA fragment(s), provisionally regarded as a primer, and two enzyme fractions (called S and P; previously[1] called A and B, respectively) each of which has thus far been purified more than 100-fold (Table I). Preliminary studies suggest that TDP can replace TTP and has the same requirements for incorporation into DNA; a decision as to the more immediate precursor requires further purification of the system.

"Primer" for the *crude* enzyme fraction was obtained (1) by the action of crystalline pancreatic DNAase on *E. coli* DNA or (2) on thymus DNA, or (3) by an *E. coli* enzyme fraction (SP) acting on DNA contained in it. However, "primer" for the *purified* enzyme fraction was obtained only with method (3); the action of pancreatic DNAase on either *E. coli* or thymus DNA did not yield "primer". These findings imply the existence of an activity in the crude enzyme fraction responsible for the formation of active "primer". The chemical properties of the unpurified "primer" resemble those of a partial digest of DNA.

Utilization of the polyphosphates (presumably triphosphates) of adenine, guanine and cytosine deoxynucleosides for DNA synthesis occurs at rates approximately equal to those for TTP in crude enzyme fractions, but at appreciably slower rates with the enzyme purified for TTP polymerization (Table II). These changes in ratio suggest the presence of different enzymes for each of the deoxyribonucleoside triphosphates. Mixtures of these triphosphates, each tested at concentrations near enzyme saturation, gave additive or superadditive rates, further suggesting different enzymes for each of the substrates and a facilitation of polymerization by such mixtures.

Studies are in progress to define the mechanism of the polymerization reaction and the

---

* Abbreviations used are: DNA, deoxyribonucleic acid; ATP, adenosine triphosphate; T5P, thymidine-5'-phosphate; TDP, thymidine diphosphate; TTP, thymidine triphosphate; DNAase, deoxyribonuclease; RNAase, ribonuclease.

linkages and sequences in the DNA-like product formed. Further investigations with phage-infected *E. coli*[1] and studies with biologically active DNA may begin to clarify the question of how genetically specific DNA is assembled.

TABLE I

REQUIREMENTS OF THE PURIFIED SYSTEM

Extracts of *E. coli* B prepared by sonic disintegration were treated with streptomycin to yield a precipitate (fraction SP) and a supernatant fluid (fraction SS). Ammonium sulfate, gel and acid fractionation procedures applied to fractions SP and SS yielded fractions P and S, respectively. *E. coli* DNA was prepared by heating fraction SP (optical density at 260 mμ = 15) at 70° for 10 minutes. To produce "primer", 0.1 ml of *E. coli* DNA was combined with 40 γ of fraction SP; after 1 hour at 37° in the presence of $5 \cdot 10^{-3} M$ MgCl$_2$, the mixture was heated for 10 minutes at 80°. The complete system contained (in 0.3 ml) 0.014 μmole of TTP ($1.5 \cdot 10^6$ c.p.m./μmole), 0.1 μmole of ATP, 0.10 ml of "primer", 10 γ of fraction S, 1 γ of fraction P, 1 μmole of MgCl$_2$, and 20 μmoles of glycine buffer, pH 9.2. After incubation for 30 minutes at 37°, 0.05 ml of crude *E. coli* extract ("carrier") and 0.3 ml of 7% perchloric acid were added. The precipitate was washed, plated and its radioactivity measured.

	mμmoles DNA-P/hour
Complete system	1.48
No ATP	0.20
No "primer"	0.11
No enzyme fraction S	0.07
No enzyme fraction P	0.04

TABLE II

CONVERSION OF FOUR DEOXYNUCLEOSIDE TRIPHOSPHATES

The incubation mixtures and assays were as described in Table I except that (1) the concentrations of deoxynucleoside triphosphates were $1.5 \cdot 10^{-5} M$, and (2) the crude enzymes were 60 γ of fraction SP and 240 γ of fraction SS.

Triphosphates	Tested with crude enzymes	Tested with purified enzymes (for TTP)
	mμmoles DNA-P/hour	
Thymidine (T)	0.8	5.48
Deoxyguanosine (G)	0.6	0.98
Deoxycytidine (C)	0.8	1.44
Deoxyadenosine (A)	0.6	1.28
T + G	2.2	14.6
T + G + C	4.4	19.6
T + G + C + A	6.4	22.0[*]
T + G + C + A (no "primer")	2.0	0.28

[*] 65% conversion of substrate.

Fellowship support of I. R. LEHMAN by the American Cancer Society, of M. J. BESSMAN by the Public Health Service, and grants to A. KORNBERG by the Public Health Service and the National Science Foundation are gratefully acknowledged.

Department of Microbiology, Washington University School of Medicine,
St. Louis, Mo. (U.S.A.)

ARTHUR KORNBERG
I. R. LEHMAN
MAURICE J. BESSMAN
E. S. SIMMS

[1] A. KORNBERG, I. R. LEHMAN AND E. S. SIMMS, *Federation Proc.*, 15 (1956) 291.
[2] H. Z. SABLE, P. B. WILBER, A. E. COHEN AND M. R. KANE, *Biochim. Biophys. Acta*, 13 (1954) 156. L. I. HECHT, V. R. POTTER AND E. HERBERT, *ibid.*, 15 (1954) 134.
[3] R. L. POTTER AND S. SCHLESINGER, *J. Am. Chem. Soc.*, 77 (1955) 6714.

Received May 2nd, 1956

THE ORGANIZATION AND DUPLICATION OF GENETIC MATERIAL[1]

J. Herbert Taylor[2]

ONE of the well-known achievements of cytogenetics is the discovery that genetic material is organized into discrete units, the chromosomes. Although the number and size of these units vary greatly among the many species of organisms, their individuality and characteristic structure are among the most permanent features of a species. When genetic analysis is extended to micro-organisms and viruses where cytological evidence is still incomplete, the same principle applies. However, in spite of their individuality and characteristic structure, chromosomes are capable of breaking and rejoining with each other, not only at homologous loci, but presumably at any locus. Therefore, they must have some common structural feature. Whether this cytological similarity extends to the micro-organisms and viruses remains uncertain, but genetic analysis of recombination suggests that they too share some common structural features.

Since their discovery chromosomes have been recognized as rod-shaped bodies that typically appear at division stages. For more than twenty-five years, these rod-shaped bodies have been generally recognized to be formed by a helical coil of a much longer filament. The structure and the three-dimensional shape of this filament still remain in doubt in spite of the fact that it is frequently described as a string of chromomeres or a beaded filament. The cytologist's concept of this filament has often been that of a bundle of fibrils which are subdivided into the two chromatids at prophase. Evidence has been brought forward at various times to indicate that the chromatids are further subdivided into half-chromatids and sometimes into quarter-chromatids (see Ris, 1957, for a detailed presentation of this concept). On the other hand, the well-known fact that crossing-over regularly occurs at the chromatid level would tend to discount the validity of any functional subdivision beyond the level of the chromatid.

NEW APPROACHES IN CHROMOSOME ANALYSIS

In view of this perplexing situation, which has failed to yield to the methods available to cytogeneticists during the last twenty-five or thirty years, new methods of analysis are most welcome. There are several of these which I believe will give us a much clearer picture of the organization of genetic material within the next decade. The first break came with the discovery that DNA (deoxyribonucleic acid) was genetic material (Avery *et al.*, 1944). It is not necessary to recount for geneticists the developments that followed in that field. As a result of the renewed interest in DNA, biochemists and crystallographers have given us a picture of its structure.

[1]The original experiments reported are part of an investigation supported by grants from the Atomic Energy Commission, Contract AT(30–1) 1304, and the Higgins Fund of Columbia University. Technical assistance of Miss Dorothy Pfeffer is gratefully acknowledged.

[2]Department of Botany, Columbia University.

Proc. X Int. Cong. Genetics, Vol. I
PRINTED IN CANADA

SELECTED PAPERS ON MOLECULAR GENETICS

With this as a basis for a more refined type of genetic analysis (discussed by Benzer, 1957, and by Benzer, Demerec, and Levinthal in this symposium) and a more critical and careful analysis of aberrant genetic recombinations in tetrads, we have the beginnings of a new understanding of genetic fine structure that may extend from the phages to higher organisms. At the cytological level information from biochemistry and biophysics has provided us with a powerful new tool. The first step was the discovery that thymidine is a highly selective precursor for DNA (Reichard and Estborn, 1951; and Friedkin *et al.*, 1956). The next step was the demonstration that tritium would give excellent resolution in autoradiography because most of its soft radiation is stopped in the first micron of photographic emulsion applied to an object (Fitzgerald *et al.*, 1951). It remained then to label thymidine with tritium in a stable position at high specific activity and use it for tracing the behavior of DNA during chromosome duplication (Taylor, Woods, and Hughes. 1957; Taylor, 1958a, 1958b, 1958c). These experiments gave us for the first time a clear picture of the number of functional units or strands of a chromosome and the mode of segregation of these strands during duplication and the subsequent divisions.

AUTORADIOGRAPHIC STUDIES WITH THYMIDINE-H[3]

Chromosomes can be labelled with thymidine-H[3] only during the interphase when they are duplicating. Several hours are then required before the labeled chromosomes appear in division figures. In root cells of *Bellevalia* this period is about six to eight hours at 25° C. When they do appear, each of the two chromatids is labeled (Fig. 1) and furthermore, is equally labeled within the limits of error of the autoradiographic method (Taylor, 1958a).

Colchicine is a convenient tool for increasing the frequency with which the chromosomes may be separated and flattened for autoradiography. The spindle is destroyed and the two chromatids often remain united at the centromere for a longer period. However, they frequently spread far enough apart in squashes to allow good resolution of the label in each.

The equal distribution of the label at the first division after a single duplication in thymidine-H[3] tells us very little by itself. Each chromosome either could have divided and built a new half, or all the DNA could have been destroyed and replaced by new DNA. But at the next division, after one duplication free of the labeled precursors, the autoradiographs yielded the significant answer. The labeled chromosomes regularly produced one labeled chromatid and one completely free of label (Fig. 2). Since these labeled anaphase chromosomes, which had duplicated once in thymidine-H[3], conserved this DNA and passed it on to only one of their daughter chromosomes, the original unlabeled DNA must likewise have been conserved and passed on to the other daughter. Therefore, the chromosomes must have been composed of two sub-units of DNA. One was the original unlabeled unit inherited during duplication and the other was a new unit built when duplication occurred in thymidine-H[3].

Chromosomes, then, are composed of two and only two functional sub-units of DNA. These are conserved at each duplication with two new sub-units built, one for each chromatid. A chromatid at each division is one-half old and one-half new.

The second division was first studied by leaving the labeled cells in colchicine from just before the first division, that is, after eight hours in thymidine-H[3], until they reached a second division. Since the chromosomes from the first division were held in one cell under the action of colchicine, the second divisions could be recog-

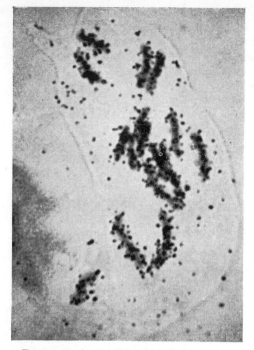 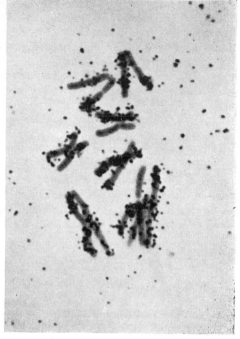

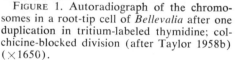

FIGURE 1. Autoradiograph of the chromosomes in a root-tip cell of *Bellevalia* after one duplication in tritium-labeled thymidine; colchicine-blocked division (after Taylor 1958b) (×1650).

FIGURE 2. Autoradiograph of a similar cell fixed after one duplication in tritium-labeled thymidine and one duplication in a medium free of labeled precursors; colchicine-blocked metaphase (after Taylor, 1958a) (×1650).

nized because the cells regularly contained double the usual number of chromosomes. In later experiments roots were grown for eight hours in thymidine-H^3, washed, and transferred to isotope-free solutions until some labeled chromosomes were estimated to have duplicated again. Colchicine was then added to accumulate division figures, some of which contained the labeled chromosomes. These cells regularly had chromosomes with one chromatid labeled and the other free of label (Fig. 2). However, a complication was noted in the very first cells examined. A chromatid frequently would be labeled for only a part of its length, and its sister would be labeled from the point where the labeling stopped to the end or to another point of exchange. With rare exceptions, which will be discussed later, each chromosome had the equivalent of a completely labeled chromatid and a completely unlabeled chromatid when account was taken of the exchanges.

Since chromosome duplication in these cells requires several hours, the question of the sequence of synthesis along a chromosome should be subject to investigation with the autoradiographic technique. The first labeled chromosomes to arrive at division after roots have been placed in thymidine-H^3 should have spent only a part of the replication cycle in contact with the isotope. Would they be labeled throughout their entire length with less radioactivity than those arriving at divisions a few hours later? Or might they be labeled only in the small regions that duplicated after thymidine-H^3 was available? Although more investigations are required, species appear to vary in this respect. In root cells of *Crepis capallaris* small regions appear labeled, and the regions are those adjacent to the centromeres. From this evidence chromosome duplication appears to begin at the ends of the arms and proceeds toward the centromere (Taylor, 1958c). A few groups of prophase chromosomes were found with a gradient of labeling from the ends toward the centromeres in all six chromosomes. Since the two arms of a chromosome were not necessarily equally labeled, they apparently began and finished duplication at different times. In *Vicia faba* a few cells were seen in which whole chromosomes, in a complement of labeled and partially labeled chromosomes, were without label (Woods, unpublished). On the other hand, chromosomes of *Bellevalia* are usually all labeled simultaneously along most of their length with only rare cells showing localized regions with little or no label when the remainder of the complement is labeled. Cells arriving at divisions a few hours later in both *Bellevalia* and *Crepis* have much more uniformly labeled chromosomes, which indicates that the differences in labeling are not due to intrinsic variations in DNA concentrations along the chromosomes.

AUTORADIOGRAPHIC STUDIES OF SISTER CHROMATID EXCHANGES

The experiments cited above show that a chromosome before duplication has two sub-units of DNA, one of which it contributes to each daughter chromatid at duplication. Are these sub-units separate structures, half-chromatids, or do they perhaps represent the two polynucleotide chains of DNA molecules with the structure and mode of replication proposed by Watson and Crick (1953)? Both DNA molecules and chromosomes have the duplex structure in common, but of course they are vastly different in size. The chromosome would more likely be an array of such molecules organized in a manner that would allow them to uncoil and separate at each duplication cycle.

The regular segregation of a new and old unit into each chromatid suggests that the units of DNA are not identical, and therefore might be complementary structures like the two chains of the DNA molecule, in which the original could act as the template for the synthesis of the new unit. At the suggestion of Dr. Max Delbrück advantage was taken of the sister-chromatid exchanges to get additional evidence on this point. In addition some evidence on the natural frequency of sister-chromatid exchanges during the mitotic cycle has been obtained.

However, a quantitative study of the exchanges is not easy. A cell with a few large, morphologically recognizable chromosomes was a primary requirement. *Bellevalia romana* ($2n = 8$) appeared to be the best material available. An additional advantage, not realized at the beginning, was the relatively more synchronous duplication of all chromosomes of *Bellevalia* compared to some other species. This reduces the number of unlabeled segments present in the first labeled chromosomes. These would be confusing in the analysis of exchanges. The exchanges had to be analyzed at the second division, after one duplication in the absence of labeled precursors. It would likewise be very important to have cells without a pool of labeled precursors remaining after the first duplication in thymidine-H³. Fortunately, the cells that we have studied do not accumulate a pool at the concentrations of thymidine used. However, there is still a chance of finding cells which had thymidine available during the last part of a duplication and which then passed through a division and began a second duplication before depletion of the labeled precursors. By leaving roots in thymidine only six hours and then transferring them to colchicine for about thirty-six hours at 25°C., this labeling during two duplications was almost completely avoided (see page 76 for exceptions). Under these experimental conditions, only rarely are cells, with sixteen c-metaphase or thirty-two c-anaphase chromosomes labeled, separated and flattened sufficiently for determining all the exchanges in any four chromosomes of one morphological type.

Figure 3 shows diagrammatically the sixteen c-metaphase chromosomes from one cell, the chromosomes of which duplicated with thymidine-H[3] available. At the first division after labeling, the anaphase was prevented, but the chromosomes finally separated and duplicated again. The autoradiograph was prepared at the time the cell had reached a second c-metaphase, with sixteen instead of eight chromosomes.

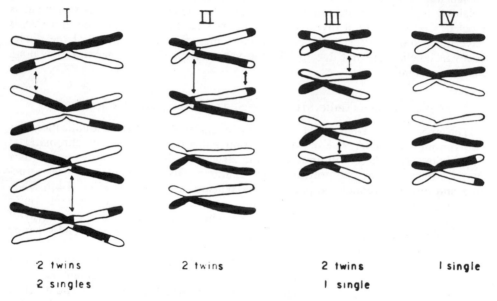

I   II   III   IV

2 twins   2 twins   2 twins   I single

2 singles   2 twins   I single

FIGURE 3. Diagrammatic sketch of the sixteen c-metaphase chromosomes at the second division after labeling with thymidine-H[3]. The dark regions represent labeled parts; the regions in outline are unlabeled (after Taylor, 1958a).

TWIN AND SINGLE EXCHANGES

One of the first characteristics of the exchanges noted is their tendency to occur in pairs, that is, twin exchanges. For example, in the four large chromosomes (Fig. 3), there are exchanges in the two upper chromosomes which are at the same locus in the left arms. Likewise, in the two lower chromosomes an exchange occurs in each just to the right of the centromere. Two other exchanges have no matching exchange at homologous positions. Chromosomes with twin exchanges must have descended from the same original labeled chromosome. Therefore, the exchanges result from some rearrangement of strands that occurred before the two chromosomes separated at the first c-anaphase. If the two strands of each chromatid underwent breakage and reunion as shown in the upper diagram of Figure 4, there would result either a bridge at the following anaphase or, if the two strands of a chromatid distal to an exchange could separate and segregate with a strand of the other chromatid, unlabeled segments at the first anaphase after labeling. Since neither of these results has been observed in cells allowed to complete duplication with thymidine-H[3]

available, the exchanges must involve both strands of each chromatid as shown in
the lower diagram of Figure 4. The half-exchanges should also result in chromosomes with both chromatids labeled distally to the point of exchange (upper diagram, Fig. 4). Since these are very rare, the half-exchanges, if they occur at all,
make no significant contribution to the frequency of sister-chromatid exchanges
observed.

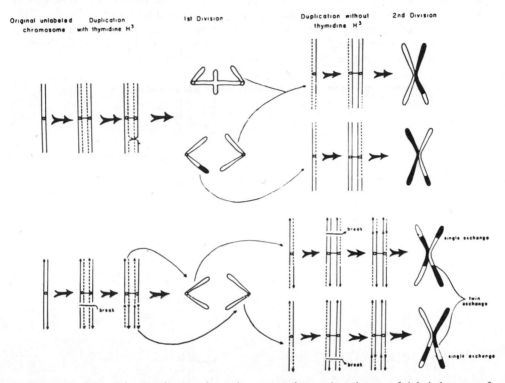

FIGURE 4. Schematic drawing to show the segregation and exchange of labeled parts of
chromosomes after one duplication in thymidine-H³. *Upper* diagram shows the results of
exchanges between two of the four DNA sub-units of sister chromatids. The *lower* diagram
shows the expected frequency of single and twin exchanges if a difference between the DNA
sub-units exists. The difference is represented by arrows. The dashed lines and the regions of
chromatids in outline represent labeled parts. Solid lines and regions in black represent unlabeled parts.

What would occur if the exchanges regularly involved all four strands of the two
chromatids? First, we must consider the situation in which the two strands of a
chromatid are different, as they would be if they represent complementary structures. The difference is represented for convenience by arrows to show opposite
directional sense although any structural difference that would limit rejoining to like
strands gives the same result (Fig. 4). The exchanges will produce no visible change
at the first division; each anaphase chromosome will be labeled along the entire
length. However, at the next division both chromosomes descended from such a
one, with exchange and rejoining limited to like strands, will have exchanges at the
same locus, that is, twin exchanges. In addition, any exchanges that occur after the
second duplication will yield single exchanges. If the frequency of exchanges is equal

in the two interphases, we predict a ratio of one twin pair of exchanges to each two singles.

On the other hand, if the four strands of sister chromatids are all alike and capable of reunion in a random fashion, quite a different ratio is predicted. The original exchange at the first interphase (Fig. 5) can result in four types of reunions. One will yield a twin at the second division, one will be undetected, and two will yield single exchanges. These exchanges plus an equivalent number of exchanges at the second interphase should produce a ratio of one twin pair to ten singles. This is the minimum ratio for, if there were no difference between the two strands of a chromatid, breaks in a single chromatid at any time before the second duplication with reunion after rotation of 180° would yield a single exchange.

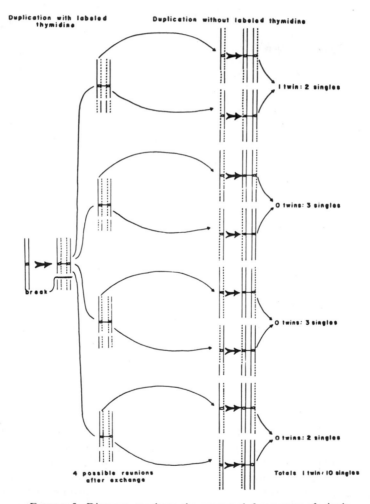

FIGURE 5. Diagram to show the expected frequency of single and twin exchanges if the two sub-units of each chromatid are alike and are capable of reunion at random. Dashed lines represent labeled parts. Exchanges following the second duplication are not shown in detail, but each chromosome is assumed to have one exchange at the second interphase after or during duplication.

FIRST EXPERIMENT ON EXCHANGES

In the first experiment, in which roots were placed in colchicine after six hours in thymidine-H³, the frequency of twins to singles was greater than two to one (Table I). Data are given only for the large chromosome 1. In seventy-two chromosomes examined, four in eighteen different cells, there were seventy-two exchanges, that is, thirty-six· twin pairs, plus fifteen single exchanges. This ratio does not fit either prediction. There are too many twins. However, if we assume that the hypothesis

TABLE I

FREQUENCY OF SINGLE AND TWIN EXCHANGES IN THE TETRAPLOID CHROMOSOME SETS OF *Bellevalia romana**

Experiment†	Number of chromosomes	Twin exchanges	Single exchanges	Frequency per chromosome	
				1st interphase	2nd interphase
1	72(18 cells)	36	15	1.00	0.21
2	112(28 cells)	39	36	0.70	0.28
3	96(24 cells)	14	26	0.29	0.27

*Data for only the largest chromosome are given.
†Data for the first two experiments are from Taylor (1958a and 1958b).

of a difference between the two strands is the correct one and that all twins were produced by exchange in the first interphase and all of the singles by exchanges in the second interphase, we can calculate the frequency of exchanges (Table I). The frequency for the large chromosome is one exchange per division cycle for the first interphase, but only 0.21 exchanges during the second interphase. Some factor appears to be increasing exchanges during the first interphase or reducing them during the second interphase. Two conditions are different. Colchicine is present during the duplication in the second interphase, but not during the first. The radioactivity per chromosome is also different; there should be about twice as much in the first interphase chromosomes as in the second interphase chromosomes.

SECOND AND THIRD EXPERIMENTS

The factor most easily varied is the colchicine; therefore, a second experiment was carried out with colchicine supplied simultaneously with the thymidine-H³. The ratio of twins to singles in this experiment was close to 1:1 (Table I). From this result colchicine appeared to be reducing the number of exchanges since the frequency of twins fell.

Since a lag might be occurring in the colchicine effect, a third experiment was set up in which the roots were pretreated two hours in colchicine before thymidine-H³ was added. The ratio of twins to singles was now very near the predicted 1:2 ratio. The frequency of exchanges in the first interphase had fallen to the level occurring in the second interphase, 0.29 and 0.27, respectively.

CONCLUSIONS

From these results several conclusions can be drawn. (1) The two strands of a chromosome or a chromatid are structurally different in a way that prevents reunion of unlike strands. (2) The frequency of exchanges is probably not significantly affected by the endogenous radiation from the tritium; otherwise the higher frequency of exchange in the first interphase should have persisted in all experiments (Taylor, 1958b). After incorporation of the thymidine-H^3 each chromosome consists of two chromatids and has two labeled strands while its descendants will have only one labeled strand at the second interphase, and therefore less endogenous radiation. (3) In the first experiment the frequency of exchanges without colchicine at first interphase is approximately the natural frequency of sister-chromatid exchanges. For the large chromosome of *Bellevalia*, this frequency is about one exchange per chromosome per division cycle. (4) The exchanges appear to occur during duplication since a two-hour pretreatment with colchicine was so much more effective in reducing the number of exchanges than simultaneous administration of colchicine and thymidine-H^3.

THE NATURE OF THE TWO DNA SUB-UNITS OF CHROMOSOMES

Since our primary concern is the organization of genetic material, let us consider the possible structural nature of the DNA sub-units of a chromosome. The autoradiographic results tell us that there are two of these units which are structurally different, as they would be if they were complementary. Are they the two polynucleotide chains of a Watson-Crick double helix? The evidence suggests that they are. However, for mechanical reasons chromosomes are likely to be arrays of molecules rather than single continuous double helices (Taylor, 1957). An experiment performed by Meselson and Stahl (1958) on the replication of DNA in *Escherichia coli* gives some very valuable clues. The treatment of cells with a detergent and centrifugation in a cesium chloride solution yields DNA particles or molecules of quite uniform size and a molecular weight of 7×10^6. This and other evidence on the disintegration of chromosomes by detergents and strong salt solutions suggests that the chromosome is an aggregate of DNA particles of rather uniform size. More important was the finding by Meselson and Stahl that the DNA of these particles behaved like that in the whole chromosome in its replication. By the use of N^{15} to produce density differences between new and original DNA, they showed with density gradient centrifugation experiments that each particle consisted of two physically continuous sub-units. After duplication each particle or molecule receives one of the sub-units which, like the sub-units in the chromosome, are conserved through many duplications. The genetic material, or chromosome if you like, is composed of a group of these particles. While Meselson and Stahl were not certain that the particles are double helices and that the DNA sub-units are single polynucleotide chains, we may at least use this concept as a working hypothesis.

The possibility has also been considered that the sub-units are double helices, that is, the DNA particles are two double helices associated into particles of 7×10^6 molecular weight. The DNA units of the chromosome, on the other hand, could not be two double helices for these would be identical rather than structurally different. The tentative conclusion then is that they are single polynucleotide chains. Could the chromosome be a bundle of these chains? The answer is that no satisfactory model has been built which will explain how the segregation of the complementary chains, new labeled and original unlabeled ones, could be regulated if the chromosomes were a bundle of DNA double helices.

Chromosome Models

Several attempts have been made to construct a workable model of a chromosome based on the structure of DNA and the information gained from autoradiography and genetic recombination (Schwartz, 1955; Bloch, 1955; Taylor, 1957, 1958d, 1958e; Freese, 1958). The first one proposed, which was based on the duplex structure of chromosomes, was the "centipede" model (Taylor, 1957, 1958e). It was proposed because it would explain how an array of DNA molecules could replicate according to the Watson-Crick scheme and segregate as shown by the experiments with thymidine-H³. More important, the model appeared to be testable by recombination studies. If correct, certain loci on different side-chains would show non-linear linkage relations.

In addition, recombination between homologous side-arms could occur without exchange of outside markers. This property might explain certain instances of negative interference.

A limited amount of testing has shown the model to be inadequate to explain the data (Freese, 1957; Levine, 1958; Pritchard, 1957). Although the "centipede" model cannot be ruled out, a better one has been suggested (Freese, 1958; Taylor,

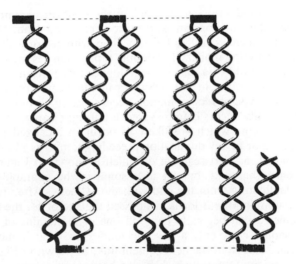

FIGURE 6. Diagrammatic representation of the linear model of a chromosome. The DNA particles (molecules) are linked together by protein links. The chromosome is assumed to be able to stretch out into a linear structure or to fold so that a ribbon is formed.

1958e). This duplex linear model retains many of the features of the "centipede" but places the DNA molecules in a linear array (Fig. 6). The DNA molecules are joined by blocks which we will assume are protein. The model is only a skeleton, of course, and does not account for the other proteins and the various longitudinal variations such as heterochromatin and constrictions. These features can be added when more information is available. For the present, the model can be used to explain duplication, segregation of DNA sub-units, the structural difference between the two sub-units, and genetic recombination.

First of all, the duplex linear model has the same advantages as the "centipede" in explaining the duplication and segregation of an array of DNA molecules. At one end each molecule is bonded to the linking blocks by only one polynucleotide chain and at the opposite end by the other chain. This allows the molecules to rotate freely in either direction around the single bonds and to unwind during replication. The linear model also has a difference between the two sub-units of DNA which becomes obvious when the linear structure is folded as in Figure 6. The group of polynucleotide chains attached along the upper side are complementary to those attached along the lower side. This feature was not incorporated into the "centipede" model. However, it could be added by having the DNA molecules attached by one polynucleotide chain to a single axis instead of a double one (Forro, 1957). The principal advantage of the linear model is that it appears to explain the recombination data better. In addition, it is adapted to the extreme elongation apparently necessary for the formation of lampbrush and salivary-gland chromosomes. Yet, it can fold into a ribbon, curl into a tube, and coil as explained by Taylor *et al.* (1957) and in more detail by Taylor (1958d, 1958e).

ABERRANT SEGREGATION IN TETRADS

Finally, the linear model appears to explain the data on recombination in complex loci. The tendency for aberrant segregation, resulting from "copy choice" or "double replication" mechanisms, to be associated with reciprocal-type recombination is also predicted by the model. By "double replication" is meant the copying of a portion of one chromatid of a pair of homologues twice in one duplication cycle, while the homologous region in the other chromatid is not replicated at all. We must assume that this type of recombination occurs during chromosome duplication. Since duplication usually occurs before zygotene-pairing (Taylor, 1957), we assume that these are rare events which are likely to occur in localized paired regions at premeiotic interphase or at any duplication preceding a mitosis (Pontecorvo, 1958).

In the linear model, a short segment of which is shown in Figure 7, duplication may proceed from either end, but let us assume in the example shown that the chromatids are duplicating from the end with the A locus. After replication of the DNA molecule containing the B locus has passed the site of b^1, the new polynucleotide chain for some reason begins to copy off one of the chains of the homologous chromatid. If it should copy only a few nucleotides, or what is more likely, to the end of the molecule, that is, to the next protein link, as shown in Figure 7B and then wind back on the original strand which it had been copying, the result would be a "hybrid" molecule in chromatid 2. This will yield at the next replication an $A+b^2C$ and an $A++C$ chromatid; therefore, after the first postmeiotic division, the ratio of spore or cell types would be one $++$: three $+2$: four $1+$. This type of double replication should be carefully looked for in tetrad analysis. Perhaps it is a very unlikely event.

If there is to be a 3:1 segregation in the tetrad, as has been frequently reported in recent years, following Lindegren's reports, (1953; 1956) on yeast, at least one of the original strands of one chromatid must break. If the break occurs as shown in Figures 7A and 7C with reunion of an original strand with the new left strand of chromatid 1, the left strand of chromatid 2 should now replicate off the right as it unwinds from the right strand of chromatid 3. The left strand of chromatid 3 should then continue its replication off the right strand. When both the left strand of chromatid 2 and the right strand of chromatid 4 arrive at the link distal to the B

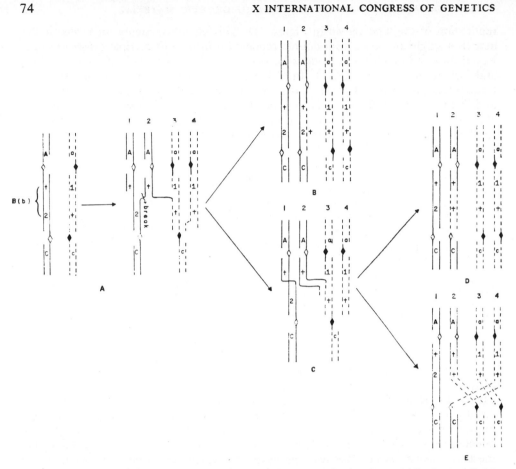

FIGURE 7. Diagram to show non-reciprocal (double replication) recombination and the predicted associated reciprocal exchanges between two duplicating chromatids. Only a very short segment of each is shown. This is the same model as that shown in Figure 6, but it is stretched out and the coiling of DNA molecules is eliminated for clarity.

locus, there may be a competition for attachment to the new connecting link. If chromatid 2 becomes attached, then chromatid 4 would have to make its attachment to the link associated with chromatid 1. The result would be a reciprocal exchange (crossover) associated with the non-reciprocal event (Fig. 7E), that is, a double replication or "conversion" as reported by Mitchell (1955a and 1955b) and Case and Giles (1958). However, if the right strand of chromatid 4 becomes attached at the new link associated with chromatid 3, the result will be a segment copied from the homologue and inserted into chromatid 2 (Fig. 7D). The first instance above might be recorded, in terms of conventional crossing-over, as a single crossover; the second instance as a double crossover, although actually the latter may be called a non-crossover. The ratio of the two events should be 1:1. The two chromatids would be $A++c$ and $A++C$. If a similar type of replication event proceeding from the other end produced a $++$ at the B locus, the chromatids would be $A++c$ and $a++c$. The triple crossover class $a+·+C$ would be produced very rarely when a crossover between the A and the B locus occurred in conjunction with double replication of the type shown in Figure 7D. This class is actually, in terms of the model, a single crossover with double replication instead of a triple crossover as it would appear in a classical model of crossing-over (see the data of Freese, 1957; and Levine and Curtiss, 1958). In Table II are listed the approximate expected frequencies of chromatids with $++$ at the B locus, if the map distance between A and B and between B and C is in each instance two crossover units. Reciprocal classes with b^1b^2 at the B locus are not shown since their frequencies should be similar. Class II and III events would be increased if "double replication" of the

TABLE II

PREDICTED RECOMBINATION OF OUTSIDE MARKERS COINCIDENT WITH DOUBLE REPLICATION AMONG PSEUDO-ALLELES AT THE B LOCUS*

Chromatid formulae after recombination		Percentages expected	Classification of crossovers	
			Duplex linear model	Conventional model
Class I	$A++c$	50.0	Single	Single
Class II	$A++C$	24.5	Non-crossover	Double
Class III	$a++c$	24.5	Non-crossover	Double
Class IV	$a++C$	1.0	Single	Triple

*Shown in Figure 7.

type shown in Figure 7B occurred, for these probably would not be associated with reciprocal exchanges. These two classes will be equal only if replication has an even chance of occurring from either end of the molecule containing the locus. The "centipede" model cannot have this property unless Forro's modification with only one polynucleotide chain attached to the axis is used. A ratio of one will not be affected very much by differences in map distances between the complex locus and the two outside markers because the associated reciprocal exchanges occur at the first link and should be much more frequent events than other non-associated reciprocal exchanges in the short region involved. The realization of this prediction should be one good test for the model; a confusing factor would be introduced, however, if replication proceeded in one direction more often than in the other. The rare Class IV events are subtracted from Class II and III, because they represent non-associated exchanges that occur in the chromatids that would have yielded Class II and Class III chromatids. The frequency of Class IV events should be equal to one-fourth the map distance between the outside markers if interference is not a factor. Some negative interference might be predicted, however, since the events are assumed to occur in regions with localized pairing; other recombination events might also have more chance of occurring in the same paired region than in other parts of the chromosome. Furthermore, if a reciprocal-type exchange occurred, the two chromatids would be held together and would be already paired at the beginning of zygotene. If one outside marker should occur on the same molecule, that is, between the B locus and a protein link, the frequency of single exchanges should then rise to near 75 per cent and one non-crossover class should be infrequent. In tetrad analysis the two loci should show "conversion" or double replication simultaneously.

When the data of Freese (1957) for *Neurospora* and those of Levine and Curtiss (1958) for a temperate phage are compared with those predicted by the model

(Table II), the fit is remarkably good. This agreement may be taken as evidence not only for the model, but for a similar organization of the genetic material in *Neurospora* and phage.

The above discussion leads to another question. What contribution would the reciprocal exchanges associated with "double replication" make to the total reciprocal-type recombinations? The answer undoubtedly varies with the organism. For the higher organism, the proportion would probably be small; reciprocal exchange of the conventional type may very well occur at a different time and by a different mechanism. In phage the only type of recombination may be the non-reciprocal "double replications" and the associated reciprocal exchanges.

Case and Giles (1958) report that typical reciprocal exchanges as well as non-reciprocal events occur between pseudo-alleles at the *pan* locus in *Neurospora*. If these pseudo-alleles are on one molecule, the possibility of reciprocal "copy-choice" events is presented. These require breaks of one original strand in each chromatid and would not represent double replication of one chromatid. They would add to the single crossover class, but should not affect the ratio of Class II and Class III chromatids. If one accepts the model, all reciprocal crossovers, besides such reciprocal copy-choice events, would be expected to occur at the protein links where there are single bonds. Likewise the sister-chromatid exchanges should occur at these loci. This would explain why conventional crossing-over always involves whole chromatids. It would also explain our failure to detect exchanges of only two of the four DNA sub-units in sister chromatids (Fig. 4).

RESERVATIONS AND UNCERTAINTIES

After using considerable space in speculations, intriguing though they may be for those who like puzzles, we will return to reality with a few comments on classical crossing-over. In the absence of data on exchange of tritium-labeled segments during meiosis, there is little if anything new to be added. However, it should be stated that speculations on various schemes of recombination should not ignore the accumulated evidence from classical cytogenetics that reciprocal exchanges between homologous chromatids occur after zygotene-pairing in meiosis. Although this may be more a statement of faith than of fact, the conventional type of crossover in higher organisms need not be associated with the replication process and may occur at a different time and by a mechanism different from that which is associated with aberrant segregation in tetrads.

We will end this paper with one other reservation. After presenting the evidence that the DNA units of chromatids are single polynucleotide chains, a short defense of the opposing view may be in order. Rare instances of chromosomes, at the second division after labeling, with both chromatids labeled for a part of their length have been observed (Taylor, 1958a; LaCour and Pelc, 1958). These could occur as pointed out above as a result of exchanges in which the DNA sub-units acted independently of each other, that is, exchanges between an original non-labeled sub-unit and a new labeled sub-unit of the sister chromatid. However, each of these events should yield a chromosome with no label in either chromatid at a similar locus (Fig. 4). These were not observed. Another possibility to explain their occurrence is that the cells had thymidine-H^3 available for one replication cycle and for a part of another, coupled with asynchronous initiation of synthesis in the various chromosomes. A third possibility is the occurrence of several sister-chromatid exchanges in an arm of a chromosome. Because of the limits of resolution both arms will appear nearly uniformly labeled. A fourth possibility related to the one above is that the observations are meaningless because they are based on rare instances in which the various artifacts inherent in the autoradiographic technique produced the result. A final possibility recently suggested by LaCour and Pelc (1958) is that the DNA sub-units are composed of two strands which occasionally fail to segregate together. Considerably more evidence is necessary before an interpretation of the apparent instances of aberrant segregation of DNA sub-units can be evaluated.

Nevertheless, the possibility that the DNA sub-units are multiple-stranded structures (Taylor *et al.*, 1957) should not be completely excluded for higher organisms. The lack of a satisfactory model of this nature to explain replication, the presence of non-reciprocal recombination, and the idea that mutations may result from changes in individual molecules of DNA are difficult obstacles for a multi-stranded model. On the other hand, an opinion expressed by Rhoades (1959), after discussing the mutations so far intensively studied in maize and other higher organisms, conveys an idea of the state of knowledge, or lack of it, concerning the mechanism of mutation in these groups. None of the mutations has been demonstrated by cytogenetic evidence to be an intragenic change. Surely such changes occur, he adds, but they remain to be demonstrated. Therefore, we may conclude this paper with an obvious inference, namely, that various kinds of changes other than alterations in nucleotide sequence in DNA molecules may be involved in the phenomena which are called mutations.

REFERENCES

AVERY, O. T., C. M. MACLEOD, and M. McCARTY. 1944. Studies on the chemical nature of the substance inducing transformation of pneumococcal types: Induction of transformation by a desoxyribonucleic acid fraction isolated from *Pneumococcus* Type III. J. Exp. M. *79*: 137–158.

BENZER, S. 1957. The elementary units of heredity. *In* Symposium on the Chemical Basis of Heredity, ed. W. D. McELROY and B. GLASS, pp. 70–93. Baltimore: Johns Hopkins Press.

BLOCH, D. 1955. A possible mechanism for the replication of the helical structure of deoxyribonucleic acid. Proc. Nat. Acad. Sc. U.S. *41*: 1058–1064.

CASE, M. E., and N. H. GILES. 1958. Evidence from tetrad analysis for both normal and aberrant recombination between allelic mutants in *Neurospora crassa*. Proc. Nat. Acad. Sc. U.S. *44*: 378–390.

FITZGERALD, P. J., M. L. EIDINOFF, J. E. KNOLL, and E. B. SIMMEL. 1951. Tritium in radioautography. Science *114*: 494–498.

FORRO, F. 1957. Personal communication, Biophysic Dept., Yale University.

FREESE, E. 1957. Ueber die Feinstruktur des Genoms im Bereich eines Pab locus von *Neurospora crassa*. Zeitsch. indukt. Abstam. vererb. *88*: 388–406.

———— 1958. The arrangement of DNA in the chromosome. Cold Spring Harbor Sympos. Quant. Biol. *23*: (in press).

FRIEDKIN, M., D. TILSON, and D. ROBERTS. 1956. Studies of deoxyribonucleic acid biosynthesis in embryonic tissues with thymidine-C14. J. Biol. Chem. *220*: 627–637.

LaCOUR, L. F., and S. R. PELC. 1958. The effect of colchicine on the utilization of labelled thymidine during chromosomal reproduction. Nature *182*: 506–508.

LEVINE, M., and R. CURTISS. 1958. A genetic test for side-chains in a phage chromosome. Nature *182*: 126–127.

LINDEGREN, C. C. 1953. Gene conversion in *Saccharomyces*. J. Genet. *51*: 625–637.

———— 1956. Stability of the gene. Science *124*: 26–27.

MESELSON, M., and F. W. STAHL. 1958. The replication of DNA in *Escherichia coli*. Proc. Nat. Acad. Sc. U.S. *44*: 671–682.

MITCHELL, M. B. 1955a. Aberrant recombination of pyridoxine mutants of *Neurospora*. Proc. Nat. Acad. Sc. U.S. *41*: 215–220.

———— 1955b. Further evidence of aberrant recombination in *Neurospora*. Proc. Nat. Acad. Sc. U.S. *41*: 935–937.

PRITCHARD, R. H. 1957. Personal communication, Genetics Dept., Univ. of Glasgow.

PONTECORVO, G. 1958. Trends in Genetic Analysis. New York: Columbia Univ. Press.

REICHARD, P., and B. ESTBORN. 1951. Utilization of desoxyribosides in the synthesis of polynucleotides. J. Biol. Chem. *188*: 839–846.

RHOADES, M. M. 1959. The Cytogenetics of Maize: Jessup Lectures at Columbia University for 1958. New York: Columbia Univ. Press (in press).

RIS, H. 1957. Chromosome structure. *In* Symposium on the Chemical Basis of Heredity, ed. W. D. McELROY and B. GLASS, pp. 23–69. Baltimore: Johns Hopkins Press.

SCHWARTZ, D. 1955. Studies on crossing over in maize and *Drosophila*. J. Cellul. Physiol. *45* (suppl. 2): 171–188.

TAYLOR, J. H. 1957. The time and mode of duplication of chromosomes. Am. Natur. *91*: 209–221.

———— 1958a. Sister chromatid exchanges in tritium-labeled chromosomes. Genetics *43*: 515–529.

———— 1958b. Further studies on the mechanism of chromosome duplication. Proc. Nat. Biophys. Conf. U.S. (in press).

———— 1958c. The mode of chromosome duplication in *Crepis capillaris*. Exp. Cell. Res. *15*: 350–357.

———— 1958d. Autoradiographic studies of the organization and mode of duplication of chromosomes. *In* Symposium on Molecular Biology, ed. R. E. ZIRKLE. Chicago: Univ. of Chicago Press.

———— 1958e. The duplication of chromosomes. Sc. Am. *198*(6): 36–42.

TAYLOR, J. H., P. S. WOODS, and W. L. HUGHES. 1957. The organization and duplication of chromosomes as revealed by autoradiographic studies using tritium-labeled thymidine. Proc. Nat. Acad. Sc. U.S. *43*: 122–128.

WATSON, J. D., and F. H. C. CRICK. 1953. Genetical implications of the structure of deoxyribonucleic acid. Nature *171*: 964–967.

Reprinted from the Proceedings of the NATIONAL ACADEMY OF SCIENCES
Vol. 44, No. 7, pp. 671–682. July, 1958.

THE REPLICATION OF DNA IN ESCHERICHIA COLI*

By MATTHEW MESELSON AND FRANKLIN W. STAHL

GATES AND CRELLIN LABORATORIES OF CHEMISTRY,† AND NORMAN W. CHURCH LABORATORY OF
CHEMICAL BIOLOGY, CALIFORNIA INSTITUTE OF TECHNOLOGY, PASADENA, CALIFORNIA

Communicated by Max Delbrück, May 14, 1958

Introduction.—Studies of bacterial transformation and bacteriaphage infection[1-5] strongly indicate that deoxyribonucleic acid (DNA) can carry and transmit hereditary information and can direct its own replication. Hypotheses for the mechanism of DNA replication differ in the predictions they make concerning the distribution among progeny molecules of atoms derived from parental molecules.[6]

Radioisotopic labels have been employed in experiments bearing on the distribution of parental atoms among progeny molecules in several organisms.[6-9] We anticipated that a label which imparts to the DNA molecule an increased density might permit an analysis of this distribution by sedimentation techniques. To this end, a method was developed for the detection of small density differences among

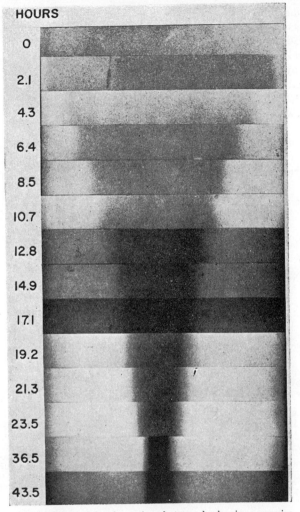

Fig. 1.—Ultraviolet absorption photographs showing successive stages in the banding of DNA from *E. coli*. An aliquot of bacterial lysate containing approximately 10^8 lysed cells was centrifuged at 31,410 rpm in a CsCl solution as described in the text. Distance from the axis of rotation increases toward the right. The number beside each photograph gives the time elapsed after reaching 31,410 rpm.

macromolecules.[10] By use of this method, we have observed the distribution of the heavy nitrogen isotope N^{15} among molecules of DNA following the transfer of a uniformly N^{15}-labeled, exponentially growing bacterial population to a growth medium containing the ordinary nitrogen isotope N^{14}.

Density-Gradient Centrifugation.—A small amount of DNA in a concentrated solution of cesium chloride is centrifuged until equilibrium is closely approached.

The opposing processes of sedimentation and diffusion have then produced a stable concentration gradient of the cesium chloride. The concentration and pressure gradients result in a continuous increase of density along the direction of centrifugal force. The macromolecules of DNA present in this density gradient are driven by the centrifugal field into the region where the solution density is equal to their own buoyant density.[11] This concentrating tendency is opposed by diffusion, with the result that at equilibrium a single species of DNA is distributed over a band whose width is inversely related to the molecular weight of that species (Fig. 1).

If several different density species of DNA are present, each will form a band at the position where the density of the CsCl solution is equal to the buoyant density of that species. In this way DNA labeled with heavy nitrogen (N^{15}) may be

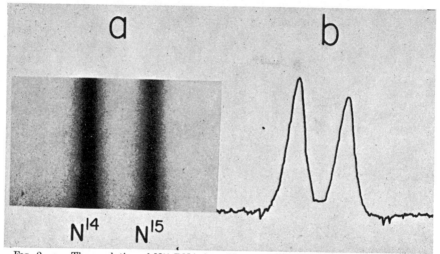

FIG. 2—*a:* The resolution of N^{14} DNA from N^{15} DNA by density-gradient centrifugation. A mixture of N^{14} and N^{15} bacterial lysates, each containing about 10^8 lysed cells, was centrifuged in CsCl solution as described in the text. The photograph was taken after 24 hours of centrifugation at 44,770 rpm. *b:* A microdensitometer tracing showing the DNA distribution in the region of the two bands of Fig. 2*a*. The separation between the peaks corresponds to a difference in buoyant density of 0.014 gm. cm.$^{-3}$

resolved from unlabeled DNA. Figure 2 shows the two bands formed as a result of centrifuging a mixture of approximately equal amounts of N^{14} and N^{15} *Escherichia coli* DNA.

In this paper reference will be made to the apparent molecular weight of DNA samples determined by means of density-gradient centrifugation. A discussion has been given[10] of the considerations upon which such determinations are based, as well as of several possible sources of error.[12]

Experimental.—*Escherichia coli* B was grown at 36° C. with aeration in a glucose salts medium containing ammonium chloride as the sole nitrogen source.[13] The growth of the bacterial population was followed by microscopic cell counts and by colony assays (Fig. 3).

Bacteria uniformly labeled with N^{15} were prepared by growing washed cells for

14 generations (to a titer of 2×10^8/ml) in medium containing 100 μg/ml of $N^{15}H_4Cl$ of 96.5 per cent isotopic purity.   An abrupt change to N^{14} medium was then accomplished by adding to the growing culture a tenfold excess of $N^{14}H_4Cl$, along with ribosides of adenine and uracil in experiment 1 and ribosides of adenine, guanine, uracil, and cytosine in experiment 2, to give a concentration of 10 μg/ml of each riboside.   During subsequent growth the bacterial titer was kept between

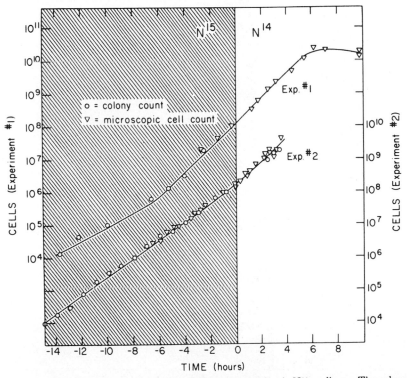

Fig. 3.—Growth of bacterial populations first in N^{15} and then in N^{14} medium.   The values on the ordinates give the actual titers of the cultures up to the time of addition of N^{14}. Thereafter, during the period when samples were being withdrawn for density-gradient centrifugation, the actual titer was kept between 1 and 2×10^8 by additions of fresh medium.   The values on the ordinates during this later period have been corrected for the withdrawals and additions.   During the period of sampling for density-gradient centrifugation, the generation time was 0.81 hours in Experiment 1 and 0.85 hours in Experiment 2.

1 and 2×10^8/ml by appropriate additions of fresh N^{14} medium containing ribosides.

Samples containing about 4×10^9 bacteria were withdrawn from the culture just before the addition of N^{14} and afterward at intervals for several generations. Each sample was immediately chilled and centrifuged in the cold for 5 minutes at 1,800$\times$ *g*.   After resuspension in 0.40 ml. of a cold solution 0.01 *M* in NaCl and 0.01 *M* in ethylenediaminetetra-acetate (EDTA) at pH 6, the cells were lysed by the addition of 0.10 ml. of 15 per cent sodium dodecyl sulfate and stored in the cold.

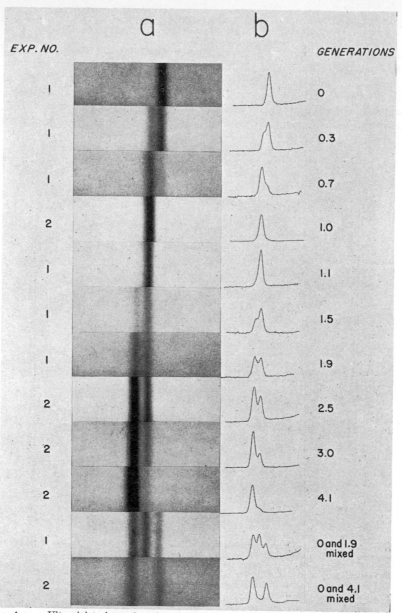

FIG. 4—*a:* Ultraviolet absorption photographs showing DNA bands resulting from density-gradient centrifugation of lysates of bacteria sampled at various times after the addition of an excess of N^{14} substrates to a growing N^{15}-labeled culture. Each photograph was taken after 20 hours of centrifugation at 44,770 rpm under the conditions described in the text. The density of the CsCl solution increases to the right. Regions of equal density occupy the same horizontal position on each photograph. The time of sampling is measured from the time of the addition of N^{14} in units of the generation time. The generation times for Experiments 1 and 2 were estimated from the measurements of bacterial growth presented in Fig. 3. *b:* Microdensitometer tracings of the DNA bands shown in the adjacent photographs. The microdensitometer pen displacement above the base line is directly proportional to the concentration of DNA. The degree of labeling of a species of DNA corresponds to the relative position of its band between the bands of fully labeled and unlabeled DNA shown in the lowermost frame, which serves as a density reference. A test of the conclusion that the DNA in the band of intermediate density is just half-labeled is provided by the frame showing the mixture of generations 0 and 1.9. When allowance is made for the relative amounts of DNA in the three peaks, the peak of intermediate density is found to be centered at 50 ± 2 per cent of the distance between the N^{14} and N^{15} peaks.

For density-gradient centrifugation, 0.010 ml. of the dodecyl sulfate lysate was added to 0.70 ml. of CsCl solution buffered at pH 8.5 with 0.01 M tris(hydroxy-methyl)aminomethane. The density of the resulting solution was 1.71 gm. cm.$^{-3}$ This was centrifuged at 140,000$\times$ g. (44,770 rpm) in a Spinco model E ultracentrifuge at 25° for 20 hours, at which time the DNA had essentially attained sedimentation equilibrium. Bands of DNA were then found in the region of density 1.71 gm. cm.$^{-3}$, well isolated from all other macromolecular components of the bacterial lysate. Ultraviolet absorption photographs taken during the course of each centrifugation were scanned with a recording microdensitometer (Fig. 4).

The buoyant density of a DNA molecule may be expected to vary directly with the fraction of N^{15} label it contains. The density gradient is constant in the region between fully labeled and unlabeled DNA bands. Therefore, the degree of labeling of a partially labeled species of DNA may be determined directly from the relative position of its band between the band of fully labeled DNA and the band of unlabeled DNA. The error in this procedure for the determination of the degree of labeling is estimated to be about 2 per cent.

Results.—Figure 4 shows the results of density-gradient centrifugation of lysates of bacteria sampled at various times after the addition of an excess of N^{14}-containing substrates to a growing N^{15}-labeled culture.

It may be seen in Figure 4 that, until one generation time has elapsed, half-labeled molecules accumulate, while fully labeled DNA is depleted. One generation time after the addition of N^{14}, these half-labeled or "hybrid" molecules alone are observed. Subsequently, only half-labeled DNA and completely unlabeled DNA are found. When two generation times have elapsed after the addition of N^{14}, half-labeled and unlabeled DNA are present in equal amounts.

Discussion.—These results permit the following conclusions to be drawn regarding DNA replication under the conditions of the present experiment.

1. *The nitrogen of a DNA molecule is divided equally between two subunits which remain intact through many generations.*

The observation that parental nitrogen is found only in half-labeled molecules at all times after the passage of one generation time demonstrates the existence in each DNA molecule of two subunits containing equal amounts of nitrogen. The finding that at the second generation half-labeled and unlabeled molecules are found in equal amounts shows that the number of surviving parental subunits is twice the number of parent molecules initially present. That is, the subunits are conserved.

2. *Following replication, each daughter molecule has received one parental subunit.*

The finding that all DNA molecules are half-labeled one generation time after the addition of N^{14} shows that each daughter molecule receives one parental subunit.[14] If the parental subunits had segregated in any other way among the daughter molecules, there would have been found at the first generation some fully labeled and some unlabeled DNA molecules, representing those daughters which received two or no parental subunits, respectively.

3. *The replicative act results in a molecular doubling.*

This statement is a corollary of conclusions 1 and 2 above, according to which each parent molecule passes on two subunits to progeny molecules and each progeny molecule receives just one parental subunit.   It follows that each single molecular reproductive act results in a doubling of the number of molecules entering into that act.

The above conclusions are represented schematically in Figure 5.

The Watson-Crick Model.—A molecular structure for DNA has been proposed by Watson and Crick.[15] It has undergone preliminary refinement[16] without alteration of its main features and is supported by physical and chemical studies.[17] The structure consists of two polynucleotide chains wound helically about a common axis.   The nitrogen base (adenine, guanine, thymine, or cytosine) at each level

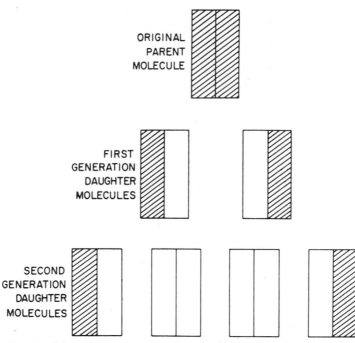

ORIGINAL PARENT MOLECULE

FIRST GENERATION DAUGHTER MOLECULES

SECOND GENERATION DAUGHTER MOLECULES

Fig. 5.—Schematic representation of the conclusions drawn in the text from the data presented in Fig. 4.   The nitrogen of each DNA molecule is divided equally between two subunits.   Following duplication, each daughter molecule receives one of these.   The subunits are conserved through successive duplications.

on one chain is hydrogen-bonded to the base at the same level on the other chain. Structural requirements allow the occurrence of only the hydrogen-bonded base pairs adenine-thymine and guanine-cytosine, resulting in a detailed complementariness between the two chains.   This suggested to Watson and Crick[18] a definite and structurally plausible hypothesis for the duplication of the DNA molecule. According to this idea, the two chains separate, exposing the hydrogen-bonding sites of the bases.   Then, in accord with the base-pairing restrictions, each chain serves as a template for the synthesis of its complement.   Accordingly, each daughter molecule contains one of the parental chains paired with a newly synthesized chain (Fig. 6).

The results of the present experiment are in exact accord with the expectations of the Watson-Crick model for DNA duplication. However, it must be emphasized that it has not been shown that the molecular subunits found in the present experiment are single polynucleotide chains or even that the DNA molecules studied here correspond to single DNA molecules possessing the structure proposed by Watson and Crick. However, some information has been obtained about the molecules and their subunits; it is summarized below.

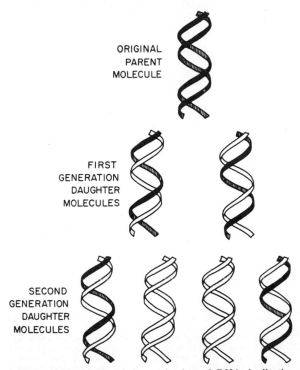

ORIGINAL
PARENT
MOLECULE

FIRST
GENERATION
DAUGHTER
MOLECULES

SECOND
GENERATION
DAUGHTER
MOLECULES

FIG. 6.—Illustration of the mechanism of DNA duplication proposed by Watson and Crick. Each daughter molecule contains one of the parental chains (*black*) paired with one new chain (*white*). Upon continued duplication, the two original parent chains remain intact, so that there will always be found two molecules each with one parental chain.

The DNA molecules derived from *E. coli* by detergent-induced lysis have a buoyant density in CsCl of 1.71 gm. cm.$^{-3}$, in the region of densities found for T2 and T4 bacteriophage DNA, and for purified calf-thymus and salmon-sperm DNA. A highly viscous and elastic solution of N^{14} DNA was prepared from a dodecyl sulfate lysate of *E. coli* by the method of Simmons[19] followed by deproteinization with chloroform. Further purification was accomplished by two cycles of preparative density-gradient centrifugation in CsCl solution. This purified bacterial DNA was found to have the same buoyant density and apparent molecular weight, 7×10^6, as the DNA of the whole bacterial lysates (Figs. 7, 8).

Heat Denaturation.—It has been found that DNA from *E. coli* differs importantly from purified salmon-sperm DNA in its behavior upon heat denaturation.

Exposure to elevated temperatures is known to bring about an abrupt collapse of the relatively rigid and extended native DNA molecule and to make available for acid-base titration a large fraction of the functional groups presumed to be blocked by hydrogen-bond formation in the native structure.[19, 20, 21, 22] Rice and Doty[22] have reported that this collapse is not accompanied by a reduction in molecular weight as determined from light-scattering. These findings are corroborated by density-gradient centrifugation of salmon-sperm DNA.[23] When this material is

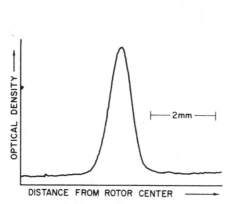

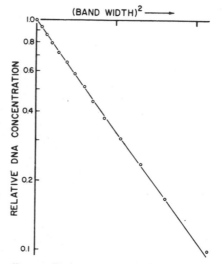

Fig. 7.—Microdensitometer tracing of an ultraviolet absorption photograph showing the optical density in the region of a band of N^{14} *E. coli* DNA at equilibrium. About 2 μg. of DNA purified as described in the text was centrifuged at 31,410 rpm at 25° in 7.75 molal CsCl at pH 8.4. The density gradient is essentially constant over the region of the band and is 0.057 gm./cm.[4] The position of the maximum indicates a buoyant density of 1.71 gm. cm.[-3] In this tracing the optical density above the base line is directly proportional to the concentration of DNA in the rotating centrifuge cell. The concentration of DNA at the maximum is about 50 μg./ml.

Fig. 8.—The square of the width of the band of Fig. 7 plotted against the logarithm of the relative concentration of DNA. The divisions along the abscissa set off intervals of 1 mm.[2] In the absence of density heterogeneity, the slope at any point of such a plot is directly proportional to the weight average molecular weight of the DNA located at the corresponding position in the band. Linearity of this plot indicates monodispersity of the banded DNA. The value of the the slope corresponds to an apparent molecular weight for the Cs·DNA salt of 9.4 × 10⁶, corresponding to a molecular weight of 7.1 × 10⁶ for the sodium salt.

kept at 100° for 30 minutes either under the conditions employed by Rice and Doty or in the CsCl centrifuging medium, there results a density increase of 0.014 gm. cm.[-3] with no change in apparent molecular weight. The same results are obtained if the salmon-sperm DNA is pre-treated at pH 6 with EDTA and sodium dodecyl sulfate. Along with the density increase, heating brings about a sharp reduction in the time required for band formation in the CsCl gradient. In the absence of an increase in molecular weight, the decrease in banding time must be ascribed[10] to an increase in the diffusion coefficient, indicating an extensive collapse of the native structure.

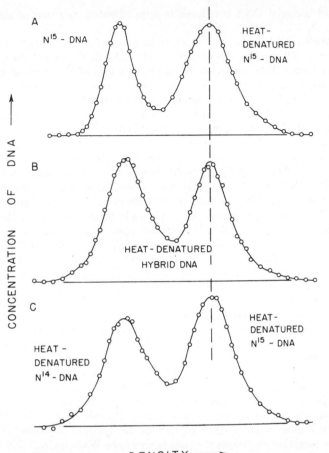

FIG. 9.—The dissociation of the subunits of *E. coli* DNA upon heat denaturation. Each smooth curve connects points obtained by micro-densitometry of an ultraviolet absorption photograph taken after 20 hours of centrifugation in CsCl solution at 44,770 rpm. The baseline density has been removed by subtraction. *A:* A mixture of heated and unheated N¹⁵ bacterial lysates. Heated lysate alone gives one band in the position indicated. Unheated lysate was added to this experiment for comparison. Heating has brought about a density increase of 0.016 gm. cm. $^{-3}$ and a reduction of about half in the apparent molecular weight of the DNA. *B:* Heated lysate of N¹⁵ bacteria grown for one generation in N¹⁴ growth medium. Before heat denaturation, the hybrid DNA contained in this lysate forms only one band, as may be seen in Fig. 4. *C:* A mixture of heated N¹⁴ and heated N¹⁵ bacterial lysates. The density difference is 0.015 gm. cm. ^{3}

The decrease in banding time and a density increase close to that found upon heating salmon-sperm DNA are observed (Fig. 9, *A*) when a bacterial lysate containing uniformly labeled N¹⁵ or N¹⁴ *E. coli* DNA is kept at 100° C. for 30 minutes in the CsCl centrifuging medium; but the apparent molecular weight of the heated bacterial DNA is reduced to approximately half that of the unheated material.

Half-labeled DNA contained in a detergent lysate of N^{15} *E. coli* cells grown for one generation in N^{14} medium was heated at 100° C. for 30 minutes in the CsCl centrifuging medium. This treatment results in the loss of the original half-labeled material and in the appearance in equal amounts of two new density species, each with approximately half the initial apparent molecular weight (Fig. 9, *B*). The density difference between the two species is 0.015 gm. cm.$^{-3}$, close to the increment produced by the N^{15} labeling of the unheated DNA.

This behavior suggests that heating the hybrid molecule brings about the dissociation of the N^{15}-containing subunit from the N^{14} subunit. This possibility was tested by a density-gradient examination of a mixture of heated N^{15} DNA and heated N^{14} DNA (Fig. 9, *C*). The close resemblance between the products of heating hybrid DNA (Fig. 9 *B*) and the mixture of products obtained from heating N^{14} and N^{15} DNA separately (Fig. 9, *C*) leads to the conclusion that the two molecular subunits have indeed dissociated upon heating. Since the apparent molecular weight of the subunits so obtained is found to be close to half that of the intact molecule, it may be further concluded that the subunits of the DNA molecule which are conserved at duplication are single, continuous structures. The scheme for DNA duplication proposed by Delbrück[24] is thereby ruled out.

To recapitulate, both salmon-sperm and *E. coli* DNA heated under similar conditions collapse and undergo a similar density increase, but the salmon DNA retains its initial molecular weight, while the bacterial DNA dissociates into the two subunits which are conserved during duplication. These findings allow two different interpretations. On the one hand, if we assume that salmon DNA contains subunits analogous to those found in *E. coli* DNA, then we must suppose that the subunits of salmon DNA are bound together more tightly than those of the bacterial DNA. On the other hand, if we assume that the molecules of salmon DNA do not contain these subunits, then we must concede that the bacterial DNA molecule is a more complex structure than is the molecule of salmon DNA. The latter interpretation challenges the sufficiency of the Watson-Crick DNA model to explain the observed distribution of parental nitrogen atoms among progeny molecules.

Conclusion.—The structure for DNA proposed by Watson and Crick brought forth a number of proposals as to how such a molecule might replicate. These proposals[6] make specific predictions concerning the distribution of parental atoms among progeny molecules. The results presented here give a detailed answer to the question of this distribution and simultaneously direct our attention to other problems whose solution must be the next step in progress toward a complete understanding of the molecular basis of DNA duplication. What are the molecular structures of the subunits of *E. coli* DNA which are passed on intact to each daughter molecule? What is the relationship of these subunits to each other in a DNA molecule? What is the mechanism of the synthesis and dissociation of the subunits in vivo?

Summary.—By means of density-gradient centrifugation, we have observed the distribution of N^{15} among molecules of bacterial DNA following the transfer of a uniformly N^{15}-substituted exponentially growing *E. coli* population to N^{14} medium.

We find that the nitrogen of a DNA molecule is divided equally between two physically continuous subunits; that, following duplication, each daughter molecule receives one of these; and that the subunits are conserved through many duplications.

* Aided by grants from the National Foundation for Infantile Paralysis and the National Institutes of Health.

† Contribution No. 2344.

[1] R. D. Hotchkiss, in *The Nucleic Acids*, ed. E. Chargaff and J. N. Davidson (New York: Academic Press, 1955), p. 435; and in *Enzymes: Units of Biological Structure and Function*, ed. O. H. Gaebler (New York: Academic Press, 1956), p. 119.

[2] S. H. Goodgal and R. M. Herriott, in *The Chemical Basis of Heredity*, ed. W. D. McElroy and B. Glass (Baltimore: Johns Hopkins Press, 1957), p. 336.

[3] S. Zamenhof, in *The Chemical Basis of Heredity*, ed. W. D. McElroy and B. Glass (Baltimore: Johns Hopkins Press, 1957), p. 351.

[4] A. D. Hershey and M. Chase, *J. Gen. Physiol.*, **36**, 39, 1952.

[5] A. D. Hershey, *Virology*, **1**, 108, 1955; **4**, 237, 1957.

[6] M. Delbrück and G. S. Stent, in *The Chemical Basis of Heredity*, ed. W. D. McElroy and B. Glass (Baltimore: Johns Hopkins Press, 1957), p. 699.

[7] C. Levinthal, these Proceedings, **42**, 394, 1956.

[8] J. H. Taylor, P. S. Woods, and W. L. Huges, these Proceedings, **43**, 122, 1957.

[9] R. B. Painter, F. Forro, Jr., and W. L. Hughes, *Nature*, **181**, 328, 1958.

[10] M. S. Meselson, F. W. Stahl, and J. Vinograd, these Proceedings, **43**, 581, 1957.

[11] The buoyant density of a molecule is the density of the solution at the position in the centrifuge cell where the sum of the forces acting on the molecule is zero.

[12] Our attention has been called by Professor H. K. Schachman to a source of error in apparent molecular weights determined by density-gradient centrifugation which was not discussed by Meselson, Stahl, and Vinograd. In evaluating the dependence of the free energy of the DNA component upon the concentration of CsCl, the effect of solvation was neglected. It can be shown that solvation may introduce an error into the apparent molecular weight if either CsCl or water is bound preferentially. A method for estimating the error due to such selective solvation will be presented elsewhere.

[13] In addition to NH_4Cl, this medium consists of 0.049 M Na_2HPO_4, 0.022 M KH_2PO_4, 0.05 M NaCl, 0.01 M glucose, 10^{-3} M $MgSO_4$, and 3×10^{-6} M $FeCl_3$.

[14] This result also shows that the generation time is very nearly the same for all DNA molecules in the population. This raises the questions of whether in any one nucleus all DNA molecules are controlled by the same clock and, if so, whether this clock regulates nuclear and cellular division as well.

[15] F. H. C. Crick and J. D. Watson, *Proc. Roy. Soc. London, A*, **223**, 80, 1954.

[16] R. Langridge, W. E. Seeds, H. R. Wilson, C. W. Hooper, M. H. F. Wilkins, and L. D. Hamilton, *J. Biophys. and Biochem. Cytol.*, **3**, 767, 1957.

[17] For reviews see D. O. Jordan, in *The Nucleic Acids*, ed. E. Chargaff and J. D. Davidson (New York: Academic Press, 1955), **1**, 447; and F. H. C. Crick, in *The Chemical Basis of Heredity*, ed. W. D. McElroy and B. Glass (Baltimore: Johns Hopkins Press, 1957), p. 532.

[18] J. D. Watson and F. H. C. Crick, *Nature*, **171**, 964, 1953.

[19] C. E. Hall and M. Litt, *J. Biophys. and Biochem. Cytol.*, **4**, 1, 1958.

[20] R. Thomas, *Biochim. et Biophys. Acta*, **14**, 231, 1954.

[21] P. D. Lawley, *Biochim. et Biophys. Acta*, **21**, 481, 1956.

[22] S. A. Rice and P. Doty, *J. Am. Chem. Soc.*, **79**, 3937, 1957.

[23] Kindly supplied by Dr. Michael Litt. The preparation of this DNA is described by Hall and Litt (*J. Biophys. and Biochem Cytol.*, **4**, 1, 1958).

[24] M. Delbrück, these Proceedings, **40**, 783, 1955.

III. DNA STRUCTURE AND REPLICATION

Reprinted from Science, May 20, 1960, Vol. 131, No. 3412, pages 1503-1508

Biologic Synthesis of Deoxyribonucleic Acid

An isolated enzyme catalyzes synthesis of this nucleic acid in response to directions from pre-existing DNA.

Arthur Kornberg

The knowledge drawn in recent years from studies of bacterial transformation (1) and viral infection of bacterial cells (2), combined with other evidence (3), has just about convinced most of us that deoxyribonucleic acid (DNA) is the genetic substance. We shall assume then that it is DNA which not only directs the synthesis of the proteins and the development of the cell but which must also be the substance which is copied so as to provide for a similar development of the progeny of that cell for many generations. Deoxyribonucleic acid, like a tape recording, carries a message in which there are specific instructions for a job to be done. Also, exact copies can be made from it, as from a tape recording, so that this information can be used again and elsewhere in time and space.

Are these two functions, the expression of the code (protein synthesis) and the copying of the code (preservation of the race), closely integrated or are they separable? What we have learned from our studies over the past 5 years is that the replication of DNA can be examined and at least partially understood at the enzymatic level even though the secret of how DNA directs protein synthesis is still locked in the cell.

Structure

First I should like to review very briefly some aspects of DNA structure which are essential for this discussion. Analysis of the composition of samples of DNA from a great variety of sources, and by many investigators (4), has revealed the remarkable fact that the purine content always equals the pyri-midine content. Among the purines, the adenine content may differ considerably from the guanine, and among the pyrimidines, the thymine from the cytosine. However, there is an equivalence of the bases with an amino group in the 6-position of the ring to the bases with a keto group in the 6-position. These facts were interpreted by Watson and Crick (5) in their masterful hypothesis of the structure of DNA. As shown in Fig. 1, they proposed in connection with their double-stranded model for DNA, discussed below, that the 6-amino group of adenine is linked by hydrogen bonds to the 6-keto group of thymine and that in a like manner guanine is hydrogen-bonded to cytosine, thus accounting for the equivalence of the purines to the pyrimidines.

On the basis of these considerations and the results of x-ray crystallographic measurements by Wilkins and his associates (6), Watson and Crick proposed a structure for DNA in which two long strands are wound about each other in a helical manner. Figure 2 is a diagrammatic representation of a fragment of a DNA chain about 10 nucleotide units long. According to physical measurements, DNA chains are, on the average, 10,000 units long. We see here the deoxypentose rings linked by phosphate residues to form the backbone of the chain; the purine and pyrimidine rings are the planar structures emerging at right angles from the main axis of the chain. Figure 3 is a more detailed molecular model (7) and gives a better idea of the packing of the atoms in the structure. The purine and pyrimidine bases of one chain are bonded to the pyrimidine and purine bases of the complementary chain by the hydrogen bonds described in Fig. 1.

The x-ray measurements have indicated that the space between the opposing chains in the model agrees with the calculated value for the hydrogen-bond linkage of a purine to a pyrimidine; it is too small for two purines and too large for two pyrimidines. Most rewarding from the biological point of view, the structure provides a useful model to explain how cellular replication of DNA may come about. For, if you imagine that these two chains separate and that a new chain is formed complementary to each of them, the result will be two pairs of strands, each pair identical to the original parent duplex and each member of the pair identical to the other.

Enzymatic Approach to Replication

Although we have in the Watson and Crick proposal a mechanical model of replication, we may at this point pose the question: What is the chemical mechanism by which this super molecule is built up in the cell? Some 60 years ago the alcoholic fermentation of sugar by a yeast cell was a "vital" process inseparable from the living cell, but through the Buchner discovery of fermentation in extracts and the march of enzymology during the first half of this century, we understand fermentation by yeast as a (now familiar) sequence of integrated chemical reactions.

Five years ago the synthesis of DNA was also regarded as a "vital" process. Some people considered it useful for biochemists to examine the combustion chambers of the cell, but tampering with the very genetic apparatus itself would surely produce nothing but disorder. These gloomy predictions were not justified then, nor are similar pessimistic attitudes justified now with regard to the problems of cellular structure and specialized function which face us. High adventures in enzymology lie ahead, and many of the explorers will come from the training fields of carbohydrate, fat, amino acid, and nucleic acid enzymology.

I feel now, as we did then, that for an effective approach to the problem of nucleic acid biosynthesis it is essential

The author is professor and executive head of the department of biochemistry of Stanford University School of Medicine, Stanford, California. He was joint winner, with Severo Ochoa, of the Nobel prize in medicine and physiology for 1959. This article is adapted from his Nobel lecture, delivered in Stockholm, Sweden, 11 December 1959. It is published with the permission of the Nobel Foundation.

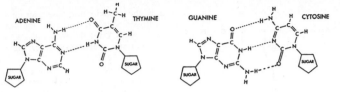

Fig. 1. Hydrogen bonding of bases.

to understand the biosynthesis of the simple nucleotides and the coenzymes and to have these concepts and methodology well in hand. It was from these studies that we developed the conviction that an activated nucleoside 5'-phosphate is the basic biosynthetic building block of the nucleic acids (8). You will recall that the main pathways of purine and pyrimidine biosynthesis all lead to the nucleoside 5'-phosphate (8); they do not usually include the free bases or nucleosides, except as salvage mechanisms. While the 2' and 3' isomers of the nucleotides are known, they probably arise mainly from certain types of enzymatic degradation of the nucleic acids. You will also recall from the biosynthesis of coenzymes (9), the simplest of the nucleotide condensation products, that it is adenosine triphosphate (ATP) which condenses with nicotinamide mononucleotide to form diphosphopyridine nucleotide, with riboflavin phosphate to form flavine adenine dinucleotide (FAD), with pantetheine phosphate to form the precursor of coenzyme A, and so forth. This pattern has been amplified by the discovery of identical mechanisms for the activation of fatty acids and amino acids, and it has been demonstrated further that uridine, cytidine, and guanosine coenzymes are likewise formed from the respective triphosphates of these nucleosides.

This mechanism (Fig. 4), in which a nucleophilic attack (10) on the pyrophosphate-activated adenyl group by a nucleoside monophosphate leads to the formation of a coenzyme, was adopted as a working hypothesis for studying the synthesis of a DNA chain. As illustrated in Fig. 5, it was postulated that the basic building block is a deoxynucleoside 5'-triphosphate which is attacked by the 3'-hydroxyl group at the growing end of a polydeoxynucleotide chain; inorganic pyrophosphate is eliminated, and the chain is lengthened by one unit. The results of our studies of DNA synthesis, as is shown below, are in keeping with this type of reaction.

Properties of the Enzyme

First let us consider the enzyme and comment on the way in which it was discovered (8, 11). Mixing the triphosphates of the four deoxynucleosides which commonly occur in DNA with an extract of thymus or of bone marrow or of Escherichia coli would not be expected to lead to the net synthesis of DNA. Instead, as might be expected, the destruction of DNA by the extracts of such cells and tissues was by far the predominant process, and one had to resort to more subtle devices to detect such a biosynthetic reaction. We used a C14-labeled substrate of high specific radioactivity and incubated it with adenosine triphos-

phate and extracts of *Escherichia coli*, an organism which reproduces itself every 20 minutes. The first positive results represented the conversion of only a very small fraction of the acid-soluble substrate into an acid-insoluble fraction (50 or so counts out of a million added). While this represented only a few micromicromoles of reaction, it was something. Through this tiny crack we tried to drive a wedge, and the hammer was enzyme purification (12).

This has been and still is a major preoccupation. Our best preparations are several thousand-fold enriched with respect to protein over the crude extracts, but there are still contaminating quantities of one or more of the many varieties of nuclease and diesterase present in the E. coli cell. The occurrence of what appears to be a similar DNA-synthesizing system in animal cells as well as in other bacterial species has been observed (13). We must wait

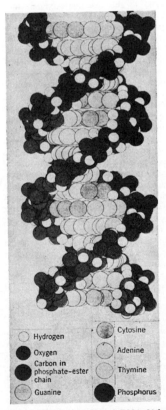

⦾ Hydrogen	◉ Cytosine
● Oxygen	○ Adenine
● Carbon in phosphate–ester chain	○ Thymine
○ Guanine	● Phosphorus

Fig. 3. Molecular model of DNA [After M. Feughelman *et al.* (7)]

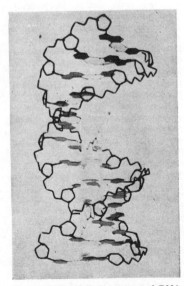

Fig. 2. Double helical structure of DNA (Watson and Crick model).

for purification of the enzymes from these sources in order to make valid comparisons with the *E. coli* system.

The requirements for net synthesis of DNA with the purified *E. coli* enzyme (*14*) are shown in the equation in Fig. 6. All four of the deoxynucleotides which form the adenine-thymine and guanine-cytosine couples must be present. The substrates must be the tri- and not the diphosphates, and only the deoxy sugar compounds are active. Deoxyribonucleic acid, which must be present, may be obtained from animal, plant, bacterial, or viral sources, and the best indications are that all these DNA samples serve equally well in DNA synthesis provided their molecular weight is high. The product, which I discuss below in further detail, accumulates until one of the substrates is exhausted and may be 20 or more times greater in amount than the DNA added. and thus is composed to the extent of 95 percent or more of the substrates added to the reaction mixture. Inorganic pyrophosphate is released in quantities equimolar to the deoxynucleotides converted to DNA.

Should one of these substrates be omitted, the extent of the reaction is diminished by a factor of more than 10^4, and special methods are then required to detect it. It turns out that when one of the deoxynucleotide substrates is lacking, an extremely small yet significant quantity of nucleotide is linked to the DNA primer. My co-workers and I have described this so-called "limited reaction" (*15*) and have shown that under these circumstances a few deoxynucleotides are added to the nucleoside ends of some of the DNA chains but that further synthesis is blocked for lack of the missing nucleotide. Current studies suggest that this limited reaction represents the repair of the shorter strand of a double helix in which the strands are of unequal length, and that the reaction is governed by the hydrogen-bonding of adenine to thymine and of guanine to cytosine.

When all four triphosphates are present, but when DNA is omitted, no reaction takes place at all. What is the basis for this requirement? Does the DNA function as a primer in the manner of glycogen, or does it function as a template in directing the synthesis of exact copies of itself? We have good reason to believe that it is the latter, and as the central and restricted theme of this article, I should like to emphasize that

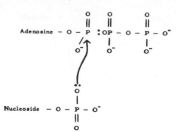

Fig. 4. Nucleophilic attack of a nucleoside monophosphate on ATP.

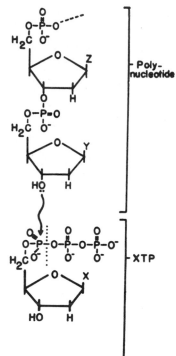

Fig. 5. Postulated mechanism for extending a DNA chain.

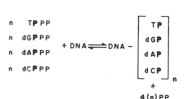

Fig. 6. Equation for enzymatic synthesis of DNA.

it is the capacity for base pairing by hydrogen-bonding between the pre-existing DNA and the nucleotides added as substrates that accounts for the requirement for DNA.

The enzyme we are studying is thus unique in our experience to date in that it takes directions from a template—it adds the particular purine or pyrimidine substrate which will form a hydrogen-bonded pair with a base on the template (Fig. 7). There are five major lines of evidence that support this thesis.

Physical Properties of Enzymatically Synthesized DNA

The first line of evidence is derived from studies of the physical nature of the DNA produced by the enzyme. I might mention again that in these descriptions as in those of the chemical nature of DNA, discussed below, 90 to 95 percent of the DNA sample comes from the substrates used in the reaction. From collaborative studies with Howard K. Schachman, to whom we are greatly indebted, it can be said that the enzymatic product is indistinguishable from high-molecular-weight. double-stranded DNA isolated from natural sources (*16*). It has sedimentation coefficients in the neighborhood of 25 and reduced viscosities of 40 deciliters per gram, and on the basis of these measurements we believe it to be a long, stiff rod with a molecular weight of about 6 million. When the DNA is heated, the rod collapses and the molecule becomes a compact, randomly coiled structure; it may be inferred that the hydrogen bonds holding the strands together have melted, and this is borne out by characteristic changes in the viscometric and optical properties of the molecule. Similar results are found upon cleavage of the molecule by pancreatic deoxyribonuclease. In all these respects the enzymatically synthesized DNA is indistinguishable from the material isolated from natural sources and may thus be presumed to have a hydrogen-bonded structure similar to that possessed by natural DNA.

Would one imagine that the collapsed, jumbled strands of heated DNA would serve as a primer for DNA synthesis? Very likely one would think not. Guided by everyday experience with a jumbled strand of twine, one might regard this as a hopeless template for replication. It turns out that the collapsed DNA is an excellent primer and that the nonviscous, randomly coiled, single-stranded DNA leads to the synthesis of highly viscous, double-stranded DNA (17). Sinsheimer has isolated from the tiny ΦX174 virus a DNA which appears to be single-stranded (18). Like heated DNA, it has proved to be an excellent primer (17) and a useful material in current studies (19) for demonstrating in density-gradient sedimentations its progressive conversion to a double-stranded condition during the course of enzymatic synthesis.

While a detailed discussion of the physical aspects of replication is not feasible in this article, it should be mentioned that the DNA in the single-stranded condition is not only a suitable primer but is the only active form when the most purified enzyme preparations are used. With such preparations of E. coli, the native, double-stranded DNA is inert unless it is heated or pretreated very slightly with deoxyribonuclease. Bollum has made similar observations with the enzyme that he has purified from calf thymus (20).

Substitution of Analogs

The second line of evidence is derived from studies of the activity of the substrates when substitutions are made in the purine and pyrimidine bases. From the many interesting reports on the incorporation of bromouracil (21), azaguanine (22), and other analogs into bacterial and viral DNA, it might be surmised that some latitude in the structure of the bases can be tolerated provided there is no interference with their hydrogen bondings. When experiments were carried out with deoxyuridine triphosphate or 5-bromodeoxyuridine triphosphate, it was found that these compounds supported DNA synthesis when used in place of thymidine triphosphate but not when substituted for the triphosphates of deoxyadenosine, deoxyguanosine, or deoxycytidine. As already described (23), 5-methyl- and 5-bromocytosine specifically replaced cytosine; hypoxanthine substituted only for guanine; and, as just mentioned, uracil and 5-bromouracil specifically replaced thymine. These findings are best interpreted on the basis of hydrogen bonding of the adenine-thymine and guanine-cytosine type.

Along these lines it is relevant to

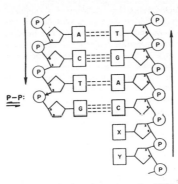

Fig. 7. Mechanism for enzymatic DNA replication.

mention the existence of a naturally occurring "analog" of cytosine, hydroxymethyl cytosine (HMC), which is found in place of cytosine in the DNA of the E. coli bacteriophages of the T-even series (24). In this case the DNA contains equivalent amounts of HMC and guanine and, as usual, equivalent amounts of adenine and thymine. Of additional interest is the fact that the DNA's of T2, T4, and T6 bacteriophages contain glucose linked to the hydroxymethyl groups of the HMC in characteristic ratios (25, 26), although it is clear that in T2 and T6 some of the HMC groups contain no glucose (26).

These characteristics have posed two problems regarding the synthesis of these DNA's which might appear to be incompatible with the simple base-pairing hypothesis. First, what mechanism is there for preventing the inclusion of cytosine in a cell which under normal conditions has deoxycytidine triphos-

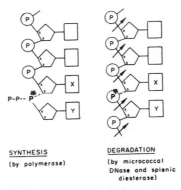

SYNTHESIS
(by polymerase)

DEGRADATION
(by micrococcal DNase and splenic diesterase)

Fig. 8. Method for determining sequences in DNA.

phate and incorporates it into its DNA? Second, how does one conceive of the origin of the constant ratios of glucose to HMC in DNA if the incorporation occurs via glucosylated and nonglucosylated HMC nucleotides? Our recent experiments have shown that the polymerase reaction in the virus-infected cell is governed by the usual hydrogen-bonding restrictions but with the auxiliary action of several new enzymes developed specifically in response to infection with a given virus (27, 28). Among the new enzymes is one which splits deoxycytidine triphosphate and thus removes it from the sites of polymerase action (28). Another is a type of glucosylating enzyme that transfers glucose from uridine diphosphate glucose directly and specifically to certain HMC residues in the DNA (28).

Chemical Composition

The third line of evidence is supplied by an analysis of the purine and pyrimidine base composition of the enzymatically synthesized DNA. We may ask two questions. First, will the product have the equivalence of adenine to thymine and of guanine to cytosine that characterize natural DNA? Second, will the composition of the natural DNA used as primer influence and determine the composition of the product? In Table 1 are the results which answer these two questions (29). The experiments are identical except that in each case a different DNA primer was used: Mycobacterium phlei, Escherichia coli, calf thymus, and phage T2 DNA, respectively.

In answer to the first question, it is clear that in the enzymatically synthesized DNA, adenine equals thymine and guanine equals cytosine, so the purine content is in every case identical to the pyrimidine. In answer to the second question, it is again apparent that the characteristic ratio of adenine-thymine pairs to guanine-cytosine pairs of a given DNA primer is imposed rather faithfully on the product that is synthesized. Whether the net DNA increase is only 1 percent, as measured with isotopic tracers, or 1000 percent, the results are the same.

It can be said further that it has not been possible to distort these base ratios by using widely differing molar concentrations of substrates or by any other means. In the last line of Table 1 is a rather novel "DNA" which is synthesized under conditions that I will not describe here (*17, 30*). Suffice it to say that after very long lag periods, a copolymer of deoxyadenylate and thymidylate (A-T) develops which has the physical size and properties of natural DNA and in which the adenine and thymine are in a perfectly alternating sequence. When this rare form of DNA-like polymer is used as a primer, new A-T polymer synthesis starts immediately, and even though all four triphosphates are present, no trace of guanine or cytosine can be detected in the product. The conclusion thus seems inescapable that the base composition is replicated in the enzymatic synthesis and that hydrogen-bonding of adenine to thymine and of guanine to cytosine is the guiding mechanism.

Enzymatic Replication of Nucleotide Sequences

The fourth line of evidence which I should like to cite is drawn from current studies of base sequences in DNA and their replication. As I have suggested already, we believe that DNA is the genetic code; the four kinds of nucleotides make up a four-letter alphabet, and their sequence spells out the message. At present we do not know the sequence; what Sanger has done for peptide sequence in protein remains to be done for nucleic acids. The problem is more difficult, but not insoluble.

Our present attempts at determining the nucleotide sequences (*31*) will be described in detail elsewhere, and I will only summarize them here. Deoxyribonucleic acid is enzymatically synthesized, with phosphorus-32 as label, in one of the deoxynucleoside triphosphates; the other three substrates are unlabeled. This radioactive phosphorus, attached to the 5-carbon of the deoxyribose, now becomes the bridge between that substrate molecule and the nucleotide at the growing end of the chain with which it has reacted (Fig. 8). At the end of the synthetic reaction (after some 10^{16} diester bonds have been formed), the DNA is isolated and digested enzymatically to yield the 3'-deoxynucleotides quantitatively. It is apparent (Fig. 8) that the phosphorus atom formerly attached to the 5-carbon of the deoxynucleoside triphosphate substrate is now attached to the 3-carbon of the nucleotide with which it reacted during the course of synthesis of the DNA chains. The phosphorus-32 content of each of the 3'-deoxynucleotides, isolated by paper electrophoresis, is a measure of the relative frequency with which a particular substrate reacted with each of the four available nucleotides in the course of synthesis of the DNA chains. This procedure, when carried out four times with a different labeled substrate in each case, yields the relative frequencies of all the 16 possible kinds of dinucleotide (nearest neighbor) sequences.

Such studies have, to date, been carried out with DNA primer samples from six different natural sources. The conclusions are as follows: (i) All 16 possible dinucleotide sequences are found in each case; (ii) the pattern of relative frequencies of the sequences is unique and reproducible in each case and is not predicted from the base composition of the DNA; (iii) enzymatic replication involves base pairing of adenine to thymine and of guanine to cytosine; and, most significantly (iv) the frequencies also indicate clearly that the enzymatic replication produces two strands of opposite direction, as predicted by the Watson and Crick model.

These studies and anticipated extensions of them should yield the dinucleotide frequencies of any DNA sample which can serve as an effective primer for enzymatic replication and thus provide some clues for deciphering the DNA code. Unfortunately, this method does not provide information about trinucleotide frequencies, but we are hopeful that, with the improvement of enzymatic tools for analysis and chromatographic techniques for isolation, some start can be made in this direction.

Requirement for Four Triphosphates and DNA for DNA Synthesis

Returning to the earlier-stated requirement for all four deoxynucleoside triphosphates and DNA for DNA synthesis, we can now regard and understand this requirement as another and final line of evidence for hydrogen bonding. Without added DNA there is no template for hydrogen bonding, and without all four triphosphates, synthesis stops early and abruptly for lack of a hydrogen-bonding mate for one of the bases in the template.

Summary

I have sketched the enzymatic approaches to the problem of DNA replication and the properties of the DNA-synthesizing enzyme purified from *Escherichia coli*. The unifying and basic generalization about the action of this enzyme is that it catalyzes the synthesis of a new DNA chain in response to directions from a DNA template; these directions are dictated by the hydrogen-bonding relationship of adenine to thymine and of guanine to cytosine. The experimental basis for this conclusion is derived from the observations of: (i) the double-stranded character of the enzymatically synthesized DNA and its origin from a single-stranded molecule, (ii) the pattern of substitution of analogs for the naturally occurring bases, (iii) the replication of the chemical composition, (iv) the replication of the nucleotide (nearest neighbor) sequences and the antiparallel direction of the strands, and (v) the requirement for all four deoxynucleoside triphosphates (adenine, thymine, guanine, and cytosine) and for DNA for DNA synthesis (*32*).

Table 1. Chemical composition of enzymatically synthesized DNA, synthesized with different primers. *A*, adenine; *T*, thymine; *G*, guanine; *C*, cytosine.

DNA	A	T	G	C	$\dfrac{A+G}{T+C}$	$\dfrac{A+T}{G+C}$
Mycobacterium phlei						
Primer	0.65	0.66	1.35	1.34	1.01	0.49
Product	0.66	0.65	1.34	1.37	0.99	0.48
Escherichia coli						
Primer	1.00	0.97	0.98	1.05	0.98	0.97
Product	1.04	1.00	0.97	0.98	1.01	1.02
Calf thymus						
Primer	1.14	1.05	0.90	0.85	1.05	1.25
Product	1.12	1.08	0.85	0.85	1.02	1.29
Bacteriophage T2						
Primer	1.31	1.32	0.67	0.70	0.98	1.92
Product	1.33	1.29	0.69	0.70	1.02	1.90
A-T copolymer	1.99	1.93	<0.05	<0.05	1.03	40

References and Notes

1. O. T. Avery, C. M. MacLeod, M. McCarty, *J. Exptl. Med.* **79**, 137 (1944); R. D. Hotchkiss, in *The Chemical Basis of Heredity*, W. D. McElroy and B. Glass, Eds. (Johns Hopkins Press, Baltimore, 1957), p. 321.
2. A. D. Hershey, *Cold Spring Harbor Symposia Quant. Biol.* **18**, 135 (1953).
3. G. W. Beadle, in *The Chemical Basis of Heredity*, W. D. McElroy and B. Glass, Eds. (Johns Hopkins Press, Baltimore, 1957), p. 3.
4. E. Chargaff, in *Nucleic Acids*, E. Chargaff and J. N. Davidson, Eds. (Academic Press, New York, 1955), vol. 1, pp. 307–371.
5. J. D. Watson and F. H. C. Crick, *Nature* **171**, 737 (1953); *Cold Spring Harbor Symposia Quant. Biol.* **18**, 123 (1953).
6. M. H. F. Wilkins, *Biochem. Soc. Symposia (Cambridge, Engl.)* **14**, 13 (1957).
7. M. Feughelman, R. Langridge, W. E. Seeds, A. R. Stokes, H. R. Wilson, C. W. Hooper, M. H. F. Wilkins, R. K. Barclay, L. D. Hamilton, *Nature* **175**, 834 (1955).
8. A. Kornberg, in *The Chemical Basis of Heredity*, W. D. McElroy and B. Glass, Eds. (Johns Hopkins Press, Baltimore, 1957), p. 579; *Revs. Modern Phys.* **31**, 200 (1959).
9. A. Kornberg, in *Phosphorus Metabolism*, W. D. McElroy and B. Glass, Eds. (Johns Hopkins Press, Baltimore 1951), p. 392; *Advances in Enzymol.* **18**, 191 (1957).
10. D. E. Koshland, Jr., in *The Mechanism of Enzyme Action*, W. D. McElroy and B. Glass, Eds. (Johns Hopkins Press, Baltimore, 1954), p. 608.
11. A. Kornberg, I. R. Lehman, E. S. Simms, *Federation Proc.* **15**, 291 (1956); A. Kornberg, *Harvey Lecture Ser.* **53**, 83 (1957–58).
12. I. R. Lehman, M. J. Bessman, E. S. Simms, A. Kornberg, *J. Biol. Chem.* **233**, 163 (1958).
13. F. J. Bollum and V. R. Potter, *J. Am. Chem. Soc.* **79**, 3603 (1957); C. G. Harford and A. Kornberg, *Federation Proc.* **17**, 515 (1958); F. J. Bollum, *ibid.* **17**, 193 (1958); ———, *ibid.* **18**, 194 (1959).
14. M. J. Bessman, I. R. Lehman, E. S. Simms, A. Kornberg, *J. Biol. Chem.* **233**, 171 (1958).
15. J. Adler, I. R. Lehman, M. J. Bessman, E. S. Simms, A. Kornberg, *Proc. Natl. Acad. Sci. U.S.* **44**, 641 (1958).
16. H. K. Schachman, I. R. Lehman, M. J. Bessman, J. Adler, E. S. Simms, A. Kornberg, *Federation Proc.* **17**, 304 (1958).
17. I. R. Lehman, *Ann. N.Y. Acad. Sci.* **81**, 745 (1959).
18. R. L. Sinsheimer, *J. Mol. Biol.* **1**, 43 (1959).
19. I. R. Lehman, R. L. Sinsheimer, A. Kornberg, unpublished observations.
20. F. J. Bollum, *J. Biol. Chem.* **234**, 2733 (1959).
21. F. Weygand, A. Wacker, H. Dellweg, *Z. Naturforsch.* **7b**, 19 (1952); D. B. Dunn and J. D. Smith, *Nature* **174**, 305 (1954); S. Zamenhof and G. Griboff, *ibid.* **174**, 306 (1954).
22. M. R. Heinrich, V. C. Dewey, R. E. Parks, Jr., G. W. Kidder, *J. Biol. Chem.* **197**, 199 (1952).
23. M. J. Bessman, I. R. Lehman, J. Adler, S. B. Zimmerman, E. S. Simms, A. Kornberg, *Proc. Natl. Acad. Sci. U.S.* **44**, 633 (1958).
24. G. R. Wyatt and S. S. Cohen, *Biochem. J.* **55**, 774 (1953).
25. R. L. Sinsheimer, *Science* **120**, 551 (1954); E. Volkin, *J. Am. Chem. Soc.* **76**, 5892 (1954); G. Streisinger and J. Weigle, *Proc. Natl. Acad. Sci. U.S.* **42**, 504 (1956).
26. R. L. Sinsheimer, *Proc. Natl. Acad. Sci. U.S.* **42**, 502 (1956); M. A. Jesaitis, *J. Exptl. Med.* **106**, 233 (1957); *Federation Proc.* **17**, 250 (1958).
27. J. G. Flaks and S. S. Cohen, *J. Biol. Chem.* **234**, 1501 (1959); J. G. Flaks, J. Lichtenstein, S. S. Cohen, *ibid.* **234**, 1507 (1959).
28. A. Kornberg, S. B. Zimmerman, S. R. Kornberg, J. Josse, *Proc. Natl. Acad. Sci. U.S.* **45**, 772 (1959).
29. I. R. Lehman, S. B. Zimmerman, J. Adler, M. J. Bessman, E. S. Simms, A. Kornberg, *ibid.* **44**, 1191 (1958).
30. C. M. Radding, J. Adler, H. K. Schachman, *Federation Proc.* **19**, 307 (1960).
31. J. Josse and A. Kornberg, *ibid.* **19**, 305 (1960).
32. Any credit for the work cited here is shared by my colleagues in New York, Bethesda, St. Louis, and Stanford, and by the whole international community of chemists, geneticists, and physiologists, which is truly responsible for the progress in nucleic acid biochemistry.

J. Mol. Biol. (1961) **3**, 756–761

An Estimate of the Length of the DNA Molecule of T2 Bacteriophage by Autoradiography

JOHN CAIRNS†

Department of Genetics, Carnegie Institution of Washington, Cold Spring Harbor, N.Y., U.S.A.

(*Received 29 June 1961*)

T2 bacteriophage, labelled with [³H]thymidine or [³H]thymine, is subject to suicide on storage. The efficiency of suicide from ³H-decay is apparently the same as that from ³²P-decay.

Autoradiography of T2 DNA, labelled with [³H]thymine and extracted in the presence of 1000-fold excess of cold T2, shows that the molecule can assume the form of an unbranched rod about 52 μ long. If the molecule is throughout its length a double helix in the *B* configuration, this indicates a molecular weight of 110×10^6.

1. Introduction

The decay of tritium gives rise to electrons whose mean range in autoradiographic emulsion is less than one micron (Fitzgerald, Eidinoff, Knoll & Simmel, 1951). It should therefore be possible to obtain a high resolution image of individual molecules of ³H-labelled DNA by autoradiography, using the very highly labelled [³H]thymine that is now available; thus DNA containing [³H]thymine of specific activity 10 c/m-mole will have roughly one disintegration per micron of double helix per week and should produce a near-continuous line of grains along its length after a few weeks' exposure.

Bacteriophage T2 seemed in most respects the best material with which to launch such a procedure. Most of the precursors for T-even thymine synthesis come from the medium after infection (Weed & Cohen, 1951; Kozloff, 1953) so there should be extensive incorporation of labelled thymine given at the time of infection; T2 DNA can be extracted in a pure and homogeneous state with phenol (Mandell & Hershey, 1960), each particle providing a single molecule with a molecular weight of over 100×10^6 (Rubinstein, Thomas & Hershey, 1961); lastly a molecule of such great size is ideal for testing a method of measuring molecular length the accuracy of which is, in theory at least, independent of length.

2. Materials and Methods

Phage. T2, strain T2H (Hershey), was used throughout.

Bacteria. Escherichia coli strain S was used for the production of stocks of unlabelled phage and for phage assays. Labelled phage was prepared in the thymineless strain B3 (Brenner).

† Present address: The Australian National University, Canberra, Australia.

Media. Stocks of unlabelled phage were prepared in M9 (Adams, 1959) supplemented with 0·5 g/l. NaCl. All experiments on the production of phage in the presence of limited thymine or thymidine were carried out using the glucose-ammonium medium described by Hershey (1955).

E. coli strain B3 was grown in the presence of 5 μg/ml. of thymine or thymidine. Phage assays were performed using the standard methods (Adams, 1959). Dilution of phage stocks was made in 10^{-3} M-MgCl$_2$, 0·05% NaCl, 0·001% gelatin, buffered with 0·01 M-tris (2-amino-2-hydroxymethylpropane-1:3-diol) pH 7·4.

[³H]Thymine and [³H]thymidine. These were obtained from the New England Nuclear Corp. and from Schwartz Inc. In the case of the former source these materials are prepared by reducing 5-hydroxymethyl-uracil with tritium so that the label is confined to one hydrogen atom in the methyl group; for this reason they can be specifically designated as 5-[³H]methyl-uracil and 5-[³H]methyldeoxyuridine.

Preparation of labelled phage. In order to ensure extensive incorporation of [³H]thymine (or thymidine) into phage it was necessary to engineer the situation so that phage would only be made if thymine was present and would then be made in an amount which was proportional to the amount of thymine present. The thymineless B3 strain of *E. coli* was used as host since this strain readily incorporates thymidine even at low concentrations, whereas the prototroph does not (Crawford, 1958). Since T2 infection causes the formation of thymidylate synthetase even in thymineless bacteria (Barner & Cohen 1959), it was necessary to block this enzyme by the addition of 5-fluorodeoxyuridine (FUDR) (Cohen, Flaks, Barner, Loeb & Lichtenstein, 1958). At the same time, uridine (UR) was added to ensure that FUDR derivatives were not incorporated into RNA. Thus the final procedure was as follows:

E. coli B3 was grown to 2×10^8 cells/ml. in glucose-ammonium medium with 5 μg/ml. thymidine, and then centrifuged and resuspended in one third volume of fresh medium without thymidine. FUDR and UR were added to give final concentrations of 10^{-5} and 10^{-4} M. Five minutes later the bacteria were infected with T2 at a multiplicity of 4. After 4 min, 0·02 ml. of these infected bacteria was added to 0·02 ml. of double strength medium (with 2×10^{-5} M-FUDR and 2×10^{-4} M-UR) and 0·02 ml. of [³H]thymidine in water. The final concentrations in this growth tube were 2×10^8 B3/ml. 10^{-5} M-FUDR, 10^{-4} M-UR, 2 to 8 μg/ml. thymidine (40 to 160 μC/ml.). (When thymine was the label, the growth tube was supplemented with 10^{-3} M-deoxyadenosine.) After aeration for a further 60 min, the bacteria were lysed with chloroform and the contents of the growth tube were made up to 10 ml. with diluting fluid.

The yield of phage from such a system was 1×10^{10} phage/μg thymidine and 6 to 8×10^9 phage/μg thymine; it was slightly less with [³H]thymidine and [³H]thymine. These yields are 2 to 4 times less than would be expected on the basis of the known thymine content of T2 (Hershey, Dixon & Chase, 1953), but they were not lowered further by raising the concentration of FUDR. In the absence of thymine or thymidine the yield was about 5 phage per bacterium. Purified phage prepared from cold thymidine in this way had the normal optical density per infective particle at 260 mμ. Phage prepared from hot or cold thymine or thymidine showed no rise in the frequency of *r* mutants.

Extraction of phage DNA. Phage was extracted with phenol according to the method of Mandell & Hershey (1960). When labelled phage was extracted, enough cold carrier phage was added to bring the concentration up to the requisite 3×10^{12} phage/ml.; the mixture was then packed in the centrifuge, resuspended and extracted with phenol.

Autoradiography. Once the DNA had been extracted it was diluted to a suitable concentration in various salt solutions and spread in various ways upon glass microscope slides which had previously been coated with various materials. These slides were, on occasion, then coated with chrome-gelatin (0·5% gelatin, 0·05% chrome alum). They were overlaid in the usual manner with Kodak autoradiographic stripping film, AR 10, and stored at 4°C over silica gel in an atmosphere of CO$_2$ to prevent latent image fading (Herz, 1959). After exposure the film was developed with Kodak D19b for 20 min at 16°C.

III. DNA STRUCTURE AND REPLICATION

3. Results

(a) *Suicide of ³H-labelled phage*

Two lots of [³H]thymidine and one of [³H]thymine were used at various times for making labelled phage. In each case the resulting phage was diluted 10² to 10⁴-fold, stored at 4°C and repeatedly assayed for surviving phage. Excess cold phage mixed with the hot phage and stored under the same conditions proved to be stable, as did phage prepared by the same procedure but with cold thymidine. Thus the observed

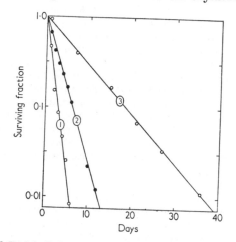

FIG. 1. The suicide of T2 labelled with (1) [³H]thymine 11·2 c/m-mole. (2) [³H]thymidine 5·2 c/m-mole and (3) [³H]thymidine 1·8 c/m-mole.

inactivation of labelled phage was due neither to indirect effects of radiation within the storage tube nor to any innate instability of phage prepared, for example, in the presence of FUDR. Since tritium has a half-life of 12 years, no correction has to be made for decline in radioactivity during the period of storage.

TABLE 1

The suicide of T2 phage labelled with [³H]thymine and [³H]thymidine.

Label	sp. A (c/m-mole)	k (lethals/phage. day)	$\frac{k.\text{m-mole}}{c}$	αN† ("lethal" methyl H atoms/phage)
(1) 5-(³H-methyl)-uracil	11·2	0·78	0·069	$3\cdot9\times10^4$
(2) 5-(³H-methyl)-deoxyuridine	5·2	0·37	0·071	$4\cdot1\times10^4$
(3) ³H-thymidine	1·8	0·13	0·072	$4\cdot1\times10^4$

$$\dagger\ \alpha N = \frac{\text{lethals}}{\text{disintegration}} \times \frac{\text{methyl H atoms}}{\text{phage}}$$

$$= \frac{\text{lethals}}{\text{phage . day}} \times \frac{\text{m-mole}}{c} \times \frac{\text{molecules}}{\text{m-mole}} \times \frac{\text{methyl H atoms}}{\text{molecule}} \times \frac{\text{Curie. day}}{\text{disintegration}}$$

$$= k \times \frac{\text{m-mole}}{c} \times 6\cdot02\times10^{20} \times 3 \times \frac{1}{3\cdot20\times10^{15}}$$

$$= 5\cdot64\times10^5 \times \frac{k.\text{m-mole}}{c}$$

The results are shown in Fig. 1 and Table 1. The suicide of phage is seen to be a first order process with a rate constant (k) which is directly proportional to the specific activity (c/m-mole) of the thymine or thymidine. From this the number, αN, of "lethal" thymine methyl H atoms per phage may be calculated to be 4×10^4. Since the burst size in these experiments was around 120, the contribution of cold thymine from the pool of bacterial DNA (about 24 phage equivalents of thymine) (Hershey *et al.*, 1953; Hershey & Melechen, 1957) will have lowered the specific activity of the incorporated thymine by 20%. Correction for this raises αN to 5×10^4.

This value is not significantly different from the number of "lethal" P atoms per phage, determined from the rate of ^{32}P-suicide (Hershey, Kamen, Kennedy & Gest, 1950; Stent & Fuerst, 1955). Since one third of the bases in T2 DNA are thymine, the total number of thymine methyl H atoms equals the total number of P atoms. It follows therefore that the efficiency of inactivation by decay of ^{32}P and ^{3}H are the same. This is an unexpected result. First, ^{32}P and ^{3}H differ greatly in the energy of the electrons they emit (max. energy 1700 and 17 kev respectively). Second, the sites of their incorporation into DNA seemingly could scarcely differ more; the decay of ^{32}P, in the sugar-phosphate chain, and its conversion to sulfur must necessarily break that chain; the decay of ^{3}H, in the methyl group of thymine, and its conversion to helium need not necessarily cause chain breakage nor perhaps any lasting local alteration in the DNA at all.

Practically, these results indicate that at least 99% of the phage is fairly uniformly labelled.

(b) *Autoradiography of* ^{3}*H-labelled T2 DNA*

Although the production and extraction of highly-labelled DNA presented no problem, there was little prior information on how best to fix this DNA in a sufficiently extended state so that its contours could be followed by autoradiography. Electron microscopy has shown that DNA can be adsorbed from phosphate-buffered solutions of pH 5 to 6 to a variety of surfaces as straight rods many microns long (Hall & Litt, 1958; Beer, 1961) and various methods have been used to ensure that at the time of adsorption the molecules are subject to sufficient shear to align them.

In the course of several months many combinations of DNA concentrations, suspending fluids, varieties of shearing force and adsorbent surfaces were tested. Interestingly, fibres drawn from DNA at high concentration show very poor extension of the minority of molecules that are labelled. The most satisfactory method was found by accident. On testing the appearance of labelled DNA adsorbed to slides partly coated with a co-polymer of polyvinylpyridine and styrene (generously supplied by Dr. Michael Beer), numerous straight molecules were seen adsorbed to the glass on either side of the area coated with polymer; this glass had been cleaned with chromic acid, coated with DNA by drawing the slide across the surface of a solution of DNA in M/15 phosphate buffer pH 5·6, drained and rinsed with distilled water, and then coated with chrome-gelatin (to ensure that the autoradiographic film remained stuck to the slide on drying). Even here, however, there were only localized regions where the DNA was suitably extended. In most regions, the individual molecules were apparently folded back on themselves several times to form a short "rod" of densely packed grains. It seems therefore that the best method for displaying DNA molecules —at least those as long as T2 DNA—has not yet been found.

The appearance of the extended DNA is shown in Plate I. Of the 13 labelled molecules (or fragments of molecules) shown, 7 have a length between 49 and 53 μ; of the remaining 6, one (immediately over the center of the scale) seems from its grain density and length to be folded about its center. Other samples of DNA prepared on different occasions likewise showed that the maximum length, when adsorbed on to glass, was slightly more than 50 μ.

As an estimate of length and hence of molecular weight this is subject to certain errors and variables. For example:

(i) There are several configurations which the molecules might assume, giving values of 2·55 to 3·46 Å per base pair (Langridge, Wilson, Hooper, Wilkins & Hamilton, 1960). Of these the most likely, particularly in the case of T2 DNA (Hamilton *et al.*, 1959), is the *B* configuration with 3·4 Å per base pair.

(ii) Since it is the autoradiographic image and not the molecule itself which is seen, any stretching of the film between exposure and measuring will produce an apparent lengthening. This, however, seems to be a rare occurrence with stripping film.

(iii) Since the molecule is indicated as a series of grains which one may assume to be randomly placed along its length, it is simple to show for this case, where the mean number of grains (M) per molecule of length L is more than about 10, that the mode, mean and variance of observed lengths (that is, between the centres of the outermost grains) will be approximately $L(1 - 1/M)$, $L(1 - 2/M)$ and $L^2(2/M^2)$ respectively. One would therefore expect for molecules such as these, marked with 50 to 100 grains, that the length of the average molecule would be underestimated by 2 to 4%.

(iv) The resolution of the technique can best be judged by the fact that the grains appear to deviate little to either side of the apparent line of each labelled molecule. It is therefore unlikely that the length of any molecule is overestimated by more than 1μ for the reason of poor resolution.

Thus if any single length has to be selected as the most likely for T2 DNA, that length is probably 52 μ. Taking a value of 3·4 Å per base pair and 357 as the average molecular weight of a base in the sodium salt of T2 DNA, this indicates a molecular weight of 110×10^6 and a phosphorus content of $3·0 \times 10^5$. These are slightly below the accepted values though probably not by enough to warrant, at this stage, postulating anything other than an uncomplicated double helix as the form of the T2 DNA molecule.

I am greatly indebted to Dr. A. D. Hershey for his advice and encouragement and for the hospitality of his laboratory, to Dr. Michael Beer for information and advice on spreading DNA, and to the National Institutes of Health (U.S.A.) for a post-doctoral fellowship during which this work was done.

REFERENCES

Adams, M. H. (1959). *The Bacteriophages*. New York: Interscience Publishers.
Barner, H. D. & Cohen, S. S. (1959). *J. Biol. Chem.* **234**, 2987.
Beer, M. (1961). *J. Mol. Biol.* **3**, 263.
Crawford, L. V. (1958). *Biochim. biophys. Acta*, **30**, 428.
Cohen, S. S., Flaks, J. G., Barner, H. D., Loeb, M. R. & Lichtenstein. J. (1958). *Proc. Nat. Acad. Sci., Wash.* **44**, 1004.
Fitzgerald, P. J., Eidinoff, M. L., Knoll, J. E. & Simmel, E. B. (1951). *Science*, **114**, 494.
Hall, C. E. & Litt, M. (1958). *J. Biophys. Biochem. Cytol.* **4**, 1.

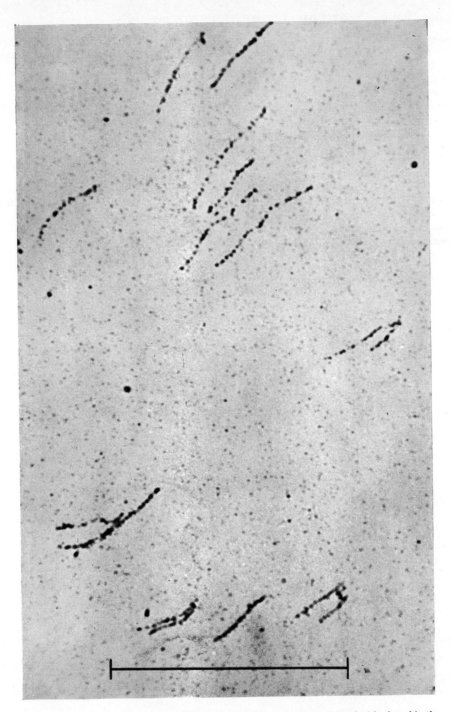

PLATE I. T2 DNA, labelled with [³H]thymine (11·2 c/m-mole), extracted with phenol in the presence of 1000-fold excess of cold T2, and adsorbed to glass at a total DNA concentration of 25 μg/ml. in M/15 phosphate buffer pH 5·6. The autoradiographic exposure was 63 days. The scale shows 100 μ.

[*To face page* 760

Hamilton, L. D., Barclay, R. K., Wilkins, M. H. F., Brown, G. L., Wilson, H. R., Marvin, D. A., Ephrussi-Taylor, H. & Simmons, N. S. (1959). *J. Biophys. Biochem. Cytol.* **5**, 397.

Hershey, A. D. (1955). *Virology*, **1**, 108.

Hershey, A. D., Dixon, J. & Chase, M. (1953). *J. Gen. Physiol.* **36**, 777.

Hershey, A. D., Kamen, M. D., Kennedy, J. W. & Gest, H. (1950). *J. Gen. Physiol.* **34**, 305.

Hershey, A. D. & Melechen, N. E. (1957). *Virology*, **3**, 207.

Herz, R. H. (1959). *Lab. Investigation*, **8**, 71.

Kozloff, L. M. (1953). *Cold Spr. Harb. Symp. Quant. Biol.* **18**, 209.

Langridge, R., Wilson, H. R., Hooper, C. W., Wilkins, M. H. F. & Hamilton, L. D. (1960). *J. Mol. Biol.* **2**, 19.

Mandell, J. D. & Hershey, A. D. (1960). *Analyt. Biochem.* **1**, 66.

Rubinstein, I., Thomas, C. A. & Hershey, A. D. (1961). *Proc. Nat. Acad. Sci., Wash.* **47**, 1113.

Stent, G. S. & Fuerst, C. R. (1955). *J. Gen. Physiol.* **38**, 441.

Weed, L. L. & Cohen, S. S. (1951). *J. Biol. Chem.* **192**, 693.

J. Mol. Biol. (1963) **6**, 208–213

The Bacterial Chromosome and its Manner of Replication as seen by Autoradiography

JOHN CAIRNS

*Department of Microbiology, Australian National University,
Canberra, A.C.T., Australia*

(Received 19 November 1962)

In order to determine the form of replicating DNA, *E. coli* B3 and K12 Hfr were labelled for various periods with [³H]thymidine. Their DNA was then extracted gently and observed by autoradiography. The results and conclusions can be summarized as follows.

(1) The chromosome of *E. coli* consists of a single piece of two-stranded DNA, 700 to 900 μ long.

(2) This DNA duplicates by forming a fork. The new (daughter) limbs of the fork each contain one strand of new material and one strand of old material.

(3) Each chromosome length of DNA is probably duplicated by one fork. Thus, when the bacterial generation time is 30 min, 20 to 30 μ of DNA is duplicated each minute.

(4) Totally unexpected was the finding that the distal ends of the two daughter molecules appear to be joined during the period of replication. The reason for this is obscure. Conceivably the mechanism that, *in vivo*, winds the daughter molecules lies at the point of their union rather than, as commonly supposed, in the fork itself.

(5) The chromosomes of both B3 (F⁻) and K12 (Hfr) appear to exist as a circle which usually breaks during extraction.

1. Introduction

The semiconservative nature of DNA replication, predicted on structural grounds by Watson & Crick (1953), was demonstrated experimentally first for bacterial DNA (Meselson & Stahl, 1958), but how the two strands of the double helix come to separate during replication is not known. There must be formidable complexities to any process which, however feasible energetically (Levinthal & Crane, 1956), at once unwinds one molecule and winds two others. So a study was undertaken of the shape and form of replicating DNA.

Bacteria, despite their complexity, promised to be the most accessible source of replicating DNA. Each bacterium in an exponentially growing culture of *E. coli* makes DNA for more than 80% of the generation time (McFall & Stent, 1959; Schaechter, Bentzon & Maaløe, 1959); if, as seems likely, the bacterial chromosome is a single molecule of DNA, this molecule must be engaged in replication most of the time. A method had already been devised for extracting this DNA with little degradation (Cairns, 1962*a*) and it seemed probable that, with more care, the chromosome could be isolated intact and, caught in the act of replication, its DNA be displayed by autoradiography.

2. Materials and Methods

Bacteria. Since the chromosomes of F⁻ and Hfr bacteria differ in the type of their genetic linkage (Jacob & Wollman, 1958) and in the manner of their duplication (Nagata, 1962), two strains of *E. coli* were used, B3 (F⁻) (Brenner) and K12 3000 *thy⁻ B_1^-* (Hfr). Both strains require thymine or thymidine.

Medium. The *A* medium of Meselson & Weigle (1961) was used. To this was added 3 mg/ml. casein hydrolysate, which had first been largely freed of thymine by steaming with charcoal. In this medium, supplemented with 2 µg/ml. TDR,† both strains have a generation time of 30 min.

Preparation of labelled bacteria for autoradiography. The bacteria were grown with aeration to 10⁸/ml., centrifuged and resuspended in an equal volume of medium containing 2 µg/ml. [³H]TDR (9 c/m-mole). In pulse-labelling experiments, incorporation of label was stopped by diluting the bacteria either 50-fold into medium containing 20 µg/ml. TDR or 250-fold into cold 0·15 M-NaCl containing 0·01 M-KCN and 0·002% bovine serum albumin. In long-term experiments, the bacteria were labelled for two generations (1 hr) so that roughly half of the DNA would be fully labelled and half would be a hybrid of labelled and unlabelled strands.

Lysis of bacteria. Only in a few minor respects has the procedure been altered from that already published (Cairns, 1962a). Labelled bacteria are lysed after dilution to a final concentration of about 10⁴/ml. Since it was important in certain experiments to be sure that DNA synthesis did not continue beyond the time the bacteria were sampled, 0·01 M-KCN was added to the lysis medium (1·5 M-sucrose, 0·05 M-NaCl, 0·01 M-EDTA). Various types of cold carrier DNA (4·7 µg/ml. calf thymus, *E. coli* or T2 DNA) were used at various times without apparently influencing the results. As before, lysis was obtained by dialysis against 1% Duponol C (Dupont, Wilmington, Delaware, U.S.A.) in lysis medium for 2 hr at 37°C. The Duponol was then removed by dialysis for 18 to 24 hr against repeated changes of 0·05 M-NaCl, 0·005 M-EDTA. As before, the DNA was collected on the dialysis membrane (VM Millipore filter, Millipore Filter Corporation, Bedford, Mass., U.S.A.).

Autoradiography. As before, Kodak AR10 stripping film was used and the exposure was about 2 months.

Thymidine incorporation experiments. To determine whether incorporation was delayed following transfer to a medium containing [³H]TDR, bacteria were grown in cold medium to 5 × 10⁸/ml., centrifuged and resuspended in medium containing 2 µg/ml. [³H]TDR (1 c/m-mole). Samples were then removed into cold 5% TCA and washed on Oxoid membrane filters (average pore diameter 0·5 to 1·0 µ, Oxo Ltd, London, England) with cold TCA and finally with 1% acetic acid. The filters were dried, placed in scintillator fluid (0·4% 2,5-diphenyloxazole, 0·01% 1,4-bis-2[5-phenyloxazolyl]-benzene in toluene) and counted in a scintillation counter.

3. Results

In interpreting autoradiographs of extracted DNA certain assumptions are necessary. These can be stated at the outset.

(1) It is not clear why some molecules of bacterial DNA choose to untangle whereas others do not. However, the few that do are assumed to be a fairly representative sample; specifically we assume that they do not belong to some special class that is being duplicated in some special way.

(2) The ratio of mass to length for this untangled DNA is taken to be at least that of DNA in the B configuration, namely 2 × 10⁶ daltons/µ (Langridge, Wilson, Hooper, Wilkins & Hamilton, 1960). We assume that single-stranded DNA will not be found in an extended state and so, even if present, will not contribute to the tally of untangled DNA.

† Abbreviation used: TDR stands for thymidine.

(3) The density of grains along these labelled molecules is assumed to be proportional to the amount of incorporated label. Specifically we assume that if one piece of DNA has twice the grain density of another this shows that it is labelled in twice as many strands.

(a) *Pulse labelling experiments*

Simple pulse-labelling experiments could tell much about the process of DNA replication. As pointed out already, DNA synthesis in *E. coli* is virtually continuous. If, therefore, the bacterial chromosome is truly a single piece of two-stranded DNA and if, at any moment, duplication is occurring at only a single point on this molecule, then the length of DNA labelled by a short pulse will be just that fraction of the total length of the chromosome that the duration of the pulse is a fraction of the generation time; if there are several points of simultaneous duplication on the single molecule, or several molecules which are duplicated in parallel, then the length of DNA labelled will be appropriately less. Further, from such pulse experiments it should be possible to determine whether one or two new strands are being made in each region of replication.

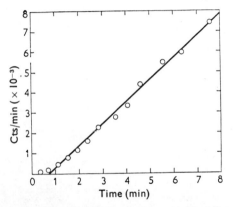

FIG. 1. Incorporation of ³H into cold TCA-insoluble material, following transfer of *E. coli* B3 to medium containing [³H]TDR.

However, first it was necessary to find out how quickly [³H]TDR gets into DNA when the bacteria are transferred from a medium containing cold TDR. The result of such an experiment with *E. coli* B3 is shown in Fig. 1 (see also Materials and Methods). A similar result was obtained for *E. coli* K12. So it seems that, under these particular conditions, the error in timing a pulse will be less than 1 minute.

Autoradiographs of *E. coli* B3 DNA were prepared following (i) a 3 minute pulse of [³H]TDR, (ii) a 3 minute pulse, followed by 15 minutes in cold TDR, and (iii) a 6 minute pulse, followed by 15 minutes in cold TDR. Examples of what was found are shown in Plate I. Similar results were obtained using *E. coli* K12.

From these experiments the following conclusions can be drawn.

(1) Immediately after a 3 minute pulse of label (Plate I(a), (b) and (c)) the labelled DNA consists of two pieces lying in fairly close association. Fifteen minutes later (Plate I(d), (e) and (f)) these pieces have moved apart and can be photographed separately. It seems therefore that *two* labelled molecules are being formed in the region of replication.

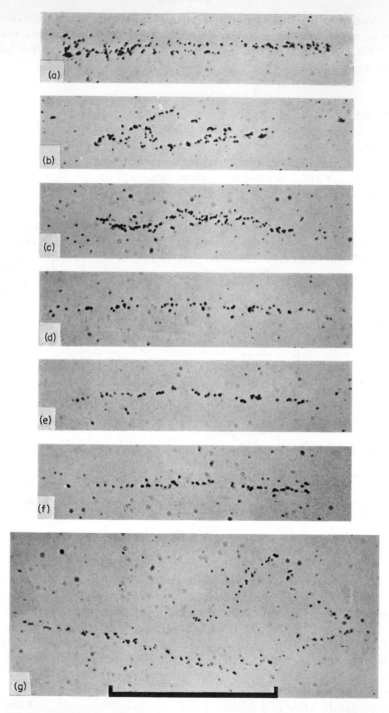

Plate I. Autoradiographs of *E. coli* B3 DNA labelled by a pulse of [³H]TDR. Exposure time was 61 days. The scale shows 50μ.

(a), (b), (c): Immediately after a 3 min pulse; (d), (e), (f): 15 min after a 3 min pulse; (g): 15 min after a 6 min pulse.

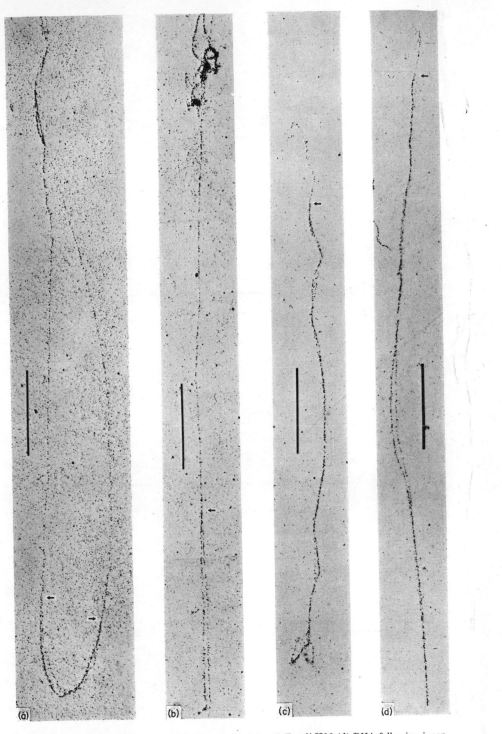

PLATE II. Autoradiographs of *E. coli* B3 (a), (b), (c) and *E. coli* K12 (d) DNA following incorporation of [³H]TDR for a period of 1 hr (two generations). The arrows show the point of replication. Exposure time was 61 days. The scales show 100 μ.

III. DNA STRUCTURE AND REPLICATION

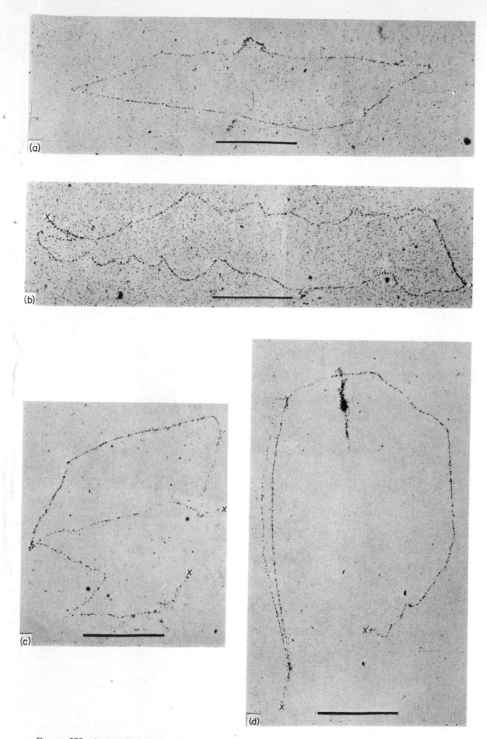

PLATE III. Autoradiographs of *E. coli* B3 (a), (b), (c) and *E. coli* K12 (d) DNA following incorporation of [³H]TDR for a period of 1 hr. In (b), (c), and (d), the postulated break is marked ×——×. Exposure time 61 days. The scales show 100 μ.

(2) There is approximately 1 grain per micron in these labelled regions. Since similarly labelled T2 and λ bacteriophage DNA, both of which are known to be largely two-stranded, show about twice this grain density (Cairns, 1962b), the two molecules being created at the point of duplication must each be labelled in one strand.

(3) A 3 minute pulse labels two pieces of DNA each 60 to 80 μ long (Plate I(a) to (f)); a 6 minute pulse labels about twice this length (Plate I(g)). In one generation time (30 minutes) the process responsible for this could cover 600 to 800 μ, or slightly more than this if the duration of the pulse is being over-estimated (see Fig. 1). There is unfortunately no precise estimate for the DNA content of the *E. coli* chromosome. When the generation time is 1 hour, each cell contains 4×10^9 daltons DNA (Hershey & Melechen, 1957). If each cell contained only one nucleus, this value would have to be divided by 1·44 (1/ln 2) to correct for continuous DNA synthesis. However, as such cells are usually multinucleate (see Schaechter, Maaløe & Kjeldgaard, 1958), this corrected value of $2·8 \times 10^9$ daltons (or 1400 μ DNA) must be too high. There is therefore no marked discrepancy between the total length of DNA that has to be duplicated ($< 1400 \mu$) and the distance traversed by the replication process in one generation (at least 600 to 800 μ). This suggests that one or at the most two regions of the chromosome are being duplicated at any moment.

These various conclusions are reinforced by the results reported in the next section.

(b) *Two-generation labelling experiments*

One conspicuous feature of the pulse experiments is not apparent from the photographs and was not listed. The proportion of the labelled DNA that had untangled, and could therefore be measured, was far lower immediately after the 3 minute pulse than 15 minutes later. Thus the replicating region of a DNA molecule is apparently less readily displayed than the rest. It was not surprising therefore that considerable search was necessary before untangled and replicating molecules were found in the two-generation experiments. Since the products of such searches are generally somewhat suspect, the guiding principles of this particular search will be given.

As pointed out earlier there are reasons for assigning the hypothetical DNA molecule of *E. coli* a length of less than 1400 μ. Therefore no molecules were accepted whose length, presumably through breakage, was much less than 700 μ. No replicating (forking) molecules were accepted unless both limbs of their fork were the same length. Lastly many extended molecules were excluded because of the complexity of their form; although perhaps interpretable in terms of a known scheme they could not be used to provide that scheme. Samples of what remained are shown in Plate II. They have been selected to illustrate what appear to be various stages of DNA replication.

First, the rough agreement between the observed length of *E. coli* DNA (up to 900 μ) and the estimated DNA content of its chromosome ($< 1400 \mu$) supports the conclusion, arising from the pulse experiments, that this chromosome contains a piece of two-stranded DNA.

Second, it seems clear that this DNA replicates by forking and that new material is formed along both limbs of the fork. This latter was shown by the pulse experiments and is confirmed here. In each of the forks shown, one limb plainly has about twice the grain density of the other and of the remainder of the molecule. The simplest hypothesis is that we are watching the conversion of a molecule of hybrid (hot–cold)

DNA into one hybrid and one fully-substituted (hot–hot) molecule. It is not surprising that, nominally after two generations of labelling, the process is seen at various stages of completion. In Plate II(a), duplication has covered about a sixth of the visible distance in what appear to be two sister molecules. In Plate II(b) and (c), duplication has gone about a third and three-quarters of the distance, respectively. In Plate II(d), duplication is almost complete, about 800 μ of DNA having been replicated. So these pictures support what seemed likely from the pulse experiments—namely, that the act of replication proceeds from one end of the molecule to the other.

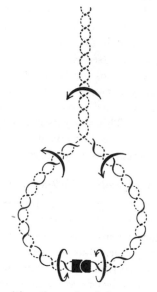

Fig. 2. The consequence of uniting the ends of the replicating fork. The arrows show the direction of rotation, as the parent molecule unwinds and the two daughter molecules are formed (modified from Delbrück & Stent, 1957).

The most conspicuous and totally unexpected feature of these pictures has been left for discussion last. In the case of each replicating molecule, the ends of the fork are joined. This complication seems to have been taken one stage further in Plate II(a); here the two limbs of the fork may be joined to each other but they also appear to be joined to their opposite numbers which are being formed from the sister molecule. Conceivably such terminal union of the new double helices (which must be alike in their base sequence) is the artificial consequence of a freedom to unite that only comes with lysis; this union may not exist inside the bacterium. Alternatively, terminal union may be the rule during the period of replication. If so, whatever unites the two ends must have the freedom to rotate so that the new helices can rotate as they are formed (Fig. 2). This uniting structure, or swivel, could in fact be the site of the mechanism that, *in vivo*, spins the parent molecule and its two daughters.

(c) *The bacterial chromosome*

The primary object of this work was to determine the form of DNA when it is replicating, not the form of the entire bacterial chromosome. The pictures presented so far give little indication of the latter as they show molecules that are either broken

(Plate II(c)) or partly tangled (Plate II(a) and (b)). It seemed possible, however' that out of all the material that had been collected some model for the shape of the whole chromosome might emerge.

In searching for such a model that could account for all the kinds of structure seen, the premise was adopted that since excess cold carrier DNA was invariably present these structures must be related to the model by breakage, if needs be, but not by end-to-end aggregation. Granted this premise, there seems to be only one model that

FIG. 3. Two stages in the duplication of a circular chromosome. (B) and (D) mark the positions of the breaks postulated to have produced the structures shown in Plate III(b) and (d), respectively.

could generate every structure merely by breakage. This model supposes that the chromosome exists as a circle. Duplication, as in Fig. 2, proceeds by elongation of a loop at the expense of the remainder of the molecule; since, however, the distal end of the molecule is also attached to the swivel, duplication creates a figure 8 each half of which ultimately constitutes a finished daughter molecule (Fig. 3). Depending on how this structure breaks at the time of extraction, it may form a rod with a terminal loop (Plate II), a rod with a subterminal loop (Plate III(c) and (d)), or a circle (Plate III(a) and (b)); in the case of a circle, the circumference may be up to twice the length of the chromosome. All structures seen, including circles of varying circumference, can be readily derived from this model whereas they do not conform to any other obvious scheme. It is, however, possible that the process of duplication may vary; that, for example, the structure shown in Plate II(a) was genuinely an exceptional case. In any event, here as elsewhere no significant difference was detected between the chromosomes of *E. coli* B3 (F⁻) and *E. coli* K12 (Hfr).

I am greatly indebted to Dr. A. D. Hershey and Professor Max Delbrück for helpful criticism and to Miss Rosemary Henry for able technical assistance.

REFERENCES

Cairns, J. (1962a). *J. Mol. Biol.* **4**, 407.
Cairns, J. (1962b). *Cold Spr. Harb. Symp. Quant. Biol.* **27**. In the press.
Delbrück, M. & Stent, G. S. (1957). In *The Chemical Basis of Heredity*, ed. by W. D. McElroy & B. Glass. Baltimore: Johns Hopkins Press.
Hershey, A. D. & Melechen, N. E. (1957). *Virology*, **3**, 207.
Jacob, F. & Wollman, E. L. (1958). *Symp. Soc. Exp. Biol.* **12**, 75.
Langridge, R., Wilson, H. R., Hooper, C. W., Wilkins, M.H.F. & Hamilton, L.D. (1960). *J. Mol. Biol.* **2**, 19.
Levinthal, C. & Crane, H. R. (1956). *Proc. Nat. Acad. Sci., Wash.* **42**, 436.
McFall, E. & Stent, G. S. (1959). *Biochim. biophys. Acta*, **34**, 580.
Meselson, M. & Stahl, F. W. (1958). *Proc. Nat. Acad. Sci., Wash.* **44**, 671.
Meselson, M. & Weigle, J. J. (1961). *Proc. Nat. Acad. Sci., Wash.* **47**, 857.
Nagata, T. (1962). *Biochem. Biophys. Res. Comm.* **8**, 348.
Schaechter, M., Bentzon, M. W. & Maaløe, O. (1959). *Nature*, **183**, 1207.
Schaechter, M., Maaløe, O. & Kjeldgaard, N. O. (1958). *J. Gen. Microbiol.* **19**, 592.
Watson, J. D. & Crick, F. H. C. (1953). *Cold Spr. Harb. Symp. Quant. Biol.* **18**, 123.

ɔl. Biol. (1959) **1**, 87-105

The Specific Mutagenic Effect of Base Analogues on Phage T4

ERNST FREESE †

Biological Laboratories, Harvard University, Cambridge, Massachusetts, U.S.A.

(*Received 3 December 1958*)

Several purine and pyrimidine analogues which are sterically very similar to the normal nucleic acid bases have been tested for their mutagenic effect upon T4 phages. Besides 5-bromodeoxyuridine only 2-aminopurine and 2,6-diaminopurine were effective.

Most of the base analogues tested inhibit bacterial growth when present in sufficiently high concentrations, and some of them show an additional effect upon phage growth. Thus 5-bromodeoxyuridine and 5-bromouracil inhibit phage growth (especially in the derivatives of bacteria K-12), and 2-aminopurine depresses lysis inhibition under certain growth conditions.

The "mutability spectrum" of T4 *r*II-type phage mutants induced by 5-bromo-deoxyuridine was found to be essentially the same as that of 5-bromouracil-induced mutants studied by Benzer & Freese (1958). In contrast, the mutability spectrum of 2-aminopurine-induced mutants was different from both spontaneous and bromouracil-induced mutants. The genetic coincidence, however, of some 2-amino-purine-induced mutants with some bromouracil-induced mutants indicates some mutagenic similarity between the two base analogues.

The high frequency of phage mutants after growth in the presence of the base analogue is not due to selection of pre-existing mutants, as shown by a fluctuation test. Again, the differences between the mutability spectra are not due to any selection but are caused by preferential mutagenic actions at certain sites of the genome.

1. Introduction

A new method of investigation promises an understanding of mutations in molecular terms. It now seems clear that most hereditary information is carried by deoxyribo-nucleic acid (DNA) ‡, and that this information is determined by the precise sequence of purine and pyrimidine bases in DNA. Most mutations, therefore, should be due to changes in the base-sequence of DNA or to alterations in the number of DNA molecules. Recently new mutagenic chemicals have been found whose mutagenic reactions with DNA inside the living cell may be analyzed. Especially promising are certain highly mutagenic analogues of the normal DNA bases, since their action may be expected to be simple and rather direct. In addition, genetic fine structure analysis is now possible in several micro-organisms, and this can reveal the mutagenic specificity of a base analogue. The correlation of this genetic specificity with bio-chemical observations should lead to a clear picture of the underlying mutagenic events.

---

† Research Fellow of the Damon Runyon Memorial Fund for Cancer Research.

‡ The following abbreviations are used in this paper: AICAR, 5-amino-4-imidazole-carboxamide ribotide; AM, aminopterin; AMP, adenosine monophosphate; AP, 2-aminopurine; BD, 5-bromo-deoxyuridine; BU, 5-bromouracil; DNA, deoxyribonucleic acid; GMP, guanosine monophosphate; HMC, 5-hydroxymethyl uracil; IMP, inosine monophosphate.

G   87

Dunn & Smith (1954) found that 5-bromouracil (BU) can quantitatively replace thymine in the DNA of phage T2, and Litman & Pardee (1956) showed that BU is also highly mutagenic for these phages. These encouraging biochemical findings stimulated Benzer & Freese (1958) to compare phage T4 mutants induced by BU with those which occur spontaneously, by means of a genetic fine structure analysis. They found that most BU-induced mutations occurred at locations genetically different from most of the spontaneous ones. In addition this analysis revealed a more elaborate mutagenic specificity than any simple model of mutation would have predicted. The mutations of many independently isolated *spontaneous* mutants are not randomly distributed, but recur frequently at certain genetic sites. Such sites of high mutability ("hot spots") have also been found among the *BU-induced* mutants, but their genetic locations are different from the spontaneous ones. The existence of sites of high mutability in itself indicates a specificity of the mutagen, while the difference in location shows that different mutagens have different specificity.

However, a direct correlation of the genetic specificity and the molecular specificity of mutagens cannot be obtained from these observations, especially since the origin of spontaneous mutations is unclear. In an attempt to obtain such a correlation, two approaches have been used in the present work.

(1) The same base analogue, BU, has been applied again for the induction of mutations under different growth conditions to see whether or not the mutagenic specificity changes. No significant change has been observed.

(2) A number of other base analogues which might possibly be incorporated into DNA have been analysed for their mutagenicity. Only two showed a significant mutagenic effect, namely 2-aminopurine (AP) and 2,6-diaminopurine. AP was used to induce a new set of T4 mutants. These exhibited a mutability spectrum (Fig. 2) different from both the spontaneous and the BU spectra, although it had some similarity with the latter.

2. Materials

(a) *Bacteria*

(i) *Derivatives of Escherichia coli B*

B (Benzer), T1 resistant.

BB (Stent), T1 resistant.

B-96 and *B-97* (Gots), both purine-deficient; both were obtained by UV irradiation and penicillin selection from the same *E. coli* B (Gots). *B-96* is blocked in the transformylase reaction between 5-amino-4-imidazole-carboxamide ribotide and inosinic acid and grows on H-medium with supplements of adenine, hypoxanthine, xanthine, or guanine (Gots & Love, 1954). *B-97* is blocked in the desuccinylation of both adenylosuccinic acid ribotide and succinyl-aminoimidazole-carboxamide ribotide, and grows with adenine but with none of the other three bases (Gots & Gollub, 1957).

(ii) *Derivatives of E. coli K12*

S (Benzer); λ-sensitive, T1 resistant.

K (Benzer); lysogenic for prophage λ, T1 resistant.

(b) *Phages*

T4 (Benzer) standard type and several *r*II-type mutants: spontaneous *r*-mutants and 5-bromouracil induced N-mutants.

(c) *Media*

Broth, 1 % bacto-tryptone (Difco) plus 0·5 % NaCl.

Synthetic medium, per 1 liter distilled water: 17·7 g $Na_2HPO_4.12 H_2O$; 3 g KH_2PO_4; 1 g NH_4Cl; 5 g glucose; 10^{-3} M-$MgSO_4$; 10^{-4} M-$CaCl_2$; 10^{-6} M-$FeCl_3$; 20 mg L-tryptophan, necessary for phage T4 adsorption and for growth of the T1-resistant bacteria (which are tryptophan-dependent).

H-Medium, synthetic medium plus 20 μg/ml. histidine.

F8 Medium, a synthetic medium which contains per liter: 20 mg L-glycine, 20 mg L-methionine, 10 mg L-leucine, 10 mg L-valine, 10 mg L-serine, 10 mg adenine, 10 mg guanine, 5 mg uracil, 10 mg deoxycytidine, 0·2 mg calcium pantothenate, 0·2 mg thiamine, 0·2 mg pyridoxine, 10 μg vitamin B_{12}.

(d) *Analogues*

Aminopterin (J. M. Ruegsegger, Lederle Medical Research Department, American Cyanamide Company, Pearl River, New York) was kept dark in the cold as a solution of 2 mg/ml. in 1/100 N-NaOH.

2-chloro-6-oxypurine (J. Montgomery, Southern Research Institute, Kettering Meyer Lab., Birmingham, Alabama).

6-methylaminopurine (G. H. Hitchings, Wellcome Research Lab., Tuckahoe 7, New York).

Purine-9-riboside (G. B. Brown, Sloan Kettering Inst. for Cancer Research, New York 21, New York.)

The other base analogues are commercially available (California Foundation, Sigma, Nutritional Biochemicals).

(e) *Plates*

Plates contain either broth or a synthetic medium, plus 1·5 % agar (Difco) with a top layer of the same medium plus 0·7 % agar.

3. Experimental

(a) *Growth of bacteria under conditions of pyrimidine and purine limitation*

The mutagenic effect of base analogues is strongly dependent on the concentration of the natural nucleic acid precursors. With some base analogues any significant mutagenesis can be found only when the formation of the normal base is partially suppressed. In the following we shall describe methods for obtaining limitation in the supply of one or another of the natural pyrimidine or purine nucleotides. It may be recalled that each of the natural nucleotides can be obtained in two different ways, either by *de novo* formation from simple building blocks, or by a "salvage" pathway, using externally provided purines, pyrimidines, or their nucleosides. Generally a limitation of a natural nucleotide will be obtained by inhibiting the corresponding *de novo* pathway and providing only a limited amount of the base which can enter the salvage pathway. We shall describe how the *de novo* pathway of thymine and hydroxymethyl cytosine (HMC) can be inhibited by counteracting folic acid with aminopterin, and how the *de novo* pathway of adenine and guanine can be shut off by using purine-dependent bacteria.

(i) *Bacterial growth in aminopterin-containing medium*

Aminopterin (AM) is a folic acid analogue which inhibits growth and duplication of bacteria *E. coli* B. Webb & Nickerson (1956) showed that it induces the development of long bacterial filaments when certain growth conditions are applied. Such growth conditions are obtained, for example, when bacteria B are grown logarithmically in F8 medium to a titer of 5×10^7/ml. and 50 μg/ml. AM are added. Within 5 hours all bacteria develop into long threads (about 1/50 mm length). Comparison of the microscope count with the colony count on broth plates shows that the bacteria rapidly die under these growth conditions. When the medium also contains 20 μg/ml. (or more) thymine the bacteria develop normally. These observations resemble those of Cohen & Barner (1956) concerning growth in sulfanilamide-containing medium. While sulfanilamide competes with *p*-aminobenzoic acid and thereby prevents the formation of folic acid, aminopterin competes with folic acid itself. Folic acid is known to be necessary for the methylation and hydroxymethylation of a number of compounds including the *de novo* formation of thymine (Friedkin & Kornberg, 1957). Its partial inhibition therefore results in the inhibition of the methyl transfer and the above observations can be attributed to "thymine-less death".

At higher concentrations of AM, e.g. 200 μg/ml., the bacteria stay small and grow very slowly in F8 and much faster when 20 μg/ml. or more thymine are present. At this AM concentration another metabolite besides thymine is probably partially suppressed and the imbalance between cell surface and cell content is less pronounced.

(ii) *The metabolic block of the purineless bacteria*

The *de novo* pathway of purine compounds goes via 5-amino-4-imidazole-carboxamide ribotide (AICAR) to inosinic acid (IMP) and then branches to give both adenosine monophosphate (AMP) and guanosine monophosphate (GMP) (Buchanan *et al*, 1957). AMP is subsequently used not only for the production of other adenosine nucleotides but also for the formation of histidine (Magasanik, personal communication). AICAR is re-formed as a by-product of histidine synthesis. Externally-given adenine which is converted into AMP by a "salvage pathway" can give rise to the formation of IMP, and thus GMP, by two pathways. On the one hand it can be converted to AICAR and thence to IMP, and on the other hand AMP can be directly deaminated to IMP.

With this knowledge the biochemical blocks of the two purine-less bacterial mutants are easily described. *B-96* is blocked in one of the enzymes that convert AICAR to IMP and therefore can grow on any externally-given purine. *B-97* is blocked in the enzyme which removes succinic acid from purine compounds. This enzyme is used at two places, once in the *de novo* synthesis of AICAR and again in the conversion of IMP to AMP. *B-97* therefore can only grow on externally-given adenine but not on any other of the three purine bases.

It should be mentioned that the amount of histidine or thiamine in the bacterium regulates how much AMP enters the histidine pathway (Magasanik, personal communication). This feedback mechanism is disturbed in purineless bacteria when they are grown in synthetic medium plus adenine alone; the bacterial growth is appreciably inhibited. This inhibition can be removed by the addition of 20 μg/ml. histidine or by 0·25 μg/ml. thiamine. Therefore H-medium was usually used for these bacteria.

(iii) *Bacterial growth in 2-aminopurine-containing medium*

When bacteria *B-96* or *B-97* are grown in H-medium plus 10 μg/ml. adenine and 500 μg/ml. or more AP, *B-96* cells develop into long threads while *B-97* cells divide nearly normally, after some transitory lengthening. The lengthening of *B-96* is more pronounced when 0·25 μg/ml. thiamine replaces the histidine in the medium; after 15 hours practically all of the *B-96* cells are long, up to 0·1 mm, and 97 % are unable to proliferate. The essential difference between the two bacteria, when they are grown in adenine, is that *B-97* can make IMP from AMP using either of the two above-mentioned pathways while *B-96* can do so only by the deamination of AMP. The different effects of AP upon these two bacteria may therefore suggest that AP interferes with the deamination of adenine compounds (e.g. AMP to IMP) and in *B-96* prevents sufficient production of GMP. Indeed *B-96* shows less filament formation when it is grown with AP together with xanthine, hypoxanthine or guanine.

(b) *The mutagenicity of different base analogues for T4 phages*

In order to find another mutagenic base analogue which could possibly be incorporated into DNA, a number of closely related DNA base analogues was tested for their mutagenic effect on phage T4.

The simplest way to detect a large mutagenic effect consists of a spot test for the induction of reversions. Phages of a reverting *r*II-type mutant are plated on a mixture of bacteria K and B, and the base analogue is added to one spot of the plate. An appreciable increase in the number of plaques around the spot can be attributed to the ability of the base analogue to increase the reversion frequency. This spot test has the further advantage that each revertant phage which arises produces only one plaque; the large fluctuation in the number of mutants which one observes in liquid cultures (jackpots) are thereby eliminated. Two reverting *r*II-type mutants were used, the spontaneous $r131$ and the BU-induced N19. The results, summarized in Table 1, columns 1 and 2, show that 2-aminopurine (AP), 2,6-diaminopurine, 5-bromouracil, and 5-bromodeoxyuridine exhibited a mutagenic effect for the reversion of N19, while no increase in plaque numbers was observed with the mutant $r131$. No normal DNA bases, or their deoxyribonucleosides, had any effect.

TABLE 1

Effect of different base analogues upon bacteria and phages

Mutagenic effect upon phages: 2×10^7 phages T4 N19 (rII-type mutant, induced by 5-bromo-uracil, spontaneous reversion index $= 0.05 \times 10^{-6}$) and T4 $r131$ (rII-type spontaneous mutant, spontaneous reversion index $= 0.5 \times 10^{-6}$) were each plated on broth with 2×10^8 bacteria K and 2×10^7 bacteria B. Some of the base analogue was placed in powder form at the center of each plate, which was then immediately put into a refrigerator for 3 hr in order to permit diffusion. During the subsequent over-night incubation at 37°C all phages infecting B are able to multiply and to undergo mutations. When all bacteria B are destroyed by lysis only the phage revertants can continue to multiply on K and give rise to a plaque. The test is positive if many plaques appear in the neighbourhood of the spotted base analogue.

Effect upon bacteria and plaques: 200 phages (standard, or one of the r types) were plated with 2×10^8 bacteria on broth, and the base analogue was placed in powder form in the center of the plate. After 12 hr diffusion time in the cold the plate was incubated overnight at 37°C. For the bacterial inhibition: — = no effect observed, + = little inhibition, ++ = strong inhibition.

Base analogue	1 Induction of reversions for the T4 rII-type phages		3 Inhibition of bacteria	4 Effect on T4 phages
	$r131$	N19		
2-aminopurine	—	++	+	standard type gives large plaques on B, BB. No effect on S, K.
2-amino-6-oxypyrimidine	—	—	—	none
2-amino-6-thiopurine	—	—	—	none
8-azaguanine	—	—	+	none
6-azathymine	—	—	+	none
2-chloro-6-hydroxypurine	—	—	+	none
2,6-diaminopurine	—	+	++	none
5-hydroxymethylcytosine	—	—	—	none
6-mercaptopurine	—	—	+	none
6-methyladenine	—	—	++	none
5-methylcytosine	—	—	—	none
6-methylpurine	—	—	++	none
purine	—	—	++	none
purine-9-riboside	—	—	++	inhibits slightly
2-thioadenine	—	—	—	none
5-bromouracil	—	+	+	inhibits
5-bromo-deoxyuridine	—	++	+	inhibits slightly
2-thiocytosine	—	—	—	none

In this reversion test only those mutations can be detected which restore the ability of the genome to make a functioning protein (enzyme). For the *r*II locus these reversions do not seem to arise as the result of a "suppressor mutation" at another locus, because the existence of several non-reverting "point" mutations (see Fig. 2) makes such a suppressor effect improbable and because crosses between some revertants and standard type phages have shown that the reversion involves a mutation closely linked to, or at, the original mutational site. Thus only mutations at one or a very small number of genetic sites within the *r*II region will be able to cause the reversion of a given mutation.

The reversion test for a given *r*II mutant may therefore reveal the mutagenicity of *some* mutagens by the induction of reversions, and be inert to others. Such a specificity of different mutable sites is demonstrated in the foregoing test, in which phage N19, but not *r*131, responded to base analogues. The mutagenic response should be much less specific if the induction of *forward* mutations is measured. For in this case changes at any one DNA site necessary for a functioning protein can be detected. The number of these indispensable sites is large and at least some of them should respond to the mutagen.

Therefore all the purine analogues were tested once more, this time for the induction of forward mutations under partial purine deprivation. The purine-less bacteria *B-96* were grown and infected under conditions (described in a later section) which give a strong mutagenic effect of 2-aminopurine. The base analogue was added in amounts of 100 μg/ml. and of 500 μg/ml. A significant mutagenic effect was found only for AP and 2,6-diamino-purine. In repeated tests between 0·5 % and 1·5 % *r*-mutants were produced.

The inhibition of bacterial growth, displayed on plates by a less turbid or even clear circle around the base analogue, is qualitatively summarized in Table 1, column 3. Most of the analogues inhibit the bacterial growth more or less.

(c) *The effect of different base analogues on T4 phage growth*

In addition to the inhibition of bacterial growth, some base analogues also affect normal phage growth. This additional effect can be observed, for example, in phage platings, beyond the area in which the base analogue spot exerts a strong bacterial inhibition. Table 1, column 4 summarizes the results. Of the base analogues used, only purine 9-riboside, 5-bromouracil (BU), 5-bromodeoxyuridine (BD), and 2-amino purine (AP) showed such an additional effect; it will be described in somewhat more detail, as far as this seems necessary for the study of the mutagenic effect of these base analogues.

Both BU and BD inhibit phage growth on plates strongly in bacteria S and K, and little in B. For smaller concentrations of BD (50 μg/ml.) the mutagenic effect is dominant while for higher concentrations the inhibition becomes more effective. When phages are grown in broth, BU shows a stronger inhibitory and a much weaker mutagenic effect than does BD.

AP depresses lysis inhibition under certain growth conditions. This can be seen most simply when *r*- and standard-type T4 phages are plated together with B on broth, or with *B-96* or *B-97* on synthetic medium plus 0·25 μg/ml. thiamine and 10 μg/ml. adenine. When 10 mg or more AP is added to the top layer the standard type phages produce plaques which are nearly (B) or completely indistinguishable from those of the *r*-type phages. Simultaneously, all "plaque interaction" between *r*- and standard-type phages vanishes. These large plaques, to which a standard-type phage gives rise, are not caused by a selection of *r*-mutants, since upon isolating and replating the phages with B on broth, most of them (about 95 %) again give standard-type plaques. The effect of AP is counteracted completely by the addition of adenine in the same concentration.

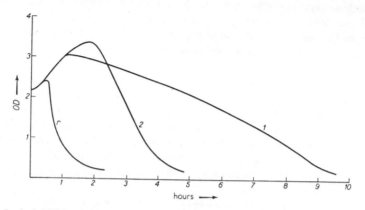

FIG. 1. *Lysis inhibition under different growth conditions. First infection with r-phage:* rapid lysis (curve *r*) independent of medium. *First infection with standard type phage:* B-97 with thiamine, histidine, or both: curve 1. B-97 with same, plus AP: curve 2. With histidine alone the decrease is less rapid than with thiamine. B-96 with histidine: decrease slower than in curve 1. AP only slightly effective. B-96 with thiamine, or both: curve 2. AP only slightly effective.

The effect of AP upon lysis inhibition in liquid medium is summarized in Fig. 1. For bacteria *B-96* the presence of thiamine alone reduces lysis inhibition and AP is only slightly effective at the concentrations used. For bacteria *B-97*, however, AP markedly accelerates lysis.

The measurements summarized in Fig. 1 were done under the following conditions. Bacteria were grown overnight in synthetic medium plus 40 μg/ml. adenine and either 20 μg/ml. histidine, 0·25 μg/ml. thiamine, or both. They were resuspended in the same medium, but with 10 μg/ml. adenine, at a concentration of 10^8/ml. and grown to 2×10^8/ml. After chilling, T4 standard type phages were added to give a multiplicity 2 and AP to give 500 μg/ml. After 8 min adsorption the culture was aerated at 37°C and 15 min later superinfected with *r*II-type phages at a multiplicity 10. The development of lysis was recorded by measuring the optical density at 600 mμ, calling O the time of incubation at 37°C. The curves given are typical for the *relative* differences under different growth conditions. The *quantitative* time-course of lysis depends on the concentration of the bacteria and of the residual adenine in the medium.

(d) *The mutability spectrum of rII-type mutants induced by 5-bromodeoxyuridine*

A mutability spectrum of T4 *r*II-type mutants included by BU has been reported by Benzer & Freese (1958). These mutants had been induced in a sulfanilamide-containing medium in which the formation of folic acid was suppressed. Flaks & Cohen (1957) have shown that bacteria B, after infection with T6 phage, synthesize an enzyme which converts deoxycytidylic acid into 5-hydroxymethyldeoxycytidylic acid and which requires tetrahydrofolic acid as a cofactor. It may therefore be presumed that sulfanilamide depressed the synthesis not only of thymidylic acid but also of HMC. We wanted to know whether the same or a different spectrum would be produced under different growth conditions using a medium in which folic acid was again counteracted, but to which excess thymidine was added to depress the incorporation of bromouracil into DNA. The addition of thymidine should not influence HMC formation since Cohen (1956) has shown that the methyl groups of thymine and methionine are not converted to the hydroxymethyl group of HMC. The mutants were induced by BD in a synthetic medium, using aminopterin as a folic acid antagonist, and thymidine was added to give a 4 : 1 ratio of thymidine to BD.

(i) *Production of mutants*

E. coli B was grown in F8 medium supplemented with 200 μg/ml. AM and 200 μg/ml. thymidine. In this medium the bacteria duplicate and stay very small. When they were grown for 6 hr to a concentration of $1\cdot5 \times 10^8$/ml. and singly infected with T4 standard type phages (multiplicity 10^{-3}) the number of infective centres (plus unadsorbed phages) decreased to about one half of its initial value by 30 min after infection. Some lysis then occurred and a burst size of 20–30 resulted. Both the loss of infective centres and the small burst size may possibly be due to a partial HMC deprivation.

BD mutants were produced in the following way: 0·1 ml. of overnight B, grown in F8, was added to 30 ml. F8 + 200 μg/ml. AM + 200 μg/ml. thymidine. The culture was aerated for 7 hr at 37°C, when the microscope count was $2\cdot3 \times 10^8$/ml. (viable count $2\cdot2 \times 10^8$/ml.). BD was added to a final concentration of 50 μg/ml. and T4 standard type phage added to give a multiplicity 2. Immediately after infection one drop of the mixture was delivered to each of 180 tubes standing in a 37°C bath. The tubes were incubated for $8\frac{1}{2}$ hr; then broth was added and each tube was diluted and plated on broth plates with B. After incubation at 37°C one r-mutant was picked from each plate on which r-mutants were found, and replated with B. From each new plate one plaque was picked and a phage stock grown with bacteria BB. The remaining undistributed mixture was aerated for 11 hr and some drops of chloroform were added to induce lysis; the lysate was plated on B for the determination of phage titer and r-mutant frequency. It showed a 20-fold increase of phage titer over the input and contained 1 % r-mutants. In the same medium without BD, the frequency of r-mutants was about 0·1 % which is higher than the usual "spontaneous" background.

(ii) *Genetic mapping of BD-induced mutants*

The series of independently arising r-type mutants were numbered N171 through N343. 103 of these were of the rII-type, the rest rI or rIII. Each of the rII-type mutants could be assigned to one of the segments into which the rII region can be subdivided by means of mutants containing large alterations (see Benzer & Freese, 1958, and Fig. 2). Further mapping could be achieved for all but three very leaky mutants. This mapping was done relative to the genetic location of all former BU-induced mutants and of all those spontaneous mutants which were available, and also with respect to all AP-mutants to be described later.

Most of the crosses were made by means of a simple spot test described previously (Benzer & Freese, 1958). About 2×10^7 phages of one mutant type were plated on a mixture of bacteria K and B (ratio 20 : 1, or 100 : 1 for leaky mutants). Phages of the other mutant type were placed on this plate as a small drop or streak as soon after plating as possible; this spot has to contain sufficient phage for recombination but not too many revertants whose frequency is checked on a control plate.

The spectrum of mutations induced under these conditions is shown in Fig. 2 (second horizontal line). Since the background of spontaneous mutants was higher than for the BU-induced spectrum of Benzer & Freese (1958) (Fig. 2, third horizontal line) it is not surprising that some mutants have the genetic location and reversion properties of the spontaneous hot spots r131 and r117. But otherwise it is obvious that essentially the same mutability spectrum has been reproduced as was reported for BU-induced mutants, with a reasonable variation in the number of mutants at each genetic site. Especially noteworthy is the recurrence of the hot spots N11, N12, and N24, and also the large number of mutants at site N29. Nearly all of the mutants revert. Only one non-reverting mutant has been found at site N29.

(e) *The mutability spectrum of rII-type mutants induced by 2-amino purine*

To obtain conditions under which the mutagenic effect is high, and therefore the background of spontaneous mutants low, the purine-less bacteria B-96 and B-97 were used, since AP is a purine analogue. Under complete purine starvation (B-96 or B-97 grown exponentially in H-medium plus 25 μg/ml. adenine, then washed and resuspended in H-medium) the phage mutation-rate did not increase appreciably. Some adenine was therefore added and a strong mutagenic effect was found.

(i) *Production of mutants*

An exponentially-growing culture of B-96 (in H-medium plus 25 μg/ml. adenine hemi-sulfate) was diluted to give a microscope count of 5×10^7 cells/ml. in an H-medium with the final concentration of 10 μg/ml. adenine and 500 μg/ml. AP. The bacteria were grown for 4 hr at 37°C at which time the microscope count was about $1\cdot2 \times 10^8$ cells/ml. (cells were about three times as long as normally). T4 standard type phages were then added to give 10^7 phages/ml., the culture was aerated for 10 hr at 37°C, and then chloroform was added. The phage titer was 3×10^9/ml. (plated on B). These phages contained many plaque-type mutants, among which r-mutants occurred with a frequency between 1 and 2 %. In controls, grown with the same amount of histidine and adenine, but without AP, the frequency of r-mutants was normally less than 0·1 %.

The same mutagenic effect was obtained with the adenine-specific purine-less mutant B-97, when grown under similar conditions. This shows that the specific inhibition, observed with B-96 and described above, has no influence upon the mutation rate.

The mutability spectrum of AP-induced mutants was determined twice, once using phage mutants arising in bacteria B-96 and once using mutants arising in B-97. The bacteria grown under the conditions described above were singly infected with standard type phages (50 to 80 phages/ml.), immediately distributed by drops to many tubes, and 60 min after infection plated with bacteria B. From each plate only one r-type mutant was picked and purified by replating, and thus a large number of independent mutants was isolated, which were numbered AP1, AP2 and so on.

(ii) *Genetic mapping of AP mutants*

Of 156 such r-type mutants arising in B-96, 53 were of the rII-type; and of the 144 r-type mutants arising in B-97, 47 were of the rII-type. Each of the rII-type mutants could be assigned to one of the rII-segments by the spot test technique. The further mapping of the AP-mutants with respect to one another, to the bromo-uracil (or bromodeoxyuridine) induced N-mutants, and to the 25 available spontaneous r-mutants, could be achieved for all but four leaky mutants of the B-96 set and one leaky mutant of the B-97 set. The results are shown in Fig. 2 (fourth and fifth horizontal lines).

Many of the phage AP-mutants induced in bacteria B-96 coincide genetically with those induced in B-97. At certain sites mutants recur frequently in both sets, and the variation of their number is within reasonable limits. Hence, the mutability spectra of AP mutants induced into the bacteria B-96 and B-97 are essentially alike, and apparently are not influenced by the difference in bacterial inhibition reported for AP earlier in this paper.

Only a small number of AP-mutants appeared at the genetic location of some spontaneous mutants; most of these have quite a different reversion index indicating a different type of mutation. The two real coincidences can be attributed to a background of spontaneous mutants among the AP-induced ones. Apparently the mutants induced by AP are of a type quite different from most spontaneous mutants.

Finally, a comparison between the AP- and the N-mutants shows again a clear difference in the mutagenic specificity of AP and BU. This is exhibited especially

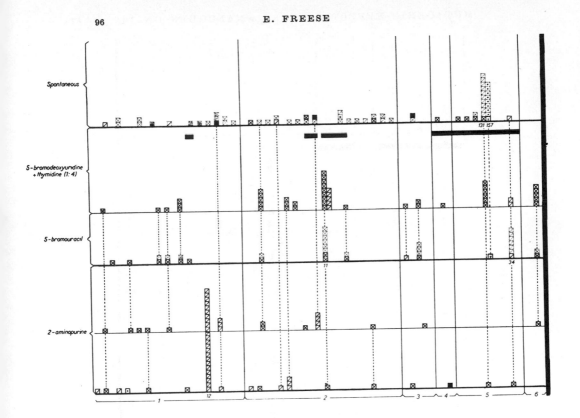

Fig. 2. Genetic map of the *r*II region of phage T4 showing the locations of mutations for independently isolated *r*II-type mutants.

The mutations induced by three different means are vertically displaced: first horizontal line: spontaneous mutations (*r*) (see Benzer & Freese, 1958); second horizontal line: mutations induced by 5-bromodeoxyuridine with the addition of four times as much thymidine (N); third horizontal line: mutations induced by 5-bromouracil (N) (see Benzer & Freese, 1958); fourth horizontal line: mutations induced by 2-aminopurine in bacteria B-97 (AP); fifth horizontal line: mutations induced by 2-aminopurine in bacteria B-96 (AP).

The *r*II region is divided into cistron A and B, and into segments 1, 2, 3, 4, 5, 6, 8; segments 7, 9, 11 are lumped together. Each mutant is represented by a box and placed in the proper segment. Mutants were assigned to a given segment by crossing each to a set of 6 large alteration mutants (see Benzer & Freese, 1958). Mostly by spot tests, and sometimes by normal crosses using a mixed infection of bacteria B, it was determined which mutants of the same segment recombine with one another and which do not. All mutants for which clearly no recombination was found are stacked at the same abscissa of the drawing. Mutants which certainly differ in

well for the hot spot AP12, at which no BU-induced mutant has been found, and for the hot spot N12 at which no AP-induced mutant has been observed.

But the difference in mutagenic specificity between BU- and AP-induced mutants is certainly less than that between induced and spontaneous mutants. As a matter of fact quite a number of AP- and N-mutants coincide genetically; e.g., at the BU hot spot N24 nine AP-mutants have been observed. This shows that some of the sites which can be mutated by BU can also be mutated by AP, while for other sites the two base analogues behave rather differently.

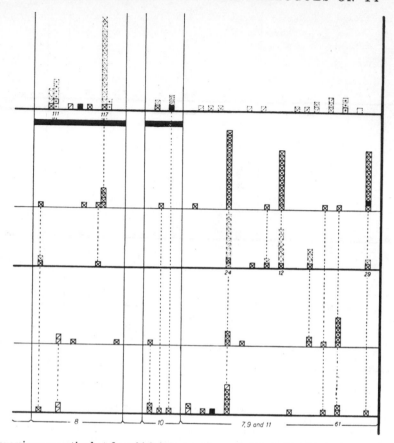

their reversion properties but for which it has not been clearly decided whether or not they can recombine, are shown immediately adjacent to one another. All other horizontally-displaced mutants do recombine. The order and position of recombining mutants within one segment have not been determined. One N-mutant was available for each genetic site at which N mutants have been reported in the previous work by Benzer & Freese (1958), while of the r-mutants only some including all hot spots, were available for this work. All mutants which were not available for crossing are indicated by dotted lines.

The reversion index of each mutant is indicated by shading. A dot ⊡ corresponds to a reversion index larger than 100×10^{-6}; a bar ⊘ corresponds to a reversion index between 1 and 100×10^{-6}; a cross ⊠ corresponds to any observed reversion with an index smaller than 1×10^{-6}; and a black box ■ indicates mutants for which no reversion has been observed. The sensitivity of detection of rare spontaneous reversions can be greatly increased when the phages are plated together with a mixture of bacteria K and B (ratio 20 : 1, for example). Applying this technique the rare reversion of some mutants was detected which had not shown any revertants in earlier work (Benzer & Freese, 1958).

Most AP-induced mutants revert, with only two exceptions among 106 mutants. Most of the reversion indices are in the neighbourhood of 10^{-6} (e.g., the hot spot AP12) or smaller.

(f) *Rejection of selection as a cause for the specific mutagenic effect*

Selection could play a role at three different stages of phage-mutant production: (i) The base analogue could select certain r-mutants present in the wild type stock, or (ii) it could select for or against certain r-type mutants in the bacteria in which they have been produced, or finally (iii) a selection could take place on the plate by preferential picking of certain phenotypes of r-type mutants. None of the three types of selection can be the cause either for the high frequency of r-type mutants, or for the difference in mutability spectra.

(i) The high selection of any r-type mutants preexisting in the wild type stock can best be excluded by a fluctuation test. For BU such a test has been reported by Litman & Pardee (1956) and it is therefore only necessary to give the similar results for AP. The bacteria *B-96* were grown under the conditions given above for a large mutagenic effect. They were singly infected with T4 standard-type phages and immediately distributed by drops into small test tubes. Each tube received about four phages. After an incubation time of 60 min in a 37°C waterbath all tubes were transferred to a 45°C bath. Soft agar and bacteria B were added to each tube, and the contents plated on broth plates. Each plate contained, on the average, 600 phages, the numbers varying between 70 and 800. (One of the 89 plates tested had no plaques.) Most plaques were of standard type. Among other mutants, varying numbers of r- and mottled plaques were found. The arithmetical mean value for the frequency of r- and mottled plaques taken together was 1·6 %. The number of plates falling into a given range of percent mutants per plate are given in Table 2. If the large

TABLE 2

Variation in the number of mutants arising under the action of 2-aminopurine

r- and (clearly) mottled plaques are both counted as mutants. Bacteria singly infected (multiplicity 4×10^{-7}).

Average number of plaques per plate about 600.

Percentage of r plus mottled plaques per plate	Number of plates
0	2
$0 < \ldots \leq 0·5$	12
$0·5 < \ldots \leq 1$	28
$1 < \ldots \leq 2$	26
$2 < \ldots \leq 3$	11
$3 < \ldots \leq 7$	9
11	1

percentage of r-mutants among the progeny phages had arisen by selection for r, one would expect a very small number of plates with a huge percentage of r-mutants, while all other plates would display only standard-type plaques. This follows from the small frequency of r-mutants among the infecting standard-type phages (less than 10^{-4}) and the small probability that an r-mutant appears spontaneously among the duplicating phages (also less than 10^{-4} per phage per duplication). Only 2 of the 88 plates had no r-mutant or mottled plaques and the largest percentage of r-plaques found on just one plate was 11 %. This clearly excludes selection.

(ii) Some of the rII mutants induced by the base analogue could possibly replicate faster than others, under the action of the base analogue (or the growth medium).

Another analogue (or growth medium) could possibly stimulate or suppress the growth of other types of rII-mutants, and thus produce the difference between the mutability spectra. *A priori* this possibility appears rather remote. Each of the rII-mutants of the same cistron probably fails to induce the formation of one and the same functioning enzyme, and it seems unlikely that different base analogues could differentiate between such differences by selective inhibition. However, this possible mechanism has also been excluded experimentally. Bacteria were grown under conditions of strong phage-mutagenic effect produced either by BD or by AP. They were then infected with different phage mixtures in different multiplicities to test for selection. The phages used were of three types—standard type, BU hot spot N12, and AP hot spot AP12. The results are summarized in Table 3. For mixed infection

TABLE 3

Effect of different mutagenic growth conditions upon the growth of different phage mutants

The growth conditions were those of high 5-bromodeoxyuridine mutagenicity and of high AP mutagenicity (bacteria *B-96*) as described in the text. The phages were absorbed to bacteria of titer 2×10^8 and the culture aerated at 37°C for 5 hr. After addition of chloroform the phages were assayed on B. *a* and *b* are two separate experiments with different concentrations of BD (0·1 and 0·2 mg/ml.) and AP (0·5 and 1 mg/ml.). r^+ = T4-standard type; N12 = rII-type mutant of a 5-bromouracil-induced hot spot; AP12 = rII-type mutant of a 2-aminopurine-induced hot spot.

Phages	Plaque types		In stock	After growth in BD		After growth in AP	
				a	*b*	*a*	*b*
N12 + standard	ratio $r : r^+$ multiplicity of infection	= =	1·8	1·2 6	1·4 6	1·8 6	1·5 6
				a	*b*	*a*	*b*
AP12 + standard	ratio $r : r^+$ multiplicity of infection	= =	1·6	1·1 5	1·1 5	1·4 5	1·4 5
			% of total	plaques	% of total	plaques	% of total
N12 + AP12	N12	=	0·55	67	0·52	70	0·52
	AP12	=	0·45	52	0·40	59	0·44
	r^+	=	0	5	(0·04)	3	(0·015)
	possible double r multiplicity of infection	= =	0	5 1	(0·04)	1 1	(0·02)

with r- and standard-type the progeny phage have in most cases a slightly higher percentage of standard-type phage than the input (probably due to lysis inhibition); but no strong selection can be observed which is specific for or against a certain rII-type mutant and which depends on the medium. The absence of selection is especially clear for the case of infection with the two rII-type phages N12 and AP12: The progeny phages were plated on B, all plaques were picked, replated on K + 1/100 B, and the plates were spotted with two large alteration mutants (of cistron A and B) to determine whether they were AP12 or N12. The phage ratios after growth in BD and AP were alike (see Table 3). These results exclude any selection between mutants of a BU and an AP hot spot, under any one of the mutagenic growth conditions used.

(iii) The final possibility is that certain plaque types are picked preferentially. A slight difference in plaque type can sometimes be observed on B between rI- and rII type mutants, the former tending to be larger with more halo. But among the different rII-type mutants no systematic difference has been seen, and hot spot and non-hot spot rII mutants could not be distinguished in mixed platings. Nevertheless, to avoid any unconscious selection, the first r-type mutant seen on a plate was picked. Apart from these precautions, the experimental evidence clearly excludes the preferential picking of certain mutants on any large scale. Either one would expect to pick the same type of plaque preferentially on every occasion, which should give rise to the same spectrum for BU and AP; or one might select a different plaque type in each experiment in which mutants are isolated, which then should yield a different spectrum each time. The evidence rules out both these alternatives.

It therefore seems to be a valid conclusion that the three different mutability spectra (spontaneous, BU or BD, and AP-induced) are caused by a difference in the mutagenic specificity of the agents responsible for the induction of the mutations, and cannot be attributed to any kind of selection.

4. Discussion

We discuss first the genetic and then the biochemical aspect of this work. The genetic analysis of the rII-type mutants induced by 5-bromouracil (BU) or 5-bromo-deoxyuridine (BD), and by 2-aminopurine (AP), showed each of the corresponding mutations to be localized in a very small area of the genome. Since nearly all of these mutants revert, perhaps most of them involve the change of just one nucleotide pair in the DNA.

The large number of sites at which mutations are observable are distributed over the whole of the rII region, as can be seen in Fig. 2. A given base analogue mutates different sites of the genome with different frequencies, which is strikingly displayed in sites of high mutability ("hot spots"). BU (or BD) and AP exhibit a difference in their mutagenic specificity, for some of their hot spots are at genetically different locations. In contrast to this difference between different analogues the same analogue gave the same mutability spectrum when applied twice under different growth conditions. These observations, in addition to mixed infection experiments and the fluctuation test, prove that the hot spots (and mutability spectra) are caused by specific mutagenesis of the base analogue at certain sites of the genome and not by any kind of selection.

Some of the BU-induced mutations coincide with some of the AP-induced ones, and thus reveal some common specificity. In contrast, practically all the mutations arising in the presence of BU or AP are different from the spontaneous ones, apart from a background of spontaneous mutants. This apparent mutual exclusion may divide the mutable sites into two or more classes so that a given base analogue can mutate the different sites of one class with varying frequency but never those of another class.

We shall now discuss the biochemical aspect and show how the two base analogues may exert their strong mutagenic effect. We first note that, since both analogues can form two hydrogen bonds to one of the normal DNA bases, their incorporation into DNA is structurally possible. BU can pair with adenine and thus replace thymine while AP can pair with thymine and replace adenine (Fig. 3). BU can quantitatively replace thymine in phage DNA, as shown by Dunn & Smith (1954); the incorporation of AP is being examined.

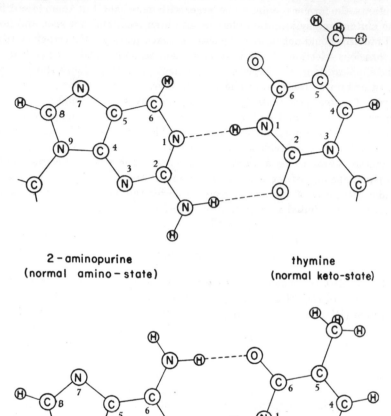

2 - aminopurine
(normal amino – state)

thymine
(normal keto-state)

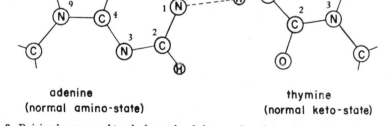

adenine
(normal amino-state)

thymine
(normal keto-state)

Fig. 3. *Pairing by means of two hydrogen bonds between 2-aminopurine and thymine, as compared to pairing between adenine and thymine.* While the latter pair uses the 1- and 6-positions of the purine and pyrimidine rings, the former occupies the 1- and 2-positions. In 5-bromouracil the methyl group of thymine is replaced by the equally large bromine atom, which has the same van der Waals radius.

It is not experimentally known whether the mutagenic action of BU or AP is direct, by incorporation into DNA, or indirect, by unbalancing the nucleic acid metabolism in the bacterial cell. But the fact that many base analogues which do not seem to be incorporated into DNA (6-mercaptopurine, etc.) inhibit bacterial growth, and yet are not highly mutagenic, makes it probable that the effect of the two base analogues used here is a direct one. We shall therefore discuss how such a direct mutagenic effect may come about using the further assumption that in DNA replication each new DNA chain is formed along a pre-existing complementary chain (e.g., according to the model proposed by Watson & Crick (1953)).

In this picture permanent mutations are not caused merely by the replacement of a DNA base by its base analogue. For, in subsequent DNA replications in a normal medium, the incorporated analogue can attach to it the base it originally paired with, and thus cause the formation of new DNA with unaltered nucleotide pairs. For instance many of the phages in which thymine has been quantitatively replaced by BU grow as well as normal phages, and 90 % of the growing ones do not exhibit any mutation. Mutations are rather induced by mistakes in base pairing which the analogue may undergo more or less frequently. We shall first examine how such mistakes in pairing can come about and then see how they may induce the transition of one nucleotide pair into another.

The possibility of rare mistaken pairings of normal DNA bases, due to tautomeric shift, has been mentioned by Watson & Crick (1953). BU should behave rather

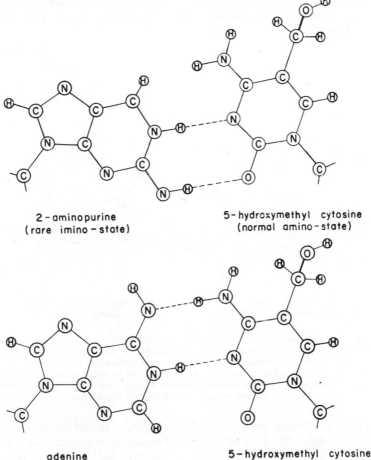

2 - aminopurine   5 - hydroxymethyl cytosine
(rare imino - state)   (normal amino - state)

adenine   5 - hydroxymethyl cytosine
(rare imino-state)   (normal amino-state)

FIG. 4. *The rare "mistake pairing", by means of two hydrogen bonds, between 2-aminopurine and 5-hydroxymethylcytosine (HMC) as compared to the pairing between adenine and HMC. For both of these pairings a tautomeric shift from the amino- into the imino-state is necessary in one of the bases.*

III. DNA STRUCTURE AND REPLICATION   361 similarly to thymine, and should therefore be able to pair by mistake with guanine. Meselson (personal communication) has pointed out that the higher electro-negativity of bromine (as compared to the 5-methyl group) should increase the frequency of tautomeric shifts in BU over that in thymine; and possibly just the loss of the hydrogen atom in the 1-position of BU could in itself give rise to a mistaken pairing by one hydrogen bond.

AP can make two hydrogen bonds with 5-hydroxymethyl cytosine (HMC), after it has undergone a tautomeric shift (Fig. 4); in this respect it is similar to adenine (Fig. 4). But in contrast to adenine, AP can make one hydrogen bond to HMC even when both bases are in their normal (amino) state (Fig. 5). This one bond alone, since no other groups are sterically hindering, may be sufficient to cause frequent pairing of AP with HMC (or another cytosine base). If this hypothesis is correct, all those 2-aminopurines should be mutagenic which bear a monovalent group at the 6-position, as long as the enzyme system can still convert them into the direct DNA precursor, and the pairing is not interfered with by steric hindrance. It might further be expected that the pairing mistakes of AP would be more frequent than those of BU, since they can occur when AP is in its normal state.

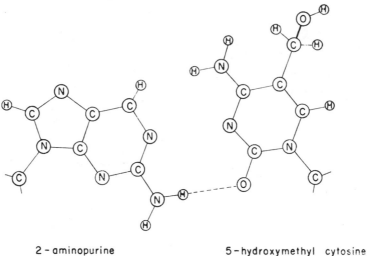

2 - aminopurine
(normal amino - state)

5 - hydroxymethyl cytosine
(normal amino - state)

FIG. 5. *The frequent "mistake pairing", by means of one hydrogen bond, between 2-aminopurine and HMC.* Both bases are in their normal amino-state. If this pairing were often fixed in duplicating DNA a high mutation rate would be expected, even under conditions of little incorporation of 2-aminopurine into DNA. Adenine cannot undergo such a frequent mistake-pairing since the two amino groups in the 6-position cannot form any strong hydrogen bonds when they are in the amino-state, nor are any other hydrogen bonds then possible.

Each pairing mistake fixed in replicating DNA by the incorporation of the attaching nucleotide ultimately gives rise to a change of one nucleotide pair in some of the progeny DNA molecules. To understand this clearly, we must consider two distinct possibilities: "mistakes in incorporation" and "mistakes in replication" (see Fig. 6). For purposes of illustration we shall take the case of BU.

A "mistake in incorporation" occurs when the DNA precursor of BU attaches to a guanine nucleotide of a pre-existing DNA chain, so that BU is incorporated in the
H

place of HMC. In the next DNA replication the incorporated BU attaches to it adenine, its normal complementary base; and in subsequent DNA replications BU can be replaced by thymine, its normal analogue. Ultimately, therefore, an HMC-guanine pair has been replaced by a thymine adenine pair in some of the progeny DNA molecules.

A "mistake in replication," on the other hand, may occur only *after* BU has been incorporated into DNA in the place of its normal analogous base thymine. When this DNA molecule replicates the incorporated BU may by mistake attach a guanine. This ultimately results in the change of a thymine-adenine pair into an HMC-guanine pair in some of the progeny DNA molecules (see Fig. 6).

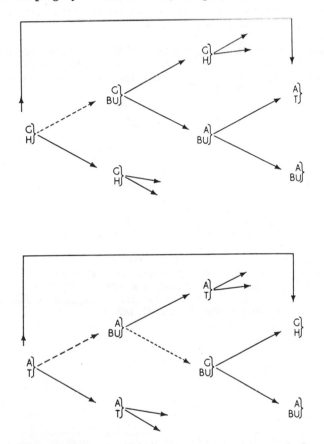

FIG. 6. *Illustration of the two types of pairing mistakes*, in the case of 5-bromouracil (BU). The normal DNA bases are indicated by H = 5-hydroxymethylcytosine, G = guanine, T = thymine, A = adenine.

(a) *Mistake in incorporation.* During DNA replication BU attaches " by mistake " to one of the G-bases, thereby initiating the change of an H—G into a T—A pair.

(b) *Mistake in replication.* During DNA replication BU attaches to adenine, with a frequency proportional to its incorporation into DNA. In one of the subsequent replications the incorporated BU may by mistake become attached to G instead of A, and thereby initiate the change of a T—A into a H—G pair. Under conditions of little BU incorporation two rare events are necessary, namely incorporation and mistake pairing.

Once a mistake in base pairing has occurred, the further development of the change is independent of the presence or absence of the base analogue in the medium. The change of a nucleotide pair will produce an observable mutation if it causes the formation of proteins with altered function (e.g., a reactivated or inactivated enzyme).

This scheme has also been proposed by Meselson & Stahl (personal communication). It predicts that such a highly mutagenic base analogue can induce the "transition" of either of the two types of nucleotide pairs, adenine-thymine into guanine-HMC and *vice versa*. The relative frequency of transitions in these two directions cannot be predicted, at present, since it depends on several unknown factors. Experimentally, however, it may be possible to enhance or suppress one direction without altering the other. In an attempt to do this we have induced mutations under different growth conditions, e.g. adding together with BD four times as much thymidine, which should depress BU incorporation. So far essentially the same mutability spectrum has been observed under such altered conditions.

I should like to thank Drs. J. D. Watson and M. Meselson for several stimulating discussions and Drs. J. S. Gots and B. Magasanik for advice concerning purine-less bacterial mutants. The material for this research was obtained by means of a grant from the Public Health Service to Dr. J. D. Watson.

REFERENCES

Benzer, S. & Freese, E. (1958). *Proc. Nat. Acad. Sci., Wash.* **44**, 112.
Buchanan, J. M., Flaks, J. G., Hartman, S. C., Levenberg, B., Lukens, L. N. & Warrens, L.
    (1957). *Ciba Foundation symposium on the chemistry and biology of purines*, p. 233.
Cohen, S. S. & Barner, H. D. (1956). *J. Bact.* **71**, 588.
Cohen, S. S. (1956). *Science*, **123**, 653.
Dunn, D. B. & Smith, J. D. (1954). *Nature*, **174**, 305.
Flaks, J. G. & Cohen, S. S. (1957). *Biochim. biophys. Acta*, **25**, 667.
Friedkin, M. & Kornberg, A. (1957). *The Chemical Basis of Heredity*, ed. McElroy and
    Glass, p. 609. Johns Hopkins Press.
Gots, J. S. & Love, S. H. (1954). *J. Biol. Chem.* **210**, 395.
Gots, J. S. & Gollub, E. G. (1957). *Proc. Nat. Acad. Sci., Wash.* **43**, 826.
Litman, R. M. & Pardee, A. B. (1956). *Nature*, **178**, 529.
Watson, J. D. & Crick, F. H. C. (1953). *Cold Spr. Harb. Symp. Quant. Biol.* **18**, 23.
Webb, M. & Nickerson, W. J. (1956). *J. Bact.* **71**, 140.

SECTION IV
Genetic Recombination

Introduction

Genetic recombination has been and remains the tool for highest resolution of genetic fine structure. While it is true that the original concept of the gene related it to a unit character rather than to a functional unit of the genetic material, the definition was soon based on genetic recombination. The gene was defined as a unit which could not be subdivided by crossing-over, but would separate from other units in the same chromosome. The first paper selected for this section (Sturtevant, 1913) shows the clarity with which the concept of genetic organization could be presented with this model. The rapid progress of genetic theory based on studies of linkage, recombination, and non-disjunction is recorded in the "Mechanism of Mendelian Heredity" by Morgan, Sturtevant, Muller, and Bridges (1922) and by Morgan (1928) in his "Theory of the Gene."

Most of the essential facts concerning the chromosomal theory of heredity were well established before a correlation could be made between the genetically observable result of crossing-over and the cytological event, i.e., the new chromosome arrangement produced by crossing-over. Two papers appeared in 1931 which established this correlation (Stern, 1931; Creighton and McClintock, 1931). We have selected the latter for the second paper of this section, because of its briefness and the simplicity of the example. It should be noted, however, that although both papers present evidence that genetic recombination is correlated with new cytological arrangements of chromosomal material, the mechanism is not revealed. The new combination could be produced by breakage and reunion or by a replication involving copy choice.

Evidence presented below indicates that breakage and exchange at molecular dimensions occurs as a part of genetic recombination in phages. Reciprocal exchange of sister chromatids by breakage and reunion has also been established during the mitotic cycle by the analysis of breakage and reunion of tritium-labeled chromosomes (Taylor, 1959; Marin and Prescott, 1964). Similar evidence which shows that reciprocal exchange of homologous chromatids occur in the meiotic division in a grasshopper has very recently been obtained (Taylor, 1965). However, these findings do not rule out copy choice or similar events at the molecular level which probably explain the phenomena of gene conversion and its consequences which are observed as aberrant segregation in tetrad analysis, particularly in ascomycetes. As an outgrowth of studies on the requirements for DNA replication in the rejoining of broken chromosomes, Taylor *et al.* (1962) suggested a repair mechanism in which small segments of DNA were lost and replaced, as the basis for this type of non-reciprocal genetic recombination. More recent studies on repair of DNA following ultraviolet irradiation and other types of damage make this scheme seem very plausible (Setlow and Carrier, 1964; Boyce and Howard-Flanders, 1964; Pettijohn and Hanawalt, 1963, 1964).

The third paper reprinted here (Lindegren, 1936) outlines the steps in mapping one chromosome of *Neurospora crassa*. Although the principles are similar to those used earlier for several other organisms, the role *Neurospora* and other ascomycetes have played in genetic analysis make this a very suitable step in developing our topic. As pointed out by B. O. Dodge, who initiated the genetic studies with *Neurospora*, one has the advantage that the results of segregation are immediately visible in the mature ascus, or if not one can make them visible by ordered isolation and growth of the linearly arranged ascospores. The segregation is regularly four of one parental type and four of the other in 8-spore asci. The adjacent pairs beginning at either end of the ascus are usually identical since they originate by a post-meiotic mitosis. However, if one observes the segregation of two pairs of factors there will be a characteristic proportion of the four-four arrangements (ditype) and the tetratype (two-four-two or two-two-two-two) depending on the independent assortment of the pairs of factors or their linkage and recombination frequencies. The regularity of segregation was taken for granted for years until Lindegren (1953) called attention to what he considered significant exceptions. In subsequent years the exceptional asci received a great amount of attention especially after evidence indicated that recombination in bacteriophages was non-reciprocal (Levinthal, 1954, 1959). We have selected one short paper (Olive, 1959) which illustrates the exceptions in a very dramatic way because the traits involve spore colors. Aberrant asci may have either 6:2 or 5:3 arrangements. Two explanations have been given for their occurrence: (1) copy choice (Lederberg, 1955) or double replication of one locus to the exclusion of the other (Taylor, 1959), or (2) crossing over in regions heterozygous for small inversions or tandem repeats. The details are beyond the scope of this presentation; for further details see Lewis and Lewis (1959); Rizet *et al.* (1960); Lissoubra *et al.* (1962); Peterson and Laughan (1963). As indicated above repair of DNA particularly in connection with breaks and exchanges now appears to be the most reasonable explanation for most cases.

For studies of genetic fine structure based on genetic recombination the viruses and bacteria have played a leading role, because extremely large populations are required. The development of these new genetic materials for recombination studies was announced in a very cautious way by papers presented at the *Cold Spring Harbor Symposium on Quantitative Biology* in the spring of 1946. Two short papers presented there are reprinted in our section on Genetic Recombination (Delbrück and Bailey, 1946 and Lederberg and Tatum, 1946).

The work on *Escherichia coli* developed rapidly under the leadership of Lederberg. His earliest definitive paper (Lederberg, 1947) is reprinted here. Many of the exciting developments in this field are recorded in detail by Jacob and Wollman (1961).

Genetic recombination studies utilizing the phages progressed more slowly, but Hershey and Chase (1951) presented an excellent paper illustrating the methods for studying recombination in phages. It is reprinted as the eighth paper in this section. They also discovered the phenomenon of heterozygosis in phages which has since played such an important role in studies of the mechanism of genetic recombination (Levinthal, 1959; Edgar, 1961).

The original idea that a gene was not subdivided by recombination began to yield because of exceptional cases observed in studies of *Drosophila* during the two decades preceding 1950. The study of several of these loci is reviewed by Lewis (1950). Studies of these so-called complex loci and position effects led some geneticists to question the concept of the gene as a unit of structure and function (see Goldschmidt, 1951). In attempts to isolate or define the functional unit Lewis utilized the *cis-trans* test. The reasoning was that if two genetic units were independent in their activity, the phenotype produced when they were located on the same chromosome (*cis* position) should be identical to that in which they were on homologous chromosomes (*trans* position). Mutants affecting the same trait were found which did not behave as independent units in the *cis-trans* test. The explanation offered at the time was that position effects might result from the utilization of the product of one gene by its near neighbor. However, the solution to the problem finally came from studies of recombination in systems where larger populations could be handled and very rare events could be detected.

The ninth paper in this section by Benzer (1957) represents both an experimental and conceptual advance. He proposed that the unit which geneticists were trying to use in an all-inclusive sense could have at least three aspects. The unit of function (cistron defined by the *cis-trans* test) might be different from the mutable unit (muton) and the unit of recombination (recon). Using the r^{II} locus in the phage T4, he showed that the trait involved, the ability to reproduce in certain strains of bacteria, depended on two functional units (cistron A and cistron B) each of which presumably controlled the formation of a different polypeptide. When the concept was applied to the DNA, the two cistrons would represent tandemly linked segments of DNA which could function equally well in the same chromosome or on separate chromosomes in the same cell. The one gene-one enzyme concept was now stated more precisely as "one cistron-one polypeptide chain." One or several of these polypeptides could conceivably form a single enzyme or protein molecule as demonstrated by the information on hemoglobins.

A cistron could mutate at numerous sites and many of these mutants were recombinable. The map produced was a linear array of mutable sites within each cistron. Studies of the mutagenic effects of base analogs and reverse mutations indicated that many mutations involved the substitution of a single base pair in the DNA duplex (see the last paper in Section III on DNA Structure and Replication by Freese, 1959). Non-reverting mutants usually represented deletion of several to many nucleotides pairs. These types failed to form functional recombinants when mated with other mutants carrying an overlapping deletion. On the other hand, non-overlapping deletions upon recombination gave rise to functional phages.

The study of mutations affecting regulatory mechanisms led to the discovery of another functional unit, the operon (see Jacob and Monod, 1961, in Section I on Biochemical Genetics). This unit is conceived as a cluster of tandemly arranged cistrons under the control of an adjacent closely linked operator locus and a regulator gene which may be anywhere in the genetic complement. In addition a unit of replication (the replicon) which may be a whole chromosome in viruses and bacteria (Jacob et al., 1963) has been defined on the basis of replication patterns. Another unit (the polaron) has been proposed by Rizet and his colleagues (1960) to describe a small region of a chromosome which yields non-reciprocal recombinants with a gradient of frequencies, which is presumably related to the unidirectional coping of the DNA segment involved.

The last paper in this section (Meselson and Weigle, 1961) and a similar study by Kellenberger et al. (1961) illustrates a molecular approach to a study of the mechanisms of genetic recombination. For the first time we have a demonstration that some genetic recombination at least involves breakage and reunion of DNA strands. The events involved in reunion are still obscure, but as knowledge is gained concerning the nature of the nucleases and polymerases involved in DNA replication and repair, we can hope that plausible schemes of genetic recombination can be devised which are testable experimentally. The idea of an enzymatically controlled process or variety of processes is replacing the older ideas of torsional breakage, and the probable importance of specific base pairing takes away much of the mystery formerly associated with concepts of genetic recombination.

REFERENCES

Boyce, R. P., and Howard-Flanders, P. (1964). *Proc. Natl. Acad. Sci. U. S.* **51**, 293.
Edgar, R. S. (1961). *Virology* **13**, 1.
Goldschmidt, R. B. (1951). *Cold Spring Harbor Symp. Quant. Biol.* **16**, 1.
Jacob, F., Brenner, S., and Cuzin, F. (1963). *Cold Spring Harbor Symp. Quant. Biol.* **28**.
Jacob, F., and Wollman, E. L. (1961). "Sexuality and the Genetics of Bacteria," 374 pp. Academic Press, New York.
Kellenberger, G., Zichichi, M. L., and Weigle, J. J. (1961). *Proc. Natl. Acad. Sci. U. S.* **47**, 869.
Lederberg, J. J. (1955). *J. Comp. Physiol.* **45** (Suppl. 2), 75.
Levinthal, C. (1954). *Genetics* **39**, 169.

Levinthal, C. (1959). *In* "The Viruses" (F. M. Burnet and W. M. Stanley, eds.), Vol. II, Chapter 8. Academic Press, New York.

Lewis, E. B. (1950). *Advan. Genet.* **3**, 73.

Lewis, K. R., and Lewis, J. B. (1959). ΦΥΤΟΝ (Gaspar Campos 841, V. Lopez, *FNGBM, Argentina* **13**, 37.

Lindegren, C. C. (1953). *J. Genet.* **51**, 625.

Lissouba, P., Mousseau, J., Rizet, G., and Rossignol, J. L. (1962). *Advan. Genet.* **11**, 343.

Marin, B., and Prescott, D. M. (1964). *J. Cell Biol.* **21**, 159.

Morgan, T. H. (1928). "Theory of the Gene," rev. ed. Yale Univ. Press, New Haven, Connecticut.

Morgan, T. H., Sturtevant, A. H., Muller, H., and Bridges, C. (1922). "Mechanism of Mendelian Heredity," 2nd ed., 262 pp. Holt, New York.

Peterson, H. M., and Laughnan, J. R. (1963). *Proc. Natl. Acad. Sci. U. S.* **50**, 126.

Pettijohn, D. E., and Hanawalt, P. C. (1963). *Biochim. Biophys. Acta* **72**, 127.

Pettijohn, D. E., and Hanawalt, P. C. (1964). *J. Mol. Biol.* **8**, 170.

Rizet, G., Lissouba, P., and Mousseau, J. (1960). *Bull. Soc. Franc. Physiol. Vegetale* **6**, 175.

Setlow, R. B., and Carrier, W. L. (1964). *Proc. Natl. Acad. Sci. U. S.* **51**, 226.

Stern, C. (1931). *Biol. Zentralbl.* **51**, 547.

Taylor, J. H. (1959). *Proc. 10th Intern. Congr. Genet., Montreal, 1958,* **1**, 63.

Taylor, J. H., Haut, W. F., and Tung, J. (1962). *Proc. Natl. Acad. Sci. U. S.* **48**, 190.

Taylor, J. H. (1963). *J. Cellular Comp. Physiol.* **62** (Suppl. 1), 73.

Taylor, J. H. (1965). *J. Cell Biol.* In press.

1

THE LINEAR ARRANGEMENT OF SIX SEX-LINKED FACTORS IN *DROSOPHILA*, AS SHOWN BY THEIR MODE OF ASSOCIATION †

Historical

   The parallel between the behavior of the chromosomes in reduction and that of Mendelian factors in segregation was first pointed out by Sutton ('02) though earlier in the same year Boveri ('02) had referred to a possible connection (loc. cit., footnote 1, p. 81). In this paper and others Boveri brought forward considerable evidence from the field of experimental embryology indicating that the chromosomes play an important rôle in development and inheritance. The first attempt at connecting any given somatic character with a definite chromosome came with McClung's ('02) suggestion that the accessory chromosome is a sex-determiner. Stevens ('05) and Wilson ('05) verified this by showing that in numerous forms there is a sex chromosome, present in all the eggs and in the female-producing sperm, but absent, or represented by a smaller homologue, in the male-producing sperm. A further step was made when Morgan ('10) showed that the factor for color in the eyes of the fly Drosophila ampelophila follows the distribution of the sex-chromosome already found in the same species by Stevens ('08). Later, on the appearance of a sex-linked wing mutation in Drosophila, Morgan ('10 a, '11) was able to make clear a new point. By crossing white eyed, long winged flies to those with red eyes and rudimentary wings (the new sex-linked character) he obtained, in F_2, white eyed rudimentary winged flies. This could happen only if 'crossing over' is possible; which means, on the assumption that both of these factors are in the sex-chromosomes, that an interchange of materials between homologous chromosomes occurs (in the female only, since the male has only one sex-chromosome). A point not noticed at this time came out later in connection with other sex-linked factors in Drosophila (Morgan '11 d). It became evident that some of the sex-linked factors are associated, i.e., that crossing over does not occur freely between some factors, as shown by the fact that the combinations present in the P_1 flies are much more frequent in F_2 than are

---

† Reprinted from The Journal of Experimental Zoology, Vol. 14, 1913, pp. 43–59.

1

new combinations of the same characters. This means, on the chromosome view, that the chromosomes. or at least certain segments of them, are more likely to remain intact during reduction than they are to interchange materials.[1] On the basis of these facts Morgan ('11 c, '11 d) has made a suggestion as to the physical basis of coupling. He uses Janssens' ('09) chiasmatype hypothesis as a mechanism. As he expresses it (Morgan '11 c):

If the materials that represent these factors are contained in the chromosomes, and if those that "couple" be near together in a linear series, then when the parental pairs (in the heterozygote) conjugate like regions will stand opposed. There is good evidence to support the view that during the strepsinema stage homologous chromosomes twist around each other, but when the chromosomes separate (split) the split is in a single plane, as maintained by Janssens. In consequence, the original materials will, for short distances, be more likely to fall on the same side of the split, while remoter regions will be as likely to fall on the same side as the last, as on the opposite side. In consequence, we find coupling in certain characters, and little or no evidence at all of coupling in other characters, the difference depending on the linear distance apart of the chromosomal materials that represent the factors. Such an explanation will account for all the many phenomena that I have observed and will explain equally, I think, the other cases so far described. The results are a simple mechanical result of the location of the materials in the chromosomes, and of the method of union of homologous chromosomes, and the proportions that result are not so much the expression of a numerical system as of the relative location of the factors in the chromosomes.

Scope of This Investigation

It would seem, if this hypothesis be correct, that the proportion of 'cross-overs' could be used as an index of the distance between any two factors. Then by determining the distances (in the above sense) between A and B and between B and C, one should be able to predict AC. For, if proportion of cross-overs really represents distance, AC must be, approximately, either AB plus BC, or AB minus BC, and not any intermediate value. From purely mathematical considerations, however, the sum and the difference of the proportion of cross-overs between A and B and those between B and C are only *limiting* values for the proportion of cross-overs between A and C. By using several pairs of factors one should be able to apply this test in several cases. Furthermore, experiments involving three or more sex-linked allelomorphic pairs together should furnish another and perhaps more crucial test of the view. The present paper is a preliminary report of the investigation of these matters.

I wish to thank Dr. Morgan for his kindness in furnishing me with material for this investigation, and for his encouragement and the suggestions he has offered during the progress of the work. I have also been greatly helped by numerous discussions of the theoretical side of the matter with Messrs. H. J.

---

[1] It is interesting to read, in this connection, Lock's ('06, p. 248–253) discussion of the matter

Muller, E. Altenburg, C. B. Bridges, and others. Mr. Muller's suggestions have been especially helpful during the actual preparation of the paper.

The Six Factors Concerned

In this paper I shall treat of six sex-linked factors and their inter-relationships. These factors I shall discuss in the order in which they seem to be arranged.

B stands for the black factor. Flies recessive with respect to it (b) have yellow body color. The factor was first described and its inheritance given by Morgan ('11 a).

C is a factor which allows color to appear in the eyes. The white eyed fly (first described by Morgan '10) is now known to be always recessive with respect both to C and to the next factor.

O. Flies recessive with respect to O(o) have eosin eyes. The relation between C and O has been explained by Morgan in a paper now in print and about to appear in the Proceedings of the Academy of Natural Sciences in Philadelphia.

P. Flies with p have vermilion eyes instead of the ordinary red (Morgan '11 d).

R. This and the next factor both affect the wings. The normal wing is RM. The rM wing is known as miniature, the Rm as rudimentary, and the rm as rudimentary-miniature. This factor R is the one designated L by Morgan ('11 d) and Morgan and Cattell ('12). The L of Morgan's earlier paper ('11) was the next factor.

M. This has been discussed above, under R. The miniature and rudimentary wings are described by Morgan ('11 a).

The relative position of these factors is B, $\dfrac{C}{O}$, P, R, M. C and O are placed at the same point because they are completely linked. Thousands of flies had been raised from the cross CO (red) by co (white) before it was known that there were two factors concerned. The discovery was finally made because of a mutation and not through any crossing over. It is obvious, then, that unless coupling strength be variable, the same gametic ratio must be obtained whether, in connection with other allelomorphic pairs, one uses CO (red) as against co (white), Co (eosin) against co (white), or CO (red) against Co (eosin) (the cO combination is not known).

Method of Calculating Strength of Association

In order to illustrate the method used for calculating the gametic ratio I shall use the factors P and M. The cross used in this case was, long

winged, vermilion-eyed female by rudimentary winged, red-eyed male. The analysis and results are seen in table 1.

Table 1

	Long vermilion ♀—MpX MpX
	Rudimentary red ♂—mPX
F_1	MpX mPX—long red ♀
	MpX —long vermilion ♂
Gametes F_1	Eggs —MPX mPX MpX mpX
	Sperm—MpX
F_2	MPX MpX ⎫ mPX MpX ⎭ —long red ♀—451
	MpX MpX ⎫ mpX MpX ⎭ —long vermilion ♀—417
	MPX —long red ♂—105
	mPX —rudimentary red ♂—33
	MpX —long vermilion ♂—316
	mpX —rudimentary vermilion ♂—4

It is of course obvious from the figures that there is something peculiar about the rudimentary winged flies, since they appear in far too small numbers. This point need not detain us here, as it always comes up in connection with rudimentary crosses, and is being investigated by Morgan. The point of interest at present is the linkage. In the F_2 generation the original combinations, red rudimentary and vermilion long, are much more frequent in the males (allowing for the low viability of rudimentary) than are the two new or cross-over combinations, red long and vermilion rudimentary. It is obvious from the analysis that no evidence of association can be found in the females, since the M present in all female-producing sperm masks m when it occurs. But the ratio of cross-overs in the gametes is given without complication by the F_2 males, since the male-producing sperm of the F_1 male bore no sex-linked genes. There are in this case 349 males in the non-cross-over classes and 109 in the cross-overs. The method which has seemed most satisfactory for expressing the relative position of factors, on the theory proposed in the beginning of this paper, is as follows. The unit of 'distance' is taken as a portion of the chromosome of such length that, on the average, one cross-over will occur in it out of every 100 gametes formed. That is, percent of cross-overs is used as an index of distance. In the case of P and M there occurred 109 cross-overs in 405 gametes, a ratio of 26.9 in 100; 26.9, the per cent of cross-overs, is considered as the 'distance' between P and M.

The Linear Arrangement of the Factors

Table 2 shows the proportion of cross-overs in those cases which have been worked out. The detailed results of the crosses involved are

Table 2

FACTORS CONCERNED	PROPORTION OF CROSS-OVERS	PER CENT OF CROSS-OVERS
BCO...............	$\frac{193}{16287}$	1.2
BO...............	$\frac{2}{373}$	0.5
BP...............	$\frac{1464}{4551}$	32.2
BR...............	$\frac{115}{324}$	35.5
BM...............	$\frac{260}{693}$	37.6
COP...............	$\frac{224}{748}$	30.0
COR...............	$\frac{1643}{4749}$	34.6
COM...............	$\frac{76}{161}$	47.2
OP...............	$\frac{247}{836}$	29.4
OR...............	$\frac{183}{538}$	34.0
OM...............	$\frac{218}{404}$	54.0
CR...............	$\frac{236}{829}$	28.5
CM...............	$\frac{112}{333}$	33.6
B(C, O)...........	$\frac{214}{21736}$	1.0
(C, O)P...........	$\frac{471}{1584}$	29.7
(C, O)R...........	$\frac{2062}{6116}$	33.7
(C, O)M...........	$\frac{406}{898}$	45.2
PR...............	$\frac{17}{573}$	3.0
PM...............	$\frac{109}{405}$	26.9

given at the end of this paper. The 16287 cases for B and CO are from Dexter ('12). Inasmuch as C and O are completely linked I have added the numbers for C, for O, and for C and O taken together, giving the total results in the lines beginning (C, O) P, B (C, O), etc., and have used these figures, instead of the individual C, O, or CO results, in my calculations. The fractions in the column marked 'proportion of cross-overs' represent the number of cross-overs (numerator) to total available gametes (denominator).

As will be explained later, one is more likely to obtain accurate figures for distances if those distances are short, i.e., if the association is strong. For

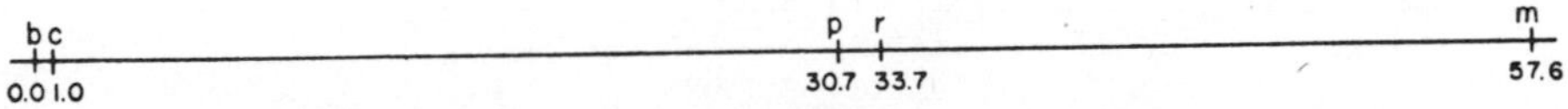

```
bc                                  p  r                          m
++                                  +  +                          +
0.0 1.0                            30.7 33.7                      57.6
```

Diagram 1

this reason I shall, in so far as possible, use the percent of cross-overs between adjacent points in mapping out the distances between the various factors. Thus, B (C, O), (C, O) P, PR, and PM form the basis of diagram 1. The figures on the diagram represent calculated distances from B.

Of course there is no knowing whether or not these distances as drawn represent the actual relative spacial distances apart of the factors. Thus the distance CP may in reality be shorter than the distance BC, but what we do know is that a break is far more likely to come between C and P than between B and C. Hence, either CP is a long space, or else it is for some reason a weak one. The point I wish to make here is that we have no means of knowing that the chromosomes are of uniform strength, and if there are strong or weak places, then that will prevent our diagram from representing actual relative distances—but, I think, will not detract from its value as a diagram.

Just how far our theory stands the test is shown by table 3, giving ob-

Table 3

FACTORS	CALCULATED DISTANCE	OBSERVED PER CENT OF CROSS-OVERS
BP....................	30.7	32.2
BR....................	33.7	35.5
BM....................	57.6	37.6
(C, O)R..............	32.7	33.7
(C, O)M..............	56.6	45.2

served per cent of cross-overs, and distances as calculated from the figures given in the diagram of the chromosome. Table 3 includes all pairs of factors given in table 2 but not used in the preparation of the diagram.

It will be noticed at once that the long distances, BM, and (C, O)M, give smaller percent of cross-overs than the calculation calls for. This is a point which was to be expected, and will be discussed later. For the present we may dismiss it with the statement that it is probably due to the occurrence of two breaks in the same chromosome, or 'double crossing over.' But in the case of the shorter distances the correspondence with expectation is perhaps as close as was to be expected with the small numbers that are available. Thus, BP is 3.2 less than BR, the difference expected being 3.0. (C, O)R is less than BR by 1.8 instead of by 1.0. It has actually been found possible to predict the strength of association between two factors by this method, fair approximations having been given for BR and for certain combinations involving factors not treated in this paper, before the crosses were made.

Double Crossing Over

On the chiasmatype hypothesis it will sometimes happen, as shown by Dexter ('12) and intimated by Morgan ('11 d) that a section of, say, maternal chromosome will come to have paternal elements at both ends, and perhaps more maternal segments beyond these. Now if this can happen it introduces a complication into the results. Thus, if a break occurs between B and P, and another between P and M, then, unless we can follow P also, there will be no evidence of crossing over between B and M, and the fly hatched from the resulting gamete will be placed in the non-cross-over class, though in reality he represents two cross-overs. In order to see if double crossing over really does occur it is necessary to use three or more sex-linked allelomorphic pairs in the same experiment. Such cases have been reported by Morgan ('11 d) and Morgan and Cattell ('12) for the factors B, CO, and R. They made such crosses as long gray red by miniature yellow white, and long yellow red by miniature gray white, etc. The details and analyses are given in the original papers, and for our present purpose it is only the flies that are available for observations on double crossing over that are of interest. Table 4 gives a graphical representation of what happened in the 10495 cases.

Double crossing over does then occur, but it is to be noted that the occurrence of the break between B and CO tends to prevent that between CO and R (or vice versa). Thus where B and CO did not separate, the gametic ratio for CO and R was about 1 to 2, but in the cases where B and CO did separate it was about 1 to 6.5.

Three similar cases from my own results, though done on a smaller scale, are given in the table at the end of this paper. The results are represented in tables 5, 6 and 7.

It will be noted that here also the evidence, so far as it goes, indicated that the occurrence of one cross-over makes another one less likely to occur in the same gamete. In the case of BOPR there was an opportunity for triple crossing over, but it did not occur. Of course, on the view here presented

Table 4

NO CROSSING OVER	SINGLE CROSSING OVER		DOUBLE CROSSING OVER
B CO R	B CO R	B CO R	B CO R
6972	3454	60	9

Table 5

NO CROSSING	SINGLE CROSSING OVER		DOUBLE CROSSING OVER
O P R	O P R	O P R	O P R
194	102	11	1

Table 6

NO CROSSING	SINGLE CROSSING OVER		DOUBLE CROSSING OVER
B O M	B O M	B O M	B O M
278	160	1	0

Table 7

B O P R	B O P R	B O P R	B O P R	B O P R	B O P R	B O P R	B O P R
393	203	19	6	2	1	1	0

there is no reason why it should not occur, if enough flies were raised. An examination of the figures will show that it was not to be expected in such small numbers as are here given. So far as I know there is, at present, no evidence that triple crossing over takes place, but it seems highly probable that it will be shown to occur.[2]

Unfortunately, in none of the four cases given above are two comparatively long distances involved, and in only one are there enough figures to form a fair basis for calculation, so that it seems as yet hardly possible to determine how much effect double crossing over has in pulling down the observed percent of cross-overs in the case of BM and (C, O)M. Whether or not this effect is partly counter-balanced by triple crossing over must also remain unsettled as yet. Work now under way should furnish answers to both these questions.

---

[2] A case of triple crossing over within the distance CR was observed after this paper went to press.

Possible Objections to These Results

It will be noted that there appears to be some variation in coupling strength. Thus, I found (CO)R to be 36.7; Morgan and Cattell obtained the result 33.9; for OR I got 34.0, and for CR, 28.5. The standard error for the difference between (CO)R (all figures) and CR is 1.84 percent, which means that a difference of 5.5 percent is probably significant (Yule '11, p. 264). The observed difference is 6.1 percent, showing that there is some complication present. Similarly, BM gave 37.6, while OM gave 54.0—and BOM gave 36.7 for BM, and 36.5 for OM. There is obviously some complication in these cases, but I am inclined to think that the disturbing factor

Table 8

(The meaning of the phrase "proportion of cross-overs" is given on p. 6)

BO. P_1: gray eosin ♀ × yellow red ♂
         F_1: gray red ♀ × gray eosin ♂
    F_2: ♀♀, g.r. 241, g.e. 196
         ♂♂, g.r.   0, g.e. 176, y.r. 195, y.e. 2

Proportion of cross-overs, $\dfrac{2}{373}$

BP. P_1: gray red ♀ × yellow vermilion ♂
         F_1: gray red ♀ × gray red ♂
    F_2: ♀♀, g.r. 98;
         ♂♂, g.r. 59, g.v. 16, y.r. 24, y.v. 33
         Back cross, F_1 gray red ♀♀ from above × yellow vermilion ♂♂
    F_2: ♀♀, g.r. 31, g.v. 11, y.r. 12, y.v. 41
         ♂♂, g.r. 23, g.v. 13, y.r. 8, y.v. 21
         P_1: gray vermilion ♀ × yellow red ♂
         F_1: gray red ♀ × gray vermilion ♂
    F_2: ♀♀, g.r. 199, g.v. 182
         ♂♂, g.r. 54, g.v. 149, y.r. 119, y.v. 41
         P_1: yellow vermilion ♀ × gray red ♂
         F_1: gray red ♀ × yellow vermilion ♂
    F_2: ♀♀, g.r. 472, g.v. 240, y.r. 213, y.v. 414
         ♂♂, g.r. 385, g.v. 186, y.r. 189, y.v. 324
         F_1: gray vermilion × yellow red (sexes not recorded)
         F_1: gray red ♀♀. These were mated to yellow vermilion ♂♂ of other stock
    F_2: ♀♀, g.r. 50, g.v. 96, y.r. 68, y.v. 41
         ♂♂, g.r. 44, g.v. 105, y.r. 86, y.v. 47

Proportion of cross-overs, adding ♀♀ from BOPR (below), $\dfrac{1464}{4551}$

BR. P_1: miniature yellow ♀ × long gray ♂
         F_1: long gray ♀ × miniature yellow ♂

Table 8 (continued)

F$_2$: ♀ ♀ l.g. 14, l.y. 2, m.g. 7, m.y. 6;

    ♂♂ l.g. 10, l.y. 1, m.g. 6, m.y. 8.

    P$_1$: long yellow ♀ × miniature gray ♂

    F$_1$: long gray ♀ × long yellow ♂

F$_2$: ♀ ♀, l.g. 148, l.y. 130

    ♂♂, l.g. 51, l.y. 82, m.g. 89, m.y. 48

Proportion of cross-overs, $\dfrac{115}{324}$

BM.   P$_1$: long yellow ♀ × rudimentary gray ♂

    F$_1$: long gray ♀ × long yellow ♂

F$_1$: ♀ ♀, l.g. 591, l.y. 549

    ♂ ♂, l.g. 228, l.y. 371, r.g. 20, r.y. 3

    P$_1$: long gray ♀ × rudimentary yellow ♂

    F$_1$: long gray ♀ × long gray ♂

F$_2$: ♀ ♀, l.g. 152

    ♂♂, l.g. 42, l.y. 29, r.g. 0, r.y. 0

Proportion of cross-overs, $\dfrac{260}{693}$

COP.   P$_1$: vermilion ♀ × white ♂

    F$_1$: red ♀ × vermilion ♂

F$_2$: ♀ ♀, r. 320, v. 294

    ♂♂, r. 86, v. 206, w. 211

(7 of the vermilion ♀ ♀ known from tests to be CC, 2 known to be Cc. 7 white ♂♂ Pp, 2 pp.)

    Back cross, F$_1$ red ♀ ♀ from above × white ♂♂, gave

F$_2$: ♀ ♀, r. 195, w. 227,

    ♂♂, r. 66, v. 164, w. 184

    Out cross, F$_1$ ♀ ♀ as above × white ♂♂ recessive in P, gave

F$_2$: ♀ ♀, r. 35, v. 65, w. 98

    ♂♂, r. 33, v. 75, w. 95

Proportion of cross-overs, $\dfrac{224}{748}$

COR.   P$_1$: miniature white ♀ × long red ♂

    F$_1$: long red ♀ × miniature white ♂

F$_2$: ♀ ♀, l.r. 193, l.w. 109, m.r. 124, m.w. 208

    ♂♂, l.r. 202, l.w. 114, m.r. 123, m.w. 174

    P$_1$: long white ♀ × miniature red ♂

    F$_1$: long red ♀ × long white ♂

F$_2$: ♀ ♀ l.r. 194, l.w. 160

    ♂♂ l.r. 52, l.w. 124, m.r. 97, m.w. 41

Proportion of cross-overs, $\dfrac{563}{1561}$; or, adding such available figures from Morgan

('11 d) and Morgan and Cattell ('12) as are not complicated by the presence of

yellow or brown flies, $\dfrac{1643}{4749}$

Table 8 (continued)

COM. P_1: long white ♀ × rudimentary red ♂
      F_1: long red ♀ × long white ♂
   F_2: ♀♀, l.r. 157, l.w. 127
        ♂♂, l.r. 74, l.w. 82, ru.r. 3, ru.w. 2

Proportion of cross-overs, $\dfrac{76}{161}$

OP. P_1: black red ♀ × black eosin-vermilion ♂
      F_1: black red ♀ × black red ♂
   F_2: (all black), ♀♀, r. 885
          ♂♂, r. 321, v. 125, e. 122, e.-v. 268

Proportion of cross-overs, $\dfrac{247}{836}$

OR. P_1: long red ♀ × miniature eosin ♂
      F_1: long red ♀ × long red ♂
   F_2: ♀♀, l.r. 408
       ♂♂, l.r. 145, l.e. 67, m.r. 70, m.e. 100
      P_1: long eosin ♀ × miniature red ♂
      F_1: long red ♀ × long eosin ♂
   F_2: ♀♀, l.r. 100, l.e. 95
       ♂♂, l.r. 27, l.e. 54, m.r. 56, m.e. 19

Proportion of cross-overs, $\dfrac{183}{538}$

OM. P_1: long eosin ♀ × rudimentary red ♂
      F_1: long red ♀ × long eosin ♂
   F_2: ♀♀, l.r. 368, l.e. 266
       ♂♂, l.r. 194, l.e. 146, ru.r. 40, ru.e. 24

Proportion of cross-overs, $\dfrac{218}{404}$

CR. P_1: long white ♀ × miniature eosin ♂
      F_1: long eosin ♀ × long white ♂
   F_2: ♀♀, l.e. 185, l.w. 205
       ♂♂, l.e. 54, l.w. 147, m.e. 149, m.w. 42
      P_1: long eosin ♀ × miniature white ♂
      F_1: long eosin ♀ × long eosin ♂
   F_2: ♀♀, l.e. 527
       ♂♂, l.e. 169, l.w. 85, m.e. 55, m.w. 128

Proportion of cross-overs, $\dfrac{230}{829}$

CM. P_1: long white ♀ × rudimentary eosin ♂
      F_1: long eosin ♀ × long white ♂
   F_2: ♀♀, l.e. 328, l.w. 371
       ♂♂, l.e. 112, l.w. 217, ru.e. 4, ru.w. 0

Proportion of cross-overs, $\dfrac{112}{333}$

Table 8 (continued)

PR.   P₁: long vermilion (yellow) ♀ × miniature red (yellow) ♂
      F₁: long red yellow ♀ × long vermilion yellow ♂

F₂: (all y.) ♀ ♀, l.r. 138, l.v. 110
          ♂ ♂, l.r.   8, l.v. 117, m.r. 97, m.v. 1

    P₁: long vermilion (gray) ♀ × miniature red ♂
    F₁: long red ♀ × long vermilion ♂

F₂: ♀ ♀, l.r. 116, l.v. 110
    ♂ ♂, l.r.   2, l.v. 81, m.r. 96, m.v. 1

    P₁: miniature red ♀ × long vermilion ♂
    F₁: long red ♀ × miniature red ♂

F₁: ♀ ♀, l.r. 45, m.r. 49
    ♂ ♂, l.r. 1, l.v. 27, m.r. 26, m.v. 0

    F₁ long red ♀ ♀ from above × miniature red ♂ ♂ of other stock, gave

F₂: ♀ ♀, l.r. 74, m.r. 52
    ♂ ♂, l.r. 3, l.v. 66, m.r. 46, m.v. 1

$$\text{Proportion of cross-overs, } \frac{17}{573}$$

PM.   P₁: long vermilion ♀ × rudimentary red ♂
      F₁: long red ♀ × long vermilion ♂

F₂: ♀ ♀, l.r. 451, l.v. 417
    ♂ ♂, l.r. 105, l.v. 316, ru.r. 33, ru.v. 4

$$\text{Proportion of cross-overs, } \frac{109}{405}$$

OPR.   P₁: long vermilion ♀ × miniature eosin ♂
      F₁: long red ♀ × long vermilion ♂

F₂: ♀ ♀, l.r. 205, l.v. 182
    ♂ ♂, l.r.   1, l.v. 109, l.e. 8, l.e.-v. 53, m.r. 49, m.v. 3, m.e. 85, m.e.-v. 0

BOM.   P₁: long red yellow ♀ × rudimentary eosin gray ♂
      F₁: long red gray ♀ × long red yellow ♂

F₂: ♀ ♀, l.r.g. 530, l.r.y. 453
    ♂ ♂, l.r.g.   1, l.r.y. 274, l.e.g. 156, l.e.y. 0, ru.r.g. 0, ru.r.y. 4, ru.e.g. 4, ru.e.y. 0

BOPR. P₁: long vermilion brown ♀ × miniature eosin black ♂
      F₁: long red black ♀ × long vermilion brown ♂

F₂: ♀ ♀, l.r.bl. 305, l.r.br. 113, l.v.bl. 162, l.v.br. 256
    ♂ ♂, l.r.bl.   0, l.r.br. 2, l.v.bl. 3, l.v.br. 185, l.e.bl. 9, l.e.br. 0, l.e.-v.bl. 127, l.e.-v.br. 0,
      m.r.bl. 1, m.r.br. 76, m.v.bl. 1, m.v.br. 10, m.e.bl. 208, m.e.br. 3, m.e.-v.bl. 0,
      m.e.-v.br. 0

discussed below (viability) will explain this. However, experiments are now under way to test the effect of certain external conditions on coupling strength. It will be seen that on the whole when large numbers are obtained in different experiments and are averaged, a fairly consistent scheme results. Final judgment on this matter must, however, be withheld until the subject can be followed up by further experiments.

Another point which should be considered in this connection is the effect of differences in viability. In the case of P and M, used above as an illustration, the rudimentary winged flies are much less likely to develop than are the longs. Now if the viability of red and vermilion is different, then the longs do not give a fair measure of the linkage, and the rudimentaries, being present in such small numbers, do not even up the matter. It is probable that there is no serious error due to this cause except in the case of rudimentary crosses, since the two sides will tend to even up, unless one is very much less viable than the other, and this is true only in the case of rudimentary. It is worth noting that the only serious disagreements between observation and calculation occur in the case of rudimentary crosses (BM, and (CO)M). Certain data of Morgan's now in print, and further work already planned, will probably throw considerable light on the question of the position and behavior of this factor M.

Summary

It has been found possible to arrange six sex-linked factors in Drosophila in a linear series, using the number of cross-overs per 100 cases as an index of the distance between any two factors. This scheme gives consistent results, in the main.

A source of error in predicting the strength of association between untried factors is found in double crossing over. The occurrence of this phenomenon is demonstrated, and it is shown not to occur as often as would be expected from a purely mathematical point of view, but the conditions governing its frequency are as yet not worked out.

These results are explained on the basis of Morgan's application of Janssens' chiasmatype hypothesis to associative inheritance. They form a new argument in favor of the chromosome view of inheritance, since they strongly indicate that the factors investigated are arranged in a linear series, at least mathematically.

LITERATURE CITED

BOVERI, T., 1902: Ueber mehrpolige Mitosen als Mittel zur Analyse des Zellkerns. Verh, Phys.-Med. Ges. Würzburg., N.F., Bd. 35, p. 67.

DEXTER, J. S., 1912: On coupling of certain sex-linked characters in Drosophila. Biol. Bull., vol. 23, p. 183.

JANSSENS, F. A., 1909: La théorie de la chiasmatypie. La Cellule, tom. 25, p. 389.

LOCK, R. H., 1906: Recent progress in the study of variation, heredity, and evolution. London and New York.

McClung, C. E., 1902: The accessory chromosome—sex determinant? Biol. Bull., vol. 3, p. 43.

Morgan, T. H., 1910: Sex-limited inheritance in Drosophila. Science, n.s., vol. 32, p. 120.

1910 a: The method of inheritance of two sex-limited characters in the same animal. Proc. Soc. Exp. Biol. Med., vol. 8, p. 17.

1911: The application of the conception of pure lines to sex-limited inheritance and to sexual dimorphism. Amer. Nat., vol. 45, p. 65.

1911 a: The origin of nine wing mutations in Drosophila. Science, n.s., vol. 33, p. 496.

1911 b: The origin of five mutations in eye color in Drosophila and their modes of inheritance. Science, n.s., vol. 33, p. 534.

1911 c: Random segregation versus coupling in Mendelian inheritance. Science, n.s., vol. 34, p. 384.

1911 d: An attempt to analyze the constitution of the chromosomes on the basis of sex-limited inheritance in Drosophila. Jour. Exp. Zoöl., vol. 11, p. 365.

Morgan, T. H. and Cattell, E., 1912: Data for the study of sex-linked inheritance in Drosophila. Jour. Exp. Zoöl., vol. 13, p. 79.

Stevens, N. M., 1905: Studies in spermatogenesis with special reference to the 'accessory chromosome.' Carnegie Inst. Washington, publ. 36.

1908: A study of the germ-cells of certain Diptera. Jour. Exp. Zoöl., vol. 5, p. 359.

Sutton, W. S., 1902: On the morphology of the chromosome group in Brachystola magna. Biol. Bull., vol. 4, p. 39.

Wilson, E. B., 1905: The behavior of the idiochromosomes in Hemiptera. Jour. Exp. Zoöl., vol. 2, p. 371.

1906: The sexual differences of the chromosome-groups in Hemiptera, with some considerations on the determination and inheritance of sex. Jour. Exp. Zoöl., vol. 3, p. 1.

Yule, G. U., 1911: An introduction to the theory of statistics. London.

Author's Notes, 1961

The terminology for the genes used is very different from that now current; the following list of equivalents may be useful in correlating this paper with later literature:

1913	B	b	C	c	O	o	P	p	R	r	M	m
Current	y^+	y	w^+	w	w^+	w^e	v^+	v	m^+	m	r^+	r

McClung's suggestion as to the relation of the X chromosome to sex-determination was made in 1901 (Anat. Anz. 20: 220–226) in a preliminary note on the material in the longer paper of 1902 which is cited in the text.

Here, and in other early papers on the genetics of Drosophila, occurs the statement that "the male has only one sex-chromosome." This was due to a misinterpretation of the work of Stevens. She described and figured the chromosomes as now known, including an XY pair, but we were misled especially by one of her figures (number 61). This confusion was not cleared up until the cytological studies of Metz and of Bridges.

There is an obvious arithmetical error in the discussion of Table 1. The total number of males is 458, not 405 as stated, and the "per cent of cross-overs" is 23.8, not 26.9. This mistake is incorporated in Tables 2 and 8, in Diagram I, and in the calculated values of Table 3.

A CORRELATION OF CYTOLOGICAL AND GENETICAL CROSSING-OVER IN ZEA MAYS

By Harriet B. Creighton and Barbara McClintock

Botany Department, Cornell University

Communicated July 7, 1931

A requirement for the genetical study of crossing-over is the heterozygous condition of two allelomorphic factors in the same linkage group. The analysis of the behavior of homologous or partially homologous chromosomes, which are morphologically distinguishable at two points, should show evidence of cytological crossing-over. It is the aim of the present paper to show that cytological crossing-over occurs and that it is accompanied by genetical crossing-over.

In a certain strain of maize the second-smallest chromosome (chromosome 9) possesses a conspicuous knob at the end of the short arm. Its distribution through successive generations is similar to that of a gene. If a plant possessing knobs at the ends of both of its 2nd-smallest chromosomes is crossed to a plant with no knobs, cytological observations show that in the resulting F_1 individuals only one member of the homologous pair possesses a knob. When such an individual is back-crossed to one having no knob on either chromosome, half of the offspring are heterozygous for the knob and half possess no knob at all. The knob, therefore, is a constant feature of the chromosome possessing it. When present on one chromosome and not on its homologue, the knob renders the chromosome pair visibly heteromorphic.

In a previous report[1] it was shown that in a certain strain of maize an interchange had taken place between chromosome 8 and 9. The interchanged pieces were unequal in size; the long arm of chromosome 9 was increased in relative length, whereas the long arm of chromosome 8 was correspondingly shortened. When a gamete possessing these two interchanged chromosomes meets a gamete containing a normal chromosome set, meiosis in the resulting individual is characterized by a side-by-side synapsis of homologous parts (see diagram, figure 1 of preceding paper). Therefore, it should be possible to have crossing-over between the knob and the interchange point.

In the previous report it was also shown that in such an individual the only functioning gametes are those which possess either the two normal chromosomes (N, n) or the two interchanged chromosome (I, i), i.e., the full genom in one or the other arrangement. The functional gametes therefore possess either the shorter, normal, knobbed chromosome (n) or the longer, interchanged, knobbed chromosome (I). Hence, when such a plant is crossed to a plant possessing the normal chromosome complement, the presence of the normal chromosome in functioning gametes of the former will be indicated by the appearance of ten bivalents in the prophase of meiosis of the resulting individuals. The presence of the interchanged

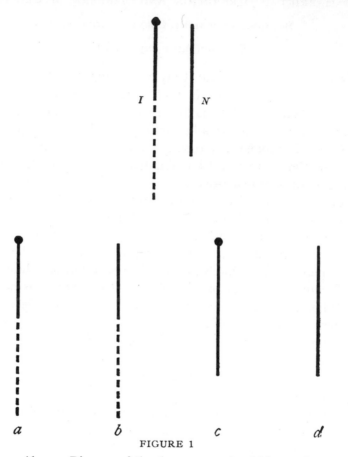

FIGURE 1

Above—Diagram of the chromosomes in which crossing-over was studied. (Labeled as in figure 1, preceding paper.)

Below—Diagram of chromosome types found in gametes of a plant with the constitution shown above.

a—Knobbed, interchanged chromosome.
b—Knobless, interchanged chromosome.
c—Knobbed, normal chromosome.
d—Knobless, normal chromosome.

a and *d* are non-crossover types.
b and *c* are crossover types.

chromosome in other gametes will be indicated in other F_1 individuals by the appearance of eight bivalents plus a ring of four chromosomes in the late prophase of meiosis.

If a gamete possessing a normal chromosome number 9 with no knob, meets a gamete possessing an interchanged chromosome with a knob, it is clear that these two chromosomes which synapse along their homologous parts during prophase of meiosis in the resulting individual are visibly different at each of their two ends. If no crossing-over occurs, the gametes formed by such an individual will contain either the knobbed, interchanged chromosome (a, Fig. 1) or the normal chromosome without a knob (d, Fig. 1). Gametes containing either a knobbed, normal chromosome (c,

TABLE 1

$\dfrac{\text{KNOB-INTERCHANGED}}{\text{KNOBLESS-NORMAL}}$ ×	KNOBLESS-NORMAL, CULTURE 337 AND KNOBBED-NORMAL CULTURES A125 AND 340			
	PLANTS POSSESSING 2 NORMAL CHROMOSOMES		PLANTS POSSESSING AN INTERCHANGED CHROMOSOMES	
CULTURE	NON-CROSSOVERS	CROSSOVERS	NON-CROSSOVERS	CROSSOVERS
337	8	3	6	2
A125	39	31	36	23
340	5	3	5	3
Totals	52	37	47	28

Fig. 1) or a knobless, interchanged chromosome (b, Fig. 1) will be formed as a result of crossing-over. If such an individual is crossed to a plant possessing two normal knobless chromosomes, the resulting individuals will be of four kinds. The non-crossover gametes would give rise to individuals which show either (1) ten bivalents at prophase of meiosis and no knob on chromosome 9, indicating that a gamete with a chromosome of type d has functioned or (2) a ring of four chromosomes with a single conspicuous knob, indicating that a gamete of type a has functioned. The crossover types will be recognizable as individuals which possess either (1) ten bivalents and a single knob associated with bivalent chromosome 9 or

TABLE 2

$\dfrac{\text{KNOB-}C\text{-}wx}{\text{KNOBLESS-}c\text{-}Wx}$		$\dfrac{c\text{-}Wx}{}$ × KNOBLESS-c-wx					
C-wx		c-Wx		C-Wx		c-wx	
Knob	Knobless	Knob	Knobless	Knob	Knobless	Knob	Knobless
12	5	5	34	4	0	0	3

(2) a ring of four chromosomes with no knob, indicating that crossover gametes of types c and b, respectively, have functioned. The results of such a cross are given in culture 337, table 1. Similarly, if such a plant is crossed to a normal plant possessing knobs at the ends of both number 9 chromosomes and if crossing-over occurs, the resulting individuals should be of four kinds. The non-crossover types would be represented by (1) plants homozygous for the knob and possessing the interchanged chromosome and (2) plants heterozygous for the knob and possessing two normal chromosomes. The functioning of gametes which had been produced as the result of crossing-over between the knob and the interchange would give rise to (1) individuals heterozygous for the knob and possessing the

interchanged chromosome and (2) those homozygous for the knob and possessing two normal chromosomes. The results of such crosses are given in cultures A125 and 340, table 1. Although the data are few, they are consistent. The amount of crossing-over between the knob and the interchange, as measured from these data, is approximately 39%.

In the preceding paper it was shown that the knobbed chromosome carries the genes for colored aleurone (*C*), shrunken endosperm (*sh*) and waxy endosperm (*wx*). Furthermore, it was shown that the order of these genes, beginning at the interchange point is *wx-sh-c*. It is possible, also, that these genes all lie in the short arm of the knobbed chromosome. Therefore, a linkage between the knob and these genes is to be expected.

One chromosome number 9 in a plant possessing the normal complement had a knob and carried the genes *C* and *wx*. Its homologue was knobless and carried the genes *c* and *Wx*. The non-crossover gametes should contain a knobbed-*C-wx* or a knobless-*c-Wx* chromosome. Crossing-over in region 1 (between the knob and *C*) would give rise to knobless *C-wx* and knobbed-*c-Wx* chromosomes. Crossing-over in region 2 (between *C* and *wx*) would give rise to knobbed-*C-Wx* and knobless-*c-wx* chromosomes. The results of crossing such a plant to a knobless-*c-wx* type are given in table 2. It would be expected on the basis of interference that the knob and *C* would remain together when a crossover occurred between *C* and *wx;* hence, the individuals arising from colored starchy (*C-Wx*) kernels should possess a knob, whereas those coming from colorless, waxy (*c-wx*) kernels should be knobless. Although the data are few they are convincing. It is obvious that there is a fairly close association between the knob and *C*.

To obtain a correlation between cytological and genetic crossing-over it is necessary to have a plant heteromorphic for the knob, the genes *c* and *wx* and the interchange. Plant 338 (17) possessed in one chromosome the knob, the genes *C* and *wx* and the interchanged piece of chromosome 8. The other chromosome was normal, knobless and contained the genes *c* and *Wx*. This plant was crossed to an individual possessing two normal, knobless chromosomes with the genes *c-Wx* and *c-wx*, respectively. This cross is diagrammed as follows:

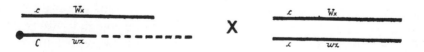

The results of the cross are given in table 3. In this case all the colored kernels gave rise to individuals possessing a knob, whereas all the colorless kernels gave rise to individuals showing no knob.

The amount of crossing-over between the knob and the interchange point is approximately 39% (Table 1), between c and the interchange approximately 33%, between wx and the interchange, 13% (preceding paper). With this information in mind it is possible to analyze the data given in table 3. The data are necessarily few since the ear contained but few kernels. The three individuals in class I are clearly non-crossover types. In class II the individuals have resulted from a crossover in region 2,

TABLE 3

KNOB-*C-wx*-INTERCHANGED / KNOBLESS-*c-Wx*-NORMAL	$\times$	KNOBLESS-*c-Wx*-NORMAL / KNOBLESS-*c-wx*-NORMAL	
PLANT NUMBER	KNOBBED OR KNOBLESS	INTERCHANGED OR NORMAL	

Class I, *C-wx* kernels			
1	Knob	Interchanged	
2	Knob	Interchanged	
3	Knob	Interchanged	
Class II, *c-wx* kernels			
1	Knobless	Interchanged	
2	Knobless	Interchanged	
			Pollen
Class III, *C-Wx* kernels			
1	Knob	Normal	$WxWx$
2	Knob	Normal	. . . .
3	. . . .	Normal	$WxWx$
5	Knob	Normal	. . . .
6	Knob	. . . . . .	. . . .
7	Knob	Normal	. . . .
8	Knob	Normal	. . . .
Class IV, *c-Wx* kernels			
1	Knobless	Normal	$Wxwx$
2	Knobless	Normal	$Wxwx$
3	Knobless	Interchanged	$Wxwx$
4	Knobless	Normal	$Wxwx$
5	Knobless	Interchanged	$WxWx$
6	Knobless	Normal	$WxWx$
7	Knobless	Interchanged	$Wxwx$
8	Knobless	Interchanged	$WxWx$
9	Knobless	Normal	$WxWx$
10	Knobless	Normal	$WxWx$
11	Knobless	Normal	$Wxwx$
12	Knobless	Normal	$Wxwx$
13	Knobless	Normal	$WxWx$
14	Knobless	Normal	$WxWx$
15	Knobless	Normal	$Wx—$

i.e., between c and wx. In this case a crossover in region 2 has not been accompanied by a crossover in region 1 (between the knob and C) or region 3 (between wx and the interchange). All the individuals in class III had normal chromosomes. Unfortunately, pollen was obtained from only 1 of the 6 individuals examined for the presence of the knob. This one individual was clearly of the type expected to come from a gamete produced through crossing-over in region 2. Class IV is more difficult to analyze.

IV. GENETIC RECOMBINATION

Plants 6, 9, 10, 13, and 14 are normal and *WxWx;* they therefore represent non-crossover types. An equal number of non-crossover types are expected among the normal *Wxwx* class. Plants 1, 2, 4, 11 and 12 may be of this type. It is possible but improbable that they have arisen through the union of a *c-Wx* gamete with a gamete resulting from a double crossover in region 2 and 3. Plants 5 and 8 are single crossovers in region 3, whereas plants 3 and 7 probably represent single crossovers in region 2 or 3.

The foregoing evidence points to the fact that cytological crossing-over occurs and is accompanied by the expected types of genetic crossing-over.

Conclusions.—Pairing chromosomes, heteromorphic in two regions, have been shown to exchange parts at the same time they exchange genes assigned to these regions.

The authors wish to express appreciation to Dr. L. W. Sharp for aid in the revision of the manuscripts of this and the preceding paper. They are indebted to Dr. C. R. Burnham for furnishing unpublished data and for some of the material studied.

[1] McClintock, B., *Proc. Nat. Acad. Sci.*, **16**, 791–796 (1930).

[From JOURNAL OF GENETICS, Vol. XXXII, No. 2,
pp. 243–256, April, 1936.]

A SIX-POINT MAP OF THE SEX-CHROMOSOME OF *NEUROSPORA CRASSA*

By CARL C. LINDEGREN

(*Department of Bacteriology, College of Letters, Arts, and Sciences,
University of Southern California, Los Angeles*)

(With Plate XIV and Two Text-figures)

INTRODUCTION

In the Ascomycete, *Neurospora crassa*, it is possible to determine whether the members of a given pair of allels were segregated from each other during the first or second reduction division. This is due to the fact that the reduction division occurs in a long narrow tube, the ascus, and results in the production of eight haploid ascospores each of which can be grown to produce a mature thallus whose genetical character can then be determined by inspection. Just prior to the reduction division the ascus contains two nuclei of opposite sex which fuse to produce the diploid zygote nucleus, so that in the life cycle of this organism there is only a single diploid nucleus which immediately undergoes reduction. With regard to the distribution of any pair of allels, the spores lie in the ascus in six different patterns, two of which result from first-division segregation and four of which result from second-division segregation. Each ascospore must be grown to maturity and the genotype determined by the growth habit of the mature thallus. It has been shown (Lindegren, 1932) that a given pair of allels may be segregated during either the first or second division and that the ratio of first- to second-division segregation is a constant. This fact was used as a means of determining the distance of the locus of two different pairs of allels from the spindle-fibre attachment (Lindegren, 1933) in accordance with the following argument: The spindle-fibre attachments do not divide at the first meiotic division, but separate from each other undivided (that is, always undergo reduction during the first division). Although the spindle-fibre attachments do not divide, each of the synapsed chromosomes divides into two strands, making a total of four strands. This has been shown in the case of *Drosophila* by genetical methods and in the case of other forms by cytological observations (Belling, 1928). It follows, therefore, that allels very close to the spindle-fibre attachment should undergo reduction practically always during the first division.

Journ. of Genetics XXXII

16

Segregation of a pair of allels during the second division is only possible if a cross-over has occurred between the locus of the gene pair and the spindle-fibre attachment. Therefore the percentage of times that a gene pair is segregated during the second division is a function of the amount of crossing-over which has occurred between the locus in question and the spindle-fibre attachment. A high percentage of second-division segregation indicates that the gene pair is far from the spindle-fibre attachment, while a low percentage of second-division segregation indicates that it is near. However, the percentage of second-division segregation does not give the distance of the locus from the spindle-fibre attachment directly in morgans. In calculating crossing-over distances the percentage of cross-over strands is determined as compared to the total number of non-cross-over strands. Since each second-division segregation produces two non-cross-over as well as two cross-over strands, the percentage of second-division segregation is twice as great as the distance from the locus to the spindle-fibre attachment in cross-over units. To convert percentages of second-division segregation into the distance of the locus from the spindle-fibre attachment, it is merely necessary to divide by two.

It was found that the ratio of first to second division of the sex factors was 87 : 13, indicating that the locus of the gene pair was 6·5 morgans from the spindle-fibre attachment. In addition it was determined that the locus of the *pale* gene was 16·5 morgans from the spindle-fibre attachment; the ratio of first- to second-division segregation being 67 : 33. These two gene pairs (*pale* and sex) were found to be linked, the distance between them amounting to 22·5 cross-over units. The sum of the two distances 6·5 and 16·5 is equal to 23. By these findings the three points (+), the spindle-fibre attachment, and *pale* were located in the sex-chromosome. Using the same method of calculation, three more points have been located on the sex-chromosome, as the result of the experiments described below.

EXPERIMENTAL

(1) *Description of mutants*

In Plate XIV are shown coloured photographs of the various mutants used in the breeding experiments. Each of the tubes contains a culture of the fungus grown from a single haploid ascospore. The first culture shown is the *normal* form, that is to say, the thallus containing nuclei which carry no mutated genes. It is characterised by its deep salmon colour and the large, thick bunches of dense conidial growth. None of the mutants obtained from *normal* produces so many conidia, although some of them may produce more rapidly growing non-conidial mycelium.

The cultures called *dirty* differ from *normal* in producing a large mass of mycelium, the upper surface of which is golden yellow and covered with a few misshapen conidia. The nuclei in this thallus differ from *normal* by a single gene *dirty* (*D*).

Gap (*G*) is differentiated from *normal* by a single gene, and the mature mycelium contains a few scattered clusters of orange conidia borne on long non-conidial hyphae.

The conidia produced by the mutant *crisp* (*C*) are very densely massed and carried on extremely short aerial hyphae. The colour of these conidial masses is much more brilliant than the *normal*. This mutant is also differentiated from *normal* by a single gene.

The mutant *pale* (*P*) produces about half as many conidia as *normal*, and these clusters of conidia are lighter in colour. This form differs from *normal* by the single gene *pale*.

These four mutants, *dirty, gap, crisp,* and *pale*, were shown by the breeding experiments to be linked to the plus-minus gene pair, which differentiates the two sexes. Another mutant producing slightly fewer conidia than *normal* was named *peach* (*Pe*), because of the delicate peach colour of its conidia. In this case the conidia are not borne in dense clusters as is characteristic of *pale* and *normal*. This is a single gene mutant.

The *dirty-gap* (*DG*) mutant is a double mutant. That is to say, in the haploid nuclei of the thallus the *dirty* (*D*) and *gap* (*G*) genes are substituted for their *normal* allels. The mutant produces rusty brown, aerial mycelium. As would be expected, the growth of the mycelium is much poorer than in the case of either of the single mutants *dirty* or *gap*. Since each of the mutant genes apparently acts to reduce the viability of the *normal* form, it would be expected that both of these genes acting together would produce much poorer growth than either one of them alone.

The *dirty-peach* (*DPe*) double mutant produces a greyish coloured, practically non-conidial mycelium, which can be distinguished from the triple mutant *dirty-gap-peach* (*DGPe*) because, in the latter, small, rusty brown drops of liquid are deposited on the aerial mycelium.

The *gap-peach* (*GPe*) double mutant is characterised by an extremely sparse growth of greyish coloured conidia. The three mutant combinations with the *peach* gene (*DPe, DGPe,* and *GPe*) all resulted in the production of a greyish coloured growth.

16-2

Normal

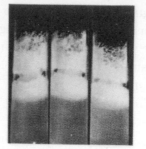

Gap

Dirty

Crisp

Pale

Peach

Dirty-gap

Gap-peach

Dirty-gap-peach

Dirty-peach

Clump-gap

Crisp-pale

The *crisp-pale* (*CP*) double mutant produced conidia on short stalks resembling those borne by the single mutant *crisp*, but were slightly less abundant and lighter in colour.

The mutant *clump* differs from those already described in that it has no effect upon the appearance of *normal*. It can only be detected when the gene *gap* is already present, and when this occurs the double mutant *clump-gap* produces large masses of conidia almost as dense as in the case of *normal*.

In the above discussion the mutants *dirty*, *gap*, *crisp*, *pale*, and *peach* have been spoken of as if each one were a simple transgenation from *normal*, in spite of the fact that it is not possible to offer conclusive evidence that this is the case. However, the facts that they do not interfere with crossing-over and are able to produce viable thalli in the haploid condition favour this view. The case of *clump* is somewhat different. It has no observable effect on *normal* and results in a decided improvement when in combination with *gap*. This could result if *clump* were a duplication carrying the *normal* allel of *gap* or if some *normal* gene had transgenated to a suppressor of *gap* (Bridges, 1932).

(2) *Heterokaryosis in the* normal *stock*

Difficulty was encountered in the analysis of the breeding experiments because the supposedly pure *normal* stock, with which the various mutants were mated, was heterokaryotic for three different kinds of nuclei. This was the result of mutations which had occurred in this stock, since it had been grown from a single ascospore several years ago. In addition to the *normal* (−) nuclei, *peach* (−) and *clump* (−) nuclei were carried in the heterokaryon. The crosses which resulted in this analysis occurred late in the course of the experiment but will be reported first.

Sixty-eight asci were analysed from five crosses between various *gap* (+) cultures and the *normal*(?) (−) heterokaryon. The zygote nucleus in 40 of these 68 asci was produced by the fusion of a *gap* (+) with a *peach* (−) nucleus. This was shown by the fact that some of the cultures grown from these asci developed the new characters *peach* and *gap-peach*, in addition to the expected *gap* and *normal*. If the *normal* culture had been pure, only *gap* and *normal* progeny would have been expected in a 1 : 1 ratio.

In 22 of the 68 asci either one or both pairs of the *gap* ascospores carried nuclei which produced the *clump-gap* type of mycelium. In these cases the *normal* thalli could not be distinguished from each other, but if an ascus contains one *clump-gap* and one *non-clump-gap* pair of ascospores, then the two pairs of *non-gap* ascospores are respectively *clump* and *non-clump*.

The cultures obtained from 6 of the 68 asci showed no evidence of either *peach* or *clump*. They could not have been produced by the reduction of a zygote heterozygous for *peach*, because the *peach* gene would have come into expression in the progeny. They might have been produced by the reduction of a zygote heterozygous for *clump*, if the *clump* genes were segregated into the *non-gap* nuclei, because this would result in their failure to come into expression.

After these experiments had shown that the supposedly pure *normal* stock was heterokaryotic, it was possible to analyse a cross of *dirty-gap* by this heterokaryon. The asci from this cross fell into three classes: (1) from zygotes heterozygous for *dirty*, *gap*, and *peach*, (2) from zygotes heterozygous for *dirty*, *gap*, and *clump*, and (3) from zygotes which were homozygous for *non-peach* and in which *clump* could not be detected.

The following tabulation shows the distribution of the different kinds of nuclei in the heterokaryon as determined by the analysis of 10 different crosses:

(a) *Asci from crosses of* gap *by* normal (?)

peach	clump	Indeterminate
4	1	0
5	0	0
3	6	0
12	7	5
16	8	1

(b) *Asci from crosses of* dirty-gap *by* normal (?)

peach	clump	Indeterminate
4	0	1
5	0	0
10	1	9
35	0	4
31	19	11

Peach nuclei apparently predominated in the heterokaryon.

Peach is a clear-cut character, and since it was not detected in earlier breeding experiments with this same *normal*(?) stock, it is apparently the result of a recent mutation. The fact that none of the zygotes heterozygous for *peach* carried the *clump* gene, while none of the zygotes heterozygous for *clump* carried the *peach* gene shows that there are at least two kinds of nuclei in the heterokaryon. Since the *clump* gene can only be detected in the presence of *gap*, the following question arises: Did the original pure *normal* strain carry the *clump* gene and did *peach* develop from it, or was the original *normal* strain *non-clump* as well as *non-peach?* Both the *peach* and *clump* mutants must have developed separately from a *non-peach—non-clump* stock, for if the *peach* nuclei had developed by mutation from *clump* nuclei they would have carried the gene *clump*, that is, they would have been double mutants with the genetical constitution *Pe Cl*. Since this was not the case, two separate mutations must have occurred.

(3) *Classification of progeny*

Recognition of the fact that the *normal* stock was heterokaryotic made it possible to classify the complex of progeny which were produced by mating this heterokaryon with the *dirty-gap* mutant. From a zygote heterozygous for *dirty, gap* and *peach*, it was possible to obtain *dirty, gap, peach, dirty-gap, peach-gap, dirty-peach, dirty-gap-peach* and *normal* progeny. These genotypes were all clearly different from each other and were easily classifiable.

In the following tabulation the asci produced from zygotes heterozygous for *gap* and *peach* are classified with regard to first- and second-division segregation of these two genes and their *normal* allels. The first column shows the division at which the gene pairs were segregated. In the next four columns are listed the four different genotypes which occurred in the ascus, without reference to end-to-end orientation. The first type of ascus *GPe GPe gpe gpe* also contains asci in which ascospore No. 1 was *gpe* and ascospore No. 8 *GPe*. Furthermore, in the case of second-division segregation, the two groups of spores (1, 2, 3, 4, and 5, 6, 7, 8) are also listed without regard to end-to-end orientation. Therefore, an ascus would fall into the classification listed in the third row if spores 1 and 2 were *gpe*; 3 and 4, *gPe*; 5 and 6, *GPe*; and 7 and 8, *Gpe*.

Division		Arrangement				*d*	*D*
I	*G/g*	*GPe*	*GPe*	*gpe*	*gpe*	18	21
I	*Pe/pe*	*Gpe*	*Gpe*	*gPe*	*gPe*	8	24
I	*G/g*	*GPe*	*Gpe*	*gpe*	*gPe*	8	9
II	*Pe/pe*						
II	*G/g*	*GPe*	*gPe*	*Gpe*	*gpe*	1	8
I	*Pe/pe*						
II	*G/g*	*GPe*	*gpe*	*GPe*	*gpe*	—	1
II	*Pe/pe*	*GPe*	*gpe*	*Gpe*	*gPe*	—	2
		Gpe	*gPe*	*Gpe*	*gPe*	1	2

Both pairs of allels are segregated more frequently during the first than during the second division, and there are two facts which show that they are not linked. In the first place, the asci in which both pairs of allels are segregated during the second division are practically equally divided between the original combination type *Gpe Gpe gPe gPe* and the recombination type *GPe GPe gpe gpe*. As has already been pointed out (Lindegren, 1933), this phenomenon can be used as a criterion of linkage in cases in which both allels are segregated with high frequency during the first division. In the second place, original combination classes (*Gpe gPe*) totalled 182 as compared to the recombination classes (*GPe gpe*) totalling 218. Percentages are respectively 45·5 and 54·5, which indicate that there is no linkage between these two genes. Since the *Pe/pe* gene pair were segregated 80 times during the first division and 23 times during the second, the locus of *Pe* is about 11 units from the spindle-fibre attachment in another chromosome than the one carrying *gap*.

The first column of figures shows the numbers of different kinds of asci obtained from the cross homozygous for *non-dirty*. The second row of figures shows the types of asci obtained from *dirty-gap* by *peach* zygotes.

As already stated, *clump* can only be detected in the presence of *gap*. However, it was not possible to distinguish two types of *dirty-gap* and this has considerably reduced the data which it was possible to obtain concerning *clump*. No tests were made to determine whether this indicates that *dirty* and *clump* are linked or that *dirty* is epistatic to *clump*.

In the following tabulation 24 asci from zygotes heterozygous for *clump* are listed. A dash indicates the cases in which *clump* cannot be detected. In 16 of the asci the *clump* gene was segregated from its *normal* allel during the second division. In seven cases the segregation occurred during the first division. This indicates that the locus is not near the spindle-fibre attachment.

Division		Arrangement				No. asci
I	*G/g*	*GCl*	*GCl*	*g—*	*g—*	7
I	*Cl/cl*					
I	*G/g*	*GCl*	*Gcl*	*g—*	*g—*	15
II	*Cl/cl*					
II	*G/g*	*g—*	*GCl*	*GCl*	*g—*	1
II	*Cl/cl*					
II	*G/g*	*g—*	*GCl*	*Gcl*	*g—*	1
?	*Cl/cl*					

(4) *Linkage*

The different types of asci with regard to the *gap*, the *non-gap*, and the (+)/(−) pairs of allels are listed in the tabulation below. The original combinations (+*G* and −*g*) total 634 as compared to the new combinations (−*G* and +*g*) which equal 58. This indicates that the distance between the loci of these two pairs of allels is equal to 8·4. The G/g pair of allels segregated from each other 165 times during the first division and 23 times during the second division, indicating a distance of 6·1 units from the spindle-fibre attachment. The $(+)/(-)$ pair of allels segregated from each other 142 times during the first division and 36 times during the second division, indicating a distance of 10·1 units from the spindle-fibre attachment. These figures indicate that G and $(+)$ are on the same side of the spindle-fibre attachment. This is the arm which we have chosen by convention to call the left arm. G is closer to the spindle-fibre attachment than $(+)$. From these data it is possible to construct a map giving the positions of these two genes with respect to the spindle-fibre attachment as shown in Text-fig. 2 (p. 254).

Row	Arrangement				D	Pe	dpe	Total	C.O.	N.C.O.	2–	3–	4–
I	$+G$	$+G$	$-g$	$-g$	79	34	22	135	0	540	—	—	—
II	$-G$	$+G$	$+g$	$-g$	16	2	2	20	40	40	—	—	—
III	$+G$	$-g$	$+G$	$-g$	11	2	1	14	28	28	—	—	—
IV	$-G$	$-G$	$+g$	$+g$	3	1	—	4	16	0	—	—	4
V	$-g$	$-G$	$+G$	$+g$	3	—	—	3	12	6	3	—	—
VI	$+G$	$-g$	$-G$	$+g$	2	—	—	2	8	2	—	2	—
				Totals	178	104		616			3	2	4

The 135 asci listed in row I represent cases in which no detectable crossing-over occurred in the two regions. In the case of the 20 asci listed in row II, a single cross-over occurred between G and $(+)$ resulting in a first-division segregation of G/g and a second-division segregation of $(+)/(-)$. Cross-overs of this type in the left arm of the chromosome are shown in Text-fig. 2 $e, f, g,$ and h. A single cross-over between G and the spindle-fibre attachment would result in the arrangement of ascospores in the ascus as shown in row III. Cross-overs of this type are shown in the left arm of the chromosome in Text-fig. 2 i and j. In this case the linkage between G and $(+)$ is not broken, but the cross-over is detected by the arrangement of the spores in the ascus.

The $-G -G +g +g$ type of ascus (row IV) would result in the event of a four-strand double exchange between the loci of G and $(+)$, in accordance with the diagrams $m, n,$ and o, Text-fig. 2. The ascus of the type shown in row V ($-g -G +G +g$) would result if a two-strand double exchange occurred with one cross-over taking place between G and the spindle-fibre attachment and the other between G and $(+)$, as indicated in the diagram r, Text-fig. 2.

The arrangement shown in row VI would result if a three-strand double exchange occurred with the first cross-over between G and $(+)$, according to the diagram p, Text-fig. 2.

These data make it possible to correct the distance between $(+)$ and the spindle-fibre attachment which was at first calculated to be 10·1. This calculation is still on the basis of the ratio of first- to second-division segregation which actually amounts to using the spindle-fibre attachment as a locus and calculating the linkage between it and the second locus. This calculation is made in the columns of the tabulation above headed C.O. (cross-over) and N.C.O. (non-cross-over). By a study of each of the different types of arrangements the number of cross-overs between the spindle-fibre attachment and (+) are calculated. In the type shown in row IV there are 4 cross-over strands in each group of 4 strands, in spite of the fact that the (+)/(−) gene pair segregated during the first division. In the type shown in row VI, there are 2 single cross-overs, 1 double cross-over, and 1 non-cross-over strand in a total of 4 strands. This is equal to 4 cross-overs between (+) and the spindle-fibre attachment in a total of 4 strands. Between the spindle-fibre attachment and (+), 104 cross-overs are shown to occur in a total of (178 × 4) 712 strands. This gives a total distance of 14·6.

In the map (Text-fig. 1) the distances 6·1 and 14·6 are calculated from data based on segregation. The distance 8·4 is calculated on data

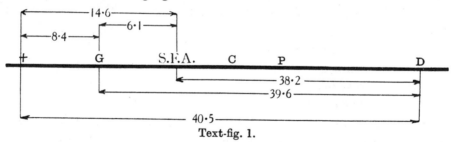

Text-fig. 1.

based on the ratio of original combination to new combination classes. The discrepancy is (14·6 − 6·1) − (8·4) = 0·1.

A two-strand double exchange between G and (+) could not be detected by any means, and a three-strand double exchange would merely register as a single cross-over. It might be objected, therefore, that two- and three-strand double exchanges had occurred between G and (+), but had escaped detection. However, the close agreement between the distances obtained by the two different methods shows that few exchanges escaped detection.

The column headed D in the tabulation on p. 250 shows the relative numbers of the different types of asci obtained from a mating between *dirty-gap* mycelia and the *normal* heterokaryon. The column headed *Pe* shows the relative frequency of the different types obtained from zygotes heterozygous for *gap* and *peach*, but homozygous for *non-dirty*.

The column headed *dpe* shows the distribution of the different types of asci obtained from zygotes heterozygous for *gap* but homozygous for *non-dirty* and *non-peach*. The close agreement between the three different crosses indicates that competition within the ascus had relatively little effect on linkage.

The gene *dirty* was found to show linkage with both *gap* and (+) indicating that it lay in the sex-chromosome. The original combinations, *GD, gd*, totalled 278 as compared to the new combinations, *Gd, gD*, which totalled 182. The linkage between *G* and *D* is therefore equal to 39·6 cross-over units. This is significantly different from equality. The original

TABLE I

The arrangement and genotypes of the ascospores in asci from zygotes heterozygous for (+), gap, and dirty

Class	Arrangements				Asci	N.C.O.	C.O.	2–	3–	4–
a	+GD	+GD	−gd	−gd	24	96	0	—	—	—
b	+GD	+Gd	−gd	−gD	46	92	92	—	—	—
c	+Gd	+Gd	−gD	−gD	5	0	20	—	—	5
d	+GD	−GD	+gd	−gd	4	16	0	—	—	—
e	+Gd	−Gd	+gD	−gD	1	0	4	—	—	1
f	−GD	+Gd	−gD	+gd	4	8	8	—	—	4
g	−Gd	+GD	+gd	−gD	2	4	4	—	2	—
h	−Gd	+GD	+gD	−gd	2	4	4	2	—	—
i	+GD	−gd	−gd	+GD	3	6	6	3	—	—
j	+GD	−gd	−gD	+Gd	2	4	4	—	2	—
k	+GD	−gD	−gd	+Gd	6	24	0	—	—	—
m	−GD	−GD	+gd	+gd	1	4	0	—	—	1
n	−Gd	−Gd	+gD	+gD	1	0	4	—	—	2
o	−Gd	−GD	+gd	+gD	1	2	2	—	—	1
p	−GD	+gd	−gD	+Gd	1	2	2	—	2	—
r	+GD	+gd	−Gd	−gD	1	2	2	1	1	—
s	−gd	−Gd	+GD	+gD	1	0	4	—	—	2
x	GD	Gd	gD	gd	6	12	12	—	—	—
y	GD	gd	gD	Gd	3	6	6	—	3	—
z	Gd	gD	Gd	gD	1	2	2	—	—	1
				Totals	284	176		6	10	17

combinations, *D* (+), *d* (−), totalled 250 as compared to 170 new combinations, *D* (−), *d* (+). This is equal to linkage of 40·5 between these two loci. According to these figures the distance between (+) and *D* is greater than between *G* and *D*. Therefore, *D* lies in the right arm of the chromosome. *Dirty* was segregated from its allel 43 times during the first reduction division and 72 times during the second reduction division. The respective percentages of first- and second-division segregation are 37·4 and 62·6, making the distance of *dirty* from the spindle-fibre attachment 31·3. This approximate distance can be corrected by a comparison of the total number of cross-over strands with the total number of strands. This comparison is made in Table I. In asci of class *a* there were no detected recombinations between the spindle-fibre attachment and *D*. Therefore, in the total of 24 asci, there were 24 × 4 = 96 non-cross-over strands between the spindle-fibre attachment and *D* and no cross-over strands. However, it is possible that a considerable amount of undetected exchanges occurred in the 24 asci listed in the table. In the 46 asci in class *b*, the *D/d* pair of allels was segregated during the second division. It is possible that in a considerable number of these asci more than one interchange may have taken place between the spindle-fibre attachment and *D* to produce the same arrangement in the ascus. Therefore, in the two columns headed N.C.O. and C.O., the figures give the recombination between the spindle-fibre attachment and *D* rather than the actual number of cross-overs. These amount respectively to 284 and 176, which is the equivalent of 38·2 per cent. of recombination between the spindle-fibre attachment and *D*. These calculations result in establishing relative distances between the different genes shown in Text-fig. 1.

The distances shown on this map are all the result of genetical measurements. None is the sum or difference of two measured distances. Between the spindle-fibre attachment and *D*, 38·2 per cent. recombinations were detected; between *G* and *D*, 39·6 per cent. recombinations were detected. 6·1 per cent. recombinations were detected between *G* and the spindle-fibre attachment as compared to the difference between 39·6 and 38·2 which is only 1·4. Therefore, many undetected multiple exchanges must have occurred between the spindle-fibre attachment and *D*. Between *G* and *D* 39·6 per cent. recombinations were detected. Between (+) and *D* 40·5 per cent. recombinations were detected. 8·4 per cent. recombinations were detected between (+) and *G*, as compared to the difference between 40·5 and 39·6, which is 0·9. This is further evidence of the fact that many undetected multiple exchanges must have occurred between the spindle-fibre attachment and *D*. In Text-fig. 2 the various possible types of double exchanges are diagrammed corresponding to the arrangement of the spores in the asci listed in Table I. Because of the evidence indicating that numerous multiple exchanges probably occur between the spindle-fibre attachment and *D*, only the double exchanges occurring between the spindle-fibre attachment and (+) can be considered.

In an earlier paper (Lindegren, 1933) it has been shown that the gene *pale* lies in the right arm of the sex-chromosome. The mutant *crisp* was mated to *pale*, and analysis of 19 asci indicated that *crisp* lay in the same chromosome as *pale* but much nearer (+). Data on the position of *pale* with respect to *gap* were obtained by the analysis of 6 asci and 62 asco-spores selected at random. The distance was shown to be about 30 cross-over units. The probable seriation of the genes *crisp* and *pale* is indicated

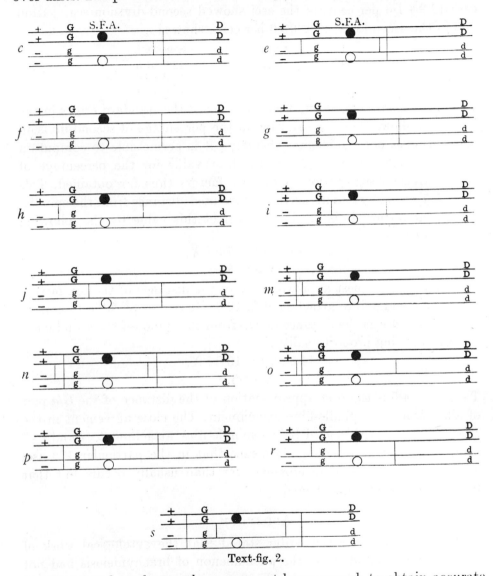

Text-fig. 2.

on the map, but the numbers were not large enough to obtain accurate distances.

In the tabulation below appear data concerning the ratio of first- to second-division segregation of the sex factors which were obtained from 449 asci and published in an earlier paper. In 391 asci the sex factors were segregated during the first division, and in 58 asci they were segregated during the second division. In the present paper 178 asci were examined. In 142 the sex factors segregated during the first division and in 36 they were segregated during the second division. In the first case $12 \cdot 9 \pm 1 \cdot 6$ per cent. of the asci showed second-division segregation and in the second case $20 \cdot 2 \pm 3 \cdot 0$ per cent. showed

I	II	% II
391	58	$12 \cdot 9 \pm 1 \cdot 6$
142	36	$20 \cdot 2 \pm 3 \cdot 0$
533	94	$15 \cdot 0 \pm 1 \cdot 4$

second-division segregation. Consideration of the standard errors in the two cases shows that the variation in the percentage of second-division segregation is not significant. Therefore, it is permissible to compute a grand average and $15 \cdot 0 \pm 1 \cdot 4$ is the best value for the percentage of second-division segregation of the sex factors thus far obtained. This gives 7·5 cross-over units as the uncorrected distance from the spindle-fibre attachment. It is possible to correct this value by the following proportionality:

$$10 \cdot 1 : 14 \cdot 6 :: 7 \cdot 5 : X,$$
$$X = 10 \cdot 8.$$

Therefore, the best approximation of the distance of the sex factors from the spindle-fibre attachment is 10·8. It is also possible to correct the value of 6·1 as the distance of *gap* from the spindle-fibre attachment by the following proportionality:

$$14 \cdot 6 : 6 \cdot 1 :: 10 \cdot 8 : X,$$
$$X = 4 \cdot 5.$$

Therefore, 4·5 is the best approximation of the distance of the *G/g* pair of allels from the spindle-fibre attachment. The close agreement in the three distances with regard to the spindle-fibre attachment, *G* and (+) shown in the map (Text-fig. 1) means that in the particular 178 asci analysed, there was more crossing-over than usually occurs but that few exchanges were undetected.

ADDENDUM.

In a recent paper the writer stated that the cytological work of Prof. Gwynne-Vaughan on the phenomenon of brachymeiosis had not been corroborated. In a personal communication she pointed out that the original discovery was made by Maire and has many times been corroborated in her laboratory. Prof. Gwynne-Vaughan had furthermore discovered that in some forms brachymeiosis occurred during the second division instead of the third. The writer had objected that in such a case the third division did not have the function of completing the reduction of the tetraploid zygote if it had already been completed in the second. Prof. Gwynne-Vaughan correctly pointed out that the third division would still be necessary to disjoin the chromosome pairs even if brachy-meiosis occurred during the second. In the case of *Neurospora crassa* it is clear that the zygote is diploid, so brachymeiosis is not a possibility.

SUMMARY

Several new genes differentiating the growth habit of *Neurospora crassa* were discovered. One of these, *clump*, was distinguished from the others by the fact that it had no effect on *normal* and improved the vigour of the mutant *gap*, when carried in the same nucleus. The standard *normal* stock which had been propagated asexually for several years was found to be heterokaryotic as result of mutations. The following seriation of loci was established for the sex chromosome: (+), *gap*, spindle-fibre attachment, *crisp*, *pale* and *dirty*.

ACKNOWLEDGMENTS

The writer is indebted to Mr P. A. Miller and Miss Pauline M. Colahan for valuable assistance. He is especially grateful to his wife, who made all the dissections of asci incidental to this study.

REFERENCES

BELLING, JOHN (1928). "Contraction of chromosomes during maturation divisions in Lilium and other plants." *Univ. Calif. Publ. Bot.* **14**, 335–43.

BRIDGES, CALVIN B. (1932). "The suppressors of purple." *Z. indukt. Abstamm.- u. VererbLehre,* **60**, 207–18.

LINDEGREN, CARL C. (1932). "The genetics of *Neurospora*. II. Segregation of the sex factors in the asci of *N. crassa, N. sitophila* and *N. tetrasperma*." *Bull. Torrey Bot. Cl.* **59**, 119–38.

—— (1933). "The genetics of *Neurospora*. III. Pure bred stocks and crossing-over in *N. crassa*" *Ibid.* **60**, 133–54.

Reprinted from the Proceedings of the NATIONAL ACADEMY OF SCIENCES
Vol. 45, No. 5, pp. 727–732.   May, 1959.

ABERRANT TETRADS IN SORDARIA FIMICOLA*

BY LINDSAY S. OLIVE

COLUMBIA UNIVERSITY

Communicated by B. O. Dodge, March 31, 1959

In an earlier paper[1] describing three ascospore color mutants in the homothallic pyrenomycete *Sordaria fimicola*, the rare occurrence of unusual tetrads with unexpected ratios of wild-type and mutant ascospores was noted for all three loci. In the course of further studies of two of these mutant loci, a number of asci showing aberrant tetrads were isolated and analyzed in an effort to obtain a clearer idea of the mechanism responsible for their occurrence.   Such tetrads in yeast had previously been explained by Lindegren[2] as resulting from "gene conversion" in a heterozygote, usually involving a change of the dominant gene to its recessive allele. Later, Mitchell[3] reported similar abnormal segregations for the pyridoxine locus in *Neurospora*, which she explained as probably resulting from double replication.

A similar explanation is offered by Case and Giles[4] in an interpretation of irregular segregation at the *pan-2* locus in *N. crassa*. These authors use the term "copy choice" suggested earlier by Lederberg.[5] Glass[6] refers to the phenomenon as "transreplication," a term that seems adequate for purposes of this discussion.

Procedure.—All asci described here were derived from crosses between cultures with the wild-type allele for the production of dark ascospores and either of two different ascospore color mutants, hyaline-spored (h) or gray-spored (g). All crosses were also heterozygous for one other mutant factor. Perithecia from the line of contact between paired cultures were pressed under a cover slip, after which the hybrid clusters of asci were removed to an adjacent drop of water on the slide and flattened out under a cover slip. These asci were then examined for aberrant tetrads showing disproportionate numbers of wild-type and mutant spores. A cluster containing such an ascus was removed to a dish of agar and the desired ascus isolated and dissected.

Results.—An analysis of 23 abnormal asci was made (Table 1). The first 12 asci were derived from crosses heterozygous for the h locus, which is situated at about 32.5 crossover units from the centromere, and for one other locus—d_1, d_2, or a-2. Unpublished data on the last three loci show that they are unlinked, but that d_1 is linked to h with a distance of about 28 crossover units between them. Both d_1 and d_2 cause dwarfness of cultures, while a-2 is recessive for ascus abortion. In asci heterozygous for the a-2 locus, the a-2 ascospores develop normally. The d_1 locus is only a few crossover units from the centromere, while d_2 is about 14.5 units out on its chromosome arm, and a-2 is far out on its chromosome arm. The h factor, in addition to causing hyaline spore color, is lethal for ascospore germination.

Asci 1–7, 10, and 11 have a ratio of $6h+:2h$ ascospores. With respect to the

TABLE 1

ASCI OF *S. fimicola* SHOWING ABERRANT SEGREGATION FOR SPORE COLOR*

Cross	Ascus No.	Spore Color Ratio	Spore No. and Genotype							
			1	2	3	4	5	6	7	8
$h+d_1+Xhd_1$	1	6+:2-	+−	+−	+−	+−	++	++	(−+)	(−+)
"	2	"	(−−)	(−−)	+−	+−	++	++	++	++
"	3	"	(−−)	(−−)	+−	+−	++	++	++	++
$h+d_1Xhd_1+$	4	"	(−+)	(−+)	++	++	+−	+−	+−	+−
"	5	"	+−	+−	+−	+−	++	++	(−+)	(−+)
"	6	"	+−	+−	+−	+−	++	++	(−+)	(−+)
"	7	"	+−	+−	+−	+−	++	++	(−+)	(−+)
"	8	5+:3-	(−+)	(−+)	++	++	+−	+−	(−−)	**+−**
"	9	"	(−+)	(−+)	(−+)	**++**	+−	+−	+−	+−
$h+d_2Xhd_2+$	10	6+:2-	(−−)	(−−)	+−	+−	++	++	++	++
$h+a\text{-}2Xha\text{-}2+$	11	"	++	++	(−+)	(−+)	+−	+−	+−	+−
"	12	5+:3-	(−−)	(−−)	++	++	+−	+−	(−+)	**++**
$gstm+Xg+stm$	13	"	+−	+−	−−	**+−**	−+	−+	++	++
"	14	"	**++**	−+	+−	+−	−+	−+	+−	+−
"	15	"	−+	−+	**++**	−+	+−	+−	+−	+−
"	16	6+:2-	+−	+−	+−	+−	−+	−+	++	++
"	17	"	+−	+−	+−	+−	−+	−+	++	++
$g+a\text{-}1+Xga\text{-}1$	18	"	+−	+−	+−	+−	−+	−+	++	++
"	19	"	++	++	+−	+−	+−	+−	−+	−+
"	20	"	(−+)	−+	++	++	+−	+−	+−	+−
"	21	5+:3-	−−	**+−**	+−	+−	−+	−+	++	+−
"	22	2+:6-	−−	−−	−−	−−	++	++	−+	−+
"	23	3+:5-	+−	+−	**−−**	+−	−+	−+	−+	−+

* Unrecovered progeny in parentheses. The h allele is lethal for ascospore germination. The aberrant alleles, where identifiable (in 5:3 asci), are indicated in bold type. The symbols + and − signify wild type and mutant alleles, respectively; the first symbol under each spore genotype refers to a spore color locus.

second locus involved in each cross, two pairs of dark spores carry the mutant allele and one pair the wild-type, or two pairs carry the wild-type and one pair the mutant allele. In other words, one pair of spores which would be expected to contain the h allele, has instead the wild-type allele at that locus. It is not possible to determine which of the three pairs is the aberrant one. Since h and d_1 are linked and d_1 is near the centromere, it is likely that in a majority of the first seven asci, the converted pair is the one adjacent to the hyaline pair. Asci 8, 9, and 12 contain ascospores in the surprising ratio of $5h+: 3h$. In each of them it is possible to identify the spore carrying the transreplicated locus, since its adjacent partner carries the h allele and is hyaline.

Asci containing an excess of h spores in proportion to $h+$ were also observed, but it was not feasible to dissect them for further analysis in view of the failure of h spores to germinate. However, an examination of 2,700 hybrid asci was made in order to obtain some idea of the relative frequency of the different types of abnormal tetrads. Of this number 11 asci, or about 0.4 per cent, contained visibly abnormal tetrads. Six showed a $6h+: 2h$ segregation, five of these having the six dark spores in a series and one having the arrangement $2h+: 2h: 4h+$; five asci showed a ratio of $2h+: 6h$, four of these having all six hyaline spores in an uninterrupted series and one having them in the order $2h: 2h+: 4h$. No 5:3 segregations were observed in this group, and in general they appear to be less common than 6:2 asci. It would appear from the data that transreplication of the h locus, if that is the phenomenon involved, is about equally common in either direction. However, in view of the fact that rare hyaline spores are produced probably as the result of other aberrations in nuclear division, it is not possible to be sure that all extra hyaline spores have developed in like manner.

The gray-spored locus (g) offers a better approach to this problem, since gray and wild-type spores are equally viable. Asci 13–23 resulted from crosses heterozygous for the g locus, which is situated far out on its chromosome arm, and for one additional factor either stm or a-1. The loci appear to be unlinked. The crosses involving stm are all homozygous for another mutant locus st-1, which causes near sterility in cultures carrying it. The stm allele converts st-1 cultures into completely self-sterile ones.[7] The a-1 allele has an effect exactly like a-2 in causing ascus abortion. There appears to be no linkage of g with either stm or a-1. The stm locus is about 6 crossover units from the centromere, while a-1 is far out on its chromosome arm. Asci 16–20 show a segregation of $6g+: 2g$, and in all of them the second locus segregated in a 4:4 ratio. Again it is not possible to identify any of the three pairs as the one which has resulted from transreplication. Figure 1 shows an ascus of this type and Figure 2, the eight cultures derived from spores of the same ascus (Ascus 19, Table 1). All of these crosses are heterozygous for unselected factors affecting growth rate and perithecial distribution. This is of some advantage to the analysis, since it offers another way of recognizing spore pairs resulting from the third division in the ascus and insures against any misinterpretation due to disorderly spore arrangement.

Asci 13–15 and 21, which show a ratio of $5g+: 3g$, are among the most revealing ones obtained. In all of them it is possible to identify the spore carrying the transreplicated locus, since it is a dark spore and its sister spore is gray. Figure 3 shows such an ascus and Figure 4, the eight cultures obtained from it (Ascus 21, Table 1).

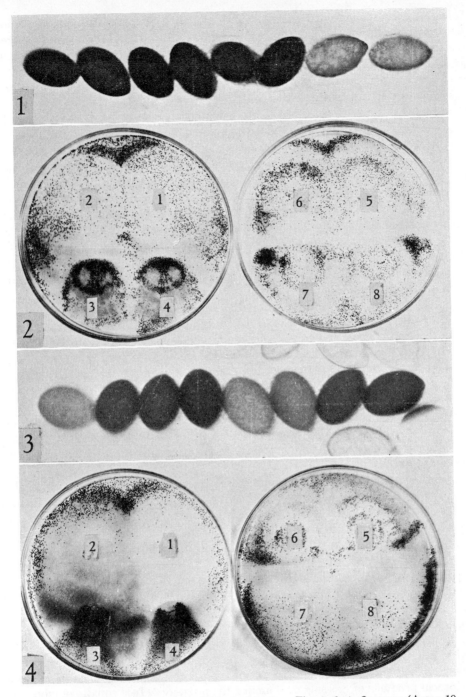

Figs. 1–4.—Aberrant tetrads in *Sordaria fimicola*. Fig. 1, 6*g*+:2*g* ascus (Ascus 19, Table 1); Fig. 2, progeny on corn meal agar plates; Fig. 3, 5*g*+:3*g* ascus (Ascus 21, Table 1); Fig. 4, progeny on corn meal agar plates. (Spores in asci are numbered from left to right.)

IV. GENETIC RECOMBINATION

It is obvious that the second spore in this ascus is the odd one. The cultures demonstrate another interesting feature, i.e., the culture derived from the odd dark spore is conspicuously darker than that derived from the gray sister spore. Our original gray-spored mutant produces a light, opaque mycelium, whereas, the wild-type produces a dark pigment, probably melanin. The difference is usually more pronounced in test tube cultures than on agar plates. In all of the $5g+:3g$ asci the unexpected dark spore gives rise to a pigmented mycelium. Also the dark spores in asci with a ratio of $6g+:2g$ produce pigmented colonies. Mycelial pigmentation is in part a pleiotropic effect of the g locus. Some of our unpublished data indicate that one or more closely linked loci may also be involved in mycelial pigmentation, but since this character is not a sharply defined one and since other unselected loci also modify the degree of pigmentation, we have not been able definitely to establish this. If such loci do exist, the data indicate that they may also undergo transreplication simultaneously with the g locus. However, it is not likely that this could be confirmed without the aid of closely linked markers with more clear-cut phenotypic effects.

Only two asci with a greater than normal number of gray spores were isolated from these crosses. They appear to be less common than the foregoing types. Ascus 22 shows a $2g+:6g$ segregation and ascus 23, a $3g+:5g$ ratio. The third spore of the latter ascus, which is obviously the odd one in the series and has apparently resulted from transreplication of the g allele instead of the normal duplication of the $g+$ allele, produced a mycelium that was lighter than that derived from the fourth, or sister, spore carrying the $g+$ allele. Otherwise the two cultures were alike in growth rate and appearance, being slower than any of the others. Abnormal tetrads resulting from crosses heterozygous for the g locus are distinctly less common than those from crosses heterozygous for the h locus. Although our observations do not at this time permit an accurate statement regarding their frequency, it is estimated that not more than one ascus in 800–1,000 show such aberrant tetrads.

The genotypes of all spore progeny from abnormal tetrads, when examined at maturity or in crossing tests, proved to carry the color factor assigned to them in direct examination of the asci. A cross between the culture derived from the odd dark spore (the fourth) in ascus 13 and a g culture resulted in further transreplication among the hybrid asci. Therefore, the transreplicated locus behaves in every way like the typical wild-type locus.

Discussion.—In an earlier paper[1] it was reported that an examination of many thousands of asci of both ultraviolet irradiated as well as non-irradiated cultures of each of the spore color mutants failed to produce any evidence of back mutation at the color loci. Although a much larger number of asci have now been observed over an additional 4-year period, there is still no evidence of back mutation at these loci in pure mutant cultures. It is also clear from the evidence that the aberrant asci described here cannot be the result of typical crossing over, since there are no reciprocal products of crossing over among the progeny. It is equally obvious that the odd ratios have not resulted from nuclear degeneration in the ascus followed by compensating nuclear divisions among the surviving genotypes, since the spores may be readily paired off by means of a second genetic marker in each cross and by unselected factors affecting growth rate. The most logical explanation would appear to be one based on a transreplication or copy choice mechanism occurring at meiotic prophase while the chromatin strands are duplicating.

The most significant asci found are those with a 5:3 ratio for spore color. While it is possible to explain 6:2 asci on the basis of transreplication within the conventional 4-strand model at meiotic prophase, this is not feasible with the 5:3 asci. Ris[8] has obtained evidence from electron microscopy that chromatids are further subdivided into half-chromatids or quarter-chromatids, depending upon the organism and varying states of the chromosomes in the same organism. Taylor[9] proposes that each chromatid is composed of two functional subunits. He has anticipated the transreplication mechanism that would lead to the production of a 5:3 ratio (see his Fig. 7, *B*). The 6:2 ratio is explained on the basis of at least one breakage among the substrands in conjunction with transreplication off both substrands of the chromatid being copied at a particular locus (see his Fig. 7, *C–E*). This interpretation would readily account for the results which we have obtained. Our 5:3 asci support the concept of the chromatid as being composed of two functional subunits.

The aberrant asci reported here could actually be more accurately referred to as octads. Certainly, the 5:3 pattern would not be readily detected in an ordinary tetrad of four meiospores, nor in an 8-spored ascus if the ascospores were isolated in pairs. The third division in the ascus is required for the separation of the transreplicated substrand from its normal partner. In a 4-spored yeast, for example, a spore carrying a heterogeneous chromatid would most likely give rise to mixed progeny and the data interpreted as resulting from a binucleate, heterokaryotic spore, back mutation in the developing colony, or contamination. The phenomenon might also contribute interesting effects elsewhere. For example, some of the reports of self-fertility among single-spore isolates of heterothallic ascomycetes and of spontaneous dikaryotization in single-spore cultures of basidiomycetes might have resulted from this mechanism.

Eight different ascospore color mutants of *S. fimicola* have now been produced in our laboratory. It would be ideal to obtain other mutant loci closely linked on either side of a color locus so that more detailed information could be obtained on the area transreplicated.

Summary.—A study of 23 asci showing aberrant segregation for ascospore color revealed that some mechanism other than crossing over, back mutation, or irregularities in nuclear survival is responsible for their occurrence. It is believed they have resulted from transreplication, by which a locus is copied more than the normal number of times during replication at meiotic prophase. The occurrence of 5:3 ratios in some asci lends confirmation to the hypothesis that each chromatid is composed of two functional subunits.

* Supported by NSF Grant G-2808 and NIH Grant E-2326.

[1] Olive, L. S., *Amer. J. Bot.*, **43**, 97–107 (1956).
[2] Lindegren, C. C., *J. Genet.*, **51**, 625–637 (1953).
[3] Mitchell, Mary B., these Proceedings, **41**, 215–220 (1955).
[4] Case, Mary E., and N. H. Giles, *Cold Spring Harbor Sympos. Quant. Biol.*, **23**, 119–135 (1958).
[5] Lederberg, J., *J. Cell. Comp. Physiol.*, **45**, Suppl. 2, 75–107 (1955).
[6] Glass, B., *Symposium on the Chemical Basis of Heredity*, 757–834 (1957).
[7] Carr, A. J. H., and L. S. Olive, *Am. J. Bot.*, **46**, 81–91 (1959).
[8] Ris, Hans, *Symposium on the Chemical Basis of Heredity*, 23–62 (1957).
[9] Taylor, J. H., Proc. 10th Int. Genet. Congress (in press).

IV. GENETIC RECOMBINATION

Reprinted from COLD SPRING HARBOR SYMPOSIA ON QUANTITATIVE BIOLOGY

VOLUME XI

INDUCED MUTATIONS IN BACTERIAL VIRUSES[1]

M. DELBRÜCK AND W. T. BAILEY, JR.

In another paper of this Symposium, to which ours is closely related and to which we refer the reader for a description of material and for terminology, Dr. Hershey (4) has described a variety of spontaneously occurring mutations of bacterial viruses. One class of mutations affects the type of plaque. These mutations occur in only one group of serologically related viruses, the group to which belong T2, T4, and T6. The most conspicuous of these mutations is the *r* mutation. Our observations are concerned exclusively with this *r* mutation. We have seen also some of the other mutations which affect the type of plaque and which Hershey has described, but we have not made systematic experiments concerning them.

We have infected bacteria simultaneously with mixtures of wild type and *r* mutant of the viruses T2, T4, and T6, and have investigated the yields of virus from such mixedly infected bacteria. These experiments are a sequel to previous studies of mixed infections with pairs of different viruses. The chief result of the studies to be reported here is the fact that the yield of virus from mixedly infected bacteria may contain a high proportion of one or more new types of virus—i.e., of a type that was not used for the infection. In all cases the new types exhibit combinations of the genetic markers of the infecting types.

MUTUAL EXCLUSION

We will begin with a recapitulation of earlier work on mixed infections (3, 6, 2). The chief finding of these earlier studies was the mutual-exclusion effect. It was found that any mixedly infected bacterium yields upon lysis only one of the infecting types of virus. The other virus does not multiply; even the adsorbed particles of the excluded type are not recovered upon lysis. Which one of the two types of virus used for infection is excluded and which one multiplies depends on the pair used and on the conditions of the experiment, such as timing and multiplicity of infection. For the pair T1, T2 the virus T1 is always excluded except when it is given a head start of at least four minutes (3). If T1 is added more than four minutes earlier than T2, then T2 will be excluded in an appreciable proportion of the infected bacteria. Lysis of any one bacterium always occurs after a time interval corresponding to the latent period of intracellular virus multiplication of the virus type which does multiply in that particular bacterium.

[1] This work was supported by grants-in-aid from The Rockefeller Foundation and from the John and Mary R. Markle Foundation.

A similar situation was encountered (2) in the study of the pair T1, T7. Here, too, the mutual-exclusion mechanism operates perfectly; in practically every bacterium either one or the other of the two viruses is excluded from multiplication. The exclusion powers of these two viruses are nearly balanced. In a bacterial culture simultaneously infected with T1 and T7 there is a clean split into T1 yielders and T7 yielders, the two types occurring with comparable frequency.

During a closer study of this pair it became evident that the excluded virus is not without effect on the course of events. The excluded virus may reduce the number of virus particles liberated upon lysis of the bacterium. This has been called the depressor effect (2).

A cursory survey of other pairs of virus particles seemed only to confirm these findings and, in particular, seemed to point to the mutual-exclusion effect as a very general phenomenon.

In these earlier investigations an attempt was made also to test whether mutual exclusion occurs when a bacterium is infected with two particles of the *same* kind. Such an assumption ("self-interference") seemed to suggest itself from the observation that bacteria infected with several particles of one kind are lysed after exactly the same latent period as are bacteria infected with only one particle. The test of mutual exclusion requires that one find out whether the yield of virus from any one bacterium is the offspring of only one or of several of the infecting particles. To make such a test one must be able to differentiate the offspring of the various infecting particles; in other words, one has to mark the infecting particles with hereditary markers. One is thus naturally led to the study of mutual exclusion between a virus and one of its mutants.

The first attempt in this direction was made by Luria (5), who studied interference between T2 and T2*h*. The difficulty with this pair lies in the fact that no indicator strain resistant to T2*h* and sensitive to T2 is available. Luria succeeded nevertheless in showing that a large proportion of the bacteria infected with T2 *and* T2*h* did not liberate any T2*h*. At least a partial functioning of the mutual-exclusion mechanism seemed to be indicated by these results.

THE BREAKDOWN OF MUTUAL EXCLUSION FOR THE PAIRS (T2*r*⁺, T2*r*) AND (T4*r*⁺, T4*r*)

The first definite indication of a new phenomenon came in March, 1945, when Hershey tried mixed infections with a wild-type strain (T2) and its *r*

[33]

mutant. Hershey observed that the mixedly infected bacteria give rise to mottled plaques, and he verified that the mottled plaques contain a mixture of the two types used for infection. Dr. Hershey communicated his discovery to us and we have since been following this promising lead.

Mixed Infections with T2r⁺, T2r

Hershey's finding that the majority of the mixedly infected bacteria give mixed yields was confirmed by two methods; viz., (1) by plating mixedly infected bacteria before lysis, (2) by plating single bursts after lysis (1).

In these experiments the infecting doses of wild type were slightly higher than those of the r mutant. Each kind of virus was in at least threefold excess over the bacteria. In the case of simultaneous infection, about one-third of the bacteria gave pure wild-type bursts. Most of the remaining bursts were mixed. These mixed bursts contained wild type and mutant in all proportions. On the average, however, wild type was predominant. The predominance may be due to an inherent advantage of wild type, or it may be due to the fact that in these experiments the infecting doses of wild type were slightly greater than those of the mutant. We have found that the wild type of this strain of virus is somewhat more rapidly adsorbed than its r mutant, and the predominance of wild type in the bursts may be due in part to the more rapid adsorption of the wild type.

If the two viruses are not given simultaneously, the ratios are shifted in favor of the virus which precedes. Thus, if wild type precedes by six minutes, almost all bursts are pure wild type. If the r mutant precedes by six minutes, there is a majority of pure r bursts and mixed bursts, but there is still a fair proportion of pure wild type.

Mixed Infections with T4r⁺, T4r

The results for this pair were similar to those for mixed infections with wild type and r mutant of T2, with the following minor differences:

(1) A greater proportion of the single bursts showed mixed yields (23 out of 25).

(2) The r mutants predominated in the mixed bursts, although all proportions were encountered. Fig. 1 shows the correlations between wild type and r mutant in the individual bursts of one large experiment, in which sixty samples were plated for bursts.

For this pair, too, it was found that wild type is adsorbed slightly more rapidly than is its r mutant.

These experiments substantiated Hershey's findings. They showed, moreover, that in the bacteria giving mixed yields all proportions of wild type to r mutant could be found. The results seemed to prove an almost complete breakdown of the mutual-exclusion mechanism, nearly every bacterium yielding virus particles of both the infecting types. However, modifications of the experimental set-up to be reported presently revealed unexpected new features, which throw the interpretation of Hershey's experiment into doubt.

It may be recalled that the first experiments on mixed infection had been undertaken in the hope of obtaining lysis of bacteria at an intermediate stage of intracellular virus multiplication. Our expectation had been that in mixed infection with (T1, T2) the bacteria would be lysed after 13

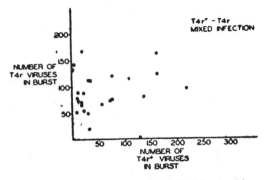

Fig. 1. T4r⁺ and T4r content of individual bursts of bacteria infected with these viruses. Each dot represents one burst. The abscissa is the T4r⁺ content, the ordinate the T4r content.

minutes, the latent period of T1, and that thus an intermediate stage in the multiplication of T2 would be revealed. T2 by itself does not lyse the bacteria until 21 minutes after infection. This hope had been frustrated when mutual exclusion was discovered. Hershey's discovery of an apparently complete breakdown of the mutual-exclusion mechanism for infections with the pair (T2r⁺, T2r) revived the hope of studying intermediate stages of intracellular multiplication of viruses. However, the study of pairs like (T2r⁺, T2r) suffers from the handicap that indicator strains are not available for obtaining separate counts of the two types. Instead, one has to rely on plaque appearance. The majority of the plaques are clearly differentiated, but there are always a few plaques whose classification is a little uncertain. These would require subculture for verification, a very laborious procedure when large numbers are involved. For this reason we eventually (October, 1945) decided to try the pairs (T2, T4), (T6, T4), and (T2, T6). These viruses are closely related to each other serologically and morphologically, but they are otherwise independent virus types, and indicator strains which sharply distinguish between them are available. The r mutation was used as an additional genetic marker.

THE BREAKDOWN OF MUTUAL EXCLUSION FOR THE PAIRS (T4, T2), (T4, T6), AND (T2, T6)

In Hershey's case of mixed infection with wild type and r mutant, a breakdown of mutual exclusion is indicated by the appearance of mottled plaques when mixedly infected bacteria are plated. For pairs with host-range differences another criterion can be employed, the appearance of clear plaques in platings on mixed indicator strains (*2*). Any bacterium that liberates at least one particle of each of the infecting types can lyse both indicator strains, while any bacterium that liberates only particles of one of the infecting types will form a plaque which is overgrown by the indicator strain for the other type and which will therefore be turbid. A comparison of plaque counts on mixed indicators and on strain B gives the fraction of the bacteria with mixed yields—i.e., the fraction of the bacteria in which the mutual-exclusion mechanism failed to operate.

Table 1 lists the fraction of mixed yielders for a variety of combinations between the wild types and

TABLE 1. THE BREAKDOWN OF THE MUTUAL-EXCLUSION PRINCIPLE

Infecting Pair		% Mixed Yielders
T6	T4	
r^+	r^+	Few
r	r	10
r	r^+	20
r^+	r	12
T2	T4	
r^+	r^+	60–90
r^+	r	60–90
r	r^+	80
T2	T6	
r^+	r	80

r mutants of T2, T4, and T6. The breakdown of the mutual-exclusion mechanism is particularly marked for the combinations involving T2. These findings would seem to fit well with Hershey's findings, and to suggest the generalization that mutual exclusion operates the more perfectly the more dissimilar the two infecting viruses. Wild type and *r* mutant give no mutual exclusion, serologically closely related viruses give partial mutual exclusion, and unrelated viruses give complete mutual exclusion.

The Nature of the T2 Particles Liberated by Mixedly Infected Bacteria Involving T2

A paradoxical feature occurred in all the combinations involving T2. When mixedly infected bacteria were plated, the number of *clear* plaques on mixed indicators was in all cases much greater than the number of plaques on the indicator for T2. The number of clear plaques *on mixed indicators* gives the number of bacteria which liberate a mixture of the infecting types. The number of plaques *on the T2 indicator* gives the number of bacteria which liberate T2, irrespective of whether or not such a bacterium also liberates the other type. The latter

plaque count comprises two classes, the mixed yielders plus the pure T2 yielders. The mixed indicators show only one of these classes, the mixed yielders. It follows that the count on mixed indicators should always be smaller than, or at most equal to, the count on the T2 indicator, contrary to the actual finding.

The possibility was considered that the clear plaques found on mixed indicators might be due, not to a mixed yield of T2 and T4 particles, but to host-range mutants. Conceivably, host-range mutants might arise during the growth of the plaques and these mutants might be responsible for the lysis of both indicator strains. It must be realized that mixed indicators constitute an ideal enrichment medium for host-range mutants.

This possibility was ruled out by two tests. First, the viruses in question were plated separately on the same pair of mixed indicators. No clear plaques were found. This shows that host-range mutants in sufficient number to cause clear plaques on mixed indicators do not occur when the viruses are plated separately. Second, the contents of ten of the clear plaques from platings of mixedly infected bacteria on mixed indicators were analyzed for their virus content. Each of these plaques contained a mixture of particles with host ranges characteristic of the infecting types, and no particles with extended host range.

It follows that the clear plaques on mixed indicators are due to genuine mixed yields of T2 and T4 particles. The low count of T2 yielders on the indicator for T2 must mean that a considerable proportion of the putative T2 particles liberated from mixedly infected bacteria fail to form plaques on the T2 indicator. The T2 particles used for infection in these experiments do not have this property; they register with the same efficiency on the T2 indicator as on mixed indicators. The low efficiency of plating of the T2 particles in the yields from mixedly infected bacteria is not a hereditary property. Their progeny registers with the same efficiency on the T2 indicator as on mixed indicators.

It might be mentioned in passing that there are many T2 indicator strains of the type B/4 on which the normal T2 exhibits a low efficiency of plating. In fact the strain of B/4 employed in these experiments is unique in registering T2 with full efficiency of plating. This strain was isolated by Dr. Hershey. The question arose whether the low efficiency of plating of the normal T2 on the other strains of B/4 is also increased by the addition of B/2. Experiments showed that this is not the case. Therefore, low efficiency of plating of the T2 particles liberated from mixedly infected bacteria must be caused by a specific property of these particles.

The findings may be summarized as follows. A large proportion of bacteria mixedly infected with T4 and T2, or T6 and T2, give mixed yields. The liberated T2 particles have a low efficiency of plating on the T2 indicator but not on mixed indicators.

The low efficiency of plating of these particles on the T2 indicator is not a hereditary property.

More experiments will be needed to clarify this situation. Specifically, the role of the second indicator strain in raising the efficiency of plating of the liberated T2 particles has to be clarified. This indicator strain by itself is totally resistant to T2. Preliminary experiments have not given any clue to the factor contributed by the second indicator strain.

INDUCED MUTATIONS

We now turn to the principal point of this paper, the occurrence in mixed infections of induced mutations at the r locus. In the experiments described in the two preceding sections, the mixedly infected bacteria were regularly plated on strain B, on each of the indicator strains separately, and on mixed indicators. In some of these experiments one of the infecting viruses was genetically marked by using the r mutant instead of the wild type. It was noted that the platings on one or the other of the indicator strains, or on both, gave a high proportion of mottled plaques. For instance, in a mixed infection with the viruses (T2r+, T4r) the plating on B/2 gave plaques the majority of which had mottled halos, indicating that the majority of the bacteria had liberated a mixture of wild-type and r-type particles which could attack B/2. Wild-type particles able to attack B/2 had not been used in this experiment. The wild-type particles, therefore, represented a new type, created during the mixed infection.

The creation of wild-type particles with the host range characteristic of T4 was verified in three ways. First, by analyzing the contents of the mottled plaques. These analyses confirmed the assumption of the presence of a mixture of T4r+ and T4r particles. Second, by plating on B/2 after lysis. These plates, too, showed the presence of T4r+, though in smaller proportion, indicating that induced mutants occur in small numbers, though they occur in the yields of the majority of the mixedly infected bacteria. Third, by plating single bursts on B/2. Small numbers of induced mutants were found in the majority of the bursts, confirming the inference of the previous test.

A priori, this new type could have arisen as a modification of either one of the infecting types: either as a modification of T4r by a mutation

$$T4r \longrightarrow T4r^+ \text{ (under the influence of } T2r^+\text{)},$$

or as a modification of T2r+ by a mutation

$$T2r^+ \longrightarrow T4r^+ \text{ (under the influence of } T4r\text{)}.$$

The first assumption implies a mutation at the r locus, the second assumption a mutation at the genetic site (or sites) determining host range. We prefer the first hypothesis for three reasons. First, the mutation at the r locus is known to occur spontaneously and is known to require only one step. Second, a change from the host range characteristic

for T2 to that characteristic for T4, as implied in the second assumption, may be expected to require several mutational steps, since T2 and T4 are independent wild types, and since at least two phenotypic changes are involved—namely, loss of activity on B/4 and gain of activity on B/2. Third, when the new type was tested serologically, it was found to be indistinguishable from the infecting type, with the same host range. We therefore believe that the new types arise by a mutation at the r locus, without change of host range.

Table 2 is a summary of the combinations of in-

TABLE 2. MIXED INFECTIONS YIELDING INDUCED MUTATIONS

Infecting Pair		Induced Types
T6	T4	
r+	r+	none
r	r	none
r	r+	T6r', T4r
r+	r	T4r+
T2	T4	
r+	r+	none
r+	r	T2r, T4r+
T2	T6	
r+	r	T2r

fecting types which have been tested for the occurrence of induced mutations at the r locus. The data point to three generalizations:

(1) Mutations occur from wild type to r type or from r type to wild type.

(2) Mutations occur only if one of the infecting types is wild type, the other r type. When both the infecting types are wild type, or both r type, no mutations are found.

(3) In the same mixed infection both infecting types may be changed, wild type to r type, and r type to wild type.

A discussion of possible theoretical interpretations of these findings does not seem warranted at this point, since our studies are far from complete. Perhaps one might dispute the propriety of calling the observed changes "induced mutations." In some respects they look more like transfers, or even exchanges, of genetic materials. We do not pretend to be able to put forward convincing arguments for either point of view.

A comment might be added with respect to Hershey's original discovery of mixed yields of wild type and r type. We now know that mutual exclusion may break down in infections with closely related viruses. Hershey's finding may therefore be interpreted as a lack of mutual exclusion. On the other hand, we know that in mixed infections with wild type and r type induced mutations do occur. To explain Hershey's findings one might assume, therefore, that only one of the infecting types multiplies while the other type induces mutations in it. A much closer study of the interrelations between the breakdown of mutual exclusion and the occurrence of induced mutations will be necessary to settle this ambiguity. For this purpose detailed studies of the contents of single bursts, and of the numerical relations between the different types of viruses in such bursts, should prove of great value.

Summary

We will briefly retrace in historical order the steps that have led to our present state of knowledge regarding mixed infections of bacteria with bacterial viruses.

Mixed infections with pairs of *unrelated* viruses, like (T1, T2) or (T1, T7), result in mutual exclusion. Only one of the infecting types multiplies, the other is lost (*3, 6, 2*).

The excluded virus may greatly reduce the yield of successful virus (depressor effect) (*2*).

Mixed infections with wild-type and *r*-type particles of the *same* strain do not, apparently, give rise to mutual exclusion (Hershey, *4*).

Mixed infections with pairs of *related* viruses of the group T2, T4, T6 give partial mutual exclusion. The T2 particles liberated in mixed infections of this type exhibit certain nonheritable peculiarities, the nature of which has not yet been ascertained.

Mixed infections with pairs of the group T2, T4, T6, in which one of the pair is used in the wild-type form, the other in the *r*-type form, give rise to the liberation of new types, which can be characterized as mutants of the infecting types. The mutations occur at the *r* locus.

References

1. DELBRÜCK, M. The burst size distribution in the growth of bacterial viruses (bacteriophages). J. Bact. 50: 131-135. 1945.
2. DELBRÜCK, M. Interference between bacterial viruses. III. The mutual exclusion effect and the depressor effect. J. Bact. 50: 151-170. 1945.
3. DELBRÜCK, M., and LURIA, S. E. Interference between bacterial viruses. I. Interference between two bacterial viruses acting upon the same host, and the mechanism of virus growth. Arch. Biochem. 1: 111-141. 1942.
4. HERSHEY, A. D. Spontaneous mutations in bacterial viruses. Cold Spring Harbor Symp. Quant. Biol. 11: 67-77. 1946.
5. LURIA, S. E. Mutations of bacterial viruses affecting their host range. Genetics 30: 84-99. 1945.
6. LURIA, S. E., and DELBRÜCK, M. Interference between bacterial viruses. II. Interference between inactivated bacterial virus and active virus of the same strain and of a different strain. Arch. Biochem. 1: 207-218. 1942.

NOVEL GENOTYPES IN MIXED CULTURES OF BIOCHEMICAL MUTANTS OF BACTERIA

JOSHUA LEDERBERG[1] AND E. L. TATUM

Hershey has reported (1) the occurrence of novel combinations of inherited characters in a bacterial virus. It may not be amiss to describe briefly some experimental fragments, relating to a situation in the bacterium *Escherichia coli,* which may be similar in some respects.

Tatum, in reviewing biochemical mutations in *E. coli* (6), has pointed out the advantages offered by these characters for genetic analysis. In particular one may note the facility and certainty with which

may be detected readily by plating heavy suspensions of the washed cells into a minimal agar medium, in which only the prototrophs will form macroscopic colonies. Their frequency is very much greater than that anticipated on the hypothesis that the prototrophs result from the coincidental occurrence, in the same clone, of reversions of two or more "loci." Furthermore, single cultures of the same multiple mutants grown and tested under comparable conditions have not been found to

TABLE 1. TYPES ISOLATED FROM SINGLE AND MIXED CULTURES. MUTANTS USED ARE INDICATED ON THE LETTERED LINES.

	From single and mixed	From mixed only		From single and mixed
A	$B^-M^-P^+T^+$ $B^+M^-P^+T^+$ $B^-M^+P^+T^+$	and $B^+M^+P^+T^+$ *	$B^+M^+P^-T^-$	$B^+M^+P^+T^-$ $B^+M^+P^-T^+$
B	**	$B^-M^-P^+T^+R$ $B^+M^+P^+T^+R$ * $B^+M^+P^+T^+$ *	and $B^+M^+P^-T^-$	**
C	**	$B^-M^-P^+T^+$ $B^+M^+P^+T^+R$ * $B^+M^+P^+T^+$ *	and $B^+M^+P^-T^-R$	**
D	**	$B^-M^-P^+T^+R$ $B^+M^+P^+T^+R$ *	and $B^+M^+P^-T^-R$	**
E	$B^-\Phi^-C^+P^+T^+$ $B^-\Phi^-C^-P^+T^+$ $B^+\Phi^-C^-P^+T^+$	$B^-\Phi^-C^-P^+T^+$ $B^+\Phi^+C^+P^+T^+$ * $B^-\Phi^+C^+P^+T^+$ $B^-\Phi^+C^+P^-T^+$	and $B^+\Phi^+C^+P^-T^-$	$B^+\Phi^+C^+P^-T^+$ $B^+\Phi^+C^+P^+T^-$

* Prototroph.
** See A for biochemical variations.
The letters refer to requirements for essential metabolites as follows:

B = biotin   M = methionine
Φ = phenylalanine   P = proline
C = cystine   T = threonine
R = Resistance to virus T1.

they can be classified, and their relative stability and independence. Since many of the single biochemical mutants of *E. coli* revert with a measurable frequency of the order of 10^{-7} (3, 5) we have used the multiple mutants, obtained by iterated mutations, referred to previously (6).

When multiple mutants are grown in mixed cultures in complete (yeast extract-peptone-glucose) medium, there have repeatedly appeared appreciable numbers of prototrophic (4), or nutritionally wild-type, cells. Although these have never been found, thus far, in a proportion higher than 10^{-7}, they

[1] Fellow of the Jane Coffin Childs Memorial Fund for Medical Research.

contain prototrophs, although small numbers of cells reverted at a single "locus" are, of course, found.

Since it has been established in this laboratory that different biochemical mutants are capable of supplying each others' growth-factor requirements by exchange through the medium, it would appear to be possible that these prototrophs represent heterogeneous aggregations of the different mutants. Attempts to detect or induce the segregation of the components of such putative aggregates by biological and physical means have, as indicated below, been uniformly unsuccessful. Therefore it seems likely that the prototrophs are genotypically unique cells.

[113]

After having passed through a single colony isolation, the prototrophs are quite stable; and of many hundreds of colonies isolated from cultures grown on complete medium, all have proved prototrophic.

Cultures of a prototroph, grown in complete medium, were irradiated with ultraviolet light of such dosage that the number of colonies which appeared on plating in complete agar medium was reduced to $1:10^5$. At this rate of killing, it is evident that most of the supposed aggregates had no surviving representatives. Of the remainder it is likely that only a single cell would survive, in most instances, to form a colony. Nevertheless, each of several hundred colonies that were tested were prototrophic.

Fortunately, the strain with which these experiments were conducted (K-12) is susceptible to the bacterial virus T1 (2). In the following experiment multiple mutant strains were used which required biotin and methionine $(B^-M^-P^+T^+)$ and threonine and proline $(B^+M^+P^-T^-)$ respectively. In addition, mutations, occurring spontaneously at a low rate, for resistance (R) to T1 were selected for by the procedure described by Luria and Delbrück (2).

Mixed cultures were plated out as before, and prototrophs isolated and tested for virus resistance. When mixtures of susceptible strains were studied, only susceptible prototrophs were found. Similarly, when resistant strains were mixed the prototrophs obtained were exclusively resistant. When, however, a mixture of $(B^-M^-P^+T^+R)$ and $(B^+M^+P^-T^-)$ was used, of ten isolated prototrophs, 8 were resistant and 2 sensitive. When $(B^-M^-P^+T^+)$ and $(B^+M^+P^-T^-R)$ were used, 3 were resistant and 7 sensitive. If the prototrophs consisted of aggregates of the original mutants,

each prototroph culture in these cases should have had a large proportion of resistant cells. Yet we have mentioned above the finding of 9 prototroph cultures which were completely lysed by T1. The occurrence of both resistant and sensitive prototrophs is evidence, also, for their internal homogeneity, as one might expect either resistance or susceptibility to be dominant (see Table 1).

Combinations of other mutants have given rise to prototrophs. In particular, isolations have been made from a mixture of proline-threonineless $(B^+\Phi^+C^+P^-T^-)$ and biotin-phenylalanine-cystineless $(B^-\Phi^-C^-P^+T^+)$ plated into agar containing biotin, phenylalanine and proline. In addition to prototrophs and single reversion types, a biotinless $(B^-\Phi^+C^+P^+T^+)$ and a biotin-prolineless $(B^-\Phi^+C^+P^-T^+)$ have been isolated.

Note added in proof: Additional experiments and an interpretation of these data have been reported by us. ("Gene recombination in *Escherichia coli*." Nature 158: 558. 1946.)

REFERENCES

1. HERSHEY, A. D. Spontaneous mutations in bacterial viruses. Cold Spring Harbor Symp. Quant. Biol. 11: 67-77. 1946.
2. LURIA, S. E., and DELBRÜCK, M. Mutations of bacteria from virus sensitivity to virus resistance. Genetics 28: 491-511. 1943.
3. RYAN, F. J. Back-mutation and adaptation of nutritional mutants. Cold Spring Harbor Symp. Quant. Biol. 11: 215-227. 1946.
4. RYAN, F. J., and LEDERBERG, J. Reverse-mutation and adaptation in leucineless Neurospora. Proc. Nat. Acad. Sci. 32: 163-173. 1946.
5. RYAN, F. J., and LEDERBERG, J. Unpublished experiments.
6. TATUM, E. L. Induced biochemical mutations in bacteria. Cold Spring Harbor Symp. Quant. Biol. 11: 278-284. 1946.

Reprinted from GENETICS 32: 505-525, September, 1947

GENE RECOMBINATION AND LINKED SEGREGATIONS
IN ESCHERICHIA COLI[1]

JOSHUA LEDERBERG[2]

*Department of Botany and Microbiology, Osborn Botanical Laboratory,
Yale University, New Haven, Conn.*

Received August 1, 1947

THE occurrence of factor recombination in the bacterium, *Escherichia coli*, has been described in previous reports (LEDERBERG and TATUM, 1946 b, c, TATUM and LEDERBERG, 1947). In an attempt to elucidate further the genetic structure of this organism, these studies have been extended to crosses involving several characters, and to the quantitative enumeration of various recombination classes. The results described in this paper provide evidence supporting the sexual basis of factor recombination and of the existence of an organized array of genes comparable to that of higher forms.

MATERIALS AND METHODS

The parent "wild-type" strain, K-12, of *E. coli* used in these experiments and the production and behavior of biochemical mutants have been described (GRAY and TATUM, 1944, LEDERBERG and TATUM, 1946a, ROEPKE, LIBBY, and SMALL, 1944, TATUM, 1945). Specific requirements, notation, and other data pertinent to the biochemical mutants are summarized in tables 1 and 2. In general, a biochemical deficiency resulting from mutation is designated by the initial of the substance required (e.g. B^- for biotinless), while the wild type alternative is written with a "$+$" sign (e.g. B^+ to emphasize the alternative to B^-). The term "prototroph" (RYAN and LEDERBERG, 1946) has been devised for strains exhibiting the nutritional behavior of the wild type, which for *E. coli* implies independence of any specific growth factors. Prototroph is, however, not synonymous with "wild type" since it refers (a) only to the phenotypic appearance of a culture and (b) only to nutritional and not to other possible mutant characteristics.

K-12 as a coliform is capable of fermenting, or producing acid, from a variety of sugars, including glucose, galactose, maltose, lactose and mannitol; however, it ferments glycerol only weakly, and sucrose even less so. Because of the ease of scoring and their biochemical specificity, mutants unable to ferment various sugars have been looked for. Particular attention was paid to the isolation of "lactose-negative" or "*Lac⁻*" mutants, because of the taxonomic significance which has been attached to this character.

---

[1] Abstracted from a dissertation offered in partial fulfillment of requirements for the degree of Doctor of Philosophy at YALE UNIVERSITY.

[2] Fellow of the JANE COFFIN CHILDS MEMORIAL FUND FOR MEDICAL RESEARCH. This work has been supported by the JANE COFFIN CHILDS MEMORIAL FUND FOR MEDICAL RESEARCH. The author's present address is: Department of Genetics, University of Wisconsin, Madison, Wis

The detection of fermentation mutants is readily accomplished by the use of indicator media. The medium "EMB-lactose" used in routine bacteriological work was found to be highly useful. It consists of the following (in g/l): peptone (or "N-Z-Case") 10, yeast extract 1, lactose 10, agar 15, eosin Y 0.4, methylene blue 0.06, sodium chloride 5, dipotassium phosphate 2. On this medium, colonies of bacteria which can ferment lactose (or any other sugar added in its place) rapidly turn a deep purple color, while colonies of non-fermenting organisms remain white or pink but may slowly turn light blue.

Lac^- mutations have been recovered in two instances. Among 15,000 colonies

TABLE 1
Symbols used for various loci.

1. Nutritional requirements. Allele for requirement of a given substance is designated by the superscript "−"; independence by "+". E.G., B^- is biotinless; B^+ is biotin-independent.

B biotin	L leucine	Pa phenylalanine (ϕ was used previously,
B_1 thiamin	M methionine	but has been modified for typographical
C cystine	P proline	reasons)
	T threonine	

2. "Sugar" fermentations. The ability to ferment is designated "+"; the inability "−".
   Lac lactose Gly glycerol

3. Bacteriophage resistance. Resistance is designated by the superscript "r"; sensitivity by "s". E.G. $V_1{}^r$.
   V_1 resistant to $T1$, $T5$
   V_{1a} resistant to $T1$; sensitive to $T5$
   V_{1b} resistant to $T1$; mucoid colonies
   V_6 resistant to $T6$.

4. Resistance to chemical agents. Resistance and sensitivity "r" and "s" respectively, as Cla^r.
   Cla sodium chloroacetate
   A sodium azide

of strain Y-10 $(T^-L^-B_1{}^-)$ obtained by spreading a culture previously treated with ultraviolet light on EMB-lactose agar, a single pink colony was noted. It proved to be the same, nutritionally, as Y-10 and was therefore regarded as a Lac^- mutant; this stock is labelled Y-53. Among 30,000 colonies of Y-40 $(B^-M^-V_1{}^r)$ a single Lac^- was recovered following treatment with nitrogen-mustard (TATUM, 1946), and was designated as Y-87. Tests showing that these independent mutations are probably allelic will be described in a later section (see table 5). Strains Y-53 and Y-87 differ in the rate at which the Lac^- character reverts to the Lac^+ condition, but whether this is due to different allelic states or to differences at other loci, cannot be definitively asserted.

Attempts to obtain maltose, mannitol, and galactose-negative mutants were not successful, presumably because the populations tested were too small. A glycerol-negative strain has been obtained, but the wild type ferments this polyalcohol so poorly to begin with that accurate scoring is difficult; studies on this character will not be further reported here.

Mutations for resistance to specific bacteriophages or bacterial viruses have proven to be exceedingly useful. They are readily obtained as spontaneous mutants by plating a large number of sensitive bacteria with the particular virus in question; only resistant mutants escape lysis and may be recovered as "secondary" colonies (fig. 1). Resistant mutants are readily freed from residual virus by serial single colony isolation. Resistance to a given virus may be

TABLE 2

A summary of the mutants used.

STRAIN NO.	GENOTYPE	ORIGIN	GENOTYPE	AGENT
K-12	prototroph.	Original wild strain		
58	B^-	K-12	B^+	X-ray
58-161	B^-M^-	58	B^-M^+	X-ray
58-278	B^-Pa^-	58	B^-Pa^+	X-ray
Y-24	$B^-Pa^-C^-$	58-278	$B^-Pa^-C^+$	ultra-violet
679	T^-	K-12	T^+	X-ray
679-680	T^-L^-	679	T^-L^+	X-ray
Y-10	$T^-L^-B_1^-$	679-680	$T^-L^-B_1^+$	X-ray
Y-46	$T^-L^-B_1^-V_1^r$	Y-10	$T^-L^-B_1^-V_1^s$	selection
Y-53	$T^-L^-B_1^-Lac^-$	Y-10	$T^-L^-B_1^-Lac^+$	ultra-violet
Y-64	$T^-L^-B_1^-Lac^-V_1^r$	Y-53	$T^-L^-B_1^-Lac^-V_1^s$	selection
Y-40	$B^-M^-V_1^r$	58-161	$B^-M^-V_1^s$	selection
Y-87	$*B^-M^-V_1^rLac^{2-}$	Y-40	$B^-M^-V_1^rLac^+$	nitrogen mustard
Y-24-V_1^r	$B^-Pa^-C^-V_1^r$	Y-24	$B^-Pa^-C^-V_1^s$	selection
679-183	T^-P^-	679	T^-P^+	X-ray
Y-88	$T^-L^-B_1^-Lac^-Cla^r$	Y-53	$T^-L^-B_1^-Lac^-Cla^s$	selection
Y-80	$B^-M^-V_1^r Gly^-$	Y-40	$B^-M^-V_1^r Gly^+$	nitrogen mustard
Y-91	$B^-M^-V_1^r Cla^r$	Y-40	$B^-M^-V_1^r Cla^s$	selection
Y-92	$B^-M^-V_1^rAz^r$	Y-40	$B^-M^-V_1^rAz^s$	selection
Y-94	$T^-L^-B_1^-Lac^-V_6^r$	Y-53	$T^-L^-B_1^-Lac^-V_6^s$	selection
Y-100	$T^-L^-B_1^-Lac^-V_{1a}^r$	Y-53	$T^-L^-B_1^-Lac^-V_{1a}^s$	selection
Y-86	$T^-L^-B_1^-Lac^-V_{1b}^r$	Y-53	$T^-L^-B_1^-Lac^-V_{1b}^s$	selection

* Lac^{2-} in mutant Y-87 differs from Lac^- in mutant Y-53 and its derivatives in the greater reverse-mutability of the latter. Lac^- and Lac^{2-} are otherwise similar, and allelic.

scored by streaking a loopful of bacteria on an EMB or nutrient agar plate at right angles to a previous streak of the virus suspension (DEMEREC and FANO, 1945, see fig. 1 of the present report.)

It was found, however, that mutations for resistance to a given virus are not entirely specific, but that resistant mutants display "cross-resistance," i.e., are also resistant to other viruses. For example, most T_1-resistant types are also resistant to T_5. (For the nomenclature of the bacterial viruses used in this investigation, and a detailed account of the cross-resistance patterns of another strain, *E. coli B*, see DEMEREC and FANO, 1945). The cross-resistance patterns of K-12 are similar to those of *E. coli B* with the exception that T_1-resistant mutants which are sensitive to T_5 are not tryptophaneless, as has been reported by ANDERSON (1946) for the corresponding mutants of *E. coli B*. In this paper, the designation V_1^r will be used for the more frequent T_1-resistant mutant, which is also resistant to T_5. The symbol V_{1a}^r is reserved for the T_5-sensitive, T_1-resistant mutant, but the evidence that distinct loci are involved will be presented *in extenso* in another place.

In addition to V_1^r and V_{1a}^r, just mentioned, a third type of "secondary colony" has been found among populations treated with the virus T_1. This type, V_{1b}^r is characterized by an exceedingly slimy or mucoid colony confor-

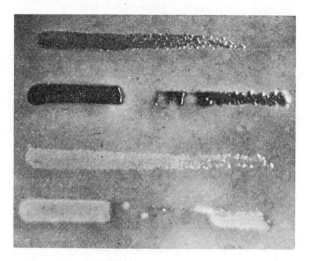

FIGURE 1.—The phenotypes of the four combinations of *Lac* and *V* are illustrated. In order they are: $Lac^+V_1^r$; $Lac^+V_1^s$; $Lac^-V_1^r$; $Lac^-V_1^s$. An EMB-lactose agar plate was first streaked vertically with the virus T_1. Subsequently, each of the bacterial types was streaked, from left to right, perpendicularly across the virus streak. After 16 hours incubation, both the *Lac* and V_1 phenotypes are well developed. Developing in the zone where $Lac^-V_1^s$ has been lysed can be seen two colonies of resistant mutants: $Lac^-V_1^r$.

mation. Recombination studies on this mutant are complicated by its genetic instability; V_{1b}^r rapidly reverts to the wild type, and in addition may also be strongly selected against in competition with V_{1b}^s. However, the locus of V_{1b} can be distinguished from the locus of the other V_1 mutants by the demonstration of a different recombination frequency with *Lac*. These data are summarized in order to emphasize the importance of genetic tests to insure the allelic identity of phenotypically similar mutants.

It is particularly fortunate that resistance tests can be conducted on EMB agar, since this allows the characterization of a strain with respect to virus-resistance and to lactose fermentation with a single streaking (see fig. 1).

Mutants resistant to sodium chloroacetate (Cla^r) were obtained by streaking a large number (about 10^7) of bacteria on nutrient agar to which filter-sterilized chloroacetate has been added to make a final concentration of 2 mg/ml. At this concentration, the wild type is substantially inhibited, while resistant mutants grow luxuriantly. This mutation is accompanied by deficiencies in the metabolism of pyruvic and acetic acids, which will be described in more detail elsewhere. Independent mutations to other inhibitors, including iodo-acetate, azide, streptomycin, streptothricin, mercuric chloride, and Brilliant Green, can be secured in a similar fashion, but genetic analysis of these mutations has not been completed.

Morphological variation has occasionally been noted (exceedingly rough or very mucoid colonial form) but is relatively unsuitable for genetic work because the presumably random choice of prototroph recombinants may be influenced.

In addition to the EMB agar already described, a number of other natural or "complete" media have been used. The Difco product "Penassay Broth" has been used most extensively, and is satisfactory for the preparation of inocula, except that it must be supplemented with cystine for the growth of cystineless organisms, such as strain Y-24. Other satisfactory media include a broth consisting of: peptone 5, glucose 5, yeast extract 3, g/l, as well as Difco Nutrient Broth, and diverse concoctions containing peptone or casein hydrolysates and meat or yeast extract.

The synthetic or minimal medium contains, in g/l: NH_4Cl 5, NH_4NO_3 1, Na_2SO_4 2, K_2HPO_4 3, KH_2PO_4 1, glucose 5, asparagine 1.5, $MgSO_4$ 0.1, trace elements (GRAY and TATUM 1944), and $CaCl_2$, a trace. The medium is made solid by the addition of agar in a concentration of 1.5 percent.

To avoid flocculation when used with agar, the glucose and agar in solution should be autoclaved separately, and mixed with the other components just before using. Unwashed agar (Difco) is sufficiently free of the growth factors under consideration to be satisfactory for many experiments; the use of washed agar, however, is recommended for the cleanest results.

The detection of recombinants is based upon the inability of biochemical mutant bacteria to proliferate in the absence of their specific growth substances. Plating in minimal agar, therefore, has the effect of a sieve for prototroph cells. To insure against contamination with prototrophs derived by reverse mutation, which has been noticed at certain loci, it has been desirable to use multiple biochemical mutants as the parental stocks in recombination studies. Coincidental reversion at two or more loci is theoretically improbable, and experimentally undemonstrable (RYAN, 1946, TATUM and LEDERBERG, 1947). For example, plating either $B^-M^+T^+L^+B_1^+$ or $B^+M^+T^-L^-B_1^-$ separately into minimal agar did not lead to the appearance of prototrophs, $B^+M^+T^+L^+B_1^+$. When, however, a mixture of these cell types was so "sieved," one prototroph was found for about each 10^7 cells inoculated. These have been assumed to arise from the recombination of "+" alleles to form the prototroph.

In previous experiments, the two multiple mutants were inoculated together into a complete medium and allowed to grow in mixed culture before plating into minimal agar. This method is not satisfactory for present purposes because it allows possible selective differentials to alter the relative frequencies of different recombination classes. A modified procedure has been developed, which will now be described in detail.

The mutant stocks are maintained on "complete" agar slants, transferred at intervals of 6–8 weeks. They are inoculated separately into test-tubes containing about ten ml of liquid complete medium and incubated overnight at 30°C with gentle shaking. The following morning, an additional ten ml of the same medium is added to each culture, and the tubes are incubated in the same manner for an additional three to five hours. These cultures contain from $1-4 \times 10^9$ cells per ml. They are then washed in the following manner: the cotton plugs are replaced with sterile corks which have been kept in 95 percent alcohol and the alcohol flamed off just before using. The cultures are then centrifuged at about 2500 r.p.m. for 20 minutes, which suffices to pack the cells in the bottom of the test tubes. The supernatant medium is carefully poured off, and the tube is rinsed with about 10 ml sterile distilled water, care being taken not to disturb the pellet. The cells are then resuspended in an additional 15–20 ml sterile water, and recentrifuged. The supernatant wash water is decanted and replaced with an equal volume of fresh sterile water, in which the cells are suspended. In the meantime, minimal agar plates are prepared. A bottom layer of about 15 ml minimal agar is poured into each Petri plate and allowed to solidify. Cell suspensions of different mutant stocks are mixed at this time and measured quantities (usually about 10^8-10^9 cells) are pipetted onto the agar surface. At this time also, one may add such growth factor supplements as are desired to permit the growth of recombination types other than prototrophs. The cell suspensions are then mixed into a layer of about ten ml molten minimal agar (at 45–50°C) which is poured onto the plates. After the agar hardens, the plates are incubated at 30°C for a period of 48 hours. At this time prototroph colonies will be found distributed throughout the plate, many of them at or near the surface and accessible to picking for further characterization.

The procedure may be varied in several ways. It is important however that the inoculum consist of "young" cells, since cultures of 24 hours or older have given quite inconsistent results. It is possible to store the inoculum in distilled water for at least twenty-four hours without appreciably affecting the yield, which suggests that the aggregation of genetic types leading to the recombination process occurs in the molten or the solidified agar. This occurrence must, however, take place within a few hours, since the recombinant prototrophs are not appreciably slower to appear than wild type cells in a similar physiological state which may be streaked on the surface of the plates. Presumably, therefore, one could increase the yield of prototrophs by making conditions more favorable for the free contact of the cells, as by packing them together in a centrifuge tube in minimal liquid medium. However the complication of proliferation of prototrophs already formed would interfere with the interpretation of such an experiment. Many physiological factors may interfere with the recombination process, and, for example, the yield may be reduced markedly by inoculating too heavily, or by omitting an under-layer of agar into which, presumably, deleterious metabolic products may diffuse. Instead of mixing the cells in semisolid agar, it is possible to streak the mixture on the surface of slightly dried minimal agar plates. Under these conditions, however, the prototroph colonies are likely to be more heavily contaminated with the residual parental mutant types.

For most purposes, however, this contamination may be ignored, as will be shown in a later section. Prototroph colonies are then fished and streaked directly on EMB plates, or otherwise tested, to classify them with respect to other factors that may be segregating.

RESULTS AND CONCLUSIONS

In most organisms inheritance is studied by the examination of zygotes carrying the gene alternatives determining a character. The segregants are chosen at random, and factor linkage is recognized by deviations in the frequency of parental and new couplings of a series of characters. In the absence of a random method of separating zygotes in *E. coli*, one is limited here to the members of specific recombination classes, namely the prototrophs. It is however, possible to introduce other factor differences into the biochemical mutants from which prototrophs are obtained, and to determine how such factors segregate into this recombination class. It was hoped in this way to obtain information concerning the haploid or diploid condition of the bacterial cell, and to determine whether factors segregated at random, or according to specific, perhaps linear chromosomal laws.

The first factor pair to which this approach was applied was V_1^r/V_1^s (LEDERBERG and TATUM, 1946b). In the cross $B^-M^-P^+T^+V_1^r \times B^+M^+P^-T^-V_1^s$, ten $B^+M^+P^+T^+$ were isolated. Eight proved to be V_1^r while two were V_1^s. This at once suggested that the vegetative cell of *E. coli* is haploid, since segregation could be observed in the first filial generation clone. It was noted also at that time that the "reversed" cross: $B^-M^-P^+T^+V_1^s \times B^+M^+P^-T^-V_1^r$ gave quite a different ratio of r/s in the prototrophs, namely 3:7. Results on so small a sample are of doubtful significance, but they suggested the technique by which the basis of this character "segregation" could be elucidated. For this reason, the study of "reversed" crosses was extended to include numerically more data, using various combinations of mutants, and involving in addition to $V_1^r/V_1^s, Lac^+/Lac^-$. The information which was obtained is summarized in tables 3 and 5. The data show clearly that neither of the factor alternatives V_1^r/V_1^s or Lac^+/Lac^- segregates at random into the prototroph recombination class. However, the occurrence of all factor combinations, albeit with different frequencies, is evident, at least with respect to Lac and V_1. It seemed clear that there are only two alternative explanations for the unequal frequencies with which alternative alleles are manifested in the prototrophs: (a) that the alleles were characterized by some differential physiological property, such as dominance, or preferential segregation, or (b) that the nonrandom segregation was due purely to the mechanics of factor recombination, which is to say a linkage system.

The results of "reversed crosses" have a distinct bearing on this problem. If nonrandom segregation into prototrophs were due to some physiological property of the allele concerned, its particular coupling in the parent in which it is introduced should have no great effect on the segregation frequency; if on the other hand, the effect were purely mechanical, the segregation would reflect entirely the couplings of the parents, and the substitution of one allele for another in the parents (as in reversed crosses) should lead to a corresponding inversion in the ratios with which that allele is found in the prototrophs. The tables cited show that in every case there is no agreement between the ratios found in reversed crosses, unless the comparison is made with one of the ratios inverted, in which case there is reasonably good agreement. This result is in accord with the hypothesis that the genes in *E. coli* are arranged in one or more linkage groups, and is in disagreement with the postulation of a diploid con-

TABLE 3

Comparisons of V_1^r segregations when introduced with alternative parents.

PARENTS			PROTOTROPHS $[B^+M^+Pa^+C^+T^+L^+B_1^+P^+]$		
			V_1^r	V_1^s	$\% \, V_1^r$
$B^-Pa^-C^-T^+P^+$		$B^+Pa^+C^+T^-P^-$			
$\cdots V_1^r$	$\times$	$\cdots V_1^s$	76	6	92
$\cdots V_1^s$	$\times$	$\cdots V_1^r$	30	107	22
$B^-Pa^-C^-T^+L^+B_1^+$		$B^+Pa^+C^+T^-L^-B_1^-$			
$\cdots V_1^r$	$\times$	$\cdots V_1^s$	80	23	77
$\cdots V_1^s$	$\times$	$\cdots V_1^r$	53	133	28
$B^-M^-T^+P^+$		$B^+M^+T^-P^-$			
$\cdots V_1^r$	$\times$	$\cdots V_1^s$	49	8	86
$\cdots V_1^s$	$\times$	$\cdots V_1^r$	5	19	21

* See LEDERBERG (1947) for a statistical analysis of tables 3, 5, and 6.

dition, or with a state of indefinite "ploidy" which would be characteristic of a system of cytoplasmic inheritance.

The results of these experiments seemed sufficiently secure that one could adopt the existence of a linkage system as a working hypothesis and on this foundation, an attempt has been initiated to "map" a number of markers in *E. coli*. It was hoped at first that there might be found linkage groups which would be independent of one another, so that recombination between biochemical markers in one group could be used to detect recombinants, yet not interfere with the segregations in the other group(s). There was, however, no immediate prospect that these relationships could be found initially, so it was decided to study linkage relationships in a single pair of mutant stocks, and their derivatives. The stocks which were selected for this study were 58–161 (B^-M^-) and Y-53 $(T^-L^-B_1^-Lac^-)$ and their V_1^r mutants. Since *Lac* and V_1 could be so readily scored, using only a single streak from each prototroph colony which appeared, it was hoped that the collection of an adequate volume of data could be accomplished with greater facility than if biochemical markers only were used.

It was, however, necessary to determine the relationships of the biochemical mutant loci of which at least four must be used to obtain recombinants. Mixtures were, therefore, plated into minimal medium supplemented with a single nutritional requirement, i.e., either biotin, methionine, threonine, leucine, or thiamin, allowing the proliferation of the corresponding single mutant as well as the prototrophic type. Colonies were then picked at random and scored according to their nutritional requirements. The results are summarized in table 4. Unfortunately, it was found that the addition of methionine to the minimal medium allowed excessive growth of B^-M^-, presumably because of a degree of contamination of the methionine with biotin. This datum is, however, not essential for the argument. In general, it will be seen that the $+$ classes are markedly and significantly more frequent than the single mutant types, with

TABLE 4

Relative frequency of various biochemical recombination classes in the cross.

$$B^-M^-T^+L^+B_1^+ \times B^+M^+T^-L^-B_1^-*$$

FROM PLATES SUPPLEMENTED WITH	NUMBER OF COLONIES TESTED	RECOMBINATION CLASSES FOUND				RATIO	χ^2
		TYPE	NUMBER	TYPE	NUMBER		
Biotin	70	B^-	10	B^+	60	0.17	36
Threonine	46	T^-	9	T^+	37	0.24	17
Leucine	56	L^-	5	L^+	51	0.096	38
Thiamin	87	B_1^-	79	B_1^+	8	9.88	56

* Cells of the parental types were mixed and plated into agar supplemented with the growth factor indicated. On this medium, the two recombination classes indicated on each line of the table could form colonies. Contrasting alleles only are specified; other loci, unless otherwise specified, have the "+" configuration. The χ^2 for the ratio of single biochemically deficient types to prototrophs is calculated for a comparison with the 1:1 expectation of a random segregation. As can be seen from the χ^2 values, the probability that the deviations are due solely to chance is, in each case, less than .001.

the exception of B_1^- which is nearly ten times as frequent as B_1^+. Writing the cross as $B^-M^-T^+L^+B_1^+ \times B^+M^+T^-L^-B_1^-$, these results may be interpreted as follows:

1. B^+M^+ $T^+L^+B_1^+$ more frequent than B^-M^+. Therefore B and M are linked.
2. T^+L^+ $B^+M^+B_1^+$ more frequent than either T^-L^+ or T^+L^-. Therefore T and L are linked.
3. $B_1^-B^+M^+$ T^+L^+ more frequent than $B_1^+B^+M^+$. Therefore B_1 is linked to B and M, but probably not between them.

One may therefore map these five loci onto not more than two linkage groups, according to the scheme in fig. 2a. In all that follows, the $[B\text{-}M]$ and $[T\text{-}L]$ combinations will be regarded as single units, since conclusive information as to their relative order has not been obtained. These data so far do not allow any conclusion to be drawn as to whether the regions $B_1^-[BM]$ and $[TL]$ are linked or are independent of each other, since a recombination between them is a necessary requirement for a detectable type.

TABLE 5

Segregation of Lac and V_1 into prototrophs issuing from various parental combinations.*

PARENTS			RECOMBINATIONS			
$B^-M^-T^+L^+B_1^+$	$B^+M^+T^-L^-B_1^-$	$B^+M^+T^+L^+$	$Lac^-V_1^r$	$Lac^-V_1^s$	$Lac^+V_1^r$	$Lac^+V_1^s$
		$\cdots B_1^+$	602 [45.8]	203 [23.1]	387 [29.4]	22 [1.7]
$Lac^+V_1^r$	$Lac^-V_1^s$	$\cdots B_1^{-***}$	13 [45]	8 [28]	8 [28]	0 [0]
		$\cdots B_1^{-**}$	244 [42.8] (D)	157 [27.5] (E)	159 [27.9] (C)	10 [1.9] (triple)
		$\cdots B_1^+$	107 [33.2]	145 [45.0]	9 [2.8]	61 [19.0]
$Lac^+V_1^s$	$Lac^-V_1^r$	$\cdots B_1^{-**}$	134 [35.8] (E)	151 [40.4] (D)	9 [2.4] (triple)	80 [21.4] (C)
		$\cdots B_1^+$	28 [23.9]	6 [5.1]	46 [39.3]	37 [31.6]
$Lac^-V_1^r$	$Lac^+V_1^s$	$\cdots B_1^{-**}$	102 [25.4] (C)	7 [1.7] (triple)	201 [50.1] (D)	91 [22.7] (E)
$†Lac^+V_1^r$	$Lac^-V_1^r$	$\cdots B_1^{-**}$	128	0	33	0
$†Lac^-V_1^r$ (Y-87)	$Lac^-V_1^s$ (Y-53)	$\cdots B_1^{-**}$	134 Lac^-; not scored for V_1			

* Cell mixtures of the indicated composition were plated into minimal agar plates or into plates supplemented with thiamin. B_1^+ types refer to scores of prototrophs picked at random from minimal plates.

** B_1^- refers to colonies picked at random from thiamin supplemented plates. Although predominantly B_1^- they contain B_1^+ colonies in the proportion 1:10 as may be seen from table 4.

*** B_1^-. In this series, colonies were scored as to B_1, and only the B_1^- are recorded.

The letters (C), (D), (E), refer to crossover types corresponding to the regions $[B\,M]-Lac$; $Lac-V_1$; and $V_1-[T\,L]$ respectively, according to the map of Fig. 2d.

† Test for allelism.

On the basis of table 5, the factors V_1 and Lac may be brought into the argument. In addition to the joint segregations of these factors, the effect of the B_1 segregation was studied in the following way. It would be uneconomical, in view of the relative paucity of B_1^+ types, to separate these from the B_1^- by nutritional testing of colonies which appear on thiamin supplemented agar. Instead, the entire sample was regarded as B_1^- with the proviso that it might be contaminated to the extent of ten percent with B_1^+. However, it has been found that the distribution of Lac and V on colonies picked from thiamin supplemented agar is homogeneous with the distribution in prototrophs, so that the segregation of these factors is not influenced by the B_1 segregation.

The data in table 5 show that Lac is inclined not to separate from BM, and is therefore regarded as linked to it, while there is a similar linkage of V_1 to TL. Since the recombination of Lac with BM is not influenced by the interchange between B_1 and BM, they are on opposite sides of BM as suggested by map 2b. Finally, a scrutiny of the interaction between the Lac and V segregations shows that these are not independent of each other, particularly because of the rarity of the least frequent class. This suggests, then, that the two linkage groups of fig. 2b be combined to give the map of fig. 2c. (The locus of V_6 on this map is obtained from additional data.) According to this interpretation, the rarity of the least frequent Lac-V combination stems from the fact that a triple-crossover is necessary for its production. In fig. 2d, the cross Y-40 × Y-53 is interpreted according to the map, with a table citing the regions in which interchange must take place to yield the given types.

That the first seven factors to be investigated should fall in the same linkage group leads to the inference that there is only a single chromosome in $E.$ $coli$. This inference is supported by incomplete analyses of the segregations of 8 other markers referred to in table 1. None of these factors has been found to segregate independently of the factors which have already been described as belonging to a single linkage group. The possibility that segregation interactions may, in some cases, be based upon an inter-chromosomal type of interference (compare STEINBERG and FRASER, 1944), has not been ruled out, however.

The distances recorded in fig. 2c are derived from the recombination totals in tables 5 and 6. However, the distance between $[BM]$ and $[TL]$ cannot be estimated directly, but only the partition of that distance among the regions BM-Lac, Lac-V_1, and V_1-TL. The relative frequency of the "triple-interchange" type can be used to estimate the absolute map distances, if it is assumed that there is no interference. This frequency, about 2.1 percent, is readily calculated to be consistent with a map length of between 75 and 80 units altogether either in a two-strand or a four-strand system (LEDERBERG, 1947). These values must be regarded as rough approximations, because they are extremely sensitive to error in the estimation of the proportion of the "triple" types.

Linearity

In constructing a map, and calculating distances, it has been taken for granted that there is in $E.$ $coli$ a system of linear linkage, such as has been demonstrated quite conclusively in Drosophila, and inferred in all higher organisms. What direct evidence may one bring to bear on this question?

The method which one is forced to employ in hybridizing this bacterium introduces certain complications. The classical proof of linearity is based on the additive character of distances, expressed in morgans, between loci occurring within the same linkage group. The determination of map distances is based upon a comparison between parental and new combinations of linked genes, as determined in the progeny of zygotes selected at random. In *E. coli*, on the other hand, one is limited to the recovery of that recombination class in which there has necessarily been an interchange between certain biochemical loci, in the cases here discussed, betwen [*BM*] and [*TL*]. For this reason, it is not possible to obtain a direct measure of the absolute distance between factors which are located within this critical region, and any argument in favor of linearity which is based on the segregations of such factors may have the

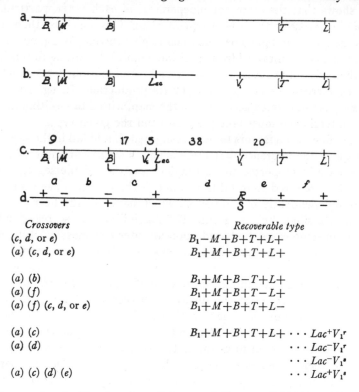

FIGURE 2.—*a*, *b*, and *c*. Mapping of genetic factors. *d*. The cross $B_1{}^+M^-B^-Lac^+V_1{}^rT^+L^+\times B_1{}^-M^+B^+Lac^-V_1{}^\bullet T^-L^-$ and some of the recoverable crossover classes. (See table 5.)

flavor of circular reasoning. It would be preferable to study the segregations of factors which are assigned to loci distal to the biochemical factors whose recombination is the basis of the detection of sexual offspring. The stocks with which this might be accomplished are not yet available, but it is hoped that they will be for future work.

That there does exist some sort of linkage system is made highly credible by the results of the "reverse crosses" tabulated in tables 3 and 5. The chief difficulty in proving that this system is linear has been to formulate the feasible alternatives, so that critical experiments, the results of which could discriminate between linearity and a given alternative, might be set up. Certain types of "linkage" can be disqualified by the data already at hand. For example, one might postulate that genes of bacteria are embedded in a two-dimensional matrix, and there occasionally occurs a gene-for-gene interchange. This is equivalent to the "Konversion" theory once proposed by WINKLER (1932), to account for interchanges in Drosophila. While this type of arrangement would account for a tendency to preserve the parental configuration, it fails to explain either quantitative linkage intensities, or the interaction of segregations which is revealed by the data on *Lac* and *V* in table 5. Naturally, one could further modify the "Konversion" theory to take these exigencies into account, but in so doing one would be elaborating an exceedingly complicated theory which would, in fact, be a re-expression of a mechanical theory of linkage.

The interaction of the *Lac* and *V* segregations is perhaps the most critical datum with which a genetic system for *E. coli* can be formulated. The interaction may be expressed as follows: the frequency of interchanges between $[BM]$ and *Lac* is dependent upon the interchanges between $[BM]$ and *V*. Specifically, in the cross $B^+M^+T^-L^-B_1^-$ $Lac^-V_1{}^s \times B^-M^-T^+L^+B_1^+$ $Lac^+V_1{}^r$, one finds in the $B^+M^+T^+L^+B_1^+$ the following distribution of classes: $Lac^-V_1{}^s$ 23 percent, $Lac^+V_1{}^r$ 29 percent (for the parental combinations) and $Lac^-V_1{}^r$ 46 percent, $Lac^+V_1{}^s$ 2 percent (for the new combinations). With reference to $[B^+M^+]$, Lac^- is the parental, Lac^+ the interchange type. The proportion of $V_1{}^r$ (representing an interchange between V_1 and $[BM]$) is different in the Lac^- and Lac^+ segregations: namely $46:23 = 2:1$ and $29:2 = 14.5:1$ respectively. This interaction between interchanges is most simply explained by the assumption that factors are located on a linear segment, so that interchanges between proximal factors also lead to the crossing over of more distal factors, barring the occurrence of additional interchanges.

Additional support for the theory of linear arrangement has been found in the segregation of V_6, summarized in table 6. It will be noted that the segregations of *Lac*, V_1, and V_6 are quite congruous in the B_1^- and B_1^+ classes. In the totals, one finds the ratios, for each factor separately, of Lac^- 78 percent; $V_6{}^r$ 82 percent; $V_1{}^s$ 36 percent; indicating that the first two are both linked to $[BM]$ while the latter is linked to $[TL]$. V_6 cannot, however, be to the left of $[BM]$ because it does not interact with B_1. If, therefore, there is a linear order of genes, V_6 must be to the right of $[BM]$, and because of its greater linkage intensity, nearer $[BM]$ than is *Lac*. This arrangement is indicated in the map in table 6, and in fig. 2c. The agreement of the data with the hypothesis can be examined at several points. In the first place, the single exchange types, as indicated in the table, should be the most frequent. Secondly, barring multiple exchanges, an interchange between V_6 and *Lac* should lead also to an interchange between V_6 and V_1. That is to say, the $Lac^+V_6{}^r$ class should be more often $V_1{}^r$ than $V_1{}^s$. Finally, in view of the similarity in linkage intensities to $[BM]$, *Lac* and V_6 must be closely linked. Although the "triple-interchange" types would seem to be rather frequent, reference to the table may suggest that these conditions are fulfilled. In particular, it will be noted that among the Lac^-, the ratio of $V_6{}^r : V_6{}^s$ is $94:3$, or $31:1$, while among the Lac^+, this same ratio is $10:29$, or $1:3$. This difference is interpreted to mean that *Lac* and V_6 are linked to each other, as demanded by the theory of linearity.

It is not, of course, proven that the gene order is not branched at some other point. The most economical hypothesis at this time, however, is that there is a single unbranched chromosome as the physical basis of inheritance in *E. coli*.

Attempts to Induce Aberrations

Using a chromosomal theory as a working hypothesis, it was hoped that some verification could be found by the study of types in which the normal order of genes was disturbed. Since there is only one chromosome (from the

TABLE 6

Segregation of Lac, V_1 and V_6.

$$B^-M^-T^+L^+B_1^+Lac^+V_1^rV_6^s \times B^+M^+T^-L^-B_1^-Lac^-V_1^sV_6^r$$

$B^+M^+T^+L^+$	Lac:	−	−	−	−	+	+	+	+	
	V_1 :	r	s	r	s	r	s	r	s	TOTAL
	V_6 :	r	r	s	s	r	r	s	s	
$\cdots B_1^+$		24	16	1	0	2	1	10	2	56
$\cdots B_1^{-**}$		52	42	2	0	6	1	16	1	120
Total		76	58	3	0	8	2	26	3	176
%		43	33	1.7	0	4.6	1.1	15	1.7	
Crossover region		e	f	cde	cdf	d	def	c	ced	

B_1	$\cdots M$	$\cdots B$	$\cdots V_6$	$\cdots Lac$	$\cdots V_1$	$\cdots T$	$\cdots L$
	a	b	c	d	e	f	
+	−	−	s	+	r	+	+
−	+	+	r	−	s	−	−

** See footnote to table 4.

genetic evidence), the only types of rearrangements would be changes leading to a series of inversion-transposition types. It was thought that such types might be detected by genetical procedures by virtue of their effect on crossing over. In particular, the occurrence of an inversion in the region $B_1 \cdots [MB]$ would be expected to have the effect of eliminating the recombination classes involving interchanges in this region. In the cross $B^-M^-T^+L^+B_1^+ \times B^+M^+T^-L^-B_1^-$ this would be equivalent to the suppression of prototroph recombinants; B_1^- types, however, would be recoverable, and allow the investigation of the extent of the changes.

Preliminary attempts to find such aberration types have, to date, been unsuccessful. The procedure was as follows:

Following treatment with nitrogen mustard (TATUM, 1946) or 20,000 r of X-rays, cells of Y-40 and of Y-53 were incubated separately for 24 hours, to allow the separation of cells or nuclei that might have been associated at the time of treatment. The cultures were then streaked out on nutrient agar plates. Single colonies of Y-40 were picked and streaked across a nutrient agar plate. Streaks of similarly treated Y-53 colonies were made from the opposite direction, so that in the center of the plate, cells of the two types were mixed, treated colony by treated colony. The plates were incubated for 24 hours, the mixed growth scraped from the plates, suspended in sterile water and plated into minimal agar. The occurrence of colonies which would not interact to produce prototrophs, as detected by plating into minimal medium, would be an indicator that the combination was heterogeneous for an aberration. Since in these experiments, both "parents" were exposed to treatment, each plating was equivalent to the testing of two chromosomes for the occurrence of an aberration. No marked variation in the yield of prototrophs was noted in tests involving 121 mustard- and 28 x-ray-treated chromosomes. This can scarcely be regarded as an adequate sample in view of the stringent selection imposed by the technique, which might be expected to eliminate any aberration types which are even slightly less vigorous than the normal. This consideration is especially relevant in view of the "hemizygous" condition of any aberrations in the probably haploid vegetative cells. These studies will be continued.

How Many Segregants per Zygote?

In the experiments detailed in this paper, recombinants were obtained from different cell types which were exposed to each other in an agar medium. Therefore each prototroph recombinant colony seen by the experimenter marks the site of formation of a zygote. The question may immediately be raised whether there are at that site other recombination classes which, by virtue of their biochemical deficiencies, remain dormant within the prototroph colony on the minimal selective medium. This is equivalent to inquiring whether there is but a single viable product of meiosis (as in megasporogenesis in many higher plants) or more than one, as in the ascomycetes. The solution to this problem would be of special interest in relation to the possible occurrence of four-strand crossing over. In addition, if an appreciable proportion of prototroph colonies consisted of two distinct segregation types, it would be necessary to isolate these types for the collection of segregation data.

There are at least three ways in which a zygote might yield more than one haploid recombinant. Firstly, the zygote might be capable of proliferation in the diplophase (or sporophyte), leading to the concurrence of several diploid cells, each of which might undergo meiosis independently, and by chance yield several segregation types. Secondly, a single zygote might produce, after meiosis, in addition to the prototroph, the *complementary* multiple mutant class. Thirdly, in a system of four-strand crossing-over, there might be two *supplementary* prototroph recombinants differing in the segregation of factors such as *Lac* and V_1 for which the diploid was heterozygous.

Obviously, the proper investigation of these possibilities requires that one stringently avoid contamination of one colony with another. For this reason, the cell suspensions used were diluted so as to yield only about five to ten recombination colonies per plate.

Crosses were made between Y-40 and Y-53 ($B^-M^-T^+L^+B_1^+Lac^+V_1^r \times B^+$-$M^+T^-L^-B_1^-Lac^-V_1^s$) on B_1-containing minimal agar medium. As already noted, about 90 percent of the colonies from such a cross are $B^+M^+T^+L^+B_1^-$. The theoretical complementary class would be $B^-M^-T^-L^-B_1^+$. Because of its nutritional deficiencies, it could not be expected to proliferate on the minimal medium even had it been produced after meiosis. The possibility remains, however, that a few cells of this constitution might still be present among the 10^8 or so B_1^- cells of the predominant type in a colony. By plating such colonies into medium lacking B_1 but containing biotin, methionine, threonine and leucine, the B_1^- cells would be suppressed, while the postulated multiple mutant type could form colonies and be recovered.

The experiment just described was carried out, testing 52 colonies for their content of other cell types. In general, a thiaminless colony could be shown to contain from 10–100 cells capable of forming colonies on the B, M, T, L medium. However, in each case investigated these have been shown to be indistinguishable from the Y-40 parental B^-M^- type, and must be presumed to arise from a surprisingly low degree of contamination of the colony with these cells from the heavily seeded plate. A few colonies were found which could be characterized as reversions from B_1^- to B_1^+. These experiments are then, inconclusive with respect to the occurrence of complementary genotypes in the same colony. With appropriate stocks, not as yet available, it should eventually be possible to manipulate the situation so that the complementary type could be recovered selectively, excluding both parents and the predominant recombination class.

A search for supplementary types was conducted with the same crosses, except that colonies appearing on B_1 agar were streaked out directly on EMB-lactose agar to determine whether any of them were heterogeneous for Lac. In some cases, a number of isolated colonies from each EMB-test plate were then also tested for homogeneity with respect to T_I-resistance. About 90 colonies were so tested; only one colony was found containing both Lac^+ and Lac^- cells. It is impossible to be certain that, with this low frequency, the single colony which was picked was not actually derived from two distinct zygotes. These experiments cannot be considered as bearing critically on the question of the occurrence of two- or four-strand crossing over because of the absence of information concerning (a) the viability of more than one meiotic product and (b) chiasma interference. The results do, however, justify the technique of picking the prototroph colonies directly, and testing them without further purification for the collection of segregation data.

A Comparison of Sexual Recombination and Transformation

The occurrence of recombination types has been interpreted by us (LEDERBERG and TATUM 1946c, TATUM and LEDERBERG 1947) as a consequence of cell fusion, "karyogamy" and meiosis with crossing over. This is, however, not the only allowable interpretation of the general phenomenon of the occurrence of new character combinations. By analogy with the systems which have been described in pneumococci (AVERY, MacLEOD and McCARTY 1944) and other strains of *E. coli* (BOIVIN and VENDRELEY 1946) one might postulate that genotypically distinct cells interact not through cell fusion, but through the release of "transforming substances" diffusing through the medium. Such transforming substances would have the property of inducing or directing mutational changes in the cell receiving them so as to lead to what appear to be recombination types. Our inability to separate such postulated transforming substances from the cells themselves is not proof of their absence but could be due to their lability in our hands.

In previous publications, certain reasons were given for the rejection of the transformation hypothesis in favor of a picture of cell fusion, and so forth. It was not our intention thereby to state, with clairvoyant insight, that no investigator will be able to duplicate the results which we have reported, using instead of living cells extracts specially prepared. It is, rather, our view that since we have been able to demonstrate no appreciable point of difference between the features of gene exchange in this strain of *E. coli* and in the classical materials of Mendelian experimentation, the most economical conclusion is that the mechanisms involved are also similar. In the absence of more detailed information on the behavior of transforming systems, a critic would be free to impute to such systems all of the properties which have been found to characterize the genetic system of *E. coli*, K-12. While this would be tailoring the cloth to suit the customer, it cannot be disputed that the only conclusive method by which it could be shown that cell fusion underlies gene recombination would be a direct cytological demonstration. The rarity with which the presumed zygote occurs, however (as indicated by the low frequency of effective recombination types) is very discouraging to attempts to find and characterize the "fusion-cell," at least in the present material.

Certain genetic experiments were performed in an attempt to characterize further the behavior of this system. On the transformation hypothesis, one must attribute the rarity of the imputed transformations primarily to restricted conditions for susceptibility to the transforming factors released into the milieu. Otherwise, one would expect to find "transformations" for single factors much more frequent than those involving more than two factors. A glance at tables 4 and 6 illustrates that certain "multiple transformed" types are much more frequent than singly transformed classes. Under these conditions, one might also anticipate that genetic materials from two different kinds of cells could mix in the medium and together transform a third. In a mixture of three cell types then, one should find cases where genes from all three have combined. Using *Lac* and V_1 as markers, this type of experiment was set up in several different ways, as summarized in table 7. Pairwise, prototrophs can be formed only from biochemically distinct and nonoverlapping parents. Combinations of B^-M^- and of $T^-L^-B_1^-$ were arranged so that taken two at a time they were heterozygous either for *Lac* or for V_1 but not both. For example, a mixture of $B^-M^-Lac^-V_1^r$, $T^-L^-B_1^-Lac^-V_1^s$ and $T^-L^-B_1^-Lac^+V_1^r$ was plated. Prototrophs could be formed by recombination between either of the two latter and the former types. In one case, only V_1 would be heterozygous, and the expected types would be $Lac^-V_1^r$ and $Lac^-V_1^s$. In the other, *Lac* would be heterozygous, and prototrophs carrying the markers $Lac^+V_1{}^r$ and $Lac^-V_1{}^r$ could be produced. The type $Lac^+V_1{}^s$ would not be expected unless, indeed, genetic material from all three types could combine in a sort of ménage à trois. As recorded in table 7, no instance of such a three-way combination was found in 628 tests, a different class being vacant, as anticipated, in each of the four parts of the experiment. It may be concluded that genetic factors from different cells are not freely miscible, as would be demanded by the most economical version of the interpretation of transformations.

From all the experiments so far cited, it must be concluded that if trans-

TABLE 7

Pairwise occurrence of recombination in mixtures of three components.

PARENTAL TYPES		RECOMBINANT PROTOTROPHS* $B^+M^+T^+L^+B_1{}^+$ or $B_1{}^-$				
$B^-M^-T^+L^+B_1{}^+$	$B^+M^+T^-L^-B_1{}^-$	$Lac^-V_1{}^r$	$Lac^-V_1{}^s$	$Lac^+V_1{}^r$	$Lac^+V_1{}^s$	TOTAL
$Lac^-V_1{}^r$	$Lac^+V_1{}^r$ $Lac^-V_1{}^s$	173	49	4	0	226
$Lac^+V_1{}^r$	$Lac^-V_1{}^r$ $Lac^+V_1{}^s$	16	0	7	28	51
$Lac^+V_1{}^s$	$Lac^+V_1{}^r$ $Lac^-V_1{}^s$	0	136	37	40	213
$Lac^+V_1{}^s$ $Lac^-V_1{}^r$	$Lac^-V_1{}^s$	65	48	0	25	138
					Total	628

* Mixtures of the three types indicated in each experiment were plated into thiamin-containing agar. The prototrophs are therefore a mixture of $B_1{}^-$ and $B_1{}^+$ types, as indicated in table 4, footnote.

forming factors are operating in this system, the diverse factors (or genes) are not independent of one another, but are grouped in separate and immiscible parcels. Such parcels would also be potentially capable of transmitting all of the genetic factors of a cell, so that there seems to be no compelling reason why such a parcel, speaking purely genetically, could not be regarded as a gamete. MULLER (1947) has interpreted the pneumococcus transformation in terms of "still viable bacterial chromosomes or parts of chromosomes floating free in the medium . . . these have penetrated the capsuleless bacteria and in part at least, taken root there, perhaps after having undergone a kind of crossing over with the chromosomes of the host." It remains to be seen whether this interpretation will be upheld by further studies on factor interaction in *bona fide* transforming systems.

Several attempts were made to determine whether "transforming activity" could be separated from the living cell under conditions comparable to the platings in minimal agar medium, or after extraction of cells by BOIVIN's method (BOIVIN et. al., 1946). No activity was found in the supernatant of a suspension of Y-40 and Y-53 together or separately in the same minimal liquid medium to which agar is added for plating experiments. The only manipulation involved here consists of the removal of most of the bacteria by ordinary centrifugation. It could thus be shown that the "activity" was associated with the cells. Equally negative results characterized attempts to reveal transforming activity on culture filtrates and cell autolysates prepared as crude fractions according to BOIVIN's procedure. Finally, the addition of desoxyribonuclease in a final concentration of .05 mg/ml to the mixing and plating medium had no effect on the number of prototrophs which appeared in the cross of Y-40 and Y-53. Tests for the destruction of enzymatic activity under these conditions were, however, not done.

The conclusions which we draw from these experiments are (a) that the existence of transforming factors is exceedingly unlikely and (b) it would be not worthwhile to go to extreme trouble to attempt to isolate such factors from this system until the study of *bona fide* transforming systems has progressed sufficiently that the genetical criteria already discussed might be applied.

DISCUSSION

Regardless of the stand that one takes on the issue of invisible zygotes versus non-extractable transforming factors, it can be asserted that *E. coli* K-12 provides a useful tool for genetic analysis. The use of biochemical mutants as parents allows crosses which are nearly as well controlled as in Neurospora. The segregational behavior of mutant factors seems to be closely analogous to that of higher forms, and seems to compel their admission into the same arena as the genes of Drosophila. However, it would be premature to transfer these conclusions to other genetic characters of other microorganisms, each of which must be examined on its own merits.

It may be wondered that the apparent recombination rate is so low. However, this is possibly not to be attributed to any sexual imperfections of *E. coli*, but to the method of enumeration. It seems likely that an analogous comparison of the number of somatic and generative cells in an organism like the oak-tree, or man (especially the female of the species) would give ratios similar to those prevailing in *E. coli*. It is also possible that the optimal conditions for zygote formation or germination have not yet been achieved and that by special procedures the rate of zygote-formation may be accelerated to the level where there might be some hope of finding it in the field of the microscope.

Attempts to detect recombination in two other strains of *E. coli*, B (DEMEREC and FANO, 1945) and L-15 (ROEPKE, LIBBY, and SMALL, 1944) by analogous methods have been unsuccessful (LURIA, 1947, TATUM and LEDERBERG, 1947). At least two strains then must be classified with the "*Fungi Imperfecti.*" This dismal conclusion is, however, illuminated by the fact that many heterothallic species have been eliminated from the *Fungi Imperfecti* with the discovery of the appropriate opposite mating-types. At the present time, one scarcely knows where to begin to look for the bacterial analogy. The application of genetic techniques to the elucidation of unusual life-cycles in diverse bacteria (BRAUN and ELROD, 1946, DIENES, 1946) cannot fail, however, to be most fruitful.

The evolutionary significance of gene recombination has been made so widely familiar by DOBZHANSKY's book (1941), and adequately discussed, more recently, by MULLER (1947), that it would be impertinent to do more than simply refer to these papers.

SUMMARY

The recombination of genetic factors and their segregation into prototroph recombinants of *Escherichia coli* have been studied. It was found that genetic markers behaved as if they were part of a system of linked genes. Some evidence for linear order of genes was obtained. Each of 15 factors studied fell into the same linkage group. Data are given in detail for the segregation of factors involved in the biosyntheses of biotin, methionine, threonine, leucine, or thiamin; in the fermentation of lactose, and in resistance to bacterial viruses $T1$ and $T6$. On the basis of these data a tentative 8-point genetic map of the chromosome of *E. coli* is presented.

ACKNOWLEDGEMENTS

The author is deeply indebted to many of his colleagues and friends, too numerous to mention, for stimulating discussions of the problems discussed in this paper. They are numbered, by and large, among the participants and discussants of the 1946 Cold Spring Harbor Symposium on Quantitative Biology. He is indebted to DR. MACLYN MCCARTY for a generous sample of purified desoxyribonuclease, and to DRS. S. E. LURIA and M. DEMEREC for cultures of the bacteriophages used in this investigation. He owes much of the genetic analysis to the criticism of DR. K. MATHER of the JOHN INNES HORTICULTURAL INSTITUTION. Above all, he is indebted to PROFESSOR E. L. TATUM for the opportunity and much of the stimulus to do these experiments.

LITERATURE CITED

ANDERSON, E. H., 1946 Growth requirements of virus-resistance mutants of *Escherichia coli* strain "*B.*" Proc. Nat. Acad. Sci. **32**: 120–128.

AVERY, O. T., C. M. MACLEOD, and M. MCCARTY, 1944 Studies on the chemical nature of the substance inducing transformation of pneumococcal types. J. Exp. Med. **79**: 137–158.

BOIVIN, A., and R. VENDRELEY, 1946 Rôle de l'acide désoxy-ribonucléique hautement polymérisé dans le déterminisme des caractères héréditaires des bactéries. Signification pour la biochemie générale de l'hérédité. Helv. Chim. Acta **29**: 1338–1344.

BRAUN, A. C., and R. P. ELROD, 1946 Stages in the life history of *Phytomonas tumefaciens*. J. Bact. **52**: 695–702.

DEMEREC, M., and U. FANO, 1945 Bacteriophage-resistant mutants in *Escherichia coli*. Genetics **30**: 119–136.

DIENES, L., 1946 Complex reproductive processes in bacteria. Cold Spring Harbor, Symposia on Quantitative Biology **11**: 51–59.

DOBZHANSKY, Th., 1941 Genetics and the Origin of Species. Rev. Ed. xviii+446 pp. New York: Columbia Univ. Press.

GRAY, C. H., and E. L. TATUM, 1944 X-ray induced growth factor deficiencies in bacteria. Proc. Nat. Acad. Sci. **30**: 404–410.

LEDERBERG, G., 1947 Genetic recombination in *Escherichia coli*. Dissertation; Yale University.

LEDERBERG, J., and E. L. TATUM, 1946a Detection of biochemical mutants of microorganisms. J. Biol. Chem. **165**: 381–382.

1946b Novel genotypes in mixed cultures of biochemical mutants of bacteria. Cold Spring Harbor, Symposia on Quantitative Biology **11**: 113–114.

1946c Gene recombination in *Escherichia coli*. Nature **158**: 558.

LURIA, S. E., 1947 Recent advances in bacterial genetics. Bact. Rev. **11**: 1–40.

MULLER, H. J., 1947 The gene. Proc. Roy. Soc., London **B134**: 1–37.

ROEPKE, R. R., R. L. LIBBY, and M. H. SMALL, 1944 Mutation or variation of *Escherichia coli* with respect to growth requirements. J. Bact. **48**: 401–412.

RYAN, F. J., 1946 Back-mutation and adaptation of nutritional mutants. Cold Spring Harbor, Symposia on Quantitative Biology **11**: 215–226.

RYAN, F. J., and J. LEDERBERG, 1946 Reverse-mutation and adaptation in leucineless Neurospora. Proc. Nat. Acad. Sci. **32**: 163–173.

STEINBERG, A. G., and F. C. FRASER, 1944 Studies on the effect of X chromosome inversions on crossing over in the third chromosome of *Drosophila melanogaster*. Genetics **29**: 83–103.

TATUM, E. L., 1945 X-ray induced mutant strains of *Escherichia coli*. Proc. Nat. Acad. Sci. **31**: 215–219.

1946 Induced biochemical mutations in bacteria. Cold Spring Harbor, Symposia on Quantitative Biology **11**: 278–284.

TATUM, E. L., and J. LEDERBERG, 1947 Gene recombination in the bacterium, *Escherichia coli*. J. Bact. **53**: 673–684.

WINKLER, H., 1932 Konversions-Theorie und Austausch-Theorie. Biol. Zentralbl. **52**: 163–189

Reprinted from COLD SPRING HARBOR SYMPOSIA
ON QUANTITATIVE BIOLOGY
Volume XVI, 1951
Made in United States of America

GENETIC RECOMBINATION AND HETEROZYGOSIS IN BACTERIOPHAGE

A. D. HERSHEY AND MARTHA CHASE

Department of Genetics, Carnegie Institution of Washington, Cold Spring Harbor, New York

In this paper we summarize the principal features of inheritance in the bacteriophage T2H, and describe some new experiments.

The genetic structure of this virus has been analyzed in terms of mutational patterns (Hershey, 1946) and by recombination tests (Hershey and Rotman, 1949). These two types of evidence agree in showing that mutational changes occur in localized regions of a complex genetic system. Mutations producing different effects usually occur at different loci, but one example of multiple allelism has been found (Hershey and Davidson, 1951). In this instance, the locus of the alternative mutations could be analyzed rather completely because most of the host-range mutations selected in a particular way proved to belong to a single allelic series. It was found that one pair of distinct mutants satisfied all three criteria of allelism listed below, and that another pair satisfied none of them. The criteria used were the following:

(1) If the second of two successive mutations from wild type occur at the locus of the first, reversion to wild-type in a single step is possible.

(2) No genetic recombination can be observed between allelic mutant pairs.

(3) The map position of the locus is independent of its allelic state.

BIPARENTAL RECOMBINATION

The production of new genetic types of phage by intracellular interaction between different bacteriophages was first observed by Delbrück and Bailey (1946), who mentioned genetic recombination as one of two possible interpretations of their result. The principle of genetic recombination was established by experiments with genetically defined stocks of the bacteriophage T2H (Hershey and Rotman, 1948, 1949).

The main facts of genetic recombination in this bacterial virus can be illustrated by examples of the interaction between two classes of mutant. Rapidly lysing (r) mutants are easily recognized by inspection of the plaques they produce on an agar plate seeded with sensitive bacteria. The plaques are larger, and have a sharper margin, than those of the wild-type. Host range (h) mutants are able to infect a suitable bacterial "indicator" strain that is resistant to the wild-type virus (Luria, 1945). The h mutants are normal with respect to type of plaque. By successive mutations, double (hr) mutants are readily obtained. The four kinds of virus, wild, h, r, and hr, can be recognized by plating on agar plates seeded with a mixture of sensitive (B) and indicator (B/2) strains of bacteria. Independently of the r character, h virus lyses both B and B/2 to produce clear plaques, and h^+ virus lyses only B to produce turbid plaques. Independently of the h character, r virus produces large plaques, and r^+ virus produces small ones.

Genetic recombination is observed in a "cross" in which sensitive bacteria are infected with a few particles of h and a few particles of r per cell. The viral progeny coming from the mixedly infected bacteria contains both parental types, together with a certain proportion of the two recombinants (Fig. 1). Analogous recombinants are found when two different r mutants are crossed. For example, the cross $r1 \times r2$ gives rise to the double mutant $r1r2$ and wild-type (Hershey and Rotman, 1948).

In both types of cross, the yield of recombinants is characteristic for the mutant pair, and the numerical results can be summarized in the form of a genetic map, as shown in Figure 2. On this map we have shown only a few markers that we wish to refer to in this paper. The letter m (minute) stands for a small plaque mutant. It is well established that the three loci, $r1$, h, and m assort independently of each other, and that the loci linked to h are arranged in linear order. Dr. N. Visconti (personal communication) has recently confirmed the earlier results on these points by a new method of three-point testing.

TRIPARENTAL RECOMBINATION

Important information about genetic recombination comes from experiments in which the frequency of triparental recombination is measured. If bacteria are infected with the three mutants h, m, and $r1$, the recombinant hmr can arise only by in-

[471]

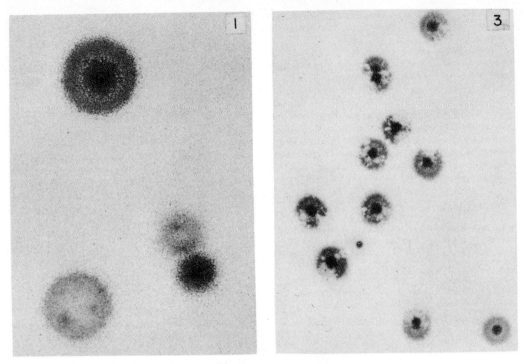

FIG. 1. Progeny of the cross *h* × *rl* plated on mixed indicator. The large clear plaque is *hr*; small clear, *h*; large turbid, *r*; small turbid, wild-type. The eccentric clearings in the *r* plaque result from secondary *h* mutations.
FIG. 3. Mottled plaques from bacteria infected with *r* and *r*+ virus.

teractions involving all three. The results for this triple infection and its reverse, *hr* × *hm* × *mr*, are shown in Table 1. About three per cent of the viral yield consists of the triparental recombinant in these crosses. This shows that interactions among three particles of virus occur with high frequency. A measure of this frequency can be expressed in terms of some artificial assumptions.

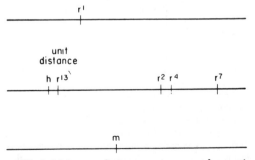

FIG. 2. Linkage relations among several genetic markers.

If we suppose that multiplication precedes recombination, and that recombinants are formed during random successive pairings between phage particles, each particle would have to pair with three other particles to explain the results shown in Table 1. The genetic factors used in these experiments are unlinked. The data for triparental recombination in experiments with linked markers (Hershey and Rotman, 1948) lead to the same quantitative conclusion.

This conclusion is a stumbling block to the further understanding of the mechanism of genetic recombination, since it is extremely difficult to distinguish between successive interactions by pairs, and other types of interaction that might involve larger groups. The available information is insufficient, therefore, to decide between alternative hypotheses of viral interaction so far considered.

EXPERIMENTS WITH CLUMPED PHAGE

The following observations are pertinent to the proper interpretation of experiments to be described in a later part of this paper. Since they are also of general interest, we record them separately.

The *r* mutants are unique among the known mutants of phage in that mixed colonies of *r* and *r*+ phage are easily recognizable as mottled plaques. Mottled plaques are conveniently prepared by infecting bacteria with *r* and *r*+ phage, and plating before lysis so that the plaques originate not from single phage particles, but from the mixed population liberated locally when the bacterium lyses (Fig. 3). We have made use of this characteristic mottling as a test for the aggregation of phage particles.

TABLE 1. TRIPARENTAL RECOMBINATION TESTS WITH THREE INDEPENDENTLY ASSORTING GENETIC FACTORS

Cross		Per cent distribution in yield							
		wild	h	r	m	hr	hm	mr	hmr
$h \times m \times rl$	(1)	25	17	22	12	9	5	7	2
	(2)	25	18	15	20	4	10	5	3
$hm \times mrl \times hrl$	(1)	3	6	5	10	17	19	14	26
	(2)	3	9	4	9	14	26	15	20

Results are shown for two independent experiments of each kind.

Platings of mixtures of *r* and *r*+ phage do not show mottled plaques (except rarely by the overlapping of plaques), even after the mixture has been packed in a centrifuge to allow every opportunity for the particles to stick together. Mottling clumps can be produced, however, by agglutinating the mixture with antiserum.

To prepare mottling clumps of phage, one adds to a mixture containing half *r* and half *r*+ phage, at a concentration of about 10^{11} particles per ml, an amount of antiphage serum just sufficient to reduce the titer of the mixture by a factor 2 to 4 after equilibrium has been reached. This requires several hours at room temperature. The mixture now yields, on plating, about two per cent of mottled plaques.

Mottled plaques coming from clumps containing the doubly marked phages *hrl* and wild-type are found, on sampling, to contain the two parental types of phage, together with the expected recombinants. The same is true of mottled plaques originating from bacteria infected with *hrl* and wild-type. This shows that there is no strong selection among the several genetic types of phage during plaque formation. It shows, incidentally, that the genetic result of a mixed infection is of the same kind whether the parental

phage particles attach to the bacterium at the same point, as with mottling clumps, or at different points, as in the usual mixed infection.

The mottling clumps are identifiable as clumps by their abnormal sensitivity to antiserum. When 90 per cent of a population containing two per cent of mottling clumps is inactivated by exposure (at low concentration, to avoid further aggregation) to antiserum, the proportion of mottling clumps among the survivors is less than 0.2 per cent.

When a population of phage containing two per cent of mottling clumps (*hrl* + wild-type) is adsorbed to B so as to infect one bacterium in ten, and the infected bacteria are plated on B after inactivating the unadsorbed phage with antiserum, two per cent of the plaques from infected bacteria are mottled. The resistance of the adsorbed clumps to antiserum shows that both members of a mottling clump infect the same bacterium. When the same population is adsorbed to B/2, and the infected cells are treated with antiserum or merely washed to remove unadsorbed phage, only *hr* plaques are formed on plates seeded with B. Evidently both members of a mottling clump have to make specific attachments to the bacterium in order to produce a mixed yield. This result probably explains why we are unable to prepare populations containing more than a small fraction of mottling clumps by agglutination with antiserum. Only those clumps in which the two kinds of virus are oriented in a manner favorable to the attachment of both to the same bacterium can produce mottled plaques.

HETEROZYGOSIS

Mixed yields of T2H from bacteria infected with *r* and *r*+ phage always contain about two per cent of particles that give rise to mottled plaques. Samples of phage from these mottled plaques consist of approximately equal numbers of typical *r* and *r*+ particles, with only traces of mottling phage particles. This distinguishes mottling phage particles from phage particles containing an unstable genetic factor affecting the *r* character (Hershey, 1946). These produce sectored rather than mottled plaques, and the sectored plaques contain sectoring particles and *r* particles, but no *r*+.

The mottling phage particles do not consist of clumps. This is shown both by the genetic data to be described presently, and more generally by the following consideration of inactivation data.

Suppose, for example, that a mottling phage particle really consists of a small clump of j normal r^+ and k normal r particles. If the population containing this clump is heated sufficiently to reduce the titer by a factor 100, the chance that the mottling property of the specified clump will survive is at most $(1 - 0.99^j) (1 - 0.99^k)$, which is very much less than the chance (0.01) that a given phage particle will survive. The proportion of mottled plaques originating from clumps in a small surviving fraction of the population will, therefore, be very much less than the proportion of mottling clumps in the original population. Mottling particles do not behave in this way. In experiments in which populations containing mottling phage were inactivated by heating, by antiserum, by ultraviolet light, or by beta rays from P^{32}, no appreciable decrease in the proportion of mottling phage among survivors was seen. (The populations were examined at ten per cent and one per cent levels of survival.) The mottling particles are inactivated as a unit by the agencies mentioned, and possess the same resistance to inactivation as the non-mottling phage particles in the population.

We conclude that mottling phage coming from bacteria infected with r and r^+ virus contains both parental markers in a particle of otherwise normal properties. Since there is adequate reason to call these markers allelic genes, the mottling particles are appropriately termed heterozygotes. We use this word without intending to imply any specific structural basis for the observed properties of the particles.

There is no evidence that the heterozygotes can multiply in the heterozygous condition. The small proportion (roughly two per cent) of mottling phage particles that is found in the mottled plaques originating from heterozygotes is also found in mottled plaques coming from bacteria infected with mixtures of r and r^+ phage. The similarity of the two proportions suggests that the mottling particles have been formed in both instances during the development of the plaque.

The proportion of r-r^+ heterozygotes produced in bacteria infected with mixtures of r and r^+ virus does not vary significantly from two per cent for five different r markers (Table 4, left half), and is also about the same in crosses between h and r mutants, to which we now turn.

Information about the structure of the heterozygotes can be sought by analyzing them in terms of the segregants they yield. For this purpose, the viruses giving rise to the heterozygotes must differ by at least two genetic factors. Our

experiments have been limited to differently linked pairs of h and r markers. The experimental method is simple. One samples mottled plaques containing the segregants from heterozygotes and replates the phage progeny on mixed indicator. The types of virus recognized in this way form the basis for classifying the original heterozygote.

By selecting mottled plaques, we limit the examination to heterozygotes segregating for r and r^+. The analysis yields information only about the pattern of segregation of the additional marker within this class. For any cross $hr \times$ wild-type, only three results are found.

TABLE 2. PER CENT DISTRIBUTION OF r-r^+ HETEROZYGOTES WITH RESPECT TO SEGREGATION PATTERN: CROSSES WITH EQUAL MULTIPLICITY OF INFECTION

Segregants found	$hr1 \times wild$ (40)	$hr7 \times wild$ (20)	$h \times r7$ (20)	$hr13 \times wild$ (2)
hr-wild	6	6	0	74
h-hr	49	44	55	15
r-wild	45	50	40	11
h-r	....	0	5	0
No. tested	253	150	129	494

Per cent yields of recombinants in each cross are shown in parentheses.

(1) Segregants h and hr, corresponding to one parent and one recombinant of the original cross. Heterozygotes of this class lack the h^+ marker, or lose it during segregation.

(2) Segregants r and wild-type, corresponding to the second parent and second recombinant of the original cross. Heterozygotes of this class lack the h marker.

(3) Segregants hr and wild-type, corresponding to the two parents of the original cross, coming from doubly heterozygous phage particles. These segregants are necessarily accompanied by their recombinants.

Two qualitative results are evident. First, the heterozygotes segregate into pairs. This shows that segregation precedes multiplication, or that daughter heterozygotes segregate in only one way. Second, the double heterozygotes do not segregate into the two recombinants, h and r, but only into the two parents, hr and wild-type. It should be noted, however, that these two alternatives could not be distinguished in the cross $hr1 \times$ wild-type, because of the large yields of recombinants in either case.

The quantitative results are summarized in Table 2. The doubly heterozygous class is a small minority in the crosses involving unlinked or distant markers, and forms a surprisingly small majority even for the closely linked factors *h* and *r13*.

The inferences that can be drawn from Table 2 are supported also by tests on a smaller scale of heterozygotes from the crosses *h* × *r1* and *h* × *r13*.

In view of the small proportion of doubly heterozygous particles produced in the crosses *hr1* × wild-type, and *hr7* × wild-type, there was some question whether we were really measuring this proportion. Two possible sources of error, namely, accidental overlaps of two plaques, and clumps containing two or more phage particles, were excluded by the following experiment. Plates showing not more than 50 plaques (as opposed to about 100 in other experiments) were prepared from a population of phage from the cross *hr1* × wild-type, of which 90 per cent had first been neutralized by antiserum. The antiserum treatment should have eliminated any clumps of phage, and the small number of plaques per plate should have eliminated overlaps. Eighty-three mottled plaques were sampled from these plates, of which five proved to contain both parental types of phage. This is the same proportion found in 170 plaques examined in other experiments. The estimate of six per cent shown in Table 2 is therefore correct.

The data of Table 2, together with the estimated total frequency (2%) of *r-r⁺* heterozygotes, measure the frequencies of three classes of heterozygotes among the progeny of crosses between *h* and *r* markers. These frequencies are, for the cross *hr7* × wild-type, 0.12 per cent *hr-wild*; 0.94 per cent *h-hr*; and 0.94 per cent *r-wild*; expressed in round numbers. The corresponding frequencies for the cross *hr13* × wild-type are 1.48, 0.26, and 0.26 per cent, respectively. What other heterozygotes might we expect to find among these progeny?

Two possible classes remain to be looked for; namely, the classes segregating into the pairs *hr*, *r*; and *h*, *wild*; coming from particles heterozygous for *h* but not for *r*. If the distribution of heterozygotes is symmetrical, that is, if the total frequency of heterozygosis for *h* is two per cent, and if the two undetected classes are of equal size, their individual frequencies would be 0.94 per cent for the cross *hr7* × wild-type, and 0.26 per cent for the cross *hr13* × wild-type.

One of the undetected classes can be efficiently measured by sampling clear *r⁺* plaques from platings of the progeny of the cross on mixed

TABLE 3. THE FREQUENCY OF *h-wild* HETERO-ZYGOTES PRODUCED IN CROSSES BETWEEN *hr* AND WILD-TYPE

	hr7 × *wild*	*hr13* × *wild*
Per cent clear *r⁺* plaques	13	1.3
No. mixed/no. tested	14/110	33/112
Per cent *h-wild* heterozygotes among progeny		
Expected	0.94	0.26
Found	1.7	0.38

indicator, and retesting to determine how many of the samples contain mixtures of *h* and wild-type phage, and how many contain *h* only. The proportion of clear *r⁺* plaques that yield mixtures, multiplied by the proportion of clear *r⁺* plaque-formers among the progeny of the cross, gives the frequency of *h-wild* heterozygotes in the population.

The results of this measurement for two crosses are compared with the expectation for symmetrical distributions of heterozygotes in Table 3. The findings are similar to those already described for *r* heterozygotes, namely:

In the cross *hr7* × *wild* (distantly linked markers) the great majority of particles heterozygous for *h* are not heterozygous for *r*.

In the cross *hr13* × *wild* (closely linked markers) the singly heterozygous class is smaller, but the proportion of heterozygotes yielding recombinants is large compared to the proportion of recombinants among the progeny as a whole.

In both crosses the total frequency of *h-h⁺* heterozygotes is roughly two per cent.

We conclude that the formation of particles heterozygous for *h* and for *r* obeys identical rules.

A method of somewhat similar principle is applicable to crosses between pairs of *r* mutants. This is important in that effects of linkage can be tested in different regions of the genetic map; unfortunately, not with very great precision. The principle of the test can be illustrated by the example *r2* × *r4*. Heterozygotes resulting from this cross should segregate to yield the following pairs: *r2* + *r2r4*, *r4* + *r2r4*, *r2* + *r4*, *r2* + *wild*, *r4* + *wild*. This list includes all possible pairs excepting the recombinant pair, which is assumed to be absent. The first two and the last two classes will all be of the same size for reasons of symmetry, and the sum of the frequencies of the last three classes will amount to two per cent of the population. If the two factors are not linked, heterozygotes belonging to the last three classes, and only these, will yield mottled plaques. If the factors are linked, only the last two classes will yield mottled plaques, and the difference between the proportion found and two per cent will measure the size of the doubly heterozygous class yielding $r2 + r4$. The assumption that particles doubly heterozygous for linked factors do not produce mottled plaques is tested by examining plaques originating from bacteria mixedly infected with r mutant pairs, which shows that for map distances up to and including 10 units ($r7 \times r13$) the mottling is negligible.

The results of tests of this kind with six pairs of r mutants are shown in Table 4. Three facts emerge. The frequency of heterozygosis with

on the work of Doermann (1948a), who has shown that infected bacteria artificially lysed at various times during the latent period of viral growth do not yield any virus during the first half of the latent period, and that the yields rise linearly from zero to a maximum during the second half of the latent period. The current interpretation of this result is that the first half of the latent period is devoted to the multiplication of non-infective virus, and the second half to the conversion of non-infective into infective virus (Doermann and Dissosway, 1949; Luria, 1950; Hershey, 1951). During the second half of the latent period, the

TABLE 4. YIELDS OF r^+ AND MOTTLING PHAGE IN r CROSSES

Cross	Per cent r^+	Per cent mottled	Cross	Per cent r^+	Per cent mottled
$r2 \times wild^*$	41	$1.64 \pm .24$	$r2 \times r4$	$0.85 \pm .17$	$0.88 \pm .17$
	37	$1.69 \pm .18$		$0.80 \pm .13$	$0.70 \pm .14$
$r4 \times wild$	41	$1.98 \pm .10$	$r2 \times r7$	$3.8 \pm .33$	$1.40 \pm .18$
$r7 \times wild$	46	$1.63 \pm .19$		$3.1 \pm .37$	$1.19 \pm .17$
	40	$1.59 \pm .21$	$r4 \times r7^*$	$3.7 \pm .32$	$1.25 \pm .19$
$r13 \times wild^*$	50	$1.88 \pm .25$		$3.5 \pm .29$	$1.90 \pm .29$
	54	$1.65 \pm .33$	$r13 \times r7^*$	$8.1 \pm .50$	$1.43 \pm .17$
$r1 \times wild^*$	45	$2.17 \pm .26$		$7.3 \pm .52$	$1.27 \pm .17$
	47	$2.43 \pm .21$	$r1 \times r7$	17.9 ± 1.2	$2.04 \pm .26$
			$r1 \times r13$	$16.7 \pm .66$	$2.00 \pm .27$

The results shown are means and their standard deviations computed from counts of about 4000 plaques on 20 plates. The duplicate counts of the crosses marked with an asterisk were made from the same population on different days; the other duplicate counts represent independent experiments. The per cent r^+ in the left half of the table measures the equality of infection with the two parental viruses; in the right half it measures the linkage between r loci.

respect to five different r loci is at least approximately the same. The effect of close linkage between the loci $r2$ and $r4$ is to produce a sufficiently large class of doubly heterozygous phage particles to cause a sharp decrease in the yield of mottling phage. No significant effect is seen for crosses between markers separated by a distance of three or four units or more. The method is evidently valid in principle, but too inaccurate to yield detailed information.

We return once more to crosses between phages carrying h and r markers to test the effect of unequal multiplicity on the pattern of segregation of the resulting heterozygotes (Table 5). The effect seen is to increase markedly the frequency of the parent-recombinant class containing the parental virus available in excess. This effect is not visible when the markers involved are closely linked.

Another experiment yields information about the sequence of events in the cell. It is based

partial yields of virus can be obtained simply by adding cyanide to the cultures. Doermann (1948b) has also shown that very large yields of virus can be obtained when lysis is delayed for several hours, as happens in cultures containing high concentrations of bacteria infected with r^+ virus.

We have compared viral yields obtained from samples of the same bacterial suspension, infected with $hr7$ and wild-type, by adding cyanide ten minutes after infection, by spontaneous lysis at the end of the normal latent period (21 to 40 minutes), and by spontaneous lysis delayed for five to six hours. The yields of virus per cell were respectively 10, 250, and 1710. The yields of recombinants were respectively 17, 29, and 42 per cent of the total virus. The yields of r-r^+ heterozygotes, however, did not differ significantly from two per cent in any of the three populations. The proportions of the different segregating classes were also the same among the heterozygotes in small samples from the first

TABLE 5. PER CENT DISTRIBUTIONS OF r-r^+
HETEROZYGOTES WITH RESPECT TO
SEGREGATION PATTERN: CROSSES
WITH 5-FOLD EXCESS OF hr OVER
WILD-TYPE

Segregants found	$hr1 \times wild$ (40)	$hr7 \times wild$ (20)	$hr13 \times wild$ (2)
hr-$wild$	2	4	71
h-hr	78	71	17
r-$wild$	20	25	12
h-r	....	0	0
No. tested	117	55	161

Per cent yields of recombinants for each cross are
shown in parentheses.

two yields. This experiment shows that the interactions between phage particles giving rise
to recombinants (Doermann and Dissosway, 1949)
and heterozygotes, are well under way by the time
infective virus begins to form in the cell. The
rise in proportion of recombinants during the latter half of the latent period, while the proportion
of heterozygotes remains constant, suggests that
the formation and segregation of heterozygotes
may be continuing during this time.

SUMMARY OF NEW FACTS

(1) When bacteria are infected with three kinds
of phage carrying unlinked genetic markers, about
three per cent of the progeny carry markers derived from all three parents.

(2) When bacteria are infected with two phages
carrying allelic markers, about two per cent of the
progeny particles segregate during further growth
to yield both kinds of phage. This is true for
five different r markers, and an h marker. The
particles segregating to yield r and r^+ phage are
conveniently studied because they produce mottled plaques.

(3) The mottle producers are not clumps of
particles because they are inactivated as single
units of normal sensitivity by antiserum, heat,
β-rays, and ultraviolet light. Artificially prepared clumps are inactivated as multiple units.

(4) There is no indication that the mottling
particles can multiply before segregating. In
view of facts (3) and (4), the segregating particles
are called heterozygotes for the specified marker.

(5) When the parental phage particles are marked
at both h and r loci, the pattern of segregation
shows the following characteristics:

(a) About two per cent of the progeny are heterozygous for h, and about two per cent for r.

(b) The particles heterozygous for a single
marker form four classes of approximately equal

size, segregating into h, hr; h, $wild$; r, hr; and
r, $wild$; respectively. Thus single heterozygotes
yield one parent and one recombinant with respect
to the original cross.

(c) When the two markers are linked, the double
heterozygotes segregate to yield the two parents
of the original cross, never the two recombinants,
and never more than two kinds of phage. When
the two markers are unlinked, these alternatives
cannot be distinguished.

(d) When the two markers are unlinked or distant, heterozygosis for one marker is almost independent of heterozygosis for the second, and
the doubly heterozygous class amounts to only
three per cent of the total number of heterozygotes.
Thus in the crosses $hr7 \times$ wild-type and $hr1 \times$
wild-type, which yield respectively 20 and 40
per cent of recombinants, the pooled heterozygotes segregate to yield about 48 per cent of
recombinants.

(e) In the cross $hr13 \times$ wild-type (closely linked
markers) the doubly heterozygous class makes up
about 59 per cent of the total number of heterozygotes. This cross yields about two per cent of
recombinants, but the pooled heterozygotes segregate to yield about 20 per cent of recombinants.

(f) If the crosses involving unlinked or distant
factors are varied by introducing a 5-fold excess
of one parent, the effect is to increase the frequency of the single heterozygotes segregating
to yield that parent. This effect is not visible
if the markers are closely linked.

(6) The frequency of heterozygosis is independent of the yield of virus per bacterium when
this is decreased by premature lysis with cyanide,
or increased under conditions of lysis-inhibition.

DISCUSSION

Information about inheritance in bacteriophage
T2H comes from the analysis of mutations and
from recombination tests. These two techniques
agree in showing that mutations occur in localized genes. Recombination tests reveal that the
genes are organized into linkage groups. For
one of these groups, it appears that the arrangement of genes is linear. Inheritance in bacteriophage is therefore amenable to the same kind of
genetic analysis that has served to elucidate
nuclear organization in other organisms. The
limitations peculiar to viral genetics should not
be overlooked. It is not possible to recover the
immediate products of recombination, unless the
heterozygotes prove to be such; the mechanism
of recombination is unknown; and cytogenetic
techniques are inapplicable.

The analysis of heterozygotes raises new questions about the mechanism of genetic recombination. The surprising result is that the great majority of the heterozygotes recovered from a two-factor cross segregate as if they were homozygous or hemizygous for one of the marked genes, unless these are very closely linked. This means that the heterozygotes found, which should perhaps be called residual heterozygotes, may not be representative of the heterozygotes formed in the cell.

One feature of the residual heterozygotes is reassuring in this respect. The total frequency of heterozygosis is the same for five different r markers and one h marker. This makes it unlikely that the formation of residual heterozygotes is contingent on structural differences between different mutants.

The questions raised by the peculiar segregation pattern of heterozygotes are clarified somewhat in terms of the following alternatives.

(1) Residual heterozygotes may not be diploid particles, but particles containing one or more small extra pieces of genetic material. Double heterozygotes for distant markers contain two or more pieces. These pieces are substituted for the homologous pieces in one of the very early progeny of the segregating heterozygote. The residual heterozygotes need not differ from intracellular heterozygotes, and their production need not involve zygote formation.

(2) Residual heterozygotes may be formed preferentially from zygotes in which recombination has occurred, and receive one parental and one recombinant set of genes. In this case the residual heterozygotes are diploid, but are not representative of the zygotes from which they come.

(3) Residual heterozygotes may be representative zygotes that are doubly heterozygous in structure, but which undergo segregations accompanied by frequent losses to yield parental and recombinant pairs.

The third alternative can be excluded. In crosses involving the markers h and $r13$, one finds only two per cent of recombinants among the whole progeny, and about 20 per cent of recombinants among the segregants of heterozygous progeny. To explain this in terms of alternative (3), one would have to assume a low frequency of intracellular zygote formation. This assumption is incompatible with the high frequency of triparental recombination observed.

The questions about structure of heterozygotes can be generalized in the following way. We find that about two per cent of the progeny of crosses are heterozygous for each marker, and that the particles heterozygous for one are mostly not the particles heterozygous for the other, excepting close linkage. Since the frequencies are not specific for individual mutants, they are presumably independent of local structure, and every phage particle must carry doublings at one or more unmarked loci if total map distances are large. The alternatives (1) and (2) are to this extent applicable to all the progeny, and take the simple form: are phage particles diploid or not?

It is reasonable to assume that the formation of heterozygotes and the formation of recombinants are related processes, but there is no evidence that recombinants have their primary origin in structures resembling the residual heterozygotes. Instead, recombinants and residual heterozygotes may be alternative products of other structures about which we have no direct information. The residual heterozygotes have one characteristic that is suggestive in this connection: they segregate to yield one recombinant per heterozygote. The recombinants that are produced in crosses also have to be assumed to come from structures yielding one recombinant, to explain the independent or nearly independent distributions of sister recombinants among single cell yields of virus (Hershey and Rotman, 1949).

The frequency of double heterozygotes provides a measure of linkage that is independent of the results of recombination tests. Both measures show that h is linked to $r13$ and that $r2$ is linked to $r4$. The new measure is insensitive for large map distances since the crosses involving h and $r7$, and h and $r1$, which yield respectively 20 and 40 per cent of recombinants, produce the same number of double heterozygotes.

CONCLUSION

A preliminary analysis of heterozygous particles of the bacteriophage T2H raises new questions about the mechanism of genetic recombination, and suggests that new ideas are needed to explain this phenomenon.

The work reported in this paper was aided by a grant from the Division of Research Grants and Fellowships, U. S. Public Health Service.

REFERENCES

DELBRÜCK, M., and BAILEY, W. T., JR., 1946, Induced mutations in bacterial viruses. Cold Spr. Harb. Symposium Quant. Biol. 11: 33–37.
DOERMANN, A. H., 1948a, Intracellular growth of bacteriophage. Yearb. Carneg. Instn. 47: 176–182. 1948b, Lysis and lysis inhibition with *Escherichia coli* bacteriophage. J. Bact. 55: 257–276.

DOERMANN, A. H., and DISSOSWAY, C. F.-R., 1949, Intracellular growth and genetics of bacteriophage. Yearb. Carneg. Instn. *48*: 170–176.

HERSHEY, A. D., 1946, Spontaneous mutations in bacterial viruses. Cold Spr. Harb. Symposium Quant. Biol. *11*: 67–77.

1951, Reproduction of bacteriophage. VIIth International Congress for Cell Biology, in press.

HERSHEY, A. D., and DAVIDSON, H., 1951, Allelic and non-allelic genes controlling host specificity in a bacteriophage. Genetics *36*: 667–675.

HERSHEY, A. D., and ROTMAN, R., 1948, Linkage among genes controlling inhibition of lysis in a bacterial virus. Proc. Nat. Acad. Sci., Wash. *34*: 253–264.

1949, Genetic recombination between host range and plaque type mutants of bacteriophage in single bacterial cells. Genetics *34*: 44–71.

LURIA, S. E., 1945, Mutations of bacterial viruses affecting their host range. Genetics *30*: 84–99.

1950, Bacteriophage: an essay on virus reproduction. Science *111*: 507–511.

DISCUSSION

VISCONTI (in reply to a comment by Horowitz): The excess of parental types in Dr. Hershey's experiments can be eliminated by selecting a class of recombinants and scoring inside this class for a third character. Making use of the three markers, rl, h and m, the following cross was made: $rl\ h\ m^+ \times rl^+\ h^+\ m$. The yield was plated on B, so that no difference could be detected between h and h$^+$. Of 1003 plaques observed, 177 were $r^+\ m^+$, thus giving a recombination value of 18 per cent. 128 of such plaques were "fished" and tested by a streaking method on B/2. Of the 128 tested, 63 were h and 65 h^+. In another experiment, 92 plaques were "fished" and tested by plating a sample on double indicator. 43 were h; 47 were h^+; and two were mixed. The two mixed plaques account for the 2 per cent of heterozygotes for the locus h.

THE ELEMENTARY UNITS OF HEREDITY*

SEYMOUR BENZER

Biophysical Laboratory, Purdue University,
Lafayette, Indiana

INTRODUCTION

THE TECHNIQUES of genetic experiments have developed to a point
where a highly detailed view of the hereditary material is attainable.
By the use of selective procedures in recombination studies with certain organisms, notably fungi (14), bacteria (2), and viruses (1), it is
now feasible to "resolve" detail on the molecular level. In fact, the
amount of observable detail is so enormous as to make an exhaustive
study a real challenge.

A remarkable feature of genetic fine structure studies has been the
ability to construct (by recombination experiments) genetic maps
which remain one-dimensional down to the smallest levels. The molecular substance (DNA) constituting the hereditary material in bacteria
and bacterial viruses is also one-dimensional in character. It is therefore tempting to seek a relation between the linear genetic map and
its molecular counterpart which would make it possible to convert
"genetic length" (measured in terms of recombination frequencies) to
molecular length (measured in terms of nucleotide units).

The classical "gene," which served at once as the unit of genetic
recombination, of mutation, and of function, is no longer adequate.
These units require separate definition. A lucid discussion of this
problem has been given by Pontecorvo (13).

The unit of recombination will be defined as the smallest element in
the one-dimensional array that is interchangeable (but not divisible)
by genetic recombination. One such element will be referred to as a

* This research has been supported by grants from the American Cancer Society,
upon recommendation of the Committee on Growth of the National Research
Council, and from the National Science Foundation.

70

"recon." The unit of mutation, the "muton," will be defined as the smallest element that, when altered, can give rise to a mutant form of the organism. A unit of function is more difficult to define. It depends upon what level of function is meant. For example, in speaking of a single function, one may be referring to an ensemble of enzymatic steps leading to *one* particular physiological end-effect, or of the synthesis of *one* of the enzymes involved, or of the specification of *one* peptide chain in one of the enzymes, or even of the specification of *one* critical amino acid.

A functional unit can be defined genetically, independent of biochemical information, by means of the elegant *cis-trans* comparison devised by Lewis (12). This test is used to tell whether two mutants, having apparently similar defects, are indeed defective in the same way. For the *trans* test, both mutant genomes are inserted in the same cell (e.g., in heterocaryon form, or, in the case of a bacterial virus, the equivalent obtained by infecting a bacterium with virus particles of both mutant types). If the resultant phenotype is defective, the mutants are said to be non-complementary, i.e., defective in the same "function." As a control, the same genetic material is inserted in the *cis* configuration, i.e., as the genomes from one double mutant and one non-mutant. The *cis* configuration usually produces a non-defective phenotype (or a close approximation to it). It turns out that a group of non-complementary mutants falls within a limited segment of the genetic map. Such a map segment, corresponding to a function which is unitary as defined by the *cis-trans* test applied to the heterocaryon, will be referred to as a "cistron."

The experiments to be described in this paper represent an attempt to place limits on the sizes of these three genetic units in the case of a specific region of the hereditary material of the bacterial virus T4. A group of *"rII"* mutants of T4 has particularly favorable properties for this kind of analysis. Mutants are easily isolated. Recombinants can be detected, even in extremely low frequency, by a selective technique. The system is sufficiently sensitive to permit extension of genetic mapping down to the molecular (nucleotide) level, so that the recon and muton become accessible to measurement. The *rII* mutants are defective in the sense of being unable to multiply in cells of a certain host bacterium (although they do infect and kill the cell). The *cis-trans* test can therefore be readily applied.

Genetic Maps

Method of Construction.

The construction of a genetic map of an organism starts with the selection of a standard ("wild") type. From the progeny of the wild type, mutant forms can be isolated on the basis of some heritable difference. When two mutants are crossed, there is a possibility that a wild-type organism will be formed as a result of recombination of genetic material. The reciprocal recombinant, containing both mutational alterations, also occurs. The proportion of progeny constituting such recombinant types is characteristic of the particular mutants used. The results of crosses involving a group of mutants can be plotted on a one-dimensional diagram where each mutant is represented by a point. The interval between two points signifies the proportion of recombinants occurring in a cross between the two corresponding mutants. Usually, it is not possible to construct a single map for all the mutants of an organism; instead the mutants must be broken up into "linkage groups." A linear map may be constructed within each linkage group, but the mutant characters assigned to different linkage groups assort randomly among the progeny. The number of linkage groups, in some cases, has been shown to correspond to the number of visible chromosomes.

The procedure for constructing a genetic map for a bacterial virus is much the same (9). A genetically uniform population of a mutant can readily be grown from a single individual. Two mutants are crossed by infecting a susceptible bacterium with both types and examining the resulting virus progeny for recombinant types. Virus T4 has been mapped in some detail (3, 1), and behaves as a haploid organism with a single linkage group (18).

Relativity of Genetic Maps.

A genetic map is an image composed of individual points. Each point represents a mutation which has been localized with respect to other mutations by recombination experiments. The image thus obtained is a highly colored representation of the hereditary material. Alterations in the hereditary material will lead to noticeable mutations only if they affect some phenotypic characteristic to a visible degree. Innocuous changes may pass unnoticed, leaving their corresponding regions on the map blank. At the other extreme, alterations having a

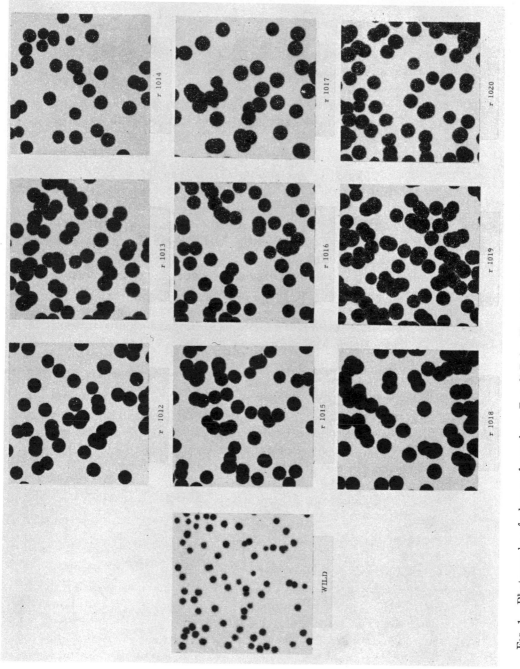

Fig. 1. Photographs of plaques formed on *E. coli* B by T4 "wild-type" and nine independently arising *r* mutants.

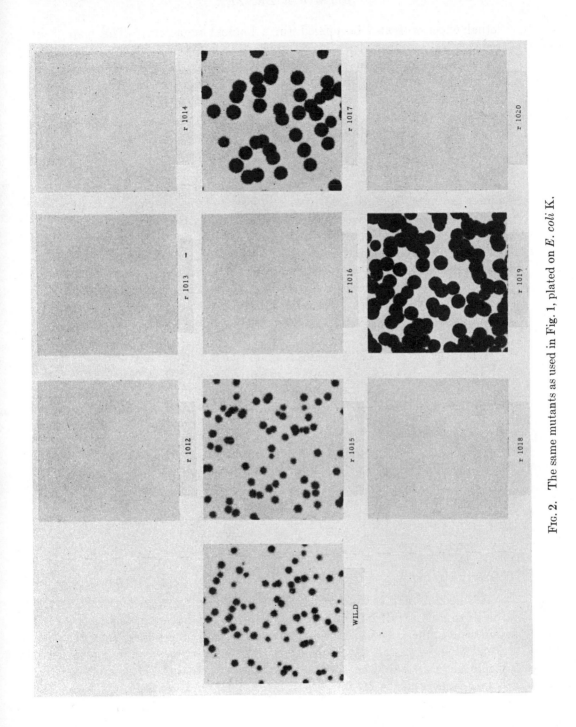

Fig. 2.   The same mutants as used in Fig. 1, plated on *E. coli* K.

lethal effect will also be missed (in a haploid organism). The map represents, therefore, only cases which fall between these extremes under the conditions of observation. By varying these conditions, a given mutational event may be shifted from one of these categories (innocuous, noticeable, or lethal) to another, thereby appearing on, or disappearing from the map.

This effect may be illustrated by the "*r*" mutants of bacterial virus T4. Wild-type T4 produces small, fuzzy plaques on *Escherichia coli* B (Fig. 1). From plaques of wild-type T4, *r*-type mutants can be isolated which produce a different sort of plaque. Fig. 1 shows the plaques of nine *r* mutants, each isolated from a different plaque of the wild type in order to assure independent origin. The similarity of plaque type of these *r*'s on B disappears when they are plated on another host strain, *E. coli* K (a lysogenic K12 strain (10) carrying phage lambda), as shown in Fig. 2. Here, they split into three groups: two mutants form *r*-type plaques, one forms wild-type plaques, and the remaining six do not register. Thus, with B as host, all three types of mutation lead to visible effects, while with K as host, the effects may be visible, innocuous, or lethal.

When the same set of mutants is plated on a third strain, *E coli* S (K12S, a non-lysogenic derivative (10) of K12) or BB (a "Berkeley" derivative (17) of B) the pattern of plaque morphology is different from that on either B or K (Table 1).

TABLE 1

Plaque Morphology of T4 Strains (Isolated in B) Plated on Various Hosts

PHAGE STRAIN	BACTERIAL HOST STRAIN		
	B	S	K
wild	wild	wild	wild
r I	r	r	r
r II	r	wild	—
r III	r	wild	wild

If a genetic map is constructed for these mutants, using B as host, the three groups fall into different map regions, as indicated in Fig. 3. On strain S, the *rII* and *rIII* types of mutation are innocuous. Thus, if S had been used as host in the isolation of *r* mutants, only the *rI* region would have appeared on the map. On K as host, the *rIII* mutation is innocuous, and the *rII* mutation is (usually) lethal, so that only the

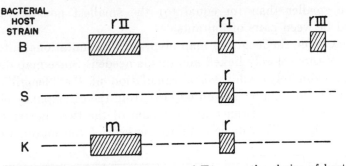

Fig. 3. Dependence of the genetic map of T4 upon the choice of host. Three regions of the map are shown as they probably would appear if *E. coli* strains B, S, or K were used as the host.

rI region would appear. Actually, a few *rII* mutants are able to multiply somewhat on K, producing visible tiny plaques. If K were used as host in the isolation and testing of mutants from wild-type T4, these mutants could be noticed and would probably be designated by some other name, perhaps "minute." The map would then appear as in the bottom row of Fig. 3. The distribution of points on the map within this "minute" region would be very different from those for the *rII* region using B as the host.

The appearance of a genetic map also depends on the choice of the standard type, which is, after all, arbitrary. For example, suppose an *r* form were taken as the standard type and non-*r* mutants were isolated from it. Then a completely different map would result. An example of this is to be found in the work of Franklin and Streisinger (5) on the $h \rightarrow h^+$ mutation in T2, as compared with that of Hershey and Davidson (7) on the $h^+ \rightarrow h$ mutation.

Another way in which the picture is weighted is by local variations in the stability of the genetic material. Certain types of structural alterations may occur more frequently than others. Thus, a perfectly stable genetic element (i.e., one which never errs during replication) would not be represented by any point on the map.

Determination of the Sizes of the Hereditary Units by Mapping.

Determination of the recon requires "running the map into the ground" (Delbrück's expression), that is, isolation and mapping of so large a linear density of mutants that their distances apart diminish to the point of being comparable to the indivisible unit. With a finite set of mutants, only an upper limit can be set upon the recon, which must be smaller than (or equal to) the smallest non-zero interval observed between pairs of mutants.

To determine the length of map involved in a mutational alteration, a group of three closely linked mutants is needed. Since map distances are (approximately) additive, a calculation of the "length" of the central mutation can be attempted (15) from the discrepancy observed between the longest distance and the sum of the two shorter ones, as shown in Fig. 4. The upper limit to the size of the muton would be

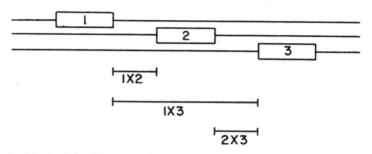

Fig. 4. Method for determining the "length" of a mutation. The discrepancy between the long distance and the sum of the two short distances measures the length of the central mutation.

the smallest discrepancy observed by this method, which can be determined accurately only if the three mutants are very closely linked. It should be noted that since the degree to which the genetic structure can be sliced by recombination experiments is limited by the size of recon, the size of the muton will register as zero by this method if it is equal to or smaller than one recon. A second method for determining the muton size is by the maximum number of mutations, separable by recombination, that can be packed into a definite length of the map.

For the cistron size, only a *lower* limit can be set with a finite group of mutants. The cistron must be at least as large as the distance between the most distant pair within it. Its boundaries become more sharply defined the larger the number of points which are shown to lie inside them.

Thus, the determination of the sizes of all three units requires the isolation and crossing of large numbers of mutants. The magnitude of this undertaking increases with the square of the number of mutants, since to cross n mutants in all possible pairs requires $n(n-1)/2$ crosses, or approximately $n^2/2$. Fortunately, however, the project can be shortened considerably by means of a trick.

The Method of Overlapping "Deletions."

Certain *rII* mutants are anomalous in the sense that they cannot be represented as *points* on the map. The anomalous mutants give no detectable wild recombinants with any of several other mutants which *do* give wild recombinants with each other. An anomalous mutant can be represented (Fig. 5) as covering a segment of the map. Reversion

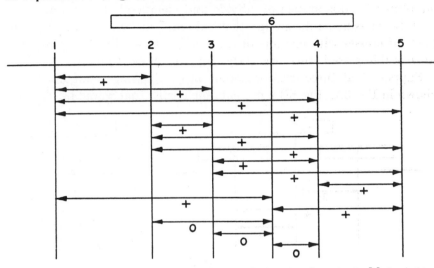

Fig. 5. Illustration of the behavior of an "anomalous" mutant. Mutant no. 6 is anomalous with respect to the segment of the map indicated by the bar; it fails to give wild recombinants with mutants (nos. 2, 3, and 4) located within that segment. A + signifies production, and 0 lack of production, of wild recombinants in a cross.

of such an *rII* mutant has never been observed; also, no mutant which does revert has been found to have this anomalous character. The properties of an anomalous mutant can be explained as owing to the deletion (i.e. loss) of a segment of hereditary material corresponding to the map span covered. However, anomalous behavior and stability against reversion are not sufficient to establish that a deletion has occurred. Similar properties could be expected of a double mutant when crossed with either of two different single mutants located at the same points. An inversion also would show the same behavior. However, the occurrence of a deletion seems to be the only reasonable explanation in the cases of several of the *rII* mutants, since they fail to give recombinants with any of three or more (in one case as many as 20) well-separated mutants.

Whether a given mutation belongs in the region covered by a deletion can be determined by the appropriate cross. If wild recombinants are produced, the mutant must have a map position *outside* the region of the deletion. This eliminates the need to cross that mutant with any of the mutants whose map positions lie *within* the region of the deletion. The problem of mapping a large number of mutants is greatly simplified by this system of "divide and conquer." The mutants can first be classified into groups that fall into different regions on the basis of crosses with mutants of the deletion-type. Further crossing in all possible pairs is then necessary only within each group.

Suppose that three deletions occur in overlapping configuration, as shown in Fig. 6A. Fig. 6B represents the results that would be obtained

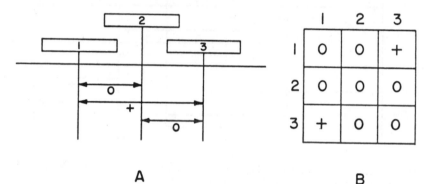

A   B

FIG. 6. The method of overlapping deletions. Three mutants are shown, each differing from wild type in the deletion of a portion of the genetic material. Mutants no. 1 and no. 3 can recombine with each other to produce wild type, but neither of them can produce wild recombinants when crossed to mutant no. 2. The matrix B represents the results obtained by crossing three such mutants in pairs and testing for wild recombinants; the results uniquely determine the order of the mutations on the map A.

in crosses of pairs of these three mutants. A diagonal element (representing a cross of a mutant with itself) is, of course, zero, since no wild recombinants can be produced. An overlap is reflected by the pattern of non-diagonal zeros. These results would establish a unique *order* of the deletions (without resort to the three-factor crosses that would ordinarily be necessary). With a sufficient number and appropriate distribution of deletions, one could hope to order a large length of map. The reader will note an analogy (not altogether without significance!) to the technique used by Sanger (16) to order the amino acids in a polypeptide chain by means of overlapping peptide segments.

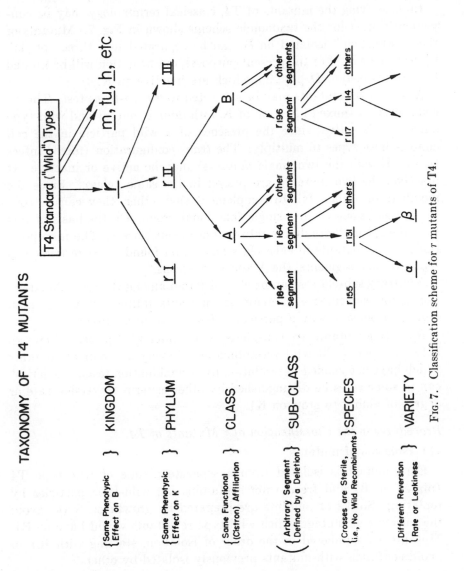

Fig. 7. Classification scheme for r mutants of T4.

Mapping the *rII* Region of T4

Taxonomy of r Mutants.

In classifying the mutants of T4, classical terminology may be conveniently used for the taxonomic scheme shown in Fig. 7. Mutants of the *r* "kingdom," isolated on B, can be separated into three "phyla" by testing on K. For the present purposes, our attention will be limited to mutants of the *rII* phylum, which are inactive on K.

A pair of *rII* mutants may be subjected to the *cis-trans* test. The *cis* configuration (mixed infection of K with double mutant and wild-type particles) is active, since the presence of a wild particle in the cell enables both types to multiply. The *trans* configuration (mixed infection of K with the two single mutants) may be active or inactive. If inactive, the two mutants are placed in the same "class." Since the members of a class fail to complement each other, they can be considered as belonging to a single functional group. On the basis of this test, the *rII* mutants divide into two clear-cut classes. The map positions of the mutants in each class have been found to be restricted to separate map segments, the A and B "cistrons."

Arbitrary sub-classes can be chosen (from among the available deletions) for convenience in mapping: mutants falling within the map region encompassed by a particular deletion form a sub-class.

Reverting mutants are considered as of different "species" if crosses between them yield wild recombinants. Among a group of mutants which have not yielded to resolution by recombination tests, "varieties" can in some cases be distinguished by other criteria (reversion rate or degree of ability to grow on K).

Procedures in the Classification of r Mutants of T4.

(1) Isolation of mutants

Each mutant is isolated from a separate plaque of wild-type T4 (plated on B) and freed from contaminating wild-type particles by replating. Stocks of mutants are prepared by growth on S (to avoid the selective advantage which wild type revertants would have on B). Mutants are numbered in the order of isolation, starting with 101 to avoid confusion with mutants previously isolated by others.

(2) Spot test on K

In this first test of a new *r* mutant, 10^8 particles are plated on K and then the plate is spotted with one drop (10^6 particles) of *r164* (a mutant having a "deletion" in an A cistron) and one drop of *r196* (a mutant having a deletion located in the B cistron). Typical examples of the results of this test are shown in Fig. 8. If the new mutant belongs either to the *rI* or the *rII* phylum, the plating bacteria will be completely lysed (except for a background of colonies formed by mutants of K which are resistant to T4), as typified by mutant *X* in Fig. 8.

Mutant *Y* in Fig. 8 is typical of a stable *rII* mutant. The background shows no plaques, indicating that the proportion of revertants in the stock is less than 10^{-8}. The spot of *r196* is completely clear, in contrast to the *r164* spot. This massive lysis is caused by the ability of mutant *Y* and *r196* to complement each other for growth on K. From this result, it may be concluded that mutant *Y* belongs to the A class. Within the *r164* spot, however, some plaques may be seen. These are due to wild recombinants arising from *r164* and mutant *Z* (by virtue of very feeble growth of *rII* mutants on K). Therefore, mutant *Y* is not in the subclass defined by *r164*.

The third test plate is typical of a reverting *rII* mutant. The stock contains a fraction 10^{-6} of wild-type particles which produce the plaques seen in the background. It is evident from the spot tests that the mutant *Z* belongs in the B class, and appears to lie within the *r196* subclass.

(3) Spot test on a mixture of K and B cells

Once the class of a new mutant is known, it can be tested on a single plate against several mutants of the same class. For this purpose, the sensitivity of the test may be increased enormously by the addition of some B cells (about one part in a hundred) to the K used for plating. The additional growth possible for the mutants on B cells enhances their opportunity to produce wild recombinants. This test gives a positive response down to the level of around 0.01 per cent recombination. A negative result does not, of course, eliminate the possibility that recombination occurs with a lower frequency.

(4) Preliminary crosses

A semiquantitative measure of recombination frequency may be obtained by mixedly infecting B with two mutants and plating the infected cells on K. B cells which liberate one or more wild-type particles can produce plaques. This method is convenient for preliminary testing for recombination in the range from 0.0001 to 0.1 per cent.

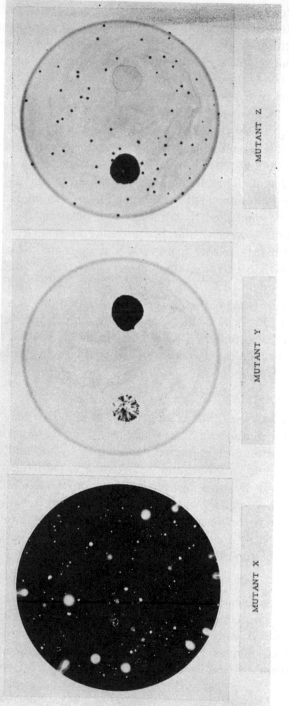

Fig. 8. Spot test used in classification of r mutants. To test a mutant, 10^8 mutant particles are plated on bacterial strain K and the plate is spotted with one drop of $r164$ (left) and one drop of $r196$ (right). Mutants X, Y, and Z illustrate typical results. Mutant X is of the $r1$ phylum. Mutant Y is a stable mutant of the rII phylum and the A class, but is not in the $r164$ sub-class. Mutant Z is a reverting mutant (wild-type plaques in background) of the rII phylum, B class, and $r196$ subclass.

With higher frequencies of recombination, approaching the point where a large fraction of the mixedly infected cells liberate recombinants, saturation sets in.

(5) Standard crosses

Standard measurements of recombination frequency are made in conventional crosses. B cells are infected with an average of three particles per cell of each phage. The infected cells are allowed to burst in a liquid medium, and the progeny are plated on K and on B to determine the proportion of wild-type particles. The reciprocal recombinant (double *rII* mutant) does not, in general, produce plaques on K, but since the two recombinant types are produced in statistically equal numbers (9), the proportion of recombinants in the progeny can be taken as twice the ratio of plaques on K to plaques on B (corrected for the relative efficiency of plating of wild type on these two strains, which is close to unity).

(6) Reversion rates

The reversion rate of a mutant is reflected in the proportion of wild-type particles present in a stock. This value is an important characteristic of each mutant, varying over an enormous range for different mutants. It may be less than 10^{-8} for "stable" (i.e., non-reverting) mutants or as high as several per cent. (For one exceedingly unstable mutant the proportion of revertants averages 70 per cent, even in stocks derived from individual mutant particles.) The precision with which a mutant can be localized on the map is inversely related to its reversion rate; only relatively stable mutants are useful for mapping. In the experiments here reported, it has been assumed that the reversion rate of a mutant is not altered during a cross; the reversion contribution is subtracted from the observed percentage of wild particles in the progeny. In most cases, this correction is negligible.

(7) "Leakiness" of *rII* mutants

rII mutants differ greatly in their ability to grow on K cells. A sensitive measure of this ability can be obtained by infecting K cells and plating them on B. Any K cell that liberates one or more virus particles can give rise to a plaque. The fraction of infected cells yielding virus progeny, which is a characteristic property of each mutant (when measured under fixed conditions), may vary from almost 100 per cent down to less than one per cent for different mutants.

Leakiness has the effect of limiting the sensitivity of K as a tool for selection of wild recombinants, thereby hampering the mapping of very leaky mutants.

TABLE 2

CLASSIFICATION OF AN UNSELECTED GROUP OF 241 *r* MUTANTS OF T4

The number of mutants in each classification is given in parentheses. An asterisk indicates that reversion of the mutant to wild type has not been detected. A few mutants (indicated as "not determined") could not be further classified due to excessively high reversion rate or leakiness.

Kingdom	Phylum	Class	Subclass	Species	Variety
			*r164** (27)	1 sp. (20) 1 sp. (2)	1 var. (11) 1 var. (9)
	rI (96)		*r184** (5)	4 sp. (1 ea.) 1 sp. (2) 1 sp. (2)*	1 var. (1) 1 var. (1)*
			*r221** (4)	1 sp. (3)	1 var. (1) 1 var. (1) 1 var. (1)
		IIA (73)	*r47** (4) *r197** (2)	1 sp. (2)* 1 sp. (1)* 1 sp. (1)	
r mutants (241)			others (29)	1 sp. (3)* 1 sp. (2) 1 sp. (2) 1 sp. (2) 1 sp. (2) 1 sp. (2) 1 sp. (2) 14 sp. (1 ea.)	1 var. (1) 1 var. (1) 1 var. (1) 1 var. (1)
	rII (134)		not determined (1)		
		IIB (60)	*r196** (34)	1 sp. (21) 1 sp. (9) 3 sp. (1 ea.)	1 var. (19) 1 var. (2) 1 var. (5) 1 var. (4)
			*r187** (6)	1 sp. (3)* 1 sp. (2) 1 sp. (3)	1 var. (1) 1 var. (1) 1 var. (2)
			others (16)	1 sp. (3) 1 sp. (2) 8 sp. (1 ea.)	1 var. (1)
	rIII (11)		not determined (4)		
		not determined (1)			

Classification of a Set of 241 r Mutants.

A set of *r* mutants was isolated, using B as host, and given numbers from *r101* to *r338*; the mutants *r47*, *r48*, and *r51*, isolated by Doermann (3), were added to this set, making a total of **241** *r* mutants. These were analyzed according to methods already described.

The results are shown in Table 2. Of these mutants, 134 fell into the *rII* phylum. Each of these (with the exception of one very leaky mutant) could be assigned unambiguously to either of two classes on the basis of the test for complementary action of pairs of mutants for growth on K. Mutants within each class were crossed with stable mutants of the same class; those giving no detectable wild recombinants with a particular stable mutant were assigned to the same subclass. Mutants of each subclass were crossed in all pairs. When two or more mutants were found to be of the same species (i.e., showed, in a "preliminary" type cross, recombination of less than about 0.001 per cent, or less than the uncertainty level set by the reversion rate, whichever was greater), one was used to represent the species in further crosses. Those mutants not falling into any of the subclasses defined by the available stable mutants were crossed with each other in pairs. By these procedures, the classification was carried to the species level for the entire set of mutants, except for six highly revertible or leaky mutants whose subclass was not established.

Several of the species showed evidence of splitting into varieties distinguishable by reversion rate or degree of leakiness. Some mutant varieties recurred frequently (e.g., 19, 11, 9 times). These recurrences were far outside the expectation for a Poisson distribution, and are indicative of local variations of mutability. The fact that many species were represented by only one occurrence suggests that many other species remain to be found.

The 33 species found in the A cistron and the 18 species found in the B cistron are sufficient to define reasonably well the limits of each cistron. The minimum size of a cistron in recombination units is determined by the maximum amount of recombination observed in standard crosses between pairs of mutants within it. On the basis of the standard crosses performed so far, this value is about 4 per cent recombination for the A cistron, and 2 per cent for the B cistron.

Study of 923 r Mutants.

While the study of the foregoing 241 mutants yielded a good idea of the sizes and complexity of the A and B cistrons, it fell short of "saturating" the map sufficiently to provide the close clusters of mutants required for the determination of the sizes of the recon and muton. To this end, it was decided to isolate many more mutants. By confining attention to those falling into the *r164* subclass, a more exhaustive study could be made of a selected portion of the map.

In a group of 923 *r* mutants (*r101* through *r1020*, plus Doermann's three), 149 were found to belong to the *r164* subclass. Four of those were stable. The remaining 145 mutants separated into the 11 species shown in Fig. 9. One of the species accounted for 123 of the mutants! As shown in Table 3, this species included three varieties as distinguished by their reversion rates; two were of roughly equal abundance, while the third occurred only once.

Results of standard crosses between the mutants of the *r164* subclass are presented in Fig. 10. The smallest recombination distance, setting an upper limit to the size of the recon, is around 0.02 per cent (between

TABLE 3

Reversion Data for Mutants of the *r131* Species

The "reversion index" is the proportion of wild-type particles in a lysate prepared from a few mutant particles (to avoid introduction of any revertants present in the original stock) using S as host. The measurement is subject to large fluctuations due to the clonal growth of the revertants formed. Therefore, four separate lysates are made for each mutant. Parentheses indicate extreme fluctuations. An asterisk indicates a background of tiny plaques (smaller than those produced by wild type) when the lysate is plated on K.

In addition to the examples listed in the table, 67 other mutants of this species are also of variety α, as judged by the proportion of revertants (from 0.2×10^{-6} to 4.0×10^{-6}) in single lysates; 45 additional mutants apparently are of variety β (having values from 300×10^{-6} to $4,000 \times 10^{-6}$).

The mutants of variety α give less than 0.001 per cent recombination with *r274*. For the more highly revertible mutants of variety β, this limit can only be set at less than 0.02 per cent recombination with *r274*. The mutant *r973*, of variety γ, gives less than 0.005 per cent (the limit set by background on K) recombination with *r274*.

	Mutant	Reversion Index (units of 10^{-6})			
variety α	*r200*	0.47	0.91	0.17	0.25
	r220	0.55	0.41	0.25	0.21
	r274	0.24	0.29	0.61	(10.)
	r930	0.17	0.66	0.19	0.21
	r1012	0.58	0.27	0.22	0.15
variety β	*r245*	420.	490.	490.	1120.
	r353	540.	530.	3900.	(500,000.)
	r376	520.	360.	1240.	450.
	r510	2000.	640.	460.	860.
	r888	610.	530.	250.	570.
variety γ	*r973*	0.01*	0.005*	0.005*	0.01*

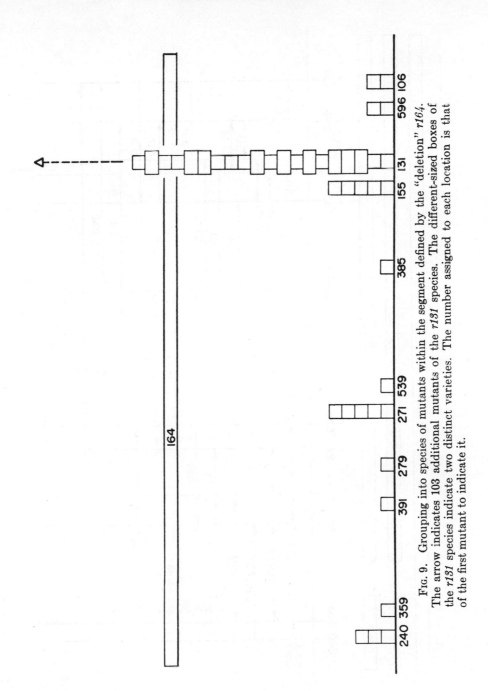

Fig. 9. Grouping into species of mutants within the segment defined by the "deletion" *r164*. The arrow indicates 103 additional mutants of the *r131* species. The different-sized boxes of the *r131* species indicate two distinct varieties. The number assigned to each location is that of the first mutant to indicate it.

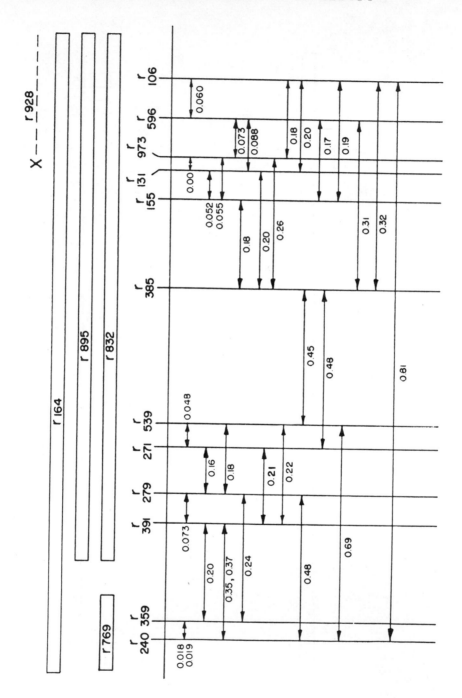

r240 and *r359*). Since only one interval has this value, the possibility of smaller values is not ruled out.

One procedure for measuring the size of the muton requires a group of three closely linked mutants in order to compare the long distance with the sum of the two shorter ones. If the central mutation has an appreciable size, there should be a discrepancy between these values. There are eight cases in Fig. 10 for which the distances have been measured for three adjacent mutants: 240-359-391, 359-391-279, 391-279-271, 279-271-539, 271-539-385, 385-155-131, 155-131-596, 131-596-106. The discrepancies for these groups are, reading from left to right, $+ 0.14$, $- 0.03$, $- 0.02$, $- 0.03$, $- 0.02$, $- 0.03$, $+ 0.03$, and $+ 0.05$ per cent recombination. The average of these values is $+ 0.01$, with an average deviation of ± 0.05. Since each measurement of recombination frequency is subject to experimental error of the order of 20 per cent of its magnitude, these determinations of mutation size (each derived from three measurements) are uncertain to plus or minus about 0.05 per cent recombination. Therefore, the latter is the smallest upper limit than can be set upon the size of the muton by these data.

Another measure of muton size can be attempted by finding the number of species that can exist within a given length of the map. As shown in Fig. 10, a map length of 0.8 per cent recombination includes 9 separable mutant species, or no more than 0.09 per cent per species. Both this determination and the previous one suffer uncertainty due to imperfect additivity of map distances ("negative interference"— see Discussion).

Stable Mutants.

Since the problem of mapping large numbers of mutants is greatly facilitated by the use of "deletions," particular attention has been paid to non-reverting mutants, in the hope of obtaining a complete set of

---

Fɪɢ. 10. Map of the mutants in the *r164* segment. The numbers give the percentage of recombination observed in standard crosses between pairs of mutants. The arrangement on this map is that suggested by these recombination values; it has not yet been verified by three-point tests. Stable mutants are represented as bars above the axis; the span of the bar covers those mutants with which the stable mutant produces no detectable wild recombinants. The stable mutant *r928* appears to be a double mutant having one mutation at the highly mutable *r131* location and a second mutation at a point in the B cistron. Mutants *r131* and *r973* are separated on the map so that the data for each can be indicated. Some of the data here given differ from (and supersede) previously published data based upon unconventional crosses which turned out to be incorrect.

overlapping deletions. Among the series of **923** r mutants, **72** stable rII mutants were found, **47** in the A cistron and **24** in the B cistron. One mutant *(r928)* was exceptional: it failed to complement mutants of either the A or B cistrons and therefore belongs to *both* classes.

The stable mutants of the B cistron have been crossed (by spot tests on K plus B) in all possible pairs. The results are shown in Fig. 11.

	r 928	r 196	r 951	r 937	r 575	r 187	r 102	r 237	r 292	r 362	r 377	r 467	r 638	r 471	r 565	r 625	r 707	r 887	r 918	r 940	r 199(R_2) r11	r 426	r 497	r 620	r 739	r 911	r 199(R_2) r4
r 928	O	O	O	+	+	+	+	+	+	+	+	+	O	+	+	+	+	+	+	+	+	+	+	+	+	+	+
r 196	O	O	O	O	+	+	+	+	+	+	+	+	O	+	+	+	+	+	+	+	+	+	+	+	+	+	+
r 951	O	O	O	O	+	+	+	+	+	+	+	+	O	+	+	+	+	+	+	+	+	+	+	+	+	+	+
r 937	+	O	O	O	+	+	+	+	+	+	+	+	O	+	+	+	+	+	+	+	+	+	+	+	+	+	+
r 575	+	+	+	+	O	O	+	+	+	+	+	+	O	+	+	+	+	+	+	+	+	+	+	+	+	+	+
r 187	+	+	+	+	O	O	O	O	O	O	O	O	O	O	O	O	O	O	O	O	O	+	+	+	+	+	+
r 102	+	+	+	+	+	O	O	O	O	O	O	O	O	O	O	O	O	O	O	O	O	+	+	+	+	+	+
r 237	+	+	+	+	+	O	O	O	O	O	O	O	O	O	O	O	O	O	O	O	O	+	+	+	+	+	+
r 292	+	+	+	+	+	O	O	O	O	O	O	O	O	O	O	O	O	O	O	O	O	+	+	+	+	+	+
r 362	+	+	+	+	+	O	O	O	O	O	O	O	O	O	O	O	O	O	O	O	O	+	+	+	+	+	+
r 377	+	+	+	+	+	O	O	O	O	O	O	O	O	O	O	O	O	O	O	O	O	+	+	+	+	+	+
r 467	+	+	+	+	+	O	O	O	O	O	O	O	O	O	O	O	O	O	O	O	O	+	+	+	+	+	+
r 638	O	O	O	O	O	O	O	O	O	O	O	O	O	O	O	O	O	O	O	O	O	O	O	O	O	O	O
r 471	+	+	+	+	+	O	O	O	O	O	O	O	O	O	O	O	O	O	O	O	O	+	+	+	+	+	+
r 565	+	+	+	+	+	O	O	O	O	O	O	O	O	O	O	O	O	O	O	O	O	+	+	+	+	+	+
r 625	+	+	+	+	+	O	O	O	O	O	O	O	O	O	O	O	O	O	O	O	O	+	+	+	+	+	+
r 707	+	+	+	+	+	O	O	O	O	O	O	O	O	O	O	O	O	O	O	O	O	+	+	+	+	+	+
r 887	+	+	+	+	+	O	O	O	O	O	O	O	O	O	O	O	O	O	O	O	O	+	+	+	+	+	+
r 918	+	+	+	+	+	O	O	O	O	O	O	O	O	O	O	O	O	O	O	O	O	+	+	+	+	+	+
r 940	+	+	+	+	+	O	O	O	O	O	O	O	O	O	O	O	O	O	O	O	O	+	+	+	+	+	+
r 199 (R_2) r11	+	+	+	+	+	O	O	O	O	O	O	O	O	O	O	O	O	O	O	O	O	+	+	+	+	+	+
r 426	+	+	+	+	+	+	+	+	+	+	+	+	O	+	+	+	+	+	+	+	+	O	+	+	+	+	+
r 497	+	+	+	+	+	+	+	+	+	+	+	+	O	+	+	+	+	+	+	+	+	+	O	+	+	+	+
r 620	+	+	+	+	+	+	+	+	+	+	+	+	O	+	+	+	+	+	+	+	+	+	+	O	+	+	+
r 739	+	+	+	+	+	+	+	+	+	+	+	+	O	+	+	+	+	+	+	+	+	+	+	+	O	+	+
r 911	+	+	+	+	+	+	+	+	+	+	+	+	O	+	+	+	+	+	+	+	+	+	+	+	+	O	+
r 199 (R_2) r4	+	+	+	+	+	+	+	+	+	+	+	+	O	+	+	+	+	+	+	+	+	+	+	+	+	+	O

FIG. 11. Recombination matrix for stable mutants of the B class. A + indicates production of wild recombinants (around 0.01 per cent recombination or more would be detected) in the cross between the indicated pair of mutants (by spot test on K plus B). All diagonal elements (self-crosses) are zero; non-diagonal zeros indicate overlaps. Two of the mutants are derived, not from the original wild type, but from a revertant of *r199*.

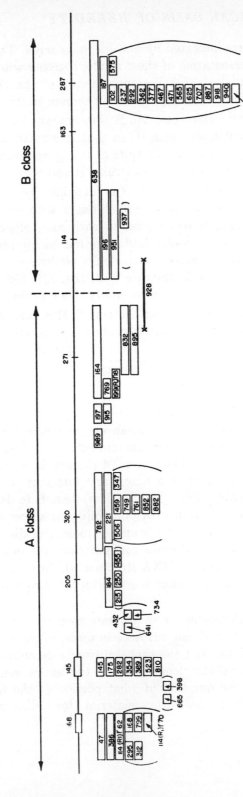

FIG. 12. Preliminary locations of stable *rII* mutants. Mutants producing no wild recombinants with each other are drawn in overlapping configuration. Pairs which produce small amounts are placed near each other. Since there remain some gaps, the order shown depends upon that established by Doermann (4) for the mutants shown on the axis. The scale is somewhat distorted in order to show the overlap relationships clearly. Brackets indicate groups, the internal order of which is not established. Ten stable mutants of the A class and six of the B class were not sufficiently close to any others to permit them to be placed on the map. (A class equals A cistron; B class equals B cistron.)

Overlapping relationships are indicated by non-diagonal zeros. Fig. 12 shows the genetic map representation of these results together with the results derived from an analysis (as yet incomplete) of the stable mutants of the A cistron. Unfortunately, gaps still remain in the map.

The mutant *r638* is of particular note. No B class mutant has been found that gives wild recombinants with it, so that it appears to be due to deletion of the entire B cistron. In spite of this gross defect, it is capable of normal reproduction on *E. coli* strains B and S.

In order to characterize a stable mutant of a "deletion" type, it is necessary to show that it gives no wild recombinants with at least three other mutants that do give recombination with each other (to exclude the possibilities that it is a double mutant or has an inversion). This criterion cannot be applied unless a suitable set of three mutants is available. Only some of the stable mutants (164, 184, 221, 196, 782, 638, 832, 895, 951) have as yet been shown to satisfy this criterion.

Stable mutations tend to occur "all over the map." However, as in the case of reverting mutants, certain localities show a strikingly high recurrence tendency, as illustrated by *r102*, et al., and by *r145*, et al.

DISCUSSION

Relation of Genetic Length to Molecular Length.

We would like to relate the genetic map, an abstract construction representing the results of recombination experiments, to a material structure. The most promising candidate in a T4 particle is its DNA component, which appears to carry the hereditary information (6). DNA also has a linear geometry (20). The problem, then, is to derive a relation between genetic map distance (a probability measurement) and molecular distance. In order to have a unit of molecular distance which is invariant to changes in molecular configuration, the interval between two points along the (paired) DNA structure will be expressed in nucleotide (pair) units, which are more meaningful for our purposes than, say, Ångstrom units.

Unfortunately, present information is inadequate to permit a very accurate calculation to be made of map distance in terms of nucleotide units. First, it is not known whether the probability of recombination is constant (per unit of molecular length) along the entire genetic structure. Second, there is the question of what portion of the total DNA of a T4 particle constitutes hereditary material (for a discussion of this problem, see the paper by Delbrück and Stent in this volume). The result of Levinthal's elegant experiment (11) suggests a value of 40 per cent. Since the total DNA content of a T4 particle is 4×10^5 nucleotides (8), it would seem that the hereditary information of T4 is carried in 1.6×10^5 nucleotides. We do not know, however, whether the information exists in one or in many copies. If there is just one copy, and if it has the paired structure of the model of Watson and Crick (20), the total length of hereditary material should be 8×10^4 nucleotide pairs.

There are difficulties on the genetic side as well. The total length of the genetic map is not well established. The determination of this length requires a number of genetic markers sufficient to define the ends of the map. It also requires a favorable distribution of markers in order that the intervals between them can be summated; if the distance between two markers is sufficiently large, the frequency of recombination between them approaches that for unlinked markers and therefore loses its value as a measure of the linkage distance. Unfortunately, the linkage data presently available for T4 leave much to be desired. The experiments of Streisinger (18) indicate that the map of T4 consists of a single linkage group. Adding up the intervals between markers (corrected for successive rounds of mating according to the theory of Visconti and Delbrück, 19) leads to a total value of the order of 200 per cent recombination units. This estimate is very rough, since the number of available markers upon which it is based is small.

A further difficulty arises from the fact that the map distances measured in standard crosses are not quite additive: a large distance tends to be less than the sum of its component smaller distances. For distances of the order of 10 per cent recombination units and more, the deviations from additivity, referred to as "negative interference," can be accounted for by the Visconti-Delbrück considerations. However, a "negative interference" effect, not accountable for by their theory, persists, and apparently gets worse, at very small distances (4). This presents a serious obstacle for our purposes, since we are interested in knowing what fraction of the total map is represented by a small distance. According to preliminary data on this point, summation of the smallest available distances between *rII* mutants yields a total length for the *rII* region which is several fold greater than that found for crosses involving distant *rII* markers. If the total T4 map length could be obtained by a similar summation of small distances, the indications are that it might be of the order of 800 per cent recombination units in length.

Thus, there are plenty of uncertainties involved in relating the genetic map quantitatively to the DNA structure. The best we can do at present is to make a rough estimate based upon the following assumptions: (1) the genetic information of T4 is carried in one copy consisting of a DNA thread 80,000 nucleotide pairs long; (2) the genetic map has a total length of about 800 per cent recombination units; (3) the probability of recombination per unit molecular length is uniform. According to these assumptions, the ratio of recombination probability (at small distances) to molecular distance would be 800 per cent recombination divided by 80,000 nucleotide pairs, or 0.01 per cent recombination per nucleotide pair. That is to say, if two mutants, having mutations one nucleotide pair apart, are crossed, the proportion of recombinants in the progeny should be 0.01 per cent. This estimate is greater, by a factor of ten, than one made a year ago, in which it was assumed that all the DNA was genetic material and that the effect of negative interference was negligible. It should become possible to improve this calculation as more information becomes available.

The estimate indicates that the level of genetic fine structure which has been reached in these experiments is not far removed from that of the individual nucleotides. Furthermore, the estimate is useful in that it defines an "absolute zero" for recombination probabilities: if a cross between two (single) T4 mutants does not give at least 0.01 per cent recombination, the locations of the two mutations probably are not separated by even one nucleotide pair.

Molecular Sizes of the Genetic Units.

Recon: The smallest non-zero recombination value so far observed among the *rII* mutants of T4 is around 0.02 per cent recombination. If the estimate of 0.01 per cent recombination per nucleotide pair should prove to be correct, the size of the recon would be limited to no more than two nucleotide pairs.

Muton: Evidently, among the stable mutants, mutations may involve varied lengths of the map. The muton is defined as the *smallest* element, alteration of which can be effective in causing a mutation. In the case of reverting mutants, it has not been possible, so far, to demonstrate any appreciable mutation size greater than around 0.05 per cent recombination. This would indicate that alteration of very few nucleotides (no more than five, according to the present estimate) is capable of causing a visible mutation.

Cistron: A cistron turns out to be a very sophisticated structure. The function to which it corresponds can be impaired by mutation at many different locations. In the study of 241 *r* mutants, 33 species were found to be located in the A cistron, of which 6 were in the *r164* subclass. In extending the survey to 923 *r* mutants, the number of known species in the *r164* subclass was doubled. Consequently, it may be expected that about 60 A cistron species will be found—when the analysis of the 923 mutants is completed. Since many species are represented by only one occurrence, implying that many more are yet to be found, it seems safe to conclude that in the A cistron alone there are over a hundred "sensitive" points, i.e., locations at which a mutational event leads to an observable phenotypic effect. Just as in the case of the entire genetic map of an organism, the portrait of a cistron is weighted by considerations of which alterations are effectual. It should be fascinating to try to translate the "topography" within a cistron into that of a physiologically active structure, such as a polypeptide chain folded to form an enzyme.

REFERENCES

1. Benzer, S., *Proc. Natl. Acad. Sci. U. S.*, **41**, 344 (1955).
2. Demerec, M., Blomstrand, I., and Demerec, Z. E., *Proc. Natl. Acad. Sci. U. S.*, **41**, 359 (1955).
3. Doermann, A. H., and Hill, M. B., *Genetics,* **38**, 79 (1953).
4. Doermann, A. H., and collaborators, pers. commun.
5. Franklin, N., and Streisinger, G., pers. commun.
6. Hershey, A. D., and Chase, M., *J. Gen. Physiol.*, **36**, 39 (1952).
7. Hershey, A. D., and Davidson, H., *Genetics,* **36**, 667 (1951).
8. Hershey, A. D., Dixon, J., and Chase, M., *J. Gen. Physiol.*, **36**, 777 (1953).
9. Hershey, A. D., and Rotman, R , *Genetics,* **34**, 44 (1949).
10. Lederberg, E. M., and Lederberg, J., *Genetics,* **38**, 51 (1953).
11. Levinthal, C., *Proc. Natl. Acad. Sci. U S.*, **42**, 394 (1956)
12. Lewis, E. B., *Cold Spring Harbor Symposia Quant. Biol.*, **16**, 159 (1951).
13. Pontecorvo, G., *Advances in Enzymol.*, **13**, 121 (1952).
14. Pritchard, R. H., *Heredity,* **9**, 343 (1955).
15. Roper, J. A., *Nature,* **166**, 956 (1950).
16. Sanger, F., *Advances in Protein Chem.*, **7**, 1 (1952).
17. Stent, G. S., pers. commun.
18. Streisinger, G., pers. commun.
19. Visconti, N., and Delbrück, M., *Genetics,* **38**, 5 (1953).
20. Watson, J. D., and Crick, F. H. C., *Cold Spring Harbor Symposia Quant. Biol.*, **18**, 123 (1953).

Reprinted from the Proceedings of the NATIONAL ACADEMY OF SCIENCES
Vol. 47, No. 6, pp. 857–868. June, 1961.

CHROMOSOME BREAKAGE ACCOMPANYING GENETIC RECOMBINATION IN BACTERIOPHAGE[*,†]

BY M. MESELSON[‡] AND J. J. WEIGLE

NORMAN CHURCH LABORATORY OF CHEMICAL BIOLOGY, CALIFORNIA INSTITUTE OF TECHNOLOGY

Communicated by G. W. Beadle, April 3, 1961

Genetic recombination in bacteriophage was first observed by Delbrück and Bailey[1] and by Hershey and Rotman,[2] who showed that cells simultaneously infected with two different mutants of phage T2 yield, in addition to the two infecting types, both doubly mutant and wild type progeny phages. Subsequently, extensive studies have been made of bacteriophage recombination, especially with the phages T1, T2, T4, and λ. Hundreds of mutants have been crossed, and for each phage type the observed recombination frequencies may be represented on a single unbranched genetic map.[3-6]

The genetic material of these bacteriophages is known to be DNA and it is commonly assumed that the genetic information resides in the linear sequence of nucleotides which comprise the DNA molecule. Under this assumption, genetic recombination in bacteriophage corresponds to the production of a nucleotide sequence derived partly from one parental line and partly from another. This may be imagined to occur in either of two ways. (1) *Copy choice:* The recombinant sequence is synthesized *de novo* by copying first one parental sequence, then another. (2) *Breakage:* The recombinant sequence is formed by the association of DNA fragments from different parental lines.

Recombinant phages produced by copy choice would be free of parental DNA, whereas breakage could result in the appearance of portions of parental DNA in recombinant phages.

In this paper, we describe experiments with the bacteriophage λ designed to see whether there is parental DNA in recombinant phages. Two-factor crosses were made between λ and λ heavily labeled with the isotopes C^{13} and N^{15}. Then density-gradient centrifugation[7, 8] was used to determine the distribution of labeled parental DNA among both parental and recombinant genotypes of the progeny. Our results demonstrate the presence of discrete portions of parental DNA in recombinant phages.

Materials and Methods.—Preparation of $C^{13}N^{15}$ media: Algal hydrolysates: Carbon-13 of 93% isotopic purity supplied in the form of methane[9] was oxidized to CO_2 by repeated passage over CuO at 850°C. The CO_2 was absorbed in saturated $Ba(OH)_2$ solution. A 6.8 gram portion of the resulting $BaC^{13}O_3$ was used along with $N^{15}H_4Cl$ of 99% isotopic purity[10] for the growth of *Ankistrodesmus* following the procedure of Davern.[11] After harvest by centrifugation, the algae were suspended in 15 ml of N HCl and kept at 100° for 6 hours. The mixture was centrifuged to yield a supernatant called H-1 and a pellet which was resuspended in 15 ml of 6 N HCl and refluxed for 20 hr. After cooling, the mixture was centrifuged to yield the supernatant H-2 and a pellet which was discarded. Hydrolysates H-1 and H-2 were separately evaporated to dryness *in vacuo* at room temperature and each residue was taken up in 5 ml of water. After three repetitions of this process, the final solutions were brought to pH 6 by the addition of carbonate-free NaOH solution. To H-2 was added 50 mg of HCl-washed decolorizing charcoal, and the mixture was shaken for 1 hr. Then both H-1 and H-2 were filtered through fine sintered-glass disks and sterilized by passage through type HA millipore filters. Both H-1 and H-2 were made up to 10 ml with sterile water and kept frozen until used.

Yeast extract: The hydrolysate H-1 was used to support the growth of yeast[12] for approximately ten generations in a medium of the following composition: $N^{15}H_4Cl$, 0.10 gm; Hydrolysate H1, 10 ml; NaCl, 0.4 gm; K_2HPO_4, 0.075 gm; $MgSO_4$, 0.30 gm: $CaCl_2$, 0.016 gm; $FeCl_3$, 7 × 10^{-5} gm; H_2O, 150 ml.

The culture was gently aerated at 30°C until the yeast attained a concentration of 4 × 10^7/ml and had just stopped budding. After harvest by centrifugation, the yeast was suspended in 5 ml of H_2O and brought to 100°C for 1 min and kept at 37°C overnight. The suspension was then centrifuged and the supernatant, called yeast infusion, was frozen. The pellet was suspended in 10 ml of 6 N HCl and refluxed 20 hours, after which the hydrolysate was repeatedly evaporated and then adjusted to pH 6 as described above. Finally, the hydrolysate was added to the yeast infusion, and the combined solution was filtered through a fine sintered-glass disk and sterilized by passage through a type HA millipore filter. This yeast extract was made up to 10 ml with sterile water and was kept frozen.

IV. GENETIC RECOMBINATION　　　　　　　　　　　　　　　　　479

The isotopic purity of the $C^{13}N^{15}$ media was verified by measurements of the buoyant density of DNA prepared from *Escherichia coli* grown for many generations in a medium containing $N^{15}H_4Cl$ and either H2 or $C^{13}N^{15}$ yeast extract as described below. In both cases, the $C^{13}N^{15}$ DNA was found to be 0.047 gm cm^{-3} more dense than unlabeled DNA from the same organism. The calculated increment for the Cs salt of *E. coli* DNA with 99% N^{15} and 93% C^{13} is 0.050 gm cm^{-3} in the absence of selective solvation.

Bacteriophages: Phage $\lambda++$ is the "wild type" of Kaiser.[13] Phage λh was derived from $\lambda++$ and has extended host range enabling it to plate on CR63. Phage $\lambda cmib_2{}^+$ is described by Kellenberger *et al.*[14] and is designated here as λcmi.

Bacteria: Strain 3110, a λ-sensitive derivative of *E. coli* K12, was used for the preparation of λcmi stocks and as host for crosses. Strain C 600[15] was used for plating as was the λ-resistant strain CR63.[16] Strain K12S made lysogenic for $\lambda++$ was used for the production of $\lambda++$ stocks by induction.

Media: Tryptone broth and suspension medium were prepared according to Weigle *et al.*,[8] and A medium is 7 gm Na_2HPO_4, 3 gm KH_2PO_4, 0.6 gm $MgSO_4$, 0.5 gm NaCl, 5×10^{-4} gm $FeCl_3$, and 1 liter H_2O, to which carbon and nitrogen sources were added separately.

Phage stocks: Phage $\lambda++$ was prepared by UV induction of $K(\lambda)$ grown in A medium containing either 1 mg/ml $N^{15}H_4Cl$ and 0.05 ml/ml each of H-2 and yeast extract or 1 mg/ml $N^{14}H_4Cl$, 3 mg/ml charcoal-treated casamino acids and 1 mg/ml Difco yeast extract. The bacteria were grown approximately 7 generations to 2×10^8/ml, centrifuged, suspended at 10^8/ml in A medium and irradiated. Carbon and nitrogen sources were then added as above and the induced culture was aerated for 100 minutes, after which the culture was lysed by saturation with chloroform. The burst size was approximately 100 for both $\lambda C^{13}N^{15}$ and $C^{12}N^{14} \lambda++$. The lysates were centrifuged at $50,000 \times g$ for 120 minutes to sediment the phage. The pellet was resuspended by standing overnight in suspension medium.

Phage λcmi was prepared by one cycle of lytic multiplication in 3110 grown in A medium with either $C^{13}N^{15}$ or $C^{12}N^{14}$ as above. The bacteria were grown approximately 8 generations to 5×10^8/ml and λcmi in suspension medium was added to a multiplicity of 3. Ten minutes after infection, a 3-fold dilution with fresh medium was made and aeration was continued for 130 minutes. The culture was then lysed by saturation with $CHCl_3$. For the preparation of the λcmi stocks used in cross II, the culture was made 0.003 M in ethylene diamine tetra-acetate, and 0.1% in lysozyme 1 min before the addition of $CHCl_3$. The burst size was approximately 60 for both labeled and unlabeled λcmi. The phages were purified by low- and high-speed centrifugation and suspended in suspension medium.

The frequency of all morphology mutants was below 0.01% in the stocks used in these experiments.

Density-gradient centrifugation: The technique of preparative density-gradient centrifugation described by Weigle *et al.*[8] was employed with several modifications. Centrifugation was at 23,000 rpm for 24 hours at 24°C. The cesium chloride solution was overlayered with mineral oil to fill the lusteroid tube in order to prevent its collapse. The initial density was chosen so that all bands formed in the lower half of the gradient. This step, recommended to us by Dr. F. Stahl, prevents the occurrence of an artifact of preparative density-gradient centrifugation which previously has caused us much difficulty. When bands formed in the upper part of the gradient are collected, one invariably finds a satellite preceding the main band. The satellite contains approximately 1% as much material as the main band and precedes it by as many as 6 drops. Phage λh was added in all centrifugations in order to serve as a density marker and to establish, by its characteristic narrow unimodal distribution, that no artifacts due to deceleration or drop collection had disturbed the distribution of the various other phage types.

In all experiments, the recovery of each genotype from the CsCl gradient was essentially complete.

Results.—Two crosses were performed with labeled phages: cross I, $\lambda ++ C^{13}N^{15}$ $\times \lambda cmi$ and cross II, $\lambda ++ \times \lambda cmi \ C^{13}/N^{15}$. In both cases, parallel crosses were made using unlabeled parents. These are referred to as dummy crosses I and II. The multiplicities of infection and yields for the various crosses are recorded in Table 1. The dummy crosses were made at approximately the same multiplicities

TABLE 1

	Multiplicities		Burst sizes		Recombinant frequencies (%)	
Crosses	++	cmi	++	cmi	c	mi
I λ++ C¹³N¹⁵ × cmi	2	3	19	46	0.88	0.56
II λ++ × cmi C¹³N¹⁵	5	2.2	33	12	0.74	0.46

and gave comparable yields.

Dummy crosses: As may be seen in Figure 1, λh and both parental and recom-

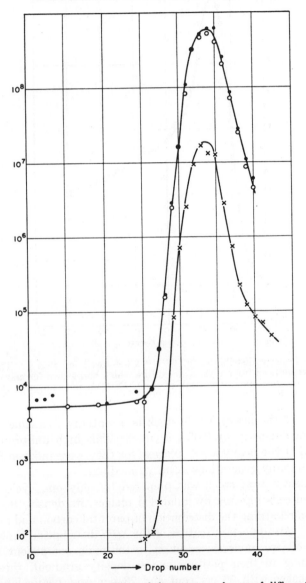

Fig. 1.—Cross λ*cmi* × λ++. Titer of the progeny phages of different genotypes in the drops collected after centrifugation. ——●—●—, *cmi*; —O—O—, ++; —x—x—, *h*. λ*h* was added as density and band shape reference. The titers of the recombinants λ + *mi* and λ*c*+ follow exactly the curve of λ*h*, and the points representing the measurements have been omitted to avoid crowding the picture.

binant types emerging from a dummy cross exhibit the same narrow unimodal distribution in the density gradient. This finding allows us to attribute any deviation of the distributions found in crosses I and II from the distribution of the λh control to the presence of the density labels C^{13} and N^{15}.

Heavy parental stocks: The density distributions of the $C^{13}N^{15}\lambda ++$ stock used in cross I and of the $C^{13}N^{15}\lambda cmi$ stock used in cross II are shown in Figures 2 and 3.

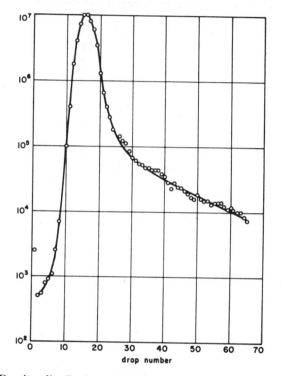

Fig. 2.—Density distribution of $C^{13}N^{15}$ $\lambda ++$ used in cross I. The $\lambda ++$ phages were induced from a lysogenic culture which had grown for many generations in heavy medium. The peak of the $C^{12}N^{14}.\lambda h$, not shown in the figure, came at drop 78.

The distribution of the heavy $\lambda ++$ stock is essentially the same as that of λh displaced to higher density by 0.05 gm cm^{-3}. This high uniformity of labeling is to be expected of the heavy $\lambda ++$ phages, for they were induced from a culture which had grown many generations in heavy medium.

Because the heavy λcmi stock was prepared by only one cycle of growth in uniformly labeled cells infected by unlabeled phages, its density distribution provides information regarding the distribution of parental carbon and nitrogen among progeny phages. An important feature of the λcmi distribution shown in Figure 3 is the existence of two modes in addition to the main component which is fully labeled. According to their position in the density gradient, these two modes correspond to phages with 56 per cent and 78 per cent heavy label. The light parental atoms are presumably harbored in their DNA and not in their protein, which is not injected upon phage infection.[17] If all of the DNA were parental and all the protein new, it may be estimated from the composition of λ and the

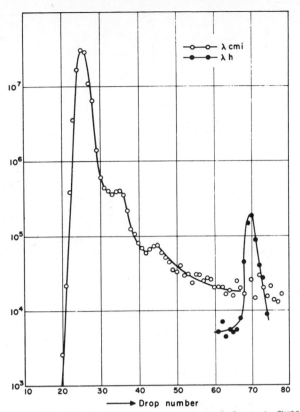

Fig. 3.—Transfer experiment with λ*cmi*. λ*cmi* grown in bacteria $C^{12}N^{14}$ were used to infect bacteria $C^{13}N^{15}$ in a $C^{13}N^{15}$ medium. After one cycle of growth, the λ*cmi* labeled with $C^{13}N^{15}$ were centrifuged. The figure gives the titers of the phages in the different drops collected after centrifugation. Phage λ*h*$C^{12}N^{14}$ was added as a density reference.

purity of the isotopes used that the phage would contain 54 per cent heavy label. We therefore presume that the phages with 56 per cent heavy label are composed of new (heavy) protein and parental (light) DNA and that the phages with 78 per cent label are composed of new protein and DNA which is half-parental. We shall refer to phages with only parental DNA as "conserved" and to those with half-parental DNA as "semiconserved." Semiconserved phages have appeared in each of the nine experiments in which we have infected labeled cells with unlabeled phages or *vice versa*. However, only when the multiplicity of infection was high have conserved phages also appeared. The yield of infectious hybrid phages has ranged between 1 and 4 per cent of the progeny phages while yields of infectious conserved phage have been found as high as 1 per cent (when $m = 7$) and less than 0.001 per cent (when $m = 0.1$).

Crosses: As may be seen in Figure 4, the density distributions of the progeny of cross I exhibit the following principal features:

(1) The distribution of the originally labeled parental genotype λ++ resembles that found when labeled phages alone are allowed to multiply in unlabeled cells. That is, modes of conserved and semiconserved phages are found in addition to unabsorbed and to essentially unlabeled phages.

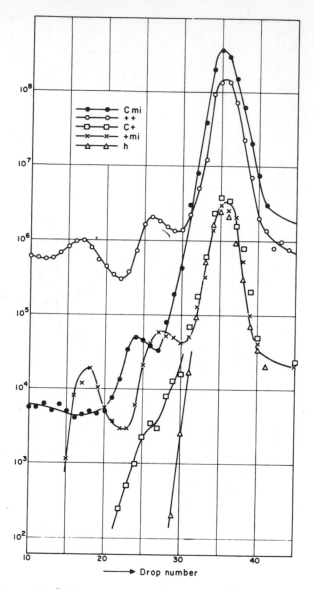

Fig. 4.—Cross $\lambda++$ $C^{13}N^{15}$ $\times$ λcmi $C^{12}N^{14}$. Titer of the progeny phages of different genotypes in the drops collected after centrifugation. λh was added as density and band shape reference.

(2) The originally unlabeled parental genotype *cmi* emerges from cross I with a very different distribution of label from that of the type $++$. Neither conserved nor semiconserved modes are found. The λcmi is essentially unlabeled but with a definite skewness toward higher density.

(3) The recombinant type $+mi$ and $c+$ are distributed in strikingly different fashion from each other. The type $+mi$ is found in three modes, one essentially unlabeled, one with slightly less label than the semiconserved $\lambda++$, and another with slightly less label than conserved $\lambda++$. The reciprocal type $c+$ is found

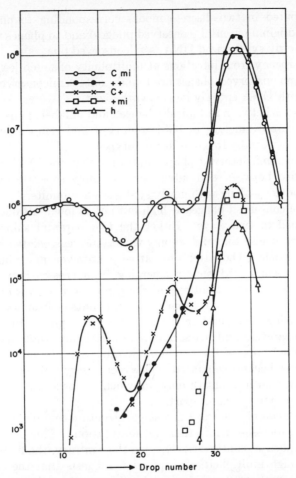

Fig. 5.—Cross λcmi $C^{13}N^{15} \times \lambda++$ $C^{12}N^{14}$. Titer of the progeny phages of different genotypes in the drops collected after centrifugation. λh was added as density and band shape reference.

in a single band which has a shoulder at a density between that of semiconserved and unlabeled phage.

To insure that the nonequivalent distributions of the two recombinant types from cross I were not due to peculiarities associated with the particular recombinant genotypes, a cross (cross II) was performed with $C^{13}N^{15}$ label in λ cmi rather than in $\lambda++$. As may be seen by comparison of Figures 4 and 5, the result of reversing the parental label is that the distributions of the two recombinants as well as the two parental types are interchanged.

Discussion.—Replication of the lambda chromosome: The maximum recombination frequency observed[6] for phage λ is only 15 per cent. This circumstance suggests that we may understand the main features of the distribution of parental DNA among progeny phages without at first considering the effects of genetic recombination. In summary, these features are:

(1) Among progeny from infections at high multiplicity, the original parental

DNA is distributed in two discrete modes corresponding to phages with DNA that is entirely original parental (conserved phages) and to phages with half original parental, half newly synthesized DNA (semiconserved phages).

(2) Among progeny from infections at multiplicity of much less than one phage per bacterium, no conserved phages are found; only semiconserved phages appear besides those with DNA entirely newly synthesized.

(3) From crosses between isotopically labeled and unlabeled phages, the genotype of the labeled parent emerges in both conserved and semiconserved modes, but these modes are essentially free of other genotypes.

The finding of semiconserved phages indicates that the DNA complement of λ is equally divided between two subunits which may separate from one another and appear in progeny along with newly synthesized subunits.

The finding of conserved phages at high but not at low multiplicities of infection may be explained in two ways. Either the two parental subunits never came completely apart or else they did so only to become reassociated by chance in the same progeny particle. The latter alternative is, however, made improbable by the finding that semi-conserved phages emerging from crosses between labeled and unlabeled parents are almost entirely of the genotype that was originally labeled. The substantial yield of labeled recombinants prevents us from ascribing this result to very poor mixing of vegetative phage in the early pool. In view of this, the hypothesis of separation and reassociation would require that the genes *c* and *mi* be restricted to only one of the two subunits and that the other never appear in progeny if the two became separated. This seems very unlikely. Accordingly we shall consider the first alternative only, in which the two parental subunits found in conserved phages never came apart.

Thus the DNA complement of λ is a single structure capable of remaining intact throughout the processes of infection and maturation. This does not imply that this structure replicates conservatively. On the contrary, the finding of conserved phages only at high multiplicities of infection suggests that the conserved phage may never have replicated; they may be "nonparticipating" phages. We are led to conclude that *the entire DNA complement of λ is a single semiconservatively replicating structure.*

In this respect, the DNA of λ behaves as a single molecule possessing the Watson-Crick structure replicating according to the scheme proposed by them.

In the remainder of this discussion, we shall refer to the DNA complement of λ as its chromosome.

The mechanism of recombination: Our main finding relevant to the mechanism of genetic recombination is that discrete amounts of original parental DNA appear in recombinant phages. This suggests that *recombination occurs by breakage of parental chromosomes followed by the reconstruction of genetically complete chromosomes from the fragments.*

Consideration of the detailed distribution of parental DNA among recombinants leads to several additional conclusions regarding the recombination process. The finding of a distinct recombinant class containing substantially more than 50 per cent original parental DNA indicates that *recombination by chromosome breakage may occur without separation of the two subunits of the parental chromosome.* If, as has been argued above, replication does not occur without separation of chromosomal subunits, it may also be concluded that *chromosomes need not replicate in order to recombine.*

From the positions of *c* and *mi* on the genetic map of λ (Fig. 6), it is seen that a break between these loci leaves an 85 per cent fragment of the map attached to the

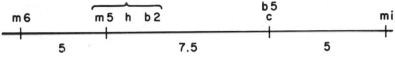

FIG. 6.—Genetic map of λ.

c locus and 15 per cent to the *mi* locus. In both crosses I and II, there occurs a mode of recombinants with approximately 86 per cent labeled parental DNA, and these recombinants carry at the *c* locus the allele contributed by the labeled parent. Thus it seems that *the probability of recombination between two loci is at least approximately proportional to the amount of DNA between them.* The recombinant type which appears with 90 per cent labeled DNA is also found in another mode with approximately 45 per cent labeled DNA. This class of recombinants could have been derived by semiconservative replication from recombinant chromosomes of the type carrying 90 per cent label or they could have been produced by breakage of hybrid chromosomes of parental genotype. It seems reasonable to suppose that both processes contribute recombinants to the mode at 45 per cent. Finally, we might expect the recombinant bearing the *c* allele brought in by the unlabeled parent to be distributed in two labeled modes at approximately 14 per cent and 7 per cent. However, phages so slightly labeled could not be resolved from the large band of unlabeled phage. Only a shoulder on the dense side of the unlabeled peak would be expected. As may be seen in Figures 4 and 5, such a shoulder is in fact observed.

The findings of this experiment thus may be understood in terms of a recombination mechanism involving breakage of a semiconservatively replicating two-stranded chromosome. The fragments produced could become incorporated into complete chromosomes either by joining of appropriate fragments (break and join) or by the completion of a fragment by copying the missing region from the homologous portion of a chromosome of different parentage (break and copy). Figures 7 and 8 show structurally plausible models for recombination by these two processes. The present experiments do not distinguish between these alternatives. Neither do they rule out the possibility of some copy choice recombination.

The contribution of original parental DNA to progeny bearing the initially unlabeled genotype does not conflict with our main conclusion that recombination occurs by breakage. However this distribution is not in simple accord with the notion that the probability of recombination between loci is always proportional to the amount of DNA separating them on the chromosome. The existence of favored breaking places as well as several other complexities, either experimental or genetic, may be invoked to explain the distribution of λ*cmi* in cross I or of λ++ in cross II. However we prefer to postpone discussion of this matter until it has been investigated further. Our conclusions are strongly supported by the experiments reported in the next paper,[18] which shows that in two-factor crosses between P[32]-labeled and unlabeled λ, more P[32] is transferred to recombinant progeny

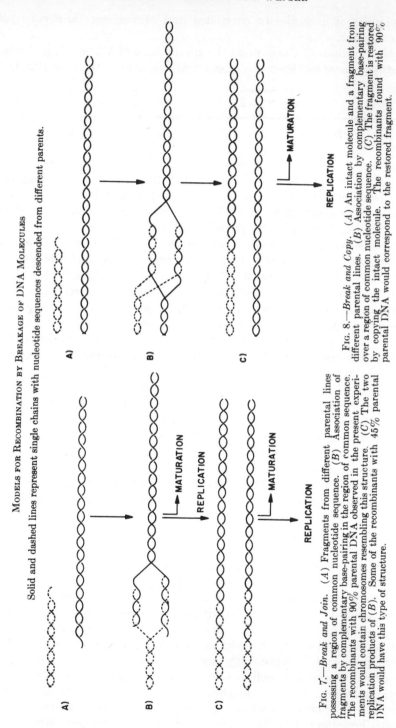

MODELS FOR RECOMBINATION BY BREAKAGE OF DNA MOLECULES

Solid and dashed lines represent single chains with nucleotide sequences descended from different parents.

FIG. 7.—*Break and Join.* (*A*) Fragments from different parental lines possessing a region of common nucleotide sequence. (*B*) Association of fragments by complementary base-pairing in the region of common sequence. The recombinants with 90% parental DNA observed in the present experiments would contain chromosomes resembling this structure. (*C*) The two replication products of (*B*). Some of the recombinants with 45% parental DNA would have this type of structure.

FIG. 8.—*Break and Copy.* (*A*) An intact molecule and a fragment from different parental lines. (*B*) Association by complementary base-pairing over a region of common nucleotide sequence. (*C*) The fragment is restored by copying the intact molecule. The recombinants found with 90% parental DNA would correspond to the restored fragment.

than to progeny with the genotype of the unlabeled parent. Although the P^{32} experiments give no information on the subunits of the DNA, they do give the integrated total amount of the original parental DNA transferred to the recombinants. This value also seems to show that distances along the genetic map are proportional to the amounts of DNA in the phage chromosomes.

Summary.—We have performed experiments designed to detect original parental DNA in recombinant phages. Density-gradient centrifugation was used to determine the distribution of labeled parental DNA among both parent and recombinant genotypes emerging from a two-factor cross between unlabeled phage λ and λ heavily labeled with the isotopes C^{13} and N^{15}. Our results demonstrate the presence of preferred quantities of original parental DNA in recombinant phages and support the following main conclusions:

(1) The DNA complement of λ is contained in a single semiconservatively replicating chromosome.

(2) Recombination occurs by chromosome breakage, although other mechanisms are not excluded.

(3) Both chromosomal subunits are broken during recombination.

(4) Distances along the genetic map are proportional to the amounts of DNA in the phage chromosome.

(5) The phage chromosome need not replicate in order to undergo recombination by breakage.

* Contribution 2674 from the Gates and Crellin Laboratories.

† Aided by grants from the National Foundation and the National Institutes of Health.

‡ Present address: Biological Laboratories, Harvard University, Cambridge, Massachusetts.

[1] Delbrück, M., and W. T. Bailey, *Cold Spring Harbor Symposia Quant. Biol.*, 11, 33 (1946).

[2] Hershey, A. D., and R. Rotman, these Proceedings, 34, 89 (1948).

[3] See Bresch, C., and H. Menningmann, *Z. Naturforsch.*, 9b, 212 (1954).

[4] See Benzer, S., these Proceedings, 41, 344 (1955).

[5] See Doermann, A. H., and M. B. Hill, *Genetics*, 38, 79 (1953).

[6] See Kaiser, A. D., *Virology*, 1, 424 (1955).

[7] Meselson, M., F. Stahl, and J. Vinograd, these Proceedings, 43, 581 (1957).

[8] Weigle, J., M. Meselson and K. Paigen, *J. Molec. Biol.*, 1, 379 (1959).

[9] We are grateful to Academician A. N. Nesmeyanov for suggesting Soyuzchimexport, Moscow, as a source of supply for high-purity C^{13}.

[10] Isomet Corporation, Palisades Park, New Jersey.

[11] Davern, C., doctoral dissertation, California Institute of Technology (1959).

[12] Strain "Y-2 original" from Wagner, R. D., *Univ. Texas Publ.* No. 4445, 104 (1944).

[13] Kaiser, A. D., *Virology*, 3, 42 (1957).

[14] Kellenberger, G., M. L. Zichichi, and J. Weigle, *Nature*, 187, 161 (1960).

[15] Appleyard, R. K., *Genetics*, 39, 440 (1954).

[16] Appleyard, R. K., J. F. McGregor, and K. M. Baird, *Virology*, 2, 565 (1956).

[17] Hershey, A. D., and M. Chase, *J. Gen. Physiol.*, 36, 39 (1952).

[18] Kellenberger, G., M. L. Zichichi, and J. Weigle, these Proceedings, 47, 869 (1961).

SECTION V

The Function of Genetic Material

Introduction

Although some of the early speculations concerning the activity of genes had attributed to them the direct role of enzyme synthesis, most later models assumed an intermediate (see the models by Wright, 1941, 1945). The best candidate for the intermediate appeared to be RNA or a ribonucleoprotein, for the studies of Caspersson (1941, 1950) and Brachet (1942) had shown that RNA was abundant in cells when protein synthesis was occurring. When growth was initiated either in bacteria in stationary phase or in higher cells, the first observable change was the accumulation of ribonucleotides. In large cells the RNA could be seen to accumulate in the nucleolus and in the cytoplasm at the periphery of the nucleus according to Caspersson (1950).

Following the early studies by Hammarsten and Hevesy (1946) on the turnover of P^{32} in nucleic acids, the results of a number of investigations were published which showed the higher turnover of RNA compared to DNA. In these early studies the relative rates of incorporation of P^{32} into the two types of nucleic acid was determined after their isolation from the tissues. The next step was to measure the specific activity of RNA in different isolated cell fractions, particularly the nucleus compared to the cytoplasm. The hypothesis that RNA originated in the nucleus had begun to influence the design of experiments. One of the earliest studies was carried out by Marshak (1948). We have selected his second paper (Marshak and Calvet, 1949) to illustrate some of the early results which showed that the nuclear RNA was labeled faster than cytoplasmic RNA. These results were interpreted to support the hypothesis that RNA was synthesized in the nucleus. Similar results were reported by Jeener and Szafarz (1950) who also believed their results indicated a nuclear origin for RNA.

As soon as the autoradiographic technique was improved to allow sufficient resolution for studies at the cellular level, the nucleolus could be shown to be the site for accumulation of the rapidly labeled RNA (Taylor, 1953; Ficq, 1953). The first of these two short papers is reprinted here as our second selection. A significant paper was published at this time by Barnum et al. (1953) who measured specific activities of RNA in nuclear, cytoplasmic particulate, and the supernatant fraction of a cell homogenate from regenerating rat liver. The supernatant fraction had RNA of the highest specific activity at an early time, with the nuclear and cytoplasmic fractions next in order. A kinetic analysis suggested to them that there existed a common precursor of both nuclear and cytoplasmic RNA, but that nuclear RNA could not be a precursor of cytoplasmic

RNA. However, a kinetic analysis of autoradiographic data on P^{32} incorporation (Taylor et al., 1955) indicated that nucleolar RNA in Drosophila salivary glands did have turnover kinetics similar to that predicted for a precursor-product relationship with cytoplasmic RNA. Quantitative data were lacking for the chromosomal RNA but its rapid labeling suggested that chromosomal RNA might be the common precursor of both nucleolar and cytoplasmic RNA.

More direct evidence utilizing cellular autoradiography and based on nuclear transplantation in amoeba, was published in the same year by Goldstein and Plaut (1955). They labeled the nuclear RNA of amoebae with P^{32} and then transplanted the radioactive nuclei into unlabeled amoebae. The distribution of the labeled RNA indicated that a large fraction of nuclear RNA later moved into the cytoplasm. The original paper is reprinted as number 3 in our collection. Further experiments utilizing this system and other enucleation experiments to study the origin of cellular RNA are summarized and reviewed by Goldstein (1963).

Our fourth paper (Zalokar, 1959) is presented to show a clever combination of the autoradiographic methods and the cell fractionation techniques of the biochemists in which the hyphae of Neurospora were utilized as micro-centrifuge tubes for producing cell fractions in vivo. This experiment showed that labeled RNA could be detected in the nuclei within one minute after presenting the cell with tritium-labeled nucleosides. When the labeled precursor was removed, the radioactive nuclear RNA was almost completely transferred to the microsomal fraction within 15 minutes.

Up to this time most of the autoradiographic studies had indicated a nuclear origin for all cellular RNA (Taylor and Woods, 1959; Woods and Taylor, 1959; Prescott, 1959). In addition a large fraction of the RNA appeared to be quite stable in spite of the faster turnover compared to DNA in some systems. Bacteria and mammalian cells grown in culture appeared to conserve most of the RNA as shown in experiments by Hershey (1954), Siminowich and Graham (1956), and Davern and Meselson (1960). However, Harris (1959) had reported the rapid turnover of a large fraction of the purine bases incorporated into RNA of rabbit macrophages in short-term cultures. Not only did his data, which later utilized both autoradiography and extraction procedures (Harris, 1960), indicate an unstable RNA, but he concluded that the rapidly labeled RNA could not be the precursor of the cytoplasmic RNA.

Another indication that RNA synthesis depended on the activity of chromosomes and presumably DNA was the behavior of RNA synthesis over the cell cycle. The fifth paper (Taylor, 1960) is an autoradiographic analysis of the labeling kinetics of nuclear and cytoplasmic RNA in rapidly growing mammalian cells in culture and a study of the variations over the cell cycle. Synthesis of RNA is continuous except for about 20 minutes during division stages, i.e., from about mid-prophase to mid-telophase when the chromosomes are extremely condensed. Holding the chromosomes in the condensed state by treatment with colchicine delays the resumption of RNA synthesis in dividing cells although it does not interfere with the process in non-dividing cells. Only a small fraction of RNA appeared to turnover in these cells and the kinetics of incorporation and transfer of label between nucleus and cytoplasm was compatible with the synthesis of all RNA in the nucleus.

In the light of present theory these results can be rationalized. Macrophages under the conditions of culture where no growth was occurring probably produced mostly messenger RNA with a short half-life. On the other hand rapidly growing cells produced a small fraction of RNA with a short half-life, but most of the RNA is ribosomal RNA which indeed does not break down. In addition the nucleotides from the unstable RNA are all eventually reincorporated into the stable ribosomal RNA in the rapidly growing cells.

Additional evidence that essentially all RNA synthesis is dependent on DNA was provided by experiments with the antibiotic, actinomycin D, which has been shown to produce its effect by reaction with DNA (Farber, 1958; Kirk, 1960; Hurwitz and August, 1963). An early paper on the *in vivo* effects of this antibiotic in relation to RNA synthesis has been selected for paper number 6 in this group (Reich *et al.*, 1961). This study and later investigations show that RNA synthesis in a variety of cells can be almost completely blocked without immediately affecting DNA synthesis. On the other hand, the RNA of viruses can in some systems replicate in the presence of the drug. Their replication apparently depends on a polymerase primed by RNA (Reddi, 1961; Baltimore and Franklin, 1962) which in these cases presumably acts as a template. However, the limited use or absence of RNA-primed synthesis of cellular RNA is indicated by the rather complete inhibition by actinomycin D in the systems tested (Reich *et al.*, 1962; Levinthal *et al.*, 1962).

By the late 1950's developments in other areas had moved so swiftly that the nuclear origin of an RNA intermediate for protein synthesis was only one small facet of the problem of the function of genetic material. Information gained from the study of cell-free systems was providing the basis for understanding how RNA could function as the intermediate in protein synthesis. Beginning with the discovery by Siekevitz (1952) that the microsomal fraction from a cell homogenate plus mitochondria incorporated C^{14}-alanine at a rate equal to that of the whole homogenate, the molecular basis for protein synthesis was rapidly elucidated. The mitochondria could be shown to provide energy for the system and when this was supplied in the form of ATP attention could be focused on other components of the system, the microsomal fraction, the soluble enzymes, and other materials in the "pH 5 fraction." Work in a number of laboratories soon identified the necessary components of the system and defined the role of a number of these (see review by Schweet and Bishop, 1963). The identification and characterization of the ribosomes as the fundamental unit of the microsomal fraction was accomplished both by the use of the electron microscope (Palade, 1955, 1958) and by studies of cell-free systems (Zamecnik, 1958; Roberts *et al.*, 1963). The unit was shown to be composed of RNA and protein. The ribosome of *Escherichia coli* consists of about 60% protein and 40% RNA, and those from other cells are similar. The stability of ribosomes is highly dependent upon the magnesium ion concentration in their environment. At $10^{-2} M$ Mg^{++} most of the particles exist in a size range characterized as 70 S on the basis of their sedimentation cofficient, but a 100 S particle also exists which apepars to be an aggregate of two 70 S particles. At lower Mg^{++} concentration $(10^{-4} M)$, the 70 S particles separate into two units of unequal size, 30 S and 50 S. The 50 S particles have two molecules of RNA with sedimentation coefficients of 23 S and 16 S, while the 30 S particles have one 16 S molecule. The specific function of the ribosomal components is still largely unknown, but as we will see presently the RNA appears to be composed of a few molecular species which are coded by a small part of the DNA.

The first RNA to which a definite role could be assigned was predicted on theoretical grounds by Crick (1957). Although it was generally believed by this time that the genetic code resided in DNA and that the intermediate in protein synthesis might be RNA, there existed no specific, satisfactory model of how this might be accomplished. Neither DNA nor RNA appeared to have the steric properties to orient amino acids directly into an ordered sequence. Crick suggested that the most likely model would be the attachment of amino acids to an adaptor molecule which could form hydrogen bonds with the hypothetical RNA template. He thought the best candidate might be a small polynucleotide. Hoagland *et al.* (1956) had already discovered amino-activating enzymes by which ATP was attached to amino acids. Further work (Hoagland *et al.*, 1958, the seventh paper in this section) disclosed the attachment of the activated amino acids to a relatively small molecular species of RNA, soluble RNA (sRNA), which also became known as transfer RNA. The transfer RNA was larger than might have been predicted, but the product of its reaction with activated amino acids, amino acyl-RNA, was demonstrated to be an intermediate in the transfer of the amino acids into peptide linkage. Since then work on sRNA has progressed rapidly (Hoagland, 1960). There is at least one type of sRNA molecule for each amino acid found in proteins and perhaps two or three for most of them. Several molecular species have been purified and progress is being made toward determining the nucleotide sequence in some of the sRNA's (Holley *et al.*, 1963; Ingram and Sjöquist, 1963).

Since the discovery of the ribosome it had generally been assumed that these particles contained the templates for protein synthesis. This concept became difficult to maintain when it was pointed out by a number of studies that the base ratio of the ribosomal RNA was quite different from that of the DNA which was supposed to be providing the template for its formation (Belozersky and Spirin, 1960). Several alternatives were suggested (Crick, 1959) but none of them appeared satisfactory. Another characteristic of the ribosomal RNA was its extreme stability. However, Jacob and Monod (1961) from studies of the kinetics of induced enzyme formation in bacteria had been led to the hypothesis that the RNA intermediate should be very labile. Actually such a fraction of RNA had been discovered several years before, but its significance was not fully appreciated. The next paper in our selection (number 8) by Volkin and Astrachan describes this RNA which was formed upon the infection of *E. coli* by phage T2. The synthesis of bacterial RNA stops quickly upon infection and the new RNA formed is a small amount of the total in the cell. When it was labeled with P^{32}, not only did the labeled RNA have a high rate of turnover, but unlike the total RNA of the cell it had a base composition very similar to that of the DNA of the infecting phage. Further studies of this unstable RNA fraction were in progress (Astrachan and Volkin, 1958; Volkin, 1963), and it appeared to be a likely candidate for the intermediate or "messenger" from the viral DNA to the cellular machinery which produced more virus.

Encouraged by the above information and inspired by their hypothesis concerning the role of messenger RNA, Brenner and Jacob came to Meselson's laboratory at the California Institute of Technology to test the idea with the phage system. If they were correct the bacterial ribosomes existing prior to infection would be used along with the newly formed messenger RNA to make the proteins required for phage reproduction. The ninth paper of this group (Brenner *et al.*, 1961) presents the results which supported their hypothesis.

On another front the role of DNA in directing synthesis of RNA was becoming testable in cell-free systems (Weiss and Gladstone, 1959; Hurwitz *et al.*, 1960; Stevens, 1960). Unlike the polynucleotide phosphorylase discovered by Grunberg-Manago and Ochoa (1955), these systems required DNA as primer and utilized ribonucleoside triphosphates as substrates. In most respects this enzyme system, now called RNA polymerase, resembled DNA polymerase except that ribonucleotides were required and the product was RNA instead of DNA. Tests of the mechanism of synthesis based on nearest neighbor frequency analysis indicated that the RNA was complementary to the DNA primer. We have selected the paper by Hurwitz *et al.* (1961) to review some of these results (number 10 in this section). Later and more extensive reviews have been written by Hurwitz and August (1963) and by Berg (1962).

Still another approach to the role of DNA in directing the synthesis of cellular RNA was introduced by Hall and Spiegelman (1961). This paper, reprinted as our eleventh selection, shows specific complex formation between single-stranded T2 DNA and the RNA synthesized subsequent to infection of the bacteria by phage T2. Subsequently, Spiegelman *et al.* (1961) found some indication for the occurrence of natural complexes of newly formed RNA and phage DNA in infected cells of *E. coli*. However, it soon became clear from a number of studies that such complexes were very unstable and transitory. True hybrid molecules of RNA and DNA could be produced by heating and slowly cooling DNA and RNA together, but such hybrid molecules probably do not exist in measurable quantities *in vivo*. Bautz and Hall (1962) devised a method for trapping denatured DNA on phosphocellulose columns and hybridizing homologous RNA's by passing them into the column at elevated temperatures. Bolton and McCarthy (1962, 1963) trapped the denatured DNA in an agar gel and hybridized the DNA with RNA by prolonged incubation at 60°–65°C. These methods, as well as Nygaard and Hall's (1964) method of trapping hybrid molecules formed in solution on methyl cellulose filters, are finding wide application in the study of homologies between DNA's and RNA's as well as DNA's from different phylogenetic groups.

The twelfth selection is another paper from Spiegelman's laboratory (Yankofsky and Spiegelman, 1962), which demonstrates that ribosomal RNA is complementary to a small part of the cellular DNA in *E. coli*. To complete the story we have reprinted another paper (number 13) from Alexander Rich's laboratory which shows complementary sequences for the soluble RNA of *E. coli* (Goodman and Rich, 1962). With this demonstration all three of the major types of RNA are shown to derive their base sequences from DNA. The total DNA which codes for these sequences is small in the case of both ribosomal and soluble RNA. Most of the DNA appears to be concerned with the synthesis of messenger RNA even though it is the smallest fraction of the total cellular RNA. According to Levinthal *et al.* (1962), the DNA-like fraction is about 10% of the total RNA in the bacterial cell. The other 90% consists of 75–80% ribosomal RNA and 10–15% soluble RNA. These results on the complementarity of RNA to the DNA taken along with the almost complete suppression of RNA synthesis by actinomycin D indicates that all cellular RNA synthesis may be primed directly by the chromosomal DNA. If the estimates of the amounts of complementary DNA are valid there would not appear to be any amplification of the system for ribosomal RNA synthesis, as for example, by extra replication of those DNA loci or cistrons which code for this fraction.

In the cell-free systems for RNA synthesis, the product is apparently complementary to both strands of primer DNA (Geiduschek *et al.*, 1961; Hurwitz and August, 1963). However, in the cell the control mechanism appears to be different for Spiegelman (1963) presents evidence that the RNA product is complementary to only one of the two strands of DNA.

The final topic to be covered in our consideration of the function of the genetic material is the nature of the code. The first approach to the coding problem was largely theoretical. The experimental facts available were the knowledge of the structure of DNA and the amino acid sequences in a few proteins. Since these aspects of the problem have been reviewed by Crick (1959, 1963) we will not dwell upon them. The best experimental approach to the problem appeared to be through the study of induced mutations in the genetic material, DNA or RNA, correlated with a study of the complete amino acid sequence in the affected protein. A limited amount could be learned with natural mutations as shown by the work with human hemoglobins (Ingram, 1963a; Baglioni, 1963). More could be learned with a system in which mutations could be readily induced, for example, tobacco mosiac virus (Tsugita and Fraenkel-Conrat, 1963). However, by far the best systems appeared to be those in which genetic crosses and fine structural mapping could be done. Three systems showed promise, the *E. coli* phosphatase system studied by Levinthal and associates (Garen, 1960), the T4 lysozyme system studied by Streisinger *et al.* (1961), and the *E. coli* tryptophan synthetase system studied by Yanofsky and associates (Yanofsky *et al.*, 1961; Yanofsky, 1963). These systems will still provide valuable information, but to everyone's surprise the rapid advances came in quite a different area. Our fourteenth paper is the original publication which describes this breakthrough (Nirenberg and Matthaei, 1961).

The work on protein synthesis in cell-free systems had developed to the point where the ribosomes could be freed of their natural messenger RNA. Addition of another kind of RNA would in some cases stimulate amino acid incorporation. In working with this system Nirenberg and Matthaei discovered that one of the synthetic polyribonucleotides, polyuridylic acid, produced by polynucleotide phosphorylase would stimulate the incorporation of only one amino acid, phenylalanine. The product appeared to be polyphenylalanine. They immediately recognized the value of the system for breaking the code. Polyribonucleotides could be prepared with various ratios and combinations of the four bases. By determining which amino acids were polymerized under the influence of such synthetic molecules, one could hope to learn the code letters (nucleotides) faster than anyone had ever imagined possible. Ochoa and several of his collaborators, especially Lengyel and Speyer, became very active in this area since their laboratory had advanced the work on polynucleotide phosphorylase to the point where they knew a great deal about the production of synthetic homo- and mixed polymers of ribotides. Papers from these laboratories came almost monthly and the scientific community became aware of molecular biology to an extent which had never occurred before. DNA, RNA, and the coding problem became familiar to anyone who attended science exhibits in world fairs or even carefully read their daily newspapers and various popular magazines.

One of the papers from Ochoa's laboratory (Speyer *et al.*, 1962) was selected to show some of the progress. By now a number of other synthetic polynucleotides have been shown to stimulate amino acid incorporation (Nirenberg *et al.*, 1963; Speyer *et al.*, 1963) and there is other evidence suggesting that the code is highly degenerate (von Ehrenstein and Dais, 1963; Weisblum *et al.*, 1962), i.e., there is more than one codon for each amino acid.

The experiments with the synthetic polynucleotides do not give the coding ratio or size of the codon. Evidence that the number is small comes from a variety of sources beginning with attempts to determine the total length of the genetic map which specifies a particular polypeptide chain. However, all such estimates leave considerable latitude, from 2 to 10 perhaps. Crick *et al.* (1962) have utilized the proflavin mutants at the rII locus in phage T4 to learn more about the coding ratio and other aspects of the translation mechanism. The findings are consistent with the idea that these mutations are produced by addition or deletion of a nucleotide pair in DNA, that the codon contains an odd number of nucleotides, probably three, and that the reading begins at a fixed point and proceeds sequential to the end of the cistron. These experiments are described in paper number 16.

The last paper (Brody and Yanofsky, 1963) expands our view of how a mutation may alter protein structure. Now that the reader is aware of various aspects of the coding problem we may return to the question which was dropped near the end of the Section I on Biochemical Genetics, namely, how do mutations change enzyme activity? We can now think of several possible ways besides alteration of the cistron which produces its structural messenger RNA. Broady and Yanofsky consider these possibilities in relation to supressor mutations, i.e., mutants which partially restore function in strains which already have a mutation from the wild-type.

REFERENCES

Astrachan, L., and Volkin, E. (1958). *Biochim. Biophys. Acta* **29**, 536.

Baglioni, C. (1963). *In* "Molecular Genetics" (J. H. Taylor, ed.), Part I, pp. 405–475. Academic Press, New York.

Baltimore, D., and Franklin, R. M. (1962). *Biochem. Biophys. Res. Commun.* **9**, 388.

Barnum, C. P., Huseby, R. A., and Vermund, H. (1953). *Cancer Res.* **13**, 880.

Bautz, E. K. F., and Hall, B. D. (1962). *Proc. Natl. Acad. Sci. U. S.* **48**, 400.

Belozersky, A. N., and Spirin, A. S. (1960). *In* "The Nucleic Acids" (E. Chargaff and J. N. Davidson, eds.), Vol. III, pp. 147–185. Academic Press, New York.

Berg, P. (1962). *In* "Basic Problems in Neoplastic Disease" (A. Gellhorn and E. Hirschberg, eds.), pp. 15–34. Columbia Univ. Press, New York.

Bolton, E. T., and McCarthy, B. J. (1962). *Proc. Natl. Acad. Sci. U. S.* **48**, 1390.

Bolton, E. T., and McCarthy, B. J. (1963). *Proc. Natl. Acad. Sci. U. S.* **50**, 157.

Brachet, J. (1942). *Arch. Biol.* (*Liege*) **53**, 207.

Caspersson, T. (1941). *Naturwissenschaften* **29**, 33.

Caspersson, T. (1950). "Cell Growth and Cell Function." W. W. Norton, New York.

Crick, F. H. C. (1957). *Biochem. Soc. Symp.* **14**, 25.

Crick, F. H. C. (1959). *Brookhaven Symp. Biol. No.* **12**, 35.

Crick, F. H. C. (1963). *In* "Progress in Nucleic Acid Research," Vol. I, pp. 163–217. Academic Press, New York.

Davern, G. I., and Meselson, M. (1960). *J. Mol. Biol.* **2**, 153.

Farber, S. (1958). *In* "Ciba Foundation Symposium on Amino Acids and Peptides with Antimetabolite Activity (G. E. W. Wolstenholme and C. M. O'Connor, eds.), p. 140. Little, Brown, Boston, Massachusetts.

Ficq, A. (1953). *Experientia* 9, 377.

Garen, A. (1960). *Symp. Soc. Gen. Microbiol.* 10, 239.

Geiduschek, E. P., Nakamoto, T., and Weiss, S. B. (1961). *Proc. Natl. Acad. Sci. U. S.* 47, 1405.

Goldstein, L. (1963). *Symp. Intern. Soc. Cell Biol.* 2, 129–149.

Grunberg-Manago, M., and Ochoa, S. (1955). *J. Am. Chem. Soc.* 77, 3165.

Hammarsten, E., and Hevesy, G. (1946). *Acta Physiol. Scand.* 11, 335.

Harris, H. (1959). *Biochem. J.* 73, 362.

Harris, H. (1960). *Biochem. J.* 74, 276.

Hershey, A. D. (1954). *J. Gen. Physiol.* 38, 145.

Hoagland, M. B. (1960). *In* "The Nucleic Acid" (E. Chargaff and J. N. Davidson, eds.), Vol. III, pp. 349–408. Academic Press, New York.

Hoagland, M. B., Keeler, E. B., and Zamecnik, P. C. (1956). *J. Biol. Chem.* 218, 345.

Holley, R. W., Apgar, J., Everett, G. A., Madison, J. T., Merrill, S. H., and Zamir, A. (1963). *Cold Spring Harbor Symp. Quant. Biol.* 28, 117.

Hurwitz, J., and August, J. T. (1963). *In* "Progress in Nucleic Acid Research" (J. N. Davidson and W. E. Cohn, eds.), Vol. I, pp. 59–92. Academic Press, New York.

Hurwitz, J., Bresler, A., and Bringer, R. (1960). *Biochem. Biophys. Res. Commun.* 3, 15.

Ingram, V. M. (1963a). "The Hemoglobins in Genetics and Evolution," 165 pp. Columbia Univ. Press, New York.

Ingram, V. M., and Sjöquist, J. A. (1963b). *Cold Spring Harbor Symp. Quant. Biol.* 28, 133.

Jacob, F., and Monod, J. (1961). *J. Mol. Biol.* 3, 318.

Jeener, R., and Szafarz, D. (1950). *Arch. Biochem.* 26, 54.

Kirk, J. M. (1960). *Biochim. et Biophys. Acta* 42, 167.

Levinthal, C., Keynan, A., and Higa, A. (1962). *Proc. Natl. Acad. Sci. U. S.* 48, 1631.

Marshak, A. (1948). *J. Cellular Comp. Physiol.* 32, 381.

Nirenberg, M. W. (1963). *Cold Spring Harbor Symp. Quant. Biol.* 28, 549.

Nygaard, A. P., and Hall, B. D. (1964). *J. Mol. Biol.* 9, 125.

Palade, G. (1955). *J. Biophys. Biochem. Cytol.* 1, 59.

Palade, G. (1958). *In* "Microsomal Particles and Protein Synthesis" (R. B. Roberts, ed.), p. 36. Pergamon Press, New York.

Prescott, D. M. (1959). *J. Biophys. Biochem. Cytol.* 6, 203.

Reddi, K. K. (1961). *Science* 133, 1367.

Reich, E., Franklin, R. M., Shatkin, A. J., and Tatum, E. (1962). *Proc. Natl. Acad. Sci. U. S.* 48, 1238.

Roberts, R. B., Britten, R. J., and McCarthy, B. J. (1963). *In* "Molecular Genetics" (J. H. Taylor, ed.), Part I, pp. 291–352. Academic Press, New York.

Schweet, R., and Bishop, J. (1963). *In* "Molecular Genetics" (J. H. Taylor, ed.), Part I, pp. 353–404. Academic Press, New York.

Siekevitz, P. (1952). *J. Biol. Chem.* 195, 549.

Siminowich, L., and Graham, A. F. (1956). *J. Histochem. Cytochem.* 4, 508.

Speyer, J. F., Lengyel, P., Basillo, C., Wahba, A. J., Gardner, R. S., and Ochoa, S. (1963). *Cold Spring Harbor Symp. Quant. Biol.* 28, 599.

Spiegelman, S., and Doi, R. H. (1963). *Cold Spring Harbor Symp. Quant. Biol.* 28, 109.

Spiegelman, S., Hall, B. D., and Starck, R. (1961). *Proc. Natl. Acad. Sci. U. S.* 47, 1135.

Stevens, A. (1960). *Biochem. Biophys. Res. Communs.* 3, 92.

Streisinger, G., Mukai, F., Dreyer, W. J., Miller, B., and Hariuchi, S. (1961). *Cold Spring Harbor Symp. Quant. Biol.* 26, 25.

Taylor, J. H., and Woods, P. S. (1959). *In* "Subcellular Particles," (T. Hayashi, ed.), pp. 172–185. Ronald Press, New York.

Taylor, J. H., McMaster, R. H., and Caluya, M. F. (1955). *Exptl. Cell Res.* **9**, 460.

Tsugita, A., and Fraenkel-Conrat, H. (1963). *In* "Molecular Genetics" (J. H. Taylor, ed.), Part I, pp. 477–520. Academic Press, New York.

Volkin, E. (1963). *In* "Molecular Genetics" (J. H. Taylor, ed.), Part I, pp. 271–289. Academic Press, New York.

von Ehrenstein, G., and Dais, D. (1963). *Proc. Natl. Acad. Sci. U. S.* **50**, 81.

Weisblum, B., Benzer, S., and Holley, R. W. (1962). *Proc. Natl. Acad. Sci. U. S.* **48**, 1449.

Weiss, S. B., and Gladstone, L. (1959). *J. Am. Chem. Soc.* **81**, 4118.

Woods, P. S., and Taylor, J. H. (1959). *Lab. Invest.* **8**, 309.

Wright, S. (1941). *Physiol. Revs.* **21**, 487.

Wright, S. (1945). *Am. Naturalist* **79**, 289.

Yanofsky, C. (1963). *In* "Cyto-differentiation and Macromolecular Synthesis," pp. 15–29. Academic Press, New York.

Yanofsky, C., Helinski, D. R., and Maling, B. D. (1961). *Cold Spring Harbor Symp. Quant. Biol.* **26**, 11.

Zamecnik, P. (1958). *Sci. Am.* **198**, 118.

Reprinted from the JOURNAL OF CELLULAR AND COMPARATIVE PHYSIOLOGY
Vol. 34, No. 3, December, 1949

SPECIFIC ACTIVITY OF P[32] IN CELL
CONSTITUENTS OF RABBIT LIVER [1]

ALFRED MARSHAK AND FERNANDO CALVET

Division of Tuberculosis and N. Y. U. College of Medicine

It has been proposed that the nucleus contains a nucleoprotein which behaves as a precursor to RNA of the cytoplasm in non-proliferating tissue (Marshak, '48). The data to be presented here furnish additional evidence in support of this hypothesis.

Rabbits were given Na_2HPO_4 containing P[32] intravenously (1 mc/kg, .025 mg P[31]/mc). At intervals after injection, the animals were anaesthetized with nembutal and the liver perfused with ice-cold Ringer solution. A portion of the tissue was taken for chemical fractionation and the remainder used for isolation of nuclei by the citric acid technique (Marshak, '40, '41). After removal of the nuclei, two particulate fractions were obtained from the liver brei in 5% citric acid, one of which sedimented at 2,500 g, the other at 24,000 g, each of which was washed several times with 5% citric acid. The tissue and each of the particulate fractions was extracted by the method of Schmidt and Thannhauser as modified by Schneider ('46). Phosphorus was determined by the method of Fiske and Subbarow ('25). P[32] was measured in solution held in a thin-walled annular glass container surrounding a thin-walled glass B-counter. All P[32] determinations were greater than 50 times the background.

The following table (table 1) gives the specific activities observed at intervals between one and 73 hours after P[32] administration. It was shown previously that the fraction iso-

[1] Supported by a grant from the Research Grants Division of the U. S. Public Health Service.

451

lated by the method for extracting PNA has the same specific activity as the nucleic acid moiety of the nuclear precursor and will be here designated as ''PNA'' (Marshak, '48).

TABLE 1

Specific activities [1]

FRACTION		HOURS AFTER INJECTION				
		1	3	12	24	73
PNA —	T	100	114	195	141	136
	N	235	1,115	945	300	207
	Cl	20	41	81	75	105
	C_s	59	104	265	. .	230
DNA —	T	18	9	63	. .	84
	N	0	13	13	11	13
Acid —	T	2,370	2,460	1,790	419	312
sol.	N	51	418	775	419	333
	Cl	378	1,185	674	715	520
	C_s	29	1,770	1,530	432	325
	T	82	65	178	245	152
Lipid —	N	53	273	400	195	195
	Cl	14	31	122	240	120
	C_s	24	55	225	238	169
Phos- —	T	3,420	2,485	2,030	605	605
pho-	N	715	1,470	956	495	276
pro-	Cl	730	715	298	512	385
tein	C_s	1,015	1,780	830	445	555

[1] P^{32} counts as of the time of injection divided by μg P^{31}.
T = whole tissue after perfusion.   N = nuclei.
Cl = larger particles. C_s = smaller particles.

''PNA'' and DNA

If the hypothesis is correct, it is expected that the specific activity of ''PNA'' of the nucleus will rise rapidly and then fall, while that of the PNA of the cytoplasm or of one of its constituents will at first be low but will eventually reach the level of the ''PNA.'' This expectation is fulfilled in the case of the small cytoplasmic particles by 73 hours. The specific activity of the larger particles is at all times lower than that of the small ones, but it increases at about the same rate during the first 12 hours.

The specific activity of the desoxyribonucleic acid (DNA) is very low and probably represents only contaminating P^{32} included as impurity in this fraction, since the specific activity of the DNA isolated from whole tissue was in all but one case several times as great as that of the same fraction obtained from nuclei alone. Previous experiments in which DNA-P^{32} was determined enzymatically also indicated no significant amount in this fraction (Marshak, '48).

Acid soluble

Since the nuclei and cytoplasmic particles had been extracted with 5% citric acid prior to the trichloracetic acid extraction while the tissue was not, the data obtained for the particulate cell components represented only minimum values for this fraction. However, significant deductions could be drawn from the relative change in these values with time after injection. From three hours onwards the specific activity of the small particles was approximately the same as that for the whole tissue suggesting equilibrium between the acid soluble component of the small particles and the inorganic phosphate and the soluble phosphate esters of the cell. The larger cytoplasmic particles, however, showed at first a lower then a higher specific activity than the fraction obtained from the whole tissue, indicating a slower rate of turnover.

The specific activity of the acid soluble portion of the whole tissue was at all times greater than that of the "PNA" of the nuclei although the factor by which they differed decreased from about 10 at one hour to about 1.5 at 73 hours. It is probable, therefore, that one or more component of the tissue acid soluble fraction contributed to the formation of nuclear "PNA" at least to the extent of being a phosphorus donor.

Lipid

The lipid specific activity of the tissue and its particulate components were at all times less than that of the nuclear "PNA" so that the phospholipids as a whole could not have behaved as phosphorus donor to "PNA" although the possibility that particular phospholipids of higher specific activity may have so acted was not excluded.

The specific activity of the lipid of the two types of cytoplasmic particles was approximately at the same level as the corresponding specific activity of the PNA of the same particles indicating comparable rates of turnover. If the specific activities were related to that of the nucleus as shown in table 2, an interesting relation between PNA and lipid became apparent. In small particles during the first 13 hours, the values for the PNA were consistently about twice those for the lipid while in the large particles, the ratio was approximately 3.

TABLE 2

Specific activities relative to the nucleus

	HOURS AFTER INJECTION				
	1	3	12	24	73
"PNA"					
$A = N/C_l$	11.7	28.2	11.7	4.0	2.0
$B = N/C_s$	4.0	11.1	3.6	. .	0.9
Lipid					
$A' = N/C_l$	3.8	8.8	3.3	0.8	1.6
$B' = N/C_s$	2.2	5.0	1.8	0.8	1.1
A/A'	3.1	3.2	3.5	5.0	1.3
B/B'	1.8	2.2	2.0	. .	0.8

Phosphoprotein

The specific activity of the phosphoprotein is surprisingly high. Since it is somewhat greater than that of the acid soluble fraction at all times, and since its actual phosphorus content is low, the result suggests the possibility that P^{32} as a contaminant in the protein may be the explanation. However, in the nucleus this fraction has a value many times greater than the acid soluble material during the first three hours, but is subsequently at about the same level. Similarly in the small cytoplasmic fragments, it is much greater at one hour but later about the same as the acid soluble fraction while in the large fragments, it is greater by a factor of 2 in the first hour but is subsequently considerably lower than its acid soluble counterpart. Although possible, it would be difficult to explain such different patterns in relationship merely to contamination so that the high specific activities observed suggest the desirability of further work with the fraction.

SUMMARY

1. Specific activity of nuclear "PNA" was at first much higher than that of the small cytoplasmic particles but decreased with time while that of the cytoplasmic particles increased until they both reached about the same level. This observation fulfilled expectations derived from the hypothesis that the nuclear "PNA" functions as a precursor for the cytoplasmic PNA.

2. P³² in DNA was very low and could be accounted for as contamination.

3. Changes in the specific activity of the phospholipid, phosphoprotein and acid soluble fractions of the tissue and of the particulate cell components are described.

4. One or more of the components of the acid soluble fraction could function as phosphorus donor to "PNA," but it was unlikely that phospholipid also functioned in this way.

5. A high specific activity of the phosphoprotein fraction was noted in the early intervals after injection, but the significance of this observation was not determined.

LITERATURE CITED

FISKE, C. H., AND Y. SUBBAROW 1925 The colorimetric determination of phosphorus. J. Biol. Chem., *66*: 375.

MARSHAK, A. 1940 Uptake of radioactive phosphorus by nuclei of liver and tumors. Science, *92*: 460–461.

———— 1941 P³² uptake by nuclei. J. Gen. Physiol., *25*: 275–291.

———— 1948 Evidence for a nuclear precursor of ribo- and desoxyribonucleic acid. J. Cell. and Comp. Physiol., *32*: 381–406.

SCHNEIDER, W .C. 1946 Phosphorus compounds in animal tissues. III. A comparison of methods for the estimation of nucleic acids. J. Biol..Chem., *164*: 747.

Reprinted from SCIENCE, November 6, 1953, Vol. 118, No. 3071, pages 555–557.

Intracellular Localization of Labeled Nucleic Acid Determined with Autoradiographs[1]

J. Herbert Taylor

Department of Botany,
Columbia University, New York City

Autoradiographs have been used to detect incorporation of phosphorus (P[32]) into the deoxyribose nucleic acids (DNA) of individual nuclei (*1, 2*). In this way the time of synthesis of DNA in relation to the division cycle during mitosis and meiosis has been determined. The method is also applicable to the study of phosphorus incorporation into the ribonucleic acids (RNA) of single cells. By applying a thin photographic emulsion layer to serial sections of large cells and making autoradiographs as previously described (*2*), the radioactive element can be located with sufficient precision to determine its intracellular distribution. For example, in the large cells of the gastric caeca and salivary glands of the third instar larvae of *Drosophila,* the relative rates of incorporation of P[32] into the RNA of cytoplasm, chromatin, and nucleolus can be followed.

Early third instar larvae of *Drosophila repleta* were fed P[32] in the form of inorganic phosphate (120 μc/ml of water containing 30 mg of gelatin and 30 mg of brewers' yeast). Incorporation occurs most rapidly in the cells of the salivary glands and the gastric caeca, and the comments here refer to the behavior of these cells. At intervals of 1 hr after beginning to feed on the labeled food, larvae were fixed in Carnoy's fluid, and prepared as paraffin sections (7 μ) on slides. After passing these slides through hot ether-alcohol, washing in lower grades of alcohol, cold 5% trichloracetic acid, and water, one of a pair of slides containing tissues of the same larvae was coated with autoradiographic stripping film. The other slide was placed in a solution of protease free ribonuclease[2] (0.2 mg/ml of water at pH 6.0 for 2 hr at 37°) (*3*). After this digestion, or in some experiments after hydrolysis and staining by the Feulgen procedure, the second slide of the pair was coated with stripping film.

A study of the autoradiographs, from those larvae fixed 1 hr after beginning to feed on the labeled food, shows that the highest concentration of P[32] that remains after fixation and the subsequent washings is in the nucleolus (Fig. 1). About one-tenth this concentration is present in the cytoplasm. Some cells at this early period also show a relatively high concentration in certain regions of the chromatin. The concentration may exceed that in the nucleolus.

Those larvae fixed 2 or 3 hr after beginning to feed show an increasing concentration of P[32] in all parts of the cell. In 2 hr the concentration of P[32] in the

[1] The work reported here is supported by a grant from the Atomic Energy Commission, Contract AT(30-1)-1804.
[2] Prepared by Worthington Biochemical Co.

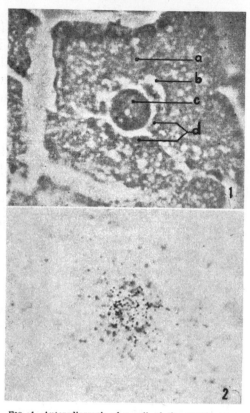

FIG. 1. Autoradiograph of a cell of the gastric caecum fixed 1½ hr after feeding food containing P[32]. 1. Phase photograph of the cell; the structures indicated are (a) cytoplasm, (b) nuclear membrane, (c) nucleolus, (d) chromatin. 2. Bright field photograph showing distribution of silver grains above the same cell. × 1220.

nucleolus is higher than in the chromatin and the cytoplasm has one-fifth to one-third the concentration present in the nucleolus. If the larvae are removed to nonradioactive food enriched with yeast after the first 2 hr, the P[32] is still higher in the nucleolus than the cytoplasm 1 hr later, but in 2–3 hr (4–5 hr after beginning to feed on the radioactive food) the P[32] is about equally distributed in various parts of the cell. Nearly all the P[32] that remains in the nucleolus and most of that in the cytoplasm and chromatin is removed from the cells on the slides digested in ribonuclease or subjected to the Feulgen hydrolysis (1N HCl for 10 min at 60°). This is interpreted to indicate that most of the P[32] is incorporated into ribonucleic acids. The P[32] remaining after digestion or hydrolysis is usually one-tenth or less of the total and its distribution is rather uniform throughout the cell.

Resolution of structures 2–3 μ apart is theoretically possible (*4*) with this type of autoradiograph. In practice one has the added advantage that adjacent structures may be separated in serial sections. If a nucleolus with surrounding chromatin and cytoplasm of a cell is included in one section, a part of the chromatin of that cell with surrounding cytoplasm in the succeeding section, and only cytoplasm in a third section, estimation of the isotope in each of these three parts can be made with greater precision than would otherwise be possible. In this way, with thinner sections, one should be able to resolve structures in smaller cells. In the cells of *Drosophila*, which are 40–50 μ in diameter with a nucleus 18–20 μ in diameter and a nucleolus 8–12 μ in diameter, resolution is not a problem.

A large proportion of the nuclear RNA of higher specific activity than cytoplasmic RNA previously reported (*5–7*) may be contributed by nucleolar RNA. The nucleolus may be a center of RNA synthesis as suggested by Pollister and Leuchtenberger (*8*) or a reservoir of RNA produced in other parts of the nucleus. The initial high specific activity of chromatin observed in these autoradiographs suggests the latter. Although one cannot definitely answer questions of sites and rates of synthesis yet, the technique provides a tool by which variations in turnover rates may be studied at the intracellular level. Perhaps the role of RNA can eventually be evaluated by application of this technique along with photometric techniques that allow measurement of relative concentration of certain cellular constituents.

References

1. HOWARD, A., and PELC, S. R. *Exptl. Cell Research,* **2**, 178 (1951).
2. TAYLOR, J. H. *Ibid.,* **4**, 164 (1953).
3. KAUFMANN, B. P., GAY, H., and McDONALD, M. R. *Am. J. Botany,* **38**, 268 (1951).
4. DONIACH, I., and PELC, S. R. *Brit. J. Radiol.,* **23**, 184 (1950).
5. MARSHAK, A., and CALVERT, F. *J. Cellular Comp. Physiol.,* **34**, 451 (1949).
6. JEENER, R., and SZAFARZ, D. *Arch. Biochem.,* **26**, 54 (1950).
7. BARNUM, C. P., and HUSEBY, R. A. *Ibid.,* **29**, 7 (1950).
8. POLLISTER, A. W., and LEUCHTENBERGER, C. *Nature,* **163**, 360 (1949).

Manuscript received June 9, 1953.

Reprinted from the Proceedings of the National Academy of Sciences,
Vol. 41, No. 11, pp. 874–880. November, 1955

DIRECT EVIDENCE FOR NUCLEAR SYNTHESIS OF CYTOPLASMIC RIBOSE NUCLEIC ACID

By Lester Goldstein* and Walter Plaut†

DEPARTMENT OF ZOÖLOGY, UNIVERSITY OF CALIFORNIA, BERKELEY

Communicated by George Wald, July 25, 1955

The question of the biosynthetic relationship of nuclear and cytoplasmic ribose nucleic acid (RNA) has received much attention in recent years. Interest has been focused on this problem by current speculation on the transmission of genetic specificity from desoxyribose nucleic acid (DNA) to cytoplasmic components. It has been suggested that RNA could serve as a receptor of a "code" from the DNA in the nucleus and could transmit this specificity to cytoplasmic proteins,[1] with the synthesis of which it may be associated. A general association of RNA with protein synthesis has been postulated by Caspersson[2] and Brachet.[3] The more recent work of Gale and Folkes[4] has helped to place this postulation on a fairly firm basis. The experiments we shall describe were designed to test directly an earlier link in the chain of transmission of specificity: the synthesis of RNA in the nucleus and its transfer to the cytoplasm.

Most of the evidence bearing on this question has been discussed in a recent review article by Brachet.[5] This article should be consulted for references to work bearing on the following discussion.

The bulk of the data which have been interpreted as favoring the hypothesis of the nuclear origin of cytoplasmic RNA fall into several major categories. Caspersson was one of the first to suggest that the accumulation of RNA in the vicinity of the nuclear membrane of many types of cells might indicate the nuclear origin of RNA. More recently, data from Mirsky's laboratory and the work of Hogeboom and Schneider indicate that enzymes concerned with purine and nucleoside metabolism are found in the nucleus in high concentrations. Both types of evidence are circumstantial; they indicate the possibility of nuclear synthesis of RNA but do not show that this is actually the case.

Many workers have shown that radioactive precursors of RNA are incorporated into nuclear RNA at a higher rate, and presumably earlier, than into cytoplasmic RNA. Barnum, Huseby, and Vermund,[6] however, have taken exception to this interpretation of precursor experiments. Brachet[7] has found that living amoebae, whose RNA has been depleted by ribonuclease, show the reappearance of cytochemically demonstrable RNA in the nucleus prior to the cytoplasm. None of this evidence is conclusive since the methods used do not exclude the possibility that RNA is synthesized in the cytoplasm and is shunted into the nucleus as rapidly as it is formed. Moreover, even if one granted that RNA synthesis occurs in the nucleus, this form of evidence could not be used to establish the passage of RNA from nucleus to cytoplasm rather than its synthesis at different rates in nucleus and cytoplasm. Rabinovitch and Plaut[8] have recently demonstrated the total loss of cytochemically demonstrable RNA from the amoeba nucleus at the time of division. Their data, however, are insufficient to establish critically the subsequent location of the nuclear RNA.

Linet and Brachet, as well as James,[9] have shown that enucleated halves of amoebae lose RNA at a more rapid rate than do nucleated halves. This could be

874

interpreted as evidence for the nuclear synthesis of cytoplasmic RNA or perhaps for the nuclear control of retention of RNA in the cytoplasm.

The lack of uniformity in biochemical composition of RNA samples derived from nucleus and cytoplasm has been felt by some workers to speak against the simple transfer of nucleus-synthesized RNA to the cytoplasm. Again, this cannot be regarded as critical evidence, since the heterogeneity is subject to alternative explanations.

A more direct approach is necessary to demonstrate the relationship between nuclear and cytoplasmic RNA, and this approach is provided, in our opinion, by the following experimental design. The RNA of the nucleus of a cell may be labeled with a radioactive tracer, and the nucleus may be transferred to a cell whose RNA is unlabeled. Transmission of labeled material from nucleus to cytoplasm may then be traced directly by autoradiographic visualization of the final distribution of the tracer atoms. The methods used were as follows: Amoebae (*A. proteus*) were labeled with P^{32} by feeding them with *Tetrahymena pyriformis* which had been cultured on a 1 per cent proteose-peptone solution with added P^{32}O$_4$. Generally, following two to three days of feeding, the amoebae were assayed at 300–1,000 counts per minute per amoeba (dried amoebae on plastic planchets in windowless Q-gas flow counter, Nuclear Instrument and Chemical Corporation Model D-46A), with perhaps 1–2 per cent of the radioactivity within the nucleus. Earlier work has indicated that essentially all the autoradiographically detectable P^{32} in the nucleus under the above labeling conditions is in RNA. That is, we found that no P^{32} was present in the nucleus following ribonuclease digestion. The fact that no detectable label could be ascribed to the DNA can be explained by the low concentration of DNA in the amoeba nucleus, as indicated by the faintness of the Feulgen reaction.

Nuclei from P^{32}-labeled amoebae were transferred by micromanipulation[10] to unlabeled, enucleated, or to normal, unenucleated, amoebae. The success of the operation could be determined from previously established criteria. We had found it possible to predict accurately, from their postoperative appearance and behavior, which of the cells would divide in time and could therefore be considered viable. Only such cells were used for subsequent analysis.

Individual amoebae were fixed at various times following the operation by flattening the cells on a slide with a cover slip carrying a small drop of 45 per cent acetic acid on the underside. After removal of the cover slip and dehydration, the slides were coated with autoradiographic stripping film (Kodak, Ltd., London, England) and stored in the dark for approximately 14 days' exposure. (See Rabinovitch and Plaut[8] for further technical details on the processing of slides.) After photographic development, the preparations were examined with bright-field and phase-contrast microscopy.

We found that in the autoradiographs of amoebae fixed less than 5 hours after the nuclear transfer operation, essentially all the significant radioactivity was still localized within the nucleus (Pl. I, Figs. 1*A* and 1*B*). Significant radioactivity denotes a silver grain density in the developed autoradiographic emulsion which is above the low general-background grain density inherent in the emulsion. The very low level of activity in the cytoplasm of these amoebae should be noted; it indicates that the cytoplasm was not significantly contaminated by the transfer oper-

V. THE FUNCTION OF GENETIC MATERIAL

ation. Amoebae fixed 12 or more hours after the operation showed appreciable activity in the cytoplasm (Pl. I, Figs. 2A and 2B). It can be concluded that material, whatever its molecular complexity, is transferred from nucleus to cytoplasm.

Although fifteen cases of successful transfers of nuclei to enucleated amoebae

PLATE I

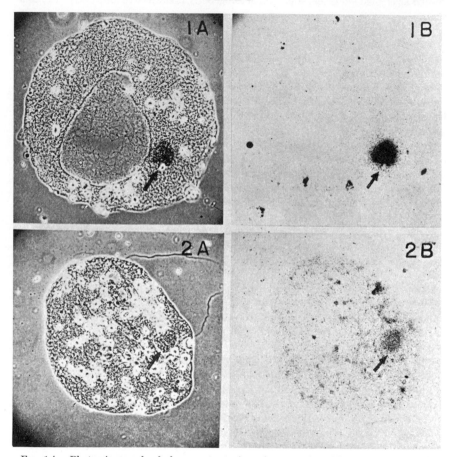

Fig. 1A.—Photomicrograph of phase-contrast view of an amoeba with a P^{32}-labeled nucleus grafted 6 minutes before fixation ($\times$117). Fig. 1B.—Photomicrograph of autoradiograph of same amoeba as in Fig. 1A. ($\times$117). Fig. 2A.—Photomicrograph of phase-contrast view of an amoeba with a P^{32}-labeled nucleus grafted 62 hours before fixation ($\times$117). Fig. 2B.—Photomicrograph of autoradiograph of same amoeba as in Fig. 2A ($\times$117). (Arrows indicate the location of the nuclei in each case.)

have been studied, the rate of transfer has not been estimated because the physiological state, i.e., the stage of cellular growth in the interphase of the mitotic cycle, of the "donor" and "host" amoebae involved in the transfers has not been controlled. We have not been able to see any consistent pattern in the change of the ratio of cytoplasmic to nuclear radioactivity with time. On the whole, of course, this ratio increases with time elasped following the transfer.   Nonetheless, we have observed instances in which a relatively short-time postoperative amoeba exhibited a higher ratio than an amoeba fixed considerably longer after the transfer operation.   This circumstance suggests that the mechanism responsible for the transfer of the labeled nuclear material to the cytoplasm is not simple diffusion.

Experiments with ribonuclease (0.04 per cent Worthington Biochemical Laboratory ribonuclease in distilled water adjusted to pH 6.7 with Na_2HPO_4, at 40° C. for 2–3 hours) have indicated that all the detectable radioactive label in nucleus and cytoplasm of these "renucleated" amoebae is in RNA.   Amoebae treated with this enzyme prior to autoradiography failed to show any significant radioactivity. Had the label left the nucleus as $P^{32}O_4$ and not as part of a more complex molecule, we would have expected some residual cytoplasmic label after ribonuclease digestion, since other phosphorus-containing compounds, such as phosphoproteins, are synthesized in significant quantities in the cytoplasm[11] and would not be removed during our processing.

Further evidence that the radioactive label leaves the nucleus as part of an entity more complex than the PO_4 ion is furnished by observations on twelve artificially binucleate amoebae in which a P^{32}-labeled nucleus had been transferred to an unlabeled cell already containing a nucleus.   After 12–90 hours of existence as binucleates, the cells were fixed and autoradiographed.   Examination of the photographically developed preparations showed that, whereas the labeled nucleus gradually lost its activity to the cytoplasm, the originally unlabeled nucleus did not acquire any significant amount of radioactivity (Pl. II, Figs. 3A and 3B).   Of the twelve cells studied, only two could be regarded as possible exceptions.   There appears, therefore, to be no transfer to the unlabeled nucleus of the labeled material the cytoplasm has received from the initially labeled nucleus.

One of the essential conditions to satisfy the hypothesis of RNA mediation between gene and cytoplasm is that the nucleus modifies the RNA that becomes localized in the cytoplasm.   It can do this either by synthesizing RNA and supplying it to the cytoplasm or by transferring to the cytoplasm a modified RNA precursor.   The evidence presented in this report suggests strongly that this required relationship between nuclear and cytoplasmic RNA exists.   We have shown that the labeled material leaves the nucleus and appears in the cytoplasm.   The labeled material in the nucleus initially, and in both nucleus and cytoplasm after a period of time, is in RNA, since all radioactivity is removed by digestion with ribonuclease.   The label is therefore in RNA at both the initial and the terminal points of its migration.   Moreover, the fact that the label demonstrated in the cytoplasmic RNA does not enter the second, initially unlabeled, nucleus of the binucleate cells leads to the conclusion that the cytoplasm does not supply RNA to the nucleus and that the nucleus, therefore, synthesizes its own.   If such a transfer were taking place, the autoradiograph of the originally unlabeled nucleus in the binucleates should show a higher level of radioactivity than that in the cytoplasm, since cytochemical evidence shows that the concentration of RNA in the nucleus of *A. proteus* is substantially higher than that in the cytoplasm.[8]   In ten of the twelve experimental binucleates studied there was no evidence for nuclear labeling in the initially unlabeled nucleus.   The other two cases (e.g., Pl. II, Fig. 4) indicated the *possibility* of some label in the second nucleus.   However, in view of the sharp

V. THE FUNCTION OF GENETIC MATERIAL

labeling contrast obtained between nucleus and cytoplasm when a labeled precursor is fed to amoebae (Pl. II, Fig. 5), such slight labeling, if significant at all, is more readily explicable as the result of a partial breakdown of labeled cytoplasmic RNA

PLATE II

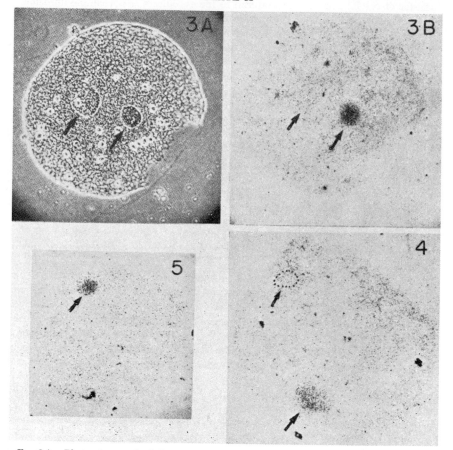

FIG. 3A.—Photomicrograph of phase-contrast view of a binucleate with one P^{32}-labeled nucleus grafted $42^1/_2$ hours before fixation ($\times$117). FIG. 3B.—Photomicrograph of autoradiograph of same amoeba as in Fig. 3A ($\times$117). The grains visible over the left nucleus are attributable to the radioactivity in the overlying and underlying cytoplasm. FIG. 4.—Photomicrograph of autoradiograph of a binucleate amoeba with one P^{32}-labeled nucleus grafted $43^1/_2$ hours before fixation ($\times$117). The dotted outline indicates the region of the originally unlabeled nucleus. (Phase-contrast view not presented because of insufficient contrast for photographic reproduction.) FIG. 5.—Photomicrograph of autoradiograph of an unoperated amoeba which was incubated in a C^{14}-adenine solution for 12 hours prior to fixation ($\times$120). (Arrows indicate the location of the nuclei in each case.)

and the consequent availability of some labeled precursor for resynthesis by the nucleus. It follows, then, that the nucleus synthesizes its RNA and that, while the nuclear RNA label appears in cytoplasmic RNA, the transfer proceeds in that direction only.

We do not know the identity of the P^{32}-containing entity which is supplied to the nucleus in the initial process of labeling. We know, however, that it is incorporated into the nuclear RNA. Similarly, we do not know the nature of the labeled material leaving the nucleus, but we know that it appears in cytoplasmic RNA. It cannot, however, be identical with the labeled entity originally incorporated into nuclear RNA. Were it identical, we would expect that it would be incorporated into the RNA of the second nucleus of a binucleate, as it was into that of the first nucleus, resulting in two labeled nuclei. This is not the case. It follows, therefore, that the labeled entity which appears first in nuclear RNA and subsequently in cytoplasmic RNA is modified by the nucleus. Thus we have shown that the relationship between nuclear and cytoplasmic RNA necessary to satisfy the hypothesis of RNA intermediacy between gene and cytoplasm exists: the evidence demonstrates that the product furnished to the cytoplasm by the nucleus, while not completely characterized, must be at least a nucleus-modified RNA precursor, if not RNA as such.

We have not proved that the labeled material migrating from nucleus to cytoplasm is the RNA as it actually existed in the nucleus, although this conclusion is consistent with our findings. Since we have shown that the nucleus is capable of synthesizing the finished RNA molecule, it appears to us most likely that it is RNA and not a precursor which is transferred. (These observations do not answer the question whether RNA as such or as ribonucleoprotein is transmitted.[12]) Moreover, the possibility of the complete synthesis of *some* RNA in the cytoplasm is not ruled out by our data. In point of fact, such synthesis has been suggested for *Acetabularia* by Brachet.[5] It would not be surprising if the amount of cytoplasmic RNA synthesis varied widely among cell types. The presence of some cytoplasmic synthesis of RNA could account for the data indicating differences in purine and pyrimidine composition of the RNA derived, respectively, from cytoplasm and nucleus. These heterogeneity data, now thought by some to rule out the possibility of nuclear synthesis of cytoplasmic RNA, could then be explained on the basis of contributory synthesis by the cytoplasm, although alternative explanations are not ruled out.

Summary.—A more direct experimental design than has heretofore been employed has been developed to test the hypothesis of nuclear synthesis of RNA and its transfer to the cytoplasm. The RNA of the nucleus was labeled with radioactive tracer, and the nucleus was grafted into a cell whose RNA was unlabeled. Transmission of labeled material from nucleus to cytoplasm was then traced directly by autoradiography. The evidence presented shows that RNA is synthesized in the nucleus and that RNA, or at least a nucleus-modified precursor of RNA, is transmitted to the cytoplasm.

We are indebted to Dr. Daniel Mazia for his generosity in providing the facilities and equipment to carry out this work and for his helpful suggestions in the preparation of the manuscript.

* Work performed during the tenure of a postdoctoral fellowship of the National Cancer Institute, United States Public Health Service. Present address: Cancer Research Institute, University of California Medical Center, San Francisco, California.

† Supported by University of California Cancer Research Funds and by grants from the American Cancer Society, recommended by the Committee on Growth, National Research Council, to Dr. Daniel Mazia.

V. THE FUNCTION OF GENETIC MATERIAL

[1] A. L. Dounce, *Nature*, **172**, 541, 1953; H. J. Muller, *Science*, **121**, 1–9, 1955; A. Rich and J. D. Watson, these Proceedings, **40**, 759–764, 1954.

[2] T. Caspersson, *Cell Growth and Cell Function* (Norton, N.Y., 1950).

[3] J. Brachet, *Arch. biol.* (*Liége*), **53**, 207–257, 1942.

[4] E. F. Gale and J. P. Folkes, *Biochem. J.*, **59**, 661–675, 675–684, 1955; *Nature*, **175**, 592–593, 1955.

[5] J. Brachet, in *The Nucleic Acids*, ed. E. Chargaff and J. N. Davidson (New York: Academic Press, Inc., 1955), Vol. **2**, chap. xxviii.

[6] C. P. Barnum, R. A. Huseby, and H. Vermund, *Cancer Research*, **13**, 880–889, 1953.

[7] J. Brachet, *Nature*, **175**, 851–853, 1955.

[8] M. Rabinovitch and W. Plaut, *Exptl. Cell Research*, (in press).

[9] T. James, *Biochim. et. biophys. acta*, **15**, 367–371, 1954.

[10] J. Commandon and P. deFonbrune, *Compt. rend. Soc. Biol.*, **130**, 740–748, 1939; I. J. Lorch and J. F. Danielli, *Quart. J. Microscop. Sci.*, **94**, 461–480, 1953.

[11] D. Mazia and S. Bendix, unpublished experiments.

[12] See particularly "Conclusions," in D. Mazia and D. M. Prescott, *Biochim. et. biophys. acta*, **17**, 23–34, 1955.

(*Reprinted from Nature*, Vol. 183, p. 1330 *only, May* 9, 1959)

Nuclear Origin of Ribonucleic Acid

LIVING hyphæ of *Neurospora crassa* were centrifuged and their contents stratified in distinct layers. Starting at the centrifugal end, the layers were as follows (Fig. 1): glycogen, ergastoplasm (microsomes), mitochondria, nuclei, 'supernatant' cytoplasm, vacuoles and fat. Each fraction could be identified by cytochemical reactions. It was found that most of the cytoplasmic ribonucleic acid resided in ergastoplasm, some in mitochondria, and none was detectable in the 'supernatant'. Nuclei were relatively poor in ribonucleic acid.

The fact that nuclei became clearly separated from the cytoplasmic ribonucleic acid enabled us to localize the site of formation of ribonucleic acid. Mycelium, in its active growth phase, was fed tritiated uridine (uridine-5,6-^{3}H, 640 mc. per m.mole, 100 μgm./ml.) for given times, centrifuged and fixed. The

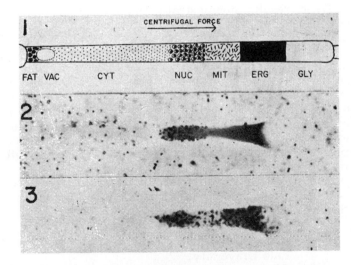

Fig. 1. Schematic presentation of a centrifuged hypha of *Neurospora*. *FAT*, fat; *VAC*, vacuole; *CYT*, 'supernatant' cytoplasm; *NUC*, nuclei; *MIT*, mitochondria; *ERG*, ergastoplasm (microsomes); *GLY*, glycogen. Centrifugal direction is to the right in all figures

Fig. 2. Autoradiograph of a centrifuged hypha fed tritiated uridine for 1 min. prior to centrifugation, stained with hæmalum. β-tracks in the nuclear layer; deeply stained layer, free of tracks, is ergastoplasm; glycogen and 'supernatant' not stained

Fig. 3. Autoradiograph of a centrifuged hypha fed tritiated uridine for 1 min. and unlabelled uridine for 1 hr., prior to centrifugation. β-tracks densest in ergastoplasm, less dense in nuclei and mitochondria; no significant increase of tracks over background in glycogen and 'supernatant'

mycelium was then washed in cold 5 per cent trichloracetic acid so that only nucleosides which were incorporated into ribonucleic acid remained. The preparation was mounted on a slide and covered with photographic emulsion[1]. After exposure and development, the autoradiographs showed tracks of β-decay at the sites of uptake of the precursor.

At short feeding times, from 1 to 4 min., the label appeared only in the nuclear fraction (Fig. 2). After 4 min., more and more label was found in cytoplasmic ribonucleic acid. In 1 hr., ergastoplasm was labelled much more heavily than the nuclei (Fig. 3), and some activity was found also in mitochondria, while the 'supernatant' remained virtually inactive. In brief, the distribution of the label became roughly proportional to the relative content of ribonucleic acid in the different fractions. When tritiated uridine was fed for 1 min. only and then washed out and replaced with an excess of non-labelled uridine, the label again appeared first in nuclei, to appear in the ergastoplasm only after several minutes. The labelling of ergastoplasm increased with time at the expense of nuclear label.

These results demonstrate that all the cellular ribonucleic acid is formed in nuclei and that it migrates into the cytoplasm later. Previous work of several investigators indicated that ribonucleic acid originated in nuclei[2] and the present experiments substantiate this hypothesis. These findings suggest that ribonucleic acid is a direct product of gene action. Ribonucleic acid is formed in nuclei, the seat of chromosomes and genes ; it migrates into the cytoplasm ; and it is required for the synthesis of proteins. A detailed report of this investigation will be published elsewhere.

This work was supported by a grant from the National Institutes of Health, U.S. Public Health Service.

M. ZALOKAR

Department of Microbiology,
    Yale University,
  New Haven, Connecticut.

[1] Ficq, A., *Arch. Biol.*, **66**, 509 (1955).
[2] Brachet, J., "Chemical Cytology" (Academic Press, New York 1957).

Reprinted from Annals of The New York Academy of Sciences
Volume 90, Article 2, Pages 409-421
October 7, 1960

NUCLEIC ACID SYNTHESIS IN RELATION
TO THE CELL DIVISION CYCLE*

J. Herbert Taylor

Department of Botany and Department of Zoology, Columbia University, New York, N. Y.

Introduction

The cyclic nature of DNA (deoxyribonucleic acid) synthesis in relation to cell division is now well established. The evidence that synthesis regularly occurs in interphase and coincides with the duplication of the chromosomes has been reviewed previously (Taylor, 1957). Studies on the distribution of tritium-thymidine incorporated into chromosomes show that duplication is accomplished by separation of the two original DNA subunits of each chromosome and by the synthesis of two new subunits. At the following division each chromatid (daughter chromosome) receives one original and one new subunit. The new subunit labeled by the tritium in each chromosome is passed on intact to one of the daughter chromosomes descended from these labeled chromosomes (Taylor et al., 1957). The subunits are conserved at each duplication and only become disrupted by an occasional sister chromatid exchange, that is, exchange between the daughter chromosomes that probably occurs during duplication (Taylor, 1959a).

Cyclic changes of RNA synthesis in relation to cell division are less well understood and appear to be less predictable. A few instances in which RNA synthesis stopped or fell to a low level during chromosome duplication have been reported (Taylor, 1958, 1959b; Sisken, 1959). However, this is not a regular occurrence (Woods and Taylor, 1959) and there are many types of cells in which the synthesis of both types of nucleic acids proceeds simultaneously.

One cyclic change that appears to be regular is the failure of cells with condensed chromosomes to form new RNA. In several types of cells indications that RNA synthesis stops during the middle stages of division have been observed (Taylor, 1958 and 1959b).

By the use of autoradiography and tritium-labeled nucleosides of high specific activity, especially with cells in sterile culture, a more critical analysis of the cyclic changes in RNA synthesis is now possible. The objective in the present work was to obtain additional information on the site of synthesis of RNA and to study cyclic variations in relation to the division stages.

Materials and Methods

Two strains of connective tissue cells ($\female$ 1404 and $\male$ A1290) isolated from embryonic tissues of Chinese hamsters by George Yerganian, Children's Cancer Research Foundation, Boston, Mass., have been used in these studies. The cells have maintained a near diploid chromosome number (2n + 1 or 2)

* The experiments described in this paper were begun while the author was a Guggenheim Fellow at the Biology Division, California Institute of Technology, Pasadena, Calif. The work done at Columbia University was supported in part by grants under Contract AT(30-1) 1304 from the Atomic Energy Commission, Washington, D. C., and the Eugene Higgins Fund, Columbia University, New York, N. Y.

V. THE FUNCTION OF GENETIC MATERIAL

during several months in culture. During these experiments they were grown in Eagle's medium with 15 per cent calf serum. Tritium-labeled thymidine (sp. act. 1.8 curies/mm.) and cytidine (sp. act. 360 mc./mm.) were mixed with a medium in which cells had been growing for 18 to 24 hours. All cultures were grown attached to cover glasses in 5 ml. of medium in small Petri dishes. These were maintained at 37° C. in an atmosphere of 5 per cent CO_2 in air. In most of these experiments the cover glasses with cells attached were immersed in the labeled medium (0.1 μc./ml. for thymidine-H^3 and 1.0 μc./ml. for cytidine-H^3) for 5 to 10 min. and, after rinsing in a medium with excess unlabeled nucleosides, were allowed to grow in the presence of an excess of the unlabeled nucleosides to quickly dilute any remaining labeled precursors. Thymidine at 100 times the concentration of the thymidine-H^3 was added to a medium in which cells had been growing for 18 to 24 hours. To dilute the cytidine-H^3 and its derivatives, unlabeled cytidine and uridine, each at 25 times the molar concentration of the cytidine-H^3, were added to a similar medium.

Cells were fixed for 5 to 10 min. after rinsing a few seconds in a balanced salt solution. Fixatives used were alcohol-acetic acid (3:1) or an alcoholic Bouin's fluid (80 per cent ethanol, 150 cc.; formalin, 60 cc.; glacial acetic acid, 15 cc; picric acid, 1 gm.). The cells were either air-dried or transferred to 95 per cent ethanol after fixing. After appropriate extraction of the cells with cold TCA (trichloroacetic acid) to retain RNA, and 1 N HCl at 60° for 7 min. or after digestion in ribonuclease for the removal of RNA (Taylor, 1959b), the preparations were again rinsed in 95 per cent alcohol and air-dried. The cover glasses were fixed by the use of Euparal or Diaphane to slides with the the cells exposed. When the preparations had dried for a few days the slides were coated with Kodak AR-10 stripping film. The autoradiograms were developed after appropriate exposure (3 days to 3 weeks). HCl-hydrolyzed material was stained by the Feulgen reaction before applying the film. The slides with unstained cells were developed and stained according to the following schedule with all solutions at 18 to 20° C.: 5 min. in one-half strength D-19 at 18° C.; 30 sec. in water for rinsing off developer; 10 min. in one-half strength Kodak acid fixer; 5 min. in water for rinsing off excess hypo; 2 min. in Kodak hypo clearing agent (one-half strength); 5 min. in several changes of fresh water; 20 min. in a staining solution (20 mg. of azure B bromide and 0.5 gm. of potassium acid phthalate in 100 ml. of distilled water); rinse for 20 to 30 sec. in water and air dry.

The stripping film was applied by floating pieces of the appropriate size on water at 25 to 26° C. The film was also dried at this same temperature. The control of temperature is important, for the film should remain expanded during drying to approximately the same extent that it will expand in the developing solution. Otherwise the film may become loose and fall off the slides.

Results

The duplication of the chromosomes (synthesis of DNA) in relation to the cell division cycle. Details of this experiment have been described elsewhere (Taylor, 1960), but a summary of the findings are necessary as a basis for the studies on RNA synthesis. Cells were exposed to thymidine-H³ for 10 min., rinsed and transferred to a medium with excess unlabeled thymidine. Samples were fixed at intervals and examined with respect to the percentage of labeled interphase nuclei and division figures. Other slides were handled in a similar way except that the contact with thymidine-H³ was 30 min. These slides were used to show that the labeled precursors were depleted or diluted within less than a minute. Grain counting in the autoradiograms showed that no detectable amount of label DNA accumulated after removing the cells to the medium with excess unlabeled thymidine. The H³ already incorporated into DNA was, however, all retained and equally distributed to each two daughter cells at division.

By counting the labeled and unlabeled interphase nuclei and division figures, the data shown in FIGURE 1 were collected. After a 10-min. labeling period, 43 per cent of the interphase nuclei were labeled. Labeled division figures did not appear for nearly two hours. This measures the shortest interval between the end of DNA replication and late prophase or metaphase. Within three hours nearly 100 per cent of the cells reaching division contained labeled chromosomes. This indicates that the interval between the end of synthesis and division is usually between two and three hours. The population of labeled cells continued to divide during the next 6 or 7 hours. However, by the eleventh hour after labeling nearly all labeled cells had divided. Most of the cells dividing between the eleventh and twelfth hours were at stages preceding DNA synthesis during the contact with thymidine-H³. The few labeled division figures were made up of cells that were slow in dividing and a few that were already at the second division after labeling; these had only one chromatid of each chromosome labeled. By twenty hours the frequency of labeled division figures was again at a peak (FIGURE 1). The length of one cycle can be estimated from the interval between the two peaks and is approximately 14 hours. The average time the cell spends in DNA replication can be calculated from the percentage of cells that were incorporating thymidine-H³ at any instant in the cycle. When the percentage of cells labeled after 10 min. is multiplied by the average generation time (0.43 × 14 hrs.) an interval of approximately 6 hours is obtained for the period of DNA replication. The division stages from mid-prophase to mid-telophase occupy about 30 min. (see section below). If 6 hours is taken as the average replication time, $2\frac{1}{2}$ hours as the interval between replication and late prophase and one-half hour for the remainder of the division stages, the difference between the sum of these times and 14 hours is 5 hours, the postdivision interval before another replication begins.

The shaded portion of the bars in FIGURE 1 shows the percentage of division figures with more than one half of the length of the chromosome complement labeled by the thymidine-H³. Duplication of the chromosomes in the cells of Chinese hamster is asynchronous for various chromosomes and different sectors of individual chromosomes. Contact with thymidine-H³ for only 10 min. of a duplication cycle of 6 hours reveals the pattern of the asynchronous duplication. Details have been reported previously (Taylor, 1960). The Y chromosome, the long arm of the X chromosome, the short arms of 2 medium-

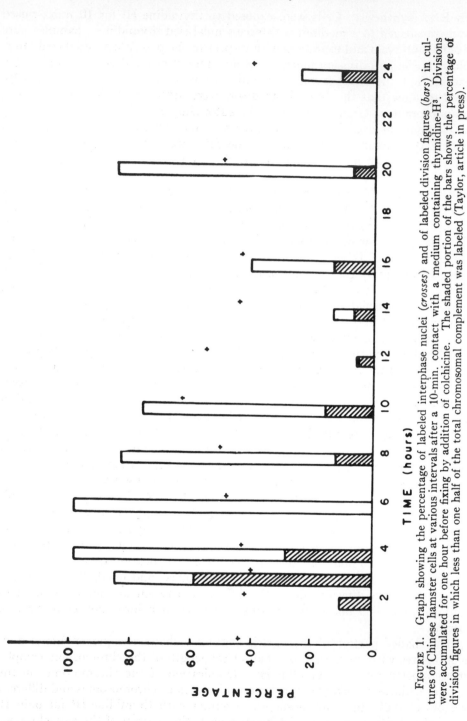

FIGURE 1. Graph showing the percentage of labeled interphase nuclei (*crosses*) and of labeled division figures (*bars*) in cultures of Chinese hamster cells at various intervals after a 10-min. contact with a medium containing thymidine-H³. Divisions were accumulated for one hour before fixing by addition of colchicine. The shaded portion of the bars shows the percentage of division figures in which less than one half of the total chromosomal complement was labeled (Taylor, article in press).

sized chromosomes, and the major portions of 2 pairs of small chromosomes were regularly duplicated in the last half of the period of DNA synthesis. When the thymidine-H³ was available only during the last 30 min. of the period of DNA replication nearly all of the isotope incorporated was in these chromosomes.

The sequence of duplication was similar in the two strains of cells examined, except that the 2 X chromosomes of the female strain were different. One had the pattern typical of the X chromosome in the male, that is, the short arm duplicated early and the long arm late. However, the other X chromosome had both arms duplicated late.

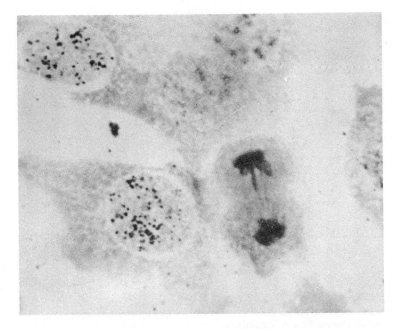

Figure 2. An autoradiogram showing cells fixed immediately after a 10-min. period in contact with a medium containing cytidine-H³. Note that only interphase nuclei are labeled; cells in division do not incorporate the cytidine into RNA.

The synthesis of RNA during the cell cycle. When the cytidine-H³ was supplied to the Chinese hamster cells for 5 to 10 min., only the nuclear RNA was labeled (FIGURE 2). The slides from which data were collected were exposed to the film for 10 days and there was an average of 86 grains over the nucleus (TABLE 1), and none detectable above background over the cytoplasm. Even when the cells were exposed to the film for 21 days, the label in the cytoplasm was not detectable. Therefore, a real lag period occurs before any labeled RNA appears in the cytoplasm. This should not occur if the difference in labeling of RNA in cytoplasm and nucleus were due to differences in turnover rates. Both should be labeled simultaneously and the amount of label in both should increase linearly until equilibration begins to produce a differential effect. The lag indicates that synthesis of RNA occurs only in the nucleus and is later transferred to the cytoplasm. This hypothesis is supported by the fact that essentially all of the label RNA has disappeared from the nuclei within four hours (FIGURE 3). Only cells that were in the period of DNA replication (about 43 per cent) take up tritium that is retained in the nucleus. Most if not all of this is incorporated into DNA.

However, to get additional evidence concerning the transfer hypothesis, the changes in distribution of the labeled RNA was observed at intervals after the removal of cells to a medium without cytidine-H³. A group of cultures were prepared from a population of cells growing in 1 culture vessel. After the new cultures had been growing for about 24 to 36 hours on cover glasses, they were placed in a medium with 1 μc. of cytidine-H³ per ml. Samples were fixed

TABLE 1

AUTORADIOGRAPHIC DATA ON INCORPORATION OF CYTIDINE-H³ INTO RNA OF CHINESE HAMSTER CELLS IN CULTURE

Time after incorporation began	Total grains with standard errors over nucleus or cytoplasm and an equivalent area without cells (background)*			
	Nucleus	Background	Cytoplasm	Background
Strain A1290				
5–6 min.	57.0 ± 2.1	2.0 ± 0.4	3.0 ± 0.3	4.0 ± 0.3
10 min.	86.3 ± 2.1	2.9 ± 0.4	3.3 ± 0.3	6.4 ± 0.6
10 + 10 min.	77.0 ± 1.8	2.9 ± 0.8	5.2 ± 0.4	5.0 ± 0.5
10 + 30 min.	57.3 ± 1.7	3.4 ± 0.4	25.2 ± 1.2	7.4 ± 0.7
10 + 60 min.	{56.1 ± 2.1}† {82.5 ± 2.3}	3.0 ± 0.4	{58.6 ± 3.0}† {67.6 ± 2.3}	6.6 ± 0.8
10 + 2½ hours	{34.5 ± 2.4}† {69.6 ± 2.1}	2.4 ± 0.6	{106.1 ± 5.9}† {127.5 ± 6.4}	6.0 ± 0.5
10 + 4 hours	{25.8 ± 2.5}† {85.8 ± 3.8}	3.4 ± 0.3	{115.8 ± 8.1}† {139.5 ± 7.4}	6.9 ± 0.5
Strain 1404				
5 min.	34.9 ± 1.5	1.2 ± 0.3	2.3 ± 0.3	4.3 ± 0.7
10 min.	64.1 ± 2.4	1.8 ± 0.5	4.3 ± 0.4	6.1 ± 0.6
10 + 10 min.	65.0 ± 3.3	0.8 ± 0.3	6.9 ± 0.4	3.4 ± 0.4

* Average number of grains over 50 cells and background count over 10 areas of the same average area as the nucleus or cytoplasm.

† Since the amount of labeled DNA in the nucleus raises the count considerably after one half hour, the cells were divided into two classes: the 56 per cent with the lowest counts and the remaining 44 per cent (number estimated to be in DNA synthesis during the 10-min. contact).

after 5 to 6 and 10 min. in an alcoholic Bouin's fluid. The remaining cultures were rinsed in an isotope-free medium with excess unlabeled cytidine and uridine added. They were then transferred to another dish of similar medium for the remaining period of culture. All of these media were conditioned by having cells growing in them for 18 to 24 hours before use, so that uninterrupted growth would be maintained. Samples were fixed at intervals, autoradiograms prepared and the grain counts over nuclei and cytoplasm are shown in TABLE 1 and interpreted in FIGURE 4. Samples of the cells were also fixed in alcohol:acetic acid (3:1), but the autoradiograms indicated that some of the RNA leaks out of the cells with this fixative. Therefore, grain counts are given only for the material fixed in alcoholic Bouin's fixative that would be expected to precipitate and bind all polynucleotides in the cell.

The data (FIGURE 4) indicate that incorporation begins immediately in the nucleus and continues at a nearly linear rate for the 10 min. of contact. After removal and transfer of the cells to a nonradioactive medium, the dilution of precursors must be very rapid, for the grain counts at 10 min. after removal were the same or slightly lower than those for cells fixed at the time of removal. From this information one may conclude that the population of cells have labeled RNA only in the nucleus and that the total amount of labeled RNA does not significantly increase after removal of the cell from medium with cytidine-H^3. Any change in total grain counts per cell will be due to changes

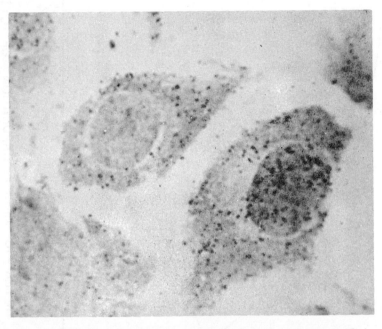

FIGURE 3. An autoradiogram showing cells treated as those in FIGURE 2, but after 10 min. the cells were washed and transferred to a medium free of cytidine-H^3 and with an excess of unlabeled cytidine and uridine for four hours. More than one half of the cells have all of the tritium in the cytoplasm where it is still incorporated in RNA. The other cells have essentially all of the labeled RNA in the cytoplasm but some tritium remains in the nucleus (lower right) of those cells that incorporate derivatives of the cytidine-H^3 into DNA.

in position of the label within the cell. The prediction would be made that as the label moves into the thin layers of cytoplasm, the efficiency of the low energy beta radiation from tritium will increase because there is less overlying shielding material. Therefore the grain counts will rise with time even though the amount of labeled RNA remains constant. Unfortunately a quantitative estimate cannot be given, for several parameters are unknown in the cells. For example, they are thickest at the nucleus and from its borders the cytoplasm tapers out to an extremely thin sheet. Usually a thin sheet of cytoplasm extends over the upper surface of the nucleus, but in some preparations this sheet bursts during fixing and drying and the naked nucleus is exposed to the film (FIGURE 3).

For the above reasons the redistribution of the label cannot be followed in

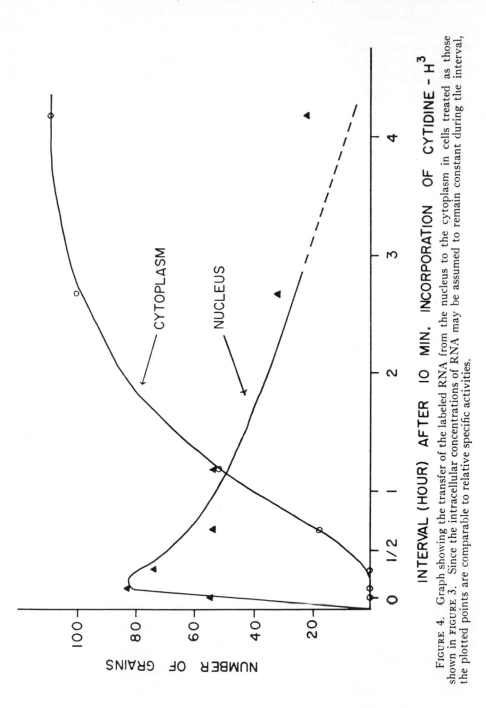

FIGURE 4. Graph showing the transfer of the labeled RNA from the nucleus to the cytoplasm in cells treated as those shown in FIGURE 3. Since the intracellular concentrations of RNA may be assumed to remain constant during the interval, the plotted points are comparable to relative specific activities.

an accurate quantitative analysis. Nevertheless the changes in geometry are not sufficient to completely distort the picture. By 10 plus 30 min. a measurable amount of the label has moved into the cytoplasm, but the total grain count per cell has not increased significantly. This might lead one to conclude that a turnover of a small fraction of the RNA is occurring that compensates for the expected increase in grain counts. By 10 plus 60 min. the expected increase in grains per cell is evident (TABLE 1). The increase was observed up to 4 hours, but the rate decreases between $2\frac{1}{2}$ and 4 hours when most of the labeled RNA has moved into the cytoplasm. All during this period as the grains over the cytoplasm increase, the labeled RNA in the nucleus decreases at the rate expected if it were contributing the label that now appears in the cytoplasm. Indeed, since there is no additional labeling indicated, the nucleus is the only source for labeled RNA. In the counts of cells at random over the slides about 43 per cent (FIGURE 1) will be selected that were in the period of DNA synthesis during the contact with cytidine-H^3. In plotting the data in FIGURE 4 account of this was taken by separating the cells into two classes (TABLE 1), those with high nuclear counts and those with low nuclear counts. Only the 56 per cent with the lowest nuclear counts were used to arrive at the points for 10 min. plus 1, $2\frac{1}{2}$, and 4 hours. A further correction should be made for the nuclei at 2 and 4 hours. By that time nearly all of the labeled RNA had moved out of the nucleus (FIGURE 3) but because many of the cells have overlying cytoplasm the count over the nucleus would be higher than its relative content of radioactivity. The dotted line in FIGURE 4 is drawn to take this into account. Since nearly all of the labeled RNA has moved out of the nucleus in 4 hours and little if any reincorporation has occurred, there is no considerable amount of RNA that is broken down into a pool of precursors that are not diluted by the cytidine and uridine from the medium. However, there is an increase in labeled DNA with time (TABLE 1). Cells digested with ribonuclease after 10 min. contact with cytidine-H^3 show very little labeled DNA. When these are removed to the medium with an excess of unlabeled cytidine and uridine, the amount of label in DNA increases so that a readily detectable amount is seen in the cells at 1, $2\frac{1}{2}$, and 4 hours after contact with cytidine-H^3. This would be predicted if some of the labeled pyridines are transferred into the pool of deoxyribotides, and if this pool is much less effectively diluted by the excess cytidine and uridine than the pool of labeled ribotides.

Altogether the above information indicates that essentially all of the RNA of these cells is produced in the nucleus and that it moves to the cytoplasm in a form that cannot be diluted by the pool of unlabeled pyrimidine derivatives. Although there is no direct evidence for a breakdown and loss of part of the labeled RNA, such a turnover of a fraction with a short half-life cannot be excluded from these experiments because of the changing geometry of the intracellular RNA with respect to the autoradiographic emulsion.

The role of the nucleolus in RNA metabolism is difficult to determine in these cells. Labeled RNA appears very soon in the nucleolus, but at the same time it is distributed throughout most of the nucleus. In one strain of cells (♀1404) the nucleoli are rather discrete and there are only a few in each cell.

On the other hand in the strain ($\male$A1290) there appear to be more regions on the chromosomes where nucleolar material collects and large nucleoli are not usually visible. In the early prophase cells of strain 1404, most of the labeled RNA is localized in nucleoli, but in the other strain the RNA labeled during the preceding 10 to 20 min. is more uniformly distributed over the chromosomes. When the cells are treated with colchicine during the incorporation and the succeeding period, up to 1 or 2 hours, much of the labeled RNA remains associated with the chromosomes in the colchicine blocked metaphases. In the absence of colchicine, however, most of the labeled RNA has dispersed into the cytoplasm before metaphase. Then during the reorganization of the nuclei at telophase, relatively little of the labeled RNA was included in the nuclei. There was variation among nuclei and sometimes a detectable amount of the label that remained nearby appeared to be included in the reorganizing nucleus as if by accident.

TABLE 2

RATIOS OF CELLS AT VARIOUS STAGES OF DIVISION WITH OR WITHOUT LABELED RNA (LABELED:UNLABELED) AT VARIOUS INTERVALS AFTER INCORPORATION OF CYTIDINE-H³ BEGAN

Stages of division	5 min.	10 min.	10 + 10 min.*	10 + 30 min.*	10 + 60 min.*
Early prophase	15:8	35:0	25:0	28:0	32:0
Mid-prophase	13:7	17:4	15:0	19:0	14:0
Late prophase	1:30	11:12	19:4	24:0	16:0
Metaphase	0:49	0:50	35:23	54:2	29:1
Anaphase	0:34	0:26	6:36	28:0	28:1
Early telophase	0:12	0:12	0:23	17:1	14:0
Late telophase	18:19	25:12	9:9	27:0	23:0

* Ten minutes in a medium with cytidine-H³ with the additional period in the medium with an excess of unlabeled cytidine and uridine.

Discontinuities in RNA synthesis associated with mitosis. Incorporation of cytidine-H³ occurred at all stages in interphase and in mitosis until about mid-prophase. As the chromosomes became condensed the synthesis of RNA stopped (TABLE 2 and FIGURE 2) even though the nucleoli were still present. This observation might be used as evidence that the expanded chromosomes are essential for RNA synthesis, for during about 30 min. from mid-prophase to mid-telophase there is no synthesis of RNA detectable by incorporation of cytidine-H³. This is not due to the failure of the dividing cell to take up and incorporate materials from the medium, for arginine-H³ is incorporated into proteins of the cytoplasm at about the rate characteristic of interphase stages.

Another difference between the behavior of RNA in prophase and interphase is the rate at which it moves to the cytoplasm. The movement is faster in late prophase. The more rapid dispersion may be associated with the breakdown of the nuclear membrane. In the cells fixed 30 min. after removal from the medium with cytidine-H³, less than one third of the label had moved to the cytoplasm in cells at interphase (TABLE 1). However, if the cells were at late prophase or metaphase when fixed, most of the labeled RNA was already in the cytoplasm. As mentioned above, an exception was found when the cells were treated with colchicine.

Colchicine was utilized in another way to find whether synthesis or turnover of RNA could be detected in the cytoplasm after longer periods of contact than from mid-prophase to mid-telophase. Cells were placed in a medium with colchicine for 2 hours and then in a medium with both colchicine and cytidine-H^3 for 2 hours. When the cells were fixed and autoradiograms prepared, about 50 per cent of the cells blocked at division were labeled and about 50 per cent were almost unlabeled. Those with label were cells that had reached division during the 2 hours in cytidine-H^3 and therefore had a chance to incorporate label before the chromosomes condensed. Those without label had been blocked during the two hours before being placed in the medium with cytidine-H^3. Therefore during the whole period in contact with label, the chromosomes had been supercondensed according to the reaction typical with colchicine.

Cells that were in isotope for 2 hours with colchicine contained a trace of label, perhaps 2 to 3 per cent of the amount present in interphase cells. No tests were performed to show that the trace of label was in RNA, but in alcohol-acetic acid fixed cells it did not appear to be retained. Perhaps it was a soluble RNA or protein-bound nucleotide. The principal result is clear; although colchicine has no effect on synthesis of RNA in interphase cells, it prevents synthesis in cells by holding the chromosomes in a condensed metaphase state for prolonged periods. The uptake and incorporation of arginine-H^3 into the cytoplasm of cells held in division by colchicine was little if any diminished during a two-hour period with conditions similar to those used for the experiments on cytidine incorporation.

The data recorded in TABLE 2 show the interruption of RNA synthesis associated with division and also provide a measure of the duration of some of the division stages. After 5 min. contact with cytidine-H^3 early and midprophases and late telophases were labeled. By 10 min. late prophases but no metaphases were labeled. Therefore synthesis of RNA ceases 10 min. or more before metaphase. Within another 10 min. nearly all metaphases and a few anaphases were labeled. No early telophases were labeled, but 40 min. after contact with cytidine-H^3 all anaphases and nearly all early telophases were labeled. Therefore, the duration of all stages from mid-prophase to mid-telophase is about 30 min.

Discussion

Tritium-labeled nucleosides of high specific activity and cells in culture provide favorable materials for studying short term incorporation. This allows an analysis of the sequence of duplication of the chromosomes, for the events in 5 to 10 min. of a DNA synthetic period of about 6 hours can be seen. The analysis clearly shows that not all parts of the chromosome complement are duplicated simultaneously. The sequence of duplication is a strain characteristic, but since only two strains, one isolated from a male and one from a female embryo, have been examined generalizations should be made with caution. However, the different timing in duplication of the long arm of the two X chromosomes in the female suggests that heterozygosity with respect to duplication time may exist (Taylor, article in press).

The experiments show that dilution of the thymidine-H^3 in the cells at the concentrations used is almost instantaneous. Once incorporated into DNA, however, the tritium is conserved and equally distributed to the daughter cells.

Similar experiments with cytidine-H^3 as the source of label reveal that the labeled precursors can be diluted quite rapidly but the quantitative aspects of the study do not exclude a turnover of a fraction of the RNA. Cytidine-H^3 is rapidly deaminated in higher plant cells (Taylor, 1959b) and in HeLa cells (Taylor, unpublished) so that uracil and, to a lesser extent, thymine-containing nucleotides are labeled. Addition of an excess of unlabeled uridine and cytidine can rapidly dilute the pool of labeled nucleotides so that increase in labeled RNA was prevented in these Chinese hamster cells. However, this conclusion had to be based on evidence collected over a very short time interval. As soon as significant amounts of labeled RNA moves from the nucleus to the cytoplasm, the geometrical relations of film and site of radioactive material are changed and further quantitative comparisons cannot be made. Since no increase in labeled RNA occurred during the first 10 min. interval after removal from the medium with isotope, one may conclude that the precursors were effectively diluted by the excess cytidine and uridine. After this inital period, the total grain count per cell increased, but this increase would be predicted without a net increase in labeled RNA if it moves from the nucleus to the cytoplasm.

Failure to take this change into account may have led Harris (1959) to reach a different interpretation of autoradiographic data on cells in culture. Harris assumed that no change in efficiency would occur and therefore considered the increase in grains to be due to incorporation of soluble precursors that could not be diluted by excess uridine and cytidine from the medium. Although independent evidence indicated that the specific activity of the RNA continued to increase, the autoradiographic data probably reflect both changes, the actual increase and the increase due to change in geometry. In his experiments the grains over the nucleus did not begin to decrease immediately as the cytoplasmic labeling rose. Although he reached the conclusion that nuclear and cytoplasmic synthesis were independent events, his data are compatible with the hypothesis that all RNA is formed in the nucleus. The residual precursors, if only utilized for synthesis of RNA in the nucleus followed by transport to the cytoplasm, would have kept the grain count over the nucleus from dropping immediately.

Since in the Chinese hamster cells there is no increase in labeled RNA after the 10-min. labeling period, all of the label that later appears in the cytoplasm must have come from the nucleus. If there were an apreciable turnover of RNA, the amount of labeled RNA in the nucleus would not have fallen to such a low level as shown in FIGURE 3 because the concentration of RNA in the nucleus is as high or higher than in the cytoplasm. From these experiments no quantitative measure of turnover can be given because the grain count increases during the four-hour period studied. A small amount of turnover could have been compensated for by the change in geometry. However, there is no evidence indicating that a measurable turnover occurs in cells in log-phase growth. Indeed the evidence is on the other side. Siminovitch and Graham (1956) found none and the data of Harris (1959) indicate that connective tissue cells in culture show no turnover between 4 and 12 hours after incorporating adenosine-H^3 into RNA. Harris found a turnover in macrophages in cultures that were not growing. Perhaps in these most of the label was incorporated in the soluble RNA which may turnover during protein synthesis, while in rapidly growing cells most of the label is incorporated into RNA of ribosomes.

Summary

Nucleic acid metabolism was studied with cells of Chinese hamster in culture by use of tritium-labeled nucleosides and autoradiography. Chromosomes of a single complement were shown to duplicate asynchronously. Difference in timing occurred among the different chromosomes and within a single chromosome. The patterns of duplication are a strain characteristic, but vary in the two strains examined.

RNA synthesis was shown to be confined to the nucleus in these cells. Incorporation of nucleosides was continuous in the rapidly growing cells except that it stopped when the chromosomes were condensed during division. In the same cells protein synthesis as measured by amino acid incorporation in the cytoplasm was unaffected by the division stage. After cells incorporate cytidine-H^3 for only 5 to 10 min. all of the labeled RNA is in the nucleus. By washing and removing the cells to a medium free of labeled nucleosides and with excess unlabeled cytidine and uridine further incorporation of the labeled precursors in RNA could be effectively stopped. The labeled RNA of such cells is nearly all found in the cytoplasm after about four hours.

Acknowledgment

The able technical assistance of Jeanne Tung is gratefully acknowledged.

References

HARRIS, H. 1959. Turnover of nuclear and cytoplasmic ribonucleic acid in two types of animal cell, with some further observations on the nucleolus. Biochem. J. **73:** 362–369.

SIMINOVITCH, L., & A. F. GRAHAM. 1956. Significance of ribonucleic acid and deoxyribonucleic acid turnover studies. J. Histochem. Cytochem. **4:** 508–515.

SISKEN, J. E. 1959. The synthesis of nucleic acids and proteins in the nuclei of *Tradescantia* root tips. Exptl. Cell Research. **16:** 602–614.

TAYLOR, J. H. 1957. The time and mode of chromosome duplication. Am. Naturalists. **91:** 209–221.

TAYLOR, J. H. 1958. Incorporation of phosphorus-32 into nucleic acids and proteins during microgametogenesis of Tulbaghia. Am. J. Botany. **45:** 123–131.

TAYLOR, J. H. 1959a. The organization and duplication of genetic material. Proc. 10th Intern. Congr. Genetics. **1:** 63–78.

TAYLOR, J. H. 1959b. Autoradiographic studies of nucleic acids and proteins during meiosis in Lilium longiflorum. Am. J. Botany. **46:** 477–484.

TAYLOR, J. H. Asynchronous duplication of chromosomes in cultured cells of Chinese hamster. J. Biophys. Biochem. Cytol. **7.** In press.

TAYLOR, J. H., P. S. WOODS & W. L. HUGHES. 1957. The organization and duplication of chromosomes as revealed by autoradiographic studies using tritium-labeled thymidine. Proc. Natl. Acad. Sci. U. S. **43:** 122–128.

WOODS, P. S. & J. H. TAYLOR. 1959. Studies of ribonucleic acid metabolism with tritium-labeled cytidine. Lab. Invest. **8:** 309–318.

Reprinted from Science, August 25, 1961, Vol. 134, No. 3478, pages 556-557

Table 1. Incorporaton of precursors into protein, RNA, and DNA*

Compound	Control	Actino-mycin treated
Leucine-H³ into protein	50,980	49,620
Uridine-H³ into RNA	160,500	66,500
Thymidine-H³ into DNA	194,000	181,000

* Values expressed as total counts per minute for infinitely thin platings' of equal aliquots obtained as follows: one pair of replicate cultures incubated in Eagle's medium containing 0.2 mmole of L-leucine received DL-leucine-H³ (1 μc/ml) and thymidine-H³ (0.5 μc, 0.4 μg/ml) and the second pair uridine-H³ (0.5 μc, 0.8 μg/ml). One culture of each pair was exposed to actinomycin (0.2 μg/ml) for 30 min before and 3½ hours after addition of labeled compounds. Samples of 25 ml each were centrifuged and carriers added: they were then washed with phosphate-buffered saline, extracted with cold 0.25N HClO₄ for 1 hour, and washed with ethanol and ethanol-ether. For leucine and thymidine determinations the washed pellets were hydrolyzed in 0.5N HClO₄, washed with ethanol and ethanol-ether and the pellets and hydrolysates were counted. For uridine measurement the pellets were incubated with ribonuclease (150 μg/ml) for 2 hours at 37°C in .005M tris buffer, pH 8, made 0.2N with HClO₄, centrifuged, and the supernatant was counted.

Effect of Actinomycin D on Cellular Nucleic Acid Synthesis and Virus Production

Abstract. Actinomycin D inhibits the synthesis of ribonucleic acid in L cells and the yield of vaccinia virus containing deoxyribonucleic acid, but it does not inhibit cellular deoxyribonucleic acid synthesis or the multiplication of Mengo virus containing ribonucleic acid. These observations serve to distinguish the replication of viral ribonucleic from ribonucleic acid synthesis which is controlled by viral or cellular deoxyribonucleic acid.

Actinomycin D is a bright red antibiotic containing two peptides, which was first reported by Vining and Waksman [1]. It possesses strong antibacterial activity against gram-positive organisms [2] and, on a weight basis, is the most potent chemotherapeutic antitumor agent known [3]. It has been reported to be antimutagenic [4].

Mammalian cells grown in the presence of actinomycin D lose their nucleoli and much of their histochemically demonstrable ribonucleic acid (RNA) [5, 6]. In the present study we report that actinomycin selectively and irreversibly suppresses mammalian cellular RNA biosynthesis, at least up to 48 hours after exposure—the period during which affected cells have been observed.

Strain 929 L-cells monolayers were maintained and propagated as previously described [6]. In addition, spinner cultures [7] were employed. Cell monolayers, seeded on cover slips and exposed to suitable radioactive nucleic acid precursors, were examined autoradiographically by the method of Doniach and Pelc [8].

When normal L cells are incubated with H³-cytidine (0.5 μc, 0.4μg/ml, 3 to 6 hours) and inspected after radioautography, a portion of the radioactivity incorporated into acid-insoluble material may be solubilized by deoxyribonuclease. The remainder can be rendered acid-soluble by digestion with ribonuclease.

After exposure to actinomycin D (1.0 μg/ml for 8 hours) and subsequent incubation for 16 hours, L cells continue to incorporate H³-cytidine into acid-insoluble material. In this case, however, none of the incorporated radioactivity becomes acid-soluble after ribonuclease treatment; all of it is solubilized by deoxyribonuclease. We conclude that cellular RNA synthesis, but not DNA synthesis, has been completely arrested by antecedent incubation with actinomycin.

Similar findings are shown in Table 1, in which pairs of spinner cultures are compared with respect to the incorporation of H³-leucine into protein, H-uridine into RNA, and H³-thymidine into DNA 4 hours after initial exposure to actinomycin. One pair of cultures contained actinomycin D (0.2 μg/ml), the other served as control. While the incorporation of leucine into protein and of thymidine into DNA were not affected by the antibiotic, uridine incorporation into RNA was depressed. After 24 hours, uridine uptake into RNA of the cells growing in the presence of actinomycin was still further decreased relative to the control.

The effect of actinomycin on virus growth has also been investigated. In some experiments cells had been treated previously with appropriate concentrations of the antibiotic, while in others actinomycin was present throughout the period of virus absorption and growth. The results were independent of the type of exposure.

The multiplication of vaccinia, a DNA virus, is sensitive to actinomycin, but somewhat less so than division of the host cell: 0.1 μg/ml inhibited vaccinia growth by 99 percent, whereas 0.005 μg/ml suppressed host cell di-

vision. On the other hand, concentrations of actinomycin in as high as 10 μg/ml did not inhibit the growth, or affect the yield of Mengo virus, a ribonucleic acid virus.

Parallel findings have been obtained with mitomycin, high concentrations of which inhibit cellular but not viral RNA synthesis [9]. Whereas mitomycin appears to affect RNA synthesis by destroying the genes under whose control the various cellular RNA species are synthesized, actinomycin would seem to leave the genetic apparatus intact since DNA replication is not abolished. This is supported by studies on the effects of actinomycin S on phage synthesis [10]. The inhibition of T2-phage reproduction by actinomycin does not result in inhibition of DNA synthesis in the phage-infected cell, whereas no phage protein appears to be made. Actinomycin thus appears to block the expression of genetic potentialities by interfering with that portion of RNA synthesis which is dependent on or governed by cellular or viral DNA. This is, therefore, a second line of evidence serving to differentiate replication of viral RNA from that of cellular RNA. Reduplication of viral RNA is not necessarily inhibited by factors capable of interfering with RNA synthesis which is governed by viral or host DNA. Presumably, therefore, the two RNA synthetic processes are enzymatically or topographically distinct [11].

E. REICH, R. M. FRANKLIN,
A. J. SHATKIN, E. L. TATUM
Rockefeller Institute, New York

References and Notes

1. L. C. Vining and S. A. Waksman, *Science* **120**, 389 (1954).
2. L. H. Pugh, E. Katz, S. A. Waksman, *J. Bacteriol.* **72**, 660 (1956).
3. S. Farber, in *Amino Acids and Peptides with Antimetabolic Activity*, Ciba Foundation Symposium, G. E. W. Wolstenholme and C. M. O'Connor, Eds. (Little, Brown, Boston, Mass., 1958), p. 140.
4. W. J. Burdette, *Science* **133**, 40 (1961).
5. D. E. Rounds, Y. H. Nakanishi, C. M. Pomerat, *Antibiotics and Chemotherapy* **10**, 597 (1960); M. N. Goldstein, E. Pfendt, J. D'Arrigo, *Anat. Record* **139**, 231 (1961).
6. A. J. Shatkin, E. Reich, R. M. Franklin, E. L. Tatum, *Biochim. et Biophys. Acta*, in press.
7. W. F. McLimans, E. V. Davis, F. L. Glover, G. W. Rake, *J. Immunol.* **79**, 428 (1957).
8. I. Doniach and S. R. Pelc, *Brit. J. Radiol.* **23**, 184 (1950).
9. E. Reich and R. M. Franklin, *Proc. Natl. Acad. Sci. U.S.*, in press.
10. A. Nakata, M. Sekiguchi, J. Kawamata, *Nature* **189**, 246 (1961).
11. Miss Joan Callender provided excellent technical assistance. This study was aided by grants from the National Foundation and from the National Cancer Institute, U.S. Public Health Service (C-3610).

21 June 1961

1

Reprinted from The Journal of Biological Chemistry
Vol. 231, No. 1, March, 1958
Made in United States of America

A SOLUBLE RIBONUCLEIC ACID INTERMEDIATE IN PROTEIN SYNTHESIS*†

By MAHLON B. HOAGLAND,‡ MARY LOUISE STEPHENSON, JESSE F. SCOTT, LISELOTTE I. HECHT, AND PAUL C. ZAMECNIK

(From the John Collins Warren Laboratories of the Huntington Memorial Hospital of Harvard University at the Massachusetts General Hospital, Boston, Massachusetts)

(Received for publication, September 27, 1957)

The cell-free rat liver system in which C^{14}-amino acids are incorporated irreversibly into α-peptide linkage in protein has been used in our laboratories for a number of years as a measure of protein synthesis. The essential components of this system are the microsomal ribonucleoprotein particles, certain enzymes derived from the soluble protein fraction, adenosine triphosphate, guanosine di- or triphosphate, and a nucleoside triphosphate-generating system (1–3). The ribonucleoprotein particles of the microsomes appear to be the actual site of peptide condensation. The soluble enzymes and ATP[1] have been found to effect the initial carboxyl activation of the amino acids (4). The role of GTP is not yet understood, although the present paper sheds light on its probable locus of action.

Much evidence has accumulated in the past 8 years, beginning with the studies of Caspersson (5) and Brachet (6), implicating a role for cellular RNA in protein synthesis. The intermediate stages between amino acid activation and final incorporation into protein in the rat liver *in vitro* system offered us unexplored regions in which to seek more direct evidence for a chemical association of RNA and amino acids. A preliminary report of such an association has recently been presented by us (7). There it was shown that the RNA of a particular fraction of the cytoplasm hitherto uncharacterized became labeled with C^{14}-amino acids in the presence of ATP and the amino acid-activating enzymes, and that this labeled RNA subsequently was able to transfer the amino acid to microsomal protein

---

* This work was supported by grants from the United States Public Health Service, the American Cancer Society, and the United States Atomic Energy Commission.

† This is publication No. 916 of the Cancer Commission of Harvard University.

‡ Scholar in Cancer Research of the American Cancer Society. Present address, Cavendish Laboratory, Cambridge University.

[1] The abbreviations used in this paper are as follows: RNA, ribonucleic acid; pH 5 RNA, ribonucleic acid derived from the pH 5 enzyme fraction; AMP, adenosine 5′-phosphate; ATP, GTP, CTP, UTP, the triphosphates of adenosine, guanosine, cytosine, and uridine; PP, inorganic pyrophosphate; PPase, inorganic pyrophosphatase; PEP, phosphoenol pyruvate; Tris, tris(hydroxymethyl)aminomethane; and ECTEOLA, cellulose treated with epichlorohydrin and triethanolamine.

241

in the presence of GTP and a nucleoside triphosphate-generating system. This paper is a more definitive report on these studies.

Materials and Methods

Cellular fractions (microsomes and pH 5 enzymes) of rat liver and mouse Ehrlich ascites tumor were prepared by methods previously described (2, 3). Microsomes were generally sedimented at 105,000 $\times$ g for 90 to 120 minutes instead of the usual 60 minutes in order to insure more complete sedimentation of microsome-like particles. pH 5 enzymes were precipitated from the resulting supernatant fraction by adjusting the pH to 5.2.

Preparation of Labeled pH 5 Enzyme Fraction—The labeling of the pH 5 enzyme fraction was carried out by incubating 10 ml. of pH 5 enzyme preparation (containing 100 to 200 mg. of protein) dissolved in buffered medium (2) with 4.0 μmoles of C^{14}-L-leucine (containing 7.2 $\times$ 10^6 c.p.m.) and 200 μmoles of ATP in a final volume of 20 ml. for 10 minutes at 37°. The reaction mixture was then chilled to 0°, diluted 3-fold with cold water, and the enzyme precipitated by addition of 1.0 M acetic acid to bring the pH to 5.2. The precipitate was redissolved in 5 to 10 ml. of buffered medium, diluted again (to 60 ml.) with water, and the enzyme reprecipitated at pH 5.2 with M acetic acid. This final precipitate was washed with water and dissolved in 5.0 to 10.0 ml. of the cold buffered medium.

Isolation of pH 5 RNA—Isolation of pH 5 RNA was carried out by a minor modification of the method of Gierer and Schramm (8) and Kirby (9). The labeled pH 5 enzyme solution as prepared above was shaken in a mechanical shaker at room temperature for 1 hour with an equal volume of 90 per cent phenol, followed by centrifugation at 15,000 $\times$ g for 10 minutes. The top aqueous layer containing the RNA-leucine-C^{14} was removed with a syringe, more water was added, and, after thorough mixing, the centrifugation and withdrawal of the aqueous solution were repeated. Phenol was removed from the pooled aqueous solutions by three successive ether extractions. 0.1 volume of 20 per cent potassium acetate (pH 5) was then added, and the RNA was precipitated with 60 per cent ethanol at $-10°$, redissolved in water, and again precipitated from 60 per cent ethanol. The final precipitate was dissolved in a small volume of water and dialyzed against water for 4 hours in the cold. This method of extraction was used as a preparative procedure and yielded 50 to 70 per cent of the RNA initially present in the enzyme preparation, and was also used to prepare microsomal and unlabeled pH 5 RNA.

For analysis of pH 5 RNA-leucine-C^{14} in smaller incubations, NaCl was used to extract the RNA. To the incubation mixture (usually a volume of 2.0 ml.), 10 volumes of cold 0.4 N perchloric acid were added. The resulting acid-insoluble precipitate, containing RNA and protein, was washed four times with cold 0.2 N perchloric acid, once with 5:1 ethanol-0.2 N perchloric acid, once with ethanol in the cold, and once with 3:1 ethanol-ether at 50°. The RNA was then extracted with 10 per cent NaCl at 100° for 30 minutes. (During this extraction, the pH drops to around 2 to 3 and it is essential to permit this to occur; if the pH is held above 6, the isolated RNA contains little or no radioactivity.) The RNA was precipitated from the NaCl extract with 60 per cent ethanol at $-10°$, and was dissolved in water and again precipitated with ethanol. The final ethanol suspension was filtered by suction onto disks of No. 50 Whatman paper. The dried RNA was counted by using a Nuclear micromil window gas flow counter, was then eluted from the paper with 0.005 N alkali, and the concentration determined by measuring the absorption at 260 mμ in a Beckman spectrophotometer by using an extinction coefficient of 34.2 mg.$^{-1}$ cm.^{2} (10). This extraction procedure yielded 30 to 35 per cent of the RNA originally present in the incubation mixture. In experiments in which total counts are recorded, the specific activity of this NaCl-extracted RNA was multiplied by the total quantity of RNA initially added as determined by the method of Scott et al. (10). This was based on the assumption that the RNA extracted was a representative sample of the total.

For the determination of the specific activity of the protein, the methods described previously (1, 2) were employed.

The nucleoside triphosphate preparations, the triphosphate-generating system, and the C^{14}-amino acids used in these studies were the same as those used in other recent work reported from this laboratory (2). 1 μmole of Mg^{++} was added per micromole of nucleoside triphosphate in all cases.

Results

Labeling of RNA Cellular Fractions with Amino Acids—In the complete system required for incorporation of C^{14}-amino acids into protein (microsomes, pH 5 enzymes, ATP, GTP, nucleoside triphosphate-generating system, and C^{14}-amino acids), the RNA subsequently isolated was found to be labeled with C^{14}-amino acids. Incubation of the pH 5 enzyme fraction without microsomes under these conditions resulted in substantially more RNA labeling than in the complete system. Little labeling of RNA was observed when microsomes were incubated alone under the above conditions. Further analysis of the requirements for labeling of pH 5 RNA revealed that ATP alone was sufficient and that GTP and the generating system were not necessary. A survey of the extent of labeling of the RNA of various isolated liver cellular fractions with leucine is shown in Fig. 1, which shows that pH 5 RNA has the highest specific activity.

Fig. 2 shows the dependence of labeling of pH 5 RNA upon leucine concentration. Glycine-C^{14}, valine-C^{14}, or alanine-C^{14} gave about the same

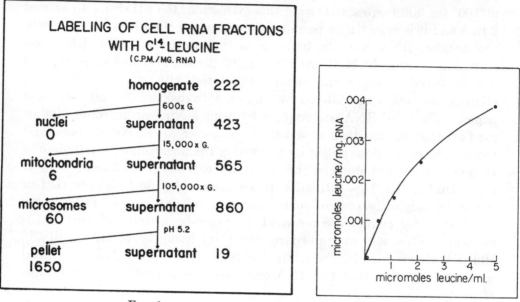

FIG. 1.

FIG. 2.

FIG. 1. Cellular fractions were prepared from rat liver and resuspended or dissolved in buffered medium (2). 0.75 ml. of each fraction was then incubated at 37° for 10 minutes with 10 μmoles of ATP, 0.1 μmole of L-leucine-C^{14} containing 180,000 c.p.m., 5 μmoles of PEP, and 0.04 mg. of pyruvate kinase in a final volume of 1.0 ml. 4 μmoles of potassium fumarate, 10 μmoles of potassium glutamate, and 10.0 μmoles of orthophosphate were added to the incubation mixtures containing the original homogenate, the 600 $\times$ g supernatant fraction, and the mitochondrial fraction, and these were shaken in an atmosphere of 95 per cent oxygen-5 per cent CO_2 during the incubation.

FIG. 2. Leucine concentration curve for labeling of pH 5 RNA. 1.2 ml. of rat liver pH 5 enzyme preparation (approximately 13 mg. of protein), in buffered medium were incubated for 10 minutes at 37° with 20 μmoles of ATP, L-leucine-C^{14} containing 3.6 $\times$ 10^5 c.p.m. at the concentrations indicated, in a final volume of 2.0 ml.

extent of labeling as leucine-C^{14} when each was present at a concentration of 0.007 M. When these amino acids were combined (0.007 M each), the labeling was approximately additive. The addition of a mixture containing fifteen C^{12}-amino acids (lacking leucine) did not affect the extent of labeling with leucine-C^{14}. Maximal labeling of 0.04 μmole of leucine per mg. of RNA was attained with the most active liver preparations by using 0.005 M leucine and 0.01 M ATP.

ATP was necessary for the labeling of the RNA with amino acids, and the extent of labeling depended upon the concentration of ATP (Fig. 3).

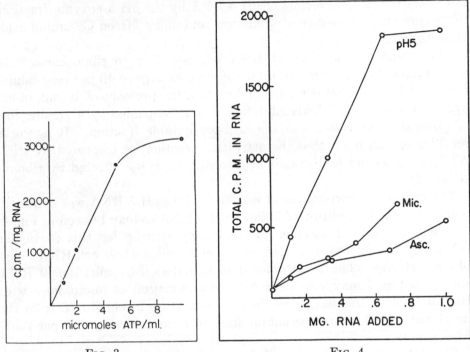

FIG. 3.   FIG. 4.

FIG. 3. ATP concentration curve for labeling of pH 5 RNA. 1.8 ml. of rat liver pH 5 enzyme preparation (20 mg. of protein) in buffered medium were incubated for 20 minutes at 37° with 0.2 μmole of L-leucine-C^{14} containing 3.6 $\times$ 10^5 c.p.m. and ATP at the concentrations indicated, in a final volume of 2.0 ml.

FIG. 4. Effect of addition of certain RNA preparations upon the labeling of pH 5 RNA with leucine-C^{14}. RNA was prepared from the pH 5 enzyme (pH 5) and microsome (Mic.) fractions of rat liver and from whole ascites cells (Asc.) by the phenol method. The quantities of RNA indicated, dissolved in 0.02 M Tris buffer, pH 7.6 (0.5 μmole of MgCl$_2$ added per mg. of RNA), were incubated at 37° for 10 minutes in 1.0 ml. volumes with pH 5 enzyme obtained from Ehrlich ascites cells (containing 0.12 mg. of RNA), and the following final concentrations of additions: 0.01 M ATP; 0.01 M PEP; 0.0038 M MgCl$_2$; 0.038 M Tris, pH 7.6; 0.018 M KCl; and 0.04 mg. of pyruvate kinase. The total radioactivity in RNA plotted was calculated as the product of the specific activity of the RNA isolated by extraction by the NaCl method and the total quantity of RNA present at the end of the incubation period. Addition of liver pH 5 RNA to the liver pH 5 enzyme fraction produces a similar enhancement of incorporation to that shown here with the tumor enzyme.

Maximal incorporation was reached at about 0.01 M. A similarly shaped ATP concentration curve had earlier been found for the amino acid activation reaction, as measured by hydroxamic acid formation (4). Also, as in the activation reaction, the requirement for ATP was specific since GTP, CTP, and UTP did not replace this nucleotide. GTP, which is necessary for the over-all incorporation of amino acids into protein, did not affect the rate of labeling of pH 5 RNA by the pH 5 enzyme fraction, in the presence or absence of a mixture containing fifteen C^{12}-amino acids (lacking leucine).

The amino acid labeling of RNA was sensitive to ribonuclease. 10 γ per ml. of Worthington crystalline ribonuclease gave 40 per cent inhibition, and 40 γ gave 90 per cent inhibition in the presence of 10 mg. of enzyme protein per ml. This inhibition was accompanied by a smaller loss of absorbance at 260 mμ in the acid-precipitable fraction. It is worth recalling at this point that the activation reaction, as measured by PP^{32}-ATP exchange and hydroxamic acid formation, is *not* affected by ribonuclease (4).

The extent of incorporation of leucine-C^{14} into pH 5 RNA was markedly stimulated by the addition of isolated pH 5 RNA as may be seen in Fig. 4. The enhancement of labeling was relatively specific for this particular RNA, rat liver microsomal RNA and mouse ascites whole cell RNA being of low activity. The small amount of stimulation by microsomal RNA shown in Fig. 4 may well be due to contamination of microsomes with the supernatant fraction, since the microsomes were centrifuged from the undiluted 15,000 $\times$ g supernatant fluid of a concentrated (30 per cent) homogenate.

The labeling reaction proceeded linearly with time for 3 minutes and was complete in 10 minutes. In those preparations in which precaution was taken to minimize contamination with microsomes (by preparing pH 5 enzymes from a 105,000 $\times$ g supernatant fraction obtained after a centrifugation for 90 to 120 minutes), there was no loss of leucine-C^{14} for a period of 20 minutes after maximal labeling had been reached. Slight microsomal contamination, however, resulted in a loss of leucine from RNA after maximal labeling had been reached.

After incubation of the pH 5 enzyme fraction with leucine-C^{14} and ATP, these latter compounds could be largely removed by reprecipitation of the pH 5 enzyme from dilute solution, as described. Upon subsequent incubation of this reprecipitated fraction, the leucine label was rapidly lost from the RNA unless ATP was added (Table I). The equivalent effect of a nucleoside triphosphate-generating system (PEP and pyruvate kinase), also shown in Table I, was probably mediated through the presence of very small amounts of adenylates which coprecipitate with the pH 5 enzyme. PP, on the other hand, increased the extent of loss of label from the RNA. These findings suggested that the labeling process might be *reversible*. This possibility was rendered more probable by the finding that, in the presence of added ATP, the addition of leucine-C^{12} produced a dilution of the leucine-C^{14} labeling, as shown in Experiment 2, Table I. This would be expected if the following reactions were occurring:

$$\text{ATP} + \text{leucine-}C^{14} + E \rightleftharpoons E(\text{AMP} \sim \text{leucine-}C^{14}) + \text{PP} \qquad (1)$$

$$E(\text{AMP} \sim \text{leucine-}C^{14}) + \text{RNA} \rightleftharpoons \text{RNA} \sim \text{leucine-}C^{14} + E + (\text{AMP}) \qquad (2)$$

The loss of label in the absence of added ATP would depend upon the presence of small amounts of indigenous PP. The failure of leucine-C^{12}

TABLE I

Effect of Various Additions upon Loss of Leucine-C^{14} from Labeled pH 5 Enzyme

Experiment No.	Addition	Amount	Per cent initial specific activity lost
		M	
1	None	0	75
	ATP	0.001	44
	"	0.005	35
	" + AMP	0.005 each	37
	PP	0.01	96
	PEP	0.01	24
2	None	0	79
	Leucine-C^{12}	0.01	84
	ATP	0.01	39
	" + leucine-C^{12}	0.01 each	68

L-Leucine-C^{14}-labeled pH 5 enzyme (0.4 ml.) was incubated at 37° for 7 minutes in a volume of 2.0 ml. with the concentrations of additions indicated. A concentration of $MgCl_2$ equal to that of PP was added with the latter. Pyruvate kinase (0.04 mg. per ml.) was added with the PEP. The initial specific activities of the RNA which were isolated from the pH 5 enzymes labeled during the preincubation were: Experiment 1, 770 c.p.m. per mg.; Experiment 2, 440 c.p.m. per mg.

to effect a dilution in the absence of added ATP would be anticipated since, due to the high ATPase activity of the preparation and the absence of a generating system, the ATP concentration would be effectively zero and the reaction would proceed rapidly to the left. It is of interest in this connection that Holley (11) has described an alanine-dependent, ribonuclease-sensitive incorporation of C^{14}-AMP into ATP catalyzed by the pH 5 enzyme preparation. This would suggest a reversal of an ATP-dependent reaction between alanine and RNA. However, other amino acids have not been found to stimulate such an exchange, suggesting that AMP is generally not a free product of reaction (2). The possibility must still be entertained, however, that ATP has some stabilizing effect upon the pH 5 RNA-amino acid bond not related to mass action.

A high concentration of NH_2OH such as 1.2 M, which was used to obtain amino acid hydroxamic acid formation with this preparation (4), also inhibits (90 per cent) the labeling of RNA with leucine.

Some Properties of pH 5 RNA-Leucine-C^{14}—The RNA of the enzyme pH 5 fraction of rat liver represents 2 per cent of the total RNA of the cell and only 20 per cent of the RNA of the 105,000 × g 2 hour supernatant fraction. It is present in a concentration of 3 mg. of RNA per 100 mg. of protein. In the mouse ascites tumor essentially all the RNA of the 105,000 × g supernatant fraction precipitates at pH 5.2 and amounts to 20 per cent of the total RNA of the cell.

The active component of the pH 5 enzyme fraction does not sediment at 105,000 × g in 3 hours. If one compares the activity and RNA content of the pH 5 enzyme prepared from a supernatant fraction obtained after 1 hour or 3 hour centrifugations at 105,000 × g, one finds that the latter preparation contains only 50 per cent as much RNA as the former. The amount of leucine incorporated into the RNA of both preparations is, however, the same, suggesting that the RNA sedimented during the additional centrifugation time is not active.

RNA-leucine-C^{14} gave a mean sedimentation constant of 1.85 $s_{20,w}$ at a concentration of 0.003 per cent in 0.15 M NaCl, 0.015 M citrate, pH 6.8.[2] Preliminary studies indicate that this value is lower when effort is made to remove magnesium ion first by dialysis against citrate buffer. The material does not appear homogeneous, however, and probably represents a range of molecular sizes. Preliminary results with paper electrophoresis suggest at least two major components.

A sample of pH 5 RNA-leucine-C^{14} extracted by the phenol method was fractionated on ECTEOLA (12). 1 mg. of RNA, dissolved in 0.01 M phosphate buffer at pH 7 and containing 4040 c.p.m. as leucine-C^{14}, was placed on a column 0.2 cm. in diameter containing 50 mg. of ECTEOLA-SF (0.16 meq. of N per gm.).[3] Elution was carried out with a gradient of NaCl in 0.01 M phosphate buffer at pH 7, which was established by feeding buffer containing 2.5 M NaCl into a 500 ml. mixing flask. 1.5 ml. fractions were collected at a flow rate of 1.8 ml. per hour. The NaCl gradient was continued until the molarity of the effluent was about 2. In accordance with the general procedure of Bradley and Rich (12), the gradient was discontinued, the column washed with water, and 10 ml. of 1 N NaOH were run through. Three fractions emerged: Fraction 1 failed to adhere to the exchanger and contained 14 per cent of the ultraviolet absorbance and 8 per cent of the radioactivity (*free* leucine, if present

[2] We wish to thank Dr. J. Fresco and Dr. P. Doty of Harvard University for performing these analyses.

[3] Kindly furnished by Dr. Alexander Rich.

would have been found in this fraction); Fraction 2 emerged at a mean molarity of 0.15 NaCl and contained 48 per cent of the absorbance and 2 per cent of the radioactivity; and Fraction 3 was eluted with NaOH and contained 36 per cent of the absorbance and 68 per cent of the radioactivity. The final recovery amounted to 98 per cent of the ultraviolet absorbance and 78 per cent of the radioactivity. The low recovery of the radioactivity is most likely due to self-absorption in the NaOH-eluted fractions when plated for counting. These results, compared with those published by Bradley and Rich, suggest that at least 68 per cent of the leucine is bound to 36 per cent of the RNA of high sedimentation coefficient relative to that of the bulk of the sample.

pH 5 RNA-leucine-C^{14} isolated from the pH 5 enzyme fraction by both the phenol and NaCl methods was readily bound by Dowex 1 and charcoal at neutral pH value. However, when the RNA-leucine-C^{14} was associated with pH 5 enzyme protein in the natural state, these agents did not take up the RNA. The isolated RNA-leucine-C^{14} was non-dialyzable and stable against water, 10 per cent NaCl, or 8 M urea. There was no detectable acid-precipitable protein in the RNA extracted by the phenol method (1 per cent contamination could have been detected (13)).

The leucine was completely released from the pH 5 RNA by 0.01 N KOH in 20 minutes at room temperature. At pH 4 to 6, it was relatively stable and the labeled material as prepared by the phenol method could be kept some weeks in the frozen state. The leucine appeared to be covalently linked to the RNA, as judged from the following indirect evidence. Treatment of the RNA-leucine-C^{14} with the ninhydrin reagent indicated the absence of free leucine, although leucine is slowly released from the RNA during the course of the ninhydrin procedure. Treatment with anhydrous hydroxylamine, followed by chromatography of the products on paper (75 per cent secondary butanol, 15 per cent formic acid, 10 per cent water), resulted in a spot corresponding to leucine hydroxamic acid which contained all the radioactivity originally bound to the RNA. (A control of this experiment, in which the RNA-leucine-C^{14} bond was first hydrolyzed in 0.01 N alkali, gave no radioactivity associated with the leucine hydroxamic acid spot.)

Labeling of RNA with Leucine-C^{14} in Intact Cell—If pH 5 RNA were on the pathway of protein synthesis, it would be reasonable to expect that in the intact cell it would become labeled with leucine-C^{14} earlier than microsome protein. Previous studies in this laboratory by Littlefield and Keller (3) had shown that treatment of mouse ascites tumor microsomes with 0.5 M sodium chloride facilitates the centrifugal separation of ribonucleoprotein particles rich in RNA (about 50 per cent RNA, 50 per cent protein). The protein moiety of these "sodium chloride-insoluble" particles was found to be the most highly labeled protein fraction after incorporation of leucine-C^{14} by intact cells. A preliminary experiment in the rat showed that, at the earliest time point which it was possible to obtain after injection of leucine-C^{14} (1 minute), both RNA of the pH 5 fraction and the protein of the ribonucleoprotein particles of the microsomes were already maximally labeled. By use of mouse ascites tumor cells, it was possible to slow down the reaction by reducing the temperature of incubation. After incubation of these cells with leucine-C^{14} at 25°, the cells were washed and lysed, and concentrated solutions were added to give a final concentration of 0.5 M NaCl, 0.005 M $MgCl_2$, and 0.01 M Tris buffer, pH 7.6 (3). "NaCl-insoluble" (NaCl particles) and "soluble" fractions of a 10 minute 15,000 × g supernatant fraction were separated by centrifugation at 78,000 × g for 2 hours. Both the protein and RNA were isolated. Since almost all of the RNA present in the soluble fraction of the ascites cells precipitates at pH 5, the RNA of this fraction may be considered pH 5 RNA. The proteins of the soluble fraction represent the proteins of the NaCl-soluble components of the microsomes and the soluble cell proteins. Littlefield and Keller (3) have shown that these two fractions become labeled at a slow rate and therefore they were not separated. The results of this experiment are shown in Fig. 5. Soluble and particle RNA became labeled maximally in 2 minutes and remained so as if a steady state had been reached, while the protein of the ribonucleoprotein particles continued to acquire new amino acid content throughout the incubation period. Incorporation into the other cell proteins started after an initial lag period and proceeded at the slowest rate. The rate of labeling of the pH 5 RNA is so rapid that it occurs to some extent at 0° and no satisfactory rate curve for this labeling process could be obtained, since the reaction is proceeding even during centrifugal separation of the fractions. Similar results were obtained when the cell fractions were prepared from a sucrose homogenate and the pH 5 RNA and the protein of the deoxycholate-soluble and -insoluble fractions of the microsomes were isolated. These data suggest that the pH 5 RNA-amino acid compound *could* be an intermediate in the incorporation of amino acids into the proteins of the ribonucleoprotein particles of the microsomes.

Transfer of Leucine-C^{14} from Labeled pH 5 Enzyme Fraction to Microsomal Protein—We have reported (7) that the leucine-C^{14}-labeled pH 5 enzyme fraction, freed from ATP and leucine-C^{14} by reprecipitation at pH 5.1 from dilute solution, will transfer the RNA-bound leucine-C^{14} to microsomal protein upon subsequent incubation with microsomes, a nucleoside triphosphate-generating system, and GTP (Table II). The other nucleoside triphosphates, including ATP, would not replace GTP in this reaction; ATP also failed to stimulate the transfer in the presence of GTP.

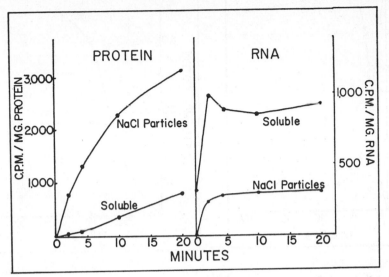

FIG. 5. Time-curve of incorporation of L-leucine-C[14] into the RNA and protein of the ribonucleoprotein particles and the soluble fraction in intact ascites cells. Ascites tumor cells (approximately 10 gm. of packed cells) were incubated at 25° in 50 ml. of their own ascitic fluid fortified with glucose (0.04 M), Tris buffer, pH 7.6 (0.02 M), and containing 3 μmoles of L-leucine (3.5 × 10⁶ c.p.m. per μmole). Aliquots were taken at the time points shown; NaCl-insoluble and -soluble fractions were prepared from the 15,000 × g supernatant fraction. The specific activities of the RNA and protein of these fractions are shown.

TABLE II

Transfer of Leucine-C[14] from Labeled pH 5 Enzyme Fraction to Microsome Protein

	Total c.p.m. in	
	RNA	Protein
Before incubation: complete system.............................	478	22
After " : " "	182	433
Complete system minus GTP.................................	116	67
" " " generating system...................	62	101
" " " " " and minus GTP.....	29	23
" " " " " but with 5 × GTP..	176	91
Complete system CTP replacing GTP.........................	98	79
" " UTP " "	117	100
" " plus 0.005 M leucine-C[12].....................	178	371

The results shown are averaged values from two experiments. In each experiment 0.6 ml. of a microsome suspension containing about 15 mg. of protein and 0.4 ml. of a pH 5 enzyme fraction prelabeled with leucine-C[14], containing about 5 mg. of protein, were incubated for 15 minutes at 37° with the nucleoside triphosphates (0.0005 M), PEP (0.01 M), and pyruvate kinase (0.04 mg.) as indicated, in a final volume of 2.0 ml.

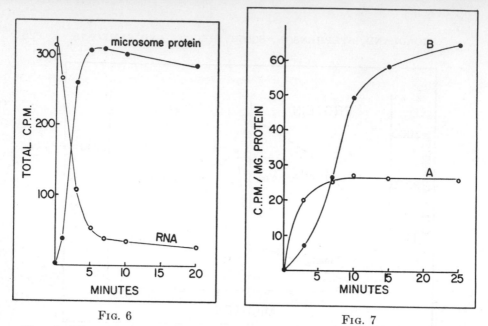

FIG. 6

FIG. 7

FIG. 6. Time-curve of transfer of leucine-C14 from prelabeled pH 5 enzyme fraction to microsome protein. 4.0 ml. of a leucine-C14-labeled pH 5 enzyme preparation (containing 2.6 mg. of RNA), and 6.0 ml. of microsomes (21 mg. of RNA) were incubated at 37° with 20 μmoles of GTP, 200 μmoles of PEP, and 0.8 mg. of pyruvate kinase in a volume of 20.0 ml. 2.5 ml. aliquots were taken at the time points shown. These were chilled, diluted to 12.5 ml., and centrifuged at 105,000 × g for 60 minutes in the cold. The RNA and protein of the supernatant fluid and of the microsomes were separated. The total counts per minute in the pH 5 RNA (○) and in the microsomal protein (●) is plotted. Since there is about 50 per cent enzymatic loss of leucine-C14 from pH 5 RNA during the hour's centrifugation (determined directly by centrifuging an aliquot of labeled pH 5 enzyme of known specific activity under the same conditions), a correction for this loss was applied to the specific activity of RNA to give the final figures used.

FIG. 7. A comparison of the rates of the over-all incorporation reaction and the incorporation when starting with labeled pH 5 enzyme fraction. 40 ml. of an enzyme preparation at pH 5 were incubated for 10 minutes at 37° with 100 μmoles of ATP and 2 μmoles of leucine-C14 (3.6 × 10⁶ c.p.m.) in a volume of 10 ml. An equal aliquot of the same enzyme was incubated identically with ATP and leucine-C12. Both enzymes were then precipitated twice at pH 5.1 from dilute solution. An aliquot of the labeled enzyme was taken for determination of RNA content and another for determination of specific activity of RNA-leucine-C14. 1.8 ml. of leucine-labeled enzyme, dissolved in buffered medium and containing 1540 c.p.m. of bound leucine-C14, were then incubated with 1.8 ml. of microsomes, 3 μmoles of GTP, 60 μmoles of PEP, and 0.24 mg. of pyruvate kinase in a volume of 6.0 ml. The same volume and amount of unlabeled enzyme were incubated with the same quantity of microsomes, GTP, PEP, and pyruvate kinase, plus 3 μmoles of ATP and 0.6 μmole of leucine-C14 containing 1.1 × 10⁶ c.p.m. The incubation mixtures were equilibrated at 30° for 1 minute before addition of microsomes and incubation was carried out at 30°. 1.0 ml. aliquots of each incubation were taken, each containing approximately 9 mg. of protein, at the times indicated and the protein of the samples was precipitated, washed, plated, and counted. Curve A, reaction with prelabeled pH 5 enzyme; Curve B, over-all reaction.

In the absence of GTP there was an equally rapid microsome-dependent loss of leucine-C^{14} from the intermediate, without concomitant appearance of amino acid in protein. (Rat liver microsomes contain considerable "ATPase" activity. Whether the loss of label is due to destruction of ATP still present in the system, thus permitting reversal of the reaction, or a manifestation of an uncoupling of the basic mechanism for trans-

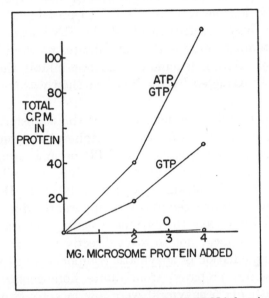

Fɪɢ. 8. Transfer of leucine-C^{14} from isolated pH 5 RNA-leucine-C^{14} to microsomal protein. 0.40 mg. of RNA, prepared by the phenol method, containing 600 c.p.m. of bound leucine-C^{14}, was incubated at 37° for 15 minutes in buffered medium (0.5 ml.) with the amount of microsomes indicated with added PEP (0.01 ᴍ), pyruvate kinase (0.04 mg.) in a volume of 1.0 ml. 0.5 µmole of ATP and GTP was added as indicated (0 = no addition of nucleotide). ATP alone gave the same activity as with no nucleotide additions. The microsomes used were sedimented from a 15,000 $\times$ g supernatant fraction which was diluted 3.5-fold before centrifugation at 105,000 $\times$ g.

ferring amino acid to microsomes is not known.) GTP had no effect on the considerably slower rate of loss of label from   pH 5 enzyme   in the absence of microsomes. The addition of a relatively high concentration of leucine-C^{12} did not appreciably dilute the radioactivity transferred to protein. Fig. 6 shows a time-curve for the transfer reaction and emphasizes the high efficiency of the transfer as well as its relatively rapid rate. Fig. 7 presents a comparison of the rates of the transfer of leucine-C^{14} to microsomal protein from free leucine-C^{14} and ATP (Curve B) and from the prelabeled intermediate in the absence of free leucine and ATP (Curve A). When starting with the labeled intermediate, the lag in the initial rate of the over-all reaction was absent, the efficiency of transfer was much greater, and the reaction attained completion at an earlier time.

Transfer of Leucine-C^{14} from Isolated Labeled pH 5 RNA to Microsomal Protein—pH 5 RNA-leucine-C^{14}, extracted from labeled pH 5 enzyme by the phenol method, precipitated twice from ethanol and dialyzed against water, will, upon incubation with microsomes, transfer leucine-C^{14} to microsomal protein. In seven experiments of this type, an average of 20 per cent of the leucine was transferred to protein (25 per cent maximum). In every case, pretreatment of the RNA-leucine-C^{14} with 0.01 N KOH at room temperature for 10 to 20 minutes resulted in lack of transfer of the leucine. Again, leucine-C^{12} did not inhibit the transfer. pH 5 RNA-leucine-C^{14} extracted by the NaCl method was consistently found to be inactive.

GTP was again found to be necessary for this transfer, and there was no transfer in the absence of a nucleoside triphosphate-generating system. Furthermore, a partial requirement for ATP became apparent with this simplified system as shown in Fig. 8. The failure to elicit an ATP requirement for the transfer of amino acid from labeled pH 5 enzyme fraction to microsomes (previous section) was apparently due to the presence of ATP not washed free from the enzyme when reprecipitated at pH 5.

Microsomes alone appear not to react directly with pH 5 RNA-leucine but to require the mediation of enzymatic components of the pH 5 enzyme fraction. Microsomes prepared from dilute homogenates (to minimize contamination with pH 5 enzymes) were low in activity when incubated with pH 5 RNA-leucine-C^{14}, ATP, GTP, and the generating system but activity could be restored by addition of the pH 5 enzyme fraction.

DISCUSSION

The evidence presented supports the conclusion that there occur ATP-dependent enzymatic reactions between ribonucleic acid and amino acids. These reactions are catalyzed by an enzyme preparation which is known to activate the carboxyl groups of amino acids in the presence of ATP. The product formed, an RNA or ribonucleoprotein to which amino acids are apparently covalently linked, is capable of interacting with enzymatic components of the activating enzyme preparation and with microsomes to effect the transfer of the amino acid to peptide linkage in protein. It is therefore suggested that this particular RNA fraction functions as an intermediate carrier of amino acids in protein synthesis. A growing body of evidence from other laboratories also suggests the presence of an intermediate similar to the one herein described (14, 15, 11, 16).

Since the amino acid activation reaction is insensitive to ribonuclease and since an activating enzyme has been isolated relatively free from RNA (17), it is still necessary to invoke an initial enzymatic activation reaction as originally postulated (4), followed by a transfer of amino acid to linkage on RNA. Because of the impurity of the pH 5 enzyme system it cannot be stated that pH 5 RNA is naturally linked to amino acid-activating enzymes or that other enzymatic steps intervene between activation and linkage to RNA. The relative specificity of the reaction of the pH 5 enzyme fraction with pH 5 RNA shown in Fig. 4, does, however, emphasize the uniqueness of this particular RNA fraction in regard to ATP-dependent amino acid binding.

The present data suggest that the pH 5 RNA molecules, when associated with protein in the natural state, are considerably lower in average sedimentation coefficient than are the ribonucleoprotein particles of the microsomes. The latter are probably of the order of 80 S (18), while the former appear to be much lower. Furthermore, the results of other experiments from this laboratory, in which pH 5 RNA is enzymatically terminally labeled with the nucleoside monophosphate moieties of nucleoside triphosphates (19), suggest that the average molecular weight of the RNA is not likely to exceed 20,000 (based on maximal labeling, and assuming no branching). The sedimentation constant of 1.85 would be consistent with a molecular weight considerably lower than this.

Thus far we cannot assign a specific structure to the amino acid-RNA linkage. An attractive possibility is an acyl anhydride involving internucleotide phosphate groups or a terminal nucleotide residue. The acid stability and alkali lability of the linkage, qualitatively similar to the behavior of the synthetic amino acyl adenylates (20, 21), the formation of a hydroxamic acid, and the relative high energy of the linkage suggested by the possible reversibility of the reaction would support this type of anhydride linkage. The linkage would appear, however, to be more stable than a phosphate diester anhydride might be expected to be. We have also given thought to the possibility that internucleotide P—O bonds may be opened by reaction with an amino acyl adenylate, with resulting attachment of the amino acyl group to one of the opened ends of the nucleotide chain and adenylate to the other. Other possible linkages to be considered are carboxyl bonding to 2'-OH on ribose and bonding involving groups on the nucleotide bases themselves. It is, nevertheless, likely that, regardless of the type of bonding, amino acids are individually linked to pH 5 RNA and do not *condense* at this stage, for the amino acid may be recovered as the specific hydroxamic acid upon treatment with hydroxylamine.

The high efficiency of the GTP-dependent transfer of amino acid from intermediate to microsome protein is striking. There is no evidence that GTP is concerned either in the activation step or in the transfer of amino acid to pH 5 RNA. Its locus of action is thus narrowed down to the area of interaction between pH 5 RNA-amino acid and microsomes. The fact that enzymatic components of the pH 5 fraction are still required for the transfer from pH 5 RNA-leucine to microsomes could mean either that a new transfer enzyme is required or that reassociation of intermediate with activating enzymes is necessary. If this latter is the case, the possibility that pH 5 RNA acts simply as a storage site for activated amino acids must be considered.

Other studies in this laboratory to be reported have shown that the same pH 5 enzyme fraction also catalyzes a rapid incorporation of the nucleotide monophosphate moieties of ATP, CTP, and UTP into pH 5 RNA. The appearance of these reactions in the same fraction which catalyzes the amino acid binding to RNA is intriguing, but thus far it has not been possible to obtain evidence for any clear direct link between the two reactions.

We have suggested elsewhere (22) a hypothetical reaction sequence for protein synthesis which accounts for the findings presented in this paper. Its central idea is that pH 5 RNA molecules, each charged with amino acids in characteristic sequence, polymerize in microsomes (in specific order determined by the complementary structure of microsomal RNA) to higher molecular weight units with resultant configurational changes which permit peptide condensation between contiguous amino acids. This working hypothesis will form the basis for further studies in these laboratories on the mechanism of protein synthesis.

SUMMARY

Evidence is presented that a soluble ribonucleic acid, residing in the same cellular fraction which activates amino acids, binds amino acids in the presence of adenosine triphosphate. Indirect evidence indicates that this reaction may be reversible. The amino acids so bound to ribonucleic acid are subsequently transferred to microsomal protein, and this transfer is dependent upon guanosine triphosphate.

The authors wish to thank Dr. Robert B. Loftfield for the radioactive amino acids used as well as for helpful criticism.

BIBLIOGRAPHY

1. Zamecnik, P. C., and Keller, E. B., *J. Biol. Chem.*, **209,** 337 (1954).
2. Keller, E. B., and Zamecnik, P. C., *J. Biol. Chem.*, **221,** 45 (1956).
3. Littlefield, J. W., and Keller, E. B., *J. Biol. Chem.*, **224,** 13 (1957).
4. Hoagland, M. B., Keller, E. B., and Zamecnik, P. C., *J. Biol. Chem.*, **218,** 345 (1956).
5. Caspersson, T. O., Cell growth and cell function, New York (1950).

6. Brachet, J., in Chargaff, E., and Davidson, J. E, The nucleic acids, New York, **2** (1955).
7. Hoagland, M. B., Zamecnik, P. C., and Stephenson, M. L., *Biochim. et biophys. acta*, **24**, 215 (1957).
8. Gierer, A., and Schramm, G., *Nature*, **177**, 702 (1956).
9. Kirby, K. S., *Biochem. J.*, **64**, 405 (1956).
10. Scott, J. F., Fraccastoro, A. P., and Taft, E. B., *J. Histochem. and Cytochem.*, **4**, 1 (1956).
11. Holley, R., *J. Am. Chem. Soc.*, **79**, 658 (1957).
12. Bradley, D. F., and Rich, A., *J. Am. Chem. Soc.*, **78**, 5898 (1956).
13. Nayyar, S. N., and Glick, D., *J. Histochem. and Cytochem.*, **2**, 282 (1954).
14. Hultin, T., *Exp. Cell Res.*, **11**, 222 (1956).
15. Hultin, T., von der Decken, A., and Beskow, G., *Exp. Cell Res.*, **12**, 675 (1957).
16. Koningsberger, V. V., van der Grinten, C. O., and Overbeek, J. T., *Ned. Akad. Wetnsch, Proc.*, series B, **60**, 144 (1957).
17. Davie, E. W., Koningsberger, V. V., and Lipmann, F., *Arch. Biochem. and Biophys.*, **65**, 21 (1956).
18. Petermann, M. L., and Hamilton, M. G., *J. Biol. Chem.*, **224**, 725 (1957).
19. Zamecnik, P. C., Stephenson, M. L., Scott, J. F., and Hoagland, M. B., *Federation Proc.*, **16**, 275 (1957).
20. DeMoss, J. A., Genuth, S. M., and Novelli, G. D., *Proc. Nat. Acad. Sc.*, **42**, 325 (1956).
21. Berg, P., *Federation Proc.*, **16**, 152 (1957).
22. Hoagland, M. B., Zamecnik, P. C., and Stephenson, M. L., Current activities in molecular biology, in press.

V. THE FUNCTION OF GENETIC MATERIAL

Reprinted from VIROLOGY, Volume 2, No. 4, August 1956
Academic Press Inc.   *Printed in U.S.A.*

VIROLOGY **2**, 433–437 (1956)

Intracellular Distribution of Labeled Ribonucleic Acid After Phage Infection of *Escherichia coli*[1]

ELLIOT VOLKIN AND L. ASTRACHAN

(with the technical assistance of M. H. Jones)

Biology Division, Oak Ridge National Laboratory, Oak Ridge, Tennessee

Accepted April 2, 1956

By rupture of T2r+-infected bacterial cells, and differential centrifugation into component subcellular parts, it can be shown that, during the course of infection, isotopic phosphate is incorporated into the RNA of these constituents in a diverse manner. The RNA of one particulate fraction, though only a small part of the total cell RNA, has the highest specific activity, whereas the major portion of cell RNA, found in another particulate fraction, has extremely low activity. RNA found in the soluble fraction is intermediate in specific activity.

INTRODUCTION

The ability of T2r+-infected *Escherichia coli* to incorporate radioactive inorganic phosphate from the medium into ribonucleic acid (RNA) has been previously described (Volkin and Astrachan, 1956). Because the specific activities of the RNA mononucleotides were unequal, it was suggested that cellular RNA contained a minor species which incorporated isotope at an enhanced rate. By partial separation of the host's morphological constituents it now has been demonstrated that the RNA's localized in different bacterial subcellular parts attain widely divergent specific activities.

MATERIALS AND METHODS

A previous report (Volkin and Astrachan, 1956) describes the bacterial and phage stocks, the biological assay procedures, the composition of the synthetic and peptone broth media, the phosphorus and radioactivity determinations, and the methods of chemical fractionation and ion-exchange chromatography.

[1] Work performed under U. S. Atomic Energy Commission Contract No. W-7405-eng-26.

433

Conditions of Infection

Logarithmic growth of bacteria in peptone broth at 37° was allowed to proceed to a titer of 4×10^8/ml, at which point the bacteria were infected with T2r+, at an input ratio of 11 phage per bacterium. After 5 minutes for phage adsorption, neutralized $P^{32}O_4$ was added, and the culture incubated for an additional 25 minutes. In synthetic medium a similar protocol was followed, except that phage infection took place at a bacterial titer of 1×10^8/ml and the culture was incubated for 55 minutes after addition of isotopic phosphate.

Separation of Subcellular Constituents

The chilled cultures were centrifuged to collect infected bacteria, which were washed with broth or synthetic medium and then ground in a mortar with alumina (Linde A, Carbide and Carbon Chemical Corporation) as described by McIlwain (1948). The mixture of ground cells and alumina was suspended in buffered saline solution (0.1 M NaCl, 0.001 M MgCl$_2$, 0.0001 M CaCl$_2$, 0.01 M tris, 0.01 M KCN, pH 7.7) and centrifuged to yield two particulate components and a soluble fraction, each containing some portion of the cell RNA (Schachman et al., 1952; Siegel et al., 1952; Billen and Volkin, 1954).

Alumina and any unbroken cells were removed by preliminary centrifugation at 3500 g for 20 minutes, after which the supernatant was centrifuged at 20,000 g for 15 minutes to yield particulate fraction P_1. This pellet, which consists mainly of bacterial membranes, also has been shown to contain high succinoxidase activity (Billen and Volkin, 1954). Centrifugation of the supernatant at 140,000 g for 90 minutes yielded a pellet (P_2) that contains the bulk of the morphologically identifiable particulates of the cell (Schachman et al., 1952; Wyckoff, 1949) and is particularly rich in RNA. The supernatant (S) contains an additional large amount of the cell RNA and almost all the deoxyribonucleic acid (DNA). It appears likely that the grinding process has disrupted most of the intracellular phage, since little DNA appears in pellets P_1 and P_2. All operations were carried out below 4°.

The two pellets and final supernatant were fractionated for the separation of the cell nucleic acids and subsequent ion-exchange analysis of the RNA mononucleotides (Volkin and Astrachan, 1956).

It should be mentioned that in the peptone broth experiment only about 50% of the phosphorylated compounds was recovered. The loss was probably a result of rupture of the rather fragile infected cells during the initial centrifugation and washing processes.

RESULTS AND DISCUSSION

Assays for free phage, infective centers, and uninfected bacteria demonstrated that at the time of isotope addition over 98% adsorption of phage had taken place and the uninfected bacterial population had decreased to less than 5×10^3/ml. No significant rise in uninfected bacteria and less than 5% lysis of infected cells occurred by the time the cultures were chilled.

The results of the RNA analyses, summarized in Tables 1 and 2, point out a wide divergence in the ability of the cellular components to incorporate isotope into RNA. Thus, although particulate fraction P_2 contains most of the host RNA, the specific activity of this RNA is by far the lowest of the three fractions. On the other hand, the RNA in P_1, though a very low proportion of the total RNA, has the highest specific activity. Soluble RNA is intermediate in both amount and specific activity. The relative specific activities of RNA in P_1, P_2, and S are, respectively, 16.6, 1.0, and 5.5 in the peptone broth experiment, and 8.8, 1.0, and 6.1 in synthetic medium.

Too much value should not be placed on the relative quantitative results for the three fractions because of possible cross-contamination inherent in such a method of separation. Such cross-contamination would arise from incomplete separation by the centrifugation procedure, and rupture or lysis of the particulate components. Thus it may be noted that P_1-RNA, with the highest specific activity, still exhibits

TABLE 1
NUCLEIC ACID RECOVERIES AND SPECIFIC ACTIVITIES (PEPTONE BROTH)

	P_1			P_2			S		
	Total radio-activity, ct/sec	Total phosphorus, μg	Specific activity, (ct/sec)/μg P	Total radio-activity ct/sec	Total phosphorus, μg	Specific activity, (ct/sec)/μg P	Total radio-activity, ct/sec	Total phosphorus, μg	Specific activity, (ct/sec)/μg P
RNA cytidylic	735	5.6	131	1040	132	8.0	2070	46	45
RNA adenylic	1220	6.4	191	1635	138	12.0	2690	41	66
RNA uridylic	1130	5.0	226	1490	125	12.0	2510	33	76
RNA guanylic	860	7.5	115	1180	155	7.5	2720	67	41
Total RNA	3940	24.5	161	5345	550	9.7	9990	187	53.5
Percentage of total cell RNA	20	3		28	72		52	25	
DNA	12,300	13	947	24,300	25	972	301,000	308	975

TABLE 2

NUCLEIC ACID RECOVERIES AND SPECIFIC ACTIVITIES (SYNTHETIC MEDIUM)

	P_1			P_2			S		
	Total radio-activity, ct/sec	Total phos-phorus, μg	Specific activity, (ct/sec)/μg P	Total radio-activity, ct/sec	Total phos-phorus, μg	Specific activity, (ct/sec)/μg P	Total radio-activity, ct/sec	Total phos-phorus, μg	Specific activity, (ct/sec)/μg P
RNA cytidylic	640	2.3	278	1070	36.0	30	4,600	25.5	180
RNA adenylic	915	2.8	323	1510	37.5	40	4,680	22.0	213
RNA uridylic	1000	2.8	360	1460	34.5	42	5,220	21.5	242
RNA guanylic	820	4.2	195	1300	57.0	23	6,100	36.5	167
Total RNA	3375	12.0	282	5340	165.0	32	20,600	105.5	195
Percentage of total cell RNA	12	4		18	58		70	38	
DNA	44,000	22	2000	148,500	74	2010	1,332,000	671	1990

heterogeneity with respect to its mononucleotide specific activities. Although other processes may account for this, such values could result from contamination of a P_1-RNA of uniform specific activity with RNA of different mononucleotide composition and/or lower specific activity. In addition, it cannot be determined whether (1) the RNA's in all fractions incorporate medium phosphate to some definite but varying extent, or (2) only some small fraction of the total RNA, such as that localized in P_1, incorporates most of the radioactivity, the latter having become distributed to other fractions because of particle breakage or incomplete centrifugation. It is conceivable that a small pool of active RNA may exist which attains a specific activity approaching that of DNA. If only a single, active pool of uniformly labeled RNA is present, it is possible to calculate its mononucleotide composition from the percentages of *total* radioactivity in the constituent mononucleotides. These ratios would be maintained in all fractions if this single RNA pool became distributed into other nonradioactive RNA fractions. Although such ratios for RNA in P_1 and P_2 are quite similar, the values for RNA in fraction S are different, possibly indicating a similarity in origin of labeled P_1- and P_2-RNA, but a divergence in the synthetic pathway of radioactive S-RNA.

In spite of the uncertainty in quantitative comparisons, it is apparent that isotopic labeling of RNA in the host's subcellular components has taken place to widely divergent extents.

REFERENCES

BILLEN, D., and VOLKIN, E. (1954). The effect of X rays on the macromolecular organization of *Escherichia coli*. *J. Bacteriol.* **67**, 191–197.

MCILWAIN, H. (1948). Preparation of cell-free bacterial extracts with powdered alumina. *J. Gen. Microbiol.* **2**, 288–291.

SCHACHMAN, H. K., PARDEE, A. B., and STANIER, R. Y. (1952). Studies on the macromolecular organization of microbial cells. *Arch. Biochem. and Biophys.* **38**, 245–260.

SIEGEL, A., SINGER, S. J., and WILDMAN, S. G. (1952). A preliminary study of the high-molecular-weight components of normal and virus-infected *Escherichia coli*. *Arch. Biochem. and Biophys.* **41**, 278–293.

VOLKIN, E., and ASTRACHAN, L. (1956). Phosphorus incorporation in *Escherichia coli* ribonucleic acid after infection with bacteriophage T2. *Virology* **2**, 149–161.

WYCKOFF, R. W. G. (1949). *Electron Microscopy, Techniques and Applications*, pp. 130–133. Interscience Publishers, New York.

(Reprinted from Nature, Vol. 190, No. 4776, pp. 576–581,
May 13, 1961)

AN UNSTABLE INTERMEDIATE CARRYING INFORMATION FROM GENES TO RIBOSOMES FOR PROTEIN SYNTHESIS

By Dr. S. BRENNER

Medical Research Council Unit for Molecular Biology, Cavendish Laboratory,
University of Cambridge

Dr. F. JACOB

Institut Pasteur, Paris

AND

Dr. M. MESELSON

Gates and Crellin Laboratories of Chemistry, California Institute of Technology,
Pasadena, California

A LARGE amount of evidence suggests that genetic information for protein structure is encoded in deoxyribonucleic acid (DNA) while the actual assembling of amino-acids into proteins occurs in cytoplasmic ribonucleoprotein particles called ribosomes. The fact that proteins are not synthesized directly on genes demands the existence of an intermediate information carrier. This intermediate template is generally assumed to be a stable ribonucleic acid (RNA) and more specifically the RNA of the ribosomes. According to the present view, each gene controls the synthesis of one kind of specialized ribosome, which in turn directs the synthesis of the corresponding protein—a scheme which could be epitomized as the one gene–one ribosome–one protein hypothesis. In the past few years, however, this model has encountered some difficulties : (1) The remarkable homogeneity in size[1] and nucleotide composition[2] of the ribosomal RNA reflects neither the range of size of polypeptide chains nor the variation in the nucleotide composition observed in the DNA of different bacterial species[2,3]. (2) The capacity of bacteria to synthesize a given protein does not seem to survive beyond the integrity of the corresponding gene[4]. (3) Regulation of protein synthesis in bacteria seems to operate at the level of the synthesis of the information intermediate by the gene rather than at the level of the synthesis of the protein[5].

These results are scarcely compatible with the existence of stable RNA intermediates acting as templates for protein synthesis. The paradox, however, can be resolved by the hypothesis, put forward by Jacob and Monod[5], that the ribosomal

RNA is not the intermediate carrier of information from gene to protein, but rather that ribosomes are non-specialized structures which receive genetic information from the gene in the form of an unstable intermediate or 'messenger'. We present here the results of experiments on phage-infected bacteria which give direct support to this hypothesis.

When growing bacteria are infected with a virulent bacteriophage such as $T2$, synthesis of DNA stops immediately, to resume 7 min. later[6], while protein synthesis continues at a constant rate[7]. After infection many bacterial enzymes are no longer produced[8] ; in all likelihood, the new protein is genetically determined by the phage. A large number of new enzymatic activities appears in the infected cell during the first few minutes following infection[9], and from the tenth minute onwards some 60 per cent of the protein synthesized can be accounted for by the proteins of the phage coat[7]. Surprisingly enough, protein synthesis after infection is not accompanied, as in growing cells, by a net synthesis of RNA[10]. Using isotopic labelling, however, Volkin and Astrachan[11] were able to demonstrate high turnover in a minor RNA fraction after phage infection. Most remarkable is the fact that this RNA fraction has an apparent nucleotide composition which corresponds to that of the DNA of the phage and is markedly different from that of the host RNA[11]. Recently, it has been shown that the bulk of this RNA is associated with the ribosomes of the infected cell[12].

Phage-infected bacteria therefore provide a situation in which the synthesis of protein is suddenly

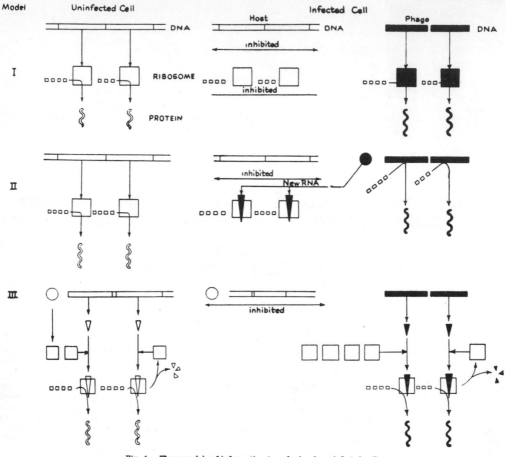

Fig. 1. Three models of information transfer in phage-infected cells

switched from bacterial to phage control and proceeds without the concomitant synthesis of stable RNA. *A priori*, three types of hypothesis may be considered to account for the known facts of phage protein synthesis (Fig. 1). Model I is the classical model. After infection the bacterial machinery is switched off, and now ribosomes are then synthesized by the phage genes. The *ad hoc* hypothesis has to be added that these ribosomes are unstable, to account for the turnover of RNA after phage infection. This is, in fact, the model favoured by Nomura *et al.*[12]. Model II assumes that in the particular case of phage the proteins are assembled directly on the DNA ; the new RNA is a special molecule which enters old ribosomes and destroys their capacity for protein synthesis. At the same time, synthesis of ribosomes is switched off. Model III implies that a special type of RNA molecule, or 'messenger RNA', exists which brings genetic information from genes to non-specialized ribosomes and that the consequences of phage infection are two-fold : (*a*) to switch off the synthesis of new ribosomes ; (*b*) to substitute phage messenger RNA for bacterial messenger RNA. This substitution can occur quickly only if messenger RNA is unstable ;

the RNA made after phage infection does turn over and appears, therefore, as a good candidate for the messenger.

It is possible to distinguish experimentally between these three models in the following way : Bacteria are grown in heavy isotopes so that all cell constituents are uniformly labelled 'heavy'. They are infected with phage and transferred immediately to a medium containing light isotopes so that all constituents synthesized after infection are 'light'. The distribution of new RNA and new protein, labelled with radioactive isotopes, is then followed by density gradient centrifugation[13] of purified ribosomes.

Density gradient centrifugation was carried out in a preparative centrifuge, and the ribosomes were stabilized by including magnesium acetate (0·01–0·06 M) in the cæsium chloride solution. Ribosomes show two bands, a heavier A band and a lighter B band, the relative proportions of which, for a given preparation, depend on the magnesium concentration used. The lower the magnesium concentration, the smaller the proportion of B band ribosomes and the larger the proportion of A band ribosomes.

2

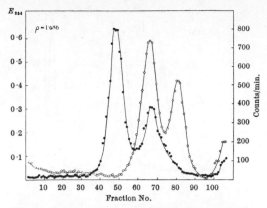

Fig. 2. Distribution of heavy and light ribosomes in a density gradient. *E. coli* B, grown in 5 ml. of a medium containing ^{15}N (99 per cent) and ^{13}C (60 per cent) algal hydrolysate and ^{32}PO$_4$, were mixed with a fifty-fold excess of cells grown in nutrient broth, the ribosomes extracted by alumina grinding in the presence of 0·01 *M* Mg^{++} and purified by centrifugation. 1 mgm. of ribosomes was centrifuged in 3 ml. of cæsium chloride buffered to pH 7·2 with 0·1 *M tris* and containing 0·03 *M* magnesium acetate for 35 hr. at 37,000 r.p.m. in the *SW*39 rotor of the Spinco model *L* ultracentrifuge. After the run, a hole was pierced in the bottom of the tube and drops sequentially collected. Ultra-violet absorption at 254 mμ detects the excess of light ribosomes (○), ^{32}P counts detect the heavy ribosomes (●)

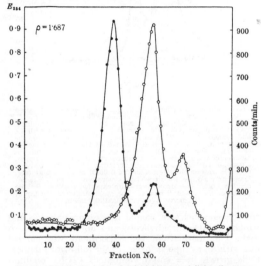

Fig. 3. Distribution of randomized heavy and light ribosomes in a density gradient. The mixture of ^{15}N^{13}C^{32}P and ^{14}N^{12}C^{31}P ribosomes was dialysed first for 18 hr. against 0·0005 *M* magnesium acetate in 0·01 *M* phosphate buffer pH 7·0, and then for 24 hr. against two changes of 0·01 *M* magnesium acetate in 0·001 *M tris* buffer pH 7·4. 1 mgm. of ribosomes was centrifuged for 38 hr. at 37,000 r.p.m. in cæsium chloride containing 0·03 *M* magnesium acetate. The drops were assayed for ultra-violet absorption (○) and ^{32}P content (●)

In order to show that there is no aggregation of ribosomes during preparation and density gradient centrifugation an experiment was carried out on ribosomes extracted from a mixture of ^{15}N^{13}C and ^{14}N^{12}C bacteria. The results are shown in Fig. 2, from which it can be seen that ribosomes of different isotopic compositions band independently and that there are no intermediate classes. The same preparation was then dialysed against low magnesium

to dissociate the ribosomes into their 50 *S* and 30 *S* components and then against high magnesium to re-associate the sub-units[14]. This should have resulted in distributing heavy 30 *S* and 50 *S* sub-units into mixed 70 *S* and 100 *S* ribosomes. Surprisingly enough, density gradient centrifugation of this preparation (Fig. 3) yields the same bands as found in the original ribosomes except for a decrease in the proportion of the *B* bands. This means that both bands contain units which do not undergo reversible association and dissociation and that the mixed 70 *S* ribosomes prepared by dialysis separate

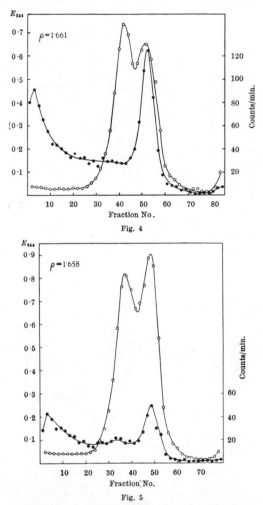

Fig. 4

Fig. 5

Figs. 4 and 5. Distribution and turnover of RNA formed after phage infection. A 600 ml. culture of *E. coli* B6 (mutant requiring arginine and uracil) was infected with *T*4*D* (multiplicity 30) and fed ^{14}C-uracil (10 mc./m*M*) from third to fifth min. after infection. One half of the culture was removed and ribosomes prepared (Fig. 4). The other half received a two hundred-fold excess of ^{12}C-uridine for a further 16 min. and ribosomes prepared (Fig. 5). In both experiments approximately 3 mgm. of purified ribosomes were centrifuged for 42 hr. at 37,000 r.p.m. in cæsium chloride containing 0·05 *M* magnesium acetate. Alternate drops were collected in *tris*-magnesium buffer for ultra-violet absorption (○) and on to 0·5 ml. of frozen 5 per cent trichloroacetic acid. These tubes were thawed, 1 mgm. of serum albumin added, and the precipitates separated and washed by filtration on membrane filters for assay of radioactivity (●)

3

into their components in the density gradient. Other experiments to be reported elsewhere suggest that the A band is composed of free 50 S and 30 S ribosomes and that the B band contains undissociated 70 S particles.

The bulk of the RNA synthesized after infection is found in the ribosome fraction, provided that the extraction is carried out in 0·01 M magnesium ions[12]. We have confirmed this finding and have studied the distribution of the new RNA among the ribosomal units found in the density gradient. Fig. 4 shows that this RNA, labelled with ^{14}C-uracil, bands in the same position as B band ribosomes. There is no peak corresponding to the A band. In addition, there is radioactivity at the bottom of the cell. This is free RNA as its density is greater than 1·8, and, moreover, it must have a reasonably high molecular weight to have sedimented in the gradient. Lowering of the magnesium concentration in the gradient, or dialysing the particles against low magnesium, produces a decrease of the B band and an increase of the A band. At the same time, the radioactive RNA leaves the B band to appear at the bottom of the gradient. This shows that the uracil has labelled a species of RNA distinct from that of the bulk of B band ribosomes, since the specific activity of the RNA at the bottom of the cell is much higher than that of the B band. Fig. 5 shows that this RNA turns over during phage growth. There is a decrease by a factor of four in the specific activity of the B band after 16 min. of growth in ^{14}C-uridine. Similar results have been obtained using [32]PO$_4$ as a label.

These results do not distinguish between a messenger fraction and a small proportion of new

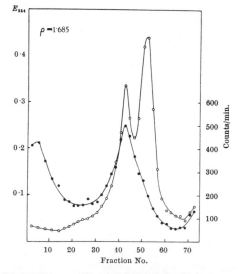

Fig. 6. RNA after isotope transfer in phage-infected cells. *E. coli* B grown in 10 ml. of [15]N (99 per cent) and [13]C (60 per cent) algal hydrolysate medium were starved in buffer, infected with $T4$ and growth initiated by addition of glucose and dephosphorylated broth ([14]N[12]C). [32]PO$_4$ was fed from the second to seventh min. after infection. The culture was mixed with a fifty-fold excess of *E. coli* B grown in nutrient broth, and then grown for 7 min. in dephosphorylated broth medium. 1 mgm. of purified ribosomes was centrifuged for 36 hr. at 37,000 r.p.m. in cæsium chloride containing 0·03 M magnesium acetate. Ultra-violet absorption (○) detects the [14]N[12]C[31]P carrier, radioactivity (●) detects the new RNA in the heavy cells transferred to light medium

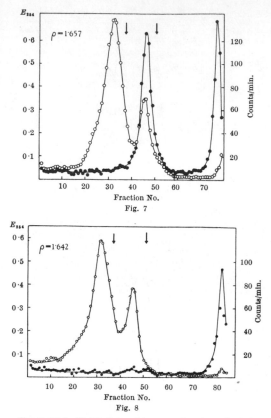

Figs. 7 and 8. Distribution and turnover of newly synthesized protein in ribosomes of phage-infected cells after transfer. *E. coli* B grown in 600 ml. of a salt glucose medium containing [15]NH$_4$Cl (99 per cent) were starved in buffer, infected with $T4$ and transferred to [14]NH$_4$Cl medium. [35]SO$_4$ was fed for the first 2 min. of infection and one half of the culture removed (Fig. 7). The other half received an excess of [32]SO$_4$ and ^{35}S-methionine and growth was continued for a further 8 min. (Fig. 8). 1 mgm. of purified ribosomes was centrifuged for 39 hr. at 37,000 r.p.m. in cæsium chloride containing 0·05 M magnesium acetate. Drops were assayed for ultra-violet absorption (○) and for radioactivity (●). The arrows mark the expected positions for the peaks of [14]N A and B bands. The radioactivity at the top of the gradient is contaminating protein

ribosomes which are fragile in cæsium chloride and which are also metabolically unstable. In order to make the distinction, the experiment was carried out with an isotope transfer, in the following manner: Cells grown in a small volume of [15]N[13]C medium were infected with $T4$, transferred to [14]N[12]C medium and fed [32]PO$_4$ from the second to the seventh minute. They were mixed with a fifty-fold excess of cells grown and infected in [14]N[12]C[31]P medium. Fig. 6 shows that the RNA formed after infection in the heavy cells has a density greater than that of the B band of the carrier. Its peak corresponds exactly with the density of the B band of [15]N[13]C ribosomes (Fig. 2) although it is skewed to lighter density, and its response to changing the magnesium concentration was that of a B band. There is no radioactive peak corresponding to the B band of the carrier : this means that no wholly new ribosomes are synthesized after phage infection. As already shown, the new RNA does not represent random labelling of B band ribosomes ; therefore it con-

4

stitutes a fraction which is added to pre-existing ribosomes the bulk of the material of which has been assimilated before infection. This result conclusively eliminates model I.

To distinguish between models II and III an experiment was carried out to see whether pre-existing ribosomes participate in protein synthesis after phage infection. Cells were grown in ^{15}N medium, infected with phage, transferred to ^{14}N medium and fed $^{35}SO_4$ for the first 2 min. of phage growth. Fig. 7 shows that only the B band of pre-existing ribosomes becomes labelled with ^{35}S and there is no peak corresponding to a ^{14}N B band. All this label can be removed by growth in non-radioactive sulphate and methionine (Fig. 8). In this experiment, the incorporation of ^{35}S into the total extract was measured and the amount in the B band found to correspond to 10 sec. of protein synthesis. This is probably an over-estimate since it is unlikely that pool equilibration was attained instantaneously. This value corresponds quite closely with the ribosome passage time of 5–7 sec. for the nascent protein in uninfected cells[15]. In addition, electrophoresis of chymotrypsin digests of B band ribosomes shows that the radioactivity is already contained in a variety of peptides. It would therefore appear that most, if not all, protein synthesis in the infected cell occurs in ribosomes. The experiment also shows that pre-existing ribosomes are used for synthesis and that no new ribosomes containing stable sulphur-35 are synthesized. This result effectively eliminates model II.

We may summarize our findings as follows: (1) After phage infection no new ribosomes can be detected. (2) A new RNA with a relatively rapid turnover is synthesized after phage infection. This RNA, which has a base composition corresponding to that of the phage DNA, is added to pre-existing ribosomes, from which it can be detached in a cæsium chloride gradient by lowering the magnesium concentration. (3) Most, and perhaps all, protein synthesis in the infected cell occurs in pre-existing ribosomes.

These conclusions are compatible only with model III (Fig. 1), which implies that protein synthesis occurs by a similar mechanism in uninfected cells. This, indeed, appears to be the case: exposure of uninfected cells to a 10-sec. pulse of $^{32}PO_4$ results in labelling of the RNA in the B band and not in the A band of ribosomes, and this RNA can be detached from the ribosomes by lowering the concentration of magnesium ions. Similarly the nascent protein can be labelled by a short pulse of $^{35}SO_4$; it is located in the B band and most of the label is removed by growth in non-radioactive sulphate. In contrast to what was observed in infected cells, residual stable radioactivity is found in both bands, reflecting the synthesis of new ribosomes.

In order to act as an intermediate carrier of information from genes to ribosomes, the messenger has to fulfil certain prerequisites of size, turnover and nucleotide composition. In the accompanying article, Gros et al.[16] have analysed the distribution of pulse-labelled RNA in sucrose gradients. They have shown that in uninfected cells there is an RNA fraction which has a rapid turnover and which can become attached reversibly to ribosomes depending on the magnesium concentration. The $T2$ phage-specific RNA shows the same behaviour and both are physically similar, with sedimentation constants of 14–16 S. We have carried out similar experiments[17] independently and our results confirm their findings. These suggest that, although the messenger RNA is a minor fraction of the total RNA (not more than 4 per cent), it is not uniformly distributed over all ribosomes, and may be large enough to code for long polypeptide chains. When ribosomes, from phage-infected cells labelled with $^{32}PO_4$ for five min., are separated by centrifugation in a sucrose density gradient[18] containing 0.01 M Mg^{++}, most of the messenger is found in 70 and 100 S ribosomes, contrary to previous reports[12]. When the magnesium concentration is lowered, the radioactivity is found in three peaks of roughly equal amount: (1) corresponding to a small residual number of 70 S ribosomes; (2) corresponding to 30 S ribosomes; (3) a peak of very high specific activity at 12 S. Separation of the RNA extracted from such ribosomes with detergent shows all the counts to be located in a peak at 12 S, skewed towards the heavier side. These results suggest that the messenger is heterogeneous in size and may have a minimum molecular weight of about $\frac{1}{4}$ to $\frac{1}{2}$ million. Similar results have been obtained in uninfected cells[17].

The undissociable 70 S ribosomes are enriched for messenger RNA over the total ribosomes of this type and it has been shown that they are also enriched for the nascent protein[17]. These ribosomes have been called "active 70 S" ribosomes, by Tissières et al.[19], and they appear to be the only ribosomes which preserve the ability to synthesize protein in vitro. This leads one to suspect that there is a series of successive events involved in protein synthesis, and that at any time we investigate a temporal cross-section of the process.

The exact determination of the rate of turnover of the messenger RNA should give information about the process of protein synthesis. This might be stoichiometric, in the sense that each messenger molecule functions only once in information transfer before it is destroyed. Its rate of turnover should then be the same as that of the nascent protein; but experiments to test this idea have been limited by difficulties in pool equilibration with nucleotide precursors.

It is a prediction of the hypothesis that the messenger RNA should be a simple copy of the gene, and its nucleotide composition should therefore correspond to that of the DNA. This appears to be the case in phage-infected cells[11,20], and recently Yčas and Vincent[21] have found a rapidly labelled RNA fraction with this property in yeast cells. If this turns out to be universally true, interesting implications for coding mechanisms will be raised.

One last point deserves emphasis. Although the details of the mechanism of information transfer by messenger are not clear, the experiments with phage-infected cells show unequivocally that information for protein synthesis cannot be encoded in the chemical sequence of the ribosomal RNA. Ribosomes are non-specialized structures which synthesize, at a given time, the protein dictated by the messenger they happen to contain. The function of the ribosomal RNA in this process is unknown and there are also no restrictions on its origin in the cell: it may be synthesized by nuclear genes or by enzymes or it may be endowed with self-replicating ability.

This work was initiated while two of us (S. B. and F. J.) were guest investigators in the Division of

5

Biology, California Institute of Technology, Pasadena, during June 1960. We would like to thank Profs. G. W Beadle and M. Delbrück for their kind hospitality and financial support.

[1] Hall, B. D., and Doty, P., *J. Mol. Biol.*, **1**, 111 (1959). Littauer, U. Z., and Eisenberg, H., *Biochim. Biophys. Acta*, **32**, 320 (1959). Kurland, C. G., *J. Mol. Biol.*, **2**, 83 (1960).

[2] Belozersky, A. N., *Intern. Symp. Origin of Life*. 194 (Publishing House of the Academy of Sciences of the U.S.S.R., 1957).

[3] Chargaff, E., *The Nucleic Acids*, **1**, 307 (Academic Press, New York, 1955). Lee, K. Y., Wahl, R., and Barbu, E., *Ann. Inst. Pasteur*, **91**, 212 (1956).

[4] Riley, M., Pardee, A. B., Jacob, F., and Monod, J., *J. Mol. Biol.*, **2**, 216 (1960).

[5] Jacob, F., and Monod, J., *J. Mol. Biol.* (in the press).

[6] Cohen, S. S., *J. Biol. Chem.*, **174**, 218 (1948). Hershey, A. D., Dixon, J., and Chase, M., *J. Gen. Physiol.*, **36**, 777 (1953). Vidaver, G. A., and Kozloff, L. M., *J. Biol. Chem.*, **225**, 335 (1957).

[7] Koch, G., and Hershey, A. D., *J. Mol. Biol.*, **1**, 260 (1959).

[8] Monod, J., and Wollman, E., *Ann. Inst. Pasteur*, **73**, 937 (1947). Cohen, S. S., *Bact. Rev.*, **13**, 1 (1949). Pardee, A. B., and Williams, I., *Ann. Inst. Pasteur*, **84**, 147 (1953).

[9] Kornberg, A., Zimmerman, S. B., Kornberg, S. R., and Josse, J., *Proc. U.S. Nat. Acad. Sci.*, **45**, 772 (1959). Flaks, J. G., Lichtenstein, J., and Cohen, S. S., *J. Biol. Chem.*, **234**, 1507 (1959).

[10] Cohen, S. S., *J. Biol. Chem.*, **174**, 281 (1948). Manson, L. A., *J. Bacteriol.*, **66**, 703 (1953).

[11] Volkin, E., and Astrachan, L., *Virology*, **2**, 149 (1956). Astrachan, L., and Volkin, E., *Biochim. Biophys. Acta*, **29**, 544 (1958).

[12] Nomura, M., Hall, B. D., and Spiegelman, S., *J. Mol. Biol.*, **2**, 306 (1960).

[13] Meselson, M., Stahl, F. W., and Vinograd, J., *Proc. U.S. Nat. Acad. Sci.*, **43**, 581 (1957).

[14] Tissières, A., Watson, J. D., Schlessinger, D., and Hollingworth, B. R., *J. Mol. Biol.*, **1**, 221 (1959).

[15] McQuillen, K., Roberts, R. B., and Britten, R. J., *Proc. U.S. Nat. Acad. Sci.*, **45**, 1437 (1959).

[16] Gros, F., Hiatt, H., Gilbert, W., Kurland, C. G., Risebrough, R. W., and Watson, J. D., see following article.

[17] Brenner, S., and Eckhart, W. (unpublished results).

[18] Britten, R. J., and Roberts, R. B., *Science*, **131**, 32 (1960).

[19] Tissières, A., Schlessinger, D., and Gros, F., *Proc. U.S. Nat. Acad. Sci.*, **46**, 1450 (1960).

[20] Volkin, E., Astrachan, L., and Countryman, J. L., *Virology*, **6**, 545 (1958).

[21] Ycas, M., and Vincent, W. S., *Proc. U.S. Nat. Acad. Sci.*, **46**, 804 (1960),

Reprinted from COLD SPRING HARBOR SYMPOSIA ON QUANTITATIVE BIOLOGY
Volume XXVI, 1961
Printed in U.S.A.

The Enzymatic Incorporation of Ribonucleotides into RNA and the Role of DNA

JERARD HURWITZ, J. J. FURTH, MONIKA ANDERS, P. J. ORTIZ AND J. T. AUGUST

New York University-Bellevue Medical Center, Department of Microbiology, New York, New York

During the past year, we have studied a number of enzyme catalyzed reactions which lead to the incorporation of ribonucleotides into RNA (Hurwitz, Bresler, and Diringer, 1960; Furth, Hurwitz, and Goldmann, 1961a, 1961b; Ortiz and August, 1961). We shall present evidence concerning two of these reactions, both of which lead to the incorporation of the four commonly occurring ribonucleoside triphosphates. One is dependent on DNA addition for nucleotide incorporation; the other is dependent on RNA. We shall devote most of this discussion to the DNA-dependent reaction.

RNA-DNA POLYMERASE

The DNA-dependent reaction, shown in Fig. 1, is catalyzed by an enzyme obtained from *E. coli* W The overall reaction consists of the polymerization of the four nucleoside triphosphates to RNA with the concomitant release of pyrophosphate. The reaction is completely dependent on DNA and the presence of a divalent metal such as Mn^{++} or Mg^{++}. This reaction has been studied in other laboratories and appears to be widely distributed in nature. Weiss and co-workers (Weiss, 1960; Weiss and Nakamoto, 1961) have detected the activity in rat liver nuclei and *Micrococcus lysodeikticus*. Stevens (1960), using an enzyme partially purified from *E. coli*, has obtained results similar to our own. A DNA-dependent reaction has also been demonstrated in extracts obtained from *Lactobacillus* and *Azotobacter* (Ochoa *et al.*, 1961), pea seedlings (Huang, Maheshwari, and Bonner, 1960), and rabbit and human reticulocytes (P. Marks, personal communication).

CHARACTERIZATION OF THE REACTION

The assay that we have routinely used (Table 1) consists of incubating the nucleoside triphosphates, one of which is labeled with C^{14} (or P^{32} in the α-phosphate), with enzyme and DNA in the presence of buffer, Mg^{++} and Mn^{++}, and a sulfhydryl compound. The incorporation of the labeled nucleoside into an acid-insoluble form is determined with a gas flow counter. Using this assay we have purified this enzyme approximately 100-fold.

The requirements for the fixation of ribonucleotides are summarized in Table 1. In this experiment, 20 mumoles of α-P^{32}-labeled GTP, 50 mumoles of

each of the other nucleoside triphosphates, and 1 optical density unit (at 260 mu) of calf thymus-DNA are added. With all components present 0.6 mumoles of GMP^{32} are converted to acid-insolubility. If DNA, or any of the nucleoside triphosphates are omitted, there is no detectable conversion. DNA cannot be replaced by RNA, e.g., tobacco mosaic virus RNA (a generous gift of Dr. K. K. Reddi), yeast and *E. coli* soluble RNA, *E. coli* ribosomal RNA, and synthetic polyribocytidylate (a gift from Dr. S. Ochoa) are completely inactive. The reaction shows an absolute dependence on Mn^{++} or Mg^{++}, and if the reaction mixture to which DNA has been added is preincubated for 30 minutes with DNase prior to the addition of enzyme, there is no detectable conversion of the $GRP^{32}PP$ into an acid insoluble product. If GTP is replaced by GDP, the rate of the reaction is decreased approximately 20-fold.

That the overall reaction is primarily synthetic is supported by the affinity constants of the substrates (Table 2). The Ks values for the 4 nucleoside-triphosphates are between 6 to 10 $\times 10^{-5}$ M. In addition, the enzyme is saturated by relatively small amounts of DNA. The ½ Vmax for thymus DNA is 0.25 optical density units or approximately 14 μg of DNA. This value is even lower for other DNA preparations (ϕX-174, d-AT-copolymer).

The product of the RNA-DNA polymerase activity contains only ribonucleotides. After acid precipitation and neutralization, the radioactivity present is rendered acid-soluble by either RNase or alkaline digestion, while DNase is without effect (Table 3).

Further support for the RNA-like nature of the product was obtained by studying the products produced after alkaline hydrolysis. RNA, in contrast to DNA, is quantitatively converted to the $2'(3')$-mixture of mononucleotides after alkaline degradation. The hydrolysis of the phosphodiester linkage as depicted in Fig. 2 occurs between the 5'-hydroxyl of the ribose and the phosphate moiety. This cleavage results in a quantitative transfer of the phosphate group to the adjacent nucleoside. As shown, AMP^{32} incorporation followed by alkaline degradation leads to the transfer of P^{32} to the neighboring nucleoside, X. When the mononucleotides formed are separated electrophoretically, all are labeled. Similar results have been obtained in separate experiments using GTP, CTP, and UTP

91

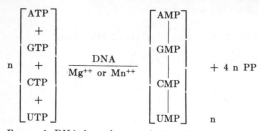

FIGURE 1. DNA-dependent synthesis of RNA.

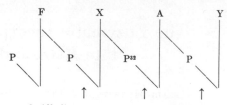

FIGURE 2. Alkaline transfer reaction with RNA.

TABLE 1. REQUIREMENT FOR INCORPORATION SUBSTRATE GR-P^{32}-P-P

Addition	mumole incorporated/20'
1. Complete	0.57
2. Omit 1 or 3 Nucleoside Triphosphates	<0.01
3. Omit DNA	<0.01
4. RNA in place of DNA	<0.01
5. Omit Mg^{++} and Mn^{++}	<0.01
6. Preincubation with DNase for 30'	<0.01

The reaction mixture (0.5 ml) contained P^{32}-GTP (1 × 10^6 cpm/μM) 20 mumoles; ATP, UTP and GTP, 50 mumoles of each; thymus DNA, 1 optical density unit at 260 mu; Tris buffer, pH 7.5, 20 μmoles; MgCl$_2$, 4 μmoles; MnCl$_2$, 2 μmoles; mercaptoethylamine, 1 μmole; Ammonium Sulfate II, 4 μg. Where indicated, 2 to 5 optical density units (at 260 mu) of TMV-RNA or E. coli ribosomal RNA or yeast or E. coli soluble RNA was used in place of DNA.

TABLE 2. KS OF VARIOUS SUBSTRATES

Substrate	Ks
ATP	9.6 × 10^{-6} M
GTP	9.6 × 10^{-6} M
UTP	6.4 × 10^{-6} M
CTP	8.0 × 10^{-6} M
Thymus DNA	0.28 optical density units at 260 mu

TABLE 3. HYDROLYSIS OF PRODUCT BY RNASE AND ALKALI

	Acid-Insoluble, cpm
1. No treatment—20' at 38°	1550
2. DNase (1 μg)— " " "	1450
3. RNase (1 μg)— " " "	<20
4. NaOH (1 M for 12 hrs)	<20

labeled with P^{32} in the α-phosphate; after alkaline hydrolysis of the reaction product, radioactivity is found in each of the four 2'(3') mononucleotides (Table 4).

TABLE 4. DISTRIBUTION OF P^{32} AFTER ALKALINE DEGRADATION (THYMUS DNA AS PRIMER)

Labeled Nucleotide	% Distribution of P^{32} After Alkaline Degradation			
	Ap	Cp	Gp	Up
AP*-PP	38	18	27	17
UP*-PP	24	24	17	35
CP*-P-P	22	21	21	36
GP*-P-P	21	18	21	40

The conditions used were as described in Table 1. The products were isolated by acid precipitation and subjected to alkaline degradation. The 2'(3') mononucleotides were then separated by electrophoresis.

TABLE 5. STOICHIOMETRY OF INCORPORATION OF THE FOUR NUCLEOTIDES

	Incorporated mumoles
1. C^{14}-ATP + UTP + GTP + CTP	21.4
2. ATP + C^{14}-UTP + GTP + CTP	19.6
3. ATP + UTP + P^{32}-GTP + CTP	16.8
4. ATP + UTP + GTP + P^{32}-CTP	17.0
Sum	74.8
Total increase in acid-insoluble orcinol material	81.5

The incubation mixture and assay were as described in Table 1 except that the additions were increased 10-fold.

The stoichiometry of the reaction is shown in Table 5. When calf thymus DNA is used as a primer, all four nucleotides are incorporated. The sum of radioactive nucleotides incorporated, 75 mumoles, is in agreement with the 82 mumoles of acid insoluble orcinol reacting material·formed. In addition there is a quantitative relationship between the amount of nucleotide incorporated and the release of inorganic pyrophosphate. α-P^{32}-labeled· UTP addition resulted in 1.3 mumoles of nucleotide incorporated. In a parallel experiment in which β-P^{32} labeled UTP was used, 1.2 mumoles of inorganic pyrophosphate was formed. The pyrophosphate was also identified by chromatographic techniques.

The requirements for the release of inorganic pyrophosphate from nucleoside triphosphates are the same as those for the incorporation of nucleotides into an acid insoluble form (Table 6). In the absence of added DNA, the reaction is reduced nearly 10-fold while the omission of any one of the ribonucleoside triphosphates results in a marked decrease in the amount of inorganic pyrophosphate formed.

THE ROLE OF DNA

A variety of DNA preparations activated the enzyme system. These preparations included calf thymus and heated calf thymus DNA, T2-DNA (kindly supplied by Dr. A. Hershey), *Pneumococcus* DNA (kindly supplied by Dr. Harriet Bernheimer) which is biologically active as transforming agent, *E. coli* DNA, *Micrococcus lysodeikticus* DNA, the phage ϕX-174 DNA (kindly supplied by Dr. R. L. Sinsheimer) which has the unique property of being single-stranded, and *Streptococcus* DNA. The chemically synthesized polydeoxythymidylate (Poly T) which is a homopolymer of deoxythymidylate was also active. This material was a generous gift of Dr. G. Khorana and had an average chain length greater than 14 nucleotide units. In addition, the enzymatically synthesized polymer, deoxyadenylate-deoxythymidylate copolymer, was also active. This compound was kindly supplied by Drs. C. Radding and A. Kornberg.

The fact that DNA of varied base composition would meet the requirement for RNA synthesis by the enzyme preparations prompted a quantitative study of the base ratios of the ribonucleotides incorporated into the product. In Table 7 is summarized the effect of four different DNA primers derived from different sources. The base ratios $(A + T)/(C + G)$ in the DNA preparations ranged from 0.4 in *Micrococcus* DNA to 1.86 in T2-DNA, and these ratios were closely reflected in the pattern of incorporation of ribonucleotides into the product. It is also significant that the sum of the purines incorporated into RNA equals the sum of the pyrimidine, reflecting the deoxynucleotide components in double-stranded DNA.

These results are consistent with the hypothesis that incorporation is determined by the ability of the ribonucleotides to form hydrogen bond pairs with the bases in the primer DNA. This bonding appears to be similar to that proposed by Watson and Crick (1953) for DNA, and found for DNA polymerase by Kornberg and his associates (Lehman *et al.*, 1958).

The observation that ϕX-174 DNA primed the incorporation of ribonucleotides was of particular interest because this DNA, in contrast to the DNA preparations previously described, is single-stranded. We have examined the influence of the base composition of this DNA on the ribonucleotides incorporated. Sinsheimer has reported (1959) that the base composition of ϕX-174 DNA is A = 1, T = 1.33, G =

TABLE 6. REQUIREMENTS FOR RELEASE OF RADIOACTIVITY FROM UR-P P* P

	mumoles
1. Complete system	1.18
2. Omit DNA	0.14
3. Omit either ATP or GTP or CTP	0.24
4. Omit Mn++	1.31

All conditions were as described in Table 1 except that β-P^{32} UTP was used. The reaction was terminated with acid, and the nucleic acid removed by centrifugation. The supernatant solutions were then treated with 0.1 ml of a 30% suspension of charcoal which was washed 3 times by centrifugation and resuspension. The charcoal was suspended in 1.0 ml of an ethanolic NH_3-H_2O solution, plated, and its radioactivity measured.

TABLE 7. INFLUENCE OF DIFFERENT DNA PREPARATIONS ON INCORPORATION OF NUCLEOTIDES

DNA Added	Nucleotide Incorporation in mμmoles						
	$\dfrac{A + T}{C + G}$ reported	AMP	UMP	GMP	CMP	$\dfrac{A + U}{C + G}$ observed	$\dfrac{A + G}{U + C}$
T2-DNA	1.86	0.54	0.59	0.31	0.30	1.85	0.96
Thymus-DNA	1.35	3.10	3.30	2.0	2.2	1.52	0.93
E. coli DNA	1.0	2.70	2.74	2.90	2.94	0.93	0.98
Micrococcus DNA	0.40	0.55	0.52	1.10	1.12	0.48	1.01

The complete system contained: ATP, GTP, CTP, and UTP (50 mumoles each), $MgCl_2$ (4 μmoles), $MnCl_2$ (2 μmoles), mercaptoethylamine (1 μmole), Tris buffer (25 μmoles, pH 7.5), 12 to 24 μg of protein and DNA. The DNA additions were as follows: T2—0.56 optical density units at 260 mu and Mn++ was omitted; thymus, 1 optical density unit; *E. coli*, 1 optical density unit; *Micrococcus* DNA, 1 optical density unit.

0.98, and C = 0.75. Using complementarity of base pairing we would expect that the RNA formed from this primer would have the base ratio of U = 1, A = 1.33, C = 0.98, and G = 0.75. As shown in Table 8, this ratio is found when ϕX-174 is used as the primer DNA.

Further evidence for complementary base pairing in this RNA forming reaction was obtained using the synthetic polydeoxythymidylate polymer and the deoxyadenylate-deoxythymidylate copolymer as primers. A comparison of the results with Poly T and thymus DNA is shown in Table 9. In the presence of all 4 nucleoside triphosphates both primers lead to extensive AMP incorporation. However, when the other three nucleoside triphosphates are omitted, there is a marked decrease in AMP incorporation with thymus DNA as a primer, while there is an increase in AMP incorporation with Poly T as the primer. The addition of RNase markedly reduced AMP incorporation in

TABLE 8. BASE COMPOSITION OF RNA USING ϕX-174 DNA AS PRIMER

Nucleotide Incorporated	mumoles per 20 min.	Base Ratio	
		Observed	Theoretical*
AMP	1.02	1.25	1.33
UMP	0.82	1	1
CMP	0.75	0.91	0.98
GMP	0.66	0.80	0.75

ϕX-174 DNA = 0.1 optical density unit at 250 mu; all other additions were as described in Table 1.

*Theoretical ratio is based on Sinsheimer's reported ratio of A = 1, T = 1.33, G = 0.98, C = 0.75.

TABLE 9. REQUIREMENTS FOR AMP INCORPORATION WITH POLY T AND THYMUS DNA AS PRIMERS

Additions	Thymus DNA	Poly T
	mμmoles incorporated	
1. Complete System	1.47	4.25
2. Omit GTP, UTP and CTP	0.15	6.80
3. 1 + RNase (5 μg)	0.22	—
4. 2 + RNase (5 μg)	—	7.0
5. 1 + DNase (5 μg)	0.18	—
6. 2 + DNase (5 μg)	—	2.84

The following additions were made: C[14]-ATP (50 mumoles), GTP, UTP and CTP (80 mumoles each), Poly T (0.5 optical density units at 250 mu), MgCl$_2$ (4 μmoles), MnCl$_2$ (2 μmoles), mercaptoethylamine (1 μmole), Tris buffer (25 μmoles, pH 7.5) and 12 μg of a 100-fold purified enzyme preparation obtained from E. coli W.

RNase and DNase were added before the E. coli enzyme. If DNA were pretreated with DNase, no detectable acid-insoluble radioactivity was found.

the thymus DNA primed reaction but was without effect when Poly T was used. This suggests that the product of the Poly T primed reaction is polyriboadenylate. This polymer, as has been shown by a number of investigators, is cleaved at a very slow rate by pancreatic RNase. In contrast, DNase addition results in decreased incorporation with both the thymus DNA and Poly T primed reactions.

The specificity of Poly T and thymus DNA in governing nucleotide incorporation is summarized in Table 10. With thymus DNA as primer, all four ribonucleotides are incorporated. In contrast, with Poly T as a primer, only AMP is extensively incorporated, either in the presence or absence of the other nucleoside triphosphates. The product of the Poly T primed system has been further characterized as polyriboadenylate by alkaline degradation of both C[14] and P[32]-labeled material.

In experiments with the d-AT copolymer as primer, only AMP and UMP are incorporated, and UMP incorporation is not dependent on the presence of CTP and GTP (Tables 11, 12). Both ATP and UTP are required. There is no detectable incorporation of C[14]-UTP in the absence of ATP. Similarly, incorporation of C[14]-ATP is dependent on the addition of UTP. The small incorporation of AMP in the absence of UTP is due to the contamination of these enzyme fractions with an enzyme which leads to the formation of polyriboadenylate from ATP. As

TABLE 10. SPECIFICITY OF POLY T AND THYMUS DNA IN GOVERNING NUCLEOTIDE INCORPORATION

	Labeled Precursor Incorporated			
	C[14]-AMP	P[32]-GMP	P[32]-UMP	P[32]-CMP
	mμmoles incorporated			
Thymus DNA + Complete System	1.95	1.40	1.06	1.20
Poly T + Complete System	4.4	0.05	0.11	<0.02
Poly T + labeled nucleotide only	6.15	0.09	<0.02	<0.02

The complete system contained 40 mumoles each of all 4 nucleoside triphosphates with one labeled as indicated. The specific activities (cpm per μmole) of the labeled nucleotides were: C[14]-ATP, 1.95 × 10[6]; GTP[32], 1.78 × 10[6]; UTP[32], 0.64 × 10[6]; CTP, 1.66 × 10[6]. All other additions were as described in Table 9.

TABLE 11. SPECIFICITY OF THE d-AT COPOLYMER AS PRIMER

Labeled precursor as substrate	mμmoles incorporated
C[14]-ATP	0.97
C[14]-UTP	1.10
P[32]-GTP	<.03
P[32]-CTP	<.03
C[14]-UTP (omit CTP and GTP)	1.06

The additions were as follows: MgCl$_2$ (4 μmoles), MnCl$_2$ (2 μmoles), mercaptoethanol (1 μmole), Tris buffer pH 7.5 (25 μmoles), d-AT copolymer (0.22 optical density units at 262 mu), 12 μg of a 100-fold purified enzyme preparation and all 4 ribonucleoside triphosphates. One of the nucleoside triphosphates was labeled with either C[14] or P[32] in the α-phosphate group. The amounts and specific activities of the labeled nucleotides were: C[14]-ATP, 50 mumoles (1950 cpm/mumole), C[14]-UTP, 21 mumoles (637 cpm/mumole), P[32]-GTP, 41 mumoles (780 cpm/mumole) and P[32]-CTP, 35 mumoles (738 cpm/ mumole). 80 mumoles of the three other nucleoside triphosphates were added in each experiment except where otherwise indicated.

TABLE 12. REQUIREMENTS FOR AMP AND UMP
INCORPORATION WITH THE D-AT COPOLYMER
AS PRIMER

Additions	mμmoles incorporated
C¹⁴-ATP + UTP	1.0
C¹⁴-ATP, omit UTP	0.17
C¹⁴-UTP + ATP	1.03
C¹⁴-UTP, omit ATP	<0.04

The additions were as in Table 11 except that the nucleoside triphosphates were added as indicated, CTP and GTP were omitted, and 0.11 optical density units of d-AT copolymer were added. The reaction was terminated after 20 minutes.

shown here C¹⁴-UTP is not incorporated to any detectable extent in the absence of ATP.

Figure 3 summarizes schematically the results which we have obtained. In the case of the homopolymer, Poly T, the RNA synthesized resembles the homopolymer polyriboadenylate. In the case of the d-AT copolymer, only AMP and UMP are incorporated into an acid-insoluble form. It has been demonstrated (Schachman *et al.*, 1960) that there is a unique sequence of dAMP and dTMP in the d-AT-copolymer. dAMP and dTMP are not randomly distributed in this DNA but are always present in alternating se-

quence. This sequence should also be reflected in the RNA that is formed in this reaction. The presence of dAMP in the DNA chain should "direct" UMP incorporation into the RNA chain and dTMP of the DNA chain should "direct" AMP fixation in the RNA chain. This model predicts that fixation of AMP³², followed by alkaline degradation, should result in a quantitative transfer of the P³² from AMP to UMP; similarly, label introduced with UMP³² should be recovered exclusively as AMP.

This has proven to be the case (Table 13). Alkaline degradation of the product formed with α-P³²-labeled ATP resulted in the transfer of 94% of the isotope to 2'(3')-UMP. The small but detectable activity in the 2'(3') AMP is probably due to the presence of the polyriboadenylate forming enzyme as a contaminant in these enzyme preparations. In the reverse experiment, in which P³²-labeled UTP was used, the radioactivity was recovered exclusively in AMP. In both instances, there was no detectable radioactivity in CMP or GMP.

The results summarized here indicate that not only does the base composition of the DNA influence the base composition of the RNA formed, but more precisely (at least in a special case), the sequence of the deoxynucleotides in the DNA-primer determines the sequence of the ribonucleotides in the product.

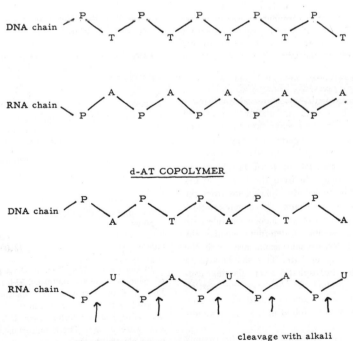

FIGURE 3. Results with Poly T and d-AT Copolymer as Primers.

TABLE 13. DISTRIBUTION OF P^{32} FOLLOWING ALKALINE
DEGRADATION OF THE PRODUCT PREPARED USING
THE D-AT COPOLYMER AS PRIMER

Substrates	mμmoles Incorporated	Distribution of Radioactivity after alkaline hydrolysis (%)			
		AMP	CMP	GMP	UMP
AP^{32}PP + UTP	16.3	6	<0.5	<0.5	94
ATP + UP^{32}PP	19.5	100	<0.5	<0.5	<0.5

The reaction vessels contained (in 5.0 ml) either 400 mumoles of AP^{32}-PP (765 cpm/mumole) plus 800 mumoles of UTP or 472 mumoles of UP^{32}-PP (242 cpm/mumole) plus 800 mumoles of ATP. Both contained d-AT copolymer (0.44 optical density units), MgCl$_2$ (40 μmoles), MnCl$_2$ (20 μmoles), Tris buffer, pH 7.5 (250 μmoles), mercaptoethanol (10 μmoles) and 120 μg of enzyme protein. After 30 minutes at 38°, the reaction was stopped with perchloric acid and 1.2 mg of bovine serum albumin were added. The acid-insoluble material was washed with 1% perchloric acid, dissolved in 1.5 ml of 1N NaOH and incubated for 16 hours at 38°. The hydrolysates were then adsorbed to Norit, washed with water, and the nucleotides eluted with ethanolic-NH$_3$. The nucleotides plus carrier amounts of each of the 2′(3′) mononucleotides were then fractionated by paper electrophoresis, located by ultraviolet light examination, eluted with water and their radioactivity determined.

Approximately 75% of the radioactivity in the alkaline hydrolysate was eluted from Norit. The elution of the material after paper electrophoresis was quantitative. The amounts of the alkaline hydrolysate used for electrophoresis were 2.53 and 3.94 mumoles for the experiments with AP^{32}-PP and UP^{32}-PP, respectively.

CHARACTERIZATION OF THE PRODUCT

While the above experiments indicated the decisive role of DNA in the system, and indirectly suggested that RNA as such does not enter into the initiation of this reaction, another experimental approach was utilized to establish this point directly. As shown in Fig. 2, alkaline degradation of RNA results in the formation of the nucleoside from the free 2′, 3′ hydroxyl end and the nucleoside diphosphate from the 5′-phosphate end of the chain. The endonucleotides yield the 2′(3′) mixtures of the mononucleotides. By this technique it is possible to determine whether the newly synthesized RNA chain commences with the labeled nucleoside triphosphate. This should lead to labeled nucleoside diphosphate after alkaline degradation of the product. If, however, pre-existing RNA is required (as a primer) to initiate the reaction, then no activity should be found in the nucleoside diphosphate moiety.

As shown in Table 14, when Poly T or thymus

DNA was the primer and C^{14}-ATP the labeled nucleotide, the isolated nucleoside diphosphate contained C^{14}. This suggested that at least part of the RNA chains began with the added nucleoside triphosphates. However, examination of the radioactivity content of the products produced after alkaline degradation revealed that the nucleoside liberated after alkaline degradation was not equivalent to the amount of nucleoside diphosphate formed. In the Poly T primed system, approximately 30% more adenosine than adenosine diphosphate was detected chromatographically, while in the case of thymus DNA this discrepancy is even more pronounced. One possible explanation for this discrepancy could be the addition of ribonucleotides to the end of DNA chains. For example, the addition of 2 AMP units to the end of DNA followed by alkaline hydrolysis (DNA----pApA) would yield only adenosine and no nucleoside diphosphate. Preliminary evidence suggests that this is the reason for the disparity between adenosine and adenosine diphosphate found experimentally.

That the discrepancy in the case of the thymus DNA primed system is due to the preferential ending of the RNA chain by AMP appears unlikely since a comparison of C^{14}-labeled nucleosides isolated from alkaline digests using all 4 C^{14}-labeled nucleoside triphosphates shows no preferential yield of C^{14}-labeled adenosine. In fact, the nucleosides isolated are very nearly equally labeled.

While these results are not unambiguous, they still demonstrate that the 5′-phosphate end of the RNA chain can be formed de novo.

TABLE 14. END GROUP ANALYSIS AFTER ALKALINE
DEGRADATION

	Thymus DNA	Poly T
mumoles C^{14}-AMP Incorporated	312	17.3

Alkaline Degradation

Product Isolated	Thymus DNA		Poly T	
	cpm	% of total	cpm	% of total
Adenosine 5′-2′(3′) diphosphate	1,830	0.38	518	2.26
2′(3′) AMP	465,000	96.91	21,500	94.01
Adenosine	13,000	2.71	852	3.73

In the case of the Thymus DNA primed system, the reaction mixture was increased 50-fold. In the case of the Poly T primed system, the reaction mixture was increased 3-fold. After alkaline degradation, carrier adenosine 5′-2′(3′)-diphosphate, 2′(3′)-AMP and adenosine were added. These materials were separated by paper electrophoresis.

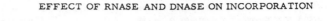

EFFECT OF RNASE AND DNASE ON INCORPORATION

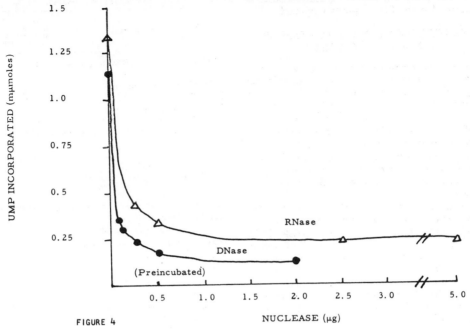

FIGURE 4   NUCLEASE (µg)

As already mentioned, the radioactivity incorporated into the product is completely susceptible to RNase after the product is acid-precipitated. However, when RNase or DNase was added to the incubation mixture, a small amount of activity is still found. This is shown in Fig. 4. The addition of small amounts of RNase markedly reduced the incorporation of UMP but increasing amounts of RNase did not further affect the reaction rate. A qualitatively similar observation was noted with DNase. However, if the DNA was preincubated for 30 minutes with DNase, there was no detectable UMP incorporated into an acid-insoluble form.

The product formed in the reaction was isolated by phenol addition and then subjected to nuclease treatment (Table 15). DNase still had no effect, and RNase led to a solubilization of only 60% of the radioactivity. Prolonged incubation of this reaction mixture was without any further effect, and the combined effect of RNase and DNase was similar to that observed with RNase alone. However, if the phenol isolated material was heated at 100°C or acidified and then neutralized, the product remained unaffected by DNase addition but was now rendered completely acid-soluble by RNase treatment.

These results suggest that part of the product may exist as a complex between RNA and DNA. Recently

TABLE 15. PRODUCT SENSITIVITY TO DNASE AND RNASE

Treatment of Product	Time of Incubation	
	15'	30'
	Acid-insoluble Radioactivity, cpm	
A. Phenol Isolated Product		
1. No addition	475	450
2. DNase (5 µg)	450	435
3. RNase (5 µg)	200	175
4. RNase + DNase	200	175
B. Phenol Product Heated at 100° or Acid-treated		
1. No Addition	450	420
2. DNase	420	400
3. RNase	<50	<50

such complexes have been shown to occur. Rich (1960) has chemically produced such a complex, as have Schildkraut, Marmur, Fresco, and Doty (1961). Hall and Spiegelman (1961) have shown this to occur also between the RNA produced after T2 infection and T2 DNA. Schildkraut et al. demonstrated that the RNA-DNA complex is resistant to pancreatic RNase and DNase (Schildkraut, Marmur, Fresco, and

Doty, 1961). Further work is now in progress to show directly that DNA is involved in a complex with the RNA formed in the DNA-dependent reaction.

RNA-DEPENDENT INCORPORATION OF RIBONUCLEOTIDES

Another ribonucleotide-incorporating reaction is present in the ribosomes of *E. coli* and leads to the incorporation of all four nucleotides. This reaction is inhibited by RNase but not by DNase.

We first came across this system while studying the effect of phage infection on RNA metabolism. Cohen (1948) demonstrated that phage infection results in the cessation of net RNA synthesis. We were interested in determining what enzyme systems involved in RNA metabolism were affected by phage infection.

We examined the enzymes involved in the activation of ribonucleotides and, as summarized in Table 16, the level of the enzymes which phosphorylate GMP, CMP, and UMP are not altered after T2 infection. There is also no detectable change in the level of either the RNA-DNA polymerase or polynucleotide phosphorylase. The latter enzyme was measured by the P_i^{32}-nucleoside diphosphate exchange reaction as well as by phosphorolysis of polyriboadenylate and by the polymerization of ADP to an acid-insoluble form (Grunberg-Manago, Ortiz, and Ochoa, 1956). In

TABLE 16. SUMMARY OF EFFECT OF T2 INFECTION ON ENZYMES INVOLVED IN RNA METABOLISM

Enzyme System
A. Not Affected
KINASES: GMP, UMP, CMP
RNA-DNA Polymerase
Polynucleotide Phosphorylase
CMP-Incorporation⎫In the presence of yeast
AMP-Incorporation⎭S-RNA
B. Affected
AMP Incorporation (in the absence of yeast S-RNA)

TABLE 17. AMP INCORPORATION IN THE ABSENCE OF EXOGENOUS RNA AND THE EFFECT OF PHAGE INFECTION

Sample	$m\mu M$/mg protein/20'
Uninfected	10.0
2 minutes	6.6
4 minutes	1.5
8 minutes	1.0
12 minutes	<1.0

The reaction mixture (0.5 ml) contained: Tris buffer, pH 8.5 (10 μmoles), MgCl$_2$ (8 μmoles), C^{14}-ATP (90 mumoles) and extracts of *E. coli* B/1, 5.

TABLE 18. PARTICULATE NATURE OF NUCLEOTIDE INCORPORATING SYSTEM

Procedure	Total Units mμ-moles per 20 min.	Specific Activity mμmoles/ mg protein
1. Alumina Extract (8000 × *g* super-natant)*	6950	9.5
2. 78,000 × *g* supernatant	1835	3.1
3. 78,000 × *g* pellet (2 hrs)	6000	45.0
4. 100,000 × *g* super	23	—
5. 100,000 × *g* pellet (1 hr)	5700	61
6. 100,000 × *g* pellet (1 hr)† (repeated centrifugation of No. 5)	4920	57

* 20 g of *E. coli* B/1, 5

† Predominantly 70 S particles

all cases, no differences were noted between uninfected and T2 infected extracts.

We also examined the effect of T2 infection on the enzyme system responsible for the addition of CMP and AMP to the terminal end of soluble RNA (Preiss, Dieckmann, and Berg, 1961; Furth, Hurwitz, Alexander, and Krug, in press). This activity, in the presence of acceptor soluble RNA, is also not changed by phage infection. However, it was noted that uninfected extracts of *E. coli* in the absence of added acceptor RNA catalyzed the conversion of significant amounts of AMP into an acid-insoluble form. After phage infection, this activity rapidly disappeard. The kinetics of this disappearance are summarized in Table 17. In the absence of exogenous RNA, uninfected extracts incorporated 10 mumoles of AMP per mg of protein into an acid insoluble form in 20 minutes. Within 2 minutes after T2 infection this activity was reduced 40%, and after 8 minutes there was virtually no activity. The addition of infected extracts to uninfected extracts did not reduce the extent of AMP incorporation.

In view of our ignorance of this enzymatic reaction, we turned our attention to uninfected extracts. It was hoped that a clearer understanding of the mechanism of AMP incorporation would aid in the elucidation of the manner in which phage infection altered this reaction.

In uninfected extracts it was observed that the enzyme activity was chiefly associated with the particles of *E. coli*. Using alumina extracts prepared in the presence of Mg^{++}, approximately 70% of the activity was sedimented after centrifugation at 78,000 × *g*. This procedure can be repeated a number of times, and all of the activity is associated with the particles (Table 18). The final preparation consists largely of 70 S particles (sucrose gradient centrifugation), and all of the enzyme activity is associated with these particles. Examination of the particles in the analytical ultracentrifuge also indicated that this material is predominantly 70 S.

Extracts prepared from the particles by sonic oscillation have been partially purified (Table 19). With the partially purified enzyme fractions, maximal ATP incorporation requires Mg^{++} and ribosomal RNA. RNase addition greatly reduced the incorporation while DNase addition had no effect. The Ks for ATP is about 7.5×10^{-5} M. The particulate preparation, after a number of high speed centrifuging and resuspension, is free of polynucleotide phosphorylase.

The product produced in this system resembles polyriboadenylate. After C^{14}-AMP incorporation followed by alkaline degradation, only a small amount of the radioactivity is released as adenosine while over 90% is released as the $2'(3')$ mixture of AMP.

The particulate fraction as well as the partially purified fraction catalyzes the incorporation of all 4 ribonucleotides. The results with the ribosomal particles are shown in Table 20. Incubation of ribosomes with any one of the labeled nucleotides results in its incorporation. However, when all four nucleoside triphosphates are combined, incorporation of the labeled nucleotide is inhibited. The significance of this inhibition is not self-evident at the present time.

Our present efforts are directed to the elucidation of the reaction. After this is realized, we will be in a position to return to the study of the mechanism by which phage infection stops the incorporation of ribonucleotide.

SUMMARY

Evidence for the participation of DNA in the biosynthesis of RNA has been presented. It has been observed that DNA acts as a primer in this reaction in a manner analogous to that proposed by Watson and Crick for DNA replication. This interpretation is based on the findings that the base composition of the RNA formed is quantitatively similar to the base composition of the primer DNA. It has also been shown that in the presence of the homopolymer, polydeoxythymidylate, AMP is incorporated into a complementary homopolymer, polyriboadenylate. This occurs even in the presence of the other nucleoside triphosphates. Evidence indicating that the sequence of the deoxynucleotide components of the DNA is reflected in a complementary sequence of the RNA has also been found. In the case of the deoxyadenylate-deoxythymidylate copolymer, deoxyadenylate is always adjacent to deoxythymidylate. The RNA-like polymer synthesized in the deoxyadenylate-deoxythymidylate primed reaction only contains uridylate and adenylate and those ribonucleotides are present in an alternating sequence analogous to that observed in the primer DNA.

It has been found that the RNA product of the DNA dependent reaction at least in part (if not all) is composed of completely new chains and does not require

TABLE 19. REQUIREMENTS FOR AMP INCORPORATION

Additions	AMP Incorporated, mμM/20 min.	
	Exp. 1	Exp. 2
Complete system	0.88	1.37
Omit Mg^{++}	.08	
Omit RNA	.46	0.22
Complete system + 5 μg RNase	.11	

The reaction mixture (0.5 ml) contained 10 μmoles Tris buffer, pH 8.5, 8 μmoles $MgCl_2$, 90 mμM ATP-C^{14}, 1.5 O.D. units of *E. coli* RNA and 17 μg protein of $(NH_4)_2SO_4$ 30–60 fraction.

TABLE 20. RIBONUCLEOTIDE INCORPORATION WITH PARTICULATE SUSPENSION

Substrate	Additions	Ribonucleotide incorporation mμM/ mg protein/ 20 min.
ATP-C^{14}	none	9.6
	UTP, CTP, GTP	3.3
UTP^{32}	none	10.0
	ATP, GTP, CTP	1.0
GTP^{32}	none	14.0
	ATP, UTP, CTP	4.6
CTP^{32}	none	11.0
	ATP, UTP, GTP	1.2

All additions were as described in Table 17 with the addition of labeled nucleotide where indicated. The same amount of unlabeled nucleotides was added.

pre-existing RNA to initiate synthesis. This is based on the isolation of C^{14}-labeled adenosine $5', 2'(3')$ diphosphate after alkaline degradation of a product containing C^{14}-AMP.

While the product isolated after acid precipitation is quantitatively rendered acid-soluble by RNase treatment, this is not the case when the product is isolated by phenol extraction. In the latter case 40% is resistant to the action of RNase. However, when the phenol-isolated product is heated at 100° or treated with acid it becomes completely susceptible to RNase. These results suggest that part of the RNA product is in a form resistant to RNase and may exist as an RNA-DNA complex.

In addition to the RNA-DNA polymerase, another mechanism for incorporating all four ribonucleotides into RNA is present in *E. coli*. This activity appears to be localized in the ribosomes, and it is inactivated by RNase but not by DNase treatment. After T2-phage infection, the incorporation of ribonucleotides by ribosomal preparations rapidly disappears. At present, the precise nature of this reaction is not clear.

ACKNOWLEDGMENTS

This work is supported by research grants from the National Institutes of Health.

Dr. Hurwitz is a Senior Postdoctoral Fellow of the National Institutes of Health; Dr. Furth is a Postdoctoral Fellow of the National Institutes of Health.

REFERENCES

COHEN, S. S. 1948. The synthesis of bacterial viruses. J. Biol. Chem., *174*: 281.

FURTH, J. J., J. HURWITZ, M. ALEXANDER, and R. KRUG. RNA-ATP(CTP) pyrophosphorylase. J. Biol. Chem., in press.

FURTH, J. J., J. HURWITZ, and M. GOLDMANN. 1961a. The directing role of DNA in RNA synthesis. Biochem. Biophys. Res. Comm., *4:* 362.

——, ——, ——. 1961b. The directing role of DNA in RNA synthesis. Specificity of the deoxyadenylate deoxythymidylate copolymer as a primer. Biochem. Biophys. Res. Comm., *4:* 431.

GRUNBERG-MANAGO, M., P. J. ORTIZ, and S. OCHOA. 1956. Enzymic synthesis of polynucleotides. Biochim. Biophys. Acta, *20:* 269.

HALL, B. D., and S. SPIEGELMAN. 1961. Sequence complementarity of T2-DNA and T2-specific RNA. Proc. Nat. Acad. Sci. U.S., *47:* 137.

HUANG, R. C., N. MAHESHWARI, and J. BONNER. 1960. Enzymatic synthesis of RNA. Biochem. Biophys. Res. Comm., *3:* 689.

HURWITZ, J., A. BRESLER, and R. DIRINGER. 1960. The enzymic incorporation of ribonucleotides into polyribonucleotides and the effect of DNA. Biochem. Biophys. Res. Comm., *3:* 15.

LEHMAN, I. R., S. B. ZIMMERMAN, J. ADLER, M. J. BESSMAN, E. S. SIMMS, and A. KORNBERG. 1958. Chemical composition of enzymatically synthesized deoxyribonucleic acid. Proc. Nat. Acad. Sci. U.S., *44:* 1191.

OCHOA, S., D. P. BURMA, H. KROGER, and J. D. WEILL. 1961. Deoxyribonucleic acid-dependent incorporation of nucleotides from nucleoside triphosphates into ribonucleic acid. Proc. Nat. Acad. Sci. U.S., *47:* 670.

ORTIZ, P. J., and J. T. AUGUST. 1961. The effect of T2 infection on the nucleic acid metabolism of *E. coli.* Federation Proc., *20:* 439.

PREISS, J., M. DIECKMANN, and P. BERG. 1961. The formation of 3'-hydroxyl terminal trinucleotide sequences of amino acid-acceptor ribonucleic acid. J. Biol. Chem., *236:* 1748.

RICH, A. 1960. A hybrid helix containing both deoxyribose and ribose polynucleotides and its relation to the transfer of information between the nucleic acids. Proc. Nat. Acad. Sci. U.S., *46:* 1044.

SCHACHMAN, H. K., J. ADLER, C. H. RADDING, J. R. LEHMAN, and A. KORNBERG. 1960. Synthesis of a polymer of deoxyadenylate and deoxythymidylate. J. Biol. Chem., *235:* 3242.

SCHILDKRAUT, C. L., J. MARMUR, J. R. FRESCO, and P. DOTY. 1961. Formation and properties of polyribo-nucleotide-polydeoxyribonucleotide helical complexes. J. Biol. Chem., *236:* PC2.

SINSHEIMER, R. L. 1959. A single-stranded deoxyribonucleic acid from bacteriophage φX-174. J. Mol. Biol., *1:* 43.

STEVENS, A. 1960. Incorporation of the adenine ribonucleotide into RNA by cell fractions from *E. coli* B. Biochem. Biophys. Res. Comm., *3:* 92.

WATSON, J. D., and F. H. C. CRICK. 1953. Genetic implications of the structure of deoxyribonucleic acid. Nature, *171:* 964.

WEISS, S. B. 1960. Enzymatic incorporation of ribonucleoside triphosphates into the interpolynucleotide linkages of ribonucleic acid. Proc. Nat. Acad. Sci. U.S., *46:* 1020.

WEISS, S. B., and T. NAKAMOTO. 1961. Net synthesis of ribonucleic acid with a microbial enzyme requiring deoxyribonucleic acid and four ribonucleoside triphosphates. J. Biol. Chem., *236:* PC18.

DISCUSSION

STEVENS: We have been studying the same reaction as just described by Dr. Hurwitz, i.e., the formation of polyribonucleotide as a process dependent on the four ribonucleoside triphosphates, DNA, and Mg^{++}.

The enzyme fraction is about 100-fold purified from *E. coli*. In the presence of ATP, UTP, CTP, and GTP, native DNA, and Mg^{++}, a five- to twenty-fold net formation of RNA can be measured by 260 mμ absorbancy or by the orcinol reaction. The base composition of the polyribonucleotide which is formed is analogous to the DNA which is added to stimulate its formation. With the complete system and native DNA it has been possible to show that more polyribonucleotide is formed than DNA added to stimulate the reaction.

Most of the studies with the enzyme have been carried out using the incorporation of ATP-C^{14} into acid insoluble material as a measure of the reaction. In comparison to the system just described by Dr. Hurwitz, we find a different situation with heated DNA. With heated DNA, an incorporation of the adenine nucleotide which is not dependent on the presence of the other nucleoside triphosphates can be demonstrated. The incorporation is not RNase sensitive. The product is alkali-labile, suggesting a sequence of adenine nucleotides. In the presence of all four nucleoside triphosphates, they are all incorporated. We think that the adenine nucleotide incorporation alone involves an addition of the adenylic units unto the ends of the DNA chains.

A study of the product, isolated from the reaction mixtures by the Sevag procedure, by sucrose density-gradient centrifugation, indicates that the RNA may be associated with the DNA.

Reprinted from the Proceedings of the NATIONAL ACADEMY OF SCIENCES
Vol. 47, No. 2, pp. 137–146. February, 1961.

SEQUENCE COMPLEMENTARITY OF T2-DNA AND T2-SPECIFIC RNA*

BY BENJAMIN D. HALL AND S. SPIEGELMAN

DEPARTMENTS OF CHEMISTRY AND MICROBIOLOGY, UNIVERSITY OF ILLINOIS

Communicated by H. E. Carter, December 8, 1960

Investigations of the functional interrelations among DNA, RNA, and protein are most conveniently performed under conditions which limit the synthesis of each macromolecular class to a few chemical species. A situation of this type obtains in *E. coli* cells infected with bacteriophage T2. Volkin and Astrachan[1] examined the nature of the RNA synthesized in the T2-coli complex by means of P[32]-labeling. Estimation of the relative P[32] content of the 2',3'-nucleotides isolated from an alkaline hydrolysate led Volkin and Astrachan to deduce that the RNA formed in the infected cell possessed an apparent base ratio analogous to that of T2-DNA. Subsequently, Volkin[2] obtained data suggesting that the synthesis of a specific RNA is a prerequisite for the intracellular production of bacteriophage.

Nomura, Hall, and Spiegelman[3] confirmed the observations on the apparent base ratios. In addition, they offered independent evidence for the existence of a "T2-Specific RNA" by demonstrating that RNA molecules synthesized after infection differed from the bulk of the *E. coli* RNA in electrophoretic mobility and average sedimentation coefficient. Because the procedures employed (zone electrophoresis and sedimentation) led to a selective separation of T2-specific RNA from the normal RNA of *E. coli*, they open up possibilities of further experiments relevant to an understanding of the nature of T2-RNA.

The fact that "T2-RNA" possesses a base ratio analogous to that of T2-DNA is of interest because it suggests that the similarity may go further and extend to a detailed correspondence of base sequence. The central issue of the significance and meaning of "T2-RNA" is whether or not this is in fact the case. A direct attack on this problem by complete sequence determination is technically not feasible at the moment. However, some recent findings of Marmur, Doty, *et al.*[4,5] suggest the possibility for an illuminating experiment. These authors demonstrated the specific reformation of active double-stranded DNA when heat-denatured DNA is subjected to a slow-cooling process. Such reconstitution of the double-stranded structure occurs only between DNA strands which originate from the same or closely related organisms. Presumably, the specificity requirement for a successful union of two strands reflects the need for a perfect, or near-perfect, complementarity of their nucleotide sequences. We have here then a possible method for detecting complementary nucleotide sequences. The formation of a double-stranded hybrid during a slow cooling of a mixture of two types of polynucleotide strands can be accepted as evidence for complementarity of the input strands.

We have used this procedure to examine for complementarity of sequence between "T2-RNA" and T2-DNA. Purified T2-RNA was used in order to provide an optimal opportunity for the T2-RNA to combine with its DNA complement, unhindered by non-specific interactions involving irrelevant RNA. Since the hybrid would have a lower density than uncombined RNA, a separation of the two might be attainable by equilibrium centrifugation in CsCl gradients.[6] To insure a sensitive and unambiguous detection of the hybrid, should it occur, double labeling was used. The T2-RNA was marked with P^{32} and the T2-DNA with H^3. Two isotopes emitting β-particles differing in their energies are conveniently assayed in each other's presence in a scintillation spectrometer.[7] This device, coupled with the use of the swinging-bucket rotor for the equilibrium centrifugation, permits the actual isolation of the pertinent fractions along with a ready and certain identification of any hybrids formed.

The primary purpose of the present paper is to present the results of such experiments. The data obtained demonstrate that specific complexes are indeed formed between "T2-RNA" and its homologous DNA. Their occurrence offers strong presumptive evidence for a detailed complementarity of the nucleotide sequences in these two macromolecules.

1. *Preparation and denaturation of DNA:* Tritiated phage were prepared by the addition of H^3-thymidine to a T2-infected culture of *E. coli* B. The cells were treated with 5-fluorouracil deoxyriboside (0.5 µg/ml) prior to infecton. The phage were purified by treatment of the lysate with DNAase and RNAase followed by three cycles of high- and low-speed centrifugation. DNA was extracted from the purified phage by treatment with sodium dodecyl sulfate followed by chloroform-iso-amyl alcohol deproteinization and ethanol precipitation of the DNA.[8] This preparation will be designated by H^3-DNA(T2). DNA from other sources was similarly purified.

Tritiated *E. coli* DNA was prepared from cells of a thymineless mutant (15T⁻) grown in a synthetic medium supplemented with tritiated thymidine. This preparation will be designated by H^3-DNA (*E. coli*).

DNA used for complex formation with RNA was first denatured by heating for 15 minutes at 95°C in 0.15 M NaCl + 0.01 M sodium citrate (pH 7.8), after which the tube containing the DNA was quickly placed in an ice bath. In all cases, the denaturation was carried out at a DNA concentration of 130 µg/cc.

2. *Preparation of T2-specific RNA labeled with P^{32}:* P^{32}-labeled ribosome RNA was obtained from *E. Coli* B grown in synthetic medium, infected with T2 at a multiplicity of 3.8, and labeled with 10 millicuries of P^{32} between three and eight minutes after infection. The infection and radioisotope incorporation were done at 37°C in medium C (Roberts *et al.*)[9] modified to include 5 gm NaCl, 0.37 gm KCl, and 1 gm casamino acids per liter. The phosphate concentration was lowered to 10^{-3} M and 0.1 M tris (hydroxymethyl) aminomethane (tris), pH 7.3, was used for buffering. The number of infective centers and uninfected survivors (2.5%) agreed with the multiplicity of infection. The procedures used for stopping incorporation, washing and disrupting cells, and preparing ribosomal RNA were those described previously (Nomura, Hall, and Spiegelman[3]).

3. *Purification of T2-specific RNA:* Enrichment of the ribosomal RNA preparation in its content of T2-specific RNA (as judged by an eightfold increase in specific activity of P^{32}) was obtained by zone centrifugation through a sucrose gradient. One ml of a 1.5% sucrose solution (w/w) + one ml of P^{32} ribosome RNA solution (1 mg/ml, 106,000 cpm/ml) were layered, with an inverted gradient of RNA on 20 ml of a 2 to 15 per cent sucrose gradient. All solutions were 0.05 M in KCl and 10^{-2} M in tris buffer at a pH of 7.3. Following centrifugation for eight hours at 25,000 rpm in the SW-25 rotor of the Spinco preparative ultracentrifuge, the contents of the tube were removed by dripping through a hole punctured in the bottom of the tube. Fractions of 1.2 ml were collected by drop counting. The ultraviolet absorption at 260 mµ and P^{32} content of the fractions are shown in Figure 1. The two fractions at the peak of P^{32} activity (corresponding

to 18 and 19.8 ml) were used for hybrid formation.   These will be referred to in the text as P^{32}-RNA(T2).   In the experiments described below, the two fractions exhibited identical properties.

4. *Slow cooling of DNA and RNA:* Slow cooling of RNA and DNA was done in solutions 0.03 M in sodium citrate and 0.3 M in NaCl at a pH of 7.8.   An insulated water bath having a capacity of 40 liters was used to provide slow cooling as follows:

Time (hr.)	Temperature (°C)
0	65
3.5	52
7.5	44
13.5	36
24.5	28.5
30.5	26

When the bath temperature reached 26°, the tubes containing RNA and DNA were removed and brought to a volume of 5.1 cc and a density of 1.74 gm/cc by addition of suitable amounts of water and saturated CsCl solution.   Twenty-five μg of unlabeled, undenatured DNA were added to the solution as a reference density marker.

5. *Separation of RNA from DNA by density-gradient centrifugation:* The solutions of RNA and DNA containing CsCl were centrifuged at 33,000 rpm in the SW-39 rotor at a temperature of 25°C.   At the end of each run, fractions corresponding to various density levels in the tube were obtained by piercing the bottom of the tube and collecting drops, 30 for each fraction.   These were diluted to a volume of 1.2 cc for measurement of ultraviolet absorption and radioisotope concentration.

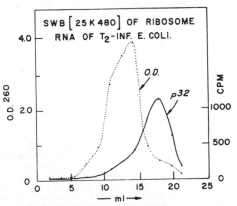

6. *Counting of H³-DNA and P³²-DNA:* To an aliquot from each swinging-bucket fraction 250 μg herring sperm DNA was added as carrier.   The nucleic acid was then precipitated with trichloracetic acid (final concentration 10%) in the cold, collected, and washed on a millipore filter (course, 50 mm dia.).   The filter was air-dried for one hour and placed in a cylindrical glass vial filled with 15 ml redistilled toluene containing 1.5 mg of 1,4-bis-2-(5-phenyloxazolyl)benzene (POPOP) and 60 mg of 2,5-diphenyloxazole (PPO). P^{32} and H^3 were counted in a Packard Tri-Carb liquid scintillation counter.

Fig. 1.—Separation of P^{32}-RNA(T2) from *E. Coli* RNA by sucrose-gradient sedimentation.   One ml. of ribosome RNA solution containing 1 mg RNA and 106,000 cpm P^{32} + 1 ml 1.5% sucrose solution were layered on 20 ml of a 2–15% sucrose gradient. Centrifugation: 8 hours at 25,000 rpm.   Cpm shown refer to 0.05 ml fractions of the swinging-bucket fractions.

Separation of T2-Specific RNA in a CsCl Gradient.—It was first necessary to establish the conditions required for an adequate separation of T2-specific RNA from T2-DNA.   Whereas *E. coli* ribosome RNA formed a narrow band within two days, T-2 RNA, because of its smaller size, required five days to form a band near the bottom of the tube.

Figure 2 shows the result of a five-day run carried out under the conditions specified above.   The mixture being separated consisted of 6.5 μg of heat-denatured H^3-DNA(T2), 25 μg of unlabeled and undenatured T2-DNA, and 14 μg of the purified P^{32}-RNA(T2).   Here, the three nucleic acids were not exposed to a slow-cooling operation but were mixed at 25°C, immediately put in the CsCl solution, and centrifuged. It will be noted that there is no appreciable interaction between the RNA and DNA as evidenced by the absence of any appreciable overlapping of the P[32]- and H[3]-containing regions. The small "tail" of P[32] which extends to the top of the tube is presumably a consequence of the low molecular weight of the T2-specific RNA.

Hybrid Formation between Denatured T2-DNA and T2-Specific RNA.—The results described in Figure 2 show that CsCl density gradient centrifugation permits a clear separation of H[3]-DNA(T2) from P[32]-RNA(T2) and provides, therefore, a test for interactions leading to the formation of RNA-DNA hybrids. Any distortion of the distribution of H[3]-DNA or P[32]-RNA from that observed in Figure 2 which leads to regions of overlap between H[3] and P[32] would be indicative of such interactions.

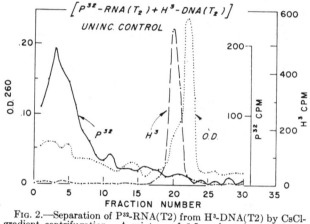

Fig. 2.—Separation of P[32]-RNA(T2) from H[3]-DNA(T2) by CsCl-gradient centrifugation. A mixture of 6.5 µg heat-denatured H[3]-DNA, 14 µg P[32]-RNA and 25 µg undenatured, unlabeled T2 DNA was made at 25°C, immediately diluted with CsCl, and then centrifuged for five days at 33,000 rpm.

1. *The effect of temperature during slow cooling on hybrid formation:* The influence of the starting temperature of the slow-cooling process was examined in a number of runs. In all cases, the nucleic acid mixture incubated consisted of 6.5 µg of heat-denatured H[3]-DNA(T2) and 14 µg of P[32]-RNA(T2). The rate and conditions of the cooling were as described earlier.

Three tubes containing this RNA-DNA mixture were placed in the slow-cooling bath at starting temperatures of 65°, 52°, and 40°C respectively. Slow cooling was followed by CsCl gradient centrifugation.

Figure 3 shows the optical density profiles and distributions of H[3] and P[32] obtained at the three temperatures. Comparison of the profiles of H[3] and P[32] with those of the control (Fig. 2) shows clearly that in all three cases, slow cooling of the DNA and RNA has produced a new peak of P[32] approximately centered on the band of H[3] (denatured DNA). This new P[32]-containing band must contain an RNA-DNA hybrid having approximately the same density as denatured T2-DNA. The amount of complex formed on cooling from the three temperatures was the

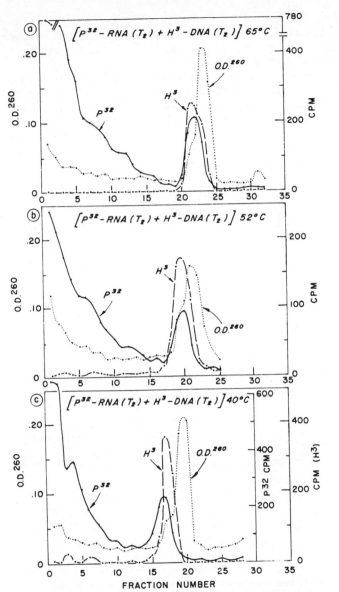

Fig. 3.—Formation of DNA-RNA hybrid at various temperatures. CsCl-gradient centrifugation analysis. P^{32}-RNA(T2) (14 μg) and H^3-DNA(T2) (6.5 μg) were mixed in 0.6 ml 0.3 M NaCl and 0.03 M Na citrate, (pH 7.8); then the solution was immediately placed in the slow-cooling bath. Three identical solutions were made; (a) was placed in the bath at 65°, (b) at 52°, and (c) at 40°C. When the bath temperature reached 26°, CsCl and 25 μg T2 DNA were added to each solution; then they were centrifuged for five days at 33,000 rpm.

same within experimental error. The three differ slightly in the density of the complex relative to DNA, the complex formed at low temperature being apparently more dense. This may be explained by the occurrence of partial renaturation of the H^3-DNA at the higher temperatures.

2. *Requirement for presence of single-stranded DNA during cooling:* In order to successfully complex with T2-RNA, the molecules of T2-DNA must be present in the single-stranded state. This was shown by an experiment in which a mixture of native H^3-DNA(T2) (13 μg) and P^{32}-RNA(T2) (15μg) was subjected to slow cooling, starting from 40°C. No evidence of hybrid formation is observed (Fig. 4). In a companion run (a repetition of the experiment of Fig. 3c) with denatured H^3-DNA(T2), approximately 10 per cent of the P^{32}-RNA was included in the hybrid region.

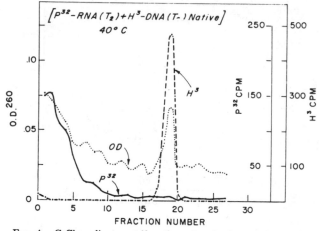

Fig. 4.—CsCl-gradient centrifugation of a slowly cooled mixture of native H^3 DNA (T2) with P^{32}-RNA(T2). 13 μg DNA and 15 μg RNA were mixed in 1.2 ml 0.3 M NaCl. 0.03 M Na citrate, slowly cooled from 40° to 26°, diluted with saturated CsCl solution, and centrifuged.

3. *Stoichiometry of hybrid formation:* Assuming the specific activity of P^{32} to be equal in all RNA molecules, one can estimate the amount of RNA which formed hybrid. From the data of Figure 3, this would be 1.4 μg RNA. (This figure is a maximum value, for some of the RNA which failed to form hybrid may be pre-existing *E. coli* RNA and, therefore, devoid of P^{32}.) The amount of DNA in the hybrid cannot exceed 6.5 μg, the total amount of denatured T2-DNA present. Because the hybrid and denatured T2-DNA have the same density, no more precise estimate can be made. From these considerations, it appears probable that the ratio of DNA to RNA in the hybrid does not exceed 5. That the complex does in fact contain considerably more DNA than RNA is suggested by its density, which is very nearly that of T2-DNA. A further indication that the entire 6.5 μg of T2-DNA has participated in complex formation is the proportionality observed between the amount of hybrid formed and the amount of DNA present when the ratio of DNA to RNA is varied. Experiments completely comparable to those

described by Figure 3 were carried out with the same concentration of P^{32}-RNA(T2) but with $1/5$ the quantity of denatured T2-DNA. In these cases, the amount of P^{32}-RNA found associated with the denatured DNA band was approximately two per cent of the input RNA which compares with the average of ten per cent observed when five times as much T2-DNA is included in the cooling mixture.

4. *On the specificity of the interaction leading to hybrid formation:* Having established the existence of the phenomenon and the conditions required for its occurrence, it became of obvious interest to examine the specificity requirements of hybrid formation. This was tested by carrying out the cooling process with mixtures of P^{32}-RNA(T2) and denatured DNA from heterologous sources. These included DNA of *Ps. aeruginosa, E. coli,* and bacteriophage T5. The DNA of the *E. coli* was labeled with H^3-thymidine whereas the others were unlabeled. The mixtures of P^{32}-RNA(T2) and denatured DNA preparations were subjected to a 52°C slow-cooling incubation under conditions identical to those described for the experiment of Figure 3b. Upon completion of the incubation, unlabeled native DNA was added to each tube as a density marker.

Figure 5 gives the optical density profiles and distributions of radioactivities. There is a suggestion of a very slight peak of P^{32} in the DNA region of the mixture containing *E. coli* DNA. It coresponds to $1/30$ the amount of hybrid produced with T2-DNA in a similar experiment. This may reflect the presence of the small amount of non-infected cells present during the P^{32}-labeling of the material from which the T2-RNA was obtained. However, it is too small to be considered seriously without further investigation. None of the other heterologous mixtures tested yielded detectable amounts of hybrid. It is of interest to note that although T5 has the same over-all base ratio as T2, no evidence of interaction between T2-RNA and T5-DNA was observed.

Interpretation of the Results.—The data presented here show that RNA molecules synthesized in bacteriophage-infected cells have the ability to form a well-defined complex with denatured DNA of the virus. That this interaction is unique to the homologous pair is shown by the virtual absence of such complexes when T2-specific RNA is slowly cooled with heterologous DNA. The fact that T2-RNA and DNA do satisfy the specificity requirement must reflect a correspondence in structure between the two. Structural specificity of this order in single polynucleotide strands can only reside in definite sequences of nucleotides. We conclude that the most likely interrelationship of the nucleotide sequences of T2-DNA and RNA is one which is complementary in terms of the scheme of hydrogen bonding proposed by Watson and Crick.[10]

Extension to Other Systems.—The bulk of the RNA in *E. coli* corresponds to the 18S and 25S[11] components of the ribosomes. These are metabolically stable,[12] remain firmly attached to ribosome protein at 10^{-4} M Mg^{++},[13] and have a base composition[14] not related in any obvious way to the DNA of the cells. In addition to the lack of correspondence in base ratio, two other reasons can be advanced for doubting the suitability of the large ribosomal RNA molecules for directing the synthesis of proteins as specified by the genetic material. First, the experiments of Riley *et. al.*[15] suggest that the intermediary between the genome and the protein-synthesizing mechanism is metabolically unstable. Second, the formation of the larger RNA components is virtually absent in T2-infected cells (cf. Fig. 1) despite

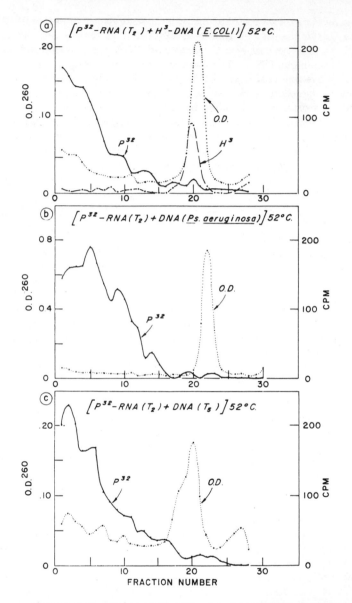

Fig. 5.—CsCl-gradient centrifugation of slowly cooled heterologous DNA-RNA mixtures. (a) P³²-RNA(T2) + H³-DNA (*E. coli*), (b) P³²-RNA(T2) + DNA (*Ps aeruginosa*), (c) P³²-RNA(T2) + DNA (T5).

In each case, 14 μg P³²-RNA and 6.5 μg heat-denatured·heterologous DNA were mixed in 0.6 ml 0.3 *M* NaCl, 0.03 *M* sodium citrate and slowly cooled from 52° to 26°C. Before CsCl-gradient centrifugation, 25 μg T2 DNA was added to (a) and (c) and 25 μg *Pseudomonas* DNA to (b).

the fact that they are actively synthesizing a variety of new protein species.

It seems more likely that the RNA molecules directly concerned with specifying protein synthesis in normal cells would have a base ratio corresponding to DNA and would possess other properties analogous to those found for T2-specific RNA. Its principle characteristics may be summarized as follows:[1, 3] (1) a weak linkage with the ribosome fractions since it can be broken by dialysis against $10^{-4} M$ Mg^{++}, (2) an active metabolic turnover, (3) an average sedimentation coefficient of about 8S, (4) a base composition which is closely analogous to its homologous DNA (considering thymidine equivalent to uridine and similarly for cytidine and hydroxymethyl cytidine), and (5) a sequence complementary to its homologous DNA.

The detection of the complementary RNA in T2-infected cells was greatly facilitated by the fact that the larger ribosomal components are not synthesized. Indeed, it would appear as if RNA synthesis in the T2-coli complex is largely confined to the class which is complementary to DNA. This advantage is not present in uninfected cells. Consequently the search for normal complementary RNA will be technically more difficult. That it is nevertheless feasible is suggested by the experiments of Yčas and Vincent[16] with yeast. These authors used P^{32} in a manner comparable to the procedures of Volkin and Astrachan and, despite surprisingly long pulses, they were able to detect the formation of a fraction with a high metabolic turnover and possessing a base composition analogous to yeast DNA.

Ultimately, attempts at establishing the presence in normal cells of RNA complementary to the genetic material will require that it be separated from the other RNA components. If all complementary RNA molecules possess physical chemical characteristics analogous to those of T2-specific RNA, the same methods which effected a successful isolation in this case may well serve in others. Once isolated, sequential complementarity to relevant DNA can be examined by the methods described above.

Some Implications of Complementary RNA.—An increasing amount of attention is currently being focused on the possibility of forming hybrid helical complexes composed of DNA and RNA strands. Interest in this originates quite naturally from its obvious implication for translating the genetic information coded in DNA to a functional RNA complement. Previous experiments[17, 18] had already demonstrated that paired helices were generated in mixtures of the synthetic polyribonucleotides of uridylate and adenylate. More recently,[19, 20] this has been extended to combinations involving synthetic polydeoxyribonucleotides and polyribonucleotides. It is of some interest that the experiments reported in the present paper lend support to the concepts underlying such model experiments by exhibiting hybrid formation between natural polynucleotides which are complementary and biologically related.

The demonstration of sequence complementarity between homologous DNA and RNA is happily consistent with an attractively simple mechanism of informational RNA synthesis in which a single strand of DNA acts as a template for the polymerization of a complementary RNA strand.

Summary.—Experiments are described showing specific complex formation between single-stranded T2-DNA and the RNA synthesized subsequent to infection of *E. coli* with bacteriophage T2. No such hybrid formation is observed with heterologous DNA even if it has the same over-all base composition as T2-DNA. It is concluded that T2-DNA and T2-specific RNA form hybrids because they possess complementary nucleotide sequences. The generality of the existence of complementary RNA and its possible role as a carrier of information from the genetic material to the site of protein synthesis is briefly discussed.

We are indebted to Drs. Noboru Sueoka and John Drake for providing the T5 DNA and *Pseudomonas* DNA used in this work and to Miss Cherith Watson for her assistance in performing the experiments.

* This investigation was aided by grants in aid from the U.S. Public Health Service, National Science Foundation, and the Office of Naval Research.

[1] Volkin, E., and L. Astrachan, *Virology*, 2, 149 (1956).
[2] Volkin, E., these PROCEEDINGS, 46, 1336 (1960).
[3] Nomura, M., B. D. Hall, and S. Spiegelman, *J. Mol. Biol.*, 2, 306 (1960).
[4] Marmur, J., and D. Lane, these PROCEEDINGS, 46, 453 (1960).
[5] Doty, P., J. Marmur, J. Eigner, and C. Schildkraut, *ibid.*, 46, 461 (1960).
[6] Meselson, M., F. W. Stahl, and J. Vinograd, *ibid.*, 43, 581 (1957).
[7] Okita, G. T., J. J. Kabara, F. Richardson, and G. V. Le Roy, *Nucleonics*, 15, 111 (1957).
[8] Marmur, J., personal communication.
[9] Roberts, R. B., P. H. Abelson, D. B. Cowie, E. T. Bolton, and R. J. Britten, "Studies of Biosynthesis in *Escherichia coli*," Carnegie Institution of Washington, Publication #607 (1957), p. 5.
[10] Watson, J. D., and F. H. C. Crick, *Nature*, 171, 964 (1953).
[11] Kurland, C. G., *J. Mol. Biol.*, 2, 83 (1960).
[12] Davern, C. I., and M. Meselson, *ibid.*, 2, 153 (1960).
[13] Tissières, A., J. D. Watson, D. Schlessinger, and B. R. Hollingworth, *ibid.*, 1, 221 (1959).
[14] Spahr, P. F., and A. Tissières, *ibid.*, 1, 237 (1959).
[15] Riley, M., A. B. Pardee, F. Jacob, and J. Monod, *ibid.*, 2, 216 (1960).
[16] Yčas M., and W. S. Vincent, these PROCEEDINGS, 46, 804 (1960).
[17] Warner, R. C., *Fed. Proc.*, 15, 379 (1956).
[18] Rich, A., and D. R. Davies, *J. Am. Chem. Soc.*, 78, 3548 (1956).
[19] Rich, A., these PROCEEDINGS, 46, 1044 (1960).
[20] Schildkraut, C. L., J. Marmur, J. R. Fresco, and P. Doty, *J. Biol. Chem.* (in press).

Reprinted from the Proceedings of the NATIONAL ACADEMY OF SCIENCES
Vol. 48, No. 8, pp. 1466–1472.   August, 1962.

THE IDENTIFICATION OF THE RIBOSOMAL RNA CISTRON BY SEQUENCE COMPLEMENTARITY,* II. SATURATION OF AND COMPETITIVE INTERACTION AT THE RNA CISTRON

BY S. A. YANKOFSKY† AND S. SPIEGELMAN

DEPARTMENT OF MICROBIOLOGY, UNIVERSITY OF ILLINOIS, URBANA, ILLINOIS

Communicated by H. S. Gutowsky, May 7, 1962

The presence of a sequence in DNA complementary to homologous ribosomal RNA is indicated by experiments described in a preceding paper.[1]   The data showed that a hybrid complex resistant to RNAase is formed when mixtures of ribosomal RNA and denatured DNA from the same cell are heated and then subjected to a slow cool.[2]   When DNA from a heterologous source is substituted, no such complex is observed.   The specific pairing of ribosomal RNA with a complementary sequence in DNA leads to the following two predictions: (1)   The ratio of RNA to DNA in the specific complex should approach a maximum value at levels indicating the involvement of a minor fraction of the DNA; (2)   Nonribosomal RNA should not compete for the same site.

Experiments relevant to these two issues have been performed.   It is the intent of the present paper to describe the results obtained and discuss their implications. The data are consistent with the existence of a specific sequence in DNA capable of complexing with homologous ribosomal RNA and not occupiable by nonribosomal RNA from the same organism.

Materials and Methods.—Strain and preparation of materials: *E. coli* strains BB and A-155, a uracilless derivative of *B* were used in the present study.   The methods of growth, labeling, counting, CsCl density gradient centrifugation, and the preparation of the following materials are detailed in the earlier papers;[1-3] heat-denatured DNA, free of RNAase; P32 and H3-labeled 23S RNA free of "informational" RNA.   The methods of assaying for RNAase activity and sensitivity of RNA-DNA complexes to nuclease degradation are the same as used in the earlier[1] study.

"Step-down" labeling of cells for informational RNA preparations: The procedure used is essentially that of Hayashi and Spiegelman.[3]   Logarithmically growing *E. coli* A-155 cells in nutrient broth were collected by centrifugation, washed twice

in SC minimal broth, and resuspended in the minimal medium to an O.D.$_{660}$ of 0.360. The cells were aerated for 10 min at 37°C; then 1.48 µg/ml of H³-uridine was added (New England Nuclear Corporation, 3.28 c/mM) and aeration at 37°C continued for 10 min. Isotope incorporation was halted by pouring the cultures into 1/3 their volume of frozen, crushed minimal medium. The cells were collected by centrifugation, then concentrated 20-fold in TM buffer. The RNA was purified and fractionated in linear sucrose gradients by the methods described previously.[1, 3] The fractions corresponding to 8–12S were pooled, concentrated, and used in the experiments described.

Experimental Results.—A. *Saturation curve of the ribosomal RNA-DNA complex:* The detection of a saturation plateau requires the performance of experiments involving the following steps: (1) Mixtures containing fixed amounts of heat-denatured DNA and varying amounts of labeled ribosomal RNA are exposed to a slow cool from 55°C to 30°C; (2) The resulting products are then subjected to equilibrium density centrifugations in CsCl solutions to separate free RNA from that which is complexed to DNA. The sorts of hybrids observed are exemplified by the two cases in Figure 1. It will be seen that at the lower level of input, most of the RNA in the reaction mixture is complexed to the DNA. The proportion of the input fixed decreases as the concentration of RNA is increased.

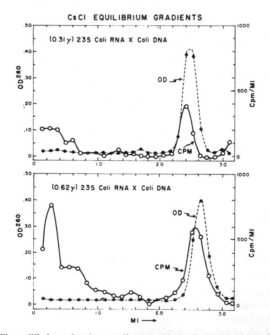

FIG. 1.—CsCl equilibrium density gradient profiles. Buffer used was TMSV (0.03 *M* tris, pH 7.3; 0.001 *M* MgCl$_2$; 0.3 *M* NaCl 0.005 *M* EDTA. Both contained 71 µg per ml of heat-denatured *E. coli* DNA. Upper contained 0.31 µg and the lower 0.62 µg of P³²– 23S RNA (6.7 × 10⁴ cpm/µg) of *E. coli*. Reaction mixtures slow (*ca.* 13 hr) cooled from 55°C to 33°C. Mixtures were then brought to a density of 1.73 with CsCl and a total volume of 3 ml. They were centrifuged for 52 hr at 33,000 rpm and 25°C.

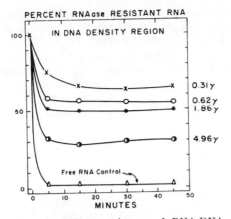

Fig. 2.—RNAase resistance of RNA-DNA complexes. 109 μg/ml of heat-denatured *E. coli* DNA were slow-cooled in TMSV with the indicated concentrations of *E. coli* 23S-P³²-RNA (6.7 × 10⁴ cpm/μg). After separation of hybrids by centrifugation as in Figure 1, sensitivity to RNAase was examined as described previously.[1]

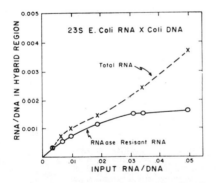

Fig. 3.—Saturation curves of total and RNAase-resistant counts in DNA region of CsCl equilibrium gradients. Details of incubations and centrifugation are as noted in Figures 1 and 2.

From our previous experience[1] with ribosomal RNA, it might be expected that nonspecific binding involving incidental coincidences over small regions will inevitably complicate such experiments. Adventitious complexing of this sort could become quantitatively serious at high levels of RNA input. Fortunately, as has been shown,[1] sensitivity to RNAase permits a ready distinction between nonspecific and specific complexes. This same device was used in the present study. Fractions in the hybrid regions of the density gradients were pooled, dialyzed, and exposed to RNAase.[1] The results obtained for four levels of RNA are detailed in Figure 2. In each case, free P³²-labeled RNA was included as an internal control in the reaction mixture. The behavior of only one control is depicted since they were all identical. It will be noted that the free RNA is almost completely solubilized in 5 min, whereas the H³-labeled RNA from the hybrid regions exhibit RNAase-resistant residues of varying percentages. The data of Figure 2 are in agreement with what would have been expected from increasing amounts of nonspecific complexing at higher concentration levels of RNA. The greater the input of RNA, the larger is the proportion of the counts in the hybrid region which are found to be sensitive to RNAase.

A composite summary of these and similar experiments are plotted in Figure 3. We have here a comparison of the total RNA found in the DNA density region with that which resists degradation by RNAase. The behavior of these two are strikingly different. The total RNA shows no signs of saturation, whereas the resistant residue clearly approaches a plateau, corresponding approximately to an RNA: DNA ratio of 0.0015. The existence of this maximal level is consistent with the view that the DNA contains a restricted region capable of specifically complexing with ribosomal RNA.

B. *Competitive and noncompetitive interaction in the course of hybrid formation:*
Competition experiments can also be used to reveal the existence of a localized
specific interaction between ribosomal RNA and its homologous DNA. In the
present system this can be realized by using two identifying isotopic labels on different RNA preparations. If the two RNA molecules are competing for the same
site and the total concentration is at or near the saturation level, one label will
displace the other as its proportion is increased in the reaction mixture. If they
do not compete for the same site, fixation to the DNA of one will be essentially in-
different to the presence of the other.

To examine questions of this nature, the following types of experiments were
performed with *E. coli* RNA and DNA. Mixtures containing fixed levels of P^{32}-
23S RNA, heat-denatured DNA, and varying amounts of H^3-23S RNA were incubated and then centrifuged in CsCl. The amounts of P^{32} and H^3-labeled RNA fixed
in the DNA and resistant to enzyme were then determined. For purposes of comparison, similar experiments were carried out with H^3-informational RNA (8–
12S) replacing the H^3-23S RNA in the mixtures. The informational variety was
chosen since it was known to complex well with DNA and thus provides a test for
the specificity of the ribosomal combination with DNA.

Figure 4 gives two examples of the hybrid regions observed in CsCl gradients.

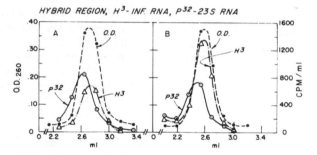

FIG. 4.—Hybrid regions in CsCl gradients of mixtures containing ribosomal and informational RNA. Both incubation mixtures contain 63 μg/ml of heat-denatured *E. coli* DNA and 2.66
μg/ml of *E. coli* P^{32}-23S RNA. (A) contained in addition 2.9 μg
of H^3-informational RNA and (B) 5.7 μg of H^3-informational
RNA per ml. Details of incubations and centrifugations are as
in Figures 1 and 2.

Both types of nucleic acids have hybridized with, however, an interesting and consistent difference. The H^3-labeled informational RNA appears to be symmetrically
distributed among the denatured strands of the DNA. This is clearly not the
case with the ribosomal complex which is distinctly displaced toward the heavy
side of the mean density of denatured DNA. The likely significance of this will be
briefly noted in the *Discussion*.

Again, to avoid confusion with irrelevant complexes, the fractions in the hybrid
regions were pooled and the RNAase-resistant residue of complexed radioactivity
determined. Figure 5 summarizes the resulting data. There is clear evidence
(Fig. 5*A*) of displacement of the P^{32}-labeled ribosomal RNA as more H^3-labeled
RNA of the same kind is incorporated into the complex. Further, a saturation

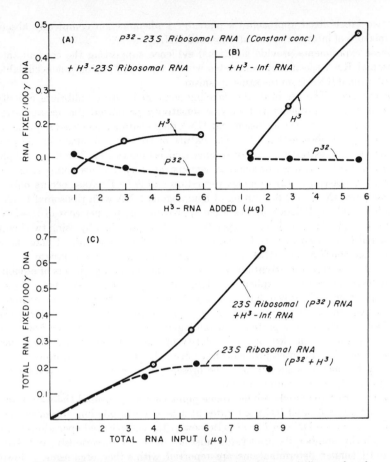

Fig. 5.—Tests for competitive interactions in mixtures of ribosomal and informational RNA molecules.   (A) All mixtures contained 63 μg/ml of heat-denatured *E. coli* DNA and 2.66 μg/ml of *E. coli* P³²-23S ribosomal RNA.   H³-23S ribosomal RNA of *E. coli* varied as shown.   (B) DNA and P³²-RNA same as (A) except that H³-informational RNA was added in the amounts indicated. (C) The same preparations as (A) and (B).   The plot here is total (P³² + H³) RNAase stable counts per 100 μg of DNA as a function of total input of RNA. All incubations during slow cool and equilibrium centrifugations were carried out as described in Figure 1.

plateau in the H³-RNA complexed is observed within the concentration range tested. On the other hand, when the H³-label is on informational RNA, its hybridization with the DNA has no effect on the ability of the DNA to combine with the P³²-labeled ribosomal material (Fig. 5B).   In addition, no evidence of saturation is observed with the informational variety within the concentration range tested. This difference in saturation behavior is more clearly illustrated in Figure 5C in which the total (P³² + H³) RNA fixed per 100 γ of DNA is plotted against the total RNA in the mixture.   When the ribosomal varieties alone are present, the sum of the two labels fixed approaches a plateau—a phenomenon completely absent in the mixture of informational and ribosomal RNA.

These experiments provide additional evidence supporting the contention that ribosomal RNA specifically complexes with a restricted region not occupiable by nonribosomal RNA from the same organism.

Discussion.—The use of double labeling combined with equilibrium centrifugations in density gradients and enzyme sensitivity permitted the accumulation of data which leads to the conclusion that DNA does contain a localized sequence complementary to ribosomal RNA. The nature of the data obtained in the present and previous investigation[1] may be summarized as follows: (1) The RNA complexed in a hybridization test is ribosomal as demonstrated by the base composition of the hybridized material. (2) Complex formation stable to RNAase occurs only with homologous DNA. (3) Saturation of homologous DNA with ribosomal RNA in a complex stable to RNAase occurs when approximately 0.2 per cent of the DNA is occupied. (4) Competition for a specific site was established by using two identical ribosomal RNA preparations distinguishable by isotopic labeling. Under the same conditions, nonribosomal RNA from the same organism does not compete.

It will not escape the attention of the reader that certain problems of obvious interest have not received explicit mention. We may briefly cite a few. First, all the experiments described have employed only the 23S ribosomal component. This raises the obvious question of sequence similarity with the 16S variety. Further, no details are reported on heterologous tests among the bacteria, a point of obvious interest in view of the similarity of the ribosomal RNA base compositions. These, and related problems have been the subject of continuing investigations by the methods developed in the present investigation. The results will be reported in separate communications.

We may perhaps briefly allude to one point centering around the significance of the fact that ribosomal RNA saturates at a level corresponding to approximately 0.2 per cent of the DNA in *E. coli.* In view of the complicated operations required to obtain this number, its exact value must not be taken too seriously, and certainly not until similar determinations are reported with other organisms. However, values similar to this have been repeatedly obtained in independent experiments, and it would seem that it is certainly correct as to order of magnitude. This, however, is about 10 times greater than one would calculate from the DNA content per nucleus[4] and the assumption that there is only one complementary sequence per genome. We conclude, therefore, that there must be repeating units of this kind. They could be similar in sequence, or identical, depending on whether the population of ribosomal RNA molecules are identical or different. There is one highly suggestive observation which leads us to conclude that, whichever is the case, these repeating units are not scattered throughout the genome, but contiguous. A persistent pecularitiy observed with homologous ribosomal RNA-DNA hybrids (Fig. 1 and P[32] curves of Figs. 4*A* and 4*B*) is the pronounced displacement of the complex towards the heavy side of the mean density of the heat-denatured DNA. This displacement is not observed with the heterologous complexes.[1] Furthermore, it is not seen with informational RNA-DNA hybrids at this level of RNA input (H[3]-curves of Figs. 4*A* and 4*B*). The simplest interpretation for this shift is to assume that the repeating units complementary to ribosomal RNA are contiguous and that any DNA strand which has one such sequence is likely to have another. Consequently, this selected set of strands complex with several ribosomal RNA molecules, resulting in the observed increase in density.

Summary.—The experiments reported offer further evidence for the presence in DNA of a sequence complementary to ribosomal RNA. Saturation experiments suggest that the particular region involved corresponds to between 0.1 and 0.2 per cent of the total genome. Competition for a restricted DNA region can be exhibited by the use of variously labeled homologous ribosomal RNA. Nonribosomal RNA from the same organism does not compete for the same site. The amount of ribosomal RNA complexed per unit of DNA at saturation suggests a number of repeating, similar, or identical sequences. Further, the density shift of the hybrids suggests that these units are not scattered but contiguous in the DNA structure.

* This investigation was aided by grants in aid from the U.S. Public Health Service, National Science Foundation, and the Office of Naval Research.

† Predoctoral fellow trainee in Molecular Genetics (USPH 2G-319).

[1] Yankofsky, S., and S. Spiegelman, these PROCEEDINGS, **48**, 1069 (1962).

[2] Hall, B. D., and S. Spiegelman, these PROCEEDINGS, **47**, 137 (1961).

[3] Hayashi, M., and S. Spiegelman, these PROCEEDINGS, **47**, 1564 (1961).

[4] Barner, H., and S. S. Cohen, *J. Bacteriol.*, **72**, 115 (1956).

Reprinted from the Proceedings of the NATIONAL ACADEMY OF SCIENCES
Vol. 48, No. 12, pp. 2101–2109.   December, 1962.

FORMATION OF A DNA-SOLUBLE RNA HYBRID AND ITS RELATION TO THE ORIGIN, EVOLUTION, AND DEGENERACY OF SOLUBLE RNA

BY HOWARD M. GOODMAN AND ALEXANDER RICH

DEPARTMENT OF BIOLOGY, MASSACHUSETTS INSTITUTE OF TECHNOLOGY

Communicated by Paul Doty, September 25, 1962

It has been known for a long time that transfer or soluble RNA (sRNA*) molecules play a central role in the organization of amino acids into polypeptide chains during protein synthesis.   Individual sRNA molecules combine with a particular amino acid to produce a complex which is active on the ribosomal particle.   Recent experiments[1] make it likely that a sequence of nucleotides in sRNA carry the specificity for determining the position of the amino acid in the polypeptide chain. However, as yet little is known regarding the origin of sRNA.   These molecules could arise from DNA in a manner similar to the production of messenger RNA. On the other hand, it has been demonstrated that the sRNA molecule is largely folded back upon itself with a regular system of hydrogen bonding,[2] and this has given rise to the suggestion that the RNA may act as a template for manufacturing itself.[2, 3]   These alternative possibilities have prompted us to carry out a series of experiments in which we look for the presence of a complementary sequence of bases in the DNA molecule by the formation of specific hybrids involving sRNA. This was stimulated by the work of Hall and Spiegelman,[4] who demonstrated that specific hybrids can be formed between T2 DNA and the RNA which is synthesized in *E. coli* during the T2 viral infection.   In these experiments, the hybrids were formed by a heating and slow cooling process such as was first used by Doty, Marmur, and co-workers[5a] in their experiments on DNA.   If hybrids are formed, the material can then be isolated through the use of density gradient centrifugation.

An important property of a DNA-RNA hybrid is the resistance which the RNA shows to ribonuclease digestion.   This was first demonstrated by Schildkraut *et al.*[5b] using synthetic polynucleotides and has been employed by Yankofsky and Spiegelman[6] in their recent work on hybrid formation between ribosomal RNA and DNA.   This property can be used to differentiate true hybrid formation involving systematic hydrogen bonding in a helical array from false hybrid formation such as may arise from "tangling" or other nonspecific interactions.   In the work reported here, we have demonstrated the formation of *E. coli* sRNA-DNA complexes and, by saturating all the sRNA sites on the DNA, we have been able to obtain an estimate of their number.   In addition, we have carried out a series of cross hybridizations between *E. coli* sRNA and a variety of bacterial DNAs.   This is a technique for learning something about the persistence of the sRNA nucleotide sequence in other bacterial species which may be close or distant relatives of *E. coli*.   Thus, the results tell us something about the evolutionary history of the sRNA molecules.

Methods and Materials.—Preparation of DNA and P^{32} sRNA: An overnight culture of *E. coli* strain B was grown in H medium.[7]   A portion of the culture was added to sterile H medium containing varying amounts of carrier-free $NaHP^{32}O_4$ (0.05 mc/ml, 0.5 mc/ml, 0.25 mc/ml in separate experiments) to bring the bacterial titer to $3-5 \times 10^7$/ml.   The flask was incubated at 37°C in a rotary shaker bath.   When a bacterial density of 5×10^8/ml was reached, the culture was flooded with unlabeled inorganic phosphate and the cells were allowed to grow for an additional 2–3 generations.   After the cells were harvested and washed, sRNA was isolated by a phenol extraction of the whole cells.[8]   The phenol-extracted sRNA was then carried through a further purification procedure using a methylated albumin column as described by Sueoka and Cheng.[9] Three different preparations were made in this way which had specific activities at the time of isolation of 1.4×10^5, 1.2×10^6, and 1.1×10^6 cpm per γ of sRNA respectively.

The unlabeled bacterial DNAs used in this investigation were prepared by the method of Marmur.[10]   Calf thymus and salmon sperm DNA were obtained from Sigma Chemical Company and California Corporation for Biochemical Research, respectively.   The DNAs from the bacteriophages were prepared by phenol extraction.[11]   Prior to annealing, the DNA was denatured by heating at 95–98°C for 15 min in 0.015 M NaCl, 0.0015 M sodium citrate, pH 7.4, and then quickly chilled in an ice bath.   Denaturation was followed by measuring the change in optical density at 260 mμ.

Annealing of sRNA to DNA and density gradient centrifugation: A variety of annealing experiments was carried out to determine optimal conditions.   The following standard procedure was then adopted: 1 ml of 0.25 M NaCl, 0.015 M sodium citrate, pH 7.4, contained 45 γ of heat-denatured DNA and varying amounts of P^{32}-labeled sRNA.   This solution was sealed in a glass ampule, quickly heated to 70°C, and then maintained at this temperature for 2 hr, after which it was slowly cooled over a 15-hr period to room temperature.   By this means, the solution was kept at a temperature over 50°C for approximately 8–10 hr.   This solution was layered below 3 ml of cesium chloride solution of density 1.72 in a 5-ml Lusterloid centrifuge tube and then spun in a

Model L ultracentrifuge (35,000 rpm, 65 hr, 25°C). Using this layering procedure, the lighter DNA and attached sRNA rises in the tube as the gradient is established, leaving the residual sRNA at the bottom. At the termination of the centrifugation, the bottom of the tube was pierced and drops were collected to divide the entire tube into approximately 35 fractions. Each fraction was diluted to 1.1 ml with distilled water and its optical density read at 260 mμ. The fraction was then split and part saved for ribonuclease digestion. To the remaining portion of the fraction 0.1 mg of carrier bovine serum albumin was added, and the nucleic acid plus carrier was precipitated with TCA (final concentration 5%). The precipitate was collected on Millipore filters, (0.45 μ pore size), air-dried, and counted in a Nuclear-Chicago low-background counter.

Ribonuclease digestion: A standard procedure was adopted for ribonuclease digestion. The solution contained 0.18 M CsCl, 5 × 10^{-3} M MgCl$_2$, 0.01 M Tris buffer, at pH 7.4, and 3.5 γ/ml of ribonuclease (crystalline pancreatic ribonuclease obtained from Worthington Biochemical Corporation). The incubations were carried out for 1 hr at 37°C. In the kinetic hydrolysis experiments, aliquots were removed from the reaction mixture at various time periods after the addition of ribonuclease and the digestion stopped by precipitation with TCA. The samples were then plated and counted as previously described.

Base ratio analysis: The P^{32}-labeled sRNA plus nonradioactive carrier sRNA prepared by the phenol method were hydrolyzed in 0.2 M KOH at 80°C for 45 min. The cooled hydrolysate was spotted on carboxymethylcellulose paper (Whatman CM50), and the nucleotides were eluted with distilled water. After suitable concentration, the hydrolysate was applied onto Whatman 3 MM filter paper and electrophoresis was carried out in 0.05 M citrate buffer, pH 3.4. The nucleotide spots were identified by their mobility, and the base ratios were determined by counting P^{32} on the paper. Pseudouridylic acid, a minor component of sRNA, was isolated on a Dowex-1 formate column as described by Cohn.[12]

Results.—It has been shown that DNA hybrids can be formed both by messenger RNA and ribosomal RNA. Accordingly, great care was taken in the isolation of sRNA to be certain that it was pure. The first precaution was the use of a "cold chase" of inorganic phosphate to allow the rapidly metabolized messenger RNA to lose its P^{32} label. In addition, two quite different isolation procedures were carried out sequentially. The sRNA base ratios are listed in Table 1, and it can be seen that they differ substantially from either ribosomal or messenger RNA. The possibility of trace P^{32} DNA contamination was eliminated because the sRNA preparations were completely digested by ribonuclease and, in addition, no P^{32} material banded in the DNA region when the sRNA was centrifuged by itself. P^{32}-labeled pseudouridylic acid isolated from the sRNA digest was identified by its characteristic absorption spectrum at pH 12.[12] This trace component has not been isolated from either ribosomal or messenger RNA and is therefore characteristic of sRNA alone. The labeled sRNA was centrifuged in a sucrose gradient, and the P^{32} counts migrated as a single peak with a sedimentation constant of 4 svedbergs. Thus, the preparations have properties characteristic of *E. coli* sRNA.

TABLE 1

BASE RATIOS OF sRNA

	Zubay[18]	Preiss *et al.*[19]	Dunn, Smith, and Spahr[20]	This work	Ribosomal[20] RNA	DNA[20] (or messenger RNA)
A	19.6	18.4	20.3	19.8	25.2	24.5
C	28.1	28.4	28.9	27.4	21.6	25.5
G	31.0	31.0	32.1	33.0	31.5	25.5
U*(T)	21.4	20.7	18.7	19.8	21.7	24.5
Purine/ pyrimidine	1.00	0.99	1.12	1.12	1.30	1.0
$\dfrac{A + U^*(T)}{G + C}$	0.69	0.66	0.64	0.66	0.88	0.96

U* includes pseudouridylic acid.

Figure 1a shows the results of annealing *E. coli* DNA with *E. coli* sRNA. It can be seen that almost half of the sRNA radioactivity is found associated with the DNA band. After ribonuclease digestion for 1 hr at 37°C, the sRNA at the bottom of the tube has been digested completely; however, less than 25 per cent of the sRNA in the band has been digested. In Figure 1b approximately ten times the amount of sRNA was annealed with the same amount of DNA as shown in Figure 1a. Under these circumstances a smaller proportion of the total radioactivity is found in the DNA band, and a larger proportion is digested off by ribonuclease. This suggests that the sRNA molecules may be competing for a limited number of annealing sites and consequently an increase in the number of sRNA molecules results in a larger number of imperfect annealings. Using a smaller amount of P³² sRNA than is illustrated in Figure 1a, 85 per cent of the total counts are found in the hybrid band. This clearly shows that it is not a small contaminant which is binding to the DNA but the bulk of the preparation. Furthermore, base ratios were de-

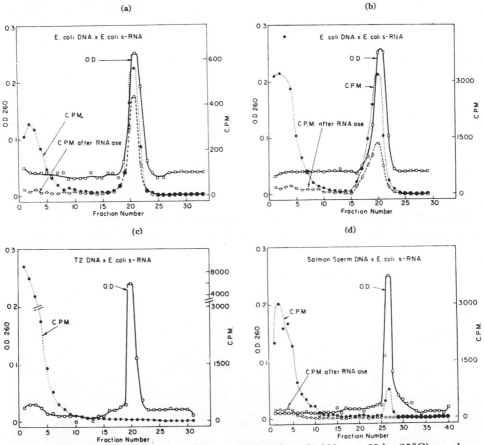

Fig. 1.— Cesium chloride density gradient centrifugations (35,000 rpm, 65 hr, 25°C) are shown for annealed *E. coli* sRNA and a variety of DNAs. Fractions were collected, diluted to 1.1 ml and the O.D.$_{260}$ was read. The fractions were then split. One part was counted directly; the other part was treated with ribonuclease (3.5 γ/ml, 1 hr, 37°C) as described under *Methods*.
   (a) 45 γ *E. coli* B DNA + 0.011 γ P³² sRNA.   (b) 45γ*E. coli* B DNA + 0.13 γP³² sRNA.   (c) 45 γ T2 DNA + 0.13 γ P³² sRNA.   (d) 45 γ Salmon sperm DNA + 0.13γ P³² sRNA.

termined on the sRNA in the hybrid band, and these gave results similar to those shown in Table 1. It should be noticed in Figure 1a and b that the radioactivity peak is not found directly under the peak of optical density but is shifted toward higher density. Since the sRNA molecules are comparatively small, we can use shifts of this type to draw some conclusions concerning the grouping of sRNA annealing sites on the DNA. If they were randomly distributed, the optical density band would be symmetric with the count band. Because of the shift, we have evidence that the sRNA positions are located near each other. This subject will be explored more fully in another publication.

In experiments using materials of high specific activity, one has to be very careful about potential artifacts, among which may be included nonspecific trapping due to the presence of short sequences of nucleotides in the DNA which are the same as those found in sRNA. Negative controls are thus very important. In addition, it is of great importance to carry out the ribonuclease digestions, as has been emphasized by Yankofsky and Spiegelman[6] in their work on ribosomal RNA. An example of a negative result is shown in Figure 1c, in which the sRNA was heated and slowly cooled together with T2 viral DNA. It can be seen that none of the sRNA is banding with the DNA. Similar results were obtained with DNA from the bacteriophages T7 and ϕX 174. Another kind of negative result is indicated in Figure 1d, which shows an annealing experiment with salmon sperm DNA. A small peak of radioactivity is found in the DNA region, but it is digested away by the treatment with ribonuclease, thereby indicating that it was an artifact rather than a true complex. It should be noted that in this case the band of radioactivity is symmetric with the band of optical density which implies that the sRNA molecules may be randomly attached to the DNA. Similar negative results were obtained with calf thymus DNA and DNA obtained from the P22 virus. However, in the latter two cases the amount of radioactivity in the band before digestion was less than 20% of that observed with the salmon sperm DNA.

The kinetics of ribonuclease digestion are shown in Figure 2. It can be seen that the control sRNA, to which DNA had been added without annealing, is rapidly di-

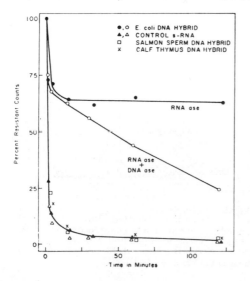

FIG. 2.—The time course of enzymatic digestion. All solutions contained 0.18 M CsCl, 5 × 10^{-3} M MgCl$_2$, 0.01 M Tris buffer, at pH 7.4 and 3.5 γ/ml ribonuclease. Aliquots were collected and precipitated for counting at various time periods. Resistant counts are shown for the *E. coli* DNA + P^{32} sRNA complex with ribonuclease alone (●) and with added DNAase, (○). Control P^{32} sRNA with added (but not annealed) *E. coli* DNA is shown with ribonuclease alone (▲) and with added DNAase (△). Ribonuclease digestion of salmon sperm DNA hybrid (□) and calf thymus DNA hybrid (×) is also shown.

gested down to a very low level. The rate at which it is digested is indistinguishable from the rate at which the false positives are digested, i.e., the salmon sperm and calf thymus DNA-*E. coli* sRNA complexes. In the true hybrid (Fig. 2), about 30% of the radioactivity is digested away almost immediately and thereafter there is a plateau of radioactivity even after 2-hr incubation at 37°C. However, the addition of DNAase to the system yields a slow digestion of the sRNA, as the DNA is digested enzymatically and the sRNA is liberated. These results are quite similar to those obtained with true and false hybrids involving ribosomal RNA.[6]

Saturation experiments: The experiments described in Figure 1a and b showed that more sRNA could be annealed to the DNA if a larger amount was added to the annealing mixture. This immediately suggests the possibility of attempting to saturate the sRNA sites on the DNA by increasing the amount of sRNA in the annealing mixture. The results of experiments of this type are shown in Figure 3.

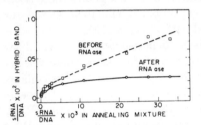

FIG. 3.—The amount of *E. coli* P[32] sRNA found in the *E. coli* DNA band is plotted as a function of increasing amounts of P[32] sRNA in the annealing mixture. All preparations were annealed with 45 γ DNA and varying amounts of P[32] sRNA (0.005 to 1.50 γ P[32] sRNA, specific activity = 5.6 × 10[6] cpm/γ). The O.D._260 and cpm before and after ribonuclease digestion were measured through the band region as described in *Methods*.

A constant amount of DNA (45 γ) was annealed with varying amounts of sRNA over a 300-fold range in concentration. The dashed curve shows that the amount of attached sRNA in the hybrid band goes up steadily while the solid curve shows that the ribonuclease-resistant part saturates. A plateau appears as a mass ratio of sRNA to DNA of 0.025 per cent. Thus, only a very small portion of the DNA is able to accept an sRNA molecule in hybrid formation. Furthermore, these results show that the preparation does not contain ribosomal RNA, since DNA-ribosomal RNA hybrids contain six times more RNA.[6] If cold ribosomal RNA is added to the annealing mixture, it does not compete with the bonding of sRNA, thereby suggesting that the ribosomal RNA sites are different from the sRNA sites.

The genome in *E. coli* contains a DNA molecular weight equivalent of 4×10^9.[13] Knowing this, and using the molecular weight of *E. coli* sRNA (25,500), we may calculate from the plateau in Figure 3 that there are approximately 40 sRNA sites in the *E. coli* genome. If we assume that there is one site per sRNA molecule, this number provides a direct estimate of the degeneracy of the amino acid code.

Inter-species hybrid formation: Having shown that it is possible to form hybrids between sRNA and its homologous DNA, we thought it would be of interest to examine the formation of hybrids between *E. coli* sRNA and other bacterial DNAs both from closely related and more distantly related species. These DNA preparations were all annealed with the same amount of *E. coli* sRNA under identical conditions in order to compare the amount of ribonuclease-resistant material produced by these cross hybridizations. Figure 4 shows that more hybrid is formed when the sRNA is annealed with the DNA from a closer relative than from a more distant relative. These initial experiments prompted us to survey a series of bacterial DNAs to see whether any trends could be observed as a function of varying guanine-cytosine (G-C) content in the DNA or familial proximity.

DNAs from five different bacterial families were used. The largest group is from the family Enterobacteriaceae to which *E. coli* belongs. In Figure 5, the results of the cross hybridization experiments are shown. The most striking feature of the figure is the fact that the results clearly fall into two different classes. Those points shown below the dashed line are all ribonuclease-resistant sRNA annealed to DNA from a different bacterial family than that of *E. coli* B. These are all at the level of 5 to 15 per cent of the amount of *E. coli* sRNA which is annealed to its homologous DNA. Furthermore, the figure shows that the G-C content is not an important distinguishing parameter. Thus, for example, *Brucella abortus* retains approximately 10 per cent of the radioactivity in its DNA band even though it has a G-C content which is reasonably close to that found in *E. coli* B. It is interesting that the three highest points in Figure 5 all belong to the same genus, *Escherichia*. Most of the Enterobacteriaceae fall in the region 50 to 70 per cent of *E. coli* B. *Proteus vulgaris* is known to be a quite distant relative of *E. coli* B and these results are consistent with the comparatively low level (30%) of ribonuclease-resistant hybrid which is formed when its DNA is annealed with *E. coli* sRNA.

Discussion.—DNA-RNA hybrids have now been demonstrated in several systems. The initial demonstrations by Rich[14] and by Schildkraut *et al.*[5b] involved synthetic polynucleotides and led to later experiments by Spiegelman and his collaborators which demonstrated the formation of these hybrids with both T2-specific messenger RNA,[4] naturally occurring messenger RNA,[15] and ribosomal RNA.[6] The present experiments deal with a much smaller molecular species, soluble RNA. The conclusion from these experiments is that the DNA is also the primary site for the manufacture of sRNA. This does not, of course, rule out the possibility

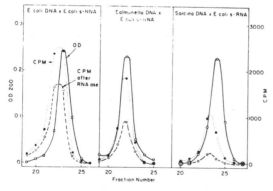

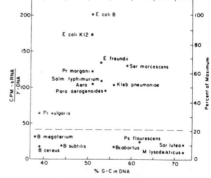

FIG. 4.—The results of cesium chloride density gradient centrifugations are shown for annealing experiments involving *E. coli* B P[32] sRNA (0.11 γ) and 45 γ of DNA from (a) *E. coli* B. (b) *Salmonella typhimurium* and (c) *Sarcina lutea*. Only the fractions containing the DNA band region are shown. Solid curve is O.D.$_{260}$; dotted curve is cpm before ribonuclease digestion; dashed curve is cpm after ribonuclease digestion under conditions described in *Methods*.

FIG. 5.—The amount of ribonuclease resistant P[32] sRNA per γ of DNA in the band after annealing is shown for a variety of different bacterial DNAs. Each annealing mixture contained 45 γ of the DNA named in the figure and 0.11 γ of P[32] sRNA. The results are plotted against the guanine-cytosine content of the DNA in the annealing mixture.[21] The dashed line separates the family Enterobacteriaceae from the four other bacterial families: Bacillaceae, Brucellaceae, Pseudomonadaceae, and Micrococcaceae. Aero is "Aerobacter" (1041).

that sRNA molecules may also be produced by RNA-RNA replications but rather demonstrates that the sequences involved originate from the DNA.

The quantitative interpretation of these experiments rests heavily on the ability of ribonuclease to digest away the parts of the sRNA molecule which are not systematically hydrogen-bonded to DNA. This resistance was first demonstrated in synthetic polynucleotides and has now also been shown in double-stranded RNA-RNA helices which have been annealed together.[16] We would like to know the extent to which irregularities in the hydrogen bonding would make the RNA strand susceptible to enzymatic degradation. Perhaps some indication of this can be seen in the fact that sRNA itself is readily digested by ribonuclease even though it has considerable internal hydrogen bonding. This suggests that a high degree of regularity may be necessary to bring on this resistance to enzymatic digestion.

Interpretation of the saturation data in Figure 3 depends upon the extent to which the enzymatic digestion is carried out to completion without denuding DNA stretches of sRNA which should be annealed there. It is not likely that this occurs, but we have no direct evidence on this point. Bearing in mind these assumptions, we can ask how much reliance may be placed on the calculation of 40 sRNA sites from the data in Figure 3. Although the molecular weight of sRNA is only slightly uncertain, the uncertainty in the total amount of DNA in the *E. coli* genome may be considerable. Thus, we cannot regard the figure of 40 sRNA sites as a very accurate determination. Nonetheless, this result suggests that there is considerable degeneracy in the amino acid code, a finding which is given indirect support from the genetic experiments of Crick *et al.*[17]

The cross species hybrid experiments suggest the existence of some common nucleotide sequences in *E. coli* B sRNA and a variety of closely related bacterial DNAs. Thus they give us some information about the evolutionary history of the sRNA molecules. Closer relatives are able to form a greater stretch of regular hydrogen bonding than are more distant neighbors. When experiments of this type are carried out on individually purified sRNA molecules, we will be able to trace the extent of the modifications which have occurred in the course of evolution.

Summary.—It is possible to form ribonuclease-resistant hybrid complexes between sRNA and DNA. This suggests the existence of a sequence of nucleotides in the DNA complementary to the sRNA. When this complex is formed with an excess of sRNA, the DNA in one *E. coli* genome is saturated with approximately 40 sRNA molecules. If there is one site per sRNA molecule, this suggests that there is considerable degeneracy in the amino acid code. Hybrids have been formed between *E. coli* sRNA and DNA from a variety of bacterial species. Closer relatives form larger amounts of ribonuclease-resistant hybrid than distant relatives.

Note added in proof: We have learned that specific *E. coli* DNA-sRNA hybrids have also been made by D. Giacomoni and S. Spiegelman. They observed a saturation plateau value similar to that shown above.

We wish to thank J. Marmur for his generous gift of several DNAs and R. L. Sinsheimer for his gift of φX 174 DNA. We acknowledge Melissa Quinn's capable technical assistance. This research was supported by grants from the U.S. Public Health Service and the National Science Foundation.

* The following abbreviations are used: DNA, deoxyribonucleic acid; sRNA, soluble ribonucleic acid; Tris buffer, tris (hydroxymethyl) aminomethane buffer; O.D.$_{260}$, optical density at

260 mμ; cpm, counts per minute; DNAase, deoxyribonuclease; RNAase, ribonuclease; γ, microgram; mc, millicurie; TCA, trichloracetic acid.

[1] Chapeville, F., F. Lipmann, G. von Ehrenstein, B. Weisblum, W. J. Ray, Jr., and S. Benzer, these PROCEEDINGS, **48**, 1088 (1962).

[2] Spencer, M., W. Fuller, M. H. F. Wilkins, and G. L. Brown, *Nature*, **194**, 1014 (1962).

[3] McCully, K. S., and G. L. Cantoni, *J. Mol. Biol.*, **5**, 80 (1962).

[4] Hall, B. D., and S. Spiegelman, these PROCEEDINGS, **47**, 137 (1961).

[5a] Doty, P., J. Marmur, J. Eigner, and C. Schildkraut, these PROCEEDINGS, **46**, 461 (1960).

[5b] Schildkraut, C. L., J. Marmur, J. Fresco, and P. Doty, *J. Biol. Chem.*, **236**, PC 4 (1961).

[6] Yankofsky, S. A., and S. Spiegelman, these PROCEEDINGS, **48**, 1069, 1446 (1962).

[7] Stent, G. S., and C. R. Fuerst, *J. Gen. Physiol.*, **38**, 441 (1954).

[8] Ehrenstein, G. von, and F. Lipmann, these PROCEEDINGS, **47**, 941 (1961).

[9] Sueoka, N., and T. Cheng, *J. Mol. Biol.*, **4**, 161 (1961).

[10] Marmur, J., *J. Mol. Biol.*, **3**, 208 (1961).

[11] Mandell, J. D., and A. D. Hershey, *Anal. Biochem.*, **1**, 66 (1960).

[12] Cohn, W. E., *J. Biol. Chem.*, **235**, 1488 (1960).

[13] Fuerst, C. R., and G. S. Stent, *J. Gen. Physiol.*, **40**, 73 (1956).

[14] Rich, A., these PROCEEDINGS, **46**, 1044 (1960).

[15] Hayashi, M., and S. Spiegelman, these PROCEEDINGS, **47**, 1564 (1961).

[16] Geiduschek, E. P., J. W. Moohr, and S. B. Weiss, these PROCEEDINGS, **48**, 1078 (1962).

[17] Crick, F. H. C., L. Barnett, S. Brenner, and R. J. Watts-Tobin, *Nature*, **192**, 1227 (1961).

[18] Zubay, G., *J. Mol. Biol.*, **4**, 347 (1962).

[19] Preiss, J., M. Dieckmann, and P. Berg, *J. Biol. Chem.*, **235**, 1754 (1961).

[20] These analyses are listed in Gros, F., W. Gilbert, H. H. Hiatt, G. Attardi, P. F. Spahr, and J. D. Watson, in *Cellular Regulatory Mechanisms*, Cold Spring Harbor Symposia on Quantitative Biology, vol. 26 (1961), p. 111.

[21] The G-C contents are listed in Schildkraut, C. L., J. Marmur, and P. Doty, *J. Mol. Biol.*, **4**, 430 (1962).

Reprinted from the Proceedings of the NATIONAL ACADEMY OF SCIENCES
Vol. 47, No. 10, pp. 1588–1602. October, 1961.

THE DEPENDENCE OF CELL- FREE PROTEIN SYNTHESIS IN E. COLI UPON NATURALLY OCCURRING OR SYNTHETIC POLYRIBONUCLEOTIDES

BY MARSHALL W. NIRENBERG AND J. HEINRICH MATTHAEI*

NATIONAL INSTITUTES OF HEALTH, BETHESDA, MARYLAND

Communicated by Joseph E. Smadel, August 3, 1961

A stable cell-free system has been obtained from *E. coli* which incorporates C[14]-valine into protein at a rapid rate. It was shown that this apparent protein synthesis was energy-dependent, was stimulated by a mixture of L-amino acids, and was markedly inhibited by RNAase, puromycin, and chloramphenicol.[1] The present communication describes a novel characteristic of the system, that is, a requirement for template RNA, needed for amino acid incorporation even in the presence of soluble RNA and ribosomes. It will also be shown that the amino acid incorporation stimulated by the addition of template RNA has many properties expected of *de novo* protein synthesis. Naturally occurring RNA as well as a synthetic polynucleotide were active in this system. The synthetic polynucleotide appears to contain the code for the synthesis of a "protein" containing only one amino acid. Part of these data have been presented in preliminary reports.[2, 3]

Methods and Materials.—The preparation of enzyme extracts was modified in certain respects from the procedure previously presented.[1] *E. coli* W3100 cells harvested in early log phase were washed and were disrupted by grinding with alumina (twice the weight of washed cells) at 5° for 5 min as described previously.[1] The alumina was extracted with an equivalent weight of buffer containing 0.01 M Tris(hydroxymethyl)aminomethane, pH 7.8, 0.01 M magnesium acetate, 0.06 M KCl, 0.006 M mercaptoethanol (standard buffer). Alumina and intact cells were removed by centrifugation at $20,000 \times g$ for 20 min. The supernatant fluid was decanted, and 3 µg DNAase per ml (Worthington Biochemical Co.) were added, rapidly reducing the viscosity of the suspension, which was then centrifuged again at $20,000 \times g$ for 20 min. The supernatant fluid was aspirated and was centrifuged at $30,000 \times g$ for 30 min to clear the extract of remaining debris. The liquid layer was aspirated (S-30) and was centrifuged at $105,000 \times g$ for 2 hr to sediment the ribosomes. The supernatant solution (S-100) was aspirated, and the solution just above the pellet was decanted and discarded. The ribosomes were washed by resuspension in the standard buffer and centrifugation again at $105,000 \times g$ for 2 hr. Supernatant fluid was discarded and the ribosomes were suspended in standard buffer (W-Rib). Fractions S-30, S-100, and W-Rib were dialyzed against 60 volumes of standard buffer overnight at 5° and were divided into aliquots for storage at −15°.

In some cases, fresh S-30 was incubated for 40 min at 35°. The reaction mixture components in µmoles per ml were as follows: 80 Tris, pH 7.8; 8 magnesium acetate; 50 KCl; 9 mercaptoethanol; 0.075 each of 20 amino acids;[1] 2.5 ATP, K salt; 2.5 PEP, K salt; 15 µg PEP kinase (Boehringen & Sons, Mannheim, Germany). After incubation, the reaction mixture was dialyzed at 5° for 10 hr against 60 volumes of standard buffer, changed once during the course of dialysis. The incubated S-30 fraction was stored in aliquots at −15° until needed (Incubated-S-30).

RNA fractions were prepared by phenol extraction using freshly distilled phenol. Ribosomal RNA was prepared from fresh, washed ribosomes obtained by the method given above. In later RNA preparations, a 0.2% solution of sodium dodecyl sulfate recrystallized by the method of Crestfield *et al.*[4] was added to the suspension of ribosomes before phenol treatment. The suspension was shaken at room temperature for 5 min. Higher yields of RNA appeared to be obtained when the sodium dodecyl sulfate step was used; however, good RNA preparations were also obtained when this step was omitted. An equal volume of H_2O-saturated phenol was added to ribosomes suspended in standard buffer after treatment with sodium dodecyl sulfate, and the suspension was shaken vigorously at room temperature for 8–10 min. The aqueous phase was aspirated from the phenol phase after centrifugation at $1,450 \times g$ for 15 min. The aqueous layer was extracted two more times in the same manner, using 1/2 volume of H_2O-saturated phenol in each case. The final aqueous phase was chilled to 5° and NaCl was added to a final concentration of 0.1%. Two volumes of ethyl alcohol at −20° were added with stirring to precipitate the RNA. The suspension was centrifuged at $20,000 \times g$ for 15 min and the supernatant solution was decanted and discarded. The RNA pellet was dissolved in minimal concentrations of standard buffer (minus mercaptoethanol) by gentle homogenization in a glass Potter-Elvehjem homogenizer (usually the volume of buffer used was about 1/3 the volume of the original ribosome suspension). The opalescent solution of RNA was dialyzed for 18 hr against 100 volumes of standard buffer (minus mercaptoethanol) at 5°. The dialyzing buffer was changed once. After dialysis, the RNA solution was centrifuged at $20,000 \times g$ for 15 min and the pellet was discarded. The RNA solution, which contained less than 1% protein, was divided into aliquots and was stored at −15° until needed.

Soluble RNA was prepared from $105,000 \times g$ supernatant solution by the phenol extraction method described above. Soluble RNA was also stored at −15°. Alkali-degraded RNA was prepared by incubating RNA samples with 0.3 M KOH at 35° for 18 hr. The solutions then were neutralized and dialyzed against standard buffer (minus mercaptoethanol). RNAase-digested samples of RNA were prepared by incubating RNA with 2 µg per ml of crystalline

RNAase (Worthington Biochemical Company) at 35° for 60 min. RNAase was destroyed by four phenol extractions performed as given above. After the last phenol extraction, the samples were dialyzed against standard buffer minus mercaptoethanol. RNA samples were treated with trypsin by incubation with 20 μg per ml of twice recrystallized trypsin (Worthington Biochemical Company) at 35° for 60 min. The solution was treated four times with phenol and was dialyzed in the same manner.

The radioactive amino acids used, their source, and their respective specific activities are as follows: U-C14-glycine, U-C14-L-isoleucine, U-C14-L-tyrosine, U-C14-L-leucine, U-C14-L-proline, L-histidine-2(ring)-C14, U-C14-L-phenylalanine, U-C14-L-threonine, L-methionine (methyl-C14), U-C14-L-arginine, and U-C14-L-lysine obtained from Nuclear-Chicago Corporation, 5.8, 6.2, 5.95, 6.25, 10.5, 3.96, 10.3, 3.9, 6.5, 5.8, 8.3 mC/mM, respectively; C14-L-aspartic acid, C14-L-glutamic acid, C14-L-alanine, obtained from Volk, 1.04, 1.18, 0.75 m C/mM, respectively; D-L-tryptophan-3 C14, obtained from New England Nuclear Corporation, 2.5 mC/mM; S35-L-cystine obtained from the Abbott Laboratories, 2.4 mC/mM; U-C14-L-serine obtained from the Nuclear-Chicago Corporation, 0.2 mC/mM. Other materials and methods used in this study are described in the accompanying paper.[1] All assays were performed in duplicate.

Results.—Stimulation by ribosomal RNA: In the previous paper,[1] it was shown that DNAase markedly decreased amino acid incorporation in this system after 20 min. For the purpose of this investigation, 30,000 × *g* supernatant fluid fractions previously incubated with DNAase and other components of the reaction mixtures (Incubated-S-30 fractions) were used for many of the experiments.

Figure 1 shows that incorporation of C14-L-valine into protein by Incubated-S-30 fraction was stimulated by the addition of purified *E. coli* soluble RNA. Maximal stimulation was obtained with approximately 1 mg soluble RNA. In some experiments, increasing the concentration 5-fold did not further stimulate the system. Soluble RNA was added to all reaction mixtures unless otherwise specified.

Figure 2 demonstrates that *E. coli* ribosomal RNA preparations markedly stimu-

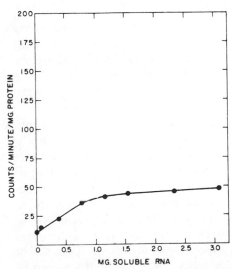

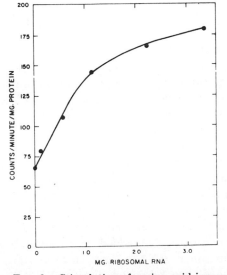

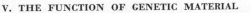

Fig 1.—Stimulation of amino acid incorporation into protein by *E. coli* soluble RNA. Composition of reaction mixtures is specified in Table 1. Samples were incubated at 35° for 20 min. Reaction mixtures contained 4.4 mg. of Incubated-S-30 protein.

Fig. 2.—Stimulation of amino acid incorporation into protein by *E. coli* ribosomal RNA in the presence of soluble RNA. Composition of reaction mixtures is specified in Table 1. Samples were incubated at 35° for 20 min. Reaction mixtures contained 4.4 mg of Incubated-S-30 protein and 1.0 mg *E. coli* soluble RNA.

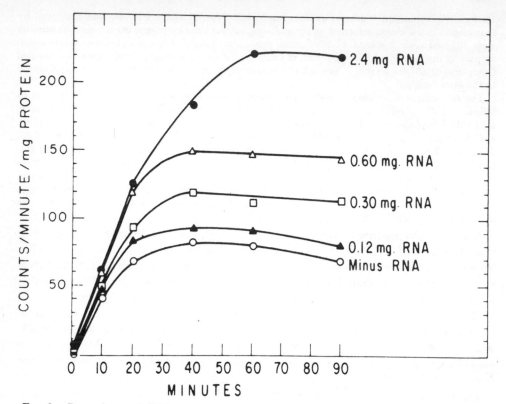

FIG. 3.—Dependence of C^{14}-L-valine incorporation into protein upon ribosomal RNA. The composition of the reaction mixtures and the incubation conditions are presented in Table 1. Reaction mixtures contained 0.98 mg of *E. coli* soluble RNA and 4.4 mg of Incubated-S-30-protein.

lated incorporation of C^{14}-valine into protein even though maximally stimulating concentrations of soluble RNA were present in the reaction mixtures. A linear relationship between the concentration of ribosomal RNA and C^{14}-valine incorporation into protein was obtained when low concentrations of ribosomal RNA were used. Increasing the soluble RNA concentration up to 3-fold did not replace the effect observed when ribosomal RNA was added.

The effect of ribosomal RNA in stimulating incorporation of C^{14}-valine into protein is presented in more detail in Figure 3. In the absence of ribosomal RNA, incorporation of C^{14}-valine into protein by the incubated-S-30 fraction was quite low when compared with S-30 (not incubated before storage at $-15°$) and stopped almost completely after 30 min. At low concentrations of ribosomal RNA, maximum amino acid incorporation into protein was proportional to the amount of ribosomal RNA added, suggesting stoichiometric rather than catalytic action of ribosomal RNA. Total incorporation of C^{14}-valine into protein was increased more than 3-fold by ribosomal RNA in this experiment even in the presence of maximally stimulating concentrations of soluble RNA. Ribosomal RNA may be added at any time during the course of the reaction, and, after further incubation, an increase in incorporation of C^{14}-valine into protein will result.

Characteristics of amino acid incorporation stimulated by ribosomal RNA: In Table 1 are presented the characteristics of C^{14}-L-valine incorporation into protein

TABLE 1

CHARACTERISTICS OF C^{14}-L-VALINE INCORPORATION INTO PROTEIN

Experiment no.	Addition				Counts/min/mg protein
1	− Ribosomal RNA				42
	+	"	"		204
	+	"	"	+ 0.15 μmole Chloramphenicol	58
	+	"	"	+ 0.20 μmole Puromycin	7
	+	"	"	deproteinized at zero time	8
2	− Ribosomal RNA				35
	+	"	"		101
	+	"	"	− ATP, PEP, PEP kinase	7
	+	"	"	+ 10 μg RNAase	6
	+	"	"	+ 10 μg DNAase	110
	+ Boiled Ribosomal RNA				127
	+ Ribosomal RNA, deproteinized at zero time				8
3	− Ribosomal RNA				34
	−	"	"	− 20 L amino acids	21
	+	"	"		99
	+	"	"	− 20-L-amino acids	52

The reaction mixtures contained the following in μmole/ml: 100 Tris(hydroxymethyl) aminomethane. pH 7.8; 10 magnesium acetate; 50 KCl; 6.0 mercaptoethanol; 1.0 ATP; 5.0 phosphoenolpyruvate, K salt; 20 μg phosphoenolpyruvate kinase, crystalline; 0.05 each of 20 L-amino acids minus valine; 0.03 each of GTP, CTP, and UTP; 0.015 C^{14}-L-valine (~70,000 counts); 3.1 mg. *E. coli* ribosomal RNA where indicated, and 1.0 mg *E. coli* soluble RNA; 3.2, 3.2, and 1.4 mg of incubated-S-30 protein were present in Experiments 1, 2, and 3, respectively. In addition 4.4 mg protein of W-Rib were added in Experiment 3. Total volume was 1.0 ml. Samples were incubated at 35° for 20 min, were deproteinized with 10 per cent trichloroacetic acid, and the precipitates were washed and counted by the method of Siekevitz.[22]

stimulated by the addition of ribosomal RNA. Amino acid incorporation was strongly inhibited by 0.15 μmoles of chloramphenicol and 0.20 μmoles/ml reaction mixture of puromycin. Furthermore, the incorporation was completely dependent upon the addition of ATP and an ATP-generating system and was totally inhibited by 10 μg/ml RNAase. Equivalent amounts of DNAase had no effect upon the incorporation stimulated by the addition of ribosomal RNA. Placing a ribosomal RNA preparation in a boiling water bath for 10 min did not destroy its C^{14}-valine incorporation activity; instead, a slight increase in activity was consistently observed. However, when these RNA preparations were placed in a boiling water bath, a copious, white precipitate resulted. Upon cooling the suspension in an ice bath, the precipitate immediately dissolved.

The data of Table 1 also demonstrate that the incorporation of amino acids into protein in the presence of ribosomal RNA was further stimulated by the addition of a mixture of 20 L-amino acids, suggesting cell-free protein synthesis.

C- and N-terminal analyses of the ribosomal RNA-dependent product of the reaction were performed with carboxypeptidase and 1-fluoro-2,4-dinitrobenzene respectively (Dr. Frank Tietze kindly performed these analyses). Four per cent of the radioactivity was released from the C-terminal end and 1% was associated with the N-terminal end. The remainder of the C^{14}-label was internal. Similar results were obtained when reactions were performed using S-30 enzyme fractions which had not been treated with DNAase. Protein precipitates isolated from reaction mixtures after incubation were completely hydrolyzed with HCl, and the C^{14}-label incorporated into protein was demonstrated to be valine by paper chromatography.

Many of the experiments presented in this paper were performed with enzyme fractions prepared with DNAase added to reduce their viscosity. Ribosomal

RNA also stimulated C^{14}-valine incorporation when enzyme extracts prepared in the absence of DNAase were used.

To be effective in stimulating amino acid incorporation into protein, the ribosomal RNA *required the presence of washed ribosomes*. The data of Table 2 show

TABLE 2

THE INEFFECTIVENESS OF RIBOSOMAL RNA IN STIMULATING C^{14}-L-VALINE INCORPORATION INTO PROTEIN IN THE PRESENCE OF RIBOSOMES OR 105,000 × g SUPERNATANT SOLUTIONS ALONE

Additions	Counts/min
Complete	51
" + 2.1 mg Ribosomal RNA	202
" − Ribosomes	17
" − Ribosomes + 2.1 mg Ribosomal RNA	20
" − Supernatant solution	36
" − Supernatant solution + 2.1 mg Ribosomal RNA	45
" Deproteinized at zero time	25

The components of the reaction mixtures and the incubation conditions are presented in Table 1.   0.86 and 3.3 mg protein were present in the ribosome (W-Rib) and 105,000 × g supernatant (S-100) fractions, respectively.

that both ribosomes and 105,000 × g supernatant solution were necessary for ribosomal RNA-dependent amino acid incorporation. No incorporation of amino acids into protein occurred when the 105,000 × g supernatant solution alone was added to ribosomal RNA preparations, demonstrating that ribosomal RNA preparations were not contaminated with intact ribosomes. This conclusion also was substantiated by showing that the activities of ribosomal RNA preparations were not destroyed by boiling, although the activities of the ribosomes were destroyed by such treatment.

The effect of ribosomal RNA upon the incorporation of seven different amino acids is presented in Table 3. The addition of ribosomal RNA increased the incorporation of every amino acid tested.

The effect shown by ribosomal RNA was not observed when other polyanions were used, such as polyadenylic acid, highly polymerized salmon sperm DNA, or a high-molecular-weight polymer of glucose carboxylic acid (Table 4). Pretreatment of ribosomal RNA with trypsin did not affect its biological activity. However, treatment of the ribosomal RNA with either RNAase or alkali resulted in a complete loss of stimulating activity. The active principle, therefore, appears to be RNA.

The sedimentation characteristics of the ribosomal RNA preparations were examined in the Spinco Model E ultracentrifuge (Fig. 4A). Particles having the characteristics of S-30, S-50, or S-70 ribosomes were not observed in these preparations. The S_{20}^{W} of the first peak was 23, that of the second peak 16, and that of the third, small peak, 4. Pretreatment with trypsin did not affect the S_{20}^{W} values of the peaks appreciably (Fig. 4C); however, treatment with RNAase completely destroyed the peaks (Fig. 4B), confirming the ancillary evidence which had suggested that the major component was high-molecular-weight RNA.

Preliminary attempts at fractionation of the ribosomal RNA were performed by means of density-gradient centrifugation employing a linear sucrose gradient. The results of one such experiment are presented in Figure 5. Amino acid incorporation activity of the RNA did not follow absorbancy at 260 mμ; instead, the activity seemed to be concentrated around fraction No. 5, which was approximately one-third of the distance from the bottom of the tube. These results again

TABLE 3

SPECIFICITY OF AMINO ACID INCORPORATION STIMULATED BY RIBOSOMAL RNA

C^{14}-Amino Acid	Addition	Counts/min/mg protein
C^{14}-L-Valine	Complete	25
"	" + Ribosomal RNA	137
C^{14}-L-Threonine	"	31
"	" + Ribosomal RNA	121
C^{14}-L-Methionine	"	121
"	" + Ribosomal RNA	177
C^{14}-L-Arginine	"	49
"	" + Ribosomal RNA	224
C^{14}-L-Phenylalanine	"	77
"	" + Ribosomal RNA	147
C^{14}-L-Lysine	"	36
"	" + Ribosomal RNA	175
C^{14}-L-Leucine	"	134
"	" + Ribosomal RNA	272
"	" Deproteinized at zero time	6

The composition of the reaction mixtures are presented in Table 1. The mixture of 20 L-amino acids included all amino acids except the C^{14}-amino acid added to one reaction mixture. Reaction mixtures contained 4.4 mg Incubated-S-30 protein. Samples were incubated at 35° for 60 min. 2.1 mg ribosomal RNA were added where indicated.

TABLE 4

RIBOSOMAL RNA CONTROL EXPERIMENTS DESCRIBED IN TEXT

Experiment No.	Addition	Counts/min/mg protein
1	Complete	54
	" + 2.4 mg Ribosomal RNA	144
	" + 2.0 mg Polyadenylic acid	10
	" + 2.0 mg Salmon sperm DNA	41
	" + 2.0 mg Polyglucose carboxylic acid	49
	" + 2.4 mg Ribosomal RNA, deproteinized at zero time	7
2	Complete	39
	" + 2.0 mg Ribosomal RNA*	150
	" + 2.1 mg Ribosomal RNA preincubated with trypsin*	166
	" + 2.0 mg Ribosomal RNA preincubated with RNAase*,†	47
	" Deproteinized at zero time	8
3	Complete	20
	" + 1.2 mg Ribosomal RNA	82
	" + 1.2 mg Alkali degraded ribosomal RNA†	21
	" Deproteinized at zero time	7

The composition of the reaction mixtures and the incubation conditions are given in Table 1. 4.4, 3.2, and 4.4 mg Incubated-S-30 protein were present in Experiments 1, 2, and 3, respectively. 2.4, 0.98, and 0 mg E. coli soluble RNA were present in Experiments 1, 2, and 3, respectively.
* Ribosomal RNA preparations were deproteinized by phenol extraction after enzymatic digestion as specified under *Methods and Materials*.
† mg Ribosomal RNA refers to RNA concentration before digestion.

demonstrate that the activity was not associated with a soluble RNA fraction, present in maximum concentration in fraction No. 11, near the top of the tube. In addition, all amino acid incorporation analyses were performed in the presence of added soluble RNA, and the addition of more soluble RNA would not stimulate C^{14}-L-valine incorporation into protein.

Effects of RNA obtained from different species: The data of Table 5 demonstrate that RNA from different sources stimulates C^{14}-valine incorporation into protein. Yeast ribosomal RNA prepared by the method of Crestfield et al.[4] was considerably more effective in stimulating incorporation than equivalent amounts of E. coli ribosomal RNA. Yeast ribosomal RNA prepared by this method has little or no amino acid acceptor activity and has a molecular weight of about 29,000.[7] Tobacco mosaic virus RNA prepared by phenol extraction and having a molecular weight of

TABLE 5

STIMULATION OF AMINO ACID INCORPORATION BY RNA FRACTIONS PREPARED FROM DIFFERENT
SPECIES

Additions	Counts/min/mg protein
None	42
+ 0.5 mg *E. coli* ribosomal RNA	75
+ 0.5 mg Yeast ribosomal RNA	430
+ 0.5 mg Tobacco mosaic virus RNA	872
+ 0.5 mg Ehrlich ascites tumor microsomal RNA	65

The components of the reaction mixtures and the incubation conditions are presented in Table 1.   Reaction
samples contained 1.9 mg Incubated-S-30 protein.

approximately 1,700,000[†] stimulated amino acid incorporation strongly.   Marked
stimulation due to tobacco mosaic virus RNA was observed also with *E. coli* enzyme extracts which had not been treated with DNAase.   More complete details
of this work will be presented in a later publication.

Stimulation of amino acid incorporation by synthetic polynucleotides: The data
of Figure 6 show that the addition of 10 μg of polyuridylic acid[‡] per ml of reaction
mixture resulted in a remarkable stimulation of C^{14}-L-phenylalanine incorporation.
Phenylalanine incorporation was almost completely dependent upon the addition
of polyuridylic acid, and incorporation proceeded, after a slight lag period, at a
linear rate for approximately 30 min.

. The data of Table 6 demonstrate that no other polynucleotide tested could replace polyuridylic acid.   The absolute specificity of polyuridylic acid was con-

TABLE 6

POLYNUCLEOTIDE SPECIFICITY FOR PHENYLALANINE INCORPORATION

Experiment no.	Additions	Counts/min/mg protein
1	None	44
	+ 10 μg Polyuridylic acid	39,800
	+ 10 μg Polyadenylic acid	50
	+ 10 μg Polycytidylic acid	38
	+ 10 μg Polyinosinic acid	57
	+ 10 μg Polyadenylic-uridylic acid (2/1 ratio)	53
	+ 10 μg Polyuridylic acid + 20 μg polyadenylic acid	60
	Deproteinized at zero time	17
2	None	75
	+ 10 μg UMP	81
	+ 10 μg UDP	77
	+ 10 μg UTP	72
	Deproteinized at zero time	6

Components of the reaction mixtures are presented in Table 1.   Reaction mixtures contained 2.3 mg Incubated-
S-30 protein.   0.02 μmoles U-C^{14}-L-phenylalanine (~125,000 counts/minute) was added to each reaction mixture.
Samples were incubated at 35° for 60 min.

firmed by demonstrating that randomly mixed polymers of adenylic and uridylic
acid[‡] (Poly A-U, 2/1 ratio and 4/1 ratio) were inactive in this system.   A solution
of polyuridylic acid and polyadenylic acid (which forms triple-stranded helices)
had no activity whatsoever, suggesting that single-strandedness is a necessary
requisite for activity.   Experiment 2 in Table 6 demonstrates that UMP, UDP, or
UTP were unable to stimulate phenylalanine incorporation.

The data of Table 7 demonstrate that both ribosomes and 100,000 $\times$ g supernatant solution, as well as ATP and an ATP-generating system, were required
for the polyuridylic acid–dependent incorporation of phenylalanine.   Incorporation was inhibited by puromycin, chloramphenicol, and RNAase.   The incorpora-

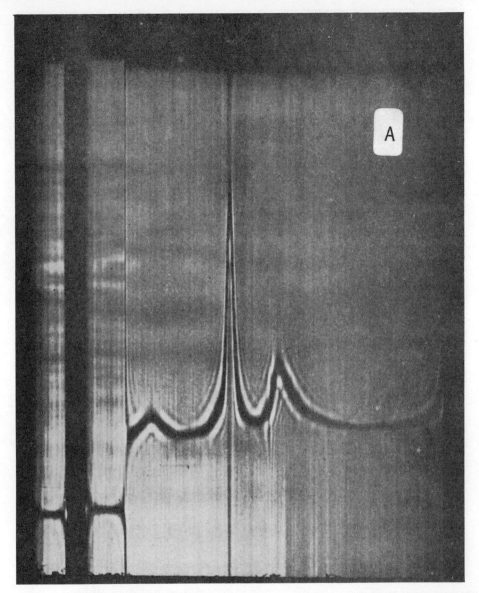

Fig. 4.—*E. coli* ribosomal RNA preparations. (*A*) Untreated (above). (*B*) digested with RNA-aase; (*C*) digested with trypsin. Preparation and digestion of samples presented under *Methods and Materials*. 9.8 and 10.5 mg/ml RNA were present in *A* and *C*. 11.5 mg/ml RNA was present in *B*
(*Continued on facing page*)

tion was not inhibited by addition of DNAase. Omitting a mixture of 19 L-amino acids did not inhibit phenylalanine incorporation, suggesting that polyuridylic acid stimulated the incorporation of L-phenylalanine alone. This conclusion was substantiated by the data presented in Table 8. Polyuridylic acid had little effect in stimulating the incorporation of 17 other radioactive amino acids. Each labeled amino acid was tested individually, and these data, corroborating the results given in Table 8, will be presented in a subsequent publication.

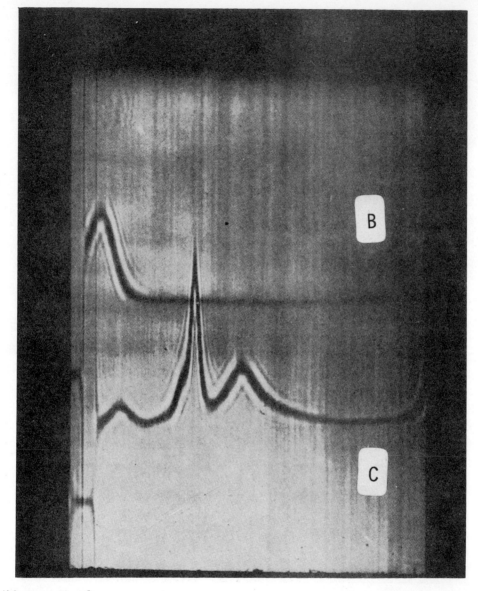

(*Fig. 4—continued*)
before digestion. Photographs were taken in a model E Spinco ultracentrifuge equipped with schlieren optics.

The product of the reaction was partially characterized and the results are presented in Table 9. The physical characteristics of the product of the reaction resembled those of authentic poly-L-phenylalanine, for, unlike many other polypeptides and proteins, both the product of the reaction and the polymer were resistant to hydrolysis by 6N HCl at 100° for 8 hr but were completely hydrolyzed by 12N HCl at 120–130° for 48 hr.

Poly-L-phenylalanine is insoluble in most solvents[25] but is soluble in 33 per cent

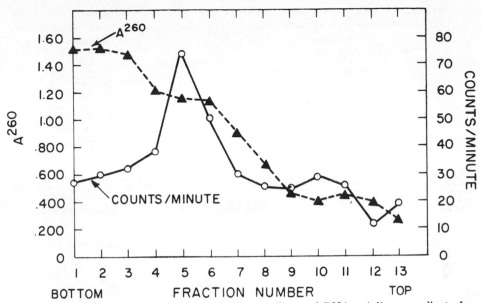

Fig. 5.—Sucrose density-gradient centrifugation of ribosomal RNA. A linear gradient of sucrose concentration ranging from 20 per cent at the bottom to 5 per cent at the top of the tube was prepared.[23] The sucrose solutions (4.4 ml total volume) contained 0.01 M Tris, pH 7.8, 0.01 M Mg acetate and 0.06 M KCl. 0.4 ml of ribosomal RNA (4.6 mg) was layered on top of each tube which was centrifuged at 38,000 × g for 4.5 hours at 3° in a swinging bucket rotor, Spinco type SW-39, using a Spinco Model L ultracentrifuge. 0.30 ml fractions were collected after piercing the bottom of the tube.[24]

0.025 ml aliquots diluted to 0.3 ml with H_2O were used for A^{260} measurements. 0.25 ml aliquots were used for amino acid incorporation assays. Reaction mixtures contained the components presented in Table 1. 0.7 mg of *E. coli* soluble RNA and 2.2 mg Incubated-S-30 protein were added. Control assays plus 0.25 ml 12.5 per cent sucrose in place of fractions gave 79 counts/min. This figure was subtracted from each value. Total volume was 0.7 ml. Samples were incubated at 35° for 20 min.

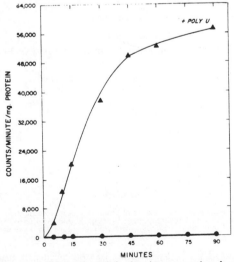

Fig. 6.—Stimulation of U-C[14]-L-phenylalanine incorporation by polyuridylic acid. ● without polyuridylic acid; ▲ 10 μg polyuridylic acid added. The components of the reaction mixtures and the incubation conditions are given in Table 1. 0.024 μmole U-C[14]-L-phenylalanine (~500,000 counts/min) and 2.3 mg Incubated-S-30 protein were added/ml of reaction mixture.

V. THE FUNCTION OF GENETIC MATERIAL   607

TABLE 7

CHARACTERISTICS OF POLYURIDYLIC ACID–DEPENDENT PHENYLALANINE INCORPORATION

Additions	Counts/min/mg protein
Minus polyuridylic acid	70
None	29,500
Minus 100,000 × *g* supernatant solution	106
Minus ribosomes	52
Minus ATP, PEP, and PEP kinase	83
+ 0.02 μmoles puromycin	7,100
+ 0.31 μmoles chloramphenicol	12,550
+ 6 μg RNAase	120
+ 6 μg DNAase	27,600
Minus amino acid mixture	31,700
Deproteinized at zero time	30

The components of the reaction mixtures are presented in Table 1.   10 μg of polyuridylic acid were added to all samples except the specified one.   2.3 mg of Incubated-S-30 protein were added to each reaction mixture except those in which ribosomes alone and 100,000 × *g* supernatant solution alone were tested.   0.7 mg W-Rib protein and 1.3 mg S-100 protein were used respectively.   0.02 μmoles U-C^{14}-L-phenylalanine, Sp. Act. = 10.3 mC/mM (∼125,000 counts/minute) were added to each reaction mixture.   Samples were incubated at 35° for 60 min.

TABLE 8

SPECIFICITY OF AMINO ACID INCORPORATION STIMULATED BY POLYURIDYLIC ACID

Experiment no.	C^{14}-amino acids present	Additions	Counts/min/mg protein
1	Phenylalanine	Deproteinized at zero time	25
		None	68
		+ 10 μg polyuridylic acid	38,300
2	Glycine, alanine, serine, aspartic acid, glutamic acid	Deproteinized at zero time	17
		None	20
		+ 10 μg polyuridylic acid	33
3	Leucine, isoleucine, threonine, methionine, arginine, histidine, lysine, tyrosine, tryptophan, proline, valine	Deproteinized at zero time	73
		None	276
		+ 10 μg polyuridylic acid	899
4	S^{35}-cysteine	Deproteinized at zero time	6
		None	95
		+ 10 μg polyuridylic acid	113

Components of the reaction mixtures are presented in Table 1.   The unlabeled amino acid mixture was omitted. 0.015 μM of each labeled amino acid was used.   The specific activities of the labeled amino acids are present in the *Methods and Materials* section.   2.3 mg of protein of preincubated S-30 enzyme fraction were added to each reaction mixture.   All samples were incubated at 35° for 30 min.

TABLE 9

COMPARISON OF CHARACTERISTICS OF PRODUCT OF REACTION AND POLY-L-PHENYLALANINE

Treatment	Product of reaction	Poly-L-phenylalanine
6 *N* HCl for 8 hours at 100°	Partially hydrolyzed	Partially hydrolyzed
12 *N* HCl for 48 hours at 120–130°	Completely hydrolyzed	Completely hydrolyzed
Extraction with 33% HBr in glacial acetic acid	Soluble	Soluble
Extraction* with the following solvents: H_2O, benzene, nitrobenzene, chloroform, N,N-dimethylformamide, ethanol, petroleum ether, concentrated phosphoric acid, glacial acetic acid, dioxane, phenol, acetone, ethyl acetate, pyridine, acetophenone, formic acid	Insoluble	Insoluble

* The product was said to be insoluble if <0.002 gm of product was soluble in 100 ml of solvent at 24°.   Extractions were performed by adding 0.5 mg of authentic poly-L-phenylalanine and the C^{14}-product of a reaction mixture (1800 counts/min) to 5.0 ml of solvent.   The suspensions were vigorously shaken for 30 min at 24° and were centrifuged.   The precipitates were plated and their radioactivity was determined.

HBr in glacial acetic acid.§   The product of the reaction had the same apparent solubility as authentic poly-L-phenylalanine.   The product of the reaction was purified by means of its unusual solubility behavior.   Reaction mixtures were deproteinized after incubation, and precipitated proteins were washed in the usual manner according to the method of Siekevitz.[22] Dried protein pellets containing added carrier poly-L-phenylalanine were then extracted with 33 per cent HBr in glacial acetic acid, and the large amount of insoluble material was discarded. Polyphenylalanine was then precipitated from solution by the addition of H_2O and was washed several times with H_2O. Seventy per cent of the total amount of C^{14}-L-phenylalanine incorporated into protein due to the addition of polyuridylic acid could be recovered by this procedure. Complete hydrolysis of the purified reaction product with $12N$ HCl followed by paper electrophoresis** demonstrated that the reaction product contained C^{14}-phenylalanine. No other radioactive spots were found.

Discussion.—In this investigation, we have demonstrated that template RNA is a requirement for cell-free amino acid incorporation. Addition of soluble RNA could not replace template RNA in this system. In addition, the density-gradient centrifugation experiments showed that the active fractions in the ribosomal RNA preparations sedimented much faster than soluble RNA. It should be noted that ribosomal RNA is qualitatively different from soluble RNA, since bases such as pseudouracil, methylated guanines, etc., found in soluble RNA, are not present in ribosomal RNA.[5]

The bulk of the RNA in our ribosomal RNA fractions may be inactive as templates, for tobacco mosaic virus RNA was 20 times as active in stimulating amino acid incorporation as equivalent amounts of *E. coli* ribosomal RNA. In addition, preliminary fractionation of ribosomal RNA indicated that only a portion of the total RNA was active.

It should be emphasized that ribosomal RNA could not substitute for ribosomes, indicating that ribosomes were not assembled from the added RNA *in toto*. The function of ribosomal RNA remains an enigma, although at least part of the total RNA is thought to serve as templates for protein synthesis and has been termed "messenger" RNA.[12-14] Alternatively, a part of the RNA may be essential for the synthesis of active ribosomes from smaller ribosomal particles.[15-21]

Ribosomal RNA may be an aggregate of subunits which can dissociate after proper treatment.[6-8] Phenol extraction of *E. coli* ribosomes yields two types of RNA molecules with S_w^{20} of 23 and 16 (Fig. 4), equivalent to molecular weights of 1,000,000 and 560,000, respectively.[9, 10] These RNA species can be degraded by boiling to products having sedimentation coefficients of 13.1, 8.8, and 4.4, corresponding to molecular weights of 288,000, 144,000, and 29,000. Although the sedimentation distributions of the latter preparations suggest a high degree of homogeneity among the molecules of each class, these observations do not eliminate the possibility that the subunits are linked to one another *via* covalent bonds.[8] Preliminary evidence indicates that the subunits may be active in our system, since the supernatant solution obtained after boiling *E. coli* ribosomal RNA for 10 min and centrifugation at 105,000 $\times$ g for 60 min was active. Examination of boiled ribosomal RNA with the Spinco Model E ultracentrifuge showed a dispersed peak with a sedimentation coefficient of 4–8. This may be the same material found in the sucrose density-gradient experiment (using non-boiled RNA preparations), where a small peak of activity somewhat heavier than soluble RNA was usually noted (Fig. 5).

In our system, at low concentrations of ribosomal RNA, amino acid incorporation into protein was proportional to the amount of ribosomal RNA added, suggesting a stoichiometric rather than a catalytic action of ribosomal RNA. In contrast, soluble RNA has been shown to act in a catalytic fashion.[11]

The results indicate that polyuridylic acid contains the information for the synthesis of a protein having many of the characteristics of poly-L-phenylalanine. This synthesis was very similar to the cell-free protein synthesis obtained when naturally-occurring template RNA was added, i.e., both ribosomes and 100,000 × g supernatant solutions were required, and the incorporation was inhibited by puromycin or chloramphenicol. One or more uridylic acid residues therefore appear to be the code for phenylalanine. Whether the code is of the singlet, triplet, etc., type has not yet been determined. Polyuridylic acid seemingly functions as a synthetic template or messenger RNA, and this stable, cell-free *E. coli* system may well synthesize any protein corresponding to meaningful information contained in added RNA.

Summary.—A stable, cell-free system has been obtained from *E. coli* in which the amount of incorporation of amino acids into protein was dependent upon the addition of heat-stable template RNA preparations. Soluble RNA could not replace template RNA fractions. In addition, the amino acid incorporation required both ribosomes and 105,000 × g supernatant solution. The correlation between the amount of incorporation and the amount of added RNA suggested stoichiometric rather than catalytic activity of the template RNA. The template RNA–dependent amino acid incorporation also required ATP and an ATP-generating system, was stimulated by a complete mixture of L-amino acids, and was markedly inhibited by puromycin, chloramphenicol, and RNAase. Addition of a synthetic polynucleotide, polyuridylic acid, specifically resulted in the incorporation of L-phenylalanine into a protein resembling poly-L-phenylalanine. Polyuridylic acid appears to function as a synthetic template or messenger RNA. The implications of these findings are briefly discussed.

Note added in proof.—The ratio between uridylic acid units of the polymer required and molecules of L-phenylalanine incorporated, in recent experiments, has approached the value of 1:1. Direct evidence for the number of uridylic acid residues forming the code for phenylalanine as well as for the eventual stoichiometric action of the template is not yet established. As polyuridylic acid codes the incorporation of L-phenylalanine, polycytidylic acid‡ specifically mediates the incorporation of L-proline into a TCA-precipitable product. Complete data on these findings will be included in a subsequent publication.

* Supported by a NATO Postdoctoral Research Fellowship.

† Dr. Frankel-Conrat, personal communication.

‡ We thank Drs. Leon A. Heppel and Maxine F. Singer for samples of these polyribonucleotides, and Dr. George Rushizky for TMV-RNA.

§ We thank Dr. Michael Sela for this information.

** We thank Drs. William Dreyer and Elwood Bynum for performing the high-voltage electrophoretic analyses.

[1] Matthaei, J. H., and M. W. Nirenberg, these PROCEEDINGS, **47**, 1580 (1961).

[2] Matthaei, J. H., and M. W. Nirenberg, *Biochem. & Biophys. Res. Comm.*, **4**, 404 (1961).

[3] Matthaei, J. H., and M. W. Nirenberg, *Fed. Proc.*, **20**, 391 (1961).

[4] Crestfield, A. M., K. C. Smith, and F. W. Allen, *J. Biol. Chem.*, **216**, 185 (1955).

[5] Davis, F. F., A. F. Carlucci, and I. F. Roubein. *ibid.*, **234**, 1525 (1959).

[6] Hall, B. D., and P. Doty, *J. Mol. Biol.*, **1**, 111 (1959).

[7] Osawa, S.. *Biochim. Biophys. Acta*, **43**, 110 (1960).

[8] Aronson, A. I., and B. J. McCarthy, *Biophys. J.*, **1**, 215 (1961).

[9] Kurland, C. G., *J. Mol. Biol.*, **2**, 83 (1960).

[10] Littauer, U. Z., H. Eisenberg, *Biochim. Biophys. Acta*, **32**, 320 (1959).

[11] Hoagland, M. B., and L. T. Comly, these Proceedings, **46**, 1554 (1960).

[12] Volkin, E., L. Astrachan, and J. L. Countryman, *Virology*, **6**, 545 (1958).

[13] Nomura, M., B. D. Hall, and S. Spiegelman, *J. Mol. Biol.*, **2**, 306 (1960).

[14] Hall, B. D., and S Spiegelman, these Proceedings, **47**, 137 (1961).

[15] Bolton, E. T., B. H. Hoyen, and D. B. Ritter, in *Microsomal Particles and Protein Synthesis*, ed. R. B. Roberts (New York: Pergamon Press, 1958), p. 18.

[16] Tissières, A., J. D. Watson, D. Schlessinger, and B. R. Hollingworth, *J. Mol. Biol.*, **1**, 221 (1959).

[17] Tissières, A., D. Schlessinger, and F. Gros, these Proceedings, **46**, 1450 (1960).

[18] McCarthy, B. J., and A. I. Aronson, *Biophys. J.*, **1**, 227 (1961).

[19] Hershey, A. D., *J. Gen. Physiol.*, **38**, 145 (1954).

[20] Siminovitch, L., and A. F. Graham, *Canad. J. Microbiol.*, **2**, 585 (1956).

[21] Davern, C. I., and M. Meselson, *J. Mol. Biol.*, **2**, 153 (1960).

[22] Siekevitz, P., *J. Biol. Chem.*, **195**, 549 (1952).

[23] Britten, R. J., and R. B. Roberts, *Science*, **131**, 32 (1960).

[24] Martin, R., and B. Ames, *J. Biol. Chem.*, **236**, 1372 (1961).

[25] Bamford, C. H., A. Elliott, and W. E. Hanby, *Synthetic Polypeptides* (New York: Academic Press, 1956), p. 322.

Reprinted from the Proceedings of the NATIONAL ACADEMY OF SCIENCES
Vol. 48, No. 3, pp. 441–448.   March, 1962.

SYNTHETIC POLYNUCLEOTIDES AND THE AMINO ACID CODE, IV*

BY JOSEPH F. SPEYER, PETER LENGYEL, CARLOS BASILIO,† AND SEVERO OCHOA

DEPARTMENT OF BIOCHEMISTRY, NEW YORK UNIVERSITY SCHOOL OF MEDICINE

Communicated January 30, 1962

Triplet code letter assignments (of as yet unknown sequence) for fourteen amino acids have been made on the basis of experiments with a cell-free *Escherichia coli* system and synthetic polynucleotides.[1-3]   Continuation of this work has led to assignments for five of the remaining six amino acids, namely alanine, asparagine, aspartic acid, glutamic acid, and methionine.   An experimental value for the code

TABLE 1

AMINO ACID INCORPORATION IN E. coli SYSTEM WITH VARIOUS POLYNUCLEOTIDES*

Amino acid	None			UC(5:1)			UA(5:1)			UAC(6:1:1)			UCG(6:1:1)		UAG(6:1:1)			Code letter
	1	2	3	1	2	3	1	2	3	1	2	3	1	2	1	2	3	
Phe	0.12	0.34	0.26	18.5	32.0	23.6	5.7	20.6	13.4	5.8	20.0	14.8	14.0	11.9	5.3	9.0	6.6	UUU
Ala	0.47			0	0							1.06	1.01		0.32	0.54	0.24	1U 1C 1G
AspN†	0.23	0.40	0.32	0	0		0.35	1.36	0.96		1.34		0		0.11	0.24	0.18	1U 2A
Asp	0.25	0.38	0.26												0.10	0.16	0.08	1U 1A 1G
Glu	0.16	0.28	0.20												0.15	0.80		1U 1A 1G
Met	0.05	0.22		0	0		0	0	0.30	1.08			0					1U 1A 1G
His		0.12	0.26						0.30	1.58								1U 1A 1C
Lys		0.20						2.94	8.70	1.90			0					1U 2A
Pro					3.96					4.16								1U 2C
Ser		0.40	0.38			0.16				1.16			2.28					2U 1C
Thr			0.48				0		2.94	3.50								1U 1A 1C‡
Tyr	0.08												1.30			1.46		2U 1A
Val	0.08																	2U 1G

* mμmoles/mg ribosomal protein. Values without polynucleotide subtracted from those with polynucleotide. In other experiments not recorded in the table, the incorporation of phenylalanine with poly UCG was 7.13; that of alanine, 0.14; poly UG did not stimulate the incorporation of alanine, asparagine, aspartic acid, or glutamic acid. The ribosomes used in experiment 1 had been kept frozen for several weeks, those used in experiments 1 and 2 for only a few days.
† Not previously tested, except with poly UG and poly UCG. These polymers did not stimulate the incorporation of asparagine.
‡ Previously given[2] as 1U 2C. This might be another letter for threonine (degenerate code).

letter of glutamine is still unavailable but a 1U 1C 1G letter for this amino acid can be predicted from replacement data of Tsugita[4] in nitrous acid mutants of tobacco mosaic virus. In the meantime, our assumption, for simplicity's sake, of a triplet code found experimental support in the elegant genetic experiments of Crick, Barnett, Brenner, and Watts-Tobin.[5]

In presenting the experimental evidence for the last assignments it will be desirable to make a general survey of all of our results and to compare them in detail with the available amino acid replacement data in nitrous acid mutants of tobacco mosaic virus (Tsugita,[4, 6] Tsugita and Fraenkel-Conrat,[7] Wittmann[8]).

Preparations and Methods.—These have been the same as in previous work[1, 3] except for the following changes: (1) during preincubation all twenty C^{12} amino acids were present at 0.045 μmole/ml each; (2) in the incubation mixture nineteen C^{12} amino acids and one C^{14} amino acid were present at 0.2 μmole/ml each.

Results.—*Experiments with alanine, asparagine, aspartic acid, glutamic acid, and methionine:* The results of several experiments with these amino acids are recorded in Table 1. Alanine incorporation was stimulated only by poly UCG. A slight stimulation by this polymer of alanine incorporation had previously been observed but not recorded as it appeared too small and inconsistent. The average phe/ala incorporation ratio in two experiments was 31 (Table 2). Since the calculated frequency ratio of UUU to 1U 1C 1G triplets in poly UCG (6:1:1) is 36,[9] this suggests 1U 1C 1G as the code letter. Incorporation of asparagine was stimulated by poly UA, poly

UAC and poly UAG. Asparagine had not been available to us until recently and had not previously been tried with these polymers. The average incorporation ratio phe/aspN with poly UA, UAC, and UAG, was 15, 15, and 20, respectively (Table 2). The calculated frequency ratios of UUU to 1U 2A in

TABLE 2

CODE LETTER ASSIGNMENTS*

Amino acid	UC (5:1)	UA (5:1)	Polynucleotides UG (5:1)	UAC (6:1:1)	UCG (6:1:1)	UAG (6:1:1)	Code letter (unknown sequence)
Ala	. . .	. . .	. . .	. . .	31	. . .	1U 1C 1G
Arg	. . .	. . .	. . .	. . .	30	. . .	1U 1C 1G
AspN	. . .	15	. . .	15	. . .	20	1U 2A (1U 1A 1C)
Asp	. . .	. . .	. . .	. . .	. . .	41	1U 1A 1G
Cys	. . .	. . .	5	. . .	1	. . .	2U 1G
Glu	. . .	. . .	. . .	. . .	. . .	64	1U 1A 1G
GluN	. . .	. . .	. . .	. . .	. . .	. . .	1U 1C 1G†
Gly	. . .	. . .	24	. . .	40	. . .	1U 2G
His	. . .	. . .	. . .	29	. . .	. . .	1U 1A 1C
Ileu	. . .	5	. . .	6	. . .	. . .	2U 1A
Leu	5	7	8	4	4	. . .	2U 1C (2U 1A, 2U 1G)
Lys	. . .	32	. . .	46	. . .	. . .	1U 2A
Met	. . .	. . .	. . .	. . .	. . .	23	1U 1A 1G
Pro	13	. . .	.	29	. . .	. . .	1U 2C
Ser	4	. . .	. . .	4	. . .	. . .	2U 1C
Thr	‡	. . .	. . .	11	. . .	. . .	1U 1A 1C (1U 2C)
Try	. . .	. . .	20	. . .	24	. . .	1U 2G
Tyr	. . .	4	. . .	4	. . .	5	2U 1A
Val	. . .	. . .	5	. . .	5	4	2U 1G

* The experimental values given are ratios of stimulation of phenylalanine incorporation to that of the amino acid in question by different polynucleotides and are in all cases averages of two or more experiments from this and previous papers of this series. Code letters in parentheses indicate other possible code letters for a given amino acid (degenerate code).

† No experimental value available. Code letter predicted from glutamine→valine replacement in HNO₂ mutant of tobacco mosaic virus (Tsugita[4]).[2, 3]

‡ In previous experiments[2] the phenylalanine/threonine ratio with poly UC (5:1) was 17. In more recent experiments, stimulation of threonine incorporation by this polymer was negligible in one and nil in another. This will be reinvestigated.

poly UA (5:1), UAC (6:1:1), and UAG (6:1:1) is 25, 36, and 36 respectively. This suggests 1U 2A and 1U 1A 1C (poly UAC was twice as effective as expected from its 1U 2A content alone) as code letters for asparagine. Since the code may be degenerate,[5] the existence of more than one code letter for a given amino acid is not improbable. Aspartic acid poses no problems as its incorporation was stimulated only by poly UAG and the phe/asp incorporation ratio, 41 (Table 2), was not far from the calculated value, i.e. 36, for a 1U 1A 1G letter. Glutamic acid behaved similarly except that stimulation of its incorporation by poly UAG was smaller and the phe/glu ratio of 64 was almost twice as high as theory for a 1U 1A 1G letter. However, no other polymer stimulated incorporation of this amino acid and the code letter 1U 1A 1G may tentatively be assigned to it. This assignment is in line with amino acid replacement data (cf. Table 5). The code letter assignment 1A 1U 1G is amply justified for methionine. Its incorporation was stimulated only by poly UAG and the phe/met ratio of 23 (Table 2), although lower than the theoretical 36, is not too far off.

Repetition of experiments with other amino acids: Since the modifications in methods introduced here and in the preceding paper[3] considerably increased the effect of synthetic polynucleotides on the incorporation of amino acids we reinvestigated certain previously described code triplet assignments.

The results, shown in Table 1, agree with the earlier data in the case of histidine, lysine, proline, serine, tyrosine and valine. In the case of threonine, in contrast with previous results,[2] poly UC (5:1) was relatively ineffective. On the other hand, stimulation of the incorporation of this amino acid by poly UAC (6:1:1) was high, relative to stimulation of phenylalanine incorporation, in the present as well as in the former experiments. A phe/thr ratio of 11 was obtained (Table 2) whereas the expected ratio for a 1U 1A 1C letter is 36. Since our sample of threonine-C^{14} had a very low specific radioactivity, repetition of these experiments with a sample of higher specific activity is clearly desirable. For the present, 1U 1A 1C may tentatively be taken as a code letter for threonine with 1U 2C as a possible additional letter for this amino acid. There is some support for this assumption in the fact that, in recent experiments, poly CU (5:1) promoted threonine incorporation although to a lesser extent than that of proline for which a 1U 2C code letter is definitely established.

In preliminary experiments it has been found that inosinic acid (I) can replace G. Thus, like poly UG (5:1), poly UI (5:1) stimulated the incorporation of phenylalanine, cysteine, glycine, tryptophan, and valine. The phe/cys and phe/val ratio was close to 5 (theory for 2U 1I letters); the phe/gly and phe/try ratio was about 25 (theory for 1U 2I letters). This is as expected since hypoxanthine resembles guanine in its hydrogen bonding properties.

Discussion.—Survey of code letter assignments: With the experimental results reported in the preceding section, code letter assignments are now available for 19 amino acids. A directly determined code letter for glutamine is still lacking.[3] However, a 1U 1C 1G letter may be predicted for this amino acid as previously discussed.[2] Table 2 summarizes the experimental basis for our code letter assignments. As previously explained,[1-3] the assignments are based on a comparison of the ratio of stimulation by a given polymer of the incorporation of phenylalanine to that of another amino acid with the calculated frequency ratio of UUU triplets to other triplets in this polymer. For ease of comparison of these two ratios the calculated UUU to other triplet frequency ratios are given in Table 3. It may be seen that in most cases the assignment is made on the basis of a very close agreement of the phenylalanine to other amino acid incorporation ratio with one of the calculated UUU to other triplet ratios for one or more of the polymers. This statement is definitely borne out in the case of the following amino acids (cf. Tables 2 and 3): Alanine, arginine, aspartic acid, cysteine, glycine, histidine, isoleucine, serine, tryptophan, tyrosine, and valine. The agreement is not as good with the remaining amino acids. These give phenylalanine to other amino acid incorporation ratios either higher (glutamic acid, lysine) or lower (asparagine, histidine, methionine, proline, threonine) than corresponds to the code letter assignment made. Since the calculated UUU to other triplet ratios are based on a random distribution of nucleotides in the synthetic copolymers,[10, 11] a slight deviation from randomness could explain the lack of perfect agreement in some cases. In spite of this we feel that the data taken as a whole bear out the proposed code letter assignments. If we take glutamic acid and methionine as examples of too high and too low ratios, respectively, it is clear that their code letters must contain 1U 1A 1G since their incorporation was stimulated only by poly UAG of the six different copolymers tested.

From the data in Table 2, it appears that three amino acids, namely asparagine, leucine, and threonine, may have more than one code letter or, in other words, that the code for these amino acids is degenerate.   The reasons for assigning more than one code letter to each asparagine, and threonine have been given in the preceding

TABLE 3

FREQUENCY RATIOS OF UUU TO OTHER TRIPLETS IN SYNTHETIC POLYNUCLEOTIDES*

	Polynucleotide					
Triplets	UC (5:1)	UA (5:1)	UG (5:1)	UAC (6:1:1)	UCG (6:1:1)	UAG (6:1:1)
2U 1C	5	...	...	6	6	...
1U 2C	25	...	...	36	36	...
2U 1A	...	5	...	6	...	6
1U 2A	...	25	...	36	...	36
2U 1G	...	...	5	...	6	6
1U 2G	...	...	25	...	36	36
1U 1A 1C	...	...	...	36	...	...
1U 1C 1G	...	...	...	...	36	...
1U 1A 1G	...	...	...	...	...	36
Triplets without U†	125	125	125	216	216	216

* Calculated frequency ratios based on the composition of the polymers with assumption of complete randomness.   The frequency ratios are for each one of the possible sequences for a given triplet, e.g. UUU/UUC or UUU/UCU or UUU/CUU = 5 in case of the 2U 1C triplets.
† In the polymers used, e.g. CCC in poly UC; or AAA, AAC, ACA, CAA, ACC, CAC, CCA, CCC in poly UAC, etc.

section.   As regards leucine it will be remembered that its incorporation into acid insoluble products was stimulated by most of the polynucleotides tested.[1, 2]   With a sample of leucine-C^{14} of high purity[12] we obtained essentially the same result (Table 2) except for a negligible stimulation by poly U.   The phe/leu incorporation ratio of 5 with poly UC (5:1), as before, was exactly that expected for a 2U 1C code letter.   The ratios of 7 and 8 obtained with poly UA (5:1) and poly UG (5:1), respectively, are not too far from 5, the expected value for a 2U 1A or a 2U 1G letter.   Further, the ratio of 4 in the case of each poly UAC (6:1:1) and poly UCG (6:1:1) is close to 3, the expected value if stimulation of leucine incorporation by these polymers were caused by 2U 1C + 2U 1A triplets in poly UAC and by 2U 1C + 2U 1G triplets in poly UCG.   The possibility must therefore be considered, as indicated in Table 2, that the results with leucine may be due to the existence of three code letters, namely 2U 1C, 2U 1A, and 2U 1G, for this amino acid.

A striking feature of the code triplets is that they all contain U.   In fact, each of 8 triplets (those for cysteine, isoleucine, leucine, serine, tyrosine, and valine) out of the 23 listed in Table 2 contains two U residues and the phenylalanine triplet contains three.   Since out of $4^3 = 64$ triplets, 37 contain U (cf. Table 3) and only 24 of these are accounted for, there remain 13 triplets some, or all, of which might be "nonsense."   How many of the 27 non-U triplets are "nonsense" cannot be decided by our present methodology which, due to limited sensitivity (cf. Table 3), can only be used for the detection of U-containing code letters.   However, the code might be degenerate to a greater extent than is apparent from our present data and there could be additional code letters consisting of triplets without U.

With copolymers of similar composition to those used by us, Martin *et al.*[13] have recently reported results for 15 amino acids largely in agreement with ours.

Distribution of code letters among various triplets: It is interesting to note from Table 4 that in no case does the number of code letters of the same composition exceed the number of possible sequences in the corresponding triplet group. Had this occurred, some of the assignments would have been undoubtedly in error.

In Table 4 the triplets of the 2U 1A and 1U 2A and those of the 1A 1U 1C and 1U 1A 1G series have been paired so that every triplet in each of the two groups is

TABLE 4
DISTRIBUTION OF CODE LETTER AMONG VARIOUS TRIPLETS*

Amino acid	UUU	2U 1C UUC UCU CUU	1U 2C UCC CUC CCU	2U 1A UUA UAU AUU	1U 2A AAU AUA UAA	2U 1G UUG UGU GUU	1U 2G UGG GUG GGU	1U 1C 1G UCG UGC CUG CGU GUC GCU	1U 1A 1C UAC UCA AUC ACU CUA CAU	1U 1A 1G AUG AGU UAG UGA GAU GUA
Ala	..	..	..	..	..	..	..	+	..	..
Arg	..	..	..	..	..	..	..	+	..	..
AspN	..	..	..	..	+	..	..	..	(+)	..
Asp	..	..	..	..	..	..	..	..	..	+
Cys	..	..	..	..	..	+	..	..	..	..
Glu	..	..	..	..	..	..	..	..	..	+
GluN†	..	..	..	..	..	..	..	+	..	..
Gly	..	..	..	..	..	..	+	..	..	..
His	..	..	..	..	..	..	..	..	+	..
Ileu	..	..	..	+	..	..	..	..	..	..
Leu	..	+	..	(+)	..	(+)	..	..	..	..
Lys	..	..	..	..	+	..	..	..	..	..
Met	..	..	..	..	..	..	..	..	..	+
Phe	+	..	..	..	..	..	..	..	..	..
Pro	..	..	+	..	..	..	..	..	..	..
Ser	..	+	..	..	..	..	..	..	..	..
Thr	..	..	(+)	..	..	..	..	..	+	..
Try	..	..	..	..	..	..	+	..	..	..
Tyr	..	..	..	+	..	..	..	..	..	..
Val	..	..	..	..	..	+	..	..	..	..

* Individual sequences are given under the nucleotide composition of each triplet. Plus signs in parentheses denote possible additional code letters for a given amino acid.
† Predicted.

next to its complementary. Since only three triplets out of six appear to be utilized in each of the 1U 1A 1C and 1U 1A 1G series, it is possible that only one triplet in each complementary pair is a code letter. If so, there would be no complementary code letters in this group. Some exclusion of complementarity occurs in the 2U 1A and 1U 2A series as only two positions are occupied by code letters in the latter. The more or less complete elimination of complementary triplets in the code letters would have the advantage of restricting hydrogen bonding (both intra- and inter-molecular) in messenger RNA an occurrence that could interfere with its function.

Correlation with amino acid replacement data in nitrous acid mutants of tobacco mosaic virus: With the availability of experimentally determined code letters for 19 amino acids and of new data on amino acid replacements in nitrous acid mutants of tobacco mosaic virus[6−8] it is of interest to examine the latter in the light of our code letter assignments. This has been done in Table 5. In recording agreement or lack of agreement, on the last column of the table, it was assumed that the only well established changes brought about by treatment of RNA with nitrous acid are (1) conversion of C to U, and (2) conversion of A to G.[8] On this basis 11 out of 16 replacements (or approximately two-thirds of the replacements thus far observed) can be explained by our code letter assignments. However, it is possible that base changes other than C→U and A→G occur as a result of nitrous acid treatment.[6]

TABLE 5

AMINO ACID REPLACEMENTS IN HNO$_2$ MUTANTS OF TOBACCO MOSAIC VIRUS†

Replacement	Times observed	Reference	Code letter change	Agreement**
Asp*→Ser	4	Tsugita & Fraenkel-Conrat,[7] Wittmann[8]	UAG, UAA(UAC)→UUC	—
Asp*→Ala	6	Tsugita,[4] Wittmann[8]	UAC→UGC	+
Asp*→Gly	2	Wittmann[8]	UAG→UGG	+
Arg→Gly	5	Tsugita[6]	UCG→UGG	—
Glu⁻→Gly	1	Tsugita[6]	UAG→UGG	+
Glu*→Gly	2	Wittmann[8]	UAG→UGG	+
GluN→Val	1	Tsugita[4]	(UCG)‡→UUG	..
Glu*→Val	2	Wittmann[8]	(UCG)→UUG	..
Ileu→Val	1	Wittmann[8]	UUA→UUG	+
Leu→Phe	1	Wittmann[8]	UUC→UUU	+
Pro→Leu	2	Tsugita,[4] Wittmann[8]	UCC→UUC	+
Pro→Ser	3	Wittmann[8]	UCC→UUC	+
Ser→Leu	1	Wittmann[8]	UUC→UUC(UUA, UUG)	—
Ser→Phe	3	Tsugita,[4] Wittmann[8]	UUC—UUU	+
Thr→Ser	1	Tsugita[4]	UCC→UUC	+
Thr→Ileu	7	Wittmann[8]	UAC→UAU	+
Thr→Met	3	Wittmann[8]	UAC(UCC)→UAG	—
Tyr→Phe	1	Tsugita[6]	UUA→UUU	—

† Asp* may be either aspartic acid or asparagine, glu*, either glutamic acid or glutamine.
‡ Letter for gluN not available experimentally; predicted from this replacement.
** + indicates that the reported replacement is in agreement with the code letter assignments in this paper on the basis that either C is converted to U or A converted to G by nitrous acid treatment of tobacco mosaic virus RNA; — indicates lack of agreement on this basis.

Moreover, some of the replacements observed only once might be the result of spontaneous mutation.

Lack of agreement in those replacements observed two or more times, e.g., asp*→ser, arg→gly, and thr→met (Table 5), is more disturbing. One possibility is that these replacements might reflect the occurrence of additional, non-U letters as considered elsewhere in this paper. The occurrence of undetected U-letters is another possibility. Thus, the asp*→ser and ser→leu replacements (Table 5) might be explained if serine had a 1U 1C 1G in addition to the 2U 1C code letter. The small stimulation of serine incorporation by 1U 1C 1G triplets in poly UCG (6:1:1) would escape detection in the presence of a six times higher stimulation due to 2U 1C triplets in this polymer (2U 1C:1U 1C 1G frequency ratio = 6). The code letter changes would then be as follows: aspN (UAC)→ser (UGC); ser (UCG)→leu (UUG).

Smith[14] has correlated single amino acid replacements in a number of human mutant hemoglobins with our code letters for 14 amino acids, under the restrictive assumption that each mutation involves replacement of only one base in a triplet, and found excellent agreement. From this comparison he was able to predict the code letters for four amino acids (alanine, asparagine, aspartic and glutamic acid) now reported in this paper.

Universality of genetic code: From the agreement between the code letters derived from work on the *E. coli* system with amino acid replacements in mutants of tobacco mosaic virus and human hemoglobins, it would appear that there is but one genetic code for all living things, i.e., that the code is universal.   A more direct answer to this important question should soon be forthcoming.

Summary.—Evidence is presented in this paper for the assignment of triplet code letters (of unspecified sequence) to the amino acids alanine, asparagine, aspartic acid, glutamic acid, and methionine.   Nineteen out of twenty amino acids are now accounted for.   An experimentally determined code letter for glutamine is not yet available but one has been predicted from amino acid replacement data in nitrous acid mutants of tobacco mosaic virus.   Three amino acids, including asparagine, leucine, and threonine, appear to have more than one letter, indicating that their code may be degenerate.   All of the present code letters contain uridylic acid residues.   However, non-uridylic code letters could not have been detected by our method and the possibility that degeneracy of the code may be more extensive than is apparent at present, to include several non-uridylic code letters, should be kept in mind.   The experimental basis for the code letter assignments, made in this and previous papers of this series, is discussed in detail and the results are compared with recent data on amino acid replacements in nitrous acid mutants of tobacco mosaic virus.

We are greatly indebted to Dr. A. Tsugita, Virus Laboratory, University of California, Berkeley, for the preprint of a paper in press and for making unpublished replacement data available to us. We are also much indebted to Dr. H. G. Wittmann, Mâx-Planck-Institut für Biologie, Tübingen, Germany, and Dr. F. H. C. Crick, Institute of Molecular Biology, Cambridge, England, for preprints of papers in press.

* Aided by grants from the National Institute of Arthritis and Metabolic Diseases (Grant A-1845) of the U.S. Public Health Service and from the Rockefeller Foundation.   The abbreviations used in this paper are the same as in previous papers of this series.   The standard abbreviations are used for amino acids.

† International Postdoctoral Fellow of the National Institutes of Health, U.S. Public Health Service.   Permanent address: Instituto de Química Fisiológica y Patológica, Universidad de Chile, Santiago, Chile.

¹ Lengyel, P., J. F. Speyer, and S. Ochoa, these Proceedings, **47**, 1936 (1961).

² Speyer, J. F., P. Lengyel, C. Basilio, and S. Ochoa, these Proceedings, **48**, 63 (1962).

³ Lengyel P., J. F. Speyer, C. Basilio, and S. Ochoa, these Proceedings, **48**, 282 (1962).

⁴ Tsugita, A., *Protein, Nucleic Acid, Enzyme (Tokyo)*, **6**, 385 (1961).

⁵ Crick, F. H. C., L. Barnett, S. Brenner, and R. J. Watts-Tobin, *Nature*, **192**, 1227 (1961).

⁶ Tsugita, A., personal communication.

⁷ Tsugita, A., and H. Fraenkel-Conrat, *J. Mol. Biol.*, in press.

⁸ Wittmann, H. G., *Naturwissenschaften*, **48**, 729 (1961).

⁹ See Table 3 for calculated frequency ratios of UUU to other triplets in the various polynucleotides used in this work.

¹⁰ Heppel, L. A., P. J. Ortiz, and S. Ochoa, *J. Biol. Chem.*, **229**, 695 (1957).

¹¹ Ortiz, P. J., and S. Ochoa, *J. Biol. Chem.*, **234**, 1208 (1959).

¹² We are indebted to Dr. Mary L. Stephenson, Massachusetts General Hospital, for a sample of leucine-C¹⁴ prepared by Dr. R. B. Loftfield.

¹³ Martin, R. G., J. H. Matthaei, O. W. Jones, and M. W. Nirenberg, *Biochem. Biophys. Res. Comm.*, **6**, 410 (1962).

¹⁴ Smith, E. L., these Proceedings (to appear, no. 4. 1962).

(*Reprinted from Nature, Vol.* 192, *No.* 4809, *pp.* 1227–1232,
December 30, 1961)

GENERAL NATURE OF THE GENETIC CODE FOR PROTEINS

By Dr. F. H. C. CRICK, F.R.S., LESLIE BARNETT,
Dr. S. BRENNER and Dr. R. J. WATTS-TOBIN

Medical Research Council Unit for Molecular Biology,
Cavendish Laboratory, Cambridge

THERE is now a mass of indirect evidence which suggests that the amino-acid sequence along the polypeptide chain of a protein is determined by the sequence of the bases along some particular part of the nucleic acid of the genetic material. Since there are twenty common amino-acids found throughout Nature, but only four common bases, it has often been surmised that the sequence of the four bases is in some way a code for the sequence of the amino-acids. In this article we report genetic experiments which, together with the work of others, suggest that the genetic code is of the following general type:

(*a*) A group of three bases (or, less likely, a multiple of three bases) codes one amino-acid.

(*b*) The code is not of the overlapping type (see Fig. 1).

(*c*) The sequence of the bases is read from a fixed starting point. This determines how the long sequences of bases are to be correctly read off as triplets. There are no special 'commas' to show how to select the right triplets. If the starting point is displaced by one base, then the reading into triplets is displaced, and thus becomes incorrect.

(*d*) The code is probably 'degenerate'; that is, in general, one particular amino-acid can be coded by one of several triplets of bases.

The Reading of the Code

The evidence that the genetic code is not overlapping (see Fig. 1) does not come from our work, but from that of Wittmann[1] and of Tsugita and Fraenkel-Conrat[2] on the mutants of tobacco mosaic virus produced by nitrous acid. In an overlapping triplet code, an alteration to one base will in general change three adjacent amino-acids in the polypeptide chain. Their work on the alterations produced in the protein of the virus show that usually only one amino-acid at a time is changed as a result of treating the ribonucleic acid (RNA) of the virus with nitrous acid. In the rarer cases where two amino-acids are altered (owing presumably to two separate deaminations by the nitrous acid on one piece of RNA), the altered amino-acids are not in adjacent positions in the polypeptide chain.

Brenner[3] had previously shown that, if the code were universal (that is, the same throughout Nature), then all overlapping triplet codes were impossible. Moreover, all the abnormal human hæmoglobins studied in detail[4] show only single amino-acid changes. The newer experimental results essentially rule out all simple codes of the overlapping type.

If the code is not overlapping, then there must be some arrangement to show how to select the correct triplets (or quadruplets, or whatever it may be) along the continuous sequence of bases. One obvious suggestion is that, say, every fourth base is a 'comma'. Another idea is that certain triplets make 'sense', whereas others make 'nonsense', as in the comma-free codes of Crick, Griffith and Orgel[5]. Alternatively, the correct choice may be made by starting at a fixed point and working along the sequence of bases three (or four, or whatever) at a time. It is this possibility which we now favour.

Experimental Results

Our genetic experiments have been carried out on the B cistron of the r_{II} region of the bacteriophage T4, which attacks strains of *Escherichia coli*. This is the system so brilliantly exploited by Benzer[6,7]. The r_{II} region consists of two adjacent genes, or 'cistrons', called cistron A and cistron B. The wild-type phage will grow on both *E. coli* B (here called B) and on *E. coli* K12 (λ) (here called K), but a phage which has lost the function of either gene will not grow on K. Such a phage produces an r plaque on B. Many point mutations of the genes are known which behave in this way. Deletions of part of the region are also found. Other mutations, known as 'leaky', show partial function; that is, they will grow on K but their plaque-type on B is not truly wild. We report here our work on the mutant P 13 (now re-named FC 0) in the B1 segment of the B cistron. This mutant was originally produced by the action of proflavin[8].

We[9] have previously argued that acridines such as proflavin act as mutagens because they add or delete a base or bases. The most striking evidence in favour of this is that mutants produced by acridines are seldom 'leaky'; they are almost always completely lacking in the function of the gene. Since our note was published, experimental data from two sources have been added to our previous evidence: (1) we have examined a set of 126 r_{II} mutants made with

2

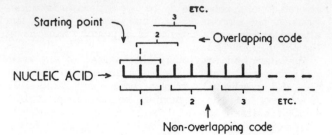

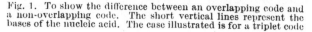

Fig. 1. To show the difference between an overlapping code and a non-overlapping code. The short vertical lines represent the bases of the nucleic acid. The case illustrated is for a triplet code

acridine yellow; of these only 6 are leaky (typically about half the mutants made with base analogues are leaky); (2) Streisinger[10] has found that whereas mutants of the lysozyme of phage $T4$ produced by base-analogues are usually leaky, all lysozyme mutants produced by proflavin are negative, that is, the function is completely lacking.

If an acridine mutant is produced by, say, adding a base, it should revert to 'wild-type' by deleting a base. Our work on revertants of FC 0 shows that it usually reverts not by reversing the original mutation but by producing a second mutation at a nearby point on the genetic map. That is, by a 'suppressor' in the same gene. In one case (or possibly two cases) it may have reverted back to true wild, but in at least 18 other cases the 'wild type' produced was really a double mutant with a 'wild' phenotype. Other workers[11] have found a similar phenomenon with r_{II} mutants, and Jinks[12] has made a detailed analysis of suppressors in the h_{III} gene.

The genetic map of these 18 suppressors of FC 0 is shown in Fig. 2, line a. It will be seen that they all fall in the $B1$ segment of the gene, though not all of them are very close to FC 0. They scatter over a region about, say, one-tenth the size of the B cistron. Not all are at different sites. We have found eight sites in all, but most of them fall into or near two close clusters of sites.

In all cases the suppressor was a non-leaky r. That is, it gave an r plaque on B and would not grow on K. This is the phenotype shown by a complete deletion of the gene, and shows that the function is lacking. The only possible exception was one case where the suppressor appeared to back-mutate so fast that we could not study it.

Each suppressor, as we have said, fails to grow on K. Reversion of each can therefore be studied by the same procedure used for FC 0. In a few cases these mutants apparently revert to the original wild-

3

type, but usually they revert by forming a double mutant. Fig. 2, lines b–g, shows the mutants produced as suppressors of these suppressors. Again all these new suppressors are non-leaky r mutants, and all map within the B1 segment for one site in the B2 segment.

Once again we have repeated the process on two of the new suppressors, with the same general results, as shown in Fig. 2, lines i and j.

All these mutants, except the original FC 0, occurred spontaneously. We have, however, produced one set (as suppressors of FC 7) using acridine yellow as a mutagen. The spectrum of suppressors we get (see Fig. 2, line h) is crudely similar to the spontaneous spectrum, and all the mutants are non-leaky r's. We have also tested a (small) selection of all our mutants and shown that their reversion-rates are increased by acridine yellow.

Thus in all we have about eighty independent r mutants, all suppressors of FC 0, or suppressors of suppressors, or suppressors of suppressors of suppressors. They all fall within a limited region of the gene and they are all non-leaky r mutants.

The double mutants (which contain a mutation plus its suppressor) which plate on K have a variety of plaque types on B. Some are indistinguishable from wild, some can be distinguished from wild with difficulty, while others are easily distinguishable and produce plaques rather like r.

We have checked in a few cases that the phenomenon is quite distinct from 'complementation', since the two mutants which separately are phenotypically r, and together are wild or pseudo-wild, must be put together in the same piece of genetic material. A simultaneous infection of K by the two mutants in separate viruses will not do.

The Explanation in Outline

Our explanation of all these facts is based on the theory set out at the beginning of this article. Although we have no direct evidence that the B cistron produces a polypeptide chain (probably through an RNA intermediate), in what follows we shall assume this to be so. To fix ideas, we imagine that the string of nucleotide bases is read, triplet by triplet, from a starting point on the left of the B cistron. We now suppose that, for example, the mutant FC 0 was produced by the insertion of an additional base in the wild-type sequence. Then this addition of a base at the FC 0 site will mean that the reading of all the triplets to the right of FC 0 will be shifted along one base, and will therefore be incorrect. Thus the amino-acid sequence of the protein

4

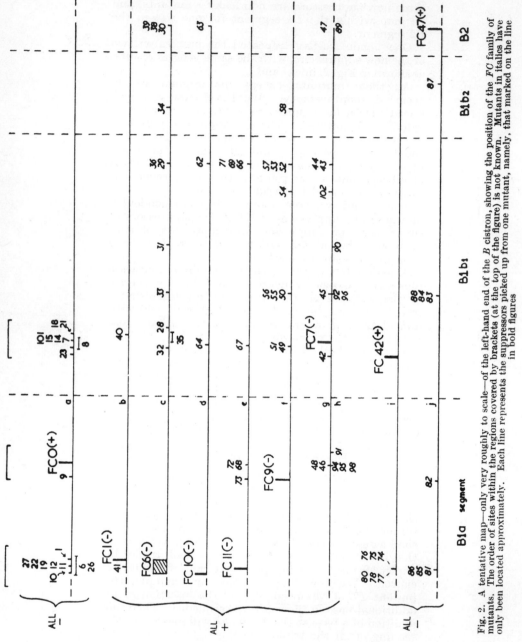

Fig. 2. A tentative map—only very roughly to scale—of the left-hand end of the *B* cistron, showing the position of the *FC* family of mutants. The order of sites within the regions covered by brackets (at the top of the figure) is not known. Mutants in italics have only been located approximately. Each line represents the suppressors picked up from one mutant, namely, that marked on the line in bold figures

which the B cistron is presumed to produce will be completely altered from that point onwards. This explains why the function of the gene is lacking. To simplify the explanation, we now postulate that a suppressor of FC 0 (for example, FC 1) is formed by deleting a base. Thus when the FC 1 mutation is present by itself, all triplets to the right of FC 1 will be read incorrectly and thus the function will be absent. However, when both mutations are present in the same piece of DNA, as in the pseudo-wild double mutant FC (0 + 1), then although the reading of triplets between FC 0 and FC 1 will be altered, the original reading will be restored to the rest of the gene. This could explain why such double mutants do not always have a true wild phenotype but are often pseudo-wild, since on our theory a small length of their amino-acid sequence is different from that of the wild-type.

For convenience we have designated our original mutant FC 0 by the symbol + (this choice is a pure convention at this stage) which we have so far considered as the addition of a single base. The suppressors of FC 0 have therefore been designated − . The suppressors of these suppressors have in the same way been labelled as + , and the suppressors of these last sets have again been labelled − (see Fig. 2).

Double Mutants

We can now ask: What is the character of any double mutant we like to form by putting together in the same gene any pair of mutants from our set of about eighty ? Obviously, in some cases we already know the answer, since some combinations of a + with a − were formed in order to isolate the mutants. But, by definition, no pair consisting of one + with another + has been obtained in this way, and there are many combinations of + with − not so far tested.

Now our theory clearly predicts that all combinations of the type + with + (or − with −) should give an r phenotype and not plate on K. We have put together 14 such pairs of mutants in the cases listed in Table 1 and found this prediction confirmed.

At first sight one would expect that all combinations of the type (+ with −) would be wild or pseudo-wild, but the situation is a little more intricate than that, and must be considered more closely. This springs

Table 1. DOUBLE MUTANTS HAVING THE r PHENOTYPE

− With −	+ With +	
FC (1 + 21)	FC (0 + 58)	FC (40 + 57)
FC (23 + 21)	FC (0 + 38)	FC (40 + 58)
FC (1 + 23)	FC (0 + 40)	FC (40 + 55)
FC (1 + 9)	FC (0 + 55)	FC (40 + 54)
	FC (0 + 54)	FC (40 + 38)

6

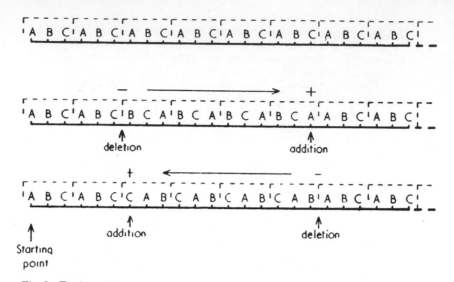

Fig. 3. To show that our convention for arrows is consistent. The letters, *A*, *B* and *C* each represent a different base of the nucleic acid. For simplicity a repeating sequence of bases, *ABC*, is shown. (This would code for a polypeptide for which every amino-acid was the same.) A triplet code is assumed. The dotted lines represent the imaginary 'reading frame' implying that the sequence is read in sets of three starting on the left

from the obvious fact that if the code is made of triplets, any long sequence of bases can be read correctly in one way, but incorrectly (by starting at the wrong point) in two different ways, depending whether the 'reading frame' is shifted one place to the right or one place to the left.

If we symbolize a shift, by one place, of the reading frame in one direction by → and in the opposite direction by ←, then we can establish the convention that our + is always at the head of the arrow, and our − at the tail. This is illustrated in Fig. 3.

We must now ask: Why do our suppressors not extend over the whole of the gene? The simplest postulate to make is that the shift of the reading frame produces some triplets the reading of which is 'unacceptable'; for example, they may be 'nonsense', or stand for 'end the chain', or be unacceptable in some other way due to the complications of protein structure. This means that a suppressor of, say, *FC* 0 must be within a region such that no 'unacceptable' triplet is produced by the shift in the reading frame between *FC* 0 and its suppressor. But, clearly, since for any sequence there are *two* possible misreadings, we might expect that the 'unacceptable' triplets produced by a → shift would occur in different places on the map from those produced by a ← shift.

Examination of the spectra of suppressors (in each

7

case putting in the arrows → or ←) suggests that while the → shift is acceptable anywhere within our region (though not outside it) the shift ←, starting from points near FC 0, is acceptable over only a more limited stretch. This is shown in Fig. 4. Somewhere in the left part of our region, between FC 0 or FC 9 and the FC 1 group, there must be one or more unacceptable triplets when a ← shift is made; similarly for the region to the right of the FC 21 cluster.

Thus we predict that a combination of a + with a − will be wild or pseudo-wild if it involves a → shift, but that such pairs involving a ← shift will be phenotypically r if the arrow crosses one or more of the forbidden places, since then an unacceptable triplet will be produced.

Table 2. DOUBLE MUTANTS OF THE TYPE (+ WITH −)

−\\+	FC 41	FC 0	FC 40	FC 42	FC 58*	FC 63	FC 38
FC 1	W	W	W		W		W
FC 86		W	W	W	W	W	
FC 9	r	W	W	W	*W*		W
FC 82	r		W	W	W	W	
FC 21	r	*W*			W		W
FC 88	r	r			W	W	
FC 87	r	r	r	r			W

W, wild or pseudo-wild phenotype; *W*, wild or pseudo-wild combination used to isolate the suppressor; r, r phenotype.
* Double mutants formed with FC 58 (or with FC 34) give sharp plaques on K.

We have tested this prediction in the 28 cases shown in Table 2. We expected 19 of these to be wild, or pseudo-wild, and 9 of them to have the r phenotype. In all cases our prediction was correct. We regard this as a striking confirmation of our theory. It may be of interest that the theory was constructed before these particular experimental results were obtained.

Rigorous Statement of the Theory

So far we have spoken as if the evidence supported a triplet code, but this was simply for illustration. Exactly the same results would be obtained if the code operated with groups of, say, 5 bases. Moreover, our symbols + and − must not be taken to mean literally the addition or subtraction of a single base.

It is easy to see that our symbolism is more exactly as follows:

+ represents + m, modulo n
− represents − m, modulo n

8

where n (a positive integer) is the coding ratio (that is, the number of bases which code one amino-acid) and m is any integral number of bases, positive or negative.

It can also be seen that our choice of reading direction is arbitrary, and that the same results (to a first approximation) would be obtained in whichever direction the genetic material was read, that is, whether the starting point is on the right or the left of the gene, as conventionally drawn.

Triple Mutants and the Coding Ratio

The somewhat abstract description given above is necessary for generality, but fortunately we have convincing evidence that the coding ratio is in fact 3 or a multiple of 3.

This we have obtained by constructing triple mutants of the form (+ with + with +) or (− with − with −). One must be careful not to make shifts

Table 3. TRIPLE MUTANTS HAVING A WILD OR PSEUDO-WILD PHENO-TYPE

$$FC\,(0\,+\,40\,+\,38)$$
$$FC\,(0\,+\,40\,+\,58)$$
$$FC\,(0\,+\,40\,+\,57)$$
$$FC\,(0\,+\,40\,+\,54)$$
$$FC\,(0\,+\,40\,+\,55)$$
$$FC\,(1\,+\,21\,+\,23)$$

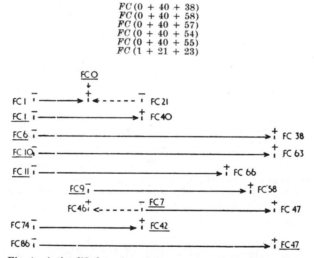

Fig. 4. A simplified version of the genetic map of Fig. 2. Each line corresponds to the suppressor from one mutant, here underlined. The arrows show the range over which suppressors have so far been found, the extreme mutants being named on the map. Arrows to the right are shown solid, arrows to the left dotted

across the 'unacceptable' regions for the ← shifts, but these we can avoid by a proper choice of mutants.

We have so far examined the six cases listed in Table 3 and in all cases the triples are wild or pseudo-wild.

The rather striking nature of this result can be

9

seen by considering one of them, for example, the triple (*FC* 0 with *FC* 40 with *FC* 38). These three mutants are, by themselves, all of like type (+). We can say this not merely from the way in which they were obtained, but because each of them, when combined with our mutant *FC* 9 (−), gives the wild, or pseudo-wild phenotype. However, either singly or together in pairs they have an *r* phenotype, and will not grow on *K*. That is, the function of the gene is absent. Nevertheless, the combination of all three in the same gene partly restores the function and produces a pseudo-wild phage which grows on *K*.

This is exactly what one would expect, in favourable cases, if the coding ratio were 3 or a multiple of 3.

Our ability to find the coding ratio thus depends on the fact that, in at least one of our composite mutants which are 'wild', at least one amino-acid must have been added to or deleted from the polypeptide chain without disturbing the function of the gene-product too greatly.

This is a very fortunate situation. The fact that we can make these changes and can study so large a region probably comes about because this part of the protein is not essential for its function. That this is so has already been suggested by Champe and Benzer[13] in their work on complementation in the r_{II} region. By a special test (combined infection on *K*, followed by plating on *B*) it is possible to examine the function of the *A* cistron and the *B* cistron separately. A particular deletion, 1589 (see Fig. 5) covers the right-hand end of the *A* cistron and part of the left-hand end of the *B* cistron. Although 1589 abolishes the *A* function, they showed that it allows the *B* function to be expressed to a considerable extent. The region of the *B* cistron deleted by 1589 is that into which all our *FC* mutants fall.

Joining two Genes Together

We have used this deletion to reinforce our idea that the sequence is read in groups from a fixed starting point. Normally, an alteration confined to the *A* cistron (be it a deletion, an acridine mutant, or any other mutant) does not prevent the expression of the *B* cistron. Conversely, no alteration within the *B* cistron prevents the function of the *A* cistron. This implies that there may be a region between the two cistrons which separates them and allows their functions to be expressed individually.

We argued that the deletion 1589 will have lost this separating region and that therefore the two (partly damaged) cistrons should have been joined together. Experiments show this to be the case,

10

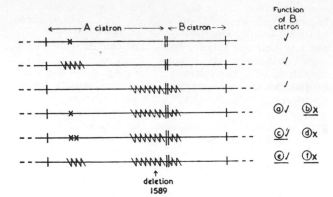

Fig. 5. Summary of the results with deletion 1589. The first two lines show that without 1589 a mutation or a deletion in the A cistron does not prevent the B cistron from functioning. Deletion 1589 (line 3) also allows the B cistron to function. The other cases, in some of which an alteration in the A cistron prevents the function of the B cistron (when 1589 is also present), are discussed in the text. They have been labelled (a), (b), etc., for convenience of reference, although cases (a) and (d) are not discussed in this paper. $\checkmark$ implies function; $\times$ implies no function

for now an alteration to the left-hand end of the A cistron, if combined with deletion 1589, can prevent the B function from appearing. This is shown in Fig. 5. Either the mutant $P43$ or $X142$ (both of which revert strongly with acridines) will prevent the B function when the two cistrons are joined, although both of these mutants are in the A cistron. This is also true of $X142\ S1$, a suppressor of $X\ 142$ (Fig. 5, case b). However, the double mutant ($X142$ with $X142\ S1$), of the type ($+$ with $-$), which by itself is pseudo-wild, still has the B function when combined with 1589 (Fig. 5, case c). We have also tested in this way the 10 deletions listed by Benzer[7], which fall wholly to the left of 1589. Of these, three (386, 168 and 221) prevent the B function (Fig. 5, case f), whereas the other seven show it (Fig. 5, case e). We surmise that each of these seven has lost a number of bases which is a multiple of 3. There are theoretical reasons for expecting that deletions may not be random in length, but will more often have lost a number of bases equal to an integral multiple of the coding ratio.

It would not surprise us if it were eventually shown that deletion 1589 produces a protein which consists of part of the protein from the A cistron and part of that from the B cistron, joined together in the same polypeptide chain, and having to some extent the function of the undamaged B protein.

Is the Coding Ratio 3 or 6?

It remains to show that the coding ratio is prob-

11

ably 3, rather than a multiple of 3. Previous rather rough estimates[10,14] of the coding ratio (which are admittedly very unreliable) might suggest that the coding ratio is not far from 6. This would imply, on our theory, that the alteration in FC 0 was not to one base, but to two bases (or, more correctly, to an even number of bases).

We have some additional evidence which suggests that this is unlikely. First, in our set of 126 mutants produced by acridine yellow (referred to earlier) we have four independent mutants which fall at or

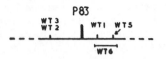

Fig. 6. Genetic map of P 83 and its suppressors, WT 1, etc. The region falls within segment B 9a near the right-hand end of the B cistron. It is not yet known which way round the map is in relation to the other figures

close to the FC 9 site. By a suitable choice of partners, we have been able to show that two are $+$ and two are $-$. Secondly, we have two mutants ($X146$ and $X225$), produced by hydrazine[15], which fall on or near the site FC 30. These we have been able to show are both of type $-$.

Thus unless both acridines and hydrazine usually delete (or add) an even number of bases, this evidence supports a coding ratio of 3. However, as the action of these mutagens is not understood in detail, we cannot be certain that the coding ratio is not 6, although 3 seems more likely.

We have preliminary results which show that other acridine mutants often revert by means of close suppressors, but it is too sketchy to report here. A tentative map of some suppressors of P 83, a mutant at the other end of the B cistron, in segment B 9a, is shown in Fig. 6. They occur within a shorter region than the suppressors of FC 0, covering a distance of about one-twentieth of the B cistron. The double mutant WT $(2 + 5)$ has the r phenotype, as expected.

Is the Code Degenerate?

If the code is a triplet code, there are 64 $(4 \times 4 \times 4)$ possible triplets. Our results suggest that it is unlikely that only 20 of these represent the 20 amino-acids and that the remaining 44 are nonsense. If this were the case, the region over which suppressors of the FC 0 family occur (perhaps a quarter of the B cistron) should be very much smaller than we observe, since a shift of frame should then, by chance, pro-

12

duce a nonsense reading at a much closer distance. This argument depends on the size of the protein which we have assumed the *B* cistron to produce. We do not know this, but the length of the cistron suggests that the protein may contain about 200 amino-acids. Thus the code is probably 'degenerate', that is, in general more than one triplet codes for each amino-acid. It is well known that if this were so, one could also account for the major dilemma of the coding problem, namely, that while the base composition of the DNA can be very different in different micro-organisms, the amino-acid composition of their proteins only changes by a moderate amount[16]. However, exactly how many triplets code amino-acids and how many have other functions we are unable to say.

Future Developments

Our theory leads to one very clear prediction. Suppose one could examine the amino-acid sequence of the 'pseudo-wild' protein produced by one of our double mutants of the (+ with −) type. Conventional theory suggests that since the gene is only altered in two places, only two amino-acids would be changed. Our theory, on the other hand, predicts that a string of amino-acids would be altered, covering the region of the polypeptide chain corresponding to the region on the gene between the two mutants. A good protein on which to test this hypothesis is the lysozyme of the phage, at present being studied chemically by Dreyer[17] and genetically by Streisinger[10].

At the recent Biochemical Congress at Moscow, the audience of Symposium I was startled by the announcement of Nirenberg that he and Matthaei[18] had produced polyphenylalanine (that is, a polypeptide all the residues of which are phenylalanine) by adding polyuridylic acid (that is, an RNA the bases of which are all uracil) to a cell-free system which can synthesize protein. This implies that a sequence of uracils codes for phenylalanine, and our work suggests that it is probably a triplet of uracils.

It is possible by various devices, either chemical or enzymatic, to synthesize polyribonucleotides with defined or partly defined sequences. If these, too, will produce specific polypeptides, the coding problem is wide open for experimental attack, and in fact many laboratories, including our own, are already working on the problem. If the coding ratio is indeed 3, as our results suggest, and if the code is the same throughout Nature, then the genetic code may well be solved within a year.

13

We thank Dr. Alice Orgel for certain mutants and for the use of data from her thesis, Dr. Leslie Orgel for many useful discussions, and Dr. Seymour Benzer for supplying us with certain deletions. We are particularly grateful to Prof. C. F. A. Pantin for allowing us to use a room in the Zoological Museum, Cambridge, in which the bulk of this work was done.

[1] Wittman, H. G., Symp. 1, Fifth Intern. Cong. Biochem., 1961, for refs. (in the press).

[2] Tsugita, A., and Fraenkel-Conrat, H., *Proc. U.S. Nat. Acad. Sci.*, **46**, 636 (1960); *J. Mol. Biol.* (in the press).

[3] Brenner, S., *Proc. U.S. Nat. Acad. Sci.*, **43**, 687 (1957).

[4] For refs. see Watson, H. C., and Kendrew, J. C., *Nature*, **190**, 670 (1961).

[5] Crick, F. H. C., Griffith, J. S., and Orgel, L. E., *Proc. U.S. Nat. Acad. Sci.*, **43**, 416 (1957).

[6] Benzer, S., *Proc. U.S. Nat. Acad. Sci.*, **45**, 1607 (1959), for refs. to earlier papers.

[7] Benzer, S., *Proc. U.S. Nat. Acad. Sci.*, **47**, 403 (1961); see his Fig. 3.

[8] Brenner, S., Benzer, S., and Barnett, L., *Nature*, **182**, 983 (1958).

[9] Brenner, S., Barnett, L., Crick, F. H. C., and Orgel, A., *J. Mol. Biol.*, **3**, 121 (1961).

[10] Streisinger, G. (personal communication and in the press).

[11] Feynman, R. P.; Benzer, S.; Freese, E. (all personal communications).

[12] Jinks, J. L., *Heredity*, **16**, 153, 241 (1961).

[13] Champe, S., and Benzer, S. (personal communication and in preparation).

[11] Jacob, F., and Wollman, E. L., *Sexuality and the Genetics of Bacteria* (Academic Press, New York, 1961). Levinthal, C. (personal communication).

[15] Orgel, A., and Brenner, S. (in preparation).

[16] Sueoka, N., *Cold Spring Harb. Symp. Quant. Biol.* (in the press).

[17] Dreyer, W. J., Symp. 1, Fifth Intern. Cong. Biochem., 1961 (in the press).

[18] Nirenberg, M. W., and Matthaei, J. H., *Proc. U.S. Nat. Acad. Sci.*, **47**, 1588 (1961).

Reprinted from the Proceedings of the National Academy of Sciences
Vol. 50, No. 1, pp. 9–16. July, 1963.

SUPPRESSOR GENE ALTERATION OF
PROTEIN PRIMARY STRUCTURE*

By Stuart Brody† and Charles Yanofsky

DEPARTMENT OF BIOLOGICAL SCIENCES, STANFORD UNIVERSITY

Communicated by V. C. Twitty, May 22, 1963

Some suppressor genes are known to act by restoring an enzymatic activity that is specifically lacking in a mutant strain. This could be accomplished in many ways, with or without the alteration of the enzyme in question.[1–3] Suppressor mutations have been detected which affect the A protein of the tryptophan synthetase of *Escherichia coli*. Previous studies have shown that alterations in the primary structure of this protein can result from forward mutation,[4, 5] reverse mutation,[6] and recombination[6] within the structural gene (the A gene) for this protein. The present paper indicates that a suppressor mutation in a region of the genome distant from the A gene also leads to a change in the primary structure of the A protein.

Pertinent Characteristics of the Tryptophan Synthetase System.—The *Escherichia coli* tryptophan synthetase consists of two separable protein subunits, designated A and B. Together these proteins catalyze the following three reactions:[7] (1) indole + L-serine → L-tryptophan; (2) indoleglycerol phosphate ⇌ indole + 3-phosphoglyceraldehyde; (3) indoleglycerol phosphate + L-serine → L-tryptophan + 3-phosphoglyceraldehyde.[8] Reaction (3) is believed to be the physiologically essential reaction in tryptophan biosynthesis.[7, 9] Many A mutant strains produce an altered A protein, designated A-CRM, which reacts with antibody to the normal A protein.[9] All of the A-CRM's detected to date can combine with the normal B protein component, and this complex can catalyze the In → Tryp reaction, but not the other two reactions, i.e., reactions (2) and (3).

Materials and Methods.—The A mutants and suppressed A mutants listed in this paper were produced by ultraviolet irradiation of the K-12 strain of *E. coli*.[9, 19] The methods employed for the preparation of transducing lysates of phage Plkc and for transduction with this phage have been described previously.[10] All cultures of suppressed A mutants used for the preparation of extracts were examined for possible changes in the cellular population, such as reversion in the A gene, by appropriate plating and transduction techniques.

Enzymatic assays,[7] and procedures for the heat-treatment and acid-treatment of crude extracts,[11] have been described previously. Procedures used for the isolation of the A protein,[12] as well as the methods for the digestion of the protein with trypsin and chymotrypsin,[13] the isolation of peptides,[13] and the analyses of peptides[4] are described elsewhere.

Results.—Genetic characterization of suppressor mutations: A certain class of tryptophan-independent strains, designated as suppressed A mutants, were isolated in reversion studies performed with various tryptophan synthetase A mutants.[14, 15] These suppressed A mutants were clearly distinguished from revertants which arose by mutation in the A gene. Transduction experiments[15] indicated that the original mutation in the A gene was still present in the suppressed A mutant, and that the site of the suppressor mutation was not linked to the A gene.[16]

Allele specificity tests performed with the suppressor genes in strains A-11 su, A-3 su, and A-36 su indicated that each suppressor gene was allele-specific. Although 50 nonidentical A mutants were examined in tests with each of the suppressor genes, suppression was not detected, i.e., no tryptophan-independent colonies were observed.

Enzymatic characterization of crude extracts of suppressed mutants: Extracts of suppressed mutants differ from extracts of A mutants in that they exhibit low levels of InGP → Tryp activity (Table 1). The level of InGP → Tryp activity restored by a suppressor gene is characteristic of each suppressed mutant. In addition, the ratio of InGP → Tryp activity to In → Tryp activity is quite characteristic for each suppressed mutant, and shows little fluctuation when cultures are grown under similar conditions.

TABLE 1

The Enzymatic Activities of the A Proteins in Extracts of Various Mutants and Suppressed Mutants

Strain	A protein-specific activity* In → Tryp	InGP → Tryp	$\frac{\text{InGP} \to \text{Tryp}}{\text{In} \to \text{Tryp}}$ per cent
Wild-type	2.5	1	40
A-36	22	0	. . .
A-36 su	6	0.25	4.2
A-3	35	0	. . .
A-3 su	44	0.19	0.44
A-11	31	0	. . .
A-11 su	55	0.48	0.87

* Units/mg protein.

Physical treatments of crude extracts of suppressed mutants: The low level of InGP → Tryp activity detected in extracts of suppressed mutants could be due to an alteration of the CRM molecules, making them all slightly active in this reaction, or it could be due to the formation of a small amount of a second A protein, which was active in the InGP → Tryp reaction. It would be possible to distinguish between these alternatives, if it could be shown that the physical properties of the A protein that is active in the InGP → Tryp reaction differed from the properties of the CRM protein. The three mutants listed in Table 1 were selected for this study because the A-CRM's in each one could be distinguished from the wild-type A protein by differences in heat- or acid-stability. In comparison to the wild-type A protein, the CRM of A-36 is heat-labile, the CRM of A-3 is heat-stable, while the CRM of A-11 is acid-precipitable.[11]

Figure 1 presents the heat inactivation curves for the two activities found in the crude extracts of two suppressed mutants.   The results obtained demonstrate two important facts about the A proteins in these extracts.   First, the bulk of the In → Tryp activity in suppressed mutant extracts is associated with an A protein with the same heat sensitivity as the CRM in the original mutant (unsuppressed) extract.[11]   Secondly, the A protein active in the InGP → Tryp reaction is clearly different from this CRM in its heat sensitivity, and furthermore resembles the wild-type A protein.   As a control for one of the heat inactivation experiments, crude extracts of the wild-type strain and of strain A-36 were mixed to simulate an extract of A-36 su, and a similar heat inactivation experiment performed.   The inactivation rates of the two activities in this mixture were the same as those observed with A-36 su extracts.

Heat treatment of an A-11 su extract did not differentially inactivate the InGP → Tryp activity or the In → Tryp activity in this extract.   Since the CRM of strain A-11 is as heat-sensitive as the wild-type A protein,[11] no differences would be expected in the two inactivation rates, if the protein bearing the InGP → Tryp activity had the same heat stability as the wild-type A protein.   However, acid treatment of an extract of A-11 su clearly showed (Table 2) that the InGP → Tryp activity was associated with a protein that was more acid-stable than the protein bearing the In → Tryp activity, and was similar in behavior to the A protein of the wild-type strain.   Here again, the bulk of the A protein resembled the A-CRM found in strain A-11.   Similar acid treatment of crude extracts of strains A-36 su and A-3 su led to a loss of activity in both reactions similar to that observed with extracts of the wild-type strain (Table 2).   Since the A-CRM's from strains A-36 and A-3 have the same acid stability as the wild-type A protein,[11] it might not be possible to distinguish these A-CRM's from a second A protein, if that protein had the same stability as the wild-type A protein.

TABLE 2

ACID TREATMENT OF EXTRACTS

Extract	Per cent activity remaining[*]	
	In → Tryp	InGP → Tryp
Wild-type	58	55
A-11	11	. . .
A-11 su	17, 11	51, 47
A-36	60	. . .
A-36 su	59	57
A-3	58	. . .
A-3 su	61	53

* A protein activity in supernatant solutions following acidification of extracts to pH 4.0.

These findings are consistent with the view that the two types of A protein found in extracts of each suppressed mutant are: an A protein active in the InGP → Tryp reaction (hereafter designated as the su-A protein), which has certain physical properties in common with the wild-type A protein; and an A protein which closely resembles the A-CRM of the parental mutant.

Purification and separation of two A proteins by DEAE column chromatography: These findings, as well as previous observations,[2] suggested the presence of a second type of A protein in extracts of suppressed mutants.   In further studies with extracts of strain A-36 su, it was possible to separate two A proteins by column

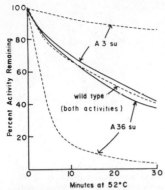

Fig. 1.—Heat inactivation of the A proteins in crude extracts of strains A-36 su, A-3 su, and the wild-type strain. InGP → Tryp activity———, In → Tryp activity - - - -.

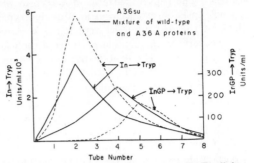

Fig. 2.—Elution pattern from DEAE-cellulose columns of the two A proteins in extracts of strain A-36 su, and of a mixture of the wild-type and A-36 A proteins. A linear phosphate gradient was employed ($0.01\ M \rightarrow 0.30\ M$, pH 7.0), and fractions of 10 ml were collected. Tube #1 refers to the first tube that contains A protein activity.

chromatography (Fig. 2). As can be seen in this figure, the In → Tryp and InGP → Tryp activity peaks are partially separated.

To determine whether the chromatographic properties of the su-A protein were similar to those of the wild-type A protein, purified A proteins from mutant A-36 and from the wild-type strain were mixed to simulate a purified preparation from strain A-36 su. When this mixture was chromatographed employing the conditions used for the first column procedure (as described above), the In → Tryp and InGP → Tryp activity peaks were partially separated (Fig. 2). As shown also in Figure 2, the activity curves were very similar to those obtained by column chromatography of the preparation from strain A-36 su.

The su-A protein was purified further by combining the fractions containing InGP → Tryp activity from several DEAE columns, concentrating by $(NH_4)_2SO_4$ precipitation, and then rechromatographing on a 100×1.2 cm DEAE-cellulose column, using a linear gradient of $0.01\ M \rightarrow 0.15\ M$ phosphate (pH 7.0). Since some of the early fractions from the previous column with InGP → Tryp activity contained the trailing portion of the In → Tryp activity peak, two activity peaks were also recovered from the second column. However, under the conditions of rechromatography, the two A proteins were completely separated. The purified su-A protein had an InGP → Tryp : In → Tryp activity ratio of 40 per cent, which is identical to that of the wild-type A protein. Heat inactivation studies showed that both of the enzymatic activities of the purified su-A protein were inactivated at the same rate, a rate identical to that for the heat inactivation of the wild-type A protein. These findings indicate that the su-A protein was completely free of the A-CRM protein. Furthermore, a comparison of the specific activities of the A protein peaks with the specific activity of pure wild-type A protein showed that the su-A protein was 50 per cent pure, while the A-CRM was greater than 90 per cent pure.

Analysis of peptides from the A-CRM and su-A proteins of A-36 su: The two A protein fractions isolated from strain A-36 su were examined in peptide pattern studies. The peptide patterns of a trypsin plus chymotrypsin digest, as well as a chymotrypsin digest of the su-A protein, were found to correspond exactly to the peptide patterns of the wild-type A protein. The peptide pattern of chymotryptic digests of the CRM protein of strain A-36 su showed one difference from a similar wild-type A protein peptide pattern, the position of peptide CP-2, as shown schematically in Figure 3. Although the chymotryptic peptide pattern of the CRM from strain A-36 su differed from the wild-type peptide pattern, it was identical to the peptide pattern of the CRM protein from the original A-36 strain. It had previously been shown that the peptide difference in mutant A-36 was due to the replacement of a particular glycine residue in CP-2 by an arginine residue.[4, 17]

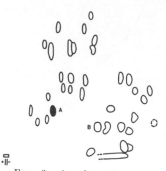

Fig. 3.—A schematic representation of the position of the major peptides in chymotryptic peptide patterns of both the A-CRM and the su-A protein of strain A-36 su. A = the position of peptide CP-2 from the su-A protein, B = the position of CP-2 from the A-CRM. Peptide CP-2 is in position A in wild-type peptide patterns and in position B in peptide patterns of the A-CRM from mutant A-36. The rectangle in the lower left-hand corner indicates the point of application of the sample.

Peptide CP-2 was isolated from the two A proteins from strain A-36 su and its amino acid composition determined. The results of these analyses are compared with the known sequence of amino acids in peptide CP-2 from the wild-type A protein,[17] and with the amino acid composition of CP-2 from A-36 CRM[17] (Table 3). The analyses indicate that peptide CP-2 from the su-A protein has the same composition as the corresponding peptide from the wild-type A protein, while CP-2 from the A-CRM of strain A-36 su has the same composition as CP-2 from the A-CRM of mutant A-36. It is clear from these data that an amino acid replacement occurs in the A protein as a result of the action of the suppressor gene.

TABLE 3

AMINO ACID COMPOSITION OF PEPTIDE CP-2 FROM VARIOUS A PROTEINS

Wild-type	AspNH₂-Ala-Ala-Pro-Pro-Leu-GluNH₂-*Gly*-Phe
A-36	(Asp*-Ala-Ala-Pro-Pro)-Leu-GluNH₂-*Arg*-Phe
A-36 su	
CRM-A	(Asp,* Ala₂, Pro₂, Leu, *Arg*, Glu*)-Phe
su-A	(Asp,* Ala₂, Pro₂, Leu, *Gly*, Glu*)-Phe

* Not determined whether present as amide.

Discussion.—Physical and chemical treatments of extracts of three suppressed A mutants indicate that there are two types of A proteins present in each extract. The majority A protein component is indistinguishable from the original CRM protein, whereas the minority component (the su-A protein) has physical and enzymatic properties characteristic of the wild-type A protein. Peptide pattern studies of the two purified A proteins from strain A-36 su also show that the su-A protein resembles the wild-type A protein, while the CRM protein resembles the A-CRM of mutant A-36. Amino acid analysis of the relevant peptides (CP-2) confirmed the fact that there is a difference in amino acid composition of the two peptides. This fact, in itself, is critical since it indicates that the presence of the suppressor gene in strain A-36 su has resulted in a change in the primary structure of the A protein.

The amino acid replacement in the A protein due to the suppressor gene of strain A-36 su is an arginine → glycine change in peptide CP-2. Only small amounts of purified su-A protein were available for study, so it was not possible to perform amino acid sequence analyses on peptide CP-2. However, if one makes the plausible assumption that the glycine residue in this peptide occupies the same position as the arginine residue that it replaces, then the effect of this suppressor gene is to restore an amino acid sequence identical to that of the wild-type A protein.[18] The presence of a glycine residue in this peptide is of particular importance in this case, since it has been shown that A proteins with any one of three other amino acids (alanine, serine, and valine) at this position are functional.[6] Although the amino acid found in the wild-type A protein (glycine) was restored in this case, it should be possible for amino acids other than the wild-type amino acid to be inserted at this position. In this regard, it is conceivable that a suppressor mutation could lead to an amino acid replacement in a protein which would not be possible by a single mutational event in the structural gene for this protein.

It has been found that the mutant phenotype of approximately one third of all the A mutants tested can be reversed by suppressor mutations.[15, 19] One mutant which is not suppressible, strain A-46, is particularly interesting in view of the studies reported in this paper. Although extensive reversion analyses and cross-suppression tests have been performed with this mutant, no suppressors have been found which restore InGP → Tryp activity. The amino acid change in the A-46 protein is a glycine → glutamic acid replacement, and this glycine residue is the same one that is replaced by arginine as a result of the A-36 mutation.[5] It is interesting that in the presence of the A-36 suppressor gene, glycine can replace arginine, but not glutamic acid, at this position in the A protein.

The results of these investigations can be most easily explained by postulating that the consequences of a mutation in a suppressor gene such as the suppressor of strain A-36 su is to produce an alteration in the specificity of incorporation of amino acids into proteins. The amino acid changes which result from this type of alteration could be called "mistakes" in protein synthesis. If the cell containing a mutated suppressor gene is incapable of always translating a certain specific DNA nucleotide sequence into the same amino acid without error, then it is important to determine the extent of this error in translation. The term "mistake level" will be used to indicate how often an amino acid at a particular position in a given protein is replaced at the same position by one or another amino acid. This definition does not include as "mistakes" the replacement of an amino acid by its analogues, or the translation of a nonsense sequence of nucleotides into a known amino acid. The "mistake level" might simply be expressed as follows: amino acid X is found to replace Y at a particular position in a protein in 8 per cent of the molecules. The "mistake level" might also be more complex if many amino acids could replace amino acid Y at this particular position and with different frequencies.[20] In any event, a given "mistake level" can be considered to denote a constant probability of misreading the genetic code independent of what proteins, or types of proteins, are being synthesized.

It is not known to what extent the bacterial cell could tolerate many types of

V. **THE FUNCTION OF GENETIC MATERIAL**

amino acid insertion mistakes. It is probable that very high "mistake levels," single or multiple, if they affected all proteins, would result in lethality. This may explain why all allele-specific suppressors of A mutants examined to date appear to have very low "mistake levels."[21] However, it could be possible to have a fairly high "mistake level" if there were more than one "coding unit" for a particular amino acid (so-called "degenerate coding units"), and if these amino acid coding units were not equally distributed in the DNA. If the suppressor mutation could lead to a translation "mistake" of a minority or infrequently found coding unit, then an amino acid switch found in one protein might not be found in other proteins. In cases where very high levels of an enzyme are restored by the action of a suppressor gene, different interpretations may be applicable.[3]

The finding that some suppressor mutations can reverse the effects of mutations in several genes lends weight to the "mistake in protein synthesis" hypothesis.[22, 23] The fact that a number of different point mutants in the T4r$_{II}$ cistron[22] or in the alkaline phosphatase gene[3] are affected by a single suppressor gene is consistent with this idea and has been interpreted in a similar manner.

There are many ways that the presumed mistake in translation in strain A-36 su might occur. According to our present knowledge of protein synthesis, which

TABLE 4

POSSIBLE SUPPRESSOR "MISTAKES" THAT WOULD LEAD TO THE OCCASIONAL INCORPORATION OF GLYCINE INSTEAD OF ARGININE IN THE A PROTEIN OF STRAIN A-36 SU

Mutationally altered component	Effect of alteration	Result
(a) Arginine-activating enzyme	Arginine enzyme activates glycine in addition to arginine	Glycine or arginine coupled to same type of arginine-tRNA
(b) Glycine-activating enzyme	Glycine enzyme pairs with arginine-tRNA in addition to pairing with glycine-tRNA	Glycine coupled to both arginine-tRNA and glycine-tRNA
(c) Arginine-tRNA	Arginine-tRNA pairs with the glycine-activating enzyme in addition to pairing with the arginine-activating enzyme	Glycine or arginine coupled to same type of arginine-tRNA
(d) Glycine-tRNA	Glycine-tRNA pairs incorrectly with messenger RNA, in addition to pairing properly	Glycine-tRNA (charged with glycine), pairs with an arginine-coding unit, in addition to pairing with a glycine coding unit in messenger RNA

tRNA = amino acid transfer RNA.

may be incomplete, the possibilities listed in Table 4 can be considered. It is assumed that all of the alterations mentioned lead only to partial losses in specificity. At the present time, the specificities of these components in strain A-36 su are being investigated to determine whether any one of the components has been altered as a result of the suppressor mutation.

We wish to express our thanks to Deanna Thorpe, Patricia Schroeder, and John Horan for their assistance with various aspects of this work.

The following abbreviations were used: Tryp = Tryptophan; In = Indole; InGP = Indoleglycerol phosphate.

* This investigation was supported by grants from the U.S. Public Health Service and the National Science Foundation.
† Predoctoral trainee of the U.S. Public Health Service.

[1] Suskind, S., and L. Kurek, these PROCEEDINGS, **45**, 193 (1959).
[2] Crawford, I., and C. Yanofsky, these PROCEEDINGS, **45**, 1280 (1959).

[3] Garen, A., and O. Siddiqi, these Proceedings, **48**, 1121 (1962).

[4] Helinski, D., and C. Yanofsky, these Proceedings, **48**, 173 (1962).

[5] Henning, U., and C. Yanofsky, these Proceedings, **48**, 183 (1962).

[6] *Ibid.*, **48**, 1497 (1962).

[7] Crawford, I., and C. Yanofsky, these Proceedings, **44**, 1161 (1958).

[8] Crawford, I., *Biochim. Biophys. Acta*, **45**, 405 (1960).

[9] Yanofsky, C., and I. Crawford, these Proceedings, **45**, 1016 (1959).

[10] Lennox, E. S., *Virology*, **1**, 190 (1955).

[11] Maling, B., and C. Yanofsky, these Proceedings, **47**, 551 (1961).

[12] Henning, U., D. Helinski, F. Chao, and C. Yanofsky, *J. Biol. Chem.*, **237**, 1523 (1962).

[13] Helinski, D., and C. Yanofsky, *Biochim. Biophys. Acta*, **63**, 10 (1962).

[14] Stadler, J., and C. Yanofsky, *Genetics*, **44**, 105 (1959).

[15] Allen, M., and C. Yanofsky, *Genetics*, in press.

[16] Preliminary transduction studies indicate that the suppressor gene of strain A-36 su is located close to the B_1 locus on the *E. coli* linkage map.

[17] Carlton, B., and C. Yanofsky, *J. Biol. Chem.*, in press.

[18] It cannot be unequivocally stated that the entire amino acid sequence of the su-A protein is identical to that of the wild-type A protein, since amino acid sequence analyses of every peptide from both of these proteins would be required to establish this point.

[19] Yanofsky, C., D. Helinski, and B. Maling, in *Cellular Regulatory Mechanisms*, Cold Spring Harbor Symposia on Quantitative Biology, vol. 26 (1961), p. 11.

[20] It was thought that perhaps a given suppressor gene, known to cause (for example) a histidine → tyrosine switch in the A protein, could be used as a genetic method for identifying tyrosine → histidine mutational changes in other proteins. However, this may not be possible until it is known whether single or multiple amino acid replacements are involved.

[21] "Mistake levels" in suppressed A mutants are estimated from the ratio of the A protein activity in the InGP → Tryp and In → Tryp reactions. If the A protein active in the InGP → Tryp reaction is similar to the wild-type A protein in its enzymatic properties, then this ratio of enzymatic activities can be taken as an indication of the amount of su-A protein relative to the A-CRM protein.

[22] Benzer, S., and S. Champe, these Proceedings, **47**, 1025 (1961).

[23] Lieb, M., and L. Herzenberg, personal communication.

Subject Index

A

Absorption spectra, of nucleoproteins, 182–183

Actinomycin D,
  RNA synthesis in cells, sensitivity to, 532
  virus multiplication, effects on, 532

Adenine, synthesis of, in *Neurospora*, 43

Adenosine triphosphate (ATP), amino acid coupling to soluble RNA dependent upon, 537

Alcaptonuria, inheritance of, 3–4, 19–21

Amino acids,
  code letters for, 617–618
  metabolism of, in man, 17–19
  quantitative analyses of, in hemoglobins, 74–83
  transfer from RNA to microsomal protein, 546

2-Aminopurine, mutagenic effects of, 346–364

Analogs, base,
  mutagenic effect of, in bacteriophage, 346–364
  substitution in DNA, 327

Anemia, sickle-cell,
  chemical differences between normal and sickle cell hemoglobins, 5, 51–52, 66–70
  genetic basis for, 5, 54–55
  nature of sickling process, 53–54

Autoradiography,
  bacterial chromosome replication studied by, 337–345
  chromatid exchange studied by, 297–310
  of DNA in T-2 bacteriophage, 333–334
  evidence for semiconservative replication of DNA, 63–78, 243
  molecular length of DNA estimated by, 330–336
  nucleic acid synthesis during the cell cycle, 519–531
  nucleic acid synthesis, effect of actinomycin D on, 532

RNA incorporation of P^{32} by salivary gland nuclei, 508–509

RNA synthesis in amoebae nuclei, 510–516
  intracellular site, 508–509, 517–518

B

Bacteria, biochemical mutants of, 419–420

Bacteriophage,
  chemical morphology of, 214–215
  DNA and protein, functions in T2, 212–229
  genetic map of, 443, 446, 449, 453–477
  genetic recombination in, 442–449
    relation to breakage and exchange, 478–489
  heterozygosity in, 444–449
  labeling with thymine-H^3, 330–336
  life cycle of T2H in bacterial cell, 447, 449
  linear gene arrangement in, 442–450
  linkage groups in, 443, 446–448
    diagram of, 119
  mutagenic effect of base analogs on, 346–364
  mutants, classification of, 461, 464, 466
  mutations induced in, 414–418
  mutual exclusion effect in, 414, 417–418
  segregation, in T2H, 444–449
  sexual reproduction in T2H, 442–450
  suicide studies by use of thymidine-H^3, 332–333

Base analogs, *see* Analogs, base

Base pairing, in DNA, 264–268, 271–276

Bromodeoxyuridine, mutagenic effect of, in bacteriophages, 346–364

C

Cesium chloride gradient,
  evidence for semiconservative replication of DNA, 243, 312–323
  for separation of T2-specific RNA, 137–146

Choline synthesis, genetics of, in *Neurospora*, 41

Chromatid exchanges,
  autoradiographic studies of, 297–310
  twin and single, 300–303
Chromatography,
  components of nucleic acids separated by,
    247–253
  hemoglobins A and S compared by, 66–70
Chromosome,
  bacterial, replication mechanism proposed
    for, 344–345
  breakage and exchange correlated with
    genetic recombination, 478–489
  evidence for, in *E. coli*, 431
  models, 304–306
  morphological markers in *Zea mays* used
    for cross-over studies, 387–392
  replication, related to DNA synthesis, 296–
    310
    in *E. coli*, 337–345
Chromosome maps,
  Drosophila, 377
  E. coli, fine structure of the tryptophan
    synthetase locus, 86
  E. coli K 12, lactose region of, 109
  Neurospora, 35, 394, 401–405
Cis-trans test, 369, 451–477
Cistron, 452, 458, 462–463, 467, 472–474, 477
  A and B in phage T4, genetic map of,
    621–624, 628
    joined together by mutation, 629–630
  competitive interaction at, 585–587
  for ribosomal RNA, identification of, 581–
    584
Code letter assignments, experimental basis
  for, 612–619
Coding, genetic, 91–92
Colchicine,
  duplication and exchanges in chromo-
    somes affected by, 301–303
  RNA synthesis affected by, 529
Controlling element, in maize, 138
Crossing-over,
  chemical nature of, 291
  cytological and genetic correlations, 387–
    392
  double, in *Drosophila*, 378–379
  genetic study of, showing linear gene
    arrangement in *Drosophila*, 372–386
  in *Neurospora crassa*, 400–403
Cytidine-H³
  incorporation to determine effect of

actinomycin on nucleic acid synthesis,
  532
incorporation to measure nucleic acid
  synthesis, 519–531

D

Density gradient centrifugation, 478–489
  genetic recombination studies in phage by,
    478–489
  messenger RNA, identification by, 556–558
Density labeling, DNA with N^{14}, 312
Deoxyribonuclease (DNase)
  sensitization of phage DNA to, 214–218
  template for RNA synthesis destroyed by,
    561–570
  transforming principle, identification by,
    165–170
Deoxyribonucleic acid (DNA)
  amounts in individual nuclei, 202–211
    in somatic cells and gametes, 197–199
  base composition compared with RNA,
    561–570
  base pairing, 264–268, 271–276
  base pairing mistakes and mutations, 361–
    364
  biosynthetic role of, in making RNA, 561–
    570
  constancy of, in plant nuclei, 200–211
  crystalline forms, 270
  duplex structure, Watson and Crick initial
    proposal, 254–256
  fibrous nature of, 269
  heat denaturation and strand separation,
    320–323
  histone complex with, 290
  hybridization of DNA and RNA, 574–577
  hydrogen bonds in, 254–256, 266
  molecular length estimated by autoradiog-
    raphy, 330–336
  molecular model, 242, 325
    critique of, 278–293
    evidence for, 272
  molecular structure of, 257–262, 327
  nucleotides, separation by chromatog-
    raphy, 247–250
  physical properties of, 326
  P^{32} incorporation, 503–507
  preparation of, 247
  replication, enzymatic, 328
    in *E. coli*, 312–323

evidence for semiconservative scheme, 243–244, 296–311, 313–323, 324–329

hypothesis for, 263–268, 273–276, 285–286

mistakes, 362–363

rate of, 340–342

structure related to, 285–290

Watson-Crick scheme, critique and difficulties of, 274–275

    evidence supporting, 318–322

sensitization to DNase by liberation from phage, 215–219

sequence complementarity between homologous DNA and RNA, 561–570, 579–580, 581–587

sodium and rubidium salts of, 282

structure, *in vivo*, 261

    X-ray diffraction studies of, 278–293

sub-units of in chromosome, 304–306

synthesis, cell division cycle, related to, 519–531

    chromosome duplication, related to, 296–310

    enzymatic steps in, 294–295

    template for, 285

DNA-RNA hybrid, 593

    isolation method, 589

    preparation method, 589

    ribonuclease test for, 590, 592, 594–595

depolymerization, enzymatic, of nucleic acids, 252–253

DNA, *see* Deoxyribonucleic acid

Drosophila, map of six sex-linked factors, 372–386

    RNA incorporation of P^{32} by salivary gland nuclei, 508–509

Duplication of DNA, *see* DNA replication

E

Electrophoresis, peptides separated by, 69

Enzyme,

    co-repressors, 115

    depolymerization of nucleic acid by, 252–253

    induction in *E. coli*, 101–105, 112

    repressors, 105–108, 112

Escherichia coli,

    autoradiographic studies of, 337–345

    chromosome, evidence for, 431

    DNA replication in, 312–323

    gene recombination in, 421–441

    genetic map of, 431–434

    linear gene arrangement in, 421–441

    linked segregations in, 427–441

    mutants, dispensable and indispensable in, 56–65

    protein synthesis in cell-free system from, 597–611

    reverse mutations in, 90–91

    sexual reproduction in, 421–441

Exchanges, chromatid

    autoradiographic studies of, 297–310

    twin and single, 300–303

F

Fingerprints,

    of hemoglobins, 6, 67–68

    of peptides of the A protein, 7, 88–90

G

β-Galactosidase, 100–112

Gene,

    chemical nature of, 43–47

    control systems in maize and bacteria, 138–149

    conversion, in *Sordaria*, 408–413

    modifier, 146–148

    molecular size of, 474–477

    one gene-one enzyme hypothesis, 4, 5, 9–16, 56–61

    operator, 137–148

    regulator, 108–110, 130–134, 137–148

    structural, 98, 137–149

        kinetics of expression, 126–129

        nature of message, 126–129

    suppressor, 634–641

    unifunctional and multifunctional, 56–62

Genes,

    cluster map of, in *E. coli*, 86

    linear arrangement of in *Drosophila*, 372–386

        in *E. coli*, 427–441

        in *Neurospora crassa*, 393–406

    regulator in temperate phage systems, 116–120

Genetic code,

    degeneracy of, 631–632

    nature of, 620–633

    universality of, 617–619

Genetic coding ratio, 630–631

Genetic map of,
E. coli, 431–434
phage λ, 487
phage T4, 353–356, 453–477
phage T2H, 443, 446, 449
Genetic markers, in Zea mays, 387–392
Genetic recombination,
in bacteria, first evidence for, 368–369,
419–441
in E. coli, 421–441
in Neurospora crassa, 368, 402, 403
original evidence for, 367, 372–386, 393–407
in phage, 368–369, 414, 417–418
associated with breakage and reunion,
478–489
density gradient studies of, 478–489
in phage T2H, 442–449
in phage T4, frequency of, 463, 465, 467–
471
Genetic segregation, nuclear and chromosomal basis of, in Neurospora, 31–33
Genetic units, relation to molecular length,
474–477
Guanosine triphosphate (GTP), role in
transfer of amino acids into microsomal
protein, 241–257

H

Hemoglobin,
chemical difference between normal and
sickle-cell, 5, 51–53, 66–70
chemical structure of A and C, 5, 71–83
end group analysis of peptides from, 71–83
Hemoglobin A, amino acid sequence in,
74–82
Hemoglobin C, amino acid sequence in, 74–
82
Hereditary units, determination of size by
mapping, 457–458
Heterozygosis, in phage T2H, 444
Histone, arrangement of in nucleohistone,
288–290
in complex with DNA, 290
Hydrogen bonds, in DNA, 254–256, 266

I

Inducers, of β-galactosidase, 115–116
Information transfer, in phage infected cells,
556–560

Isotopes,
density labeling with C^{13} and N^{15}, 478–489
P^{32} incorporation by RNA, 508–509, 510–
516
sulfur[35] and phosphorus[32] as labels for
protein and DNA in phages, 222–229
uridine-H^3, incorporation into RNA by
Neurospora, 517–518

K

Knobs, chromosome, in Zea mays, 388–389

L

Lactose system of E. coli, 100–101
Linkage, and crossing-over, early concepts,
372–386
groups in phage T2H, 443, 446–448
in Neurospora crassa, 399–406
Linked segregations in E. coli, 427–441
Leucine-C^{14}, transfer from enzyme fraction to
microsome protein, 542–544
Leucine-H^3, incorporation into mammalian
protein unaffected by actinomycin, 532

M

Maize, regulator genes in, 137–149
Messenger RNA, see RNA
Microsomal protein, leucine-C^{14} transfer to,
from labeled enzyme fraction, 542–543
Mitotic cycle, measurement in cell cultures
of Chinese hamster, 519–522
Molecular models, DNA, diagrams of, 325
Watson and Crick, for DNA, 278–293
Watson and Crick scheme, critique of,
278–293
Mutants,
classification of, in phage T4, 461, 464, 466
constitutive, 110–112
loss of dispensable and indispensable functions, 56–65
nutritional, induced in Neurospora, 9–16
nutritional (biochemical), induction and
isolation of, 27–30
reading frame, 626
temperature, in Neurospora, 58–59
Mutations,
amino acid sequence affected by, 84–97
biochemical, in bacteria, 419–420
induced in phage, 414–418

molecular investigation of, 346–364
natural, hypothetical scheme for, 275–276
operator, 120–122
reverse in *E. coli*, 90–91
suppressor, 92–95
suppressor, nature of, 634–638
Muton, 452, 458, 471, 476

N

Neurospora,
chromosome map of, 35
genetic control of biochemical reactions
in, 9–16
life cycle, 24
quantitative measurement of growth, 13–16
Neurospora crassa,
gene recombinations in, 368, 393, 402–403
linkage in, 399–406
map of sex-chromosome, 394, 401–405
RNA originating in nucleus of, 517–518
segregation, first division and second
division, 402, 404–405
Niacin synthesis, in *Neurospora*, 42
Nuclear transplantation, in amoeba, 511
Nucleic acid (nucleinic acid) physical basis
of heredity, 153–154
Nucleic acids, base composition of, 247–251
Nucleolus,
loss of in mammalian cells treated with
actinomycin D, 532
RNA incorporation of P^{32} measured in,
508–509
RNA metabolism, role in, 527–528
Nucleoprotamine,
composition of, 181–182
content estimated in trout sperm nuclei,
186–196
isolation of from trout sperm, 179–196
structure of, 287–290
Nucleoprotein, separation into component
parts, 182–186
Nucleotide sequence, in DNA complementary to soluble RNA, 588–596
Nucleus, functional role of, 3
RNA synthesis in, of amoeba, 510–516

O

Operon, 123
Ornithine cycle in *Neurospora*, 38

P

Pentose nucleic acid (PNA), *see* Ribo-
nucleic acid (RNA)
Peptides, from hemoglobin, end group anal-
ysis of, 73–82
electrophoretic separation of, 69
Permease, 101
Phenylketonuria, inheritance of, 20
Phospholipids, turnover measured by P^{32}
incorporation, 505–506
Phosphoproteins, phosphorus turnover in,
506–507
Photometric measurements, of DNA in
individual nuclei, 204–211
Pneumococcus, transformation in, 157–178
Polymerase, RNA, 561–570
Polynucleotides (synthetic) amino acid in-
corporation stimulated by 604–609, 612–
619
Polyploidy, DNA amounts associated with,
201
Polyteny, DNA amounts associated with, 201
Primer, DNA, 243, 294, 324–329
Protamines, structure in DNA complex, 286,
287–290
Protein, A type, purification and separation
of, 636
coat of phages, function of, 212–229
Protein synthesis,
cell-free, 597–611
genetically regulated in bacteria, 98–136
model for regulation of, 124
reaction sequence evidence for, 533–549
Prototroph, definition of, 419–420
Purines, analogs in DNA replication, 346–
364
chromatographic separation of, 247–251
Pyrimidines, analogs of, in DNA replication,
346–364
chromatographic separation of, 247–251

R

Recombination, *see* Genetic recombination
Recon, 451–452, 457, 476
Reconstitution of virus, 230–238
Regulatory mechanisms, genetic, 98–136, 137–
149, 370
Replication of DNA, *see* DNA replication

Replication, distribution of parental atoms among progeny molecules, 312–322

Repression, genetic, 105–107

Ribonuclease (RNase),
amino acid labeling of RNA, sensitivity to, 538
enzymatic synthesis of RNA affected by, 561–570
resistance of RNA-DNA complexes to, 583

Ribonucleic acid, (RNA)
base composition of, 250–251
related to base composition of primer DNA, 561–570
base ratio analysis, 590
base ratios compared to phage DNA following infection, 552
complex formed with DNA, 561–570
enzymic synthesis of, 561–565
independent function of, in TMV, 230–238
informational, 584–587
intracellular synthetic site indicated by autoradiographs, 508–509
messenger, 129–132
evidence for, 555–560
labeled, preparation of, 589
molecules, evolutionary history of, 593–595
nuclear origin of, in *Neurospora*, 517–518
nuclear synthesis, evidence for, 510–516
properties of pH 5 RNA-Leucine-C¹⁴, 540–541
purification of T2-specific, 572
ribosomal, 584–587
fractionation of, 602–603
stability of, 555–560
protein synthesis in cell-free system dependent upon, 597
saturation of sites on DNA, 593
soluble, evidence of a role in protein synthesis, 533
intermediate in protein synthesis, 533–549
isolation from pH 5 fraction, 534–535
preparation of, 598–599
specific activity, changes after pulse labeling with H³-cytidine, 525–527
synthesis, following phage infection of *E. coli*, 433–437
inhibited in cells by actinomycin D, 532
rate during the cell cycle, 523–526

synthetic site indicated by activity of incorporated P³², 504–506
transfer from nucleus to cytoplasm, evidence for, 519–531
turnover in phage infected cells, 555–560

RNA-DNA complexes, resistance to RNase, 583
hybrids, conditions for formation, 574–575
hybrids, separation of, from DNA by centrifugation, 573

Ribonucleotides, incorporation into RNA, 561–570

Ribosomes, required for cell-free synthesis of protein, 597
stability of RNA in, 555–560

S

Segregation, aberrant form of in *Sordaria fimicola*, 408–413
aberrant in tetrads, 306
in bacteriophage T2H, 444–449
first and second division in *Neurospora crassa*, 402, 404, 405
linked in *E. coli*, 427–441

Sequence complementavity, DNA-RNA hybrids, 581–587

Sexual reproduction, bacteriophage T2H, 442–450
E. coli, 421–441
Sordaria fimicola, 408–413

Sickle-cell anemia, *see* Anemia

Sordaria fimicola, aberrant tetrads in, 408–413

Suppressor mutation, 139

Suppressor mutations, genetic character of, 635

T

Template, in DNA replication, 243, 285

Thymidine-H³, DNA synthesis over the cell cycle studied with, 519–531
use of in autoradiography, 297

Thymine-H³, bacteriophage T2, labeled with, 330–336
chromosome of *E. coli* labeled with, 337–345

Tobacco mosaic virus (TMV), 154

Tradescantia paludosa, amounts of DNA per cell, 205–211